CAMPING

FRANCE 2014

Selection 2014

2,400 selected camping sites including:
2,100 with chalets, bungalows and mobile homes
1,200 with campervan facilities

*D*ear Reader,

The Michelin Camping Guide is perfect for all those who love the great outdoors and enjoy spending their leisure time in a tent, caravan, campervan, chalet or mobile home. We have selected the best campsites in France with our usual care, listing those with the best facilities in the most pleasant surroundings.

Using the traditional Michelin classification method, this guide provides you with an easy, speedy reference for assessing the category of each site: 1 to 5 tents (see pages 8–9).

The guide is updated each year, so consult the latest edition for the most up-to-date information and pricing.

Here are a few tips on how to use the guide

→ To select a campsite

The guide covers all 22 regions of France – see the map and list of regions on pages 4–5. Each region has been colour-coded so that you can find your way around the guide easily: the band at the top of the page matches the colour used in the map. Once you have selected a region, turn to the detailed map at the start of that region's section. It shows all the localities that have at least one campsite. The localities with campsites and their descriptions are listed alphabetically within each region section.

→ To find a specific locality

Refer to the index on page 510, where all the places are listed in alphabetical order.

→ To make a selection based on specific criteria

See the list of campsites on pages 26–32 for an at-a-glance summary of selected facilities available at sites, listed region by region.

→ For a detailed description of each individual site

The essential information and brief description given for each site are supplemented by symbols, which provide a wealth of additional information and detail. See pages 10–12 for the key to the symbols used in both the campsite entries and the maps.

→ Glossary of French terms

For a list of useful words, turn to the Glossary on page 14 for a translation of common terms.

→ Descriptions of the sites start on page 34

For more information on visiting particular towns or regions, consult the relevant regional Michelin Green Guide. We also recommend you use the appropriate Michelin regional map to locate your selected campsite, to calculate distances and to work out the best route.

→ To get the most out of this Camping Guide, read pages 6–12 carefully.

© Jharela / Fotolia.com

We welcome your feedback on our listed campsites.

Please email us at:
campingfrance@tp.michelin.com

Many thanks in advance!

Nanterre 92
Bobigny 93
PARIS 75
Créteil 94

62 NORD-PAS DE CALAIS
Lille
Arras 59
Amiens 80 02
PICARDY
Beauvais 60
Laon
Charleville-Mézières 08
76
Rouen
51 Châlons-en-Champagne 55 Metz
50 St-Lô
Caen 27
NORMANDY
14
Evreux
Pontoise 95
Versailles 78 95
ILE DE FRANCE
91 Évry
Melun
77
CHAMPAGNE-ARDENNE
Bar-le-Duc
Nancy 54
LORRAINE 57
Strasbourg 67
22 St-Brieuc
29 Quimper
BRITTANY
35 Rennes
53
61 Alençon
Chartres 28
Troyes 10
Chaumont 52
88 Epinal
Colmar 68
Belfort 90
Vesoul 70
FRANCHE-COMTÉ 25
Besançon
ALSACE
56
Vannes
PAYS DE LA LOIRE
Le Mans 72
Laval
Orléans 45
89 Auxerre
21
Dijon
Blois
41
CENTRE
Tours 37
Bourges
BURGUNDY
Lons-le-Saunier 39
44 Nantes
49
Angers
18
Châteauroux 36
Nevers 58
71
Mâcon
85 la Roche-s-Yon
79 Poitiers
Niort 86
87 Guéret 23
Moulins 03
Bourg-en-Bresse 01
74 Annecy
POITOU-CHARENTES
La Rochelle
17 16
Limoges
LIMOUSIN
Clermont-Ferrand 63
42
69 Lyon
St-Étienne
38
Chambéry 73
19 Tulle
AUVERGNE
RHÔNE-ALPES
Périgueux 24
15 Aurillac
le Puy-en-Velay 43
Grenoble
Bordeaux 33
46 Cahors
Rodez 12
Mende 48
Privas 07
Valence 26
Gap 05
Digne-les-Bains 04
06 Nice
AQUITAINE
47 Agen
Montauban 82
Albi
30 Nîmes
84 Avignon
PROVENCE-ALPES-CÔTE D'AZUR
Mont-de-Marsan 40
32 Auch
MIDI-PYRÉNÉES
Toulouse 81
Montpellier 34
13 Marseille
83 Toulon
Bastia 2B
CORSICA
Pau 64
Tarbes 65
31 Foix 09
Carcassonne 11
LANGUEDOC-ROUSSILLON
Perpignan 66
Ajaccio 2A

5

Practical information for each location with
cross reference to Michelin maps

Michelin classification of selected sites

Services and leisure facilities available

Brief description of the site and its capacity

Peak season rates

For key to the symbols, see pages 10 to 11

CENTRE

LORRIS

45260 – Michelin map **318** M4 – pop. 2 941 – alt. 126
▶ Paris 132 – Gien 27 – Montargis 23 – Orléans 55

⛰ L'Étang des Bois

℘ 02 38 92 32 00, www.canal-orleans.fr

Address : 6km west along the D 88, follow the signs for
Châteauneuf-sur-Loire, near the lake at Les Bois

Opening times : from beginning April to end Sept.

3 ha (150 pitches) grassy

Tariff : ★ 3,60€ ⇔ 🚗 5,90€ – 🔌 (10A) 4,50€
Rental rates : (from beginning April to end Sept.) – 4
Per night from 52 to 67€ – Per week from 310 to 420€
A wooded setting in a pleasant location.

Surroundings : 🏞 ♨
Leisure activities : 🎱 🎣
Facilities : 🚿 🚽 ⚰ ♿ 🍴 🖼
Nearby : ✂ 🏊 ≈ (beach) 🐎 🐴

Longitude : 2.4
Latitude : 47.87

LUÇAY-LE-MÂLE

36360 – Michelin map **323** E4 – pop. 1 496 – alt. 160
▶ Paris 240 – Le Blanc 73 – Blois 60 – Châteauroux 43

⛰ Municipal la Foulquetière

℘ 02 54 40 43 31, www.lucaylemale.fr

Address : at La Foulquetière (3.8km southwest along the D 960,
follow the signs for Loches, D 13, follow the signs for Ecueillé to
left and take the road to the right)

Opening times : from beginning April to mid Oct.

1,5 ha (30 pitches) flat and relatively flat, grassy

Tariff : ★ 2€ ⇔ 🚗 2,50€ – 🔌 (6A) 1,50€
Rental rates : Permanent 🏠 – 3 🏘 – 2 gîtes. Per night from
Per week from 263 to 330€
🚐 borne 3€
80m from a small lake that is very popular with anglers.

Surroundings : 🏞 ♨
Leisure activities : 🚣 🏊
Facilities : ♿ ⚰ 🍴 ⚰ 🖼
Nearby : 🍴 ✕ 🚴 ✂ 🏊 ≈ (beach) 🐎 pedalos

Longitude : 1.40
Latitude : 47.11

LUNERY

18400 – Michelin map **323** J5 – pop. 1 449 – alt. 150
▶ Paris 256 – Bourges 23 – Châteauroux 51 – Issoudun 28

⛰ Intercommunal de Lunery

℘ 02 48 68 07 38, www.cc-fercher.fr – 🛖

Address : 6 rue de l'Abreuvoir (in the town, near the church)

Opening times : from mid May to mid Sept.

0,5 ha (37 pitches) flat, grassy

Tariff : (2013 Price) ★ 4€ ⇔ 🚗 6€ – 🔌 (10A) 2€
*Based around the remains of an old windmill near the
river.*

Surroundings : 🌊 🏞 ♨
Leisure activities : 🎱 🚣
Facilities : ♿ 🔑 🍴 🖼
Nearby : 🍴 ✕ ✂

Longitude : 2.27
Latitude : 46.936

CILLY-SUR-VIENNE

Michelin map **317** M6 – pop. 559 – alt. 60
280 – Azay-le-Rideau 32 – Chinon 30 – Châtellerault 29

ercommunal la Croix de la Motte

7 65 20 38, www.cc-saintemauredetouraine.fr

ss : 1.2km north along the D 18, follow the signs for L'Ile-
rd and take turning to the right

g times : from mid June to mid Sept.

61 pitches) flat, grassy

(2013 Price) ⚹ 2,50€ ⟳ 🚐 🅿 3€ – (✚) (16A) 3€

rates : (2013 Price) (from mid June to mid Sept.)
– 1 tent lodge . Per night 31 € – Per week from 150 to 315€
ne 4,10€

sant, shaded surroundings near the Vienne river.

undings :
re activities :
ies :

GPS Longitude : 0.54337
Latitude : 47.05075

Directions to campsite

GPS

NETOU-SUR-CHER

– Michelin map **318** I8 – pop. 878 – alt. 100
s 209 – Bourges 56 – Romorantin-Lanthenay 18 – Selles-sur-
7

unicipal Val Rose

4 98 11 02, mairie.mennetou@wanadoo.fr

ss : rue de Val Rose (south of the town, to the right after the
over the canal, 100m from the Cher river)

g times : from beginning May to beginning Sept.

50 pitches) flat, grassy

⚹ 2€ 🚐 🅿 3€ – (✚) (2A) 2,50€

rne 2€ – 🚐 (✚)8€

undings :
re activities :
ies :
y :

GPS Longitude : 1.86173
Latitude : 47.26937

me campsites benefit from proximity to a municipal
isure centre.

Address of campsite

Sani-station (borne) and fee (see page 12)

LAND

– Michelin map **318** D6 – pop. 547 – alt. 79
s 205 – Amboise 19 – Blois 23 – Château-Renault 20

Yelloh! Village Le Parc du Val de Loire

54 70 27 18, www.parcduvaldeloire.com

ss : 155 route de Fleuray (located 1.5km west)

ng times : from beginning April to end Sept.

300 pitches)

: 18€ ⚹⚹ 🚐 🅿 (✚) (10A) – Extra per person 6€

l rates : (from beginning April to end Sept.) – 130
. Per night from 39 to 97€ – Per week from 234 to 582€

ooded setting opposite a vineyard.

undings :
re activities :
ities :

GPS Longitude : 1.10477
Latitude : 47.51001

Rental options and rates

The Michelin Camping Guide selection lists the best sites in each 'comfort' category:

⩜⩜ ⩜⩜   Extremely comfortable, equipped to a very high standard

⩜⩜ ⩜⩜   Very comfortable, equipped to a high standard

⩜⩜ ⩜⩜   Comfortable and well equipped

⩜ ⩜   Reasonably comfortable

⩜ ⩜   Satisfactory

Exceptional campsites in each category are awarded an additional rating:

⩜⩜…⩜   Particularly pleasant setting, good quality and range of services available.

How the selection works:

• Campsites are ranked according to their location, facilities, etc., and are awarded a number of tent symbols – see above.

• In order for the guide to remain wholly objective, the selection is made on an entirely independent basis. There is no charge for being selected for the guide.

• The Michelineclassification (⩜⩜…⩜) is totally independent of the official star classification system awarded by the local prefecture or other official organisation.

• All practical information and classifications are revised and updated annually so that the information is as reliable and up to date as possible. Some information or pricing may have changed since the guide went to press. We recommend you check the price list online in advance or at the entrance to the campsite and enquire about possible restrictions.

• Our inspectors make regular visits to campsites; our readers' comments are also a valuable source of information, and regular follow-up visits are undertaken.

18 campsites have been classified ⩜⩜ / ⩜⩜ and 93 ⩜ / ⩜ in 2014. This selection can be found below and opposite.

⩜⩜ 2014

BERNY-RIVIÈRE	La Croix du Vieux Pont	DOL-DE-BRETAGNE	Les Castels Domaine des Ormes
CANET-PLAGE	Yelloh! Village Le Brasilia	GHISONACCIA	Arinella-Bianca
CARNAC	Les Castels La Grande Métairie	PIERREFITTE-SUR-SAULDRE	Les Alicourts

⩜⩜ 2014

BÉNODET	Le Letty	PERROS-GUIREC	Yelloh! Village Le Ranolien
BIRON	FranceLoc Le Moulinal	PYLA-SUR-MER	Yelloh! Village Panorama du Pyla
CANET-DE-SALARS	Les Castels Le Caussanel	QUIMPER	Les Castels L'Orangerie de Lanniron
CARANTEC	Yelloh! Village Les Mouettes	RAMATUELLE	Le Kon Tiki
CHASSIERS	Sunêlia Domaine Les Ranchisses	RUOMS	Sunêlia Aluna Vacances
DIENNÉ	DéfiPlanet au Domaine de Dienné	ST-CAST-LE-GUILDO	Les Castels Le Château de la Galinée
GHISONACCIA	Homair Vacances Marina d'Erba Rossa	ST-CRÉPIN-ET-CARLUCET	Les Peneyrals
GRANVILLE	Les Castels Le Château de Lez-Eaux	ST-JULIEN-DES-LANDES	Les Castels La Garangeoire
GRIMAUD	Les Prairies de la Mer	ST-JUST-LUZAC	Les Castels Sequoia Parc
HOURTIN-PLAGE	Club Airotel La Côte d'Argent	ST-LÉON-SUR-VÉZÈRE	Le Paradis
LACANAU-OCÉAN	Yelloh! Village Les Grands Pins	SAMPZON	Yelloh! Village Soleil Vivarais
LONGEVILLE-SUR-MER	MS Vacances Les Brunelles	SARLAT-LA-CANÉDA	La Palombière
MONTCLAR	Yelloh! Village Domaine d'Arnauteille	SOMMIÈRES	Les Castels Le Domaine de Massereau
MUROL	Sunêlia La Ribeyre	VALLON-PONT-D'ARC	Les Castels L'Ardéchois
NOYAL-MUZILLAC	Moulin de Cadillac	VIAS-PLAGE	Yelloh! Village Club Farret

ᨆᨆᨆ 2014

AGAY	Esterel Caravaning	MESSANGES	Club Airotel Le Vieux Port
ARGELÈS-GAZOST	Sunêlia Les Trois vallées	ROQUEBRUNE-SUR-ARGENS	Domaine de la Bergerie
ARGELÈS-SUR-MER	La Sirène et l'Hippocampe	SÉRIGNAN-PLAGE	Yelloh! Village
BADEN	Mané Guernehué		Le Sérignan Plage
BÉNODET	Sunêlia L'Escale St-Gilles	ST-ALBAN-AURIOLLES	Sunêlia Le Ranc Davaine
BISCARROSSE	Club Airotel Domaine de la Rive	ST-AVIT-DE-VIALARD	Les Castels St-Avit Loisirs
LABENNE-OCÉAN	Yelloh! Village le Sylvamar	ST-BREVIN-LES-PINS	Sunêlia Le Fief
LECTOURE	Yelloh! Village Le Lac des 3 Vallées	VALRAS-PLAGE	Domaine de La Yole

ᨆᨆᨆ 2014

AIGUES-MORTES	Yelloh! Village La Petite Camargue	MÉZOS	Club Airotel Le Village Tropical Sen Yan
ARGELÈS-SUR-MER	Le Front de Mer	MIMIZAN-PLAGE	Club Airotel Marina-Landes
ARGELÈS-SUR-MER	Le Soleil	LA PALMYRE	Village Siblu Bonne Anse Plage
ARZANO	Les Castels Ty Nadan	PORNIC	Club Airotel La Boutinardière
AVRILLÉ	FranceLoc Le Domaine Des Forges	PORTIRAGNES-PLAGE	Les Sablons
BELVÈS	FranceLoc Les Hauts de Ratebout	RAMATUELLE	Yelloh! Village les Tournels
BIDART	Les Castels Le Ruisseau des Pyrénées	RONCE-LES-BAINS	Village Siblu La Pignade
BIDART	Yelloh! Village Ilbarritz	RUOMS	Domaine de Chaussy
BISCARROSSE	Mayotte Vacances	RUOMS	Yelloh! Village La Plaine
BONIFACIO	Pertamina Village - U-Farniente	SARLAT-LA-CANÉDA	Les Castels Le Moulin du Roch
BORMES-LES-MIMOSAS	Le Camp du Domaine	SÉRIGNAN-PLAGE	Yelloh! Village Aloha
CARNAC-PLAGE	Les Menhirs	SOUSTONS	Village Vacances Framissima Nature
CASTELLANE	Les Castels Le Domaine du Verdon	ST-AYGULF	L'Étoile d'Argens
CHAMBON-SUR-LAC	Le Pré Bas	ST-CYPRIEN-PLAGE	Cala Gogo
COL-ST-JEAN	Yelloh! Village L'Étoile des Neiges	STE-CATHERINE-DE-FIERBOIS	Les Castels Parc de Fierbois
CONTIS-PLAGE	Yelloh! Village Lous Seurrots	ST-HILAIRE-DE-RIEZ	Les Biches
CORCIEUX	Yelloh! Village en Voges Domaine des Bans	ST-JEAN-DE-LUZ	Club Airotel Itsas Mendi
DOUCIER	Domaine de Chalain	ST-JEAN-DE-MONTS	Les Amiaux
FOUESNANT	Sunêlia L'Atlantique	ST-JEAN-DE-MONTS	Le Bois Joly
FRÉJUS	La Baume - la Palmeraie	ST-RAPHAËL	Les Castels Douce Quiétude
GIEN	Les Bois du Bardelet	TALMONT-ST-HILAIRE	Yelloh! Village Le Littoral
GHISONACCIA	Sunêlia Perla Di Mare	TORREILLES-PLAGE	Sunêlia Les Tropiques
ÎLE DE RÉ	Sunêlia Interlude	TORREILLES-PLAGE	Mar I Sol
ÎLE DE RÉ	L'Océan	VARENNES-SUR-LOIRE	Les Castels Domaine de la Brèche
ÎLE D'OLÉRON	Club Airotel Les Gros Joncs	VIAS-PLAGE	Sunêlia Domaine de la Dragonnière
LACANAU-OCÉAN	Club Airotel de l'Océan	VIELLE-SAINT-GIRONS	Sunêlia Le Col Vert
LARNAS	FranceLoc Le Domaine d'Imbours	VINSOBRES	Franceloc Le Sagittaire
LES MATHES	La Pinède	VITRAC	Domaine Soleil Plage
LIT-ET-MIXE	Village Center Les Vignes	VOGÜÉ	Domaine du Cros d'Auzon
MARIGNY	Les Castels La Pergola		
MARSEILLAN-PLAGE	Les Méditerranées – Beach Club Nouvelle Floride		

You can find a particular village or town in the index on page 510.

CAMPSITES

Michelin classification

AAAA AAAA — Extremely comfortable, equipped to a very high standard

AAA AAA — Very comfortable, equipped to a high standard

AAA AAA — Comfortable and well equipped

AA AA — Reasonably comfortable

A A — Satisfactory

• **Campsites are ranked according to their location, facilities, etc., within each category and are awarded a number of tent symbols – see page 8.**

• **Michelin classification (AAAA ... A) is totally independent of the official star classification system awarded by the local prefecture or other official organisation.**

Opening times

Permanent — Site open all year round

Special features

❄ Winter caravan sites: these sites are specially equipped for a winter holiday in the mountains. Facilities generally include central heating, electricity and drying rooms for clothes and equipment.

👥 Child-friendly sites, including washing facilities for young children, playgrounds and activities monitored by professionals

Exceptional in its category

AAAA ... A — Particularly pleasant setting, quality and range of services available.

🦢🦢 — Tranquil, isolated site – quiet site, particularly at night

≼≼ — Exceptional view – Interesting or panoramic view

General information

Access — Direction from nearest listed locality: north, south, east, west

☎ — Telephone

⚿ — 24 hour security: a warden usually lives on site and can be contacted during reception hours, although this does not mean round-the-clock surveillance outside normal hours

⚷ — Day security only

🚫 — No dogs (if dogs are permitted, a current vaccination certificate is required)

Ⓟ — Cars must be parked away from pitches

R̶ — Reservations not accepted

🚫 — Credit cards not accepted

🚫 — Chèque-vacances (French holiday vouchers) not accepted

CC — Chèque-vacances accepted

Site information

3 ha — Area available in hectares (1ha = 2.47 acres)

60 ha/3 ha for camping — Total area of the property/total area available for camping

90 pitches — Number of pitches

⬜ — Marked-off pitches

♀ ♀♀ ♀♀♀ — Shade: fair amount of shade to well shaded

⚓ — Waterside location with swimming area

Facilities

🔲 — Heating facilities

♿ — Facilities for the disabled

🚼 — Baby changing facilities

⚐ ⚐ — Each bay is equipped with water/drainage

Services

🚐	Services for campervans
sani-station 4 €	Type of service points and rates (see page 12)
3 回 15.50 €	Number of pitches equipped for campervans/daily rate per pitch
8 to 13 €	Daily fee formula
🦇	Special FFCC price for campervans at site (Fédération Française de Camping et Caravaning)
回	Washing machines, laundry
🛒 🏪	Supermarket – Grocery
🍴	Takeaway meals
((•))	Internet or Wifi point

Sports and leisure facilities

🍷	Bar (serving alcohol)
✕	Eating places (restaurant, snack-bar, etc)
🏠	Common room or games room
🎭	Miscellaneous activities (sports, culture, leisure)
🧗	Children's club
🏋	Exercise room or gym
⊆s	Sauna
🛝	Playground
🚲	Cycle hire
✂ 🎾	Tennis courts: open air/indoor
⛳ m	Minigolf
🏊 🏊	Swimming pool: indoor/open air
🏊	Bathing allowed (or supervised bathing)
🛝	Waterslide
🐟	Fishing
🛶	Canoeing
⚓	Sailing (school or centre)
⚓	Mooring pontoon (river mooring)
🐎	Pony trekking or riding

• **The majority of outdoor leisure facilities are only open in season and during peak periods; opening times are not necessarily the same as those of the site and some facilities are only available during the summer season.**

Nearby The guide only features facilities that are in the vicinity of the campsite

Charges in euros

Daily charge:

🚶 5 €	per person
🚗 2 €	per vehicle
回 7.50 €	per pitch (tent/caravan)
⚡ 2.50 € (4A)	for electricity (calculated by number of ampere units)

Inclusive rates:

25 € 🚶🚶 🚗	pitch for 2 people
回 ⚡ (10A)	including vehicle and electricity

• **The prices listed were supplied by the campsite owners in Autumn 2013 (if prices were not available, those from the previous year are given). The fees should be regarded as basic charges and may fluctuate with inflation.**

• **Listings shown in** light type **(i.e. not bold) indicate that not all revised charges have been provided by the owners.**

• **Additional charges may apply for some facilities (e.g., swimming pool, tennis courts), as well as for long stays.**

• **Special rates may apply for children – ask owner for details.**

Rentals

12 🚐	Number of mobile homes
20 🏠	Number of chalets
6 🛏	Number of rooms to rent
Per night 30 to 50€	Minimum/maximum rates per night
Per week 300 to 800€	Minimum/maximum rates per week

LOCALITY INFORMATION

23700	Postcode
343 B8	Michelin map reference
Rennes 47	Distance in kilometres
1 050 pop.	Population
alt. 675	Altitude (in metres)
⚕	Spa
1200/1900m	Altitude (in metres) of resort/ highest point reached by lifts

• **Should you have grounds for complaint during your stay at a campsite about your reservation, the prices, standards of hygiene or facilities available, we recommend that you first try to resolve the problem with the proprietor or with the person responsible.**

• **If you are unable to resolve the disagreement, and if you are sure that you are within your rights, you could take the matter up with the relevant prefecture of the department.**

• **We welcome all suggestions and comments, whether in criticism or praise, relating to the campsites recommended in our guide. However, we must stress that we have neither the facilities nor the authority to deal with complaints between campers and proprietors.**

A sani-station, known in French as a 'borne', can be one of several proprietary commercial makes or a local, home-made 'artisanale' device. In return for a payment of a few euros or using a 'jeton', a pre-paid token, you receive fresh water, mains electricity and access to rubbish bins, plus grey and black waste disposal.

borne	sani-station
borne artisanale	local sani-station
borne eurorelais, flot bleu, raclet, Urbaco	different types of commercial sani-station
borne autre	other type of sani-station

accès difficile	difficult access
accès direct à	direct access to…
accidenté	uneven, hilly
adhésion	membership
aire (de repos)	rest area
après-midi	afternoon
arrêt	stop (traffic instruction)
Ascension	Feast of the Ascension
assurance obligatoire	insurance cover compulsory
août	August
automne	autumn
avenue (av.)	avenue
avril	April
baie	bay
bain	bath
base de loisirs	leisure and activity park/ centre
bois, boisé	wood, wooded
bord	shore, riverbank
au bord de la mer	by the sea
borne	sani-station (see page 12)
boucher	butcher
boulanger	baker
boulevard (bd.)	boulevard.
au bourg	in town/in the village
cadre agréable	attractive setting
cadre sauvage	natural setting
carrefour	crossroads
cases réfrigérées	refrigerated food storage facilities
cedez le passage	give way (on roads)
centre équestre	equestrian centre
chambre d'hôte	guesthouse, B&B
château	castle
chemin	path
conseillé	advised
cotisation obligatoire	membership charge obligatoire
en cours d'aménagement	rebuilding work in progress
croisement difficile	difficult access
crêperie	pancake restaurant/stall
décembre (déc.)	December
déjeuner	lunch
derrière	behind
dimanche	Sunday
dîner	dinner
douche	shower
à droite	on/to the right
église	church
embouteillage	traffic jam

emplacement (empl.)	pitch
entrée	way in, entrance
entrée fleurie	attractive floral entrance/ reception area
essence	petrol, gas
étang	lake, pool
été	summer
falaise	cliff
famille	family
fermé	closed
feu rouge	traffic lights
février (fév.)	February
forêt	forest
garage	parking
garage pour caravans	covered parking for caravans
garderie (d'enfants)	(children's) crèche
gare routière	bus/coach station
gare (S.N.C.F.)	railway station
à gauche	on/to the left
gazole	diesel
goudronné	surfaced road
GPL	LPG
gratuit	free, no charge
gravier	gravel
gravillons	fine gravel
hammam	Turkish-style steam bath with plunge pools
herbeux	grassy
hiver	winter
hors saison	out of season
île, îlot	island
incliné	sloping
indispensable	essential
interdit	forbidden, prohibited
intersection	junction
janvier (janv.)	January
jeudi	Thursday
jour	day
juillet (juil.)	July
juin	June
lac	lake
lande	heath/moorland
licence obligatoire	camping licence/ international camping carnet compulsory
au lieu-dit	in the small locality of/at the place known as
lundi	Monday

mai	May	priorité à droite	priority to right (give way to traffic from right, traffic joining roundabouts has priority, traffic on minor roads has right-of-way onto major roads, sign: black cross inside red triangle)
mairie	town hall		
marché	market		
mardi	Tuesday		
mars	March		
matin	morning		
mer	sea		
mercredi	Wednesday		
mineurs non accompagnés non admis	under 18s must be accompanied by an adult	à proximité	nearby
montagne	mountain	quartier	quarter, district, area
		Rameaux	Palm Sunday
Noël	Christmas	réservé	reserved, booked
non clos	open site (landscape)	rive droite, gauche	right, left bank
novembre (nov.)	November	rivière	river
nuit	night	rocailleux	stony, rocky, rugged
à la nuitée	per night, on a nightly basis	rocheux	rocky
		rond-point	roundabout
		route (rte)	road
octobre (oct.)	October	rue (r.)	street
ouvert	open	ruisseau	stream
ouverture prévue	opening scheduled		
		sablonneux	sandy
en panne	broken down	saison (tourist)	tourist season
Pâques	Easter	samedi	Saturday
parcours de santé	fitness trail	avec sanitaires	with sanitary facilities
passage non admis	no touring pitches	schéma	local map
péage	toll	semaine	week
pelouse	lawn	à la semaine	per week, on a weekly basis
pente	sloping/slope	septembre (sept.)	September
Pentecôte	Whitsun	soir	evening
personne (pers.)	person	sortie	way out, exit
petit-déjeuner	breakfast	sous-bois	undergrowth
pierreux	stony	(face) à la station	(opposite) at the filling station
piéton	pedestrian		
pinède	pine trees, pine wood	supplémentaire (suppl.)	extra
place (pl.)	square		
places limitées pour le passage	limited number of touring pitches	en terrasses	terraced
		toboggan aquatique	water slide
plage	beach	torrent	torrent (river/stream)
plan d'eau	stretch of water, artificial lake	Toussaint	All Saints' Day (1 Nov)
		tout compris	all inclusive
plat	flat	tout droit	straight ahead
pneu	tyre		
pont	bridge	unleaded	sans plomb
port	port, harbour		
prairie	grassland, lawn	vacances scolaires	school holidays
pré	meadow	vallonné	undulating
près de	near	vendredi	Friday
presqu'île	peninsula	verger	fruit trees, orchard
prévu	projected	vers	in the direction of/towards
printemps	spring	Voie Verte	green trail
en priorité	as a priority	voir	see

SPA FACILITIES ON THE CAMPSITES

Spas are back in fashion! And outdoor campsites are only too keen to ride the crest of this wave of enthusiasm for relaxation and health by expanding their range of services to include spa treatments. More and more tourists are attracted to the idea of spending a few hours on holiday in a spa, especially in the resort where they are actually staying.

But what do we really mean when we talk about spa facilities? The term 'spa' covers any kind of treatment with hot water (20–34°C) involving hydro massage, such as jacuzzi and whirlpool bathing. Often these are combined with other treatments using dry or wet steam (saunas and hammams), as well as massage and body sculpting massage.

Hot water and water vapour have many benefits: relaxing the muscles, stimulating blood circulation, eliminating toxins and dead skin, and dilating the pores. It is an excellent way to treat rheumatic and skin conditions and helps reduce stress.

© T. Pepeira / Iconotec / Photononstop

On campsites, spa centres – areas specifically dedicated to providing these treatments – are not medical facilities as such, but they are run by healthcare professionals. Nor are they open access, as the amenities provided generally have to be paid for.

© Image Source G / Photononstop

Particular attention is given to the decor of such centres, often utilising a Greco-Roman or contemporary type design, special lighting effects, background music and an array of aromas: everything is designed to make you feel completely relaxed. We have carefully chosen campsites with the finest spa facilities (see the names and detailed descriptions of the selected campsites), where you will find jacuzzis, saunas, hammams and massages. What a great way to relax!

Club Airotel Domaine de la Rive

ⵟⵟⵟ

AQUITAINE
Biscarrosse (40)
See page 55

This holiday village is located on the shores of a lake (Cazaux-Sanguinet) and has direct access to the beach. It offers accommodation in chalets tucked away in the pine forest with wooden terraces that provide a sense of warmth and (something important to hardcore campers) space. But the real plus point of this place is Aquarive Park, with its slides, banana boats and other colourful attractions, which children will love, whilst for adults there is a wave pool and the more adventurous can safely learn water sports (such as sailing, water skiing, racing between buoys) at La Rive Watersports.

Village Vacances Port Lalande

ⵟ

AQUITAINE
Castelmoron-sur-Lot (47)
See page 58

Port Lalande is a small harbour built on the banks of the Lot. Located in a huge area of greenery, this resort offers accommodation in extremely comfortable air-conditioned chalets with terraces and outdoor garden lounges. You can safely leave children aged 6 to 10 in the care of childminders to supervise their activities (including paddling) while you explore the area, swim in the outdoor pool or head for the spa facility, one of the best features of the place, offering sauna, hammam and massages. It has all you need to eliminate toxins or stress.

Mayotte Vacances

ⵟⵟⵟ

AQUITAINE
Biscarrosse (40)
See page 55

This feels like a tropical island! The Indian Ocean my be a long way from the Atlantic, but you could quite easily believe that's where you are once you arrive here, right down to the lovely mobile homes and tented lodges in bright colours. As well as all the usual amenities of a luxury campsite (including 450 square metres of shops), Mayotte Vacances offers a large area for aquatic activities, complete with lagoon pool, water slides and paddling pools, gym, spa, restaurant, sports facilities for beach volleyball, basketball and mini-golf, four children's clubs (grouped according to age), cabaret evenings and even a beauty salon. You almost never need to set foot outside the place!

Yelloh! Village Le Sylvamar

ⵟⵟⵟ

AQUITAINE
Labenne-Océan (40)
See page 65

If you head to the heart of the pine forest, you'll discover Le Sylvamar hidden away. Located in the Labenne-Océan district, this resort on the Landes coast offers a wide variety of camping accommodation from simple pitches to Palombière, beautiful cabins built in the trees. Comfortable cottages and chalets are also available. Then you are spoiled for choice in terms of sports; you can enjoy a huge area for aquatic activities and two heated pools. And for those who want to explore the country, Spain and the Pyrenees are virtually next door.

Yelloh! Village Les Grands Pins

AQUITAINE
Lacanau-Océan (33)
See page 66

Just a few yards from the beach, this campsite is a great holiday village, with the typical hilly terrain and shady pine trees that are common to the Landes. It has first-class amenities too, of course. These include partially covered swimming pools and a small shopping centre for everything you might need during your stay, not to mention the comfortable mobile homes located on the main site itself. Some have a tall wooden design that blends in with the surroundings and wooden decor reminiscent of the pine trees. Finally, part of the place is closed off to motor vehicles, in order to protect the environment and for the comfort of holidaymakers, especially those with children.

Village Vacances Sunêlia Le Framissima Nature

AQUITAINE
Soustons (40)
See page 86

This resort is unusual in that it was built only recently. Just a few years ago it was simply a stretch of Landes pine forest. Then the Fram Group, travel specialists, decided to open their first site here, building wooden mobile homes and tented lodges with large covered terraces and all the latest facilities on the beach, in the shade of the pine trees. To blend in with the natural environment, the buildings are made of Landes pinewood and the pool is drained naturally into the surrounding greenery. In addition to its spa facilities, this new holiday resort benefits from being close to Lake Soustons and the sea.

Airotel Le Vieux Port

AQUITAINE
Messanges (40)
See page 69

A short walk from the ocean and the large sandy Landes beaches, Le Vieux Port has a landscape lined with trees. You can even ignore the Atlantic if you like, since the aquatic area of the campsite has several pools, a paddling pool and slides for children, both younger (from aged 3) and older (from aged 10). Other attractions include an equestrian centre, activities and sports facilities. Relax and recharge your batteries at this lovely spot while all the family has fun.

Le Pré Bas

AUVERGNE
Chambon-sur-Lac (63)
See page 97

These camping facilities lie on the shore of Lake Chambon, which is overlooked by an enormous mountain range. High hedges, mostly flat or slightly inclined, surround the buildings, offering some privacy. The floral spaces are well laid out and you can swim in the lake or in one of two heated pools, complete with four slides. There is entertainment galore, plus a play area for children and fitness facilities for adults. Walkers or sports enthusiasts into hiking, biking or climbing will love the clean air in the vast surrounding open space.

Mané Guernehué

ᴧᴧᴧᴧ

BRITTANY
Baden (56)
See page 114

In the Gulf of Morbihan, the small town of Baden is home to one of the most beautiful campsites in the area, set on gently sloping grassy terrain. The accommodation consists of tents or caravans, as well as mobile homes, chalets and even traditional gypsy caravans. And, appropriately enough, there is also a riding farm. The site offers a wide selection of activities and entertainment, including a partially covered aquatic area with slides. For those who prefer to relax while on holiday, new facilities include a jacuzzi, sauna, hammam and gym, with massages and facials also available. It's a great place in which to unwind.

Yelloh! Village Les Pins

ᴧᴧᴧᴧ

BRITTANY
Erquy (22)
See page 123

This is like a small town among pine trees, but one equipped with plenty of space and gentle undulations that divide into areas offering good shade. A small swimming pool, ideal for doing lengths, is there to welcome you, along with a massive aquatic area with waterfalls and slides, all centrally located. Stay in one of the chalets with a living area of 37 square metres and let your little ones check out the kids club while you enjoy the spa, gym or tennis courts. A perfect place to enjoy a relaxing holiday en famille.

Sunêlia L'Escale St-Gilles

ᴧᴧᴧᴧ

BRITTANY
Bénodet (29)
See page 116

L'Escale St Gilles is ideally located right on the coast. There is a magnificent first class spa centre on site, a large heated and partially covered aquatic area and beautiful beaches with straw huts providing shade. It remains open on some evenings in season to the great delight of those who enjoy slides and other water games. On other nights you can enjoy cabaret entertainment, quizzes and karaoke. Whether you bring your own equipment (tents/caravans) or choose to stay in one of the very comfortable mobile homes, you will be on a clearly marked pitch covering at least 100 square metres.

Yelloh! Village Le Ranolien

ᴧᴧᴧᴧ

BRITTANY
Perros-Guirec (22)
See page 133

There is plenty of variety at Le Ranolien. The campsite has pitches for tents or caravans and boasts outdoor mobile homes, atmospheric gypsy caravans and top quality chalets. The latter are equipped with a 1.8-metre bed, two flat screen TVs, hi-fi system and dishwasher. Le Ranolien is also a holiday club with many activities, sports during the day, entertainment or cultural events in the evening, plus superb facilities for health and relaxation treatments: spa, hammam, sauna, massage. It has a unique location in the heart of a protected natural site. What more could one want?

Les Alicourts

ᨆᨆ

CENTRE
Pierrefitte-sur-Sauldre (41)
See page 181

You'll never be bored at Les Alicourts. The resort offers plenty of aquatic activities, with four swimming pools (including one wave pool), a lavish spa area and a 6-hectare lake for swimming and canoeing. You'll be spoilt for choice between relaxation (spa) and sports (fishing, golf, mini-golf, skate park, fitness facilities), and your children will be kept amused with organized activities throughout the day. Every type of accommodation is available: spacious pitches for tents and caravans, chalets, cottages, tree houses, and – the latest arrival – 'explorer' and 'safari' lodges.

Yelloh! Village Mer et Soleil

ᨆᨆ

LANGUEDOC-ROUSSILLON
Agde (34)
See page 226

Between the Rhone and the Mediterranean, this 8-hectare landscaped environment with its flat grassy or sandy terrain features mobile homes, chalets, furnished tents and simple pitches. Leisure activities involving water are a key feature at this site, with the sea just a kilometre away, an excellent aquatic area with an upstairs restaurant and, best of all for spa lovers, wonderful facilities over 650 square metres in size. In this haven of relaxation choose from such delightful options as 'Bitter Orange and Poppy', 'Volcanic Escape' or even 'Provençal Relaxation'. After treating yourself to a treatment, you will be ready for the evening activities that await.

Arinella-Bianca

ᨆᨆ

CORSICA
Ghisonaccia (20)
See page 199

Located on the east coast of Corsica, known as the 'Isle of Beauty', Ghisonaccia is a small resort offering several campsites but Arinella Bianca stands out because of the quality of its services and its great location. It is right next to the sandy beach, and the vegetation, including palm trees, eucalyptus and oleander, make this a particularly pleasant resort. Many of the available activities revolve around water: sea fishing or in the small inland lake, outdoor fitness facilities and an indoor spa, a sailing club and, for fun, buoy-to-buoy racing! There are plenty of things to do in the evening as well and sometimes it may even be your turn to take to the stage!

L'Arche

ᨆᨆ

LANGUEDOC-ROUSSILLON
Anduze (30)
See page 227

This seaside campsite seems a million miles from any urban or industrial setting. A charming and friendly welcome lends it a family atmosphere. Located at the foot of the Cevennes, it is the perfect place for a vacation in the countryside on a quiet site designed for relaxation. There isn't a great variety of properties to rent. Camping facilities predominate. Pleasant shady pitches overlook the river and the small sandy beach with rocks lying a little further on. The site's amenities include a pleasant indoor pool, while the hammam, sauna and jacuzzi complement the outdoor pool and water slides.

Domaine de Beauséjour

LANGUEDOC-ROUSSILLON
Sérignan-Plage (34)
See page 254

Nestled under a series of dunes that hide some of the most beautiful beaches of Languedoc, the Domaine de Beauséjour extends over 10 hectares. There are plenty of accommodation options, from mobile homes to comfortable chalets, as well as pitches for tents and caravans. Special mention must be made of the indoor spa area, which is lavishly decorated in a contemporary style with an oriental touch. A range of state-of-the-art treatments are offered there. You simply have to try it! Another attraction of this beautiful campsite is the sailing and water sports centre on the Séoune beach, which campers are free to use.

Albirondack Park

MIDI-PYRÉNÉES
Albi (81)
See page 286

Located near the historic city of Albi, a designated UNESCO World Heritage site, this campsite is in a hilly, shady location and provides pitches for tents, caravans and motor homes as well as chalets, mobile homes and even treehouses for the more adventurous. After a day of sightseeing or simply relaxing, you will find an on-site pool with a lovely terrace, a new indoor spa offering sauna, hammam and jacuzzi, and finally, for lunch or for dinner, a high quality restaurant with American-style interior.

Sunêlia Les Tropiques

LANGUEDOC-ROUSSILLON
Torreilles-Plage (66)
See page 255

This 8-hectare site with its lush vegetation is an established resort with pitches under palm trees and mobile homes of various sizes, some of which have been adapted to accommodate disabled persons. Naturally, there is an aquatic area with several pools, one of which has a waterslide (with four tracks). Children and younger guests are catered for too and enjoy the giant inflatable giraffe. Adults can enjoy the numerous sports on offer (tennis, petanque, archery, etc.) and can take advantage of the spa facilities, which are open 7 days a week during the summer season.

© C. Sjodin Lindqvist / Jahner / Photononstop

Village Vacances
Le Domaine du Pré

PAYS-DE-LA-LOIRE
La Chapelle-Hermier (85)
See page 358

Situated beside Lake Jaunay, Domaine du Pré offers a concept of outdoor tourism that combines ecology, health and leisure. There are 128 chalets spread over 12 hectares of natural beauty, wholly dedicated to your relaxation and well-being. As well as enjoyable amenities such as an indoor pool and a heated lake for swimming, the resort has a fitness centre where massages, chromotherapy, colonic irrigation and rebirth relaxation are all available. The activities offered vary according to the season, but all revolve around similar themes combining nature and health.

Sunêlia Interlude

POITOU-CHARENTES
Le Bois-Plage-en-Ré (17)
See page 403

This really is Ile de Ré at its best. The huge campsite is set on slightly hilly terrain with dry vegetation reminiscent of that of the south of France. Its irregularly shaped plots seem to accentuate the feeling of an untamed landscape. Mobile homes clad in dark wood on terraces blend into the landscape perfectly. Some pitches for tents and caravans are also available. The site has excellent amenities including a brasserie, a restaurant, a supermarket and a beautiful pool. In summer the atmosphere buzzes with all the events and activities taking place throughout the day.

Sunêlia Le Fief

PAYS-DE-LA-LOIRE
St-Brévin-les-Pins (44)
See page 376

This village resort lies on the Côte de Jade between the sea and the forest. It covers a large flat grassy area. In addition to traditional camping facilities, high quality mobile homes are also available. A dozen camp organizers ensure a lively atmosphere with colourful theme nights during which even children get to take part in musical extravaganzas. The area set aside for children is large and very well equipped. There is a 500-square metre aquatic area with rapids, lagoons and waterfalls, along with a wide variety of sports facilities, including archery and beach volleyball. And for those seeking tranquility and health, there is no better place to relax than the spa area with its jacuzzi and sauna.

L'Océan

POITOU-CHARENTES
La Couarde-sur-Mer (17)
See page 404

Although it was affected by Cyclone Xynthia, this campsite has made a spirited recovery. The management used the opportunity to refurbish and renew the rental accommodation and equipment to the latest standards. The result is a consistent, well-run site, with disabled access, offering a vast array of mobile homes, including an exclusive village made up of mobile homes with three bedrooms, superb bathrooms and a luxurious exclusive aquatic area with a large swimming pool under palm trees. The sports facilities include a multi-purpose sports ground, tennis courts and mini-golf. And for those who like fishing, there is a small pond containing eels, bream and bass.

DéfiPlanet au Domaine de Dienné

POITOU-CHARENTES
Dienné (86)
See page 402

In this beautiful area of 47-hectares you can choose between a small campsite, with all the modern comforts, in an environmentally friendly setting, and a range of unusual accommodation: prefab cube shelters (carré d'étoiles), gypsy caravans, cabins and treehouses or yurts, etc. All the activities are organized with health in mind: there's a variety of sports, an equestrian centre, water aerobics, fitness trails, walking and biking. There are also zip wires, a climbing tower and fishing. If you just want to relax, you can use the jacuzzi and hammam. Finally, the restaurant offers 'designer menus' (for losing weight or to help with cardiovascular problems) prepared by a doctor and a Michelin-starred chef.

Club Airotel Les Gros Joncs

POITOU-CHARENTES
St-Georges-d'Oléron (17)
See page 407

Backing onto the dunes that are lapped by the ocean, this campsite occupies a pleasant location with direct access to the beach via beautiful shady wild trails – a village hidden in the forest. The accommodation consists of mobile homes and cottages, five of which are accessible to people with reduced mobility. The site facilities offer disabled access, including to the pool. The amenities are also first rate, with a grocery store, a restaurant offering fine cuisine and a swimming pool, not to mention the spa with its counter-current pool and whirlpool. Most of all, it offers a charming and professional welcome.

Esterel Caravaning

PROVENCE-ALPES-
CÔTE-D'AZUR
Agay (83)
See page 424

At the heart of the Esterel massif, this is a very comfortable place to stay. The beautiful living space around which it is organized offers all the amenities you could ever want: a large grocery store, shop, excellent restaurant, bar with a cosy atmosphere and spa centre. The aquatic area may not be eye-catching, but it is fully equipped with covered swimming pools and paddling pools. There are other activities and a sports ground plus a ranch. You can stay in a mobile home or on one of the pitches in the hilly section of the site, shaded by pines. There are various clubs and activities to suit all ages and tastes, along with entertainment in the evenings.

Yelloh! Village L'Étoile des Neiges

⛰

PROVENCE-ALPES-CÔTE-D'AZUR
Col Saint-Jean (04140)
See page 433

Perched 1,300 metres above sea level, this family campsite is open in both winter and summer. Lying on a gentle green slope in the foothills of the Dormillouse massif, it has a panoramic outdoor pool, an indoor leisure pool and a beautiful indoor spa facility, including sauna, hammam and fitness suite. Most of the site consists of accommodation, offering a wide range of mobile homes and some beautiful cottages sheltered by pines. You can ski here in winter, using the nearby ski lifts.

Le Kon Tiki

⛰

PROVENCE-ALPES-CÔTE-D'AZUR
Ramatuelle (83)
See page 446

At the edge of Pampelonne, the most sought-after resort in Europe, Kon Tiki offers a complete change of scenery. It is a village consisting of luxurious 'Tiki Huts'. Leisure facilities include a wellness suite, hairdressing salon, bar, restaurant, beach café, and (externally supplied) jet skiing, ski-tubing, parasailing and even skiing on a slope with artificial snow! Younger visitors can enjoy a supervised Kids Club for age-appropriate play activities. However the key feature is undoubtedly the wellness centre, consisting of several spa pools, massage, hammam and sauna suites.

Les Prairies de la Mer

⛰

PROVENCE-ALPES-CÔTE-D'AZUR
Grimaud (83)
See page 438

This site is notable for its direct access to a sandy beach and stunning views of St Tropez and its gulf. In addition to a standard range of accommodation and traditional campsite pitches, it also offers original accommodation in the shape of exotic wood-clad huts (*fares*). Some of these form an unusual village with small wooden bridges, water points, internal gardens and communal areas for relaxation. Other (very popular) huts line the beach and offer a unique view of the Gulf of St Tropez. Naturally, the site also possesses all the amenities you would expect, including spa facilities and leisure activities to suit all ages.

Yelloh! Village Au Joyeux Réveil

⛰

RHÔNE-ALPES
Autrans (38)
See page 463

Nestling in a peaceful valley of the Vercors mountains, this small campsite is 1,050 metres above sea level. It is run by Christine and Franck, and is a very family friendly. Just a short distance from the village of Autrans, the site offers a nice relaxing pool area, including three heated pools, one indoor pool for the more delicate and three small slides. The pitches, which boast thick grass, are quite spacious and provide some shade. Towards the rear of the site are tastefully furnished mobile homes. In summer, a lively team organizes entertainment and fun activities for children.

Sunêlia Domaine Les Ranchisses

RHÔNE-ALPES
Chassiers (07)
See page 470

The sound of cicadas, vines, olive trees… this stunning location is in the southern part of the Regional Natural Park of Monts d'Ardèche. At the entrance stands a restored Cévennes farmhouse, now home to the reception and restaurant. The extensive range of facilities and activities include a superb pool with a variety of slides, a wellness suite (offering massages and other treatments), a fitness club, a skate park and canoeing. The well-shaded and compact camping pitches are next to the river, while further up, on the other side of the road, another part of the site consists of cottages and modern accommodation, in the form of stylish 'Taos' mobile homes.

© L. Invernizzi Tettoni / Tips / Photononstop

Sunêlia Aluna Vacances

RHÔNE-ALPES
Ruoms (07)
See page 491

White oaks, vines and scrubland surround this family campsite, which has not been over-expanded. Part of the site consists of comfortable rental cottages, some of which are accessible to disabled persons, while the rest is, of course, dedicated to traditional camping pitches. The large pool facilities, featuring an artificial 'island', offer waterslides, waterfalls, a swimming area, a paddling pool and a solarium. And there's plenty to do at night too! There is a café-theatre, where cabaret and musicals and other entertainment are organized, as well as discos on some evenings.

Sunêlia Le Ranc Davaine

RHÔNE-ALPES
St-Alban-Auriolles (07)
See page 493

This village set in the scrubland really does offer all the shops and facilities you could ever need, including internet access. On the vast site, there is a choice of accommodation in chalets and cottages of varying sizes, all with private terraces, or on a shaded campsite. Most importantly, it has extensive aquatic facilities including a swimming area with two separate pools, waterfalls, a paddling pool, a whirlpool bath and a spa centre. There are clubs for younger children and of course, evening entertainment with shows, games and a disco.

Key

On the following pages you will find a region-by-region summary of localities with at least one site with the following facilities:

BRITTANY	Name of the region
Carnac	Name of the locality
(quiet icon)	Locality with at least one quiet and peaceful campsite
P	Town with at least one campsite open all year round
(family icon)	Locality with at least one campsite suitable for families
(water park icon)	Locality with at least one campsite with a water park
B	Locality with at least one selected site with a spa centre
(entertainment icon)	Locality with at least one campsite offering entertainment/organized activities (sports, culture, leisure)

• For more details on specific sites, refer to the individual campsite entries

	Page	(quiet)	Permanent	(family)	(water park)	Spa centre	(entertainment)
ALSACE							
Burnhaupt-le-Haut	37		P				
Geishouse	38		P				
Heimsbrunn	38		P				
Munster	40						(entertainment)
Oberbronn	41					B	
Ranspach	41		P				
Rhinau	41				(water park)		
Seppois-le-Bas	42		P				(entertainment)
Wattwiller	43			(family)			
AQUITAINE							
Ainhoa	48		P				
Anglet	48				(water park)		(entertainment)
Arès	49						(entertainment)
Atur	50			(family)	(water park)		(entertainment)
Aureilhan	50			(family)			
Azur	50			(family)	(water park)		(entertainment)
Badefols-sur-Dordogne	51				(water park)		
Baudreix	51				(water park)		
Bélus	51				(water park)		
Belvès	52			(family)			(entertainment)
Bias	52			(family)			
Bidart	53	(quiet)		(family)	(water park)		(entertainment)
Biron	54			(family)	(water park)		(entertainment)
Biscarrosse	55			(family)	(water park)	B	(entertainment)
Biscarrosse-Plage	56						(entertainment)
Bordeaux	56		P				
Le Bugue	57			(family)	(water park)		
Le Buisson-de-Cadouin	57			(family)	(water park)		
Campagne	57			(family)			
Castelmoron-sur-Lot	58					B	(entertainment)
Castelnaud-la-Chapelle	58				(water park)		
Contis-Plage	60			(family)			(entertainment)
Daglan	60			(family)	(water park)		
Dax	61			(family)			
Les Eyzies-de-Tayac	62			(family)	(water park)		
Gradignan	63		P				
Groléjac	63			(family)	(water park)		
Hautefort	63	(quiet)					
Hendaye	63			(family)			(entertainment)
Hourtin	64			(family)			
Hourtin-Plage	64			(family)	(water park)		(entertainment)
Itxassou	65		P				
Labenne-Océan	65			(family)			
Lacanau	65			(family)	(water park)	B	(entertainment)
Lacanau-Océan	66			(family)		B	(entertainment)
Lamonzie-Montastruc	66			(family)	(water park)		
Lanouaille	66				(water park)		
Laruns	67		P				
Léon	67			(family)			(entertainment)
Lescun	67	(quiet)					
Linxe	68				(water park)		(entertainment)
Lit-et-Mixe	68			(family)	(water park)		(entertainment)
Mauléon-Licharre	68	(quiet)					
Messanges	69			(family)	(water park)	B	(entertainment)

	Page	🥾	Permanent	👥	🛝	Spa centre	🛡️
Mezos	69			👥	🛝		🛡️
Mimizan	70			👥	🛝		🛡️
Mimizan-Plage	70			👥			🛡️
Moliets-Plage	70			👥			🛡️
Monpazier	70			👥	🛝		🛡️
Parcoul	72		P		🛝		
Parentis-en-Born	72			👥			
Petit-Palais-et-Cornemps	72		P				
Peyrignac	72		P				
Plazac	73			👥			
Le Porge	73			👥			🛡️
Pyla-sur-Mer	74	🥾		👥	🛝		🛡️
La Roque-Gageac	75			👥			
Saint-Amand-de-Coly	75			👥	🛝		
Saint-Antoine-d'Auberoche	76				🛝		
Saint-Aulaye	76				🛝		
Saint-Avit-de-Vialard	76			👥	🛝		🛡️
Saint-Crépin-et-Carlucet	76			👥	🛝		🛡️
Saint-Émilion	77			👥	🛝		
Saint-Geniès	77			👥	🛝		
Saint-Girons-Plage	77			👥	🛝		🛡️
Saint-Jean-de-Luz	78	🥾		👥	🛝		🛡️
Saint-Laurent-Médoc	80				🛝		
Saint-Léon-sur-Vézère	80			👥			🛡️
Saint-Martin-de-Seignanx	80			👥			
Saint-Paul-lès-Dax	80			👥			
Saint-Pée-sur-Nivelle	81			👥			
Saint-Saud-Lacoussière	81			👥	🛝		
Salles	82			👥	🛝		
Sanguinet	83			👥	🛝		🛡️
Sarlat-la-Canéda	83			👥	🛝		🛡️
Saubion	85						🛡️
Seignosse-Océan	85			👥			🛡️
Soulac-sur-Mer	86			👥	🛝		🛡️
Soustons	86					B	🛡️
Le Teich	87			👥			
La Teste-de-Buch	87			👥	🛝		🛡️
Urrugne	88		P	👥			
Le Verdon-sur-Mer	89			👥			🛡️
Vielle-Saint-Girons	90			👥	🛝		🛡️
Villeréal	90			👥	🛝		🛡️
Vitrac	91			👥	🛝		🛡️
AUVERGNE							
Ambert	95				🛝		
Arnac	95						🛡️
Aydat	96						🛡️
Chambon-sur-Lac	97	🥾		👥	🛝	B	🛡️
Champagnac-le-Vieux	98						🛡️
Châtelguyon	98			👥			🛡️
Langeac	100						🛡️
Lapeyrouse	100		P				
Murat-le-Quaire	102	🥾					
Murol	102			👥	🛝		🛡️
Neuvéglise	103						🛡️
Orcet	103		P				
Royat	104			👥			🛡️
Sainte-Sigolène	108			👥			
Singles	108			👥			🛡️
Vic-sur-Cère	109	🥾			🛝		
Vorey	109				🛝		
BRITTANY							
Ambon	114				🛝		🛡️
Arradon	114			👥	🛝		
Arzano	114			👥	🛝		🛡️
Baden	114			👥	🛝	B	🛡️
Bégard	115				🛝		🛡️
Bénodet	116			👥	🛝	B	🛡️
Binic	116	🥾					
Camaret-sur-Mer	117				🛝		
Carantec	118			👥	🛝	B	🛡️
Carnac	118			👥	🛝	B	🛡️
Cléden-Cap-Sizun	121		P				
Concarneau	121			👥			
Crach	121				🛝		
Dol-de-Bretagne	122	🥾			🛝		🛡️
Erdeven	122				🛝		
Erquy	123	🥾		👥	🛝	B	🛡️
La Forêt-Fouesnant	124			👥	🛝		🛡️
Fouesnant	125			👥	🛝	B	🛡️
Guidel	126				🛝		
Guilvinec	126			👥	🛝		🛡️
Jugon-les-Lacs	126				🛝		🛡️
Kervel	127			👥	🛝		🛡️
Landeda	127			👥			🛡️
Lannion	127		P		🛝		
Marcille-Robert	129		P				
Martigné-Ferchaud	130	🥾					
Meucon	130				🛝	B	
Nevez	131			👥	🛝		🛡️
Noyal-Muzillac	131				🛝		🛡️
Le Palais (Belle-Île)	115				🛝		
Penestin	132			👥	🛝		🛡️
Pentrez-Plage	133			👥	🛝		
Perros-Guirec	133			👥	🛝	B	🛡️
Pléneuf-Val-André	134			👥			
Pleumeur-Bodou	134	🥾					
Plobannalec-Lesconil	135			👥	🛝		🛡️
Ploemel	135			👥			
Plomodiern	136				🛝		
Plouezec	136	🥾					
Plougastel-Daoulas	136			👥	🛝		
Plougoumelen	137	🥾					
Plouha	138			👥	🛝		🛡️
Plouhinec	138			👥	🛝		🛡️
Pontrieux	139		P				
Pont-Scorff	139		P				
Port-Manech	140				🛝		

Place	Page	🥿	Permanent	👥	⛷	Spa centre	📶
Le Pouldu	140				⛷		📶
Poullan-sur-Mer	141			👥	⛷		
Primel-Trégastel	142	🥿					
Quiberon	142			👥			📶
Quimper	142			👥	⛷		
Rennes	143		P				
Saint-Briac-sur-Mer	144				⛷		
Saint-Cast-le-Guildo	144	🥿		👥	⛷		📶
Saint-Gildas-de-Rhuys	145			👥	⛷		
Saint-Jouan-des-Guérets	146			👥	⛷		📶
Saint-Malo	146			👥	⛷		
Saint-Philibert	147				⛷		
Saint-Pol-de-Léon	147	🥿		👥	⛷		📶
Saint-Yvi	148				⛷		📶
Sarzeau	148			👥	⛷		📶
Sulniac	149				⛷		📶
Telgruc-sur-Mer	150				⛷		
Tréboul	151				⛷		
Trégunc	152			👥			📶
Trélevern	152	🥿					
La Trinité-sur-Mer	152			👥	⛷		📶
BURGUNDY							
Charolles	159			👥			
Dompierre-les-Ormes	161				⛷		
Gigny-sur-Saône	161			👥			
Luzy	163			👥			📶
Matour	163				⛷		
Meursault	163				⛷		
Montbard	163	🥿					
Nolay	164		P				
Saint-Honoré-les-Bains	165				⛷		
Saint-Péreuse	165		P				
Vandenesse-en-Auxois	167			👥	⛷		
Vincelles	168			👥			
CENTRE							
Bessais-le-Fromental	173				⛷		
Chaillac	174		P				
Chémery	175		P				
Cheverny	175			👥			
Chinon	176	🥿					
Cloyes-sur-le-Loir	176				⛷		
Éguzon	176		P				
Fontaine-Simon	176		P				
Gien	177			👥			📶
Mesland	178			👥	⛷		
Muides-sur-Loire	180			👥	⛷		
Pierrefitte-sur-Sauldre	181			👥	⛷	B	📶
Saint-Père-sur-Loire	182		P				
Sainte-Catherine-de-Fierbois	183			👥	⛷		📶
Savigny-en-Véron	183		P				
Senonches	184			👥			
Sonzay	184			👥	⛷		
Suèvres	184			👥	⛷		📶
La Ville-aux-Dames	185		P				
Vitry-aux-Loges	185		P				
CHAMPAGNE-ARDENNES							
Bourg-Sainte-Marie	189		P				
Braucourt	189			👥			📶
Éclaron	190			👥			📶
Giffaumont-Champaubert	191						📶
Langres	191	🥿		👥	⛷		
Mesnil-Saint-Père	191			👥	⛷		
Thonnance-les-Moulins	192			👥			📶
CORSICA							
Aléria	195			👥			
Bonifacio	195			👥	⛷		📶
Calacuccia	196	🥿					
Calvi	196			👥	⛷		
Castellare-di-Casinca	198			👥			📶
Ghisonaccia	199			👥		B	📶
Porto	200			👥		B	
Porto-Vecchio	201				⛷		
Sagone	203			👥			📶
Sainte-Lucie-de-Porto-Vecchio	203			👥			
Solenzara	203			👥			
FRANCHE-COMTE							
Bonnal	207			👥	⛷		
Champagnole	208			👥			📶
Châtillon	208			👥	⛷		📶
Clairvaux-les-Lacs	208			👥	⛷		📶
Doucier	209			👥	⛷		📶
Huanne-Montmartin	209				⛷		📶
Maisod	211						📶
Malbuisson	211			👥	⛷		📶
Marigny	211			👥			📶
Mesnois	212				⛷		
Ornans	212			👥			
Ounans	213				⛷		📶
Pontarlier	213		P				
Saint-Point-Lac	214		P				
Uxelles	215						📶
Vesoul	215						📶
ÎLE-DE-FRANCE							
Boulancourt	219		P				
Champigny-sur-Marne	219		P				
Louan-Villegruis-Fontaine	220				⛷		📶
Montjay-la-Tour	220		P				
Paris	221		P				
Pommeuse	221			👥			📶
Rambouillet	221			👥			
Touquin	221				⛷		
Tournan-en-Brie	222		P		⛷		
Villiers-sur-Orge	222		P				
LANGUEDOC-ROUSSILLON							
Agde	226			👥	⛷	B	📶
Aigues-Mortes	227			👥			

Place	Page	🥾	Permanent	👥	⛷	Spa centre	🎭
Duravel	298			👥			🎭
Estaing	298	🥾	P	👥			
Flagnac	299				⛷		
Gondrin	300			👥			
Heches	301		P				
Lau-Balagnas	302		P				🎭
Lectoure	302			👥	⛷		🎭
Loudenvielle	302	🥾					
Loupiac	302			👥			
Luz-Saint-Sauveur	303		P	👥	⛷	B	
Martres-Tolosane	304			👥			🎭
Mérens-les-Vals	305		P				
Millau	305			👥	⛷		🎭
Moissac	306			👥			
Nages	308	🥾		👥			
Nailloux	308		P				
Nant	308			👥	⛷		🎭
Ouzous	309	🥾					
Padirac	309			👥			🎭
Payrac	309			👥	⛷		
Pont-de-Salars	310			👥			🎭
Rieux-de-Pelleport	311		P				
Rivière-sur-Tarn	311			👥	⛷		🎭
Rodez	312			👥			🎭
La Romieu	312			👥			🎭
Roquelaure	312			👥			🎭
Saint-Amans-des-Cots	313			👥	⛷		🎭
Saint-Antonin-Noble-Val	313						
Saint-Cirq-Lapopie	314			👥			
Saint-Gaudens	314	🥾					
Saint-Geniez-d'Olt	314			👥	⛷		🎭
Saint-Germain-du-Bel-Air	315			👥			
Saint-Girons	315			👥			
Saint-Pantaléon	315				⛷		
Saint-Rome-de-Tarn	316		P				🎭
Sainte-Marie-de-Campan	316		P				
Salles-Curan	316			👥			🎭
Salles-et-Pratviel	317		P				
Sassis	317		P				
Sévérac-l'Église	318			👥			🎭
Sorgeat	318	🥾	P				
Souillac	318			👥	⛷		🎭
Tarascon-sur-Ariège	319			👥			🎭
Thégra	319			👥			
Thérondels	319				⛷		
Vielle-Aure	321		P				
NORD-PAS-DE-CALAIS							
Condette	325			👥			
Guines	326			👥	⛷		
NORMANDY							
Barneville-Carteret	331						🎭
Baubigny	331	🥾					
Beauvoir	332				⛷		

Place	Page	🥾	Permanent	👥	⛷	Spa centre	🎭
Bellême	332		P				
Bernières-sur-Mer	332						🎭
Les Biards	333						🎭
Blangy-le-Château	333			👥			
Bréhal	333						🎭
Bréville-sur-Mer	334			👥	⛷		🎭
Colleville-sur-Mer	334				⛷		
Fiquefleur-Equainville	336				⛷		
Genêts	337					B	
Le Gros-Theil	337		P		⛷		🎭
Honfleur	338				⛷		🎭
Houlgate	338			👥	⛷		🎭
Martigny	340	🥾					
Maupertus-sur-Mer	340			👥	⛷		🎭
Merville-Franceville-Plage	340						🎭
Moyaux	340						🎭
Les Pieux	341						🎭
Pont-Authou	341		P				
Pontorson	342			👥			
Port-en-Bessin	342			👥	⛷		🎭
Radon	342		P				
Ravenoville	342			👥			🎭
Le Rozel	342				⛷		
Saint-Arnoult	343			👥	⛷		🎭
Saint-Aubin-sur-Mer	343			👥	⛷		🎭
Saint-Jean-de-la-Rivière	344				⛷		🎭
Saint-Martin-en-Campagne	344						🎭
Saint-Pair-sur-Mer	344				⛷		🎭
Saint-Symphorien-le-Valois	345			👥	⛷		🎭
Saint-Vaast-la-Hougue	345						🎭
Surrain	345				⛷		
Surtainville	346		P				🎭
Touffreville-sur-Eu	346		P				
PAYS-DE-LA-LOIRE							
Ancenis	352				⛷		
Angers	353			👥			
Angles	353			👥	⛷		🎭
Assérac	354				⛷		
Avrille	354			👥	⛷		🎭
Barbâtre (île de Noirmoutier)	363			👥			🎭
La Baule	354			👥	⛷		
La Bernerie-en-Retz	355			👥	⛷		🎭
Brem-sur-Mer	356			👥	⛷		
Brétignolles-sur-Mer	356			👥	⛷		
La Chaize-Giraud	358				⛷		
La Chapelle-Hermier	358			👥	⛷	B	
Château-Gontier	359		P		⛷		
Cholet	359			👥	⛷		
Evron	361		P				
Fresnay-sur-Sarthe	362			👥			
Fromentine	362			👥			🎭
Givrand	362			👥	⛷		🎭

	Page	🥾	Permanent	👥	🏊	Spa centre	⚕
Le Givre	362		P				
Guémené-Penfao	363				🏊		
La Guérinière (île de Noirmoutier)	363			👥	🏊		⚕
L'Île-d'Olonne	364			👥			
Jard-sur-Mer	364			👥	🏊		⚕
Landevieille	365			👥	🏊		⚕
Longeville-sur-Mer	366			👥	🏊		⚕
Loue	366		P		🏊		
Ménil	368		P				
Mesquer	369			👥			
Mézières-sous-Lavardin	369		P				
La Mothe-Achard	370				🏊		
Mouilleron-le-Captif	370		P				
Nantes	370		P				
Olonne-sur-Mer	371			👥	🏊		
Piriac-sur-Mer	372			👥	🏊		⚕
La Plaine-sur-Mer	373			👥	🏊		
Les Ponts-de-Cé	373			👥			
Pornic	373			👥	🏊	B	⚕
Pouzauges	374		P				
Préfailles	374	🥾					
Sablé-sur-Sarthe	375			👥			
Les Sables-d'Olonne	375			👥	🏊		⚕
Saint-Brévin-les-Pins	376		P	👥	🏊	B	⚕
Saint-Hilaire-de-Riez	377			👥	🏊		⚕
Saint-Hilaire-la-Forêt	379				🏊		
Saint-Jean-de-Monts	379		P	👥	🏊	B	⚕
Saint-Julien-de-Concelles	382		P				
Saint-Julien-des-Landes	382			👥	🏊	B	⚕
Saint-Père-en-Retz	383				🏊		
Saint-Vincent-sur-Jard	383				🏊		⚕
Sainte-Luce-sur-Loire	384		P				
Saumur	384	🥾		👥			
Sille-le-Philippe	384						⚕
Talmont-Saint-Hilaire	385				🏊		⚕
La Tranche-sur-Mer	386			👥	🏊		⚕
Varennes-sur-Loire	387			👥	🏊		⚕
Vendrennes	387		P				
Villiers-Charlemagne	387		P				
PICARDY							
Berny-Rivière	391		P	👥	🏊		⚕
Cayeux-sur-Mer	391			👥			
Nampont-Saint-martin	393						⚕
Saint-Quentin-en-Tourmont	395				🏊		
Saint-Valery-sur-Somme	395						⚕
Villers-sur-Authie	395			👥			⚕
POITOU-CHARENTES							
Angoulins	400				🏊	B	⚕
Ars-en-Ré (île de Ré)	403			👥			⚕
Le Bois-Plage-en-Ré (île de Ré)	403			👥	🏊	B	⚕
Le Château-d'Oléron (île d'Oléron)	405			👥	🏊		⚕
Châtelaillon-Plage	401			👥			⚕
La Couarde-sur-Mer (île de Ré)	404			👥		B	⚕
Couhé	402			👥	🏊		⚕
Coulon	402			👥			
Dienné	402			👥		B	⚕
Dolus-d'Oléron (île d'Oléron)	406			👥			
La Flotte (île de Ré)	404			👥	🏊		⚕
Fouras	403		P	👥	🏊		⚕
Loix (île de Ré)	404			👥			
Les Mathès	409			👥	🏊		⚕
Montbron	411			👥			⚕
La Palmyre	411			👥	🏊		⚕
Pons	412		P				
Rochefort	413				🏊		
La Roche-Posay	413			👥	🏊		⚕
Ronce-les-Bains	413			👥	🏊		⚕
Royan	414			👥	🏊		⚕
Saint-Clément-des-Baleines (île de Ré)	405			👥			
Saint-Cyr	415						⚕
Saint-Georges-les-Baillargeaux	415		P		🏊		
Saint-Georges-de-Didonne	415			👥			
Saint-Georges-d'Oléron (île d'Oléron)	406			👥	🏊	B	⚕
Saint-Just-Luzac	416			👥			⚕
Saint-Laurent-de-la-Prée	416			👥			
Saint-Pierre-d'Oléron (île d'Oléron)	407				🏊		
Saint-Trojan-les-Bains (île d'Oléron)	407			👥			
Saujon	417			👥			
Secondigny	418				🏊		
Semussac	418				🏊		
PROVENCE-ALPES-CÔTE-D'AZUR							
Agay	424			👥	🏊	B	⚕
Aix-en-Provence	425		P	👥			
Arles	426			👥	🏊		⚕
Baratier	426		P				
Beaumont-du-Ventoux	428	🥾	P				
Bollène	428		P				
Bormes-les-Mimosas	428		P	👥			⚕
Cagnes-sur-Mer	429			👥			⚕
Callas	429				🏊		⚕
Castellane	430			👥	🏊		⚕
Cavalaire-sur-Mer	431	🥾					
Clamensane	432				🏊		
La Colle-sur-Loup	432			👥			
Col-St-Jean	433			👥		B	⚕
La Couronne	433			👥			⚕
La Croix-Valmer	433			👥			
Curbans	434				🏊		
Espinasses	435	🥾					
Fréjus	436			👥	🏊		⚕
Giens	437			👥			

Place	Page	🛶	Permanent	👥	⛰	Spa centre	🎭
Gréoux-les-Bains	438			👥			
Grimaud	438	🛶		👥		B	🎭
Guillestre	438	🛶					
Hyères	439			👥	⛰		
Mandelieu-la-Napoule	441		P				
Méolans-Revel	442			👥			🎭
Le Muy	443			👥	⛰		🎭
Nans-les-Pins	443			👥	⛰		🎭
Niozelles	444			👥			
Orpierre	444	🛶					
Pertuis	445			👥	⛰		🎭
Pont-du-Fossé	445		P				
Puget-sur-Argens	445			👥			
Ramatuelle	446			👥		B	🎭
Régusse	446			👥			
La Roche-de-Rame	447		P				
La Roche-des-Arnauds	447		P				
La Roque-d'Anthéron	448				⛰		🎭
Roquebrune-sur-Argens	447			👥	⛰		🎭
Saint-Apollinaire	448	🛶					
Saint-Aygulf	448						🎭
Saint-Étienne-du-Grès	449		P				
Saint-Mandrier-sur-Mer	450						🎭
Saint-Paul-en-Forêt	450			👥			
Saint-Raphaël	451			👥	⛰		🎭
Sanary-sur-Mer	452			👥	⛰		
Le Sauze-du-Lac	453	🛶					
Serres	453			👥			
Le Thor	454				⛰		
Vaison-la-Romaine	454			👥	⛰		🎭
Villecroze	456			👥	⛰		
Villeneuve-Loubet-Plage	456		P				
Volonne	457			👥	⛰		🎭
RHÔNE-ALPES							
Les Abrets	462			👥			
Aigueblanche	462		P				
Anse	462				⛰		
Aussois	463	🛶	P				
Autrans	463			👥	⛰	B	
Benivay-Ollon	464						
Berrias-et-Casteljau	464			👥			
Bourdeaux	465				⛰		
Le Bourg-d'Oisans	465		P	👥			🎭
Bout-du-Lac	467						🎭
Chabeuil	468				⛰		🎭
Chamonix-Mont-Blanc	469	🛶					
Champdor	469		P				
Chassiers	470			👥	⛰	B	
Châteauneuf-de-Galaure	470				⛰		🎭
Châteauneuf-sur-Isère	470			👥	⛰		🎭
Châtel	470			👥			
Châtillon-en-Diois	471						🎭
Crest	472			👥			
Dardilly	473		P				
Doussard	474			👥	⛰		
Excenevex	475						🎭
Faramans	475		P				
Les Gets	476	🛶					
Gresse-en-Vercors	477	🛶					
Jeansagnière	478	🛶					
Joannas	478				⛰		
Lagorce	479			👥	⛰		🎭
Larnas	480			👥	⛰		🎭
Lathuile	480				⛰		🎭
Lus-la-Croix-Haute	481	🛶					
Massignieu-de-Rives	482	🛶					
Méaudre	483		P				
Menglon	483	🛶		👥	⛰		
Montrevel-en-Bresse	484			👥	⛰		🎭
Morzine	485	🛶					
Murs-et-Gélignieux	485				⛰		
Les Ollières-sur-Eyrieux	486			👥	⛰		🎭
La Pacaudière	486				⛰		
Le Poët-Célard	487	🛶			⛰		
Pont-de-Vaux	488			👥	⛰		🎭
Pradons	488			👥			
Pralognan-la-Vanoise	489	🛶					
Praz-sur-Arly	489		P				
Privas	489			👥	⛰		
Recoubeau-Jansac	490				⛰	B	🎭
La Rosière-1850	490		P				
Rumilly	491		P				
Ruoms	491			👥	⛰	B	🎭
Saint-Alban-Auriolles	493			👥	⛰	B	🎭
Saint-Alban-de-Montbel	494			👥			
Saint-Christophe-en-Oisans	494	🛶					
Saint-Clair-du-Rhône	494				⛰		
Saint-Donat-sur-l'Herbasse	495				⛰		
Saint-Ferréol-Trente-pas	495				⛰		
Saint-Galmier	495			👥			🎭
Saint-Jorioz	496			👥	⛰		🎭
Saint-Martin-d'Ardèche	497			👥			
Saint-Maurice-d'Ardèche	498			👥	⛰		🎭
Sainte-Catherine	500	🛶					
Samoëns	501						🎭
Sampzon	501			👥			🎭
Seez	502		P				
Taninges	503		P				
Termignon	503		P				
La Toussuire	503	🛶					
Trept	503				⛰		
Ucel	504			👥			
Vallon-Pont-d'Arc	504			👥		B	🎭
Verchaix	506		P				
Vernioz	506						🎭
Villard-de-Lans	506				⛰		🎭
Vinsobres	507		P	👥	⛰		🎭

Selected **camping** sites

R. Mattes / hemis.fr

Alsace is perhaps the most romantic of France's regions, a place of fairy-tale castles, gentle vine-clad hills and picturesque villages perched on rocky outcrops or nestling in lush, green valleys. From Colmar's 'Little Venice' with its flower-decked balconies, famous storks (the region's iconic emblem) and wonderful Unterlinden Museum, to the spectacular lights and tempting delights of Strasbourg's Christmas market, via the atmospheric half-timbered houses, reflected in the meandering River Ill, Alsace radiates an inviting warmth that even the winter temperatures cannot chill. The region is known for its wonderful scenery, traditional cuisine, local produce and excellent wine. Head to a brasserie and enjoy a regional beer in a lively atmosphere or relax in a local *winstub* (wine lounge), tucking into a steaming dish of *choucroute* (sauerkraut with smoked pork) and a generous slice of *Kugelhopf* cake, all washed down with a glass of fruity Sylvaner or Riesling. Alsace has something for everyone.

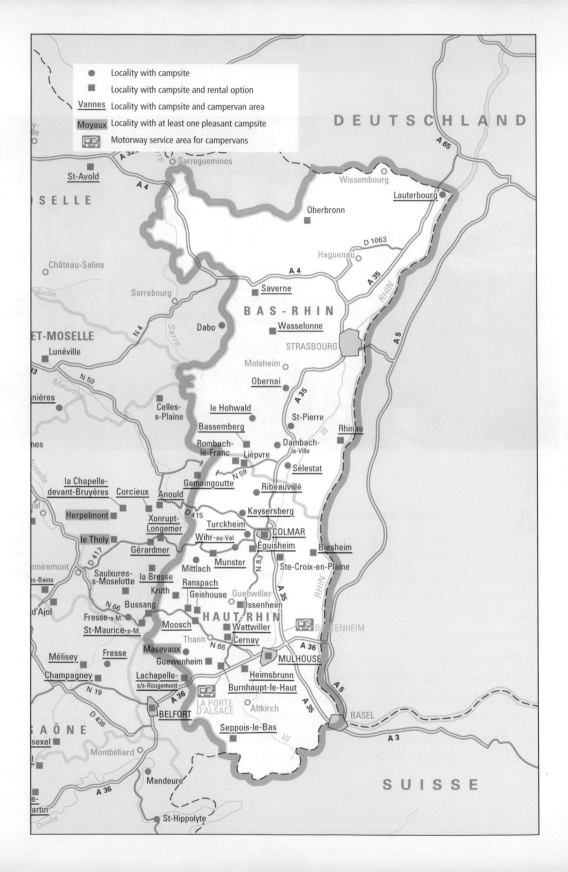

Locality with campsite
- Locality with campsite and rental option
- **Vannes** Locality with campsite and campervan area
- **Moyaux** Locality with at least one pleasant campsite
- Motorway service area for campervans

DEUTSCHLAND

SUISSE

BASSEMBERG

67220 – Michelin map **315** H7 – pop. 268 – alt. 280
▶ Paris 432 – Barr 21 – St-Dié 35 – Sélestat 19

⚠ Campéole Le Giessen

✆ 03 88 58 98 14, www.camping-vosges.net

Address : route de Villé (take northeastern exit on the D 39; beside the Giessen river)

Opening times : from beginning April to mid Sept.

4 ha (79 pitches for camping) flat, grassy

Tariff : (2013 Price) 26.80€ � ⛺ 🔲 🚻 (10A)

Extra per person 6.50€ – Reservation fee 15€

Rental rates : (from beginning April to mid Sept.) ♿ (1 mobile home) – 8 ⛺ – 5 🏠 – 8 canvas bungalows. Per night from 32 to 142€ – Per week from 239 to 994€ – Reservation fee 25€

🚐 borne 4.30€

A pretty site near a water park.

Surroundings : < ◻
Leisure activities : 🍽 🕐 daytime 🛶 🚲
Facilities : ♿ ⊶ ▥ 🛁 🚿 🚾 🚻 🔲 refrigerators
Nearby : 🍴 🎮 ⊠ ▤ 🛶 ⛷

G P S Longitude : 7.28911
Latitude : 48.33602

We have selected the best campsites in France with our usual care, listing those with the best facilities in the most pleasant surroundings.

BIESHEIM

68600 – Michelin map **315** J8 – pop. 2 398 – alt. 189
▶ Paris 520 – Strasbourg 85 – Freiburg-im-Breisgau 37 – Basel 68

⚠ Village Center L'Ile du Rhin

✆ 03 89 72 57 95, www.village-center.fr

Address : touristic area of l'Île du Rhin (5km east along the N 415, follow the signs for Fribourg)

Opening times : from beginning April to end Sept.

3 ha (220 pitches for camping)

Tariff : (2013 Price) 21€ 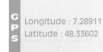 � ⛺ 🔲 🚻 (10A) – Extra per person 5€

Rental rates : (from beginning April to end Sept.) – 26 ⛺. Per night from 35 to 89€ – Per week from 245 to 770€ Reservation fee 30€

🚐 borne 3€

A pleasant site and setting between the Rhine and the Canal d'Alsace on the Franco-German border.

Surroundings : ♀
Leisure activities : ✗ ▤ 🕐 daytime 🚲
Facilities : ♿ ⊶ 🚾 🛁 🚿 🚻 launderette 🛁 🚿
Nearby : ▤ 🛶 ⛷ ⚓ water skiing

G P S Longitude : 7.57278
Latitude : 48.02746

BURNHAUPT-LE-HAUT

68520 – Michelin map **315** G10 – pop. 1 596 – alt. 300
▶ Paris 454 – Altkirch 16 – Belfort 32 – Mulhouse 17

⚠ Les Castors

✆ 03 89 48 78 58, www.camping-les-castors.fr

Address : 4 route de Guewenheim (2.5km northwest along the D 466)

Opening times : Permanent

2.5 ha (135 pitches for camping) flat, grassy

Tariff : 18€ � ☆ ⛺ 🔲 🚻 (10A) – Extra per person 4€ – Reservation fee 2.50€

Rental rates : Permanent – 3 ⛺. Per night from 40 to 60€ Per week from 300 to 600€ – Reservation fee 20€

🚐 8 🔲 18€

Rural setting beside a river and a lake. Extensive green spaces.

Surroundings : ♀
Leisure activities : 🍽 ✗ 🛶 🎣
Facilities : ♿ ⊶ 🚾 🛁 🚻 launderette

G P S Longitude : 7.12383
Latitude : 47.77455

CERNAY

68700 – Michelin map **315** H10 – pop. 11 288 – alt. 275
▶ Paris 461 – Altkirch 26 – Belfort 39 – Colmar 37

⚠ Les Cigognes

✆ 03 89 75 56 97, www.camping-les-cigognes.com

Address : 16 rue René Guibert (take the exit following signs for Belfort then take a right turn after the bridge; beside the Thur river)

Opening times : from beginning April to end Sept.

3.5 ha (138 pitches for camping) flat, grassy

Tariff : (2013 Price) 17€ ☆ ☆ ⛺ 🔲 🚻 (10A) – Extra per person 4.50€ Reservation fee 5€

Rental rates : (2013 Price) (from beginning April to end Sept.) 3 ⛺. Per week from 250 to 450€ – Reservation fee 15€

🚐 borne 5€

Pretty, green pitches within the town.

Surroundings : ♀
Leisure activities : 🏛 🎣
Facilities : ♿ ⊶ ▥ 🛁 🚻 🔲
Nearby : 🍴 🎮 ▤ (open air in season)

G P S Longitude : 7.16876
Latitude : 47.80519

Key to rentals symbols:

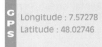

12 ⛺ *Number of mobile homes*

20 🏠 *Number of chalets*

6 🛏 *Number of rooms to rent*

Per night 30–50€ *Minimum/maximum rate per night*

Per week 300–1,000€ *Minimum/maximum rate per week*

COLMAR

68000 – Michelin map **315** I8 – pop. 67 214 – alt. 194
▶ Paris 450 – Basel 68 – Freiburg 51 – Nancy 140

⚠ Indigo L'Ill

✆ 03 89 41 15 94, www.campingdelill.fr

Address : situated 2km east along the N 415, follow the signs for Fribourg; beside the Ill river

Opening times : from mid April to beginning Jan.

2.2 ha (150 pitches for camping)

Tariff : 19.80€ ✳✳ ⬅ 🔲 💧 (10A) – Extra per person 4.20€
Reservation fee 22€

Rental rates : (from mid April to beginning Jan.) – 10 tent lodges. Per night from 39 to 62€ – Per week from 191 to 369€
Reservation fee 22€

🚐 borne 7€

A shaded site on the peaceful banks of the Ill river.

Surroundings : 🌳🌳
Leisure activities : 🍷✕ 🏠 ⛵ 🎣
Facilities : ⚐ ⚑ 🚿 🍴 🔲 🚮 ♨

Longitude : 7.38676
Latitude : 48.07838

DAMBACH-LA-VILLE

67650 – Michelin map **315** I7 – pop. 1 946 – alt. 210
▶ Paris 443 – Barr 17 – Obernai 24 – Saverne 61

⚠ L'Ours

✆ 03 88 92 46 09, alavignette@orange.fr

Address : 2 rue du stade (1.2km east along the D 210, follow the signs for Ebersheim and take road to the left)

1.8 ha (120 pitches for camping) flat, grassy

A shaded setting in the heart of the countryside with an attractive view of the mountain.

Surroundings : ⛰🌳
Facilities : ⚐ ⚑ 🚿 🔲
Nearby : ⛵ ✕ 🏊

Longitude : 7.44324
Latitude : 48.32274

ÉGUISHEIM

68420 – Michelin map **315** H8 – pop. 1 622 – alt. 210
▶ Paris 452 – Belfort 68 – Colmar 7 – Gérardmer 52

⚠ Des Trois Châteaux

✆ 03 89 23 19 39, www.eguisheimcamping.fr

Address : 10 rue du Bassin (to the west)

Opening times : from end March to end Oct.

2 ha (133 pitches for camping)

Tariff : (2013 Price) 16,90€ ✳✳ ⬅ 🔲 💧 (8A) – Extra per person 4€
Reservation fee 6€

Rental rates : (from end March to end Oct.) – 18 🚐. Per night from 40 to 111€ – Per week from 280 to 645€ – Reservation fee 6€

🚐 borne 3€

The sanitary facilities are a little old, but a pleasant location near a vineyard and the very beautiful village of Eguisheim.

Surroundings : 🌿⛰🌳
Facilities : ⚐ ⚑ 🍴 🔲

Longitude : 7.29909
Latitude : 48.04274

GEISHOUSE

68690 – Michelin map **315** G9 – pop. 484 – alt. 730
▶ Paris 467 – Belfort 53 – Bussang 23 – Colmar 55

⚠ Au Relais du Grand Ballon

✆ 03 89 82 30 47, www.aurelaisdugrandballon.com – limited spaces for one-night stay

Address : 17 Grand-Rue (southern exit)

Opening times : Permanent

0,3 ha (24 pitches for camping) flat, grassy

Tariff : 18€ ✳✳ ⬅ 🔲 💧 (10A) – Extra per person 4,80€

Rental rates : Permanent – 4 🏠. Per night from 55 to 65€
Per week from 340 to 455€

A small, pretty site in the heart of the mountains; a family atmosphere with a very busy restaurant.

Surroundings : 🌿 ▱ 🌳
Leisure activities : 🍷✕ 🏠 ⛵
Facilities : ⚐ ⚑ 🔲 ♨ 🍴 launderette

Longitude : 7.05852
Latitude : 47.88056

GUEWENHEIM

68116 – Michelin map **315** G10 – pop. 1 256 – alt. 323
▶ Paris 458 – Altkirch 23 – Belfort 36 – Mulhouse 21

⚠ La Doller

✆ 03 89 82 56 90, www.campingdoller.com

Address : rue du Commandant Charpy (located 1km north along the D 34, follow the signs for Thann and take the road to the right; beside the Doller river)

0,8 ha (40 pitches for camping) flat, grassy

Rentals : 6 🚐.

A family atmosphere in a green setting surrounded by flowers, lovely dining room.

Surroundings : 🌿 🌳
Leisure activities : 🍷 🏠 ⛵ 🎣 🐟
Facilities : ⚐ ⚑ 🔲 ♨ 🚿 ⚘ 🍴 🔲
Nearby : ✕ 🎿

Longitude : 7.09827
Latitude : 47.75597

HEIMSBRUNN

68990 – Michelin map **315** H10 – pop. 1 453 – alt. 280
▶ Paris 456 – Altkirch 14 – Basel 50 – Belfort 34

⚠ Parc la Chaumière

✆ 03 89 81 93 43, www.camping-lachaumiere.com – limited spaces for one-night stay

Address : 62 rue de Galfingue (take the southern exit along the D 19, follow the signs for Altkirch)

Opening times : Permanent

1 ha (53 pitches for camping)

Tariff : 14.20€ ✳✳ ⬅ 🔲 💧 (10A) – Extra per person 3.60€

Rental rates : Permanent – 4 🚐. Per night from 12 to 40€
Per week from 100 to 490€

🚐 borne 4€ – 6 🔲 14.20€ – 🚐 💧12€

Convivial and family-orientated site in a pleasant setting among trees.

Surroundings :
Leisure activities : 🚣 🛝 (small swimming pool)
Facilities : 🔑 🏢 🚿 🚐

GPS Longitude : 7.22477
Latitude : 47.72242

LE HOHWALD

67140 – Michelin map **315** H6 – pop. 496 – alt. 570 – Winter sports : 600/1100m
▶ Paris 430 – Lunéville 89 – Molsheim 33 – St-Dié 46

⛰ Municipal

📞 03 88 08 30 90, lecamping.herrenhaus@orange.fr – alt. 615

Address : 28 rue du Herrenhaus (take the western exit along the D 425, follow the signs for Villé)

Opening times : from end April to mid Oct.

2 ha (100 pitches for camping) very uneven, terraced, fine gravel, flat, grassy

Tariff : (2013 Price) 🚶 3.70€ – 🚗 1.80€ 🔲 2.20€ – 🔌 (6A) 2.10€

A pleasant setting in the heart of the mountains among pines, spruce and beech trees.

Surroundings : 🌳
Leisure activities : 🏛 🚣 sports trail
Facilities : 🏢 🧺

GPS Longitude : 7.32328
Latitude : 48.4063

This guide is updated regularly, so buy your new copy every year!

ISSENHEIM

68500 – Michelin map **315** H9 – pop. 3 418 – alt. 245
▶ Paris 487 – Strasbourg 98 – Colmar 24 – Mulhouse 22

⛰ Le Florival

📞 03 89 74 20 47, www.camping-leflorival.com

Address : route de Soultz (2.5km southeast along the D 430, follow the signs for Mulhouse and take D 5 to the left, follow the signs for Issenheim)

Opening times : from mid April to mid Oct.

3,5 ha (73 pitches for camping)

Tariff : (2013 Price) 17,30€ 🚶🚶 🚗 🔲 🔌 (10A)

Extra per person 3,80€

Rental rates : (from mid April to mid Oct.) ♿ (2 chalets) 🚭 20 🏠. Per night from 50 to 88€ – Per week from 262 to 568€

In a pleasant setting at the edge of the woods. Swimming facilities with an Olympic-size pool nearby.

Surroundings : ⩽ 🏕
Leisure activities : 🏛 🚣
Facilities : ♿ 🔑 🏢 🚿 🚿 launderette
Nearby : 🏊 🛝 🎿

GPS Longitude : 7.23879
Latitude : 47.90014

KAYSERSBERG

68240 – Michelin map **315** H8 – pop. 2 721 – alt. 242
▶ Paris 438 – Colmar 12 – Gérardmer 46 – Guebwiller 35

⛰ Municipal

📞 03 89 47 14 47, www.camping-kaysersberg.fr 🚭 (July–Aug.)

Address : rue des Acacias (take northwestern exit along the N 415, follow the signs for St-Dié and take a right turn)

Opening times : from beginning April to end Sept.

1,6 ha (115 pitches for camping) flat, grassy

Tariff : (2013 Price) 18.96€ 🚶🚶 🚗 🔲 🔌 (13A)

Extra per person 4.53€

🚐 borne

A charming site beside the La Weiss river.

Surroundings : ⩽ 🌳
Leisure activities : 🏛 🚣 🎿
Facilities : 🔑 🚿 🚿 🚿 🚿 launderette

GPS Longitude : 7.25404
Latitude : 48.14887

KRUTH

68820 – Michelin map **315** F9 – pop. 1 029 – alt. 498
▶ Paris 453 – Colmar 63 – Épinal 68 – Gérardmer 31

⛰ Le Schlossberg

📞 03 89 82 26 76, www.schlossberg.fr

Address : rue du Bourbaach (2.3km northwest along the D 13b, follow the signs for La Bresse and take turning to the left)

Opening times : from beginning April to beginning Oct.

5,2 ha (200 pitches for camping)

Tariff : (2013 Price) 🚶 4,70€ 🚗 🔲 4.40€ – 🔌 (6A) 3€ – Reservation fee 10€

Rental rates : Permanent – 9 🏠. Per night from 52 to 86€ Per week from 286 to 599€ – Reservation fee 10€

A pleasant location in the heart of the Parc des Ballons, close to the Magnificent Lac de Kruth. Cycle path at the entrance.

Surroundings : 🚣 ⩽ 🌳
Leisure activities : 🍴 🚣
Facilities : ♿ 🔑 🏢 🚿 🚿 launderette

GPS Longitude : 6.9546
Latitude : 47.94535

LAUTERBOURG

67630 – Michelin map **315** N3 – pop. 2 266 – alt. 115
▶ Paris 519 – Haguenau 40 – Karlsruhe 22 – Strasbourg 63

⛰ Municipal des Mouettes

📞 03 88 54 68 60, camping-lauterbourg@wanadoo.fr – limited spaces for one-night stay 🚭

Address : located 1.5km southwest along the D 3 and take road to the left, 100m from a small lake (direct access)

2,7 ha (136 pitches for camping) flat, grassy

🚐 borne – 6€ 🔲

Extensive green spaces beside a large leisure and activity park.

Leisure activities : 🍴 🍽
Facilities : ♿ 🔑 🏢 🚿 🖼
Nearby : 🚣 🛶 🎣 🛟

GPS Longitude : 8.1654
Latitude : 48.9708

LIEPVRE

68660 – Michelin map **315** H7 – pop. 1 751 – alt. 272
▶ Paris 428 – Colmar 35 – Ribeauvillé 27 – St-Dié-des-Vosges 31

⛰ Haut-Koenigsbourg

🖉 03 89 58 43 20, www.liepvre.fr/camping

Address : route de La Vancelle (900m east along the C 1 follow the signs for la Vancelle)

Opening times : from mid March to mid Oct.

1 ha (56 pitches for camping)

Tariff : 15,70€ ★★ 🚐 🔲 (½) (8A) – Extra per person 4€
Rental rates : (from mid March to mid Oct.) 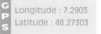 – 6 🏠 .
Per night from 60 to 95€ – Per week from 310 to 575€ .

A centuries-old sequoia beside the entrance; absolute peace in the middle of the countryside.

Surroundings : 🏞 ≤ ♀
Leisure activities : 🏛 🐎
Facilities : ⚹ ⚲ 🏢 🚰 🚿

G P S Longitude : 7.2903
Latitude : 48.27303

MASEVAUX

68290 – Michelin map **315** F10 – pop. 3 278 – alt. 425
▶ Paris 440 – Altkirch 32 – Belfort 24 – Colmar 57

⛰ Le Masevaux

🖉 03 89 82 42 29, www.camping-masevaux.com

Address : 3 rue du Stade (beside the Doller river)

Opening times : from mid March to end Oct.

3,5 ha (133 pitches for camping) flat, grassy

Tariff : (2013 Price) ★ 4€ 🚐 🔲 4€ – (½) 3,50€

A pleasant wooded setting with flowers. Numerous walking trails begin at the site.

Surroundings : ♀♀
Leisure activities : 🎭 🏛 🐎 🛶
Facilities : ⚹ ⚲ 🏢 🍴 🚰 launderette
Nearby : 🍴 🏞 🛶

G P S Longitude : 6.99093
Latitude : 47.77833

MITTLACH

68380 – Michelin map **315** G8 – pop. 323 – alt. 550
▶ Paris 467 – Colmar 28 – Gérardmer 42 – Guebwiller 44

⛰ Municipal Langenwasen

🖉 03 89 77 63 77, www.mittlach.fr – alt. 620

Address : chemin du Camping (3km southwest; beside a stream)

Opening times : from mid April to mid Oct.

3 ha (77 pitches for camping) terrace, flat and relatively flat, gravelled, grassy

Tariff : (2013 Price) ★ 3,30€ 🚐 1,15€ 🔲 2,50€ – (½) (10A) 6€

A wooded site at the bottom of a peaceful valley.

Surroundings : 🏞 ≤ ☐ ♀
Leisure activities : 🏛 🐎
Facilities : ⚲ (July–Aug.) 🚿

G P S Longitude : 7.01867
Latitude : 47.98289

To make the best possible use of this guide, please read pages 2–15 carefully.

MOOSCH

68690 – Michelin map **315** G9 – pop. 1 764 – alt. 390
▶ Paris 463 – Colmar 51 – Gérardmer 42 – Mulhouse 28

⛰ La Mine d'Argent

🖉 03 89 82 30 66, www.camping-la-mine-argent.com – limited spaces for one-night stay

Address : rue de la Mine d'Argent (located 1.5km southwest along the r. de la Mairie; beside a stream)

Opening times : from mid April to mid Oct.

2 ha (75 pitches for camping)

Tariff : 15,95€ ★★ 🚐 🔲 (½) (6A) – Extra per person 3,95€
Rental rates : (from mid April to mid Oct.) – 4 🛖 . Per night from 40 to 70€ – Per week from 220 to 400€
🚐 borne
On a lush, green, hilly site out in the mountains.

Surroundings : 🏞 ≤ ♀
Leisure activities : 🏛 🐎
Facilities : ⚲ 🚰 launderette

G P S Longitude : 7.03054
Latitude : 47.85102

MULHOUSE

68100 – Michelin map **315** I10 – pop. 111 156 – alt. 240
▶ Paris 465 – Basel 34 – Belfort 43 – Besançon 130

⛰ L'Ill

🖉 03 89 06 20 66, www.camping-de-lill.com

Address : 1 rue Pierre de Coubertin (to the southwest, along the A 36, take the exit for Dornach)

Opening times : from beginning April to end Sept.

5 ha (193 pitches for camping) flat, grassy

Tariff : 19,45€ ★★ 🚐 🔲 (½) (10A) – Extra per person 5,15€
Reservation fee 5€

Rental rates : (from beginning April to end Sept.) – 8 🛖
15 chalets (without sanitary facilities). Per night from 65 to 85€
Per week from 320 to 550€ – Reservation fee 15€
🚐 borne 5€ – 11 🔲 19,45€

A wooded setting beside river and near Euro cycle route 6.

Surroundings : ♀♀
Leisure activities : 🏛 🛶
Facilities : ⚹ ⚲ 🏢 🍴 🚰 🚿
Nearby : 🏂 🏞 skating rink, mountain biking

G P S Longitude : 7.32283
Latitude : 47.73424

MUNSTER

68140 – Michelin map **315** G8 – pop. 4 889 – alt. 400
▶ Paris 458 – Colmar 19 – Gérardmer 34 – Guebwiller 40

⛰ Village Center Le Parc de la Fecht

Interaview Production

🖉 0825 00 20 30, www.village-center.fr

Address : route de Gunsbach (located 1km east along the D 10, follow the signs for Turckheim)

Opening times : from mid April to end Sept.

4 ha (192 pitches for camping) flat, grassy

Tariff : 18€ ★★ 🚐 🔲 (½) (10A)
Extra per person 3€

Rental rates : (from beginning April to mid Oct.) – 24 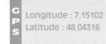.
Per night from 26 to 102€ – Per week from 182 to 851€
Reservation fee 30€

🚐 borne 5€

A wooded site beside the Fecht river, but the sanitary facilities have seen better days.

Surroundings : ♀♀
Leisure activities : 🏠 ⚓ 🚴
Facilities : ⚏ 🆑 🚿 📷
Nearby : 🛶

Longitude : 7.15102
Latitude : 48.04316

Some information or pricing may have changed since the guide went to press. We recommend you check the price list online in advance or at the entrance to the campsite and enquire about possible restrictions.

OBERBRONN

67110 – Michelin map **315** J3 – pop. 1 543 – alt. 260 – ⚓
▶ Paris 460 – Bitche 25 – Haguenau 24 – Saverne 36

⛰ Flowers L'Oasis

✆ 0388097196, www.oasis-alsace.com

Address : 3 rue du Frohret (located 1.5km south along the D 28, follow the signs for Ingwiller and take the road to the left)

Opening times : from end March to beginning Nov.

2,5 ha (139 pitches for camping)

Tariff : (2013 Price) 22€ 🎯🎯 🚐 📷 (6A) – Extra per person 5€

Rental rates : (2013 Price) (from end March to beginning Nov.) ⚒ (2 chalets) – 28 🏠 – 11 huts, 1 gîte d'étape (lodge). Per night from 71 to 98€ – Per week from 196 to 686€

On the edge of a forest with a magnificent view over the mountain and the village of Oberbronn.

Surroundings : 🌲 ≤
Leisure activities : 🍴 🍽 🏠 ⚓ 🎿 🛶
sports trail, spa centre
Facilities : ⚒ 🚿 🔲 🚽 📷 🚮
Nearby : 🐎

Longitude : 7.60347
Latitude : 48.9286

OBERNAI

67210 – Michelin map **315** I6 – pop. 10 803 – alt. 185
▶ Paris 488 – Colmar 50 – Erstein 15 – Molsheim 12

⛰ Municipal le Vallon de l'Ehn

✆ 0388953848, www.obernai.fr

Address : 1 rue de Berlin (take the western exit along the D 426, follow the signs for Ottrott, for caravans, recommended route via the bypass (rocade) south of the town)

Opening times : from beginning May to end Oct.

3 ha (150 pitches for camping) flat and relatively flat, grassy

Tariff : (2013 Price) 🎯 4,30€ 🚐 📷 5€ – (16A) 4€

🚐 borne 2€ – 30 📷 5€

A restful site with a pretty view of Mont Sainte-Odile.

Surroundings : ≤♀
Leisure activities : 🏠 ⚓ 🐎
Facilities : ⚒ 🚿 🔲 🚽 🚰 🚿 laundrette
Nearby : 🍽 🏓 🛶 🐎

Longitude : 7.46715
Latitude : 48.46505

RANSPACH

68470 – Michelin map **315** G9 – pop. 852 – alt. 430
▶ Paris 459 – Belfort 54 – Bussang 15 – Gérardmer 38

⛰ Flower Les Bouleaux

✆ 0389826470, www.alsace-camping.com

Address : 8 rue des Bouleaux (south of the town along the N 66)

Opening times : Permanent

1,75 ha (75 pitches for camping) flat, grassy

Tariff : 20,50€ 🎯🎯 🚐 📷 (6A) – Extra per person 3,50€
Reservation fee 10€

Rental rates : Permanent ⚒ (2 chalets) – 25 🏠. Per night from 46 to 100€ – Per week from 230 to 714€ – Reservation fee 10€

🚐 borne 3,50€ – 4 📷 20,50€

Extensive attractive green spaces in the shade of birch trees, but the sanitary facilities are rather jaded.

Surroundings : ≤♀
Leisure activities : 🍴 🍽 🏠 ⚓ 🚴 🛶
Facilities : ⚒ 🚿 🚽 🚿 laundrette

Longitude : 7.01037
Latitude : 47.88084

RHINAU

67860 – Michelin map **315** K7 – pop. 2 698 – alt. 158
▶ Paris 525 – Marckolsheim 26 – Molsheim 38 – Obernai 28

⛰ Ferme des Tuileries

✆ 0388746045, www.fermedestuileries.com – 🏨 ⚒

Address : 1 rue des Tuileries (take the northwestern exit, follow the signs for Benfeld)

Opening times : from beginning April to end Sept.

4 ha (150 pitches for camping) flat, grassy

Tariff : 🎯 4€ 🚐 📷 4€ – (6A) 3,20€

Rental rates : (from beginning April to end Dec.) ⚒ – 5 🏠.
Per night from 50 to 85€ – Per week from 350 to 600€

🚐 borne 2€

A well-equipped site scattered with fruit trees, next to a magnificent lake.

Surroundings : 🌲
Leisure activities : 🍽 🏠 🎿 ⚓ 🚴 🎯 🛶 🚤 (lake) ⚒ 🎣
Facilities : 🚿 📷 🔲 🚽 🚿 laundrette 🚮

Longitude : 7.6986
Latitude : 48.32224

RIBEAUVILLÉ

68150 – Michelin map **315** H7 – pop. 4 798 – alt. 240
▶ Paris 439 – Colmar 16 – Gérardmer 56 – Mulhouse 60

⛰ Municipal Pierre-de-Coubertin

✆ 0389736671, http://camping-alsace.com/camping-pierre-coubertin-ribeauville – 🏨

Address : 23 rue de Landau (take the eastern exit along the D 106 then take the turning to the left)

Opening times : from mid March to mid Nov.

3,5 ha (208 pitches for camping) flat, grassy

Tariff : 🎯 4€ 🚐 📷 5€ – (16A) 3,60€

🚐 borne – 18€ 📷

A pretty view of mountain, vineyards and château.

Surroundings : 🌲 ≤♀
Leisure activities : 🏠 ⚓ 🎿
Facilities : ⚒ 🚿 🚽 🚰 🚿 🚿 📷 🚮
Nearby : 🏊 🛶 ⚒

Longitude : 7.336
Latitude : 48.195

ROMBACH-LE-FRANC

68660 – Michelin map **315** H7 – pop. 877 – alt. 290
▶ Paris 431 – Colmar 38 – Ribeauvillé 30 – St-Dié 34

⚠ Municipal les Bouleaux

✆ 03 89 58 41 56, www.valdargent.com/camping-rombach-les-bouleaux.htm – access difficult for caravans

Address : route de la Hingrie (located 1.5km to the northwest)

Opening times : from mid April to mid Oct.

1,3 ha (38 pitches for camping)

Tariff : ✦ 2,55 € ⇔ 🅴 2,85 € – 🔌 (13A) 2,45 €
Rental rates : Permanent 🚫 – 5 🏠. Per night from 55 €
Per week from 270 to 400 €

In a valley surrounded by pines and crossed by a stream.

Surroundings : 🏊 ♨		
Leisure activities : 🏛 🚴	**G**	Longitude : 7.2402
Facilities : ♿ 🚱🏚 🍴 launderette	**P** **S**	Latitude : 48.2877

ST-PIERRE

67140 – Michelin map **315** I6 – pop. 589 – alt. 179
▶ Paris 498 – Barr 4 – Erstein 21 – Obernai 12

⚠ Les Reflets de St-Pierre

✆ 03 89 58 64 31, reflets@calixo.net

Address : 14 rue de l'Eglise (In the village, beside the Muttlbach river)

0,6 ha (47 pitches for camping) flat, grassy

A peaceful site beside the river.

Surroundings : 🏞		
Leisure activities : 🍴	**G**	Longitude : 7.47472
Nearby : 🚴	**P** **S**	Latitude : 48.38254

There are several different types of sani-station ('borne' in French) – sanitation points providing fresh water and disposal points for grey water. See page 12 for further details.

STE-CROIX-EN-PLAINE

68127 – Michelin map **315** I8 – pop. 2 661 – alt. 192
▶ Paris 471 – Belfort 78 – Colmar 10 – Freiburg-im-Breisgau 49

🏞 Clair Vacances

✆ 03 89 49 27 28, www.clairvacances.com 🚫

Address : route de Herrlisheim (On the D1)

Opening times : from end April to beginning Oct.

4 ha (145 pitches for camping) flat, grassy

Tariff : 25 € ✦✦ ⇔ 🅴 🔌 (16A) – Extra per person 7,50 € – Reservation fee 10 €
Rental rates : (from end April to beginning Oct.) 🚫 – 12 🚐. Per night from 45 to 95 € – Per week from 300 to 820 € Reservation fee 10 €

Attractive trees and shrubs; peaceful site with plenty of charm.

Surroundings : 🏞		
Leisure activities : 🏛 🚴 🛝	**G**	Longitude : 7.35289
Facilities : ♿ 🚱🏚 🍴 launderette	**P** **S**	Latitude : 48.01454

SAVERNE

67700 – Michelin map **315** I4 – pop. 12 046 – alt. 200
▶ Paris 450 – Lunéville 88 – St-Avold 89 – Sarreguemines 65

🏞 Seasonova Les Portes d'Alsace

✆ 03 88 91 35 65, www.camping-lesportesdalsace.com

Address : 40 rue du Père Libermann (1.3km southwest along the D 171)

Opening times : from beginning April to end Oct.

2,1 ha (145 pitches for camping)

Tariff : 21 € ✦✦ ⇔ 🅴 🔌 (10A) – Extra per person 6 € – Reservation fee 12 €
Rental rates : Permanent 🚫 – 10 🚐. Per night from 35 to 95 € Per week from 200 to 690 € – Reservation fee 15 €
🚐 borne 3 – 15 🅴 8 € – ♨ 8 €

A small rural oasis in an urban environment, peaceful and well appointed.

Surroundings : ⛰ ♨		
Leisure activities : 🏛 🚴 🖼 (open air in season)	**G**	Longitude : 7.35539
Facilities : ♿ 🔑 ♿🏚 🚣 🍴 launderette	**P** **S**	Latitude : 48.73095
Nearby : 🍴 🐎		

SÉLESTAT

67600 – Michelin map **315** I7 – pop. 19 332 – alt. 170
▶ Paris 441 – Colmar 24 – Gérardmer 65 – St-Dié 44

⚠ Municipal les Cigognes

✆ 03 88 92 03 98, www.selestat-tourisme.com

Address : 1 rue de la 1ère Division France Libre

Opening times : from beginning April to mid Oct.

0,7 ha (48 pitches for camping) flat, grassy

Tariff : 17,70 € ✦✦ ⇔ 🅴 🔌 (6A) – Extra per person 4,60 €
🚐 borne 5,50 €

A charming site 5 minutes from the town centre.

Surroundings : ♨		
Leisure activities : 🚴	**G**	Longitude : 7.44828
Facilities : 🔑🏚 🍴 🖼	**P** **S**	Latitude : 48.25444
Nearby : 🍴 🖼 🏊		

SEPPOIS-LE-BAS

68580 – Michelin map **315** H11 – pop. 1 164 – alt. 390
▶ Paris 454 – Altkirch 13 – Basel 42 – Belfort 38

🏞 Village Center Les Lupins

Village Center

✆ 03 89 25 65 37, www.village-center.com

Address : 1 rue de la Gare (take the northeastern exit along the D 17 2, follow the signs for Altkirch)

Opening times : Permanent

3,5 ha (158 pitches for camping)

Tariff : (2013 Price) 18 € ✦✦ ⇔ 🅴 🔌 (6A) – Extra per person 4 € Reservation fee 30 €

Rental rates : Permanent 🅿 – 10 🏠. Per night from 26 to 96 € Per week from 182 to 672 € – Reservation fee 30 €
🚐 4 🅴 18 €

On the leafy site of the old station; a linear site.

Surroundings : 🐾 ♀
Leisure activities : 🏛 🚴 🏊 🛶
Facilities : ♿ 🗑 🚿 🚰 launderette
Nearby : ✕

Longitude : 7.17893
Latitude : 47.53956

TURCKHEIM

68230 – Michelin map **315** H8 – pop. 3 747 – alt. 225
▶ Paris 471 – Colmar 7 – Gérardmer 47 – Munster 14

⛰ Le Médiéval

☎ 03 89 27 02 00, www.camping-turckheim.com

Address : quai de la Gare (to the west of the town, behind the stadium - access via the road between the level crossing and the bridge)

Opening times : from beginning April to end Oct.

2,5 ha (117 pitches for camping) flat, grassy

Tariff : 18,40€ ★★ 🚐 🔲 🔌 (16A) – Extra per person 4€ – Reservation fee 8€

🚐 borne 2,50€ – 20 🔲 18,60€

Beside a small canal and near the Fecht river.

Surroundings : 🗺 ♀
Leisure activities : 🏛
Facilities : ♿ 🔌 🗑 🚿 🚰 launderette
Nearby : 🍴

Longitude : 7.27144
Latitude : 48.08463

WASSELONNE

67310 – Michelin map **315** I5 – pop. 5 562 – alt. 220
▶ Paris 464 – Haguenau 42 – Molsheim 15 – Saverne 15

⛰ Municipal

☎ 03 88 87 00 08, www.camping-wasselonne.com

Address : rue des Sapins (located 1km west along the D 224, follow the signs for Wangenbourg)

Opening times : from mid April to mid Oct.

1,5 ha (100 pitches for camping)

Tariff : ★ 8,40€ 🚐 🔲 – 🔌 (10A) 3,30€

Rental rates : (from beginning March to end Nov.) ♿ (1 chalet) 12 🏠. Per week from 310 to 470€

🚐 borne 2€ – 10 🔲 8,40€ – 🔋 12€

Pretty green spaces within the grounds of a leisure centre.

Surroundings : ◁ ♀
Leisure activities : 🚴 🏊
Facilities : 🔌 🚰 launderette 🗑
Nearby : ✕ 🍴 🎣

Longitude : 7.44869
Latitude : 48.63691

WATTWILLER

68700 – Michelin map **315** H10 – pop. 1 734 – alt. 356
▶ Paris 478 – Strasbourg 116 – Freiburg-im-Breisgau 81 – Basel 56

☶ Les Sources 🅰

☎ 03 89 75 44 94, www.campinglessources.com

Address : route des Crêtes

Opening times : from mid April to end Sept.

15 ha (200 pitches for camping)

Tariff : 32€ ★★ 🚐 🔲 🔌 (6A) – Extra per person 7€

Rental rates : (from mid April to end Oct.) – 50 🚍 – 20 🏠. Per night from 45 to 125€ – Per week from 270 to 875€ – Reservation fee 10€

🚐 borne 5€ – 5 🔲 14€ – 🔋 🔌 17€

A pleasant wooded site, but the infrastructure and sanitary facilities are getting old.

Surroundings : 🐾 🗺 🎵
Leisure activities : 🍴 ✕ 🏛 🕐 daytime 🤾 🚴 ✂ 🌊 🏊 🛶
Facilities : ♿ 🔌 🚿 🚰 launderette 🗑 🚲
Nearby : 🐴

Longitude : 7.16736
Latitude : 47.83675

In order for the guide to remain wholly objective, the selection of campsites is made on an entirely independent basis.

WIHR-AU-VAL

68230 – Michelin map **315** H8 – pop. 1 237 – alt. 330
▶ Paris 463 – Colmar 14 – Gérardmer 38 – Guebwiller 35

⛰ La Route Verte

☎ 03 89 71 10 10, www.camping-routeverte.com

Address : 13 rue de la Gare (take the southern exit along the D 43, follow the signs for Soultzbach-les-Bains)

Opening times : from end April to end Sept.

1,2 ha (55 pitches for camping) flat and relatively flat, grassy

Tariff : (2013 Price) ★ 2,90€ 🚐 🔲 3,90€ – 🔌 (10A) 6,40€

🚐 borne 5€ – 🔋 9,80€

A small, lovely family-orientated site in the heart of a charming village surrounded by vineyards.

Surroundings : 🐾 ♀
Leisure activities : 🚴
Facilities : ♿ 🔌 🚿 🚰 📺
Nearby : 🍴 ✕

Longitude : 7.20513
Latitude : 48.05159

AQUITAINE

H. Lenain / hemis.fr

Welcome to Aquitaine, home to prehistoric remains, fortified towns and a mosaic of landscapes, as distinctive and welcoming as the hospitality and humour of its locals. A quick stop to buy *confit d'oie* (confit of goose) could lead to an invitation to look around the farm! Aquitaine has dense forests, imposing mountains and sweeping beaches; it is home to picturesque villages, bustling cities, large estates and imposing châteaux. No stay would be complete without · visiting at least one of the renowned vineyards of Bordeaux. Then head over to the 'Silver Coast', with its many surfers, rugby fans and bullfighters, all raised on *gâteau Basque*, a cake made with almond flour, and *piment d'Espelette*, a rather spicy pepper. This rugged, sunlit land between the Pyrenees and the Atlantic remains fiercely proud of its identity. Spend a little time in a sleepy Basque village and you will soon discover the region's traditional colours of red, white and green proudly displayed.

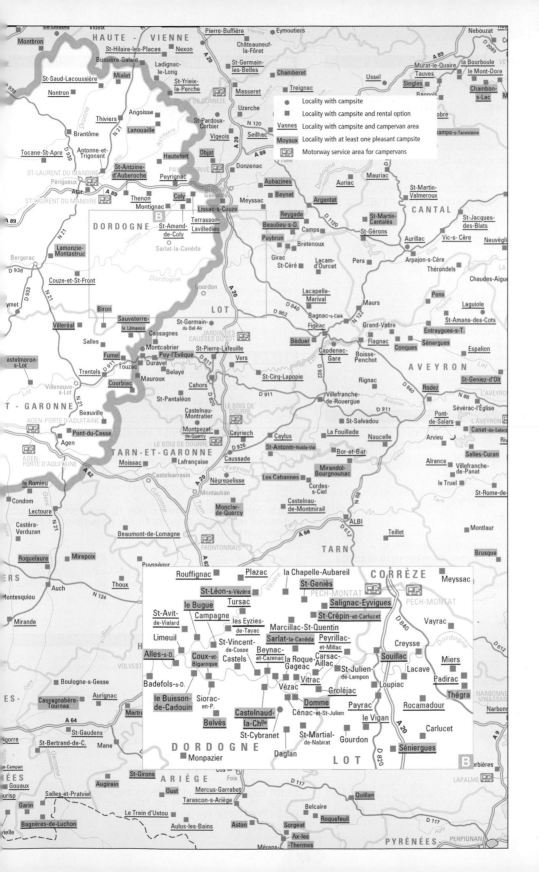

AGEN

47000 – Michelin map **336** F4 – pop. 33 920 – alt. 50
▶ Paris 662 – Auch 74 – Bordeaux 141 – Pau 159

⚠ Le Moulin de Mellet

☏ 05 53 87 50 89, www.camping-moulin-mellet.com

Address : at St Hilaire de Lusignan, route de Prayssas (head 8km northwest along the D 813 and take a right turn along the D 107)

Opening times : from beginning April to mid Oct.

5 ha/3,5 for camping (48 pitches) flat, grassy, stream, small lake

Tariff : 26,90€ ♣♣ ⇔ 🗐 🗐 (10A) – Extra per person 6,30€
Rental rates : (from beginning April to mid Oct.) – 2 🛏 – 6 🏠.
Per night from 119 to 139€ – Per week from 231 to 797€

Surroundings : ♤♤
Leisure activities : 🎣 ⛵ 🎿 🏄
Facilities : ♿ ⚡ 🏕 🍴 🔥
Nearby : paintballing

G P S Longitude : 0.54188
Latitude : 44.2436

There are several different types of sani-station ('borne' in French) – sanitation points providing fresh water and disposal points for grey water. See page 12 for further details.

AINHOA

64250 – Michelin map **342** C3 – pop. 672 – alt. 130
▶ Paris 791 – Bayonne 28 – Biarritz 29 – Cambo-les-Bains 11

⚠ Xokoan

☏ 05 59 29 90 26, etchartenea@orange.fr

Address : at Dancharia (head 2.5km southwest then take the left turn before the customs post (border with Spain)

Opening times : Permanent

0,6 ha (30 pitches)

Tariff : 19€ ♣♣ ⇔ 🗐 🗐 (10A) – Extra per person 5,50€
Rental rates : 2 🛏 – 6 🛏 – (hotel). Per night from 55 to 90€
🚰 borne 5,50€ – 4 🗐 10€
Situated alongside a stream that marks the border between France and Spain.

Surroundings : ♤♤
Leisure activities : 🍴 ✕ 🎣
Facilities : ♿ ⚡ 🗑 🏕 🍴 launderette 🧹

G P S Longitude : -1.50369
Latitude : 43.29139

⚠ Harazpy

☏ 05 59 29 89 38, etchartenea@orange.fr

Address : district Gastelu-Gaïna (to the northwest of the town, behind the church)

1 ha (25 pitches)

Rentals : 1 gîte d'étape (lodge, 12 beds)
🚰 borne
A delightful and tranquil meadow setting with a view of typical Basque countryside.

Surroundings : ♤ ♤
Leisure activities : 🎣
Facilities : ♿ ⚡ launderette

G P S Longitude : -1.50172
Latitude : 43.3089

AIRE-SUR-L'ADOUR

40800 – Michelin map **335** J12 – pop. 6 275 – alt. 80
▶ Paris 722 – Auch 84 – Condom 68 – Dax 77

⚠ Les Ombrages de l'Adour

☏ 05 58 71 75 10, www.camping-adour-landes.com

Address : rue des Graviers (located near the bridge, behind the arenas; beside the Adour river)

Opening times : from mid April to mid. Oct.

2 ha (100 pitches) flat, grassy

Tariff : (2013 price) 17,50€ ♣♣ ⇔ 🗐 🗐 (10A) – Extra per person 3,80€

Rental rates : (2013 price) (from mid April to mid Oct.) – 8 🛏
2 canvas bungalows. Per night from 40 to 64€ – Per week from 195 to 385€

🚰 borne
Near the town centre.

Surroundings : 🌳 ♤♤
Leisure activities : ⛵ 🎣
Facilities : ⚡ 🍴 launderette
Nearby : 🎿

G P S Longitude : -0.25793
Latitude : 43.70257

ALLES-SUR-DORDOGNE

24480 – Michelin map **329** G6 – pop. 344 – alt. 70
▶ Paris 534 – Bergerac 36 – Le Bugue 12 – Les Eyzies-de-Tayac 22

⚠ Port de Limeuil

☏ 05 53 63 29 76, www.leportdelimeuil.com

Address : 3km northeast on the D 51e, near the bridge at Limeuil, where the Dordogne and the Vézère rivers meet

Opening times : from beginning May to mid Sept.

7 ha/4 for camping (90 pitches)

Tariff : 33,30€ ♣♣ ⇔ 🗐 🗐 (10A) – Extra per person 7,50€
Reservation fee 15€
Rental rates : (from beginning May to end Sept.) – 13 🛏
1 gîte. Per night from 70 to 150€ – Per week from 175 to 980€
Reservation fee 15€
🚰 borne – 9 🗐 29,40€

Surroundings : 🌳 ♤♤ ⛰
Leisure activities : 🍴 🎣 ⛵ 🚲 ✕ 🎿 🏄
Facilities : ♿ ⚡ 🏕 🏕 🍴 launderette 🧹 🧺
Nearby : ✕ 🐎

G P S Longitude : 0.88599
Latitude : 44.87969

ANGLET

64600 – Michelin map **342** C2 – pop. 37 661 – alt. 20
▶ Paris 773 – Bordeaux 187 – Pamplona 108 – Donostia-San Sebastián 51

⚠ Le Parme

☏ 05 59 23 03 00, www.campingdeparme.com

Address : 2 allée Etchecopar (near the flying club)

Opening times : from end March to beginning Nov.

3,5 ha (187 pitches)

Tariff : (2013 price) 34€ ♣♣ ⇔ 🗐 🗐 (5A) – Extra per person 6,50€
Reservation fee 15€
Rental rates : (from end March to beginning Nov.) – 65 🛏
10 🏠. Per night from 49 to 135€ – Per week from 378 to 693€ – Reservation fee 15€
🚰 6 🗐 35€

A range of rental options of differing levels of comfort. Choose the pitches away from the road.

Surroundings : 🖵 ♋♋
Leisure activities : 🍴 ✗ 🚣 ⊙ 🏃 🏊 🛶 ✗ multi-sports ground
Facilities : ᵹ �o━ ⚓ 🚰 launderette 🔌 🚿

G P S Longitude : -1.53238
Latitude : 43.4643

These symbols are used for a campsite that is exceptional in its category:

🏕🏕 ...🏕 *Particularly pleasant setting, quality and range of services available*

🦢 🦢 *Tranquil, isolated site – quiet site, particularly at night*

⪡ ⪡ *Exceptional view – interesting or panoramic view*

ANGOISSE

24270 – Michelin map **329** H3 – pop. 610 – alt. 345
▶ Paris 445 – Bordeaux 180 – Périgueux 51 – Limoges 53

🏕 Rouffiac en Périgord

🖉 0553526879, www.semitour.com – traditional camp. spaces also available

Address : at the leisure centre of Rouffiac (4km southeast along the D 80, follow the signs for Payzac, 150m from a small lake (direct access)

Opening times : from beginning May to end Sept.

54 ha/6 for camping (40 pitches)

Tariff : ✶ 5,20€ 🚐 🔲 8€ ⏻ (10A)
Rental rates : Permanent – 2 🛏 – 34 🏠. Per night from 83 to 252€ – Per week from 220 to 670€
Organised cultural and sporting holidays based around the sailing centre.

Surroundings : 🦢 🖵 ♋♋
Leisure activities : 🍴 🚣
Facilities : ᵹ �o━ 🚰 🔳
Nearby : 🚴 ✗ 🏖 (beach) 🛶 🐎 forest trail

G P S Longitude : 1.16648
Latitude : 45.41449

ANTONNE-ET-TRIGONANT

24420 – Michelin map **329** F4 – pop. 1 203 – alt. 106
▶ Paris 484 – Bordeaux 139 – Périgueux 10 – Limoges 91

🏕 Au Fil de l'Eau

🖉 0553061788, www.campingaufildeleau.com

Address : in Antonne, 6 allées des Platanes (take the northeastern exit and follow the signs for Escoire to the right; beside the island, on the D 6)

Opening times : from mid April to mid Oct.

1,5 ha (50 pitches)

Tariff : 20,60€ ✶✶ 🚐 🔲 ⏻ (6A) – Extra per person 4,50€
Rental rates : (from mid April to mid Oct.) – 9 🛏 – 4 canvas bungalows. Per night from 40 to 90 € – Per week from 210 to 700€

Surroundings : ♋♋
Leisure activities : 🏊 🐎
Facilities : ᵹ ⌀━ 🚰 🔳

G P S Longitude : 0.83754
Latitude : 45.213

ARAMITS

64570 – Michelin map **342** H4 – pop. 677 – alt. 293
▶ Paris 829 – Mauléon-Licharre 27 – Oloron-Ste-Marie 15 – Pau 49

🏕 Barétous-Pyrénées

🖉 0559341221, www.camping-pyrenees.com

Address : district Ripaude (take the western exit along the D 918, follow the signs for Mauléon-Licharre; beside the Vert de Barlanes (river)

Opening times : from mid Feb. to mid Oct.

2 ha (61 pitches) flat, grassy

Tariff : 27,60€ ✶✶ 🚐 🔲 ⏻ (10A) – Extra per person 6,50€
Reservation fee 13,50€
Rental rates : (from mid Dec. to mid Oct.) ᵹ (chalet) – 10 🛏 11 🏠 – 3 canvas bungalows. Per night from 35 to 85€ – Per week from 220 to 585€ – Reservation fee 16,50€
Very comfortable wooden chalets (hotel service available on request).

Surroundings : 🖵 ♋♋
Leisure activities : 🍴 ✗ 🚣 🎣 jacuzzi 🏃 🚴 🛶
Facilities : ᵹ ⌀━ 🆒 🚰 launderette 🚿

G P S Longitude : -0.73243
Latitude : 43.12135

ARÈS

33740 – Michelin map **335** E6 – pop. 5 548 – alt. 6
▶ Paris 627 – Arcachon 47 – Bordeaux 48

🏕 Les Goëlands

🖉 0556825564, www.goelands.com

Address : 64 avenue de la Libération (1.7km southeast, near lakes and 500m from the quayside)

Opening times : from beginning March to end Oct.

10 ha/6 for camping (400 pitches)

Tariff : (2013 price) 32€ ✶✶ 🚐 🔲 ⏻ (6A) – Extra per person 9€
Reservation fee 24,50€
Rental rates : (from mid April to mid Oct.) – 16 🛏. Per night from 50 to 60€ – Per week from 305 to 865€ – Reservation fee 24,50€
🚰 borne

Surroundings : 🦢 🖵 ♋♋
Leisure activities : 🍴 ✗ ⊙ 🏃 🏊 🚴 🛶 multi-sports ground
Facilities : ᵹ ⌀━ ⚓ 🚰 launderette 🔌 🚿
Nearby : 🏖 (pond) 🦢 🛶

G P S Longitude : -1.11979
Latitude : 44.75747

🏕 Sites et Paysages La Cigale

🖉 0556602259, www.camping-lacigale-ares.com – limited spaces for one-night stay

Address : 53 rue du Général de Gaulle (take the northern exit)

Opening times : from end April to end Sept.

2,4 ha (75 pitches)

Tariff : 39,50€ ✶✶ 🚐 🔲 ⏻ (6A) – Extra per person 7,50€
Reservation fee 18€
Rental rates : (from end April to end Oct.) – 7 🏠 – 3 tent lodges. Per week from 125 to 900€ – Reservation fee 20€

Surroundings : 🦢 🖵 ♋♋
Leisure activities : 🍴 ✗ 🚣 🏃 🛶
Facilities : ᵹ ⌀━ 🚰 launderette 🚿

G P S Longitude : -1.14188
Latitude : 44.77287

⛰ Les Abberts

☎ 05 56 60 26 80, www.lesabberts.com

Address : 17 rue des Abberts (take the northern exit then take the turning to the left)

Opening times : from beginning June to mid Sept.

2 ha (125 pitches)

Tariff : 35 € ✳✳ 🚐 📺 �🚿 (6A) – Extra per person 9,50 € – Reservation fee 18 €

Rental rates : (from mid April to mid Oct.) 🚫 (from mid April to end June) – 30 🛏 – 1 🏠. Per night from 80 to 123 € – Per week from 359 to 859 € – Reservation fee 18 €

🚰 borne

Surroundings : 🏊 ♉♉		
Leisure activities : ♈ ✗ 🏛 🛶 🚴 🛶 (small swimming pool)	**G**	Longitude : -1.1444
Facilities : ♿ ⛲ ♏ launderette 🧺	**P** **S**	Latitude : 44.77163

⛺ Pasteur

☎ 05 56 60 33 33, www.atlantic-vacances.com – limited spaces for one-night stay

Address : 1 rue du Pilote (take the southeastern exit, 300m from the quayside)

Opening times : from mid March to mid Nov.

1 ha (50 pitches)

Tariff : 19 € ✳✳ 🚐 📺 �🚿 (6A) – Extra per person 4 € – Reservation fee 17 €

Rental rates : (from mid March to mid Nov.) – 16 🛏 – 14 🏠. Per night from 49 to 60 € – Per week from 230 to 760 € Reservation fee 17 €

🚰 borne 14 € – 🚐 11 €

Surroundings : 🏊 ♉♉		
Leisure activities : 🛶 🚴 🛶 (small swimming pool)	**G**	Longitude : -1.13681
Facilities : ♿ ⛲ ♏ 🧺	**P** **S**	Latitude : 44.76174

24750 – Michelin map **329** F5 – pop. 1 744 – alt. 224

▶ Paris 499 – Bordeaux 134 – Périgueux 6 – Brive-la-Gaillarde 83

⛰ Iris Parc Le Grand Dague ♣♣

☎ 05 53 04 21 01, www.legranddague.fr – limited spaces for one-night stay

Address : route du Grand Dague (3km southeast following signs for St-Laurent-sur-Manoire – if on southern diversion coming from Brive or Limoges: take the road towards Bergerac and take the road to the right)

Opening times : from end April to end Sept.

22 ha/12 for camping (382 pitches)

Tariff : 39 € ✳✳ 🚐 📺 �🚿 (10A) – Extra per person 7,50 €

Rental rates : (2013 price) (from end April to end Sept.) ♿ 🚫 Ⓟ 260 🛏 – 80 tent lodges. Per night from 25 to 139 € – Per week from 175 to 973 € – Reservation fee 20 €

A well-equipped indoor children's play area.

Surroundings : 🏊 🛒 ♉♉		
Leisure activities : ♈ ✗ 🏛 ⓘ 🏃 🛶 ♟ 🎣 paintballing	**G**	Longitude : 0.77656
Facilities : ♿ ⛲ 🏛 🧺 ♏ launderette 🧺 🛠	**P** **S**	Latitude : 45.14816

40200 – Michelin map **335** D9 – pop. 935 – alt. 10

▶ Paris 689 – Bordeaux 103 – Mont-de-Marsan 79 – La Teste 59

⛰ Village Center Aurilandes ♣♣

Interaview Production

☎ 0825 00 20 30, www.village-center.fr

Address : 1001 Promenade de l'Étang (located 1km to the northeast, near the lake)

Opening times : from end April to end Sept.

6 ha (440 pitches)

Tariff : 19 € ✳✳ 🚐 📺 �🚿 (10A) Extra per person 4 € – Reservation fee 30 €

Rental rates : Permanent – 51 🛏 – 16 canvas bungalows – 40 tent lodges. Per night from 21 to 62 € – Per week from 301 to 690 € Reservation fee 30 €

Surroundings : 🏊 ♉♉ ⛰		
Leisure activities : 🏛 ⓘ 🏃 🎿 🈳 jacuzzi 🛶 🚴 🛶 multi-sports ground	**G**	Longitude : -1.20314
Facilities : ♿ ⛲ 🆑 🏛 ♏ launderette 🧺 🛠	**P** **S**	Latitude : 44.22306
Nearby : ♿ ⚓		

There are several different types of sani-station ('borne' in French) – sanitation points providing fresh water and disposal points for grey water. See page 12 for further details.

40140 – Michelin map **335** D12 – pop. 575 – alt. 9

▶ Paris 730 – Bayonne 54 – Dax 25 – Mimizan 79

⛰ FranceLoc La Paillotte ♣♣

☎ 05 58 48 12 12, www.paillotte.com 🚫

Address : 66 route des Campings (located 1.5km southwest; beside the Lac de Soustons)

7 ha (310 pitches)

Rentals : 🚫 – 205 🛏 – 50 🏠.

Exotically decorated but pretty chalet village and a large water park beside the lake.

Surroundings : 🏊 ← 🛒 ♉♉ ⛰		
Leisure activities : ♈ ✗ 🏛 ⓘ 🏃 🛶 🐟 🛶 🎿 🏊 🛶	**G**	Longitude : -1.30875
Facilities : ♿ ⛲ 🏛 🧺 ♏ launderette 🧺 🛠	**P** **S**	Latitude : 43.78731
Nearby : 🚴 🚣 🎣 🛶 pedalos		

⛰ Azur Rivage

☎ 05 58 48 30 72, www.campingazurivage.com

Address : 720 route des Campings (situated 2km to the south, 100m from the lake at Soustons)

Opening times : from beginning April to mid Sept.

6,5 ha (250 pitches)

Tariff : 17,30 € ✳✳ 🚐 📺 �🚿 (16A) – Extra per person 6 € – Reservation fee 17 €

Rental rates : (from beginning April to mid Sept.) – 62 🚐. Per night from 38 to 115€ – Per week from 266 to 805€ Reservation fee 17€

🚐 borne 17,30€

Surroundings : ⌂ ♌
Leisure activities : ⛵🏊🛶⛵ multi-sports ground
Facilities : ♿ ⚏ (July–Aug.) 🧺🔥♨🍴📮🚰
🚰 refrigerated food storage facilities
Nearby : 🚴✂✂🏛 ⛴ pedalos

Longitude : -1.23047
Latitude : 43.78477

BADEFOLS-SUR-DORDOGNE

24150 – Michelin map **329** F6 – pop. 211 – alt. 42
▶ Paris 542 – Bergerac 27 – Périgueux 54 – Sarlat-la-Canéda 47

🛖 Club Airotel Les Bö Bains

☎ 0553735252, www.bo-bains.com – limited spaces for one-night stay

Address : route de Bergerac (take the western exit, along the D 29; beside the Dordogne)

Opening times : from beginning April to end Sept.

5 ha (97 pitches)

Tariff : 13€ ★★ 🚐 ▣ [½] (9A) – Extra per person 7€ – Reservation fee 25€

Rental rates : (from beginning April to end Sept.) ♿ – 40 🚐 34 🏠. Per night from 45 to 70€ – Per week from 350 to 500€ Reservation fee 25€

Surroundings : ≮ ♌
Leisure activities : ⛵✗ 🖼 ⛲nighttime 🏃
🏹🛶🚴🛶⛵ 🏊⛵ 🌿
Facilities : ♿ ⚏ 🚿 🍴 launderette 🚰
Nearby : ✂

Longitude : 0.78541
Latitude : 44.84155

In order for the guide to remain wholly objective, the selection of campsites is made on an entirely independent basis.

LA BASTIDE-CLAIRENCE

64240 – Michelin map **342** E4 – pop. 984 – alt. 50
▶ Paris 767 – Bayonne 26 – Hasparren 9 – Peyrehorade 29

🛖 Village Vacances Les Collines Iduki

(rental of apartment and maisonnettes only)
☎ 0559702081, www.location-vacances-paysbasque.com

Address : at Pont de Port

Opening times : Permanent

2,5 ha terraced

Rental rates : ♿ (1 apartment) – 6 🏠 – 30 apartments. Per night from 65 to 131€ – Per week from 303 to 1 097€
Pretty Basque buildings and a good quality restaurant.

Surroundings : ⌂ ≮ ♌
Leisure activities : ✗ 🖼 🛶⛵ 🏊
Facilities : ♿ ⚏ 🅿 🍴 launderette
Nearby : ✂

Longitude : -1.25742
Latitude : 43.43324

BAUDREIX

64800 – Michelin map **342** K3 – pop. 537 – alt. 245
▶ Paris 791 – Argelès-Gazost 39 – Lourdes 26 – Oloron-Ste-Marie 48

🛖 Les Ôkiri

☎ 0559929773, www.lesokiri.com ✀ (from June to Aug)

Address : avenue du Lac (At the leisure and activity park)

Opening times : from beginning April to end Sept.

20 ha/2 for camping (60 pitches) flat, grassy

Tariff : 25,50€ ★★ 🚐 ▣ [½] (10A) – Extra per person 15€

Rental rates : Permanent ✀ 🅿 – 10 🚐 – 25 🏠 – 5 canvas bungalows. Per night from 50 to 118€ – Per week from 280 to 600€ – Reservation fee 10€

A large boating centre; wooden chalets of a basic standard, mobile homes with or without sanitary facilities and a camp-site with about 50 pitches.

Surroundings : ⌂ ☷ ♌ 🏊
Leisure activities : ✗✗🛶⛵🚴⛴ (beach)
🏊⛵ pedalos 🌿 multi-sports ground
Facilities : ♿ ⚏ (July–Aug.) 🆒🍴 launderette
🚰

Longitude : -0.26124
Latitude : 43.20439

BEAUVILLE

47470 – Michelin map **336** H4 – pop. 584 – alt. 208
▶ Paris 641 – Agen 26 – Moissac 32 – Montaigu-de-Quercy 16

⛺ Les 2 Lacs

☎ 0553954541, www.les2lacs.info

Address : at Vallon de Gerbal (900m southeast along the D 122, follow the signs for Bourg de Visa)

Opening times : from beginning April to end Oct.

22 ha/2,5 for camping (80 pitches)

Tariff : ★ 5€ 🚐 ▣ 10€ – [½] (6A) 2,90€ – Reservation fee 10€

Rental rates : (from beginning April to end Oct.) – 2 🚐 – 1 🏠 2 canvas bungalows. Per week from 160 to 1 000€ – Reservation fee 10€

There's a snack-bar terrace beside the lake.

Surroundings : ⌂ ☷ ♌
Leisure activities : ✗✗🛶⛵✂⛴🌿 boats to hire 🌿
Facilities : ♿ ⚏ 🍴 launderette

Longitude : 0.88819
Latitude : 44.27142

BÉLUS

40300 – Michelin map **335** E13 – pop. 605 – alt. 135
▶ Paris 749 – Bayonne 37 – Dax 18 – Orthez 36

⛺ La Comtesse

☎ 0558576907, www.campinglacomtesse.com ✀

Address : at Claquin (2.5km northwest along the D 75 and take turning to the right)

Opening times : from beginning April to end Sept.

6 ha (115 pitches) flat, grassy

Tariff : (2013 price) ★ 3,40€ 🚐 1,70€ ▣ 6€ – [½] (10A) 3,10€

Rental rates : Permanent ✀ – 15 🚐. Per week from 260 to 610€ Reservation fee 10€

A pleasant site among poplar trees around a lake.

Surroundings : ⌂ ☷ ♌
Leisure activities : ✗✗ 🖼 🏃✂🏊⛵🌿
Facilities : ♿ ⚏ 🧺🍴 launderette 🚰

Longitude : -1.13075
Latitude : 43.60364

BELVÈS

24170 – Michelin map **329** H7 – pop. 1 432 – alt. 175
▶ Paris 553 – Bergerac 52 – Le Bugue 24 – Les Eyzies-de-Tayac 25

⚑ FranceLoc Les Hauts de Ratebout ♣♠

✆ 05 53 29 02 10, www.camping-hauts-ratebout.fr

Address : Ste-Foy-de-Belvès, at Ratebout (7km southeast along the D 710, follow the signs for Fumel, D 54 and take turning to the left)

Opening times : from end April to beginning Sept.

12 ha/6 for camping (200 pitches) terraced, flat and relatively flat, grassy

Tariff : 42€ ♣♣ ⇔ 回 (5) (10A) – Extra per person 7€ – Reservation fee 27€

Rental rates : (from end April to mid Sept.) – 156 ⏢ – 5 gîtes. Per night from 22 to 170€ – Per week from 154 to 1 190€ Reservation fee 27€

A pretty, renovated Périgord farmhouse with a top-quality children's play area.

Surroundings : ⛰ ⟨♤♤
Leisure activities : ♈ ✕ 🎣 ☷ 🚶 🏊 🚣 ✂ ♪
⊠ 🛝 ⚘
Facilities : ⚹ ⟜ 🏢 ♨ 🚿 ♿ ♨ launderette ⚗

G P S | Longitude : 1.04529
Latitude : 44.74151

⚑ RCN Le Moulin de la Pique ♣♠

✆ 05 53 29 01 15, www.rcn.fr

Address : at Moulin de la Pique (3km southeast along the D 710, follow the signs for Fumel; near the Nauze river, a lake and a millpond)

Opening times : from mid April to end Sept.

15 ha/6 for camping (200 pitches)

Tariff : 52,50€ ♣♣ ⇔ 回 (5) (10A) Extra per person 5,75€ Reservation fee 19,95€

Rental rates : (from mid April to end Sept.) – 60 ⏢ 3 apartments 5 tent lodges. Per night from 35 to 177€ – Per week from 245 to 1 239€ – Reservation fee 19,95€

🚮 borne 16€ – 20 回 16€
Based around a pretty 18th-century mill and its outbuildings.

Surroundings : ⏢♤♤
Leisure activities : ♈ ✕ 🎣 ☷ 🚶 🏊 🚴 ✂
♪ 🛝 ⚘ 🏊
Facilities : ⚹ ⟜ 🏢 ♨ 🚿 ♿ ♨ launderette
⚗

G P S | Longitude : 1.01371
Latitude : 44.7305

⚑ Flower Les Nauves ♣♠

✆ 05 53 29 12 64, www.lesnauves.com

Address : at Le Bos Rouge (4.5km southwest along the D 53, follow the signs for Monpazier and turn left following the signs for Larzac)

Opening times : from beginning April to end Sept.

40 ha/5 for camping (100 pitches)

Tariff : 26,90€ ♣♣ ⇔ 回 (5) (10A) – Extra per person 5,50€ Reservation fee 15€

Rental rates : (from beginning April to end Sept.) – 31 ⏢ – 3 🏠 3 canvas bungalows – 8 tent lodges. Per night from 30 to 102€ Per week from 150 to 714€ – Reservation fee 15€

Surroundings : ⛰ ⏢♤♤
Leisure activities : ♈ ✕ 🎣 🚶 🚣
Facilities : ⚹ ⟜ ♨ 🚿 🛝 ⚗
Nearby : 🐎

G P S | Longitude : 0.98184
Latitude : 44.75497

BEYNAC-ET-CAZENAC

24220 – Michelin map **329** H6 – pop. 522 – alt. 75
▶ Paris 537 – Bergerac 62 – Brive-la-Gaillade 63 – Fumel 60

⚑ Le Capeyrou

✆ 05 53 29 54 95, www.campinglecapeyrou.com

Address : route de Sarlat (take the eastern exit, along the D 57; beside the Dordogne river)

Opening times : from end April to end Sept.

4,5 ha (120 pitches) flat, grassy

Tariff : (2013 price) ♣ 6,50€ ⇔ 回 8,10€ – (5) (10A) 4,20€ Reservation fee 10€

Rental rates : (from end April to end Sept.) – 4 tent lodges. Per night from 55 to 93€ – Per week from 270 to 650€ Reservation fee 10€

🚮 borne

Surroundings : ⟨ Château de Beynac ♤♤
Leisure activities : ♈ 🎣 🚴 🚣 🏊 🚣
Facilities : ⚹ ⟜ ♨ ♨ 🚿 ♨ launderette
Nearby : ✕ ⚗ ✂

G P S | Longitude : 1.14843
Latitude : 44.83828

BIARRITZ

64200 – Michelin map **342** C4 – pop. 25 397 – alt. 19
▶ Paris 772 – Bayonne 9 – Bordeaux 190 – Pau 122

⚑ Club Airotel Biarritz-Camping

✆ 05 59 23 00 12, www.biarritz.camping.fr

Address : 28 rue Harcet

Opening times : from beginning April to end Sept.

3 ha (170 pitches)

Tariff : (2013 price) 38€ ♣♣ ⇔ 回 (5) (10A) – Extra per person 8€ Reservation fee 15€

Rental rates : (2013 price) (from end March to mid Nov.) ✂ 72 ⏢ – 14 canvas bungalows. Per night from 50 to 80€ Per week from 320 to 890€ – Reservation fee 15€

300m from the Cité de l'Océan (maritime museum) and 700m from the beach. Bus for the town.

Surroundings : ♤♤
Leisure activities : ♈ ✕ jacuzzi 🚴 🚣
Facilities : ⚹ ⟜ ♨ ♨ launderette ⚗ ⚗
Nearby : 🐎

G P S | Longitude : -1.56685
Latitude : 43.46199

BIAS

40170 – Michelin map **335** D10 – pop. 736 – alt. 41
▶ Paris 706 – Castets 33 – Mimizan 7 – Morcenx 30

⚑ Municipal Le Tatiou ♣♠

Le Tatiou

✆ 05 58 09 04 76, www.campingletatiou.com

Address : route de Lespecier (situated 2km west)

Opening times : from beginning April to end Sept.

10 ha (501 pitches)

Tariff : (2013 price) 21,60€ ♣♣ ⇔ 回 (5) (10A) – Extra per person 5,60€ Reservation fee 20€

Rental rates : Permanent – 6 🚐 – 5 canvas bungalows. Per night 60€ – Reservation fee 20€

Surroundings : 🏞 ♤♤
Leisure activities : ♟ ✕ 🏖 🏕 🏃 🚴 ⛳
🏊
Facilities : 🚿 ⚲ 🧺 ⛺ launderette 🗑 🛒 refrigerated food storage facilities

G P S	Longitude : -1.24029
	Latitude : 44.14531

This guide is not intended as a list of all the camping sites in France; its aim is to provide a selection of the best sites in each category.

BIDART

64210 – Michelin map **342** C2 – pop. 6 117 – alt. 40
▶ Paris 783 – Bordeaux 196 – Pau 119 – Bayonne 13

🔺 Les Castels Le Ruisseau des Pyrénées ♣♪

(rental of mobile homes, chalets and canvas bungalows only)

📞 05 59 41 94 50, www.camping-le-ruisseau.fr – traditional camp. spaces also available

Address : rue Burruntz (situated 2km east; beside the Ouhabia river and a stream – divided into two separate areas)

Opening times : from mid April to mid Sept.

15 ha/7 for camping (440 pitches) terraced, flat, grassy

Tariff : 49€ ♣♣ ⇌ 🔲 ⚡ (10A) – Extra per person 7€ – Reservation fee 20€

Rental rates : 🚿 (mobile home) – 130 🚐 – 7 🏠. Per night from 42 to 127€ – Per week from 65 to 203€ – Reservation fee 20€

Divided into 2 separate sections, with lots of green space for relaxation or leisure activities and 2 water parks, one partially indoor 'zen'-style and one with water slides.

Surroundings : 🏞 🛻 ♤♤
Leisure activities : ♟ ✕ 🏖 ⛳ 🏃 🎿 ⛳ hammam, jacuzzi 🚴 ⛳ ✂ 🏊 🛝 🛶 🏹 fitness trail, farm or petting farm multi-sports ground
Facilities : 🚿 ⚲ 🧺 launderette 🗑 🛒
Nearby : 🐎

G P S	Longitude : -1.56835
	Latitude : 43.43704

🔺 Yelloh! Village Ilbarritz ♣♪

📞 05 59 23 00 29, www.camping-ilbarritz.com

Address : avenue de Biarritz (situated 2km to the north)

Opening times : from beginning April to beginning Oct.

6 ha (374 pitches)

Tariff : 71€ ♣♣ ⇌ 🔲 ⚡ (10A) – Extra per person 9€

Rental rates : (from end March to mid Nov.) 🚿 (1 mobile home) 166 🚐 – 24 🏠. Per night from 39 to 248€ – Per week from 273 to 1 911€

An attractive and spacious entrance with pretty buildings in the Basque style.

Surroundings : 🛻 ♤♤
Leisure activities : ♟ ✕ 🏖 ⚡ 🏃 jacuzzi 🚴 🏊 🛝 🛶 surfing multi-sports ground
Facilities : 🚿 ⚲ 📺 🧺 launderette 🛒 🛒 refrigerated food storage facilities
Nearby : 🎵 disco

G P S	Longitude : -1.57374
	Latitude : 43.45315

🔺 Sunêlia Berrua ♣♪

📞 05 59 54 96 66, www.berrua.com

Address : rue Berrua (500m east, follow the signs for Arbonne)

5 ha (261 pitches) terraced, relatively flat, grassy

Rentals : 157 🚐 – 10 🏠 – 2 tent lodges.

🚐 borne

A well-maintained site with flowers; some luxurious rental options.

Surroundings : 🛻 ♤♤
Leisure activities : ♟ ✕ 🏖 ⚡ 🏃 hammam 🚴 ⛳ 🏊 multi-sports ground
Facilities : 🚿 ⚲ 🧺 launderette 🗑 🛒
Nearby : surfing

G P S	Longitude : -1.58176
	Latitude : 43.43824

🔺 Club Airotel Oyam ♣♪

📞 05 59 54 91 61, www.camping-oyam.com

Address : chemin Oyhamburua (located 1km east along the follow the signs for Arbonne then take the turning to the right)

Opening times : from mid April to mid Sept.

7 ha (350 pitches)

Tariff : 42€ ♣♣ ⇌ 🔲 ⚡ (6A) – Extra per person 7,50€ – Reservation fee 20€

Rental rates : (from mid April to mid Sept.) 🚿 (1 mobile home) 97 🚐 – 18 🏠 – 14 apartments – 3 tipis – 10 canvas bungalows – 30 tent lodges. Per night from 41 to 59€ – Per week from 196 to 994€ – Reservation fee 20€

🚐 borne 10€ – 11 🔲 36€

Many and varied rental options; some attractive pitches for tents and caravans beside a water park surrounded by vegetation.

Surroundings : 🛻 ♤♤
Leisure activities : ♟ ✕ 🏖 🏃 🚴 🏊 🛝 multi-sports ground
Facilities : 🚿 ⚲ 🧺 launderette 🛒

G P S	Longitude : -1.58278
	Latitude : 43.43501

Key to rentals symbols :

12 🚐	*Number of mobile homes*
20 🏠	*Number of chalets*
6 🛏	*Number of rooms to rent*
Per night 30–50€	*Minimum/maximum rate per night*
Per week 300–1,000€	*Minimum/maximum rate per week*

⚥ Pavillon Royal

℘ 05 59 23 00 54, www.pavillon-royal.com ✖

Address : avenue du Prince de Galles (situated 2km to the north; beside the beach)

Opening times : from mid May to end Sept.

5 ha (303 pitches) terraced, flat, grassy

Tariff : 58€ ♣♣ ⇔ ▣ ⓗ (10A) – Extra per person 14€ – Reservation fee 25€

Rental rates : (from mid May to end Sept.) ✖ – 3 ⌂. Per week from 473 to 1 085€ – Reservation fee 25€

⛽ borne

In a secluded location near a golf course, château and the sea.

Surroundings : ⋙ ◁ ▭ ♀ ⛰	
Leisure activities : ♈ ✕ ▦ ⌚daytime ⌁ ⇌ ⛵ beauty treatments, surfing	**G P S** Longitude : -1.57642 Latitude : 43.45469
Facilities : ⚒ ⚬ 🅿 ⊟ ⚐ ⚲ ⚒ 🍴 launderette ⇌ ⚒	
Nearby : ⚑nighttime ♫ disco	

⚥ Ur-Onea

GOYA

℘ 05 59 26 53 61, www.uronea.com

Address : rue de la Chapelle (300m east, 500m from the beach)

Opening times : from mid April to end Sept.

5 ha (270 pitches)

Tariff : 41€ ♣♣ ⇔ ▣ ⓗ (10A) Extra per person 7,50€ – Reservation fee 28€

Rental rates : (from mid April to end Sept.) ✖ – 51 ⛺ 51 ⌂. Per night from 40 to 120€ – Per week from 250 to 910€ Reservation fee 38€

⛽ 12 ▣ 44€

Surroundings : ♀♀	
Leisure activities : ♈ ✕ ▦ ⇌ ⛵	**G P S** Longitude : -1.59035 Latitude : 43.43416
Facilities : ⚒ ⚬ ⊟ ⚐ ⚲ 🍴 launderette ⇌ refrigerated food storage facilities	

⚥ Flower Harrobia ♣⚬

℘ 05 59 26 54 71, www.harrobia.fr

Address : rue Maurice Pierre (1.2km to the south, 400m from the beach)

Opening times : from mid June to end Sept.

3 ha (145 pitches)

Tariff : 39€ ♣♣ ⇔ ▣ ⓗ (10A) – Extra per person 8€ – Reservation fee 25€

Rental rates : (from beginning March to end Nov.) – 135 ⛺ 2 ⌂ – 5 apartments. Per night from 49 to 150 € – Per week from 196 to 1050€ – Reservation fee 25€

Near the railway line, a mobile home park with just under 10 pitches for tents and caravans.

Surroundings : ▭ ♀♀	
Leisure activities : ♈ ✕ ▦ ⚐ ⇌ ⛵	**G P S** Longitude : -1.59903 Latitude : 43.42773
Facilities : ⚒ ⚬ ⊟ 🍴 launderette	

We value your opinion and welcome your feedback.
Do email us at campingfrance@tp.michelin.com

33380 – Michelin map **335** F7 – pop. 9 464 – alt. 16

▶ Paris 629 – Andernos-les-Bains 15 – Arcachon 27 – Bordeaux 47

⚥ Le Marache

℘ 05 57 70 61 19, www.marachevacances.com

Address : 25 rue Gambetta (take the northern exit along the D 3, follow the signs for Audenge and take turning to the right)

Opening times : from beginning April to end Sept.

2 ha (115 pitches)

Tariff : 34,50€ ♣♣ ⇔ ▣ ⓗ (16A) – Extra per person 6€ – Reservation fee 15€

Rental rates : (from beginning April to end Sept.) – 35 ⛺ 6 ⌂. Per week from 225 to 805€ – Reservation fee 20€

⛽ borne 6€ – 8 ▣ 12,50€

Surroundings : ▭ ♀♀	
Leisure activities : ♈ ✕ ▦ ⛵ multi-sports ground	**G P S** Longitude : -0.97943 Latitude : 44.65081
Facilities : ⚒ ⚬ ⊟ 🍴 ▣ ⇌	

24540 – Michelin map **329** G8 – pop. 182 – alt. 200

▶ Paris 583 – Beaumont 25 – Bergerac 46 – Fumel 20

⚥ FranceLoc Le Moulinal ♣⚬

℘ 05 53 40 84 60, www.campings-franceloc.fr – limited spaces for one-night stay

Address : at Étang du Moulinal (4km to the south, follow the signs for Lacapelle-Biron then continue 2km following signs for Villeréal to the right)

Opening times : from beginning April to end Sept.

10 ha/5 for camping (300 pitches)

Tariff : (2013 price) 35€ ♣♣ ⇔ ▣ ⓗ (10A) Extra per person 7€ Reservation fee 27€

Rental rates : (from beginning April to end Sept.) – 260 ⛺ 10 ⌂. Per night from 44 to 184€ – Per week from 175 to 1 370€ Reservation fee 27€

Pleasant location beside a lake, great variety of luxuriant foliage.

Surroundings : ⋙ ◁ ▭ ♀♀	
Leisure activities : ♈ ✕ ▦ ⚑ ⚶ ⇌ ⚵ ⚹ ♫ ▣ ⛵ ⚓ (beach) ⛵ ⚓ ⚘ multi-sports ground, entertainment room	**G P S** Longitude : 0.87116 Latitude : 44.60031
Facilities : ⚒ ⚬ ⊟ ⚐ ⚲ 🍴 launderette ⇌ ⚒	

⚥ Village Vacances Castelwood

(rental of chalets only)

℘ 05 53 57 96 08, www.castelwood.fr

Address : at Bois du Château-Les Fargues (located 1km south along the D 53, follow the signs for Lacapelle-Biron)

Opening times : Permanent

1 ha

Rental rates : ⚒ (1 chalet) – 15 ⌂. Per night from 60 to 123€ Per week from 315 to 858€

Luxury chalets nestling in the Périgord Pourpre (Purple Périgord) forest.

Surroundings : ⋙ ♀♀♀	
Leisure activities : ⛵	**G P S** Longitude : 0.87701 Latitude : 44.62495
Facilities : ⚬ ⛲ 🍴 ▣	

BISCARROSSE

40600 – Michelin map **335** E8 – pop. 12 163 – alt. 22

▶ Paris 656 – Arcachon 40 – Bayonne 128 – Bordeaux 74

⚞⚞⚞⚞ Club Airotel Domaine de la Rive 👤👤

𝒫 05 58 78 12 33, www.larive.fr

Address : route de Bordeaux (8km northeast along the D 652, follow the signs for Sanguinet, then continue 2.2km along the turning to the left, beside the Étang de Cazaux (lake)

Opening times : from mid April to end Aug.

15 ha (800 pitches)

Tariff : 57 € 🚻 ⛺ 🔲 (10A) – Extra per person 10,60 €
Reservation fee 30 €

Rental rates : (from mid April to end Aug.) ♿ ⚡ – 350 ▭
40 ⌂. Per night from 60 to 309 € – Per week from 450 to 2 193 €
Reservation fee 30 €

⚟ borne

A pretty swimming area, partially covered.

Surroundings : ⛰ 🌊 ▲
Leisure activities : 🍷 ✕ 🎳 🚴 🏖 ⛵ hammam, jacuzzi ⛹ 🚲 🏊 🛝 🎣 ≋ (beach) 🏄 water skiing, multi-sports ground, spa centre, entertainment room, skate park
Facilities : ♿ ⚟ 🚿 🛁 🚮 launderette 🛒 refrigerated food storage facilities

GPS Longitude : -1.1299
Latitude : 44.46022

⚞⚞⚞⚞ Mayotte Vacances 👤👤

𝒫 05 58 78 00 00, www.mayottevacances.com

Cie BEL AIR

Address : 368 chemin des Roseaux (6km north following signs for Sanguinet then turn left at Goubern and continue for 2.5km; 150m from the Étang de Cazaux (lake, direct access)

Opening times : from beginning April to end Sept.

15 ha (709 pitches)

Tariff : 52 € 🚻 ⛺ 🔲 (16A)
Extra per person 9 € – Reservation fee 30 €

Rental rates : (from beginning April to end Sept.) – 259 ▭ – 21 tent lodges.
Per night from 46 to 287 € – Per week from 322 to 2 009 € – Reservation fee 35 €

Surroundings : ⛰ 🏞 🌊 ▲
Leisure activities : 🍷 ✕ 🎳 🏖 ⛵ hammam, jacuzzi ⛹ 🚲 🏊 🛝 🎣 fitness trail, multi-sports ground, spa centre, entertainment room
Facilities : ♿ ⚟ 🛁 🚿 launderette 🛒 refrigerated food storage facilities

GPS Longitude : -1.1538
Latitude : 44.43488

Michelin classification:

⚞⚞⚞⚞⚞ *Extremely comfortable, equipped to a very high standard*

⚞⚞⚞⚞ *Very comfortable, equipped to a high standard*

⚞⚞⚞ *Comfortable and well equipped*

⚞⚞ *Reasonably comfortable*

⚞ *Satisfactory*

⚞⚞⚞ Les Écureuils 👤👤

𝒫 05 58 09 80 00, www.ecureuils.fr – limited spaces for one-night stay

Address : 646 chemin de Navarrosse (4.2km north following signs for Sanguinet and turn left towards Navarrosse; 400m from the Étang de Cazaux (lake)

Opening times : from beginning April to end Sept.

6 ha (183 pitches)

Tariff : (2013 price) 50 € 🚻 ⛺ 🔲 (10A) – Extra per person 8 €
Reservation fee 32 €

Rental rates : (from beginning April to end Sept.) ⚡ – 3 ▭
2 ⌂. Per week from 350 to 1 100 € – Reservation fee 32 €

⚟ borne 3 €

Pretty shrubs and flowers.

Surroundings : 🏞 🌊
Leisure activities : 🍷 ✕ 🎳 🏖 jacuzzi ⛹ 🚲 🏊 🎣 ≋ (beach) 🏄
Facilities : ♿ ⚟ 🛁 launderette 🛝 🛒
Nearby : 🎣 🌊

Do not confuse:

⚞ to ⚞⚞⚞⚞ : MICHELIN classification with

★ to ★★★★★ : official classification

⚞⚞⚞ Bimbo

𝒫 05 58 09 82 33, www.campingbimbo.fr – limited spaces for one-night stay

Address : 176 chemin de Bimbo (3.5km north following signs for Sanguinet and turn left towards Navarrosse)

Opening times : from beginning April to end Sept.

6 ha (177 pitches)

Tariff : 44 € 🚻 ⛺ 🔲 (6A) – Extra per person 9 € – Reservation fee 25 €

Rental rates : (from beginning April to mid Nov.) – 32 ▭
12 ⌂ – 5 tent lodges. Per night from 38 to 177 € – Per week from 182 to 1 239 € – Reservation fee 25 €

⚟ borne

Surroundings : ⛰ 🏞 🌊
Leisure activities : 🍷 ✕ 🎳 🏖 ⛹ 🚲 🏊 🛝 multi-sports ground
Facilities : ♿ ⚟ 🛁 🚿 launderette 🛝 🛒 refrigerated food storage facilities
Nearby : 🚲

GPS Longitude : -1.16137
Latitude : 44.42588

⚞⚞ Village Vacances La Fontaine de Nava

(rental of mobile homes only)

𝒫 05 58 09 83 11, www.lesfontainesdenava.com

Address : chemin de Bimbo, at Navarrosse (3.5km north following signs for Sanguinet then follow the signs for Navarrosse)

12 ha/7 for camping

Rentals : ⚡ – 35 ▭.

Surroundings : ⛰ 🏞
Leisure activities : 🍷 ✕ 🎳 🏊 🛝 multi-sports ground
Facilities : ⚟ 🚿 📶

GPS Longitude : -1.16763
Latitude : 44.39439

△ Campéole de Navarrosse ♟♀

📞 0558098432, www.camping-navarrose.com

Address : 712 chemin de Navarrosse (5km to the north, follow the signs for Sanguinet and turn left towards Navarrosse; beside the Étang de Cazaux (lake)

Opening times : from end April to mid Sept.

9 ha (500 pitches)

Tariff : 12€ ♟♟ ⟵ ▣ 🚿 (10A) – Extra per person 9,80€ – Reservation fee 15€

Rental rates : (from end April to mid Sept.) ♿ (1 mobile home) – 46 🚐 – 11 🏠 – 139 canvas bungalows. Per night from 26 to 74€ – Per week from 294 to 1 267€ – Reservation fee 15€

🚐 borne 10€

Surroundings : ⟳ 🌿 ⛰
Leisure activities : ♟ ✗ 🏛 🎣 🏃 🛝 🎾 🛶 ≈
Facilities : ♿ ⚷ 🚿 launderette 🧺
Nearby : 🚲 🐴 ⚓

Longitude : -1.16765
Latitude : 44.42822

BISCARROSSE-PLAGE

40600 – Michelin map **335** E8
▶ Paris 669 – Bordeaux 91 – Mont-de-Marsan 100

△ Campéole le Vivier

📞 0558782576, www.camping-biscarosse.info

Address : 681 rue du Tit (north of the resort, 700m from the beach)

17 ha (830 pitches)

Rentals : ♿ (1 mobile home) – 74 🚐 – 20 🏠 – 186 canvas bungalows

Surroundings : 🌿
Leisure activities : ♟ 🏛 🎣 🏃 🛝 🚲 🎾 ≈
multi-sports ground, entertainment room
Facilities : ♿ ⚷ 🚿 launderette 🧺
refrigerated food storage facilities
Nearby : 🏖

Longitude : -1.24056
Latitude : 44.45938

BLASIMON

33540 – Michelin map **335** K6 – pop. 866 – alt. 80
▶ Paris 607 – Bordeaux 47 – Mérignac 63 – Pessac 60

△ Le Lac

📞 0556715962, www.entredeuxmers.com

Address : Domaine departemental Volny Favory (at the leisure and activity park)

Opening times : from beginning July to end Aug.

50 ha/0,5 (39 pitches) flat, grassy

Surroundings : ⟳ 🌿
Leisure activities : 🏛
Facilities : ♿ ⚷ 🚿 🚽
At the leisure/activities centre : ✗ 🧺 🛶
🎾 🏖 (beach) 🌊

Longitude : -0.08757
Latitude : 44.75541

We have selected the best campsites in France with our usual care, listing those with the best facilities in the most pleasant surroundings.

BLAYE

33390 – Michelin map **335** H4 – pop. 4 882 – alt. 7
▶ Paris 546 – Bordeaux 49 – Jonzac 52 – Libourne 45

△ Municipal de la Citadelle

📞 0557420020, www.blaye.fr

Address : to the west, inside the citadel

1 ha (47 pitches)

An amazing location within Blaye citadel, but very poor sanitary facilities.

Surroundings : ⟳ < 🌿
Facilities : ⚷

Longitude : -0.66634
Latitude : 45.12943

The prices listed were supplied by the campsite owners in 2013 (if prices were not available, those from the previous year are given). The fees should be regarded as basic charges and may fluctuate with inflation.

BORDEAUX

33000 – Michelin map **335** H5 – pop. 236 725 – alt. 4
▶ Paris 572 – Mont-de-Marsan 138 – Bayonne 191 – Arcachon 72

△ International de Bordeaux Lac

📞 0557877060, www.camping-bordeaux.com

Address : at Bordeaux Lac, Bruges, Blvd Jacques Chaban-Delmas – take exit 5 from the bypass: Parc des expositions

Opening times : Permanent

13 ha/6 for camping (193 pitches) flat, grassy

Tariff : 31€ ♟♟ ⟵ ▣ 🚿 (10A) – Extra per person 8€

Rental rates : Permanent ♿ (1 mobile home) – 231 🚐 – 9 🏠.
Per night from 29 to 125€ – Per week from 203 to 1 050€

🚐 borne 5€ – 40 ▣ 18€

Spread out around several small but pretty lakes.

Surroundings : 🌿
Leisure activities : ✗ 🏛 🛶 🚲 ≈
Facilities : ♿ ⚷ 🏢 🚿 🧺 🌿 🚽 🍴 launderette
🏖 🧺
Nearby : 🌊 🦆

Longitude : -0.5827
Latitude : 44.89759

BRANTÔME

24310 – Michelin map **329** E3 – pop. 2 140 – alt. 104
▶ Paris 470 – Angoulême 58 – Limoges 83 – Nontron 23

△ Brantôme Peyrelevade

📞 0553057524, www.camping-dordogne.net

Address : avenue André Maurois (located 1km east along the D 78; beside the Dronne river)

5 ha (170 pitches) flat, grassy

Rentals : 15 🚐 .

Surroundings : ⟳ 🌿
Leisure activities : ✗ 🛶 🎾 🏊 🏖 (beach)
🌊

Facilities : ♿ ⚷ 🏢 🚿 🍴 launderette

Longitude : 0.66043
Latitude : 45.36107

LE BUGUE

24260 – Michelin map **329** G6 – pop. 2 800 – alt. 62
▶ Paris 522 – Bergerac 47 – Brive-la-Gaillarde 72 – Cahors 86

⚑ Vagues-Océanes La Linotte 🏕

🕿 0820150040, www.vagues-oceanes.com – limited spaces for one-night stay

Address : route de Rouffignac (3.5km northeast along the D 710 following the signs for Périgueux and turn right onto D 32)

13 ha/2,5 for camping (120 pitches) terraced, flat and relatively flat, grassy

Rentals : 2 caravans – 99 🛖 – 7 🏠.

A very undulating site with few pitches for tents and caravans.

Surroundings : 🌲 ← 🏞 〰
Leisure activities : 🍽 🎬 🏓 jacuzzi ⚡ 🎿
🏊 🏄 multi-sports ground
Facilities : 🚿 ⚊ 🔥 🍴 launderette 🧺

GPS Longitude : 0.93659
Latitude : 44.93386

⚑ Les Trois Caupain

🕿 0553072460, www.camping-des-trois-caupain.com

Address : allée Paul-Jean Souriau

Opening times : from beginning April to end Oct.

4 ha (160 pitches) flat, grassy

Tariff : 19,90€ 🌲🌲 🚗 🔲 ⚡ (16A) – Extra per person 5,50€
Reservation fee 5€

Rental rates : (from beginning April to end Oct.) – 44 🛖.
Per night from 35 to 66€ – Per week from 159 to 700€
Reservation fee 15€
🚐 borne 5€ – 15 🔲 9,90€ – 🛢 9,90€

Surroundings : 🌲 〰
Leisure activities : ✗ 🏊 🏄 multi-sports ground
Facilities : 🚿 ⚊ 🔥 🍴 launderette 🧺
Nearby : 🐟 large aquarium

GPS Longitude : 0.93178
Latitude : 44.90916

Using the traditional Michelin classification method, the guide provides you with an easy, speedy reference for assessing the category of each site: 1 to 5 tents (see page 10).

LE BUISSON-DE-CADOUIN

24480 – Michelin map **329** G6 – pop. 2 143 – alt. 63
▶ Paris 532 – Bergerac 38 – Périgueux 52 – Sarlat-la-Canéda 36

⚑ Domaine de Fromengal 🏕

🕿 0553631155, www.domaine-fromengal.com

Address : at La Combe de Cussac (6.5km southwest along the D 29, follow the signs for Lalinde, turn left onto D 2, follow the signs for Cadouin and take the road to the right)

22 ha/3 for camping (90 pitches) adjacent wood

Rentals : 26 🛖 – 21 🏠 – 4 canvas bungalows

Surroundings : 🌲 🏞 〰
Leisure activities : ✗ 🎬 🏓 ⚡ 🚲 🐟
🏊 🏄
Facilities : 🚿 ⚊ 🏛 🔥 🍴 launderette
🧺

GPS Longitude : 0.86006
Latitude : 44.82292

BUNUS

64120 – Michelin map **342** F3 – pop. 147 – alt. 186
▶ Paris 820 – Bayonne 61 – Hasparren 38 – Mauléon-Licharre 22

⚑ Inxauseta

🕿 0559378149, www.inxauseta.fr

Address : In the town, near the church

Opening times : from mid June to mid Sept.

0,8 ha (40 pitches) relatively flat

Tariff : 🌲 4,50€ 🚗 🔲 4,50€ – ⚡ (5A) 3€

Lovely sitting rooms in an old renovated Basque house where painting etc. exhibitions are held.

Surroundings : 🌲 ← 〰
Leisure activities : 🎬
Facilities : 🚿 ⚊ 🧺

GPS Longitude : -1.06794
Latitude : 43.20974

CAMBO-LES-BAINS

64250 – Michelin map **342** D2 – pop. 6 466 – alt. 67 – ⚕
▶ Paris 783 – Bayonne 20 – Biarritz 21 – Pau 115

⚑ Bixta Eder

🕿 0559299423, www.campingbixtaeder.com

Address : 52 avenue d'Espagne (1.3km southwest along the D 918, follow the signs for St-Jean-de-Luz)

Opening times : from mid April to mid Oct.

1 ha (90 pitches) relatively flat, flat, grassy, gravelled

Tariff : 24€ 🌲🌲 🚗 🔲 ⚡ (10A) – Extra per person 5,50€ – Reservation fee 15€

Rental rates : (from mid March to mid Nov.) – 19 🛖 – 3 🏠.
Per night from 35 to 85€ – Per week from 207 to 620€
Reservation fee 15€
🚐 20 🔲 15€

A pleasant small site with some well-appointed mobile homes.

Surroundings : 🏞 〰
Leisure activities : 🎬
Facilities : 🚿 ⚊ 🔥 🍴 launderette 🧺
Nearby : 🎿 🏊

GPS Longitude : -1.41448
Latitude : 43.35567

CAMPAGNE

24260 – Michelin map **329** G6 – pop. 367 – alt. 60
▶ Paris 542 – Bergerac 51 – Belvès 19 – Les Eyzies-de-Tayac 7

⚑ Le Val de la Marquise 🏕

🕿 0553547410, www.levaldelamarquise.com

Address : at Le Moulin (500m east along the D 35, follow the signs for St-Cyprien)

Opening times : from beginning April to end Sept.

4 ha (104 pitches)

Tariff : 24,90€ 🌲🌲 🚗 🔲 ⚡ (15A) – Extra per person 5,80€

Rental rates : (from beginning April to end Sept.) 🐟 – 18 🛖
8 🏠. Per night from 35 to 120€ – Per week from 245 to 840€
Reservation fee 20€
🚐 borne 11,60€

Surroundings : 🏞 〰
Leisure activities : ✗ 🎬 🏓 ⚡ 🏊 🏄
Facilities : 🚿 ⚊ 🏛 🔥 🍴 launderette 🧺

GPS Longitude : 0.9743
Latitude : 44.90637

CARSAC-AILLAC

24200 – Michelin map **329** I6 – pop. 1 479 – alt. 80
▶ Paris 536 – Brive-la-Gaillarde 59 – Gourdon 18 – Sarlat-la-Canéda 9

⚠ Le Plein Air des Bories

✆ 05 53 28 15 67, www.camping-desbories.com

Address : at Les Bories (1.3km south along the D 703, follow the signs for Vitrac and take road to the left; beside the Dordogne river)

Opening times : from mid April to mid Sept.

3,5 ha (110 pitches)

Tariff : ★ 6,50€ ⚌ 🅿 8,90€ – (2) (6A) 3,50€ – Reservation fee 15€
Rental rates : (from mid April to mid Sept.) – 33 🛖 – 8 canvas bungalows. Per night from 30 to 85€ – Per week from 180 to 720€
Reservation fee 15€

Surroundings : 🏞 🚤 ♨♨
Leisure activities : 🎪 🚣 🏊 (open air in season) 🎣 🚴
Facilities : & 🚿 🍽 🍴 🅿

GPS Longitude : 1.2684
Latitude : 44.83299

⚠ Le Rocher de la Cave

✆ 05 53 28 14 26, www.rocherdelacave.com

Address : at La Pommarède (1.7km south along the D 703, follow the signs for Vitrac and take road to the left; beside the Dordogne)

Opening times : from beginning May to end Sept.

5 ha (150 pitches) flat, grassy

Tariff : ★ 6,40€ ⚌ 🅿 8,20€ – (2) (16A) 3,70€
Rental rates : (from beginning May to end Sept.) – 23 🛖 12 canvas bungalows – 5 tent lodges. Per night from 25 to 100€
Per week from 180 to 700€

Surroundings : 🏞 ♨♨
Leisure activities : 🏓 🚣 🏊 🎣 🚴
Facilities : & 🚿 🍽 🍴 launderette 🚮

GPS Longitude : 1.26719
Latitude : 44.82977

CASTELJALOUX

47700 – Michelin map **336** C4 – pop. 4 773 – alt. 52
▶ Paris 674 – Agen 55 – Langon 55 – Marmande 23

⚠ Village Vacances Castel Chalets

(rental of chalets only)

✆ 05 53 93 07 45, www.castel-chalets.com

Address : route de Mont de Marsan, at the lake Clarens (2.5km southwest along the D 933, follow the signs for Mont-de-Marsan)

Opening times : permanent

4 ha

Rental rates : & (1 chalet) – 25 🏠. Per night from 90 to 155€
Per week from 275 to 680€
🚐 borne 15€ – 15 🅿 15€

A little chalet village beside the lake, opposite the very well-equipped leisure and activity park.

Surroundings : 🏞 ≤ ♨♨ ⛰
Leisure activities : 🎪 🚣 🎣
Facilities : 🚿 🍽 🍴
Nearby : 🍴 ✗ 🚲 🎿 🚣 🏇 forest trail

GPS Longitude : 0.0725
Latitude : 44.29278

CASTELMORON-SUR-LOT

47260 – Michelin map **336** E3 – pop. 1 755 – alt. 49
▶ Paris 600 – Agen 33 – Bergerac 63 – Marmande 35

⚠ Village Vacances Port-Lalande

(rental of chalets only)

✆ 04 68 37 65 65, www.grandbleu.fr

Address : located 1.5km southeast

Opening times : from beginning April to end Oct.

4 ha flat, grassy

Rental rates : & (1 chalet) 🅿 – 60 🏠. Per night from 65 to 85€
Per week from 196 to 938€

Beside the Lot river and a marina.

Surroundings : 🏞 ≤ ♨
Leisure activities : 🎪 🎡 🏇 🎿 🛶 hammam 🏊 🧖 spa centre
Facilities : 🚿 🍴 launderette
Nearby : ⚓

GPS Longitude : 0.50661
Latitude : 44.38803

CASTELNAUD-LA-CHAPELLE

24250 – Michelin map **329** H7 – pop. 477 – alt. 140
▶ Paris 539 – Le Bugue 29 – Les Eyzies-de-Tayac 27 – Gourdon 25

⚠ Flower Lou Castel

✆ 05 53 29 89 24, www.loucastel.com

Address : at Prente Garde (take the southern exit along the D 57 then continue 3.4km along the road to the château, for caravans, access is strongly recommended via Pont-de-Cause and the D 50, follow the signs for Veyrines-de-Domme)

Opening times : from mid April to mid Sept.

5,5 ha/2,5 for camping (110 pitches) adjacent wood

Tariff : 20€ ★★ ⚌ 🅿 (2) (10A) – Extra per person 5€ – Reservation fee 10€
Rental rates : Permanent – 50 🛖 – 10 🏠. Per night from 50 to 170€ – Per week from 196 to 1 100€ – Reservation fee 18€
🚐 2 🅿 10€ – 🚌 (2) 15€

In a pleasant oak wood.

Surroundings : 🏞 🏕 ♨♨♨
Leisure activities : 🎪 🚣 🏊 🛝 multi-sports ground
Facilities : & 🚿 🍽 🍴 🍴 launderette

GPS Longitude : 1.13182
Latitude : 44.79746

⚠ Maisonneuve

✆ 05 53 29 51 29, www.campingmaisonneuve.com

Address : chemin de Maisonneuve (located 1km southeast along the D 57 and take road to the left; beside the Céou river)

Opening times : from beginning April to end Oct.

6 ha/3 for camping (140 pitches)

Tariff : (2013 price) ★ 6,80€ ⚌ 🅿 8,50€ – (2) (10A) 5€ – Reservation fee 15€
Rental rates : (from beginning April to end Oct.) – 10 🛖 2 tent lodges – 1 gîte. Per night from 48 to 70€ – Per week from 270 to 790€ – Reservation fee 15€

Based around an old renovated farmhouse and surrounded by flowers.

Surroundings : ≤ 🏕 ♨♨
Leisure activities : 🍴 ✗ 🎪 🚣 🏹 🏊 🛶 🎣
Facilities : & 🚿 🍽 🍴 launderette 🚮

GPS Longitude : 1.15822
Latitude : 44.80482

CASTELS

24220 – Michelin map **329** H6 – pop. 647 – alt. 50
▶ Paris 551 – Bordeaux 181 – Montauban 145 – Brive-la-Gaillarde 73

⚠ Village Vacances La Noyeraie (rental of chalets only)

🖉 0553312443, www.chaletlanoyeraie.fr

Address : at Le Grelat (located 1km southeast along the D 703, follow the signs for Sarlat)

Opening times : Permanent

1,5 ha flat, grassy

Rental rates : 🚱 🅿 – 19 🏠. Per night from 38 to 65€ – Per week from 220 to 680€ – Reservation fee 15€

Surroundings : ♒
Leisure activities : 🎪 🏊 🏖 (open air in season)
Facilities : ⚊ 🍴 🎯 launderette

| | Longitude : 1.08071 |
| GPS | Latitude : 44.85004 |

Do not confuse:
⚠ *to* ⚠⚠⚠ *: MICHELIN classification with*
★ *to* ★★★★★ *: official classification*

CASTETS

40260 – Michelin map **335** E11 – pop. 1 945 – alt. 48
▶ Paris 710 – Dax 21 – Mimizan 40 – Mont-de-Marsan 61

⚠ Municipal Le Galan

🖉 0558894352, www.camping-legalan.com

Address : 73 rue du Stade (located 1km east along the D 42, follow the signs for Taller and take turning to the right)

Opening times : from beginning Feb. to end Nov.

4 ha (181 pitches)

Tariff : (2013 price) 👤 3,40€ 🚗 1,10€ 🅴 6,55€ – 🔌 (10A) 2€
Rental rates : (from beginning Feb. to end Nov.) – 8 🚐 – 5 🏠.
Per night from 75 to 95€ – Per week from 125 to 580€
🚐 borne 3€
A welcome awaits pilgrims on their way to Santiago di Compostella in a small wooden cabin.

Surroundings : ♒
Leisure activities : 🎪 🏊 🏖
Facilities : 🚿 ⚊ 🍴 🎯 🎌 launderette
Nearby : 🎽 fitness trail

| | Longitude : -1.13754 |
| GPS | Latitude : 43.88059 |

CASTILLON LA BATAILLE

33350 – Michelin map **335** K5 – pop. 3 203 – alt. 17
▶ Paris 549 – Bergerac 46 – Libourne 18 – Montpon-Ménestérol 27

⚠ Municipal La Pelouse

🖉 0557400422, www.castillonlabataille.fr

Address : 2 prom. Dubourdieu (east of the town; beside the Dordogne river)

Opening times : from beginning May to end Oct.

0,5 ha (38 pitches) flat, grassy

Tariff : 14€ 👤👤 🚗 🅴 🔌 (15A) – Extra per person 4€

Surroundings : ♒
Leisure activities : 🏖
Facilities : 🚿 ⚊ 🎯 🎌 🅴

| | Longitude : -0.03569 |
| GPS | Latitude : 44.85337 |

CÉNAC-ET-ST-JULIEN

24250 – Michelin map **329** I7 – pop. 1 218 – alt. 70
▶ Paris 537 – Le Bugue 34 – Gourdon 20 – Sarlat-la-Canéda 12

⚠⚠ Le Pech de Caumont

🖉 0553282163, www.pech-de-caumont.com

Address : situated 2km to the south

Opening times : from beginning April to end Sept.

2,2 ha (100 pitches)

Tariff : 22€ 👤👤 🚗 🅴 🔌 (16A) – Extra per person 5,60€ – Reservation fee 12,50€

Rental rates : (from beginning April to end Sept.) 🚱 – 20 🚐 6 🏠. Per night from 33 to 54€ – Per week from 200 to 670€ Reservation fee 12,50€

Looking out over the Dordogne valley, opposite the village of Domme.

Surroundings : ♒ ＜ 🏕 ♒
Leisure activities : 🍷 🎪 🏊 🏖
Facilities : 🚿 ⚊ 🎯 🎌 🅴 🅰

| | Longitude : 1.20908 |
| GPS | Latitude : 44.78654 |

LA CHAPELLE-AUBAREIL

24290 – Michelin map **329** I5 – pop. 471 – alt. 230
▶ Paris 515 – Brive-la-Gaillarde 40 – Les Eyzies-de-Tayac 21 Montignac 9

⚠⚠ La Fage

🖉 0553507650, www.camping-lafage.com

Address : at La Fage (1.2km northwest following signs for St-Amand-de-Coly, head towards D 704 and take road to the left)

Opening times : from mid April to mid Oct.

5 ha (60 pitches)

Tariff : 25€ 👤👤 🚗 🅴 🔌 (10A)

Extra per person 5€ – Reservation fee 10€

Rental rates : (from mid April to mid Oct.) – 15 🚐 – 3 🏠 6 canvas bungalows. Per night from 24 to 116€ – Per week from 170 to 815€

Surroundings : ♒ 🏕 ♒
Leisure activities : ✕ 🎪 🏊 🏖
Facilities : 🚿 ⚊ 🅰 🎯 🎌 🅴 launderette 🅰

| | Longitude : 1.1882 |
| GPS | Latitude : 45.01745 |

COLY

24120 – Michelin map **329** I5 – pop. 226 – alt. 113
▶ Paris 504 – Brive-la-Gaillarde 29 – Lanouaille 45 – Périgueux 53

⚠⚠ Village Vacances Goelia Les Cottages du Lac

(rental of chalets only)

🖉 0553509442, www.vacances-lascaux-dordogne.com

Address : at La Prade (situated 2km southeast along the D 62, follow the signs for la Cassagne; beside a small lake)

18 ha flat, grassy, lakes

Rentals : 🚿 (1 chalet) – 73 🏠.

Some chalets have terraces looking out onto the water.

Surroundings : ♒ ＜ ♒
Leisure activities : 🏊 🚲 🎽 🏖 fitness trail 🎯 multi-sports ground
Facilities : ⚊ 🎌 launderette

| | Longitude : 1.27945 |
| GPS | Latitude : 45.07271 |

CONTIS-PLAGE

40170 – Michelin map **335** D10
▶ Paris 714 – Bayonne 87 – Castets 32 – Dax 52

⚲⚲ **Yelloh! Village Lous Seurrots** ⚑

☎ 05 58 42 85 82, www.lous-seurrots.com

Address : 606 avenue de l'Océan (take the southeastern exit along the D 41, near the Courant de Contis (small river), 700m from the beach)

Opening times : from end April to beginning Oct.

14 ha (610 pitches)

Tariff : 49€ ♣♣ ⇌ 🅴 🚰 (10A) – Extra per person 8€
Rental rates : (from end April to beginning Oct.) ♿ (1 chalet)
191 🚐 – 109 🏠 – 5 canvas bungalows – 30 tent lodges 3 gîtes.
Per night from 30 to 161€ – Per week from 210 to 1127€
🚐 🔋🚰18€

> Surroundings : 🗁 ♧♧
> Leisure activities : 🍴🍽️ 🏛️ ☺(open air theatre) 🏃 🚴 🎾 ⚽ multi-sports ground
> Facilities : ♿ ⛽ 🏛️ 🚰 launderette 🔌 🚿 refrigerated food storage facilities
> Nearby : 🏇 🏄 surfing

GPS Longitude : -1.31685
Latitude : 44.08878

COURBIAC

47370 – Michelin map **336** I3 – pop. 110 – alt. 145
▶ Paris 623 – Bordeaux 172 – Agen 46 – Montauban 59

⚲ **Le Pouchou**

☎ 05 53 40 72 68, www.camping-le-pouchou.com

Address : head 1.8km west following signs for Tournon-d'Agenais, take road to the left

Opening times : from beginning March to end Nov.

15 ha/2 for camping (30 pitches)

Tariff : ♣ 4,75€ ⇌ 🅴 7,30€ – 🚰 (10A) 4€
Rental rates : Permanent ♿ (1 chalet) – 1 🚐 – 7 🏠
2 canvas bungalows. Per night from 39 to 100€ – Per week from 169 to 648€
🚐 borne 3€ – 2 🅴 5€ – 🔋14€
In a pleasant setting among undulating hills, arranged around a small lake.

> Surroundings : 🏊 ♧ ♤
> Leisure activities : 🍴 🏛️ 🚴 🎾 ⚓ walking trails
> Facilities : ♿ ⛽ 🚿 🔥 🚰 launderette

GPS Longitude : 1.02293
Latitude : 44.37854

COUX-ET-BIGAROQUE

24220 – Michelin map **329** G7 – pop. 993 – alt. 85
▶ Paris 548 – Bergerac 44 – Le Bugue 14 – Les Eyzies-de-Tayac 17

⚲⚲ **Les Valades**

☎ 05 53 29 14 27, http://www.lesvalades.com

Address : at Les Valades (4km northwest along the D 703, follow the signs for Les Eyzies then take left turning)

Opening times : from beginning April to end Sept.

11 ha (85 pitches) small lake, natural setting among trees and bushes

Tariff : 29€ ♣♣ ⇌ 🅴 🚰 (10A) – Extra per person 7€ – Reservation fee 15€

Rental rates : (from beginning April to end Sept.) ♿ (1 chalet)
6 🚐 – 19 🏠 – 2 tent lodges. Per week from 230 to 850€
Reservation fee 15€

> Surroundings : 🏊 ♤ 🗁 ♧♧
> Leisure activities : 🍽️ 🏛️ 🚴 🎿 ⚓ (beach) 🏄 ♨️
> Facilities : ♿ ⛽ 🚿 – 10 individual sanitary facilities (🚽 🚿 wc) 🔥 🚰 launderette 🚿

GPS Longitude : 0.96367
Latitude : 44.8599

COUZE-ET-ST-FRONT

24150 – Michelin map **329** F7 – pop. 775 – alt. 45
▶ Paris 544 – Bergerac 21 – Lalinde 4 – Mussidan 46

⚲ **Les Moulins**

☎ 06 89 85 76 24, www.campingdesmoulins.com – limited spaces for one-night stay

Address : at Les Maury Bas (take the southeastern exit along the D 660, follow the signs for Beaumont and take a right turn, near the sports field; beside the Couze river)

Opening times : from mid March to mid Nov.

2,5 ha (50 pitches)

Tariff : 29€ ♣♣ ⇌ 🅴 🚰 (10A) – Extra per person 8€ – Reservation fee 10€
Rental rates : (from mid March to mid Nov.) – 40 🚐. Per night from 50 to 90€ – Per week from 220 to 600€ – Reservation fee 10€
🚐 borne 3€ – 8 🅴 12€ – 🔋🚰12€
In a green setting perched on a rocky spur opposite the village.

> Surroundings : ♤ 🗁 ♧♧
> Leisure activities : 🍴 🏛️ 🏃 🎿 🎾 🎿 🏄
> Facilities : ♿ ⛽ 🚰 launderette

GPS Longitude : 0.70448
Latitude : 44.82646

DAGLAN

24250 – Michelin map **329** I7 – pop. 555 – alt. 101
▶ Paris 547 – Cahors 48 – Fumel 40 – Gourdon 18

⚲⚲ **Club Airotel Le Moulin de Paulhiac** ⚑

☎ 05 53 28 20 88, www.moulin-de-paulhiac.com

Address : route de St-Cybranet (4km northwest along the D 57; beside the Céou river)

Opening times : from mid May to mid Sept.

5 ha (150 pitches) flat, grassy

Tariff : (2013 price) ♣ 8€ ⇌ 🅴 11,10€ – 🚰 (10A) 4,60€
Rental rates : (2013 price) (from mid May to mid Sept.)
13 🚐 – 2 tent lodges. Per night from 50 to 85€ – Per week from 235 to 950€

> Surroundings : 🏊 🗁 ♧♧
> Leisure activities : 🍴🍽️ 🏛️ 🏃 🚴 🖼️ (open air in season) 🎿 ⛺ 🏄
> Facilities : ♿ ⛽ 🚿 🔥 🚿 🚰 launderette 🔌 🚿

GPS Longitude : 1.17654
Latitude : 44.76772

⚲⚲ **La Peyrugue**

☎ 05 53 28 40 26, www.peyrugue.com

Address : at La Peyrugue (located 1.5km north along the D 57, follow the signs for St-Cybranet, 150m from the Céou river)

Opening times : from beginning April to end Sept.

5 ha/2,5 for camping (85 pitches)

Tariff : ♣ 7,80€ ⇌ 🅴 12,50€ – 🚰 (10A) 4,20€ – Reservation fee 10€

Rental rates : (from beginning April to end Sept.) 👤 (2 chalets) 5 🛏 – 10 🏠 – 2 canvas bungalows. Per night from 30 to 120€ Per week from 210 to 840€ – Reservation fee 10€

Surroundings : 🌳 ♤♤
Leisure activities : 🍴 🛖 🚣 🏊 ⛷
Facilities : 👤 ⚡ 🍳 🍽 launderette 🚿

GPS Longitude : 1.18798
Latitude : 44.75267

DAX

40100 – Michelin map **335** E12 – pop. 21 003 – alt. 12 – ⚕
▶ Paris 727 – Bayonne 54 – Biarritz 61 – Bordeaux 144

🏕 Les Chênes ♤♤
✆ 05 58 90 05 53, www.camping-les-chenes.fr

Address : allée du Bois de Boulogne (1.8km west of the town centre, in the Bois de Boulogne, 200m from the Adour river)

5 ha (230 pitches)
Rentals : 34 🛏 – 20 🏠.

In a pleasant wood near a lake.

Surroundings : 🌳 ⛺ ♤♤
Leisure activities : 🛖 🏃 🚣 🚲 🎿
Facilities : 👤 ⚡ 🍳 🍽 🚿 launderette 🔧
Nearby : 🍴 🍽 🎣 🐎

GPS Longitude : -1.07174
Latitude : 43.71138

🏕 Le Bascat
✆ 05 58 56 16 68, www.campinglebascat.com

Address : rue de Jouandin (2.8km west from the town centre through the Bois de Boulogne, access from the Vieux Pont (left bank) and the avenue running along the banks of the Adour)

Opening times : from beginning March to mid Nov.

3,5 ha (160 pitches)

Tariff : 15€ 👤👤 🚗 🔌 (6A) – Extra per person 4,30€ – Reservation fee 5€

Rental rates : (from mid March to mid Nov.) – 41 🛏. Per night from 45 to 60€ – Per week from 225 to 350€ – Reservation fee 5€
🚰 borne 11,50€ – 10 🔲 11,50€ – 🚐 11,50€

Surroundings : 🌳 ♤♤
Leisure activities : 🛖
Facilities : 👤 ⚡ 🍳 🍽 🚿 🍳 launderette 🔧

GPS Longitude : -1.07043
Latitude : 43.70617

DOMME

24250 – Michelin map **329** I7 – pop. 989 – alt. 250
▶ Paris 538 – Cahors 51 – Fumel 50 – Gourdon 20

🏕 Village Vacances Les Ventoulines

(rental of chalets only)
✆ 05 53 28 36 29, www.gites-dordogne-sarlat.fr

Address : at Les Ventoulines (3.6km to the southeast)

Opening times : Permanent

3 ha

Rental rates : 🅿 – 24 🏠. Per night from 76 to 86€ – Per week from 354 to 1 100€

Surroundings : 🌳 ♧♧♧
Leisure activities : 🛖 🚣 🏓 🏊
Facilities : 👤 ⚡ 🍳 🍽 launderette

GPS Longitude : 1.22588
Latitude : 44.84048

🏕 Perpetuum ♤♤
✆ 05 53 28 35 18, www.campingleperpetuum.com

Address : head 2km south along the D 50 and take road to the right; beside the Dordogne river

Opening times : from beginning May to mid Oct.

4,5 ha (120 pitches) flat, grassy

Tariff : 👤 7,10€ 🚗 🔲 7,30€ – 🔌 (10A) 4,30€ – Reservation fee 12€

Rental rates : (from beginning May to mid Oct.) 🚫 – 28 🛏. Per night from 57 to 189€ – Per week from 210 to 810€ Reservation fee 12€

🚰 borne 12€

Surroundings : 🌳 ⛺ ♤♤
Leisure activities : 🍴 🛖 🏃 🚣 🏊 ⛷ 🎣
multi-sports ground, entertainment room
Facilities : 👤 ⚡ 🍳 🍽 launderette 🔧

GPS Longitude : 1.22065
Latitude : 44.81542

🏕 Village Vacances de la Combe (rental of chalets only)
✆ 05 53 29 77 42, www.sarlat-gites-dordogne.com

Address : at Le Pradal (located 1.5km southeast)

Opening times : Permanent

2 ha terraced, flat, grassy

Rental rates : 👤 (1 chalet) 🅿 – 12 🏠 – 12 gîtes. Per night from 150 to 180€ – Per week from 350 to 850€ – Reservation fee 18€

🚰 borne – 5 🔲 15€

Surroundings : 🌳 ♤♤
Leisure activities : 🛖 🏊
Facilities : ⚡ 🍳 🍳 🍽 🍳

GPS Longitude : 1.22243
Latitude : 44.8161

🏕 Le Bosquet
✆ 05 53 28 37 39, www.lebosquet.com

Address : at La Rivière (900m south of Vitrac-Port, along the D 46)

Opening times : from beginning April to end Sept.

1,5 ha (60 pitches)

Tariff : 19,60€ 👤👤 🚗 🔲 🔌 (10A) – Extra per person 5,20€ Reservation fee 8€

Rental rates : (from beginning April to end Sept.) – 21 🛏. Per night from 35 to 65€ – Per week from 20 to 670€ – Reservation fee 8€

🚰 borne – 🚐 9€

Surroundings : 🌳 ⛵ ⛺ ♤♤
Leisure activities : 🍴 🛖 🚣 🏊
Facilities : 👤 ⚡ 🍳 🍽 🍳 🚿

GPS Longitude : 1.22555
Latitude : 44.82185

🏕 Le Moulin de Caudon
✆ 05 53 31 03 69, www.campingdordogne.com

Address : at Caudon (6km northeast along the D 46e and the D 50, follow the signs for Groléjac; near the Dordogne – recommended route for caravans via Vitrac-Port)

Opening times : from beginning June to end Sept.

2 ha (60 pitches) flat, grassy

Tariff : 👤 4€ 🚗 3,30€ 🔲 3,30€ – 🔌 (10A) 3,30€

Rental rates : (from beginning June to end Sept.) 🚫 – 4 🛏. Per night from 30 to 180€ – Per week from 180 to 500€

🚰 🚐 🔌 14€

Surroundings : ⛺ ♤♤
Leisure activities : 🛖 🚣
Facilities : 👤 ⚡ (season) 🍳 🍳 🍽
Nearby : 🚣

GPS Longitude : 1.24466
Latitude : 44.82061

EYMET

24500 – Michelin map **329** D8 – pop. 2 563 – alt. 54
▶ Paris 560 – Bergerac 24 – Castillonnès 19 – Duras 22

⚠ Le Château

✆ 05 53 23 80 28, www.eymetcamping.com

Address : rue de la Sole (behind the château; beside the Dropt river)

Opening times : from mid April to end Sept.

1,5 ha (66 pitches) flat, grassy, adjacent public garden

Tariff : 15€ ★★ ⇌ 圓 ⚡ (10A) – Extra per person 4€

In a pleasant location surrounded by the river, the municipal park and the ramparts.

Surroundings : ⅏ ⊏┐ ♤♤
Leisure activities : ⅙♤ ➲ ⚲
Facilities : & ⛷ ⛆⚗♑⚐

GPS Longitude : 0.39584
Latitude : 44.66925

LES EYZIES-DE-TAYAC

24620 – Michelin map **329** H6 – pop. 839 – alt. 70
▶ Paris 536 – Brive-la-Gaillarde 62 – Fumel 62 – Lalinde 35

⚠ Vacances Directes Le Mas ♠♠

(rental of chalets and mobile homes only)

✆ 0825 13 34 00, www.campinglemas.com

Address : 7 km east along the D 47 follow the signs for Sarlat-la-Canéda then continue 2.5km following signs for Sireuil to the left

Opening times : from mid May to mid Sept.

5 ha

Rental rates : 104 ⌦ – 6 ⌂ – 10 tent lodges. Per night from 28 to 121€ – Per week from 196 to 847€ – Reservation fee 30€

Surroundings : ⅏ ⊏┐ ♤♤
Leisure activities : ♈✗ (farm-inn) ⋌⋌ ⛷
♒ ⚘ ⚘
Facilities : & ⛷ ♗♑ launderette ⚞ ⚘

GPS Longitude : 1.0849
Latitude : 44.93675

⚠ La Rivière

✆ 05 53 06 97 14, www.larivierelesseyzies.com

Address : 3 route du Sorcier (located 1km northwest along the D 47, follow the signs for Périgueux and take the turning to the left after the bridge, 200m from the Vézère)

Opening times : from beginning April to end Oct.

7 ha/3 for camping (120 pitches) flat, grassy

Tariff : ★ 6,60€ ⇌ 圓 9,95€ – ⚡ (10A) 4,60€ – Reservation fee 4€
Rental rates : (from beginning April to end Oct.) – 13 ⌦
6 ⌸ 1 tent lodge. Per night from 35 to 95€ – Per week from 160 to 895€ – Reservation fee 4€
⛽ borne 3,50€

Surroundings : ⊏┐ ♤♤
Leisure activities : ♈✗ ⋌⋌ ⚘ ≈
Facilities : & ⛷ ♑ ♗⚘⚐♑ launderette
⚘

GPS Longitude : 1.00582
Latitude : 44.93732

⚠ La Ferme du Pelou

✆ 05 53 06 98 17, www.lafermedupelou.com

Address : at Le Pelou (4km northeast along the D 706, follow the signs for Montignac then take the turning to the right)

Opening times : from mid Feb. to mid Nov.

1 ha (65 pitches)

Tariff : 16€ ★★ ⇌ 圓 ⚡ (10A) – Extra per person 4,20€

Rental rates : (from mid April to mid Nov.) – 2 ⌦. Per night from 40 to 70€ – Per week from 310 to 495€
⛽ borne
A farm campsite.

Surroundings : ⅏ ⊏┐ ♤♤
Leisure activities : ⚞ ⚘
Facilities : & ⛷ ⚗ launderette
Nearby : ⛷

GPS Longitude : 1.04472
Latitude : 44.95527

FUMEL

47500 – Michelin map **336** H3 – pop. 5 186 – alt. 70
▶ Paris 594 – Agen 55 – Bergerac 64 – Cahors 48

⚠ Village Vacances Domaine de Guillalmes

(rental of chalets only)

✆ 05 53 71 01 99, www.domainedeguillalmes.com

Address : at La Gaillarde (3km east along the D 911, follow the signs for Cahors, at Condat exit follow right turn for 1km; beside the Lot river)

Opening times : from beginning March to end Oct.

3 ha flat, grassy

Rental rates : & (1 chalet) – 1 ⌦ – 18 ⌂. Per night from 60 to 80€ – Per week from 360 to 660€ – Reservation fee 10€
⛽ borne 20€

Surroundings : ⅏ ♤♤
Leisure activities : ♈✗ ⋌⋌ ⅙♤ ♒ ⚘ ⚘ ⚲
Facilities : ⛷ ⓟ ⚗Ⅲ♑♗⚘

GPS Longitude : 1.00955
Latitude : 44.48343

⚠ Les Catalpas

✆ 05 53 71 11 99, www.les-catalpas.com

Address : at La Tour, chemin de la plaine de Condat (situated 2km east along the D 911, follow the signs for Cahors; at the Condat exit, follow the road to the right for 1.2km; beside the Lot river)

Opening times : from beginning March to mid Nov.

2 ha (80 pitches) flat, grassy, hard surface areas

Tariff : (2013 price) 21,50€ ★★ ⇌ 圓 ⚡ (10A) – Extra per person 5€
Rental rates : Permanent – 3 ⌦ – 3 ⌂ – 1 gîte. Per night from 40 to 60€ – Per week from 200 to 550€
⛽ 10 圓 15,50€
Cycling tourists welcome.

Surroundings : ⅏ ♤♤
Leisure activities : ⋌⋌ ⚘
Facilities : ⛷ Ⅲ♑♗

GPS Longitude : 0.99737
Latitude : 44.48916

GABARRET

40310 – Michelin map **335** L11 – pop. 1 270 – alt. 153
▶ Paris 715 – Agen 66 – Auch 76 – Bordeaux 140

⚠ Parc Municipal Touristique la Chêneraie

✆ 05 58 44 92 62, la-cheneraie@orange.fr

Address : take the eastern exit along the D 35, follow the signs for Castelnau-d'Auzan and take the road to the right

Opening times : from beginning March to end Oct.

0,7 ha (36 pitches)

Tariff : (2013 price) 10,95€ ★★ ⇌ 圓 ⚡ (10A) – Extra per person 2,87€

Rental rates : Permanent – 4 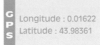 – 10 gîtes. Per night from 50 to 58€ – Per week from 168 to 305€

Surroundings : ⟳ ⌂ ♤♤
Leisure activities : 🏇 🚲
Facilities : ♿ ⚡ 📷 ▦ ⛽ 🚿
Nearby : 🏕 ⛵

GRADIGNAN

33170 – Michelin map **335** H6 – pop. 23 386 – alt. 26
▶ Paris 592 – Bordeaux 9 – Lyon 550 – Nantes 336

🏕 Beausoleil

✆ 05 56 89 17 66, www.camping-gradignan.com
Address : 371 cours du Général de Gaulle (on the bypass (rocade), take exit 16 for Gradignan)

Opening times : Permanent

0,5 ha (31 pitches)

Tariff : 20€ ✶✶ ⛟ 🔲 (10A) – Extra per person 3,50€
Rental rates : Permanent ⚡ – 4 🚐. Per week from 250 to 425€
Shuttle bus for the tram to Bordeaux.

Surroundings : . ⌂ ♤♤
Facilities : ♿ ⚡ 📷 ▦ 🚿 🚿 ⛽ launderette

Longitude : -0.6278
Latitude : 44.75573

GROLÉJAC

24250 – Michelin map **329** I7 – pop. 654 – alt. 67
▶ Paris 537 – Gourdon 14 – Périgueux 80 – Sarlat-la-Canéda 13

⛰ Les Granges 🏊♿

✆ 05 53 28 11 15, www.lesgranges-fr.com – limited spaces for one-night stay

Address : in the village

Opening times : from end April to mid Sept.

6 ha (188 pitches) terraced, flat and relatively flat, grassy

Tariff : 30,30€ ✶✶ ⛟ 🔲 (6A) – Extra per person 7,70€
Reservation fee 25€
Rental rates : (from end April to mid Sept.) – 50 🚐 – 17 🏠.
Per night from 43 to 113 € – Per week from 307 to 795 €
Reservation fee 25€

Surroundings : ⟳ ⌂ ♤♤
Leisure activities : ♟ 🍴 🎮 🌙 nighttime 🏃
🏇 🚲 🏓 ⛵ ♨
Facilities : ♿ ⚡ 🚿 ♨ ⛽ launderette 🚿
Nearby : 🏊

Longitude : 1.29117
Latitude : 44.81579

🏕 Le Lac de Groléjac

✆ 05 53 59 48 70, www.camping-dulac-dordogne.com
Address : at Le Roc Percé (situated 2km south along the D 704, D 50, follow the signs for Domme and turn left, following signs for Nabirat)

Opening times : from mid April to mid Sept.

2 ha (92 pitches)

Tariff : 16€ ✶✶ ⛟ 🔲 (10A) – Extra per person 5€ – Reservation fee 15€
Rental rates : (from mid April to mid Sept.) ⚡ – 15 🚐 – 9 canvas bungalows. Per night from 35 to 48€ – Per week from 210 to 740€ – Reservation fee 15€
⛽ borne – 🚿 ⛽8€

Surroundings : ⟳ ≪ ♤♤ △
Leisure activities : 🏇 pedalos 🪁
Facilities : ♿ ⚡ (July–Aug.) ♨ ⛽ 🚿
Nearby : ⛵

Longitude : 1.29441
Latitude : 44.802

40700 – Michelin map **335** H13 – pop. 4 539 – alt. 96
▶ Paris 737 – Aire-sur-l'Adour 34 – Dax 45 – Mont-de-Marsan 29

🏕 Municipal de la Cité Verte

✆ 05 58 79 79 79, www.laciteverte.com
Address : chemin des Loussets (to the south along the av. du Dr-Édouard-Castera, near some arenas and the swimming pool; beside a river)

0,4 ha (24 pitches) flat, grassy
Close to municipal sports buildings and lesiure facilities.

Surroundings : ⟳ ⌂ ♤♤
Leisure activities : 🍴 🏠 🏇 ⚓
Facilities : ⚡ 🅿 – 24 individual sanitary facilities (🍴 ♨ 🚻 WC) ♨ 🚿
Nearby : 🍴 🔲 ⚓ sports trail

Longitude : -0.59215
Latitude : 43.65233

Some information or pricing may have changed since the guide went to press. We recommend you check the price list online in advance or at the entrance to the campsite and enquire about possible restrictions.

24390 – Michelin map **329** H4 – pop. 1 086 – alt. 160
▶ Paris 466 – Bordeaux 190 – Périgueux 60 – Brive-la-Gaillarde 57

⛰ Village Vacances Les Sources (rental of chalets only)

✆ 05 53 51 96 56, www.dordogne-gite.fr
Address : at La Génèbre (2.6km south along the D 704 and the D 62E4)

30 ha/5 for camping, undulating
Rentals : 🅿 – 12 🏠 – 3 gîtes.

Surroundings : ⟳ ≪ Château de Hautefort
Leisure activities : ♟ 🏠 🏇 ⚓ paintballing
Facilities : ♿ ⚡ ▦ ⛽ launderette

Longitude : 1.12641
Latitude : 45.25085

64700 – Michelin map **342** B4 – pop. 14 412 – alt. 30
▶ Paris 799 – Biarritz 31 – Pau 143 – St-Jean-de-Luz 12

⛰ Eskualduna 🏊♿

✆ 05 59 20 04 64, www.camping-eskualduna.fr
Address : route de la Corniche (situated 2km east, rte da la Corniche; beside a stream)

Opening times : from beginning May to end Sept.

10 ha (330 pitches) undulating

Tariff : ✶ 9€ ⛟ 5€ 🔲 8€ – (10A) 6€ – Reservation fee 20€
Rental rates : (from mid April to end Oct.) ♿ (2 mobile homes) 60 🚐 – 11 🏠. Per night from 60 to 85€ – Per week from 220 to 1 520€ – Reservation fee 20€
⛽ borne 5€ – 30 🔲 12€
A free shuttle service to the beach, choose the pitches away from the road.

Surroundings : ♤♤
Leisure activities : ♟ 🍴 🏠 🎮 🏃 🏇 ⚓
multi-sports ground
Facilities : ♿ ⚡ ♨ ⛽ launderette 🏊
🚿 refrigerators

Longitude : -1.73925
Latitude : 43.37555

⛰ Club Airotel Ametza

℘ 0559200705, www.camping-ametza.com

Address : boulevard de l'Empereur (located 1km east)

Opening times : from beginning April to end Oct.

4,5 ha (230 pitches) terraced, relatively flat, flat, grassy

Tariff : (2013 price) 38€ ♦♦ ⇔ 🔲 (6A) – Extra per person 7,30€ Reservation fee 15€

Rental rates : (from mid April to mid Oct.) ♿ (1 mobile home) 🚵 27 🏠 – 3 🏡. Per week from 330 to 930€ – Reservation fee 15€

🚐 3 🔲 38€

Pitches for tents and caravans, as well as owner-occupied and rental mobile homes.

Surroundings : ⌐ ♤♤
Leisure activities : ♈ ✕ 🏠 🏃 🚣 ⚽ 🚴
Facilities : ♿ ⊶ 🍖 launderette 🧺 🚿

G P S Longitude : -1.75578
Latitude : 43.37285

⛰ Dorrondeguy

℘ 0559202616, www.camping-dorrondeguy.com

Address : rue de la Glacière

Opening times : from beginning April to mid Oct.

4 ha (127 pitches) terrace, relatively flat, flat, grassy

Tariff : 31€ ♦♦ ⇔ 🔲 (10A) – Extra per person 6€ – Reservation fee 15€

Rental rates : (from beginning April to end Oct.) ♿ 🚵 🅿 30 🏠 13 🏡. Per night from 40 to 150€ – Per week from 270 to 1060€ Reservation fee 20€

A pretty little chalet village.

Surroundings : 🌲 ⌐ ♤♤
Leisure activities : ♈ ✕ 🏠 🚣 🚣 Basque pelota walled court
Facilities : ♿ ⊶ 🍖 launderette 🚿

G P S Longitude : -1.74727
Latitude : 43.36867

HOURTIN

33990 – Michelin map **335** E3 – pop. 3 001 – alt. 18
▶ Paris 638 – Andernos-les-Bains 55 – Bordeaux 65 – Lesparre-Médoc 17

⛰ La Rotonde - Le Village Western ♣♠

℘ 0556091060, www.village-western.com

Address : chemin de Bécassine (head 1.5km west along the av. du Lac and take road to the left, 500m from the lake (direct access)

Opening times : from mid April to end Sept.

17 ha/11 for camping (300 pitches)

Tariff : 35€ ♦♦ ⇔ 🔲 (10A) – Extra per person 7€ – Reservation fee 20€

Rental rates : (from mid April to end Sept.) – 82 🏠 – 10 🏡 12 tipis – 5 canvas bungalows – 5 tent lodges. Per night from 38 to 90€ – Per week from 210 to 1288€ – Reservation fee 20€

🚐 borne 2€ – 🚿 💧14€

Original Wild West décor, arranged around the riding centre.

Surroundings : 🌲 ♤
Leisure activities : ♈ ✕ 🏠 🌙nighttime 🏃 🚣 🚣 ⚽
Facilities : ♿ ⊶ 🍖 🧺 🍴 launderette 🧺 🚿
Nearby : ⚽ 🐎

G P S Longitude : -1.07468
Latitude : 45.17935

⛰ Les Ourmes ♣♠

℘ 0556091276, www.lesourmes.com

Address : 90 avenue du Lac (located 1.5km west)

7 ha (300 pitches)

Rentals : 🚵 – 37 🏠.

🚐 borne

Surroundings : 🌲 ♤♤
Leisure activities : ♈ ✕ 🏠 🌙nighttime 🏃 🚣 🚣
Facilities : ♿ ⊶ 🍖 🍴 launderette 🧺 🚿
Nearby : ⚽ 🐎 🐴

G P S Longitude : -1.07584
Latitude : 45.18204

⛺ Aires Naturelles l'Acacia et le Lac

℘ 0556738080, www.campinglacacia.com

Address : route de Carcans (7km southwest along the D 3 and take the road to the right)

Opening times : from mid June to end Sept.

5 ha/2 for camping (50 pitches) adjacent pine trees

Tariff : 22€ ♦♦ ⇔ 🔲 (12A) – Extra per person 6€

Rental rates : (from mid June to end Sept.) 🚵 – 2 caravans. Per night from 50 to 67€ – Per week from 350 to 470€

Surroundings : 🌲 ♤♤
Leisure activities : 🚣 🚴
Facilities : ⊶ 🚿 launderette

G P S Longitude : -1.06361
Latitude : 45.13561

HOURTIN-PLAGE

33990 – Michelin map **335** D3
▶ Paris 556 – Andernos-les-Bains 66 – Bordeaux 76 – Lesparre-Médoc 26

⛰ Club Airotel La Côte d'Argent ♣♠

℘ 0556091025, www.cca33.com

Address : 500m from the beach

Opening times : from mid May to mid Sept.

20 ha (870 pitches)

Tariff : 58€ ♦♦ ⇔ 🔲 (10A) – Extra per person 10€ – Reservation fee 35€

Rental rates : (from mid May to mid Sept.) 🚵 – 252 🏠. Per night from 53 to 258€ – Per week from 212 to 1806€ – Reservation fee 35€

🚐 borne – 50 🔲 58€

Surroundings : 🌲 ♤♤
Leisure activities : ♈ ✕ 🏠 🌙 🏃 🚣 🚣 🚴 🐎 ⚽ 🎳 🚣 🐴 multi-sports ground
Facilities : ♿ ⊶ 🆓 🍖 🍴 launderette 🛒 🚿 refrigerated food storage facilities

G P S Longitude : -1.16446
Latitude : 45.22259

LA HUME

33470 – Michelin map **335** E7
▶ Paris 645 – Bordeaux 59 – Mérignac 62 – Pessac 56

⛺ Verdalle

℘ 0556661262, www.campingdeverdalle.com

Address : 2 allée de l'Infante (continue north along the av. de la Plage and take the road to the right; beside the Bassin d'Arcachon, direct access to the beach)

Opening times : from mid April to mid Sept.

1,5 ha (108 pitches)

Tariff : 27€ ♦♦ ⇔ 🔲 (10A) – Extra per person 6€ – Reservation fee 12€

Rental rates : (from mid April to mid Sept.) ✂ – 6 canvas bungalows. Per night from 40 to 80€ – Per week from 220 to 510€ – Reservation fee 15€

Surroundings : 🐟 ⇐ 🖵 ♨♨
Facilities : ⚹ ⚬━ 🚰 ⁇ 🏢
Nearby : 🏊

G P S Longitude : -1.11099
Latitude : 44.64397

ITXASSOU

64250 – Michelin map **342** D3 – pop. 2 031 – alt. 39
▶ Paris 787 – Bayonne 24 – Biarritz 25 – Cambo-les-Bains 5

🔺🔺 Hiriberria

𝒫 0559299809, www.hiriberria.com

Address : located 1km northwest along the D 918, follow the signs for Cambo-les-Bains and take the road to the right

Opening times : Permanent

4 ha (228 pitches)

Tariff : ⚹ 7€ ⇔ 🔲 8€ – ⑂ (10A) 4€

Rental rates : (from beginning March to end Nov.) – 14 🏠 19 🏠. Per night from 65 to 100€ – Per week from 255 to 695€

🚰 borne 3,50€ – 150 🔲 26€

A small, pretty chalet village. Choose the pitches furthest away from the road in preference.

Surroundings : ⇐ 🖵 ♨♨
Leisure activities : 🎭 🏄 🏊 (open air in season)
Facilities : ⚹ ⚬━ 🚿 ⛱ 🧺 ⁇ ⁇ launderette

G P S Longitude : -1.40137
Latitude : 43.33887

LABENNE-OCÉAN

40530 – Michelin map **335** C13
▶ Paris 763 – Bordeaux 185 – Mont-de-Marsan 98 – Pau 129

🔺🔺🔺 Yelloh! Village le Sylvamar ♠♣

𝒫 0559457516, www.sylvamar.fr

Address : avenue de l'Océan (continue along the D 126, follow the signs for the beach, near Le Boudigau)

Opening times : from beginning April to beginning Oct.

25 ha (750 pitches)

Tariff : 52€ ⚹⚹ ⇔ 🔲 ⑂ (16A)
Extra per person 9€

Rental rates : (from beginning April to beginning Oct.) ⚹ (chalets) 240 🏠 60 🏠 – 3 🛏 – 1 cabin in the trees 1 gîte. Per night from 39 to 285€ Per week from 273 to 1995€

🚰 10 🔲 67€

A large water park with a covered paddling pool and play area and a range of luxury rental options.

Surroundings : 🐟 🖵 ♨♨
Leisure activities : 🍽 ✗ 🎭 🛶 (open air theatre) 🏄 🎣 🛥 hammam, jacuzzi 🏊 🚴 ✗ 🎱 🏊 ⛸ multi-sports ground, spa centre
Facilities : ⚹ ⚬━ 🚿 ⛱ 🧺 ⁇ ⁇ launderette 🏪 🧺 refrigerated food storage facilities
Nearby : 🏇 🐾 wildlife park

G P S Longitude : -1.45687
Latitude : 43.59532

🔺🔺 Côte d'Argent ♠♣

𝒫 0559454202, www.camping-cotedargent.com

Address : 60 avenue de l'Océan (along the D 126, follow the signs for the beach)

Opening times : from beginning April to end Oct.

4 ha (215 pitches)

Tariff : 38,10€ ⚹⚹ ⇔ 🔲 ⑂ (6A) – Extra per person 5,80€

Reservation fee 25€

Rental rates : (from beginning April to end Oct.) – 23 🏠 – 35 🏠 12 canvas bungalows. Per night from 45 to 132€ – Per week from 199 to 930€ – Reservation fee 25€

🚰 borne 3,50€

Surroundings : 🖵 ♨♨
Leisure activities : 🍽 ✗ 🎮 daytime 🏄 🏊 🚴 🛶 🏊 multi-sports ground
Facilities : ⚹ ⚬━ 🏦 🚿 ⛱ ⁇ ⁇ launderette 🏪
Nearby : 🏊 ✗

G P S Longitude : -1.45687
Latitude : 43.59532

🔺🔺 Municipal Les Pins Bleus

𝒫 0559454113, www.lespinsbleus.com

Address : avenue de l'Océan (along the D 126 follow the signs for the beach; beside the Boudigau river)

Opening times : from beginning April to end Oct.

6,5 ha (120 pitches)

Tariff : 14,10€ ⚹⚹ ⇔ 🔲 ⑂ (6A) – Reservation fee 18€

Rental rates : (from beginning April to end Oct.) ⚹ (1 chalet) 14 🏠 – 22 🏠 – 10 canvas bungalows. Per night from 21 to 89€ Per week from 33 to 550€ – Reservation fee 18€

🚰 borne 2€ – 10 🔲 9€ – 🚐 9€

Surroundings : ♨♨
Leisure activities : ✗ 🎭 🏄 🏊 🚴 🛥 🚤
Facilities : ⚬━ ⁇ launderette, refrigerated food storage facilities

G P S Longitude : -1.45687
Latitude : 43.60229

*The classification (1 to 5 tents, **black** or red) that we award to selected sites in this guide is our own system. It should not be confused with the classification (1 to 5 stars) of official organisations.*

LACANAU

33680 – Michelin map **335** E5 – pop. 4 412 – alt. 17
▶ Paris 625 – Bordeaux 47 – Mérignac 45 – Pessac 51

🔺🔺🔺 FranceLoc Talaris Vacances ♠♣

𝒫 0556030415, www.talaris-vacances.fr

Address : at Le Moutchic (5km west along the D 6, follow the signs for Lacanau-Océan)

10 ha (476 pitches) flat, grassy, small lake

Rental rates : 170 🏠 – 5 🏠 – 23 canvas bungalows – 8 tent lodges.

🚰 borne

A pleasant wooded site.

Surroundings : 🐟 🌳
Leisure activities : 🍽 ✗ 🎭 🎮 🏄 🏊 🚴 ✗ 🏊 🛶 🏊 multi-sports ground
Facilities : ⚹ ⚬━ ⛱ ⁇ launderette 🏪 🧺

G P S Longitude : -1.11236
Latitude : 45.008

⛰ Le Tedey ♁♨

📞 05 56 03 00 15, www.le-tedey.com 🚫 (July–Aug.)

Address : at Le Moutchic, route de Longarisse (3km south and take road to the left)

Opening times : from end April to mid Sept.

14 ha (700 pitches) adjacent wooded dunes

Tariff : (2013 price) 31€ ♟♟ 🚐 🔲 (10A) – Extra per person 6€ Reservation fee 20€

Rental rates : (from end April to mid Sept.) 🚫 – 38 🏠. Per week from 330 to 750€ – Reservation fee 20€

A pleasant site beside the Lac de Lacanau, shaded by pine trees, but with poor sanitary facilities.

Surroundings : 🏖 ⛺ ♨♨ ⛰	
Leisure activities : 🍴🎾⛹🚣🚴🎣🛶 🏊	**G P S**
Facilities : ♿ ⛽ 🍳🍽 launderette 🏪🛒	Longitude : -1.13652 Latitude : 44.9875

⛺ Villages Vacances Le Gîte Autrement

(rental of chalets only)

📞 05 57 17 22 47, www.gite-autrement.com

Address : at Narsot (2.5km northeast along the D 104E4 follow the signs for Brach)

1 ha

Rentals : 🚫 – 9 🏠.

Surroundings : ♨♨	
Leisure activities : 🚣🚴🏊 (open air in season)	**G P S**
Facilities : ⛽🍽🍳	Longitude : -1.04908 Latitude : 44.98457

LACANAU-OCÉAN

33680 – Michelin map **335** D4 – pop. 3 142

▶ Paris 636 – Andernos-les-Bains 38 – Arcachon 87 – Bordeaux 63

⛰ Yelloh! Village Les Grands Pins ♁♨

YELLOH

📞 05 56 03 20 77, www.lesgrandspins.com

Address : Plage Nord (north of the resort, 500m from the beach - direct access-)

Opening times : from end April to end Sept.

11 ha (570 pitches) terraced, undulating, sandy

Tariff : 53€ ♟♟ 🚐 🔲 (10A) Extra per person 9€

Rental rates : (from end April to end Sept.) – 218 🏠. Per night from 35 to 267€ – Per week from 245 to 1869€

🏕 borne

No vehicle access to one part of the site.

Surroundings : 🏖 ⛺ ♨♨	
Leisure activities : 🍴🍽 🎾🎣 🚣🚴🎳🏊🏊 fitness trail, multi-sports ground, spa centre	**G P S**
Facilities : ♿ ⛽ Ⓟ 🍳🍽 launderette 🏪🛒 refrigerated food storage facilities	Longitude : -1.19517 Latitude : 45.01088

⛰ Club Airotel de l'Océan ♁♨

📞 05 56 03 24 45, www.airotel-ocean.com

Address : 24 rue du Repos (Plage Nord (North Beach)

Opening times : from beginning April to beginning Nov.

9 ha (550 pitches) terraced, undulating, sandy

Tariff : 55€ ♟♟ 🚐 🔲 (15A) – Extra per person 10€ – Reservation fee 28€

Rental rates : (from beginning April to beginning Nov.) – 250 🏠. Per night from 55 to 192€ – Per week from 385 to 1350€ Reservation fee 28€

🏕 borne – 40 🔲 25€

A pleasant water park, partly covered.

Surroundings : ♨♨	
Leisure activities : 🍴🍽🎾🚣⛹🎣🎳 hammam, jacuzzi 🚣🚴🍴🏊🏊 disco, surfing, spa centre	**G P S**
Facilities : ♿ ⛽ 🍳🍽 launderette 🏪🛒 refrigerated food storage facilities	Longitude : -1.1928 Latitude : 45.00868

LAMONZIE-MONTASTRUC

24520 – Michelin map **329** E6 – pop. 632 – alt. 50

▶ Paris 587 – Bordeaux 131 – Périgueux 46 – Agen 103

⛰ L'Escapade ♁♨

📞 05 53 57 23 79, www.campinglescapade.com

Address : at Les Roussilloux (follow the signs for St-Alvère)

Opening times : from beginning April to mid Sept.

4,5 ha (85 pitches)

Tariff : 30€ ♟♟ 🚐 🔲 (10A) – Extra per person 7,90€ – Reservation fee 26€

Rental rates : (from beginning April to mid Sept.) ♿ – 68 🏠 10 🏠. Per night from 31 to 133€ – Per week from 287 to 931€ Reservation fee 26€

Surroundings : 🏖 ⛺ ♨	
Leisure activities : 🍴🍽 🎾 ⛹ 🎳 hammam, jacuzzi 🚣🚴🏊🏊🏄 donkey rides multi-sports ground	**G P S**
Facilities : ♿ ⛽ 🍳🍽 launderette 🛒	Longitude : 0.60793 Latitude : 44.88636

LANOUAILLE

24270 – Michelin map **329** H3 – pop. 989 – alt. 209

▶ Paris 446 – Brantôme 47 – Limoges 55 – Périgueux 46

⛰ Village Vacances Le Moulin de la Jarousse

((rental of chalets, yurts, cabins in the trees and gîtes only)

📞 05 53 52 37 91, www.location-en-dordogne.com

Address : at Payzac, at La Jarousse (continue 9km northeast along the D 704 to l'Hôpital, then take right turn along the D 80)

Opening times : Permanent

8 ha terraced, lake, forest

Rental rates : ♿ (1 gîte) – 8 🏠 – 8 yurts – 9 cabins in the trees 3 gîtes. Per night 185€ – Per week 860€

In a natural wooded setting overlooking the lake.

Surroundings : 🏖 ≤ ♨♨	
Leisure activities : 🚣🚴🏊 (open air in season) 🏊 pedalos 🏄	**G P S**
Facilities : ⛽ Ⓟ 🚿🍳🍽	Longitude : 1.18411 Latitude : 45.43694

LARRAU

64560 – Michelin map **342** G4 – pop. 204 – alt. 636
▶ Paris 840 – Bordeaux 254 – Pamplona 110 – Donostia-San Sebastián 142

⚠ Village Vacances Les Chalets d'Iraty

(rental of chalets only)

✆ 05 59 28 51 29, www.chalets-iraty.com – alt. 1 327

Address : at the Col de Bagargui pass (14km west along the D 19, follow the signs for St-Jean-Pied-de-Port)

2 000 ha/4 for camping undulating

Rentals : 🏠 – 40 🏠 .

The site is spread out in the Forêt d'Iraty, between the Col de Bagargui and the Col Hegui Xouri.

Surroundings : 🐾 ♨
Leisure activities : 🚲 ✂
Facilities : ⊶ ▥ 🚩 🗑
Nearby : 🏖 🍷 ✗ 🚿 🦅 🐎 cross-country skiing

GPS
Longitude : -1.03532
Latitude : 43.03638

LARUNS

64440 – Michelin map **342** J5 – pop. 1 326 – alt. 523
▶ Paris 811 – Argelès-Gazost 49 – Lourdes 51 – Oloron-Ste-Marie 34

⚠ Les Gaves

✆ 05 59 05 32 37, www.campingdesgaves.com – limited spaces for one-night stay

Address : Pon quartier (located 1.5km southeast of Larun, follow the signs for Le Col d'Aubisque and take the road to the left; beside the Gave d'Ossau (river)

Opening times : Permanent

2,4 ha (101 pitches) flat, grassy

Tariff : (2013 price) 26,40€ 🚻 🚗 🔲 🔌 (10A)

Extra per person 4,80€ – Reservation fee 17€
Rental rates : Permanent 🏠 – 20 🛏 – 5 🏠 – 5 apartments 1 gîte. Per night 97€ – Per week 707€ – Reservation fee 20€
🚐 borne – 5 🔲 11€ – 🔋 11€

A pleasant camping area, with varied rental options, but the rather jaded sanitary facilities are not of a high standard; many owner-occupier mobile homes.

Surroundings : ❄ 🐾 ♨
Leisure activities : 🍷 🏛 🏓
Facilities : ⊶ ▥ 🚿 🚩 🍽 launderette

GPS
Longitude : -0.41772
Latitude : 42.98306

LÈGE-CAP-FERRET

33950 – Michelin map **335** E6 – pop. 7 527 – alt. 9
▶ Paris 629 – Arcachon 65 – Belin-Beliet 56 – Bordeaux 50

⚠ La Prairie

✆ 05 56 60 09 75, www.campinglaprairie.com

Address : 93 avenue du Médoc (located 1km northeast along the D 3, follow the signs for Le Porge)

Opening times : from beginning March to end Oct.

2,5 ha (118 pitches)

Tariff : 20,30€ 🚻 🚗 🔲 🔌 (10A) – Extra per person 3,80€
Rental rates : (from beginning April to end Sept.) – 16 🛏 – 4 tent lodges. Per night from 41 to 108€ – Per week from 232 to 655€
🚐 borne – 10 🔲 11€ – 🔋 9€

Surroundings : 🌳 ♨
Leisure activities : 🏛 🏓
Facilities : 🚿 ⊶ 🚿 🍽 🗑

GPS
Longitude : -1.13375
Latitude : 44.80271

LÉON

40550 – Michelin map **335** D11 – pop. 1 830 – alt. 9
▶ Paris 724 – Castets 14 – Dax 30 – Mimizan 42

⚠ Yelloh! Village Punta Lago 🛝

✆ 05 58 49 24 40, www.camping-puntalago.com

Address : 1165 avenue du Lac (1.5km northwest along the D 142, opposite the municipal stadium, 200m from the lake)

Opening times : from beginning April to end Sept.

5,5 ha (300 pitches)

Tariff : 48€ 🚻 🚗 🔲 🔌 (10A) – Extra per person 7€
Rental rates : (from beginning April to end Sept.) – 70 🛏. Per night from 39 to 208€ – Per week from 273 to 1456€

Surroundings : 🐾 🖼 ♨
Leisure activities : 🍷 🏛 🎣 🏃 🎾 ⛷ 🖼 🏊 multi-sports ground
Facilities : 🚿 🚿 🚿 🍽 launderette 🚿
Nearby : 🏖 ✗

GPS
Longitude : -1.31342
Latitude : 43.88382

LESCUN

64490 – Michelin map **342** I5 – pop. 178 – alt. 900
▶ Paris 846 – Lourdes 89 – Oloron-Ste-Marie 37 – Pau 70

⚠ Le Lauzart

✆ 05 59 34 51 77, camping-lescun.com

Opening times : from beginning April to end Sept.

1 ha (55 pitches) flat and relatively flat

Tariff : 🚹 3,50€ 🚗 1,50€ 🔲 4,50€ – 🔌 (10A) 4,50€

A magnificent mountain site, although with ageing sanitary facilities. Half board available.

Surroundings : 🐾 ⛰ ♨
Leisure activities : 🏛
Facilities : 🚿 ⊶ 🚿 ▥ 🚩 🍽 🗑

GPS
Longitude : -0.64217
Latitude : 42.92761

The Michelin classification (⚠⚠⚠ … ⚠) is totally independent of the official star classification system awarded by the local prefecture or other official organisation.

LIMEUIL

24510 – Michelin map **329** G6 – pop. 328 – alt. 65
▶ Paris 528 – Bergerac 43 – Brive-la-Gaillarde 78 – Périgueux 48

⚠ La Ferme des Poutiroux

✆ 05 53 63 31 62, www.poutiroux.com

Address : take the northwestern exit along the D 31, follow the signs for Trémolat then continue 1km along the road for Paunat to the right

Opening times : from beginning April to end Sept.

2,5 ha (45 pitches)

Tariff : 🚹 5,60€ 🚗 🔲 6,20€ – 🔌 (6A) 4€ – Reservation fee 13€
Rental rates : (from beginning April to end Sept.) 🚿 – 20 🛏. Per night 38€ – Per week 610€ – Reservation fee 13€

Surroundings : 🐾 ⛰ ♨
Leisure activities : 🏛 🏓 🏊
Facilities : 🚿 ⊶ 🚿 🚩 🍽 launderette

GPS
Longitude : 0.87946
Latitude : 44.89332

LINXE

40260 – Michelin map **335** D11 – pop. 1 236 – alt. 33
▶ Paris 712 – Castets 10 – Dax 31 – Mimizan 37

⚐ FranceLoc Domaine Lila

𝄞 05 58 43 96 25, www.franceloc.fr – limited spaces for one-night stay

Address : 190, route de Mixe (located 1.5km northwest along the D 42, follow the signs for St-Girons and take D 397, turning to the right)

2 ha (159 pitches)

Rentals : 140 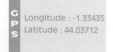.

A good number of mobile homes and pitches for tents and caravans arranged around an eco swimming pool (no chemicals).

Surroundings : 🌳		Longitude : -1.25758
Leisure activities : 🍴🏠📺🏃🚣🎣▦⛳🏊	**G P S**	Latitude : 43.93185
Facilities : ♿ ⚡ 🚿 launderette		

LIT-ET-MIXE

40170 – Michelin map **335** D10 – pop. 1 497 – alt. 13
▶ Paris 710 – Castets 21 – Dax 42 – Mimizan 22

⚐ Village Center Les Vignes 👥

(rental of mobile homes, chalets and canvas bungalows only)

𝄞 05 58 42 85 60, www.village-center.fr

Address : 2.7km southwest along the D 652 and take the D 88, to the right, follow the signs for Le Cap de l'Homy

Opening times : from beginning April to end Sept.

15 ha (495 pitches)

Rental rates : ♿ (2 mobile homes) – 280  – 40 🏠 19 canvas bungalows. Per night from 23 to 101€ – Per week from 448 to 1 218€ – Reservation fee 30€

Leisure activities : 🍴✕🏠📺🎪(big top staging activities and shows) 🏃🚴⛳✂🎣▦🏊⛱cinema, multi-sports ground	**G P S**	Longitude : -1.28275
Facilities : ♿⚡🚿🍴launderette 🐾🧺		Latitude : 44.02401

△ Municipal du Cap de l'Homy

𝄞 05 58 42 83 47, www.camping-cap.com

Address : at Cap-de-l'Homy, 600 avenue de l'Océan (8km west along the D 652 and take D 88 to the right; 300m from the beach (direct access)

Opening times : from beginning May to end Sept.

10 ha (474 pitches)

Tariff : 28,70€ ✶✶ 🚗 ▤ ⚡ (6A) – Extra per person 6,50€

Reservation fee 30€

Rental rates : (from beginning May to mid Sept.) 🐾 – 15 canvas bungalows. Per night from 35€ – Per week from 220 to 660€ Reservation fee 30€

🚰 borne 16,80€

In the shelter of a pleasant pine wood.

Surroundings : 🏞️🌲		
Leisure activities : 📺🚴		Longitude : -1.33435
Facilities : ♿⚡🚿launderette, refrigerated food storage facilities	**G P S**	Latitude : 44.03712
Nearby : 🏊🍴✕🧺surfing		

MARCILLAC-ST-QUENTIN

24200 – Michelin map **329** I6 – pop. 791 – alt. 235
▶ Paris 522 – Brive-la-Gaillarde 48 – Les Eyzies-de-Tayac 18 – Montignac 21

⚐ Les Tailladis

𝄞 05 53 59 10 95, www.tailladis.com

Address : at Les Tailladis (situated 2km to the north, near the D 48; beside the Beune river and a lake)

Opening times : from mid March to end Oct.

25 ha/8 for camping (90 pitches)

Tariff : ✶ 6,25€ 🚗 ▤ 7,50€ – ⚡ (10A) 3,90€ – Reservation fee 10€

Rental rates : (from mid March to end Oct.) – 3  – 4 🏠. Per week from 520 to 700€ – Reservation fee 10€

🚰 borne

Surroundings : 🏊🚣🌳		
Leisure activities : 🍴✕🏊🎣	**G P S**	Longitude : 1.18789
Facilities : ♿⚡▦🍴launderette 🏊🚿		Latitude : 44.97465

MAULÉON-LICHARRE

64130 – Michelin map **342** G5 – pop. 3 205 – alt. 140
▶ Paris 802 – Oloron-Ste-Marie 31 – Orthez 39 – Pau 60

⚐ Uhaitza - Le Saison

𝄞 05 59 28 18 79, www.camping-uhaitza.com

Address : located 1.5km south along the D 918, follow the signs for Tardets-Sorholus; beside the Saison river

Opening times : from beginning April to mid Oct.

1 ha (50 pitches) terraced, flat, grassy

Tariff : (2013 price) 25,28€ ✶✶ 🚗 ▤ ⚡ (10A)

Extra per person 5,85€ – Reservation fee 10€

Rental rates : (from beginning March to mid Nov.) – 2 🚐 5 🏠. Per week 599 € – Reservation fee 10€

🚰 borne 5,10€

Choose the pitches near the stream and further away from the road.

Surroundings : 🏊🚣🌳		
Leisure activities : 🍴🏠📺🏃🎣	**G P S**	Longitude : -0.8972
Facilities : ♿⚡🐾🚿🏊🍴launderette		Latitude : 43.20789

△ Aire Naturelle La Ferme Landran

𝄞 05 59 28 19 55, www.gites64.com/la-ferme-landran

Address : at Ordiarp, Larréguy quartier (4.5km southwest along the D 918, follow the signs for St-Jean-Pied-de-Port then continue 1.5km along the road for Lambarre to the right)

Opening times : from beginning April to end Sept.

1 ha (25 pitches) sloping, flat, grassy

Tariff : 14,32€ ✶✶ 🚗 ▤ ⚡ (6A) – Extra per person 3,41€

Rental rates : Permanent – 2 🏠 – 7 🛏 – 1 lodging stage (27 beds). Per night 60€ – Per week 360€

🚰 borne 3,50€

A farm campsite.

Surroundings : 🏊⛰️🌳		
Leisure activities : 📺🏃	**G P S**	Longitude : -0.93933
Facilities : ♿⚡🚿🍴▦		Latitude : 43.20185

MESSANGES

40660 – Michelin map **335** C12 – pop. 986 – alt. 8
▶ Paris 734 – Bayonne 45 – Castets 24 – Dax 33

⚠️ Club Airotel Le Vieux Port ♠♠

𝒫 0825704040, www.levieuxport.com

Address : route de la Plage Sud (2.5km southwest along the D 652, follow the signs for Vieux-Boucau-les-Bains then continue 800m along the road to the right; 500m from the beach – direct access)

Opening times : from beginning April to end Sept.

40 ha/30 for camping (1546 pitches)
undulating, flat, grassy, sandy

Tariff : (2013 price) 64€ ♦♦ ⇔ 🔲 (🔌) (8A) – Extra per person 9,50€
Reservation fee 40€

Rental rates : (from beginning April to end Sept.) ♿ (1 mobile home) ⚡ – 380 🏠 – 75 ⛺. Per night from 66 to 28€
Per week from 245 to 1960€ – Reservation fee 40€

A spacious landscaped water park with plenty of shops and services at the entrance.

Surroundings : ♒
Leisure activities : 🍴 ✗ 🎬 🎭 (cinema/theatre) 👫 🏊 hammam, jacuzzi 🚴 🚵 🏇 ⛳ 🔲 🎿 🏊 🏇 multi-sports ground, spa centre
Facilities : ♿ ⚡ 🆑 🏠 🚿 🛗 🍴 launderette 🛒 refrigerated food storage facilities

GPS Longitude : -1.39995
Latitude : 43.79773

⚠️ Village Vacances Club Airotel Lou Pignada ♠♠

(rental of caravans, mobile homes and chalets only)

𝒫 0825704040, www.loupignada.com

Address : route d'Azur (situated 2km south along the D 652 then continue 500m down road to the left)

Opening times : from beginning April to end Sept.

8 ha (430 pitches)

Rental rates : ♿ (1 mobile home) ⚡ – 120 🏠 – 25 ⛺. Per night from 46 to 220€ – Per week from 195 to 1540€ Reservation fee 40€

Surroundings : 🏕 ♒
Leisure activities : 🍴 ✗ 🎬 👫 🎣 🏊 🚴 🚵 🏇 🎿 🏊 multi-sports ground
Facilities : ♿ ⚡ 🏠 🍴 launderette 🛒 refrigerated food storage facilities

GPS Longitude : -1.38245
Latitude : 43.79747

⚠️ La Côte

𝒫 0558489494, www.campinglacote.com

Address : chemin de la Côte (2.3km southwest along the D 652, follow the signs for Vieux-Boucau-les-Bains and take the road to the right)

Opening times : from beginning April to end Sept.

3,5 ha (143 pitches)

Tariff : 30,80€ ♦♦ ⇔ 🔲 (🔌) (10A) – Extra per person 6,30€
Reservation fee 19€

Rental rates : (from beginning April to end Sept.) ⚡ – 12 🏠
1 gîte. Per night from 55 to 65€ – Per week from 250 to 830€
Reservation fee 20€

🚐 borne

Surroundings : 🏖 ♒
Leisure activities : 🏊 jacuzzi 🚴 🎿
Facilities : ♿ ⚡ 🏠 🚿 🛗 🍴 launderette, refrigerated food storage facilities

GPS Longitude : -1.39171
Latitude : 43.80035

⚠️ Les Acacias

𝒫 0558480178, www.lesacacias.com

Address : 101 chemin du Houdin, Delest quartier (situated 2km south along the D 652, follow the signs for Vieux-Boucau-les-Bains then continue 1km along the turning to the left)

Opening times : from end March to end Oct.

1,7 ha (128 pitches)

Tariff : 24,20€ ♦♦ ⇔ 🔲 (🔌) (10A) – Extra per person 4,80€
Reservation fee 15€

Rental rates : Permanent – 11 🏠. Per week from 240 to 690€
Reservation fee 15€

🚐 borne 10€ – 8 🔲 24,20€

Surroundings : 🏖 ♒
Leisure activities : 🏊 🚴
Facilities : ♿ ⚡ 🏠 🚿 🛗 🍴 launderette

GPS Longitude : -1.37567
Latitude : 43.79757

These symbols are used for a campsite that is exceptional in its category:

⚠️...⚠️ *Particularly pleasant setting, quality and range of services available*

🏖🏖 *Tranquil, isolated site – quiet site, particularly at night*

≼≼ *Exceptional view – interesting or panoramic view*

MÉZOS

40170 – Michelin map **335** E10 – pop. 866 – alt. 23
▶ Paris 700 – Bordeaux 118 – Castets 24 – Mimizan 16

⚠️ Club Airotel Le Village Tropical Sen Yan ♠♠

𝒫 0558426005, www.sen-yan.com

Address : avenue de la Gare (located 1km east, follow the signs for Le Cout)

Opening times : from beginning June to mid Sept.

8 ha (310 pitches)

Tariff : 43,60€ ♦♦ ⇔ 🔲 (🔌) (10A) – Extra per person 8,30€
Reservation fee 26,50€

Rental rates : (from mid April to mid Sept.) ⚡ – 300 🏠
40 ⛺. Per night from 64 to 177€ – Per week from 448 to 1239€
Reservation fee 26,50€

A pretty site with swimming pools, palm trees, plantations and a small ecological lake.

Surroundings : 🏖 🏕 ♒
Leisure activities : 🍴 ✗ 🎬 👫 🎣 🏊 🚴 🚵 🏇 🎿 🏊 ⚓ (lake) 🏄 multi-sports ground
Facilities : ♿ ⚡ 🏠 🚿 🛗 🍴 launderette 🛒

GPS Longitude : -1.15657
Latitude : 44.07164

MIALET

24450 – Michelin map **329** G2 – pop. 665 – alt. 320
▶ Paris 436 – Limoges 49 – Nontron 23 – Périgueux 51

⚐ Village Vacances L'Étang de Vivale

(rental of chalets only)

✆ 05 53 52 66 05, www.vivaledordogne.com

Address : 32 avenue de Nontron (700m west along the D 79; beside the lake)

Opening times : from beginning March to beginning Nov.

30 ha

Rental rates : 20 🏠. Per night from 70 to 110€ – Per week from 400 to 770€

Surroundings : 🚣 ⟨ ⌑ ♀
Leisure activities : 🍽 🎱 🏊 🚲 🎣 ⛵
boats to hire 🚤
Facilities : 🚿 ⚓ 🅿 🍴 📠

GPS	Longitude : 0.89788
	Latitude : 45.54793

MIMIZAN

40200 – Michelin map **335** D9 – pop. 7 000 – alt. 13
▶ Paris 692 – Arcachon 67 – Bayonne 109 – Bordeaux 109

⚑ Municipal du Lac

✆ 05 58 09 01 21, www.mimizan-camping.com

Address : avenue de Woolsack (situated 2km north along the D 87, follow the signs for Gastes; beside the Lac d'Aureilhan)

Opening times : from mid April to beginning Sept.

8 ha (466 pitches)

Tariff : 20,59€ ✶✶ 🚗 🔲 🔌 (6A) – Extra per person 7,85€ Reservation fee 20€

Rental rates : (from mid April to beginning Sept.) – 19 canvas bungalows. Per night from 26 to 44€ – Per week from 180 to 510€ – Reservation fee 20€

🚻 borne 2€ – 21 🔲 1€

Surroundings : ♀
Leisure activities : 🍽 🏊
Facilities : 🚿 ⚓ 🍴 🚾 ♨ 🍴
Nearby : 🏊 🎣 ♨ pedalos

GPS	Longitude : -1.2299
	Latitude : 44.21968

MIMIZAN-PLAGE

40200 – Michelin map **335** D9
▶ Paris 706 – Bordeaux 128 – Mont-de-Marsan 84

⚑ Club Airotel Marina-Landes 👥

✆ 05 58 09 12 66, www.marinalandes.com

Address : 8, rue Marina (500m from La Plage du Sud (beach))

Opening times : from mid April to end Sept.

9 ha (536 pitches)

Tariff : 55€ ✶✶ 🚗 🔲 🔌 (10A) – Extra per person 10€ – Reservation fee 35€

Rental rates : (from mid April to end Sept.) – 100 – 6 🏠 24 apartments – 10 canvas bungalows – 7 tent lodges. Per night from 30 to 186€ – Per week from 210 to 1305€ – Reservation fee 35€

🚻 borne 2€

Surroundings : ⌑ ♀♀
Leisure activities : 🍽 🍴 🎱 🏊 👥 🎿 🏊
🚲 🎾 🎱 🏊 🏊 🏄 multi-sports ground,
entertainment room
Facilities : 🚿 ⚓ 🏧 🍴 launderette 🚾 🍴
Nearby : 🐎

GPS	Longitude : -1.2909
	Latitude : 44.2043

⚐ Municipal de la Plage 👥

✆ 05 58 09 00 32, www.mimizan-camping.com

Address : boulevard de l'Atlantique (northern suburb)

Opening times : from mid April to mid Sept.

16 ha (608 pitches)

Tariff : (2013 price) ✶ 12€ 🚗 2€ 🔲 8€ – 🔌 (10A) 10€

Rental rates : (from mid April to mid Sept.) 🅿 – 32 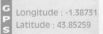 – 15 🏠. Per night from 28 to 36€ – Per week from 310 to 740€

🚻 borne 1,50€ – 18 🔲 10€
Welcomes surfer groups.

Surroundings : ⌑
Leisure activities : 🍽 🎱 🎿 🏊 climbing
wall, multi-sports ground
Facilities : 🚿 ⚓ 🍴 🍴 launderette 🚾 🍴
refrigerated food storage facilities

GPS	Longitude : -1.28384
	Latitude : 44.21719

MOLIETS-PLAGE

40660 – Michelin map **335** C11
▶ Paris 716 – Bordeaux 156 – Mont-de-Marsan 89 – Bayonne 67

⚑ Le Saint-Martin 👥

✆ 05 58 48 52 30, www.camping-saint-martin.fr

Address : avenue de l'Océan (on the D 117, direct access to the beach)

Opening times : from mid April to beginning Nov.

18 ha (660 pitches)

Tariff : 45,20€ ✶✶ 🚗 🔲 🔌 (10A) – Extra per person 8,90€ Reservation fee 35€

Rental rates : (from mid April to beginning Nov.) – 40 🚗 137 🏠 – 6 canvas bungalows. Per night from 88 to 280€ Per week from 205 to 1 540€ – Reservation fee 35€

🚻 borne – 45 🔲 51,90€

Surroundings : ⌑ ♀
Leisure activities : 🍽 🍴 🎱 🎿 🏊 🍴 🏊
🏊 🏊 multi-sports ground
Facilities : 🚿 ⚓ 🍴 🚾 🍴 🍴 launderette 🍴
refrigerated food storage facilities
Nearby : 🚲 🎾

GPS	Longitude : -1.38731
	Latitude : 43.85259

MONPAZIER

24540 – Michelin map **329** G7 – pop. 522 – alt. 180
▶ Paris 575 – Bergerac 47 – Fumel 26 – Périgueux 75

⚑ Le Moulin de David 👥

✆ 05 53 22 65 25, www.moulindedavid.com

Address : 3km southwest along the D 2, follow the signs for Villeréal and take road to the left; beside a stream

Opening times : from beginning April to end Sept.

16 ha/4 for camping (160 pitches)

Tariff : 26€ ✶✶ 🚗 🔲 🔌 (10A) – Extra per person 6€ – Reservation fee 20€

Rental rates : (from beginning April to end Sept.) 🏄 – 56 🚗 3 canvas bungalows – 6 tent lodges. Per night from 26 to 142€ Per week from 182 to 993€ – Reservation fee 20€

Surroundings : 🚣 ⌑ ♀♀
Leisure activities : 🍽 🍴 🎱 🎿 🏊 🏊 🏊 🌊
(stream) 🏊
Facilities : 🚿 ⚓ 🍴 🚾 🍴 🍴 launderette 🚾
🍴

GPS	Longitude : 0.87873
	Latitude : 44.65979

MONTIGNAC

24290 – Michelin map **329** H5 – pop. 2 851 – alt. 77
▶ Paris 513 – Brive-la-Gaillarde 39 – Périgueux 54 – Sarlat-la-Canéda 25

⛰ Le Moulin du Bleufond

☎ 05 53 51 83 95, www.bleufond.com

Address : avenue Aristide Briand (500m south along the D 65 follow the signs for Sergeac; near the Vézère river)

Opening times : from beginning April to end Sept.

1,3 ha (84 pitches) flat, grassyTariff : (2013 price) 🚶 8,50 € 🚗 🔲 7 € 🔌 (10A) 4,90 €

Rental rates : (from beginning April to end Sept.) – 21 🛖. Per night from 60 to 110 € – Per week from 282 to 750 €

The pretty pitches are spread out around the old mill.

Surroundings : 🌊 ⌂ 🎠
Leisure activities : ✗ 🏠 🏊 jacuzzi 🏄 🛶
Facilities : ♿ ⚷ 🚿 🏕 🔥 ⚒ 🍽 launderette 🚰
Nearby : 🍴 🎣

MONTPON-MÉNESTÉROL

24700 – Michelin map **329** B5 – pop. 5 535 – alt. 93
▶ Paris 532 – Bergerac 40 – Bordeaux 75 – Libourne 43

⛰ La Cigaline

☎ 05 53 80 22 16, www.lacigaline.fr

Address : 1 rue de la Paix (take the northern exit along the D 708, follow the signs for Ribérac and take the turning to the left before the bridge)

Opening times : from beginning April to end Oct.

2 ha (120 pitches) flat, grassy

Tariff : 15,50 € 🚶🚶 🚗 🔲 🔌 (10A) – Extra per person 3,80 € Reservation fee 12 €

Rental rates : (from mid April to end Oct.) – 8 🛖. Per night from 48 to 58 € – Per week from 280 to 530 € – Reservation fee 12 €

Beside the Isle river.

Surroundings : ⌂ 🎠
Leisure activities : 🏠 🎣
Facilities : ♿ ⚷ 🔥 ⚒ 🍽 🔲
Nearby : 🎣

NAVARRENX

64190 – Michelin map **342** H3 – pop. 1 104 – alt. 125
▶ Paris 787 – Oloron-Ste-Marie 23 – Orthez 22 – Pau 43

⛰ Beau Rivage

☎ 05 59 66 10 00, www.beaucamping.com

Address : allée des Marronniers (to the west of the town between the Gave d'Oloron (river) and the village ramparts)

Opening times : from end March to mid Oct.

2,5 ha (70 pitches)

Tariff : 26,75 € 🚶🚶 🚗 🔲 🔌 (10A) – Extra per person 5,85 €

Rental rates : (from end March to mid Oct.) ♿ (1 chalet) – 10 🏠 Per week from 304 to 680 €

🚐 borne

By the Gave d'Oloron river and the old village fortifications.

Surroundings : 🌊 ⌂ 🎠
Leisure activities : 🏠 🏄 🛶
Facilities : ♿ ⚷ 🏕 🚿 🔥 ⚒ 🍽 launderette
Nearby : 🍴 🎣

Longitude : -0.76121
Latitude : 43.32003

NONTRON

24300 – Michelin map **329** E2 – pop. 3 421 – alt. 260
▶ Paris 464 – Bordeaux 175 – Périgueux 49 – Angoulême 47

⛰ Camping De Nontron

☎ 05 53 56 02 04, www.campingdenontron.com

Address : at St-Martial-de-Valette (located 1km south on the D 675, follow the signs for Périgueux)

Opening times : from beginning Jan. to mid Dec.

2 ha (70 pitches) flat, grassy, beside river

Tariff : (2013 price) 15 € 🚶🚶 🚗 🔲 🔌 (10A) – Extra per person 3,90 €

Rental rates : (from beginning Jan. to mid Dec.) ♿ – 3 🛖. Per night from 47 to 57 € – Per week from 260 to 568 €

🚐 borne 3 €

Beside a large indoor water park.

Surroundings : ⌂ 🎠
Leisure activities : 🏠 🎣
Facilities : ♿ ⚷ 🏕 🚿 🍽 🔲 🚰
Nearby : 🏊 hammam, jacuzzi 🏊 🏊

For more information on visiting particular towns or regions, consult the relevant regional MICHELIN Green Guide. We also recommend you use the appropriate Michelin regional map to locate your selected campsite, to calculate distances and to work out the best route.

ONDRES

40440 – Michelin map **335** C13 – pop. 4 479 – alt. 37
▶ Paris 761 – Bayonne 8 – Biarritz 15 – Dax 48

⛰ Du Lac

☎ 05 59 45 28 45, www.camping-du-lac.fr

Address : 518 rue de Janin (2.2km north along the N 10 then take the D 26, follow the signs for Ondres-Plage then head towards Le Turc, road to the right; near a lake)

Opening times : from mid March to end Oct.

3 ha (115 pitches)

Tariff : 45 € 🚶🚶 🚗 🔲 🔌 (10A) – Extra per person 8 € – Reservation fee 18 €

Rental rates : (from mid March to end Oct.) ♿ (from mid March to end June) – 27 🛖 – 3 🏠 – 7 canvas bungalows. Per night from 32 to 237 € – Per week from 224 to 1 659 € – Reservation fee 20 €

Surroundings : 🌊 ⌂ 🎠
Leisure activities : 🍴 ✗ 🏠 🏊 hammam 🏄 🚴 🛶
Facilities : ♿ ⚷ 🏕 🚿 🍽 launderette 🚰
Nearby : 🎣

Longitude : 1.15864
Latitude : 45.05989

Longitude : 0.15839
Latitude : 45.01217

Longitude : 0.65807
Latitude : 45.51951

Longitude : -1.45249
Latitude : 43.56499

PARCOUL

24410 – Michelin map **329** B4 – pop. 363 – alt. 70
▶ Paris 503 – Bergerac 69 – Blaye 72 – Bordeaux 75

🏕 Le Paradou

𝒫 0553914278, www.leparadou24.fr

Address : at Vaures leisure centre (situated 2km southwest along the D 674, follow the signs for La Roche-Chalais)

Opening times : Permanent

20 ha/4 for camping (100 pitches)

Tariff : 24€ ♟♟ 🚐 🔲 🔌 (10A) – Extra per person 5,50€ – Reservation fee 15€

Rental rates : Permanent ♿ (1 chalet) – 56 🛏 – 4 🏠. Per night from 42 to 70€ – Per week from 220 to 720€ – Reservation fee 15€

Surroundings : 🗺 ♋♋
Leisure activities : 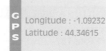 (lake)
Facilities : ♿ ⛟ ♨ 🔥 launderette, refrigerators
Nearby : 🍷 ✖ 🚲 pedalos

G P S Longitude : 0.02578
Latitude : 45.19038

PARENTIS-EN-BORN

40160 – Michelin map **335** E8 – pop. 5 187 – alt. 32
▶ Paris 658 – Arcachon 43 – Bordeaux 76 – Mimizan 25

🏕 L'Arbre d'Or

𝒫 0558784156, www.arbre-dor.com

Address : 75 route du lac (located 1.5km west along the D 43)

Opening times : from beginning April to end Oct.

4 ha (200 pitches) flat, grassy, sandy

Tariff : (2013 price) 27,60€ ♟♟ 🚐 🔲 🔌 (10A)

Extra per person 6,30€

Rental rates : (from beginning April to end Oct.) – 15 🛏 – 1 🏠 2 canvas bungalows. Per night from 60 to 100€ – Per week from 200 to 1030€

🚐 40 🔲 14€ – 🔋 🔌14€

Surroundings : ♋
Leisure activities : 🍷 ✖ 🏠 🎿 🚣 🚴 🏊 🏊 multi-sports ground
Facilities : ♿ ⛟ 🍴 launderette 🔥 refrigerators

G P S Longitude : -1.09232
Latitude : 44.34615

🏕 Le Pipiou ♟:

𝒫 0558785725, www.camping-pipiou.fr

Address : 382 route des Campings (2.5km west along the D 43 and take the turning to the right, 100m from the lake)

Opening times : from beginning March to beginning Nov.

6 ha (324 pitches)

Tariff : 25,50€ ♟♟ 🚐 🔲 🔌 (10A) – Extra per person 5€ – Reservation fee 15€

Rental rates : (from mid April to mid Oct.) – 20 🛏 3 canvas bungalows. Per night from 70 to 90€ – Per week from 150 to 670€– Reservation fee 15€

🚐 🔋 🔌14€

Surroundings : 🏊 🗺
Leisure activities : 🍷 ✖ 🎿 🚣 🚴 multi-sports ground
Facilities : ♿ ⛟ 🛁 ♨ 🔥 🍴 launderette 🔥 🔥
Nearby : 🏖 🏊 (beach) 🎣 🛶

G P S Longitude : -1.10135
Latitude : 44.3457

PAUILLAC

33250 – Michelin map **335** G3 – pop. 5 135 – alt. 20
▶ Paris 625 – Arcachon 113 – Blaye 16 – Bordeaux 54

🏕 Municipal Les Gabarreys

𝒫 0556591003, www.pauillac-medoc.com

Address : route de la Rivière (located 1km to the south, near the Gironde river)

Opening times : from beginning April to mid Oct.

1,6 ha (59 pitches)

Tariff : (2013 price) 23,30€ ♟♟ 🚐 🔲 🔌 (10A)

Extra per person 4,65€ – Reservation fee 11€

Rental rates : (from beginning April to mid Oct.) ♿ (1 mobile home) – 7 🛏. Per night from 42 to 69€ – Per week from 242 to 504€ – Reservation fee 11€

🚐 borne 4,50€ – 🔋16,30€

There's an outdoor jacuzzi upstairs, with a panoramic view of the Gironde river.

Surroundings : 🏊 🗺 ♋♋
Leisure activities : 🏠 🔋s jacuzzi 🎿 🔥
Facilities : ♿ ⛟ 🍴 launderette

G P S Longitude : -0.74226
Latitude : 45.18517

PETIT-PALAIS-ET-CORNEMPS

33570 – Michelin map **335** K5 – pop. 676 – alt. 35
▶ Paris 532 – Bergerac 51 – Castillon-la-Bataille 18 – Libourne 20

🏕 Flower Le Pressoir

CAMPING LE PRESSOIR

𝒫 0557697325, www.campinglepressoir.com

Address : at 29 Queyrai (1.7km northwest along the D 21, follow the signs for St-Médard-de-Guizières and take road to the left)

Opening times : Permanent

2 ha (100 pitches)

Tariff : (2013 price) 16,50€ ♟♟ 🚐 🔲 🔌 (10A) – Extra per person 4€ Reservation fee 15€

Rental rates : Permanent – 50 🛏 8 canvas bungalows. Per night from 32 to 76€ – Per week from 160 to 896€ – Reservation fee 15€

Surroundings : 🏊 ⬅ 🗺 ♋♋
Leisure activities : 🍷 ✖ 🔋s 🎿 🚲 🚣
Facilities : ♿ ⛟ 🍴 launderette

G P S Longitude : -0.06301
Latitude : 44.99693

PEYRIGNAC

24210 – Michelin map **329** I5 – pop. 514 – alt. 200
▶ Paris 508 – Brive-la-Gaillarde 33 – Juillac 33 – Périgueux 44

🏕 La Garenne

𝒫 0553505773, www.lagarennedordogne.com

Address : at Le Combal (800m north of the village, near the stadium)

Opening times : Permanent

4 ha/1,5 (70 pitches)

Tariff : 20,60€ ♟♟ 🚐 🔲 🔌 (16A) – Extra per person 4,80€ Reservation fee 12€

Rental rates : Permanent – 9 🚐 – 10 🏠 – 2 canvas bungalows. Per night from 32 to 98€ – Per week from 224 to 680€ Reservation fee 12€

🚐 3 ▣ 20,60€ – 🚐 ⟨𝄐⟩15,60€

Surroundings : 🐟 🎱
Leisure activities : 🎮 ⇄ hammam, jacuzzi 🚣 🏊 ⛵
Facilities : 🚿 ⚓ 🏠 🍽 🏖 🎡 🍴 📷 🎣
Nearby : 🍴 🎿

Longitude : 1.1837
Latitude : 45.16175

PEYRILLAC-ET-MILLAC

24370 – Michelin map **329** J6 – pop. 213 – alt. 88
▶ Paris 521 – Brive-la-Gaillarde 45 – Gourdon 23 – Sarlat-la-Canéda 22

⚠ Au P'tit Bonheur

☎ 0553297793, www.camping-auptitbonheur.com

Address : at Combe de Lafon (2.5km north along the follow the signs for Le Bouscandier)

Opening times : from beginning April to end Sept.

2,8 ha (113 pitches)

Tariff : 21,70€ ✚ ✚ 🚗 ▣ ⟨𝄐⟩ (10A) – Extra per person 5€ – Reservation fee 16€

Rental rates : (from beginning April to end Sept.) – 25 🚐 9 🏠 – 3 canvas bungalows – 1 gîte. Per night from 26 to 105€ Per week from 179 to 720€ – Reservation fee 16€

🚐 borne

Surroundings : 🐟 ⇄ 🎱
Leisure activities : 🍴 🍴 🎮 ⇄ jacuzzi 🚣 ⛵ 🏊 🎱 🏊
Facilities : 🚿 ⚓ 🏖 🎡 🍴 📷 🎣

Longitude : 1.40356
Latitude : 44.93214

PISSOS

40410 – Michelin map **335** G9 – pop. 1 315 – alt. 46
▶ Paris 657 – Arcachon 72 – Biscarrosse 34 – Bordeaux 75

⚠ Municipal de l'Arriu

☎ 0558089038, www.pissos.fr – 🏪

Address : 525 chemin de l'Arriu (1.2km east along the D 43, follow the signs for Sore and take the road to the right, after the swimming pool)

Opening times : from beginning July to mid Sept.

3 ha (74 pitches)

Tariff : (2013 price) ✚ 3,20€ 🚗 ▣ 4,50€ – ⟨𝄐⟩ (12A) 2,10€

Rental rates : (from beginning July to mid Sept.) – 3 canvas bungalows. Per week from 261€

Surroundings : 🐟 🎱
Facilities : 🚿 ⚓ 🏖 🎡 🍴
Nearby : 📷 🎮 🚲 🍴 🐎

Longitude : -0.77047
Latitude : 44.3027

PLAZAC

24580 – Michelin map **329** H5 – pop. 725 – alt. 110
▶ Paris 527 – Bergerac 65 – Brive-la-Gaillarde 53 – Périgueux 40

⚠ Le Lac 🚹🚺

☎ 0553507586, www.campinglelac-dordogne.com

Address : at the lake (800m southeast along the D 45, follow the signs for Thonac)

Opening times : from mid May to end Sept.

7 ha/2,5 for camping (130 pitches)

Tariff : (2013 price) ✚ 5,70€ 🚗 ▣ 5,70€ – ⟨𝄐⟩ (10A) 3,60€ Reservation fee 12€

Rental rates : (from beginning May to end Sept.) 🚿 (1 mobile home) – 45 🚐 – 4 🏠. Per night from 34 to 80€ – Per week from 235 to 720€ – Reservation fee 12€

🚐 5 ▣ 20,70€

Beside the lake, in the shade of walnut and Holm oak trees.

Surroundings : 🐟 ⇄ 🎱 ⛰
Leisure activities : 🍴 🍴 🎮 🚣 🏊 ⛵ 🎣 🏊
🎣 multi-sports ground
Facilities : 🚿 ⚓ 🏖 🎡 🍴 launderette 🎣

Longitude : 1.14794
Latitude : 45.03125

Some campsites benefit from proximity to a municipal leisure centre.

PONT-DU-CASSE

47480 – Michelin map **336** G4 – pop. 4 305 – alt. 67
▶ Paris 658 – Bordeaux 147 – Toulouse 122 – Montauban 96

⚠ Village Vacances de Loisirs Darel

(rental of chalets only)

☎ 0553679641, accueil@ville-pontducasse.fr

Address : at Darel (7km northeast along the D 656, follow the signs for Cahors and take a right turn towards St-Ferréol)

Opening times : Permanent

34 ha/2 for camping undulating

Rental rates : 🅿 – 15 🏠. Per night from 70€ – Per week from 202 to 386€ – Reservation fee 15€

In a pleasant location surrounded by trees, near a large horse riding centre.

Surroundings : 🐟 🎱
Leisure activities : 🎮 🚣 🐎
Facilities : 🏖 📷

Longitude : 0.68536
Latitude : 44.21698

LE PORGE

33680 – Michelin map **335** E5 – pop. 2 428 – alt. 8
▶ Paris 624 – Andernos-les-Bains 18 – Bordeaux 47 – Lacanau-Océan 21

⚠ Municipal la Grigne 🚹🚺

☎ 0556265488, www.camping-leporge.fr

Address : 35 avenue de l'Océan (9.5km west along the D 107, 1km from Le Porge-Océan)

Opening times : from beginning April to end Sept.

30 ha (700 pitches)

Tariff : 30,10€ ✚ ✚ 🚗 ▣ ⟨𝄐⟩ (10A) Extra per person 6€ – Reservation fee 18€

Rental rates : Permanent 🚿 (from beginning April to end Sept) 24 🚐 – 10 canvas bungalows. Per night from 82 to 147€ Per week from 305 to 895€ – Reservation fee 18€

🚐 borne 3€

Surroundings : 🎱
Leisure activities : 🍴 🍴 🎮 🎯 🚣 🚲 🍴 🎣
Facilities : 🚿 ⚓ 🏖 🎡 launderette 📷 🎣
Nearby : forest trail

Longitude : -1.20314
Latitude : 44.89363

GERMAIN

PYLA-SUR-MER

33115 – Michelin map **335** D7
▶ Paris 648 – Arcachon 8 – Biscarrosse 34 – Bordeaux 66

△△△ Yelloh! Village Panorama du Pyla ♣♪

🖉 05 56 22 10 44, www.camping-panorama.com

Address : route de Biscarrosse (7km south along the D 218)

Opening times : from mid April to end Sept.

15 ha/10 for camping (450 pitches)

Tariff : 45€ ✯✯ ⇔ 🗉 ⚡ (10A) – Extra per person 8€

Rental rates : (from mid April to end Sept.) – 80 🖭 – 10 🏠 12 tent lodges. Per night from 34 to 169€ – Per week from 238 to 1 183€

🖳 borne

Access to the beach via a pedestrian path and steep steps.

Surroundings : 🐾 ⟨ ☐ ♉♉
Leisure activities : 🍷 ✗ 🎦 🖰 ✝ 🛶 🛷 ✂
🔥 🛝 hang-gliding, skate park
Facilities : ♿ ⊶ 🛢 🍴 launderette 🍖 🚿
refrigerated food storage facilities

GPS Longitude : -1.22502
Latitude : 44.57738

△△△ FranceLoc Domaine Le Petit Nice ♣♪

🖉 05 56 22 74 03, www.petitnice.com

Address : route de Biscarrosse (at the foot of the Dune du Pyla)

Opening times : from beginning April to end Sept.

5 ha (209 pitches) extremely uneven

Tariff : 39€ ✯✯ ⇔ 🗉 ⚡ (8A) – Extra per person 7€ – Reservation fee 30€

Rental rates : (from beginning April to end Sept.) – 4 caravans 93 🖭 – 10 tent lodges. Per night from 44 to 170€ – Per week from 175 to 1 246€ – Reservation fee 30€

🖳 borne

Surroundings : 🐾 ⟨ Banc d'Arguin National Park ♉♉
Leisure activities : 🍷 ✗ 🎦 🖰 ✝ 🛶 🛝 🛷
multi-sports ground
Facilities : ♿ ⊶ 🏛 🛢 🍴 launderette 🍖 🚿
refrigerated food storage facilities
Nearby : paragliding

GPS Longitude : -1.22043
Latitude : 44.57274

Interaview Production

△△△ Village Center La Forêt ♣♪

🖉 05 56 22 73 28, www.village-center.fr

Address : 3 km at the south on the D 218, route Biscarrosse (at the foot of the Dune du Pyla)

Opening times : from beginning April to end Sept.

8 ha (460 pitches)

Tariff : (2013 price) 37€ ✯✯ ⇔ 🗉 ⚡ (10A) – Extra per person 8€

Rental rates : (2013 price) (from beginning April to end Sept.)
♿ (2 mobile homes) – 95 🖭 – 12 🏠. Per night from 25 to 80€
Per week from 500 to 1 050€ – Reservation fee 10€

🖳 60 🗉 25€

Surroundings : ♉♉
Leisure activities : 🍷 ✗ 🎦 🖰 ✝ 🛷 🚲 ✂
🔥 🛝 multi-sports ground
Facilities : ♿ ⊶ ♋ 🛢 🍴 launderette 🍖 🚿

GPS Longitude : -1.20857
Latitude : 44.58542

RAUZAN

33420 – Michelin map **335** K6 – pop. 1 148 – alt. 69
▶ Paris 596 – Bergerac 57 – Bordeaux 39 – Langon 35

△ Le Vieux Château

🖉 05 57 84 15 38, www.camping-levieuxchateau.com

Address : take the northern exit follow the signs for St-Jean-de-Blaignac and take road to the left (1.2km)

2,5 ha (74 pitches)

Rentals : 8 🖭 – 4 🏠 – 2 canvas bungalows.

At the foot of a ruined 12th-century fortress, with a pedestrian path to the village.

Surroundings : 🐾 ♉♉
Leisure activities : 🍷 ✗ 🎦 🖰 🛶
Facilities : ♿ ⊶ 🍴 🖪

GPS Longitude : -0.12715
Latitude : 44.78213

RIVIÈRE-SAAS-ET-GOURBY

40180 – Michelin map **335** E12 – pop. 1 168 – alt. 50
▶ Paris 742 – Bordeaux 156 – Mont-de-Marsan 68 – Bayonne 44

△ Lou Bascou

🖉 05 58 97 57 29, www.campingloubascou.fr – limited spaces for one-night stay

Address : 250 route de Houssat (to the northeast of the town)

Opening times :

1 ha (41 pitches) flat, grassy

Tariff : 24,50€ ✯✯ ⇔ 🗉 ⚡ (10A) – Extra per person 9€

Rental rates : Permanent – 8 🏠. Per night from 39 to 99€
Per week from 273 to 693€

🖳 borne 13€ – 12 🗉 13€

Surroundings : 🐾 ☐ ♉♉
Leisure activities : 🎦 entertainment room
Facilities : ♿ ⊶ 🍴 launderette
Nearby : 🛷 ✗

GPS Longitude : -1.14971
Latitude : 43.68203

LA ROCHE-CHALAIS

24490 – Michelin map **329** B5 – pop. 2 857 – alt. 60
▶ Paris 510 – Bergerac 62 – Blaye 67 – Bordeaux 68

△ Municipal de Gerbes

🖉 05 53 91 40 65, www.larochechalais.com

Address : at Les Gerbes (located 1km west; beside the river)

Opening times : from mid April to end Sept.

3 ha (100 pitches) small adjacent wood

Tariff : (2013 price) 11,68€ ✯✯ ⇔ 🗉 ⚡ (10A) – Extra per person 2,50€

Rental rates : (from mid April to end Sept.) – 4 🖭 – 1 gîte.
Per night from 25 to 55€ – Per week from 91 to 321€ – Reservation fee 15€

🖳 borne – 5 🗉 9€ – 🚐 9€

Surroundings : 🐾 ☐ ♉♉
Leisure activities : 🎦 🛷 🚣
Facilities : ♿ ⊶ 🚿 🍴 🖪

GPS Longitude : -0.00207
Latitude : 45.14888

LA ROQUE-GAGEAC

24250 – Michelin map **329** I7 – pop. 416 – alt. 85
▶ Paris 535 – Brive-la-Gaillarde 71 – Cahors 53 – Fumel 52

⚠ Le Beau Rivage ♣♣

📞 05 53 28 32 05, www.beaurivagedordogne.com

Address : at Le Gaillardou (4km east on the D 46; beside the Dordogne river)

8 ha (199 pitches)
Rentals : 44 ⬛ .

Surroundings : 🌊🏞⛰
Leisure activities : 🍴✗ 🏛 ⚜nighttime 🏃
🏊🎿🚣🛶
Facilities : 🚿🔌🚰 🗑 🧺launderette
🏊🚿
Nearby : 🚴

Longitude : 1.21422
Latitude : 44.81587

ROUFFIGNAC

24580 – Michelin map **329** G5 – pop. 1 552 – alt. 300
▶ Paris 531 – Bergerac 58 – Brive-la-Gaillarde 57 – Périgueux 32

⚠ La Ferme Offrerie

📞 05 53 35 33 26, www.camping-ferme-offrerie.com

Address : at Le Grand Boisset (situated 2km south along the D 32, follow the signs for Les Grottes de Rouffignac and take a right turn)

Opening times : from beginning April to end Sept.

3,5 ha (48 pitches)

Tariff : (2013 price) 23,20€ ✶✶ 🚗 🅿 [⚡] (10A) – Extra per person 5,60€

Rental rates : (from beginning April to end Sept.) – 19 ⬛
10 canvas bungalows. Per night from 25 to 55€ – Per week from 145 to 735€

🚐 borne 3€ – 1 🅿 11,50€ – 🚿11,50€

Surroundings : 🌊🏞⛰
Leisure activities : ✗ 🏛 🎿🚣🛶
Facilities : 🔌 🚿🚰 🗑 🚿

Longitude : 0.97109
Latitude : 45.02775

⚠ La Nouvelle Croze

📞 05 53 05 38 90, www.lanouvellecroze.com

Address : 2.5km southeast along the D 31, follow the signs for Fleurac and take the road to the right

Opening times : from beginning April to end Oct.

1,3 ha (40 pitches) flat, grassy

Tariff : 22€ ✶✶ 🚗 🅿 [⚡] (16A) – Extra per person 5,50€
Rental rates : (from beginning April to end Oct.) – 14 ⬛.
Per night from 38 to 61€ – Per week from 215 to 795€

Surroundings : 🌊🏞⛰
Leisure activities : 🍴✗ 🏛 🎿🛶
Facilities : 🚿🔌 🚿🚰 🗑

Longitude : 0.99783
Latitude : 45.02412

⚠ Bleu Soleil

📞 05 53 05 48 30, www.camping-bleusoleil.com

Address : at Domaine Touvent (located 1.5km north along the D 31, follow the signs for Thenon and take turning to the right)

Opening times : from beginning April to end Sept.

41 ha/7 for camping (110 pitches)

Tariff : ✶ 6€ 🚗 🅿 10€ – [⚡] (10A) 3,70€ – Reservation fee 10€

Rental rates : (from beginning April to end Sept.) – 21 🏠
2 canvas bungalows. Per night from 31 to 105€ – Per week from 378 to 735€ – Reservation fee 10€

Surroundings : 🌊≤🏞
Leisure activities : 🍴✗ 🏛 🎿🚣🛶
multi-sports ground
Facilities : 🚿🔌 🚿🗑 🅿 🚿 refrigerated
food storage facilities

Longitude : 0.98586
Latitude : 45.05507

SABRES

40630 – Michelin map **335** G10 – pop. 1 200 – alt. 78
▶ Paris 676 – Arcachon 92 – Bayonne 111 – Bordeaux 94

⚠ Le Domaine de Peyricat

📞 05 58 07 51 88, www.vtf-vacances.com

Address : take the southern exit along the D 327, follow the signs for Luglon

Opening times : from mid June to mid Sept.

20 ha/2 for camping (69 pitches)

Tariff : (2013 price) 21,80€ ✶✶ 🚗 🅿 [⚡] (10A)
Extra per person 2,60€

Rental rates : (2013 price) (from mid April to end Sept.) 🏊 – 4 ⬛
8 🏠. Per night from 33 to 59€ – Per week from 231 to 689€

🚐 borne 5€

Lots of activities at the adjacent Holiday Village.

Surroundings : 🗑
Facilities : 🚿🔌 🚿
At Village Vacances : launderette 🍴✗ 🏛
🏃🎣🚿🛶

Longitude : -0.74235
Latitude : 44.144

Some information or pricing may have changed since the guide went to press. We recommend you check the price list online in advance or at the entrance to the campsite and enquire about possible restrictions.

ST-AMAND-DE-COLY

24290 – Michelin map **329** I5 – pop. 382 – alt. 180
▶ Paris 515 – Bordeaux 188 – Périgueux 58 – Cahors 104

⚠ Yelloh! Village Lascaux Vacances ♣♣

📞 05 53 50 81 57, www.campinglascauxvacances.com

Address : at Les Malénies (located 1km south along the D 64, follow the signs for St-Geniès)

Opening times : from end May to mid Sept.

12 ha (150 pitches)

Tariff : 36€ ✶✶ 🚗 🅿 [⚡] (10A) – Extra per person 7€
Rental rates : (from end May to mid Sept.) – 80 ⬛ – 10 🏠
2 canvas bungalows – 2 tent lodges. Per night from 44 to 134€ Per week from 308 to 938€

🚐 borne – 10 🅿 19€ – 🚿 [⚡]15€

Surroundings : 🌊🗑🏔
Leisure activities : 🍴✗ 🏃🎿🚴🎣 🏛🛶
🏊 multi-sports ground
Facilities : 🚿🔌 🚿🚿🗑 🚿launderette 🚿

Longitude : 1.24191
Latitude : 45.05461

ST-ANTOINE-D'AUBEROCHE

24330 – Michelin map **329** G5 – pop. 145 – alt. 152

▶ Paris 491 – Brive-la-Gaillarde 96 – Limoges 105 – Périgueux 24

▲ La Pélonie

☎ 05 53 07 55 78, www.lapelonie.com

Address : at La Pélonie (1.8km southwest towards Milhac-Gare – from Fossemagne, continue 6 km along the RN 89 and take the road to the right)

Opening times : from mid April to end Sept.

5 ha (60 pitches) Tariff : ✦ 5,60€ ⇐ 🅴 6,90€ – 🔌 (10A) 3,80€
Reservation fee 10€

Rental rates : (from mid April to end Sept.) – 24 🛖. Per week from 510 to 715€ – Reservation fee 10€

🚐 5 🅴 18€

Surroundings : ⛲ 🏕 ♨♨
Leisure activities : 🍽 ✗ 🏛 🚣 🏊 ⛵
Facilities : 🕭 ⚡ 🖭 🕳 🚿 launderette 🧺

GPS Longitude : 0.92845
Latitude : 45.13135

ST-ANTOINE-DE-BREUILH

24230 – Michelin map **329** B6 – pop. 2 073 – alt. 18

▶ Paris 555 – Bergerac 30 – Duras 28 – Libourne 34

▲ La Rivière Fleurie

☎ 05 53 24 82 80, www.la-riviere-fleurie.com

Address : at St-Aulaye-de-Breuilh, 180 rue Théophile-Cart (3km southwest, 100m from the Dordogne river)

Opening times : from mid April to mid Sept.

2,5 ha (60 pitches) flat, grassy

Tariff : 24,90€ ✦✦ ⇐ 🅴 🔌 (10A) – Extra per person 5,80€
Reservation fee 18€

Rental rates : (from mid April to mid Sept.) – 21 🛖 – 2 studios 2 apartments. Per night from 50 to 58€ – Per week from 250 to 610€ – Reservation fee 20€

Surroundings : ⛲ 🏕 ♨♨
Leisure activities : 🍽 ✗ 🏛 🚣 ⛵
Facilities : 🕭 ⚡ 🖭 🕳 🚿 launderette 🧺
Nearby : 🍴

GPS Longitude : 0.12235
Latitude : 44.82879

ST-AULAYE

24410 – Michelin map **329** B4 – pop. 1 360 – alt. 61

▶ Paris 504 – Bergerac 56 – Blaye 79 – Bordeaux 81

▲ Municipal de la Plage

☎ 05 53 90 62 20, www.saint-aulaye.com

Address : Les Ponts (take the northern exit along the D 38, follow the signs for Aubeterre; beside the Dronne river)

Opening times : from mid June to mid Sept.

1 ha (70 pitches) flat, grassy

Tariff : 12€ ✦✦ ⇐ 🅴 🔌 (10A) – Extra per person 2€

Rental rates : (from beginning June to mid Sept.) – 11 🛖 14 🏠. Per week from 125 to 405€ – Reservation fee 30€

🚐 borne 3€

Surroundings : 🏕 ♨♨
Leisure activities : 🏛 🚣 🚲 🍴 ⛳ 🎿 🛶 ♨♨
Facilities : 🕭 ⚡ 🗜 🕳 🚿 launderette 🧺
Nearby : ✗ 🧺 🏖 (beach)

GPS Longitude : 0.13274
Latitude : 45.20786

ST-AVIT-DE-VIALARD

24260 – Michelin map **329** G6 – pop. 145 – alt. 210

▶ Paris 520 – Bergerac 39 – Le Bugue 7 – Les Eyzies-de-Tayac 17

▲▲▲ Les Castels St-Avit Loisirs ♣♠

☎ 05 53 02 64 00, www.saint-avit-loisirs.com – limited spaces for one-night stay

Address : at Malefon (1.8km to the northwest)

Opening times : from beginning April to mid Sept.

55 ha/15 for camping (400 pitches) natural setting among trees and bushes

Tariff : 46,20€ ✦✦ ⇐ 🅴 🔌 (6A)
Extra per person 11,60€ – Reservation fee 19€

Rental rates : (from beginning April to mid Sept.) – 15 🛖 – 45 🏠 30 🛏 – 15 apartments – 1 gîte. Per night from 92 to 117€ – Per week from 357 to 1 280€ – Reservation fee 25€

🚐 15 🅴 46,20€

A spacious, hilly site with trees and an attractive swimming area.

Surroundings : 🏕 🏖 ♨♨
Leisure activities : 🍽 ✗ 🏛 🎣 🏃 🏸 jacuzzi 🚣 🚲 🎯 🎿 🛶 quad biking, multi-sports ground, entertainment room
Facilities : 🕭 ⚡ 🕳 🖭 🚿 🚻 launderette 🧺 🧺

GPS Longitude : 0.84971
Latitude : 44.95174

*We value your opinion and welcome your feedback.
Do email us at campingfrance@tp.michelin.com*

ST-CRÉPIN-ET-CARLUCET

24590 – Michelin map **329** I6 – pop. 493 – alt. 262

▶ Paris 514 – Brive-la-Gaillarde 40 – Les Eyzies-de-Tayac 29 – Montignac 21

▲▲▲ Les Peneyrals ♣♠

☎ 05 53 28 85 71, www.peneyrals.com
🏊 (from mid May to mid Sept)

Address : at St Crépin (located 1km south along the D 56, follow the signs for Proissans)

Opening times : from mid May to mid Sept.

12 ha/8 for camping (250 pitches)

Tariff : ✦ 9,40€ ⇐ 🅴 13,70€
🔌 (10A) 4,20€ – Reservation fee 20€

Rental rates : (from mid May to mid Sept.) 🕭 (1 chalet) – 40 🛖 28 🏠. Per night from 41 to 75€ – Per week from 380 to 1 100€
Reservation fee 30€

🚐 borne

A hilly setting with pitches among trees or beside a lake.

Surroundings : 🏕 🏖 ♨♨
Leisure activities : 🍽 ✗ 🏛 🎣 🏃 🏸 🎯 🚲 🍴 🎿 🛶 🏊 🎣
Facilities : 🕭 ⚡ 🖭 🕳 🚿 launderette 🧺 🧺

GPS Longitude : 1.27267
Latitude : 44.95785

⚠ Village Vacances Les Gîtes de Combas

(rental of gîtes only)

📞 05 53 28 64 00, www.perigordgites.com

Address : at Les Combas (situated 2km south along the D 56, follow the signs for Proissans)

4 ha

Rentals : ♿ (1 gîte) 🅿 – 22 gîtes.

Some gîtes are in old farm buildings made of local stone.

Surroundings : 🐾 ⚘ Leisure activities : 🍷 🏠 🚣 🍴 🎯 🛝 Facilities : ⚡ 📶 🍴 🖼 🚿	**GPS** Longitude : 1.27718 Latitude : 44.94871

ST-CYBRANET

24250 – Michelin map **329** I7 – pop. 376 – alt. 78
▶ Paris 542 – Cahors 51 – Les Eyzies-de-Tayac 29 – Gourdon 21

⚠ Bel Ombrage

📞 05 53 28 34 14, www.belombrage.com

Address : on the D 50 (800m to the northwest; beside the Céou river)

Opening times : from beginning June to beginning Sept.

6 ha (180 pitches) flat, grassy

Tariff : 🚶 5,70€ 🚗 📧 7,30€ – 💡 (10A) 4€

Surroundings : 🐾 ⚘⚘ 🛝 Leisure activities : 🏠 🚣 🛝 Facilities : ♿ ⚡ 🍴 launderette Nearby : 🍴	**GPS** Longitude : 1.16244 Latitude : 44.79082

To visit a town or region, use the MICHELIN Green Guides.

ST-ÉMILION

33330 – Michelin map **335** K5 – pop. 2 005 – alt. 30
▶ Paris 584 – Bergerac 58 – Bordeaux 40 – Langon 49

⚠ Yelloh! Saint-Émilion ♟⚐

📞 05 57 24 75 80, www.camping-saint-emilion.com

Address : at Les Combes (3km north along the D 122, follow the signs for Lussac and take turning to the right – caravans and camper vans are not permitted to pass through St-Émilion)

Opening times : from end April to mid Oct.

4,5 ha (160 pitches) flat, grassy

Tariff : 39€ 🚶🚶 🚗 📧 💡 (10A) Extra per person 7€

Rental rates : (from end April to mid Oct.) – 47 🚐. Per night from 39 to 188€ – Per week from 273 to 1316€

🚐 borne 5€ – 19 📧 39€ – 💧💡11€

A free shuttle bus to St-Émilion.

Surroundings : 🐾 🚐 ⚘⚘ Leisure activities : 🍴 🏠 🏃 🚣 🚲 🎯 🛝 🛝 🏊 pedalos 🏇 Facilities : ♿ ⚡ 🍴 launderette 🚿 🛒	**GPS** Longitude : -0.14241 Latitude : 44.91675

ST-ÉTIENNE-DE-BAIGORRY

64430 – Michelin map **342** D3 – pop. 1 618 – alt. 163
▶ Paris 820 – Bordeaux 241 – Pau 160 – Pamplona 69

⚠ Municipal l'Irouleguy

📞 05 59 37 43 96, comstetiennebaigorry@wanadoo.fr

Address : Borciriette quartier (take the northeastern exit along the D 15, follow the signs for St-Jean-Pied-de-Port and take road to the left in front of the swimming pool and behind the Irouléguy wine co-operative; beside the Nive river)

Opening times : from mid March to mid Nov.

1,5 ha (67 pitches) flat, grassy

Tariff : 12,70€ 🚶🚶 🚗 📧 💡 (5A) – Extra per person 3,35€

In a green setting, part stretching along the river.

Surroundings : ⚘⚘ Leisure activities : 🚣 🏇 Facilities : ♿ ⚡ 🚿 🍴 🖼 Nearby : 🍷 🍴 🎯 🛝	**GPS** Longitude : -1.33551 Latitude : 43.18386

ST-GENIÈS

24590 – Michelin map **329** I6 – pop. 941 – alt. 232
▶ Paris 515 – Brive-la-Gaillarde 41 – Les Eyzies-de-Tayac 29 – Montignac 13

⚠ Club Airotel La Bouquerie ♟⚐

📞 05 53 28 98 22, www.labouquerie.com – limited spaces for one-night stay

Address : located 1.5km northwest along the D 704, follow the signs for Montignac and take the road to the right

Opening times : from mid April to mid Sept.

8 ha/4 for camping (183 pitches)

Tariff : 🚶 8,30€ 🚗 📧 12,80€ – 💡 (10A) 3,90€ – Reservation fee 20€

Rental rates : (from mid April to mid Sept.) ♿ (1 mobile homes) 90 🚐 – 50 🏠 . Per week from 590 to 1130€ – Reservation fee 30€

🚐 borne – 5 📧

Pretty, shady pitches by an oak grove.

Surroundings : 🐾 🚐 ⚘⚘ Leisure activities : 🍷 🍴 🏠 🎣 🏃 🛝 🏇 🎯 🛝 🏊 🏊 ⚓ paintballing, multi-sports ground Facilities : ♿ ⚡ 📶 🚿 🍴 launderette 🚿 🛒 Nearby : 🏇	**GPS** Longitude : 1.24594 Latitude : 44.99892

ST-GIRONS-PLAGE

40560 – Michelin map **335** C11
▶ Paris 728 – Bordeaux 142 – Mont-de-Marsan 79 – Bayonne 73

⚠ Eurosol ♟⚐

📞 05 58 47 90 14, www.camping-eurosol.com

Address : route de la Plage (350m from the beach)

Opening times : from mid May to mid Sept.

33 ha/18 for camping (510 pitches)

Tariff : 38€ 🚶🚶 🚗 📧 💡 (10A) – Extra per person 6€ – Reservation fee 25€

Rental rates : (from mid May to mid Sept.) 🚫 🅿 – 145 🚐 15 🏠 – 2 tent lodges. Per night from 46 to 170€ – Per week from 322 to 1190€ – Reservation fee 25€

🚐 borne 20€ – 10 📧 20€

Surroundings : 🐾 ⚘⚘ Leisure activities : 🍷 🍴 🏠 🎣 🏃 🚣 🚲 🎯 🛝 🛝 multi-sports ground Facilities : ♿ ⚡ 🚿 🏊 🚿 launderette 🛝 🛒 Nearby : 🏇	**GPS** Longitude : -1.35162 Latitude : 43.95158

🛆🛆 Campéole les Tourterelles ♣♣

🕿 05 58 47 93 12, www.camping-tourterelles.com

Address : route de la plage (5.2km west along the D 42, 300m from the ocean (direct access)

Opening times : from beginning May to end Sept.

18 ha (822 pitches)

Tariff : (2013 price) 34€ ♣♣ 🚐 🔲 🔌 (10A) – Extra per person 10,20€ Reservation fee 25€

Rental rates : (2013 price) (from beginning May to end Sept.) ♿ (2 mobile homes) – 134 🏚 – 20 🏕 – 115 canvas bungalows. Per night from 26 to 154€ – Per week from 364 to 1078€ Reservation fee 25€

🚰 borne 2€ – 49 🔲 14,10€
Welcomes groups of surfers.

Surroundings : 🌳🌳
Leisure activities : 🎮🏃 🏊 🚴🏊 multi-sports ground
Facilities : ♿ ⚲ 🛁🚿🚻 launderette 🧺 refrigerated food storage facilities

G P S Longitude : -1.35691
Latitude : 43.95439

ST-JEAN-DE-LUZ

64500 – Michelin map **342** C2 – pop. 13 742 – alt. 3
▶ Paris 785 – Bayonne 24 – Biarritz 18 – Pau 129

🛆🛆🛆 Club Airotel Itsas Mendi

🕿 05 59 26 56 50, www.itsas-mendi.com

Address : Acotz quartier, chemin Duhartia (5km to the northeast, 500m from the beach)

Opening times : from end March to end Sept.

8,5 ha (475 pitches)

Tariff : (2013 price) 20,50€ ♣♣ 🚐 🔲 🔌 (10A) Extra per person 4,10€

Rental rates : (from end March to end Sept.) ♿ – 130 🏚. Per night from 28 to 88€ – Per week from 196 to 616€ Reservation fee 15€

🚰 borne
In a green setting laid out on terraces, with half the pitches for mobile homes.

Surroundings : 🌳🌳
Leisure activities : 🍽🍴 🏛 🎮🏃 ⚓ jacuzzi 🏊 🎾 🎯🏊🏄 surfing school, multi-sports ground
Facilities : ♿ ⚲ 🔲🚻 🚿 launderette 🧺 refrigerated food storage facilities

G P S Longitude : -1.61726
Latitude : 43.41347

🛆🛆 Atlantica ♣♣

🕿 05 59 47 72 44, www.campingatlantica.com

Address : Acotz quartier, chemin Miquélénia (5km to the northeast, 500m from the beach)

Opening times : from beginning April to end Sept.

3,5 ha (200 pitches)

Tariff : (2013 price) 38€ ♣♣ 🚐 🔲 🔌 (6A) – Extra per person 7,80€ Reservation fee 25€

Rental rates : (2013 price) (from beginning April to end Sept.) ♿ – 100 🏚 – 12 tent lodges. Per night from 35 to 160€ Per week from 215 to 1120€ – Reservation fee 25€

🚰 borne
In a terraced green setting, many and varied good-quality rentals.

Surroundings : 🏕 🌳🌳
Leisure activities : 🍽🍴 🏛 🏃 ⚓ jacuzzi 🏊🏄 🏊 multi-sports ground
Facilities : ♿ ⚲ 🛁🚿🚻🍴 🚿🧺 refrigerated food storage facilities

G P S Longitude : -1.61688
Latitude : 43.41525

🛆🛆 La Ferme Erromardie

🕿 05 59 26 34 26, www.camping-erromardie.com

Address : 40 chemin Erromardie (1.8km to the northeast, near the beach)

Opening times : from mid March to end Sept.

2 ha (176 pitches) flat, grassy

Tariff : 32,50€ ♣♣ 🚐 🔲 🔌 (16A) – Extra per person 6€ – Reservation fee 19€

Rental rates : (from mid March to end Sept.) – 42 🏚. Per night from 39 to 128€ – Per week from 230 to 896€ – Reservation fee 19€

🚰 borne 8€
Divided into three separate sections, beside the beach.

Surroundings : 🏊 🏕 🌳🌳
Leisure activities : 🍽🍴 🏛 ⚓
Facilities : ♿ ⚲ 🛁🍴 launderette 🧺

G P S Longitude : -1.64202
Latitude : 43.40564

🛆🛆 Inter-Plages

🕿 05 59 26 56 94, www.campinginterplages.com

Address : Acotz quartier, 305 route des Plages (5km to the northeast, 150m from the beach (direct access)

Opening times : from beginning April to end Sept.

2,5 ha (91 pitches)

Tariff : 39€ ♣♣ 🚐 🔲 🔌 (10A) – Extra per person 8€ – Reservation fee 20€

Rental rates : (from beginning April to end Sept.) ♿ – 4 caravans 17 🏚 – 5 🏕. Per night from 40 to 65€ – Per week from 250 to 750€ – Reservation fee 20€

🚰 borne 4,50€
In an attractive location looking out over the sea.

Surroundings : 🏊 ⛰ 🏕 🌳🌳
Leisure activities : 🏛 ⚓ 🚴🏊
Facilities : ♿ ⚲ 🚿🔲 🛁🚿🚻 launderette
Nearby : 🧺 🍽🍴 🧺 🏊 surfing

G P S Longitude : -1.62667
Latitude : 43.41527

🛆 Merko-Lacarra

🕿 05 59 26 56 76, www.merkolacarra.com

Address : Acotz quartier, 820 route des Plages (5km to the northeast, 150m from the beach d'Acotz)

Opening times : from end March to beginning Oct.

2 ha (123 pitches)

Tariff : 34€ ♣♣ 🚐 🔲 🔌 (16A) – Extra per person 7€ – Reservation fee 16€

Rental rates : (from end March to beginning Oct.) ♿ 27 🏚. Per night from 49 to 67€ – Per week from 287 to 784€ Reservation fee 20€

🚰 borne 6€
A warm welcome, top-quality sanitary facilities and very close to the beach at Mayarco.

Leisure activities : 🍴 ⚓
Facilities : ♿ ⚲ 🔲 🛁🍴 launderette 🧺
Nearby : 🧺 🍽 🏊 surfing

G P S Longitude : -1.62366
Latitude : 43.41855

⛺ Les Tamaris-Plage ♠♣

📞 05 59 26 55 90, www.tamaris-plage.com

Address : Acotz quartier, 720 route de Plages (5km to the northeast, 80m from the beach)

Opening times : from mid April to beginning Nov.

1,5 ha (79 pitches)

Tariff : 33 € ♦♦ ⊞ ▣ ⚡ (7A) – Extra per person 10 € – Reservation fee 30 €

Rental rates : (from mid April to beginning Nov.) – 41 🚐. 4 studios – 10 canvas bungalows. Per night from 43 to 69 € Per week from 301 to 966 € – Reservation fee 30 €

Pleasant lawns with some trees and very close to Mayarco beach.

Surroundings : ☐ ♀
Leisure activities : 🏊 🚵 ≋ hammam, jacuzzi ♨
Facilities : ♿ ⚬ ⛁ ♨ ⚐ 🍴 launderette
Nearby : 🏊 ♀ ✗ ⚓ ⚓ surfing

GPS Longitude : -1.62387
Latitude : 43.41804

⛺ Le Bord de mer

📞 05 59 26 24 61, www.camping-le-bord-de-mer.fr

Address : 71 chemin d'Erromardie (1.8km northeast)

Opening times : from mid April to end Oct.

2 ha (78 pitches) terraced, relatively flat, flat, grassy

Tariff : 34 € ♦♦ ⊞ ▣ ⚡ (10A) – Extra per person 9 €

A small coastal footpath leads to the cliffs and the beach.

Surroundings : ≤ the ocean and La Rhune mountain ☐
Leisure activities : ✗
Facilities : ⚬ 🚰 ♨ 🍴 launderette
Nearby : 🏊 ♀ ⚓

GPS Longitude : -1.64155
Latitude : 43.40678

This guide is updated regularly, so buy your new copy every year!

ST-JEAN-PIED-DE-PORT

64220 – Michelin map **342** E4 – pop. 1 477 – alt. 159
▶ Paris 817 – Bayonne 54 – Biarritz 55 – Dax 105

⛺ Narbaïtz Vacances

📞 05 59 37 10 13, www.camping-narbaitz.com

Address : at Ascarat (2.5km northwest along the D 918, follow the signs for Bayonne and take the turning to the left; 50m from the Nive river and beside a stream)

Opening times : from mid April to mid Sept.

2,5 ha (101 pitches)

Tariff : 36,50 € ♦♦ ⊞ ▣ ⚡ (10A) – Extra per person 6 € – Reservation fee 18 €

Rental rates : Permanent ✂ – 12 🚐 – 3 🏠 – 3 gîtes. Per week from 290 to 1 200 € – Reservation fee 18 €
🚐 borne

An unrestricted view over the Irouléguy vineyards. Choose pitches furthest away from the road.

Surroundings : ≤ ♀
Leisure activities : 🏊 🚵 ⛴
Facilities : ♿ ⚬ ⛁ ♨ launderette ⚓
Nearby : ⚓

GPS Longitude : -1.25911
Latitude : 43.17835

⛺ Europ'Camping

📞 05 59 37 12 78, www.europ-camping.com

Address : at Ascarat (situated 2km northwest along the D 918, follow the signs for Bayonne and take road to the left)

Opening times : from beginning April to end Sept.

2 ha (110 pitches)

Tariff : 34,50 € ♦♦ ⊞ ▣ ⚡ (10A) – Extra per person 6 € – Reservation fee 22 €

Rental rates : (from beginning April to end Sept.) – 44 🚐. Per night from 60 to 80 € – Per week from 260 to 720 € Reservation fee 22 €

An attractive view over the Irouléguy vineyards from well-kept pitches.

Surroundings : ⛱ ≤ ♀
Leisure activities : ♀ ✗ 🏊 ≋ ⛴
Facilities : ♿ ⚬ ♨ ⚐ 🍴 launderette ⚓
Nearby : ⚓

GPS Longitude : -1.25398
Latitude : 43.17279

The pitches of many campsites are marked out with low hedges of attractive bushes and shrubs.

ST-JULIEN-DE-LAMPON

24370 – Michelin map **329** J6 – pop. 613 – alt. 120
▶ Paris 528 – Brive-la-Gaillarde 51 – Gourdon 17 – Sarlat-la-Canéda 17

⛺ Le Mondou

📞 05 53 29 70 37, www.camping-dordogne.info

Address : at Le Colombier (located 1km east along the D 50, follow the signs for Mareuil and take the road to the right)

Opening times : from beginning April to mid Oct.

1,2 ha (60 pitches)

Tariff : 12 € ♦♦ ⊞ ▣ ⚡ (6A) – Extra per person 4,40 €

Rental rates : (from beginning April to mid Oct.) ✂ – 4 🚐 1 🏠 – 8 canvas bungalows. Per night 72 € – Per week 750 €

Surroundings : ⛱ ☐ ♀
Leisure activities : 🏊 ♨ ⛴
Facilities : ♿ ⚬ 🚰 ♨ 🍴 📶 ⚓
Nearby : launderette

GPS Longitude : 1.36691
Latitude : 44.86295

ST-JULIEN-EN-BORN

40170 – Michelin map **335** D10 – pop. 1 450 – alt. 22
▶ Paris 706 – Castets 23 – Dax 43 – Mimizan 18

⛺ Municipal la Lette Fleurie

📞 05 58 42 74 09, www.camping-municipal-plage.com

Address : at La Lette, route de l'Océan (4km northwest along the D 41, follow the signs for Contis-Plage)

Opening times : from beginning April to end Sept.

8,5 ha (457 pitches)

Tariff : ♦ 5,60 € ⊞ ▣ 6,40 € – ⚡ (10A) 5,50 € – Reservation fee 15 €

Surroundings : ⛱ ♀
Leisure activities : ♀ ✗ 🏊 ♨ ⚽ ⛴
Facilities : ♿ ⚬ ♨ 🍴 launderette 🏊 ⚓
refrigerated food storage facilities

GPS Longitude : -1.26173
Latitude : 44.08139

ST-JUSTIN

40240 – Michelin map **335** J11 – pop. 922 – alt. 90
▶ Paris 694 – Barbotan-les-Thermes 19 – Captieux 41 – Labrit 31

⛰ Le Pin

𝒸 0558448891, www.campinglepin.com

Address : route de Roquefort (2.3km north on the D 626; beside a little lake)

Opening times : from beginning April to end Oct.

3 ha (80 pitches)

Tariff : 22€ ♟ ♟ ⇔ 🔳 🔌 (10A) – Extra per person 4,50€ – Reservation fee 15€

Rental rates : (from beginning April to end Oct.) – 6 🚐 – 11 🏠 8 canvas bungalows. Per night from 45 to 90€ – Per week from 180 to 695€ – Reservation fee 15€

Surroundings : 🞉🞉
Leisure activities : ♟ ✗ ⛵ 🛶 ⚲ 🐎
Facilities : ♿ ⚲ 🕳 🎪 launderette ⚲

G P S Longitude : -0.23468
Latitude : 44.00188

ST-LAURENT-MEDOC

33112 – Michelin map **335** G4 – pop. 4 054 – alt. 6
▶ Paris 603 – Bordeaux 45 – Mérignac 41 – Pessac 48

⛰ Le Paradis

𝒸 0556594215, www.leparadis-medoc.com

Address : at Fourthon (2.5km north along the D 1215, follow the signs for Lesparre)

3 ha (70 pitches) flat, grassy

Rentals : 29 🚐 – 4 🏠 – 3 canvas bungalows.

Surroundings : 🞉🞉
Leisure activities : ♟ ⛵ 🛶 🏊 🏓
Facilities : ♿ ⚲ 🎪 🔳 ⚲

G P S Longitude : -0.83995
Latitude : 45.17495

ST-LÉON-SUR-VÉZÈRE

24290 – Michelin map **329** H5 – pop. 428 – alt. 70
▶ Paris 523 – Brive-la-Gaillarde 48 – Les Eyzies-de-Tayac 16 – Montignac 10

⛰ Le Paradis ♟♟

𝒸 0553507264, www.le-paradis.fr

Address : at La Rebeyrolle (4km southwest along the D 706, follow the signs for Les Eyzies-de-Tayac; beside the Vézère)

Opening times : from beginning April to end Oct.

7 ha (200 pitches) flat, grassy

Tariff : (2013 price) 33,50€ ♟ ♟ ⇔ 🔳 🔌 (10A)
Extra per person 8,10€ – Reservation fee 20€

Rental rates : (from beginning April to end Oct.) – 41 🚐 – 3 tent lodges. Per night from 45 to 160€ – Per week from 315 to 1120€ Reservation fee 20€

🚐 borne 2€
Upmarket facilities based around an old renovated farmhouse.

Surroundings : ⚲ 🞉🞉
Leisure activities : ♟ ✗ 🎬 🎯 🏋 ⛵ 🚲 🏓 🛶 ☀ multi-sports ground
Facilities : ♿ ⚲ 📇🕳 🎪 🚿 🎪 launderette 🚿 ⚲

G P S Longitude : 1.0712
Latitude : 45.00161

ST-MARTIAL-DE-NABIRAT

24250 – Michelin map **329** I7 – pop. 666 – alt. 175
▶ Paris 546 – Cahors 42 – Fumel 45 – Gourdon 11

⛰ Calmésympa

𝒸 0553284315, www.http:camping-calmesympa.jimdo.com

Address : at Lagrèze (2.2km northwest along the D 46, follow the signs for Domme and take road to the left)

2,7 ha (50 pitches)

Rentals : 8 🚐 – 7 gîtes.
In the shade of a 500-year-old chestnut tree!

Surroundings : ⚲ 🞉🞉
Leisure activities : 🏊
Facilities : ♿ ⚲ 🎪 🔳

G P S Longitude : 1.23951
Latitude : 44.75444

ST-MARTIN-DE-SEIGNANX

40390 – Michelin map **335** C13 – pop. 4 724 – alt. 57
▶ Paris 766 – Bayonne 11 – Capbreton 15 – Dax 42

⛰ Sites et Paysages Lou P'tit Poun ♟♟

𝒸 0559565579, www.louptitpoun.com

Address : 110 avenue du district Neuf (4.7km southwest along the N 117, follow the signs for Bayonne and take road to the left)

Opening times : from mid June to mid Sept.

6,5 ha (168 pitches)

Tariff : (2013 price) 35,10€ ♟ ♟ ⇔ 🔳 🔌 (10A)
Extra per person 8,10€ – Reservation fee 30€

Rental rates : (from mid June to mid Sept.) 🏠 – 10 🚐 16 🏠. Per night from 63 to 124€ – Per week from 441 to 868€ Reservation fee 30€

🚐 borne 7€ – 🔋 🔌16€

Surroundings : ⚲ 🞉🞉
Leisure activities : 🎬 🎯 ⛵ 🏊
Facilities : ♿ ⚲ 🕳 🚿 🎪 🔳 ⚲

G P S Longitude : -1.41195
Latitude : 43.52437

ST-PAUL-LES-DAX

40990 – Michelin map **335** E12 – pop. 12 343 – alt. 21
▶ Paris 731 – Bordeaux 152 – Mont-de-Marsan 53 – Pau 89

⛰ Les Pins du Soleil ♟♟

𝒸 0558913791, www.pinsoleil.com

Address : route des Minières (5.8km northwest along the N 124, follow the signs for Bayonne and take the turning to the left along the D 459)

Opening times : from beginning April to end Sept.

6 ha (145 pitches)

Tariff : 25€ ♟ ♟ ⇔ 🔳 🔌 (10A) – Extra per person 6€ – Reservation fee 10€

Rental rates : (from beginning April to end Oct.) ♿ (1 chalet) 45 🚐 – 10 🏠 – 4 canvas bungalows. Per night from 40 to 103€ Per week from 278 to 719€ – Reservation fee 17€

🚐 borne

Surroundings : ⚲ 🞉🞉🞉
Leisure activities : ♟ ✗ 🎬 🎯 jacuzzi ⛵ 🏊
Facilities : ♿ ⚲ 📇🕳 🚿 🎪 🚿 🎪 launderette ⚲

G P S Longitude : -1.09373
Latitude : 43.72029

⛰ L'Étang d'Ardy

☎ 0558975774, www.camping-ardy.com

Address : allée d'Ardy (5.5km northwest along the N 124, follow the signs for Bayonne then take road to the left before the access road, continuing for 1.7km; beside a lake)

Opening times : from beginning April to mid Oct.

5 ha/3 for camping (102 pitches)

Tariff : 26,40€ ✶✶ ⊕ 📧 (10A) – Extra per person 6€

Rental rates : (from beginning April to mid Oct.) – 24 📦 – 7 🏠. Per night from 56 to 100€ – Per week from 245 to 630€

All the pitches for tents and caravans are equipped with individual sanitary facilities ranging from simple and basic to rather old.

Surroundings : 🦢 ⊏ ♨ Leisure activities : ⊿ 🖎 Facilities : ௰ ⊶ – 53 individual sanitary facilities (🖫 🕭 ⇧ wc) 🕭 ⇥ ⊤ launderette	**GPS** Longitude : -1.12256 Latitude : 43.72643

⚠ Abesses

☎ 0558916534, www.thermes-dax.com

Address : allée du Château (7.5km northwest following signs for Bayonne, D 16 to the right and take the Chemin d'Abesse)

4 ha (198 pitches) small lake

Rentals : 16 📦.

📦 borne
Minimum stay 20 nights.

Surroundings : 🦢 ⊏ ♨ Leisure activities : 📺 🖎 Facilities : ௰ ⊶ 🖫 🕭 ⊤ launderette	**GPS** Longitude : -1.09715 Latitude : 43.74216

For more information on visiting particular towns or regions, consult the relevant regional MICHELIN Green Guide. We also recommend you use the appropriate Michelin regional map to locate your selected campsite, to calculate distances and to work out the best route.

ST-PÉE-SUR-NIVELLE

64310 – Michelin map **342** C2 – pop. 5 550 – alt. 30
▶ Paris 785 – Bayonne 22 – Biarritz 17 – Cambo-les-Bains 17

⛰ L'Ibarron

☎ 0559541043, www.camping-ibarron.com

Address : Ibarron quartier (2km, take the western exit, on the D 918, follow the signs for St-Jean-de-Luz, near the Nivelle river)

Opening times : from beginning May to end Sept.

2,9 ha (142 pitches) flat, grassy

Tariff : (2013 price) 25,10€ ✶✶ ⊕ 📧 (6A) – Extra per person 5€ Reservation fee 10€

Rental rates : (from beginning May to end Sept.) 🏖 – 23 📦. Per night from 50 to 93€ – Per week from 230 to 650€

📦 borne 5€
Choose the pitches furthest away from the road.

Surroundings : ⊏ ♨ Leisure activities : 📺 🖙 ⊿ Facilities : ௰ ⊶ ⊤ launderette Nearby : 🍴 ✗ 🚲 ☁	**GPS** Longitude : -1.5749 Latitude : 43.3576

⛰ Goyetchea 🚻

☎ 0559541959, www.camping-goyetchea.com

Address : Ibarron quartier (1.8km north along the D 855, follow the signs for Ahetze and take a right turn)

Opening times : from beginning June to mid Sept.

3 ha (147 pitches) flat and relatively flat, grassy

Tariff : 28,50€ ✶✶ ⊕ 📧 (6A) – Extra per person 6€ – Reservation fee 13€

Rental rates : (from end April to mid Sept.) 🏖 – 2 caravans 33 📦. Per night from 53 to 63€ – Per week from 245 to 810€ Reservation fee 13€

A view of the pretty Basque houses and La Rhune (mountain).

Surroundings : 🦢 ⪻♨ Leisure activities : ✗ 📺 🖙 🖎 Facilities : ௰ ⊶ 🖫 ⊤ launderette ⇥ refrigerators	**GPS** Longitude : -1.56683 Latitude : 43.36275

ST-RÉMY

24700 – Michelin map **329** C6 – pop. 432 – alt. 80
▶ Paris 542 – Bergerac 33 – Libourne 46 – Montpon-Ménestérol 10

⛰ Les Cottages en Périgord (rental of chalets only)

☎ 0553805946, www.cottagesenperigord.com

Address : at Les Pommiers (continue north following signs for Montpon-Ménestérol along the D 708)

Opening times : from mid Jan. to mid Dec.

7 ha/1 campable flat, small lake, adjacent wood

Rental rates : ௰ (1 chalet) – 3 caravans – 8 🏠. Per night from 65 to 100€ – Per week from 250 to 650€ – Reservation fee 10€

Surroundings : 🦢 ♨ Leisure activities : 🖙 🖎 jacuzzi ⊿ 🖎 Facilities : ⊶ 🖫 ⊤ 🕭	**GPS** Longitude : 0.16333 Latitude : 44.96024

ST-SAUD-LACOUSSIÈRE

24470 – Michelin map **329** F2 – pop. 864 – alt. 370
▶ Paris 443 – Brive-la-Gaillarde 105 – Châlus 23 – Limoges 57

⛰ Kawan Village Château Le Verdoyer 🚻

☎ 0553569464, www.verdoyer.fr

Address : 2.5km northwest along the D 79, follow the signs for Nontron and take D 96, follow the signs for Abjat-sur-Bandiat; near lakes

Opening times : from mid April to end Sept.

15 ha/5 for camping (170 pitches) lakes

Tariff : 37€ ✶✶ ⊕ 📧 (10A) – Extra per person 7€ – Reservation fee 20€

Rental rates : (from mid April to end Sept.) – 25 📦 – 20 🏠 5 🛏. Per night from 34 to 100€ – Per week from 240 to 595€ Reservation fee 20€

📦 borne
Some pitches for tents and caravans wiith individual sanitary facilities and 5 converted rooms in the château.

Surroundings : 🦢 ⊏ ♨ Leisure activities : 🍴 ✗ 📺 🖙 🖎 🚲 ✂ ⊿ 🖎 🖙 🦢 Facilities : ௰ ⊶ 📧 🕭 – 4 individual sanitary facilities (🖫 ⇧ wc) 🕭 ⇥ ⊤ launderette 🕭 ⇥ refrigerated food storage facilities Nearby : 🏖 (beach)	**GPS** Longitude : 0.79595 Latitude : 45.55133

ST-VINCENT-DE-COSSE

24220 – Michelin map **329** H6 – pop. 374 – alt. 80
▶ Paris 540 – Bergerac 61 – Brive-la-Gaillarde 65 – Fumel 58

⛰ Le Tiradou

🖉 05 53 30 30 73, www.camping-le-tiradou.com

Address : at Larrit (500m southwest of the village; beside a stream)

Opening times : from beginning May to end Sept.

2 ha (60 pitches) flat, grassy

Tariff : 🛉 4,50 € 🚗 📧 6,20 € – ⛽ (6A) 3,40 € – Reservation fee 10 €
Rental rates : (from beginning May to end Sept.) 🚱 – 15 🚐
5 🏠. Per night from 72 to 102 € – Per week from 315 to 560 €
Reservation fee 15 €

Surroundings : ⌂ 🎣
Leisure activities : ✗ 🏊 jacuzzi ⛵ 🏊
Facilities : & ⛷ 🔥 🍴 launderette 🧺

G P S Longitude : 1.11268
Latitude : 44.83747

STE-EULALIE-EN-BORN

40200 – Michelin map **335** D9 – pop. 1 116 – alt. 26
▶ Paris 673 – Arcachon 58 – Biscarrosse 98 – Mimizan 11

⛰ Les Bruyères

🖉 05 58 09 73 36, www.camping-les-bruyeres.com

Address : 719 route de Laffont (2.5km north along the D 652)

Opening times : from end May to beginning Sept.

3 ha (177 pitches)

Tariff : 28,90 € 🛉🛉 🚗 📧 ⛽ (10A) – Extra per person 7,90 €
Reservation fee 16 €
Rental rates : (from beginning May to end Sept.) – 23 🚐
1 🏠. Per night from 38 to 115 € – Per week from 266 to 800 €
Reservation fee 16 €

Local home-made produce is available to taste and buy.

Surroundings : 🏊 ⌂ 🎣
Leisure activities : 🍴 ✗ 🏊 🍴 🏊
Facilities : & ⛷ 🔥 🍴 launderette 🧺 🧺

G P S Longitude : -1.17949
Latitude : 44.29387

STE-FOY-LA-GRANDE

33220 – Michelin map **335** M5 – pop. 2 544 – alt. 10
▶ Paris 555 – Bordeaux 71 – Langon 59 – Marmande 53

⛰ La Bastide

🖉 05 57 46 13 84, www.camping-bastide.com 🚱

Address : at Pineuilh, allée du Camping (take northeastern exit along the D 130; beside the Dordogne river)

1,2 ha (38 pitches) flat, grassy

Rentals : 🚱 – 10 🚐.

Surroundings : 🏊 🎣
Leisure activities : 🏊 ⛵ 🏊
Facilities : & ⛷ 🍴 launderette
Nearby : 🎣

G P S Longitude : 0.22462
Latitude : 44.84403

Routes nationales are main roads and their identifying numbers begin with N or RN. Routes départementales are generally quieter roads and begin with D or DN.

SALIES-DE-BÉARN

64270 – Michelin map **342** G4 – pop. 4 886 – alt. 50 – ⚓
▶ Paris 762 – Bayonne 60 – Dax 36 – Orthez 17

⛰ Mosqueros

🖉 05 59 38 12 94, campingsaliesdebearn@hotmail.fr

Address : avenue Al Cartero (take the western exit along the D 17, follow the signs for Bayonne, at the outdoor activity centre)

Opening times : from beginning March to mid Nov.

0,7 ha (60 pitches)

Tariff : 16 € 🛉🛉 🚗 📧 ⛽ (10A) – Extra per person 2,50 € – Reservation fee 10 €
Rental rates : (from beginning March to mid Nov.) – 2 🚐.
Per week from 199 to 580 € – Reservation fee 10 €

A pleasant site next to the municipal sports centre. Rather poor and antiquated facillities.

Surroundings : 🏊 🎣
Leisure activities : 🏊 multi-sports ground
Facilities : & ⛷ 🔥 🍴 launderette
Nearby : ✗ 🏊

G P S Longitude : -0.93814
Latitude : 43.47643

SALIGNAC-EYVIGUES

24590 – Michelin map **329** I6 – pop. 1 141 – alt. 297
▶ Paris 509 – Brive-la-Gaillarde 34 – Cahors 84 – Périgueux 70

⛰ Flower Le Temps de Vivre

🖉 05 53 28 93 21, www.temps-de-vivre.com

Address : located 1.5km south along the D 61 and take the road to the right

Opening times : from mid April to end Sept.

4,5 ha (50 pitches) adjacent wood

Tariff : 27,90 € 🛉🛉 🚗 📧 ⛽ (10A) – Extra per person 5,50 €
Reservation fee 5 €
Rental rates : (from beginning April to end Sept.) – 18 🚐
4 canvas bungalows. Per night from 32 to 96 € – Per week from 160 to 672 € – Reservation fee 20 €
🚐 5 📧 11,50 € – 🚱 ⛽ 11,50 €

Surroundings : 🏊 ⌂ 🎣
Leisure activities : 🍴 🏊 ⛵ 🏊
Facilities : & ⛷ 🔥 🍴 launderette 🧺

G P S Longitude : 1.32817
Latitude : 44.96355

SALLES

33770 – Michelin map **335** F7 – pop. 6 044 – alt. 23
▶ Paris 632 – Arcachon 36 – Belin-Béliet 11 – Biscarrosse 122

⛰ Le Park du Val de l'Eyre 🏕

🖉 05 56 88 47 03, www.valdeleyre.com

Address : 8 route du Minoy (take the southwestern exit along the D 108e, follow the signs for Lugos; beside the Eyre river and a lake – from the A 63, take exit 21)

Opening times : from beginning March to end Nov.

13 ha/4 for camping (150 pitches)

Tariff : 35 € 🛉🛉 🚗 📧 ⛽ (10A)
Extra per person 8 € – Reservation fee 20 €

Rental rates : (from beginning March to end Nov.) – 40 ⌐⊓⌐ – 8 ⌂
4 ⊨. Per night from 48 to 88€ – Per week from 253 to 545€
Reservation fee 20€
⊕ borne – 4 ▣ 7€

Surroundings : ⊗ ♉♉
Leisure activities : ♈ ✕ ⟐ ⊀⊁ ⊱⊰ ⟐
⟐ ⊛
Facilities : ♿ ⚲ ▥ ⊖ ⊿ ♒ launderette ⊱ | **G P S** | Longitude : -0.87399
Latitude : 44.54606 |

SALLES

47150 – Michelin map **336** H2 – pop. 314 – alt. 120
▶ Paris 588 – Agen 59 – Fumel 12 – Monflanquin 11

⚑ Des Bastides

✆ 05 53 40 83 09, www.campingdesbastides.com

Address : at Terre Rouge (located 1km to the northeast, follow the signs for Fumel, at junction of D 150 and D 162)

Opening times : from beginning April to end Sept.

6 ha (96 pitches)

Tariff : 33,90€ ✶ ✶ ⇆ ▣ ⧲ (6A) – Extra per person 4,70€
Reservation fee 18€
Rental rates : (from beginning April to end Sept.) ⊀ (July–
Aug.) – 7 ⌐⊓⌐ – 3 ⌂ – 1 yurt – 2 canvas bungalows – 4 tent lodges. Per night from 42 to 108€ – Per week from 294 to 756€
Reservation fee 18€

Surroundings : ⊡ ♉♉
Leisure activities : ♈ ✕ jacuzzi ⊀⊁ ⊗ ⊿ ⊰
multi-sports ground
Facilities : ♿ ⚲ ▥ ⊖ – 2 individual sanitary
facilities (⊿ ⊖ ⊔ wc) ♒ launderette ⊱ | **G P S** | Longitude : 0.88161
Latitude : 44.55263 |

There are several different types of sani-station ('borne' in French) – sanitation points providing fresh water and disposal points for grey water. See page 12 for further details.

SANGUINET

40460 – Michelin map **335** E8 – pop. 3 133 – alt. 24
▶ Paris 643 – Arcachon 27 – Belin-Béliet 26 – Biscarrosse 120

⚑ Lou Broustaricq ♠♣

✆ 05 58 82 74 82, www.lou-broustaricq.com – limited spaces for one-night stay ⊀

Address : 2315 route Langeot (2.8km northwest following signs for Bordeaux, 300m from the Étang de Cazaux (lake)

Opening times : from beginning April to end Sept.

18,8 ha (570 pitches)

Tariff : (2013 price) 42€ ✶ ✶ ⇆ ▣ ⧲ (10A) – Extra per person 7€
Rental rates : (2013 price) (from end March to beginning Nov.)
⊀ – 156 ⌐⊓⌐. Per night from 36 to 154€ – Per week from 252 to 1 078€

Surroundings : ⊗ ⊡ ♉♉
Leisure activities : ♈ ✕ ⟐ ⊛ ⊀⊁ jacuzzi
⊀⊁ ⊗ ⊚ ⟐ ⊿ ⟿ entertainment room
Facilities : ♿ ⚲ ▥ ⊖ ♒ launderette ⊿ ⊱
Nearby : ⊷ ◊ | **G P S** | Longitude : -1.0789
Latitude : 44.50006 |

SARE

64310 – Michelin map **342** C3 – pop. 2 434 – alt. 70
▶ Paris 794 – Biarritz 26 – Cambo-les-Bains 19 – Pau 138

⚑ La Petite Rhune

✆ 05 59 54 23 97, www.lapetiterhune.com – limited spaces for one-night stay

Address : Lehenbiscaye quartier (situated 2km south along the road connecting D 406 and D 306)

Opening times : from mid June to mid Sept.

1,5 ha (39 pitches) terraced, relatively flat, flat, grassy

Tariff : (2013 price) 25,80€ ✶ ✶ ⇆ ▣ ⧲ (10A)
Extra per person 5,50€ – Reservation fee 10€

Rental rates : (2013 price) Permanent ⊀ – 5 gîtes. Per week from 230 to 670 € – Reservation fee 10€

A small village painted in the Basque colours!

Surroundings : ⊗ ≤ ♉♉
Leisure activities : ⟐ ⊀⊁ ⊿ (small
swimming pool), multi-sports ground
Facilities : ♿ ⚲ ⊖ ♒ launderette
Nearby : ♈ ✕ | **G P S** | Longitude : -1.58771
Latitude : 43.30198 |

SARLAT-LA-CANÉDA

24200 – Michelin map **329** I6 – pop. 9 541 – alt. 145
▶ Paris 526 – Bergerac 74 – Brive-la-Gaillarde 52 – Cahors 60

⚑ La Palombière ♠♣

✆ 05 53 59 42 34, www.lapalombiere.fr – limited spaces for one-night stay

Address : at Sainte Nathalène, at Galmier (9km northeast on the D 43 and take the turning to the left)

Opening times : from end April to mid Sept.

8,5 ha/4 for camping (177 pitches)

Tariff : ✶ 8,90€ ⇆ ▣ 12,90€ – ⧲ (10A) 28,90€ – Reservation fee 25€
Rental rates : (from end April to mid Sept.) – 51 ⌐⊓⌐ – 10 ⌂
Per night from 45 to 160€ – Per week from 315 to 1120€
Reservation fee 25€

Surroundings : ⊗ ⊡ ♉♉♉
Leisure activities : ♈ ✕ ⊛ ⊀⊁ ⌡⊙ hammam
⊀⊁ ⊚ ⊗ ⟐ ⊿ ⊰
Facilities : ♿ ⚲ ⊖ ⟿ ♒ launderette
⊿ ⊱ | **G P S** | Longitude : 1.29157
Latitude : 44.90639 |

⚑ Les Castels Le Moulin du Roch ♠♣

✆ 05 53 59 20 27, www.moulin-du-roch.com ⊀

Address : at St-André d'Allas, on the D 47 (10km to the northwest, follow the signs for Les Eyzies; beside a stream)

Opening times : from mid May to mid Sept.

8 ha (200 pitches) small lake

Tariff : 38€ ✶ ✶ ⇆ ▣ ⧲ (6A) – Extra per person 10€ – Reservation fee 12€

Rental rates : (from mid May to mid Sept.) ⊀ – 55 ⌐⊓⌐
6 ⌂. Per night from 36 to 68€ – Per week from 420 to 1060€
Reservation fee 12€

Based around an old Périgord windmill.

Surroundings : ⊡ ♉♉
Leisure activities : ♈ ✕ ⟐ ⊛ ⊀⊁ ⊀⊁ ⊗
⊿ ⊰
Facilities : ♿ ⚲ ⊡⊡ ▥ ⊖ ⟿ ♒ launderette
⊿ ⊱ | **G P S** | Longitude : 1.11481
Latitude : 44.90843 |

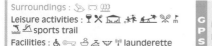 La Châtaigneraie ♠♠

☎ 05 53 59 03 61, www.camping-lachataigneraie24.com

Address : at Prats de Carlux, at La Garrigue Basse (10km east along the D 47 at take turning ot the right)

Opening times : from end May to mid Sept.

9 ha (140 pitches)

Tariff : 35,50 € ♦♦ ⟷ 🔲 🛀 (10A) Extra per person 8,90 €

Reservation fee 20 €

Rental rates : (from end May to mid Sept.) 🚫 (from end May to end June) – 60 🚐 – 11 🏠. Per night from 44 to 115 € Per week from 230 to 1310 € – Reservation fee 20 €

A pretty water and play park surrounded by low walls made of local stone.

Surroundings : 🐾 ⛺ 〰️ Leisure activities : 🍽 ✕ 🎯 🏃 🎿 🏇 🏊 ♒ sports trail Facilities : 🚿 ⚡ 🛁 ♨ 🚰 🚽 launderette 🛏 🚗	**GPS** Longitude : 1.29871 Latitude : 44.90056

🏕 Les Grottes de Roffy ♠♠

☎ 05 53 59 15 61, www.roffy.fr

Address : at Ste-Nathalène, at Roffy (8km east, along the D 47)

5 ha (165 pitches)
Rentals : 28 🚐 .

Surroundings : 🐾 ⛰ ⛺ 〰️ Leisure activities : 🍽 ✕ 🎯 🏃 🎿 🏊 ♒ Facilities : 🚿 ⚡ 🛁 ♨ 🚰 🚽 launderette 🛏 🚗	**GPS** Longitude : 1.28211 Latitude : 44.90417

🏕 Domaine de Loisirs le Montant ♠♠

☎ 05 53 59 18 50, www.camping-sarlat.com

Address : at Négrelat (situated 2km southwest along the D 57, follow the signs for Bergerac then continue 2.3km along the road to the right)

70 ha/8 for camping (135 pitches)
Rentals : 16 🚐 – 14 🏠 – 2 gîtes.

A range of luxury rental options in a naturally wooded and hilly setting.

Surroundings : 🐾 ⛰ ⛺ 〰️ Leisure activities : 🍽 ✕ 🎯 nighttime 🏃 jacuzzi 🎿 🚲 ♒ 🏊 multi-sports ground Facilities : 🚿 ⚡ 🍴 🛁 ♨ 🚰 🚽 launderette 🚗	**GPS** Longitude : 1.18903 Latitude : 44.86573

🏕 Domaine Des Chênes Verts ♠♠

☎ 05 53 59 21 07, www.chenes-verts.com – limited spaces for one-night stay

Address : route de Sarlat et Souillac (8.5km southeast)

8 ha (143 pitches)
Rentals : 72 🚐 – 31 🏠.

Surroundings : 🐾 ⛺ 〰️ Leisure activities : 🍽 ✕ 🎯 🏃 🎿 🚲 🏊 ♒ Facilities : 🚿 ⚡ ♨ 🚽 launderette 🛏 🚗	**GPS** Longitude : 1.2972 Latitude : 44.86321

🏕 La Ferme de Villeneuve ♠♠

☎ 05 53 30 30 90, www.fermedevilleneuve.com

Address : at St-André-d'Allas, at Villeneuve (8km northwest along the D 47, follow the signs for Les Eyzies-de-Tayac and take turning to the left)

Opening times : from beginning April to end Oct.

20 ha/2,5 for camping (100 pitches) natural setting among trees and bushes, lake

Tariff : ♦ 6,70 € ⟷ 🔲 7,30 € – 🛀 (10A) 4,10 € – Reservation fee 10 €

Rental rates : (from beginning April to end Oct.) 🚫 – 2 caravans 9 🚐 – 4 tipis – 2 canvas bungalows – 3 tent lodges – 1 gîte. Per night from 39 to 50 € – Per week from 290 to 698 € Reservation fee 10 €

🚐 borne 3 € – 3 🔲 12 €

Farm campsite.

Surroundings : 🐾 ⛰ ⛺ 〰️ Leisure activities : 🍽 ✕ 🏃 🎿 🚲 🏊 Facilities : 🚿 ⚡ 🛁 🚽 launderette 🚗 Nearby : cinema/activity centre	**GPS** Longitude : 1.14051 Latitude : 44.90438

🏕 Les Terrasses du Périgord

☎ 05 53 59 02 25, www.terrasses-du-perigord.com

Address : at Proissans, at Pech d'Orance (2.8km to the northeast)

Opening times : from beginning April to end Sept.

5 ha (85 pitches)

Tariff : 24,60 € ♦♦ ⟷ 🔲 🛀 (16A) – Extra per person 5,90 € Reservation fee 8 €

Rental rates : (from beginning April to end Sept.) 🚫 (from beginning July to end Aug) – 10 🚐 – 10 🏠. Per week from 195 to 730 € – Reservation fee 10 €

🚐 5 🔲 14,90 €

Surroundings : 🐾 ⛰ ⛺ 〰️ Leisure activities : ✕ 🎯 jacuzzi 🎿 ♒ 🏊 ♒ mountain biking Facilities : 🚿 ⚡ 🍴 🛁 ♨ 🚰 🚽 launderette 🛏 🚗	**GPS** Longitude : 1.23658 Latitude : 44.90617

🏕 Indigo Sarlat - Les Périères

☎ 05 53 59 05 84, www.camping-indigo.com

Address : rue Jean Gabin (located 1km to the northeast, by the exit from town)

11 ha/4 for camping (100 pitches) terraced, flat, grassy

Rentals : 4 caravans – 4 🚐 – 22 tent lodges – 15 gîtes.

🚐 borne

Surroundings : 〰️ Leisure activities : 🍽 🎯 🏖 🎿 🏇 ♒ 🏊 ♒ sports trail Facilities : 🚿 ⚡ 🍴 ♨ 🚽 launderette	**GPS** Longitude : 1.22767 Latitude : 44.89357

▲ Les Charmes

📞 05 53 31 02 89, www.campinglescharmesdordogne.com

Address : at St-André-d'Allas, at Malartigue Haut (10km west along the D 25, follow the signs for Le Bugue and take road to the right)

Opening times : from beginning April to beginning Oct.

5,5 ha/1,8 (100 pitches)

Tariff : (2013 price) 23,40€ ♣♣ 🚐 🖃 ⚡ (6A) – Extra per person 5,90€ Reservation fee 10€·

Rental rates : (from beginning April to beginning Oct.) 6 🚃.5 🏠. 4 canvas bungalows – 3 tent lodges. Per night from 30 to 85€ Per week from 169 to 789 € – Reservation fee 10€

🚐 borne

Surroundings : 🐾 ⌁ 𝄞
Leisure activities : ♟ 🏊 🐎 🏹 ⛷
multi-sports ground
Facilities : ♿ ⊶ 🚻 ⚹ 🖫 ♻

G P S Longitude : 1.11365 Latitude : 44.89412

▲ Les Acacias

📞 05 53 31 08 50, www.acacias.fr

Address : at the bourg de la Canéda, rue Louis de Champagne (6km southeast along the D 704 and take a right turn at the Leclerc hypermarket)

Opening times : from mid April to end Sept.

4 ha (122 pitches)

Tariff : 21,50€ ♣♣ 🚐 🖃 ⚡ (10A) – Extra per person 5,40€ Reservation fee 10€

Rental rates : (from mid April to end Sept.) ⛺ – 20 🚃. Per night from 41 to 63€ – Per week from 240 to 690€ – Reservation fee 10€

🚐 borne 4€
Bus shuttle service to Sarlat.

Surroundings : ⋖ ⌁ 𝄞
Leisure activities : ♟ 🏊 🚴 🏹 multi-sports ground
Facilities : ♿ ⊶ 🚿 ⚹ 🖫 launderette ♻

G P S Longitude : 1.23699 Latitude : 44.85711

SAUBION

40230 – Michelin map **335** C12 – pop. 1 323 – alt. 17
▶ Paris 747 – Bordeaux 169 – Mont-de-Marsan 79 – Pau 106

▲ Club Airotel La Pomme de Pin

📞 05 58 77 00 71, www.camping-lapommedepin.com

Address : 825 route de Seignosse (situated 2km southeast along the D 652 and take D 337, follow the signs for Saubion)

Opening times : from beginning April to beginning Oct.

5 ha (252 pitches)

Tariff : 32€ ♣♣ 🚐 🖃 ⚡ (6A) – Extra per person 6,20€ – Reservation fee 20€

Rental rates : (from beginning April to beginning Oct.) – 48 🚃 24 canvas bungalows. Per night from 35 to 59€ – Per week from 224 to 895€ – Reservation fee 20€

🚐 borne
Indoor swimming area.

Surroundings : ⌁ 𝄞
Leisure activities : ♟ ✗ 🏊 jacuzzi 🏄
🏊 (open air in season)
Facilities : ♿ ⊶ 🄲 ⚹ 🖫 launderette ♻ ♻
refrigerated food storage facilities

G P S Longitude : -1.35563 Latitude : 43.67608

SAUVETERRE-LA-LÉMANCE

47500 – Michelin map **336** I2 – pop. 587 – alt. 100
▶ Paris 572 – Agen 68 – Fumel 14 – Monflanquin 27

▲ Flower Le Moulin du Périé

📞 05 53 40 67 26, www.camping-moulin-perie.com

Address : at Moulin du Périé (3km east following signs for Loubejac; beside a stream)

Opening times : from mid May to mid Sept.

4 ha (125 pitches) flat, grassy

Tariff : 33,40€ ♣♣ 🚐 🖃 ⚡ (10A) – Extra per person 7,80€ Reservation fee 20€

Rental rates : (from mid May to mid Sept.) ⛺ (from mid May to end June) – 13 🚃 – 4 🏠 – 10 canvas bungalows. Per night from 35 to 132€ – Per week from 175 to 924€ – Reservation fee 35€

🚐 borne – 5 🖃 10,60€

Surroundings : 🐾 ⌁ 𝄞
Leisure activities : ♟ ✗ 🏊 🏄 🚴 🏹 🌊
Facilities : ♿ ⊶ 🄲 ⚹ 🖫 launderette ♻

G P S Longitude : 1.04743 Latitude : 44.5898

The guide covers all 22 regions of France – see the map and list of regions on pages 4–5.

SEIGNOSSE OCEAN

40510 – Michelin map **335** C12
▶ Paris 763 – Bordeaux 184 – Mont-de-Marsan 89 – Pau 115

▲ Océliances ♣♣

📞 05 58 43 30 30, www.oceliances.com

Address : avenue des Tucs (along the D 79e, 500m from the beach at Les Bourdaines)

13 ha (432 pitches)

Rentals : ⛺ – 75 🚃 – 20 🏠.

🚐 borne

Surroundings : 𝄞
Leisure activities : ♟ ✗ 🏊 🛝 🏃 🏇 🏇
🚴 ⛷ surfing, multi-sports ground, entertainment room
Facilities : ♿ ⊶ ⚹ 🖫 launderette 🏪 ♻ refrigerated food storage facilities

G P S Longitude : -1.43039 Latitude : 43.69358

SIORAC-EN-PÉRIGORD

24170 – Michelin map **329** G7 – pop. 1 015 – alt. 77
▶ Paris 548 – Bergerac 45 – Cahors 68 – Périgueux 60

△ Le Port

📞 05 53 31 63 81, www.campingduport.net

Address : to the northeast of the town, access via the D 25, follow the signs for Buisson-Cussac and take the road in front of Carrefour supermarket; beside the Dordogne and the Nauze rivers

2,5 ha (83 pitches) flat, grassy

Rentals : 10 🚃 – 2 tipis.

Surroundings : ⌁ 𝄞
Leisure activities : 🏊 🏄 🌊 🏹
Facilities : ♿ ⊶ 🖫
Nearby : ♟ ✗ ✗

G P S Longitude : 0.98755 Latitude : 44.82472

SORDE-L'ABBAYE

40300 – Michelin map **335** E13 – pop. 646 – alt. 17
▶ Paris 758 – Bayonne 47 – Dax 27 – Oloron-Ste-Marie 63

⚠ Municipal la Galupe

🖉 05 58 73 18 13, mairie.sordelabbaye@wanadoo.fr

Address : 242 chemin du Camping (1.3km west along the D 29, follow the signs for Peyrehorade, D 123 to the left and take the road before the bridge; near the Gave d'Oloron (river)

Opening times : from beginning July to end Aug.

0,6 ha (28 pitches)

Tariff : (2013 price) 11,50€ ♦♦ ⇔ 🗉 (9A) – Extra per person 2,50€
🚐 10 🗉 11,50€ – 🏕️🟦11,50€

Surroundings : 🌊 🗗 ♀
Facilities : ♿ 🚿

GPS Longitude : -1.0561 / Latitude : 43.52983

Do not confuse:
⚠ *to* ⚠⚠⚠ *: MICHELIN classification with*
★ *to* ★★★★★ *: official classification*

SOULAC-SUR-MER

33780 – Michelin map **335** E1 – pop. 2 711 – alt. 7
▶ Paris 515 – Bordeaux 99 – Lesparre-Médoc 31 – Royan 12

⚠⚠⚠ Les Lacs ♣♣

🖉 05 56 09 76 63, www.camping-les-lacs.com

Address : 126 route des Lacs (continue 3km east along the D 101)

Opening times : from mid April to mid Nov.

5 ha (228 pitches)

Tariff : 36,50€ ♦♦ ⇔ 🗉 (10A) – Extra per person 6€
Rental rates : (from mid April to mid Nov.) ♿ (1 mobile home) 80 🚐 – 12 🏠. Per night from 48 to 80€ – Per week from 280 to 1 080€
🚐 2 🗉 15€ – 🏕️🟦14€

Organised coach excursions are available.

Surroundings : 🌊 🗗 ♀♀
Leisure activities : 🍴 ✕ 🖼 📷 ⚡ ⛵ 🎣 🎯 ⊡ 🏊 🏖 multi-sports ground
Facilities : ♿ 🔑 🏕 🚿 🍴 launderette 🚮 🚰
Nearby : 🏇

GPS Longitude : -1.11932 / Latitude : 45.48328

⚠⚠⚠ Yelloh! Village Soulac sur Mer ♣♣

🖉 05 56 09 77 63, www.camping-club-soulac.com

Address : at L'Amélie-sur-Mer, allée Michel de Montaigne (continue 2.8km east along the D 101e 2 and take the D 101)

Opening times : from end April to mid Sept.

4 ha (170 pitches)

Tariff : (2013 price) 42€ ♦♦ ⇔ 🗉 (6A) – Extra per person 7€
Rental rates : (2013 price) (from end April to mid Sept.) – 70 🚐 10 🏠. Per night from 41 to 195€ – Per week from 287 to 1 365€

Surroundings : 🌊 ♀♀
Leisure activities : 🍴 ✕ 🖼 ⚡ ≋ jacuzzi 🎣 ⛵ 🏊
Facilities : ♿ 🔑 🏕 🍴 launderette 🚮 🚰

GPS Longitude : -1.11886 / Latitude : 45.48563

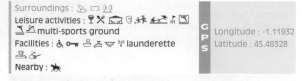

⚠ L'Océan

🖉 05 56 09 76 10, www.perso.wanadoo.fr/camping.ocean

Address : 62 allée de la Négade (take the eastern exit along the D 101e 2 and take the D 101, 300m from the beach)

Opening times : from beginning June to mid Sept.

6 ha (300 pitches)

Tariff : ♦ 5,80€ ⇔ 🗉 14€ – (10A) 4,40€ – Reservation fee 15€

In a natural wooded setting.

Surroundings : 🌊 ♫♫
Leisure activities : 🍴 🖼 🚲 ✕
Facilities : ♿ 🔑 🏕 🍴 launderette 🚮 🚰

GPS Longitude : -1.14533 / Latitude : 45.48043

This guide is updated regularly, so buy your new copy every year!

SOUSTONS

40140 – Michelin map **335** D12 – pop. 7 240 – alt. 9
▶ Paris 732 – Biarritz 53 – Castets 23 – Dax 29

⚠⚠⚠ Village Vacances Sunêlia Le Framissima Nature

(rental of mobile homes, chalets and tent lodges only)

🖉 05 58 77 70 00, www.camping-nature-soustons.fr

Address : at Nicot-les-Pins, 63 avenue Port d'Albret (follow the signs for Les Lacs)

Opening times : from mid April to end Sept.

14 ha (250 pitches)

Rental rates : ♿ (1 mobile home) 🚲 🅿 – 200 🚐 – 12 🏠 37 tent lodges. Per night from 43 to 84€ – Per week from 252 to 1 596€

Organised excursions, an eco swimming pool (filtered, no chemicals) and plenty of activities for children and teenagers.

Surroundings : 🌊 ♀♀
Leisure activities : 🍴 ✕ 🖼 📷 (open air theatre) ⚡ 🎣 ≋ hammam, jacuzzi 🎣 🚲 ✕ 🏊 multi-sports ground, spa centre, entertainment room
Facilities : 🔑 🍴 launderette 🚮 🚰

GPS Longitude : -1.35999 / Latitude : 43.75593

⚠⚠⚠ L'Airial

🖉 05 58 41 12 48, www.campinglairial.fr

Address : 67 avenue de Port d'Albret (situated 2km west along the D 652, follow the signs for Vieux-Boucau-les-Bains, 200m from the Étang de Soustons)

Opening times : from end March to beginning Oct.

13 ha (440 pitches)

Tariff : (2013 price) 33,30€ ♦♦ ⇔ 🗉 (10A)
Extra per person 6,80€ – Reservation fee 20€
Rental rates : (from end March to beginning Oct.) ♿ (2 mobile homes) 🚲 – 66 🚐 – 20 🏠. Per night from 65 to 115€ Per week from 360 to 940€ – Reservation fee 20€
🚐 80 🗉 27,30€ – 🏕️🟦14€

Surroundings : ♀
Leisure activities : 🍴 ✕ 🖼 📷 daytime ⚡ 🚲 ✕ 🎯 ⊡ 🏊 multi-sports ground
Facilities : ♿ 🔑 🏕 🍴 launderette 🚮 🚰 refrigerated food storage facilities

GPS Longitude : -1.35195 / Latitude : 43.75433

⛺ Village Vacances Le Dunéa (rental of chalets onlly)

☏ 05 58 48 00 59, www.club-dunea.com

Address : at Souston-Plage, port d'Albret sud, 1 square de l'Herté (200m from the lake)

Opening times : from beginning April to mid Oct.

0,5 ha

Rental rates : 🚫 – 20 gîtes. Per night from 90€ – Per week from 250 to 1 150€

Surroundings : 🐟 ♀
Leisure activities : 🎱 🛶
Facilities : ⌫ 🅿 🍴 🔲
Nearby : 🍽 🐎 🐴

G P S Longitude : -1.40065
Latitude : 43.7731

LE TEICH

33470 – Michelin map **335** E7 – pop. 6 485 – alt. 5
▶ Paris 633 – Arcachon 20 – Belin-Béliet 34 – Bordeaux 50

🏕 Ker Helen ♠♣

☏ 05 56 66 03 79, www.kerhelen.com

Address : 119 avenue de la Côte d'Argent (situated 2km west along the D 650, follow the signs for Gujan-Mestras)

Opening times : from beginning April to mid Oct.

4 ha (170 pitches) flat, grassy

Tariff : ♦ 5€ 🚗 🔲 13€ – ⚡ (10A) 3,70€ – Reservation fee 20€
Rental rates : (from beginning April to mid Oct.) ♿ (1 chalet) 45 🛖 – 12 🏠 – 12 canvas bungalows. Per night from 28 to 60€ Per week from 160 to 790€ – Reservation fee 20€
🚐 borne 13€

Surroundings : 🏕 ♀♀
Leisure activities : ♈ ✗ 🌙 nighttime 🤸 🏊
🚲 🛶 🏖
Facilities : ♿ ⌫ 🏖 🚿 🍴 launderette ≈

G P S Longitude : -1.04284
Latitude : 44.63975

This guide is not intended as a list of all the camping sites in France; its aim is to provide a selection of the best sites in each category.

TERRASSON-LAVILLEDIEU

24120 – Michelin map **329** I5 – pop. 6 222 – alt. 90
▶ Paris 497 – Brive-la-Gaillarde 22 – Juillac 28 – Périgueux 53

🏕 La Salvinie

☏ 05 53 50 06 11, www.camping-salvinie.com

Address : at Bouillac Sud (take the southern exit along the D 63, follow the signs for Chavagnac then continue 3.4km, following signs for Condat;on the right after the bridge)

Opening times : from beginning April to end Oct.

2,5 ha (70 pitches) flat, grassy

Tariff : 21€ ♦♦ 🚗 🔲 ⚡ (8A) – Extra per person 5,40€
Rental rates : (from beginning April to end Oct.) – 11 🛖. Per night 95€ – Per week 620€
🚐 5 🔲 13,40€ – ⚡ 14,50€

Surroundings : ≤ 🏕 ♀♀
Leisure activities : 🎱 🏊 🛶
Facilities : ♿ ⌫ 🍴 launderette

G P S Longitude : 1.26216
Latitude : 45.12069

🏔 Village Vacances le Clos du Moulin

(rental of chalets only)

☏ 05 53 51 68 95, www.leclosdumoulin.com

Address : at Le Moulin de Bouch (6km west de Terrasson-Lavilledieu along the N 89, follow the signs for St-Lazare and take the D 62 following signs for Coly; beside the river)

Opening times : Permanent

1 ha flat, grassy

Rental rates : 🅿 – 14 🏠 – 14 gîtes. Per night from 75 to 105€ Per week from 280 to 910€ – Reservation fee 16€

Surroundings : ♀
Leisure activities : ♈ 🚲 🛶
Facilities : ♿ ⌫ 🔲 🍴 🔲

G P S Longitude : 1.26337
Latitude : 45.10288

We value your opinion and welcome your feedback. Do email us at campingfrance@tp.michelin.com

LA TESTE-DE-BUCH

33260 – Michelin map **335** E7 – pop. 24 597 – alt. 5
▶ Paris 642 – Andernos-les-Bains 35 – Arcachon 5 – Belin-Béliet 44

🏔 Village Vacances FranceLoc La Pinèda ♠♣

(rental of mobile homes only)

☏ 05 56 22 23 24, www.campinglapinede.net ou franceloc.fr

Address : route de Cazaux (11km south along the D 112; beside the Les Landes canal - 2.5km from Cazaux)

Opening times : from beginning April to end Sept.

5 ha (200 pitches)

Rental rates : ♿ (1 mobile home) – 200 🛖. Per night from 37 to 166€ – Per week from 147 to 1 211€ – Reservation fee 27€

Surroundings : 🏕 🏕 ♀♀
Leisure activities : ♈ ✗ 🎱 ☕ 🤸 🏊 🚲
🛶 🛶 🏖
Facilities : ♿ ⌫ 🏖 🍴 launderette ≈
Nearby : ⚓ water skiing

G P S Longitude : -1.15055
Latitude : 44.55516

THENON

24210 – Michelin map **329** H5 – pop. 1 283 – alt. 194
▶ Paris 515 – Brive-la-Gaillarde 41 – Excideuil 36 – Les Eyzies-de-Tayac 33

🏔 Le Verdoyant

☏ 05 53 05 20 78, www.campingleverdoyant.fr

Address : route de Montignac-Lascaux (4km southeast along the D 67, near two lakes)

Opening times : from beginning April to end Sept.

9 ha/3 for camping (67 pitches)

Tariff : 20,70€ ♦♦ 🚗 🔲 ⚡ (10A) – Extra per person 5,10€
Rental rates : (from beginning April to end Sept.) – 9 🛖 – 2 🏠 2 tent lodges. Per night 111€ – Per week from 175 to 780€ Reservation fee 10€
🚐 15 🔲 16,80€

Surroundings : ≤ ♀♀
Leisure activities : ♈ ✗ 🛶 🎣
Facilities : ♿ ⌫ 🔲 🏖 🍴 launderette ≈

G P S Longitude : 1.09102
Latitude : 45.11901

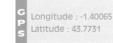

THIVIERS

24800 – Michelin map **329** G3 – pop. 3 121 – alt. 273
▶ Paris 449 – Brive-la-Gaillarde 81 – Limoges 62 – Nontron 33

🏕 Le Repaire

📞 05 53 52 69 75, www.camping-le-repaire.fr

Address : situated 2km southeast along the D 707, follow the signs for Lanouaille and take the road to the right

Opening times :

10 ha/4,5 for camping (100 pitches) adjacent wood

Tariff : 20,40 € ♟ ♦ ⇔ 🗉 🔌 (6A) – Extra per person 5 €
Rental rates : Permanent 🅿 – 9 🏠. Per night from 65 to 70 €
Per week from 350 to 500 €
🚰 borne 5 €
Attractive pitches set around a small lake.

Surroundings : ⌑ ♀
Leisure activities : 🏠 ♨ jacuzzi ⛵ 🎣
fitness trail
Facilities : 🚿 ⛽ (season) 🍴 🖥
Nearby : 🍽 ⛵ (beach)

G P S Longitude : 0.9321
Latitude : 45.41305

TOCANE-ST-APRE

24350 – Michelin map **329** D4 – pop. 1 679 – alt. 95
▶ Paris 498 – Brantôme 24 – Mussidan 33 – Périgueux 25

⚠ Municipal le Pré Sec

📞 05 53 90 40 60, www.campingdupresec.com

Address : north of the town along the D 103, follow the signs for Montagrier, near the stadium; beside the Dronne river

Opening times : from beginning May to end Sept.

1,8 ha (80 pitches)

Tariff : (2013 price) ♦ 1,95 € ⇔ 🗉 4,45 € – 🔌 (16A) 1,80 €
Rental rates : (2013 price) Permanent – 14 🏠. Per week from 245 to 380 €
🚰 borne 2 € – 🚐

Surroundings : ⤳ ⌑ ♀♀
Leisure activities : 🏠 ⛵ 🍽 ⛵ (beach)
🎣 🛹 skate park
Facilities : 🚿 ⛽ ⛺ 🍴 🖥

G P S Longitude : 0.49685
Latitude : 45.25649

TRENTELS

47140 – Michelin map **336** H3 – pop. 821 – alt. 50
▶ Paris 607 – Agen 42 – Bergerac 72 – Cahors 60

⚠ Village Vacances Municipal de Lustrac

(rental of chalets only)

📞 05 53 70 77 22, campingdelustrac.jimdo.com – traditional camp. spaces also available

Address : at Lustrac (2.5km northeast along the D 911, follow the signs for Fumel and take the road to the right, towards Lustrac; beside the Lot river)

Opening times : Permanent

0,5 ha flat, grassy
Rental rates : 🚿 – 7 🏠 – 7 gîtes. Per week from 200 to 440 €
🚰 10 🗉 3,50 €

Surroundings : ⤳ ⌑ ♀♀
Leisure activities : 🏠
Facilities : ⛽ ⛺ 🍴 launderette
Nearby : 🍽

G P S Longitude : 0.88316
Latitude : 44.4335

TURSAC

24620 – Michelin map **329** H6 – pop. 319 – alt. 75
▶ Paris 536 – Bordeaux 172 – Périgueux 48 – Brive-la-Gaillarde 57

🏕 Le Vézère Périgord

📞 05 53 06 96 31, www.levezereperigord.com

Address : 800m northeast along the D 706, follow the signs for Montignac and take the road to the right

Opening times : from mid April to end Oct.

3,5 ha (103 pitches)

Tariff : ♦ 6 € ⇔ 🗉 10,50 € – 🔌 (10A) 3,50 €
Rental rates : (from mid April to end Oct.) – 25 🚐. Per night from 40 to 95 € – Per week from 210 to 720 €
🚰 borne – 🚐 8 €

Surroundings : ⤳ ⌑ ♀♀♀
Leisure activities : 🍴 🍽 🏠 jacuzzi ⛵ 🚴
🍽 🎣 🏊
Facilities : 🚿 ⛽ ⛺ 🍴 launderette 🚿

G P S Longitude : 1.04637
Latitude : 44.97599

URDOS

64490 – Michelin map **342** I5 – pop. 69 – alt. 780
▶ Paris 850 – Jaca 38 – Oloron-Ste-Marie 41 – Pau 75

⚠ Municipal Le Gave d'Aspe

📞 05 59 34 88 26, www.campingaspe.com

Address : rue du Moulin de la Tourette (1.5km northwest along the N 134, take the road in front of the old station)

Opening times : from beginning May to end Sept.

1,5 ha (80 pitches) open site, relatively flat, flat, grassy

Tariff : 15 € ♟ ♦ ⇔ 🗉 🔌 (10A) – Extra per person 3,80 €
Rental rates : Permanent 🚿 – 2 🏠 – 1 🛏. Per night from 55 to 65 € – Per week from 290 to 400 €
🚰 borne 2 € – 🚐 10 €
Pitches with good shade beside the Aspe mountain stream.

Surroundings : ⤳ ⬗ ♀♀
Leisure activities : 🏠 ⛵ 🎣
Facilities : 🚿 ⛽ ⛺ 🍴 🖥

G P S Longitude : -0.55642
Latitude : 42.87719

URRUGNE

64122 – Michelin map **342** B4 – pop. 8 427 – alt. 34
▶ Paris 791 – Bayonne 29 – Biarritz 23 – Hendaye 8

🏕 Sunêlia Col d'Ibardin ♟♦

📞 05 59 54 31 21, www.col-ibardin.com

Address : route d'Olhette (4km south along the D 4, follow the signs for Ascain and Le Col d'Ibardin; beside a stream)

Opening times : from end March to mid Nov.

8 ha (203 pitches)

Tariff : 41 € ♟ ♦ ⇔ 🗉 🔌 (10A) – Extra per person 6,50 € – Reservation fee 30 €
Rental rates : (from end March to mid Nov.) 🚿 (1 mobile home) 🚿 – 56 🚐 – 6 tent lodges. Per night from 45 to 116 € – Per week from 284 to 812 € – Reservation fee 30 €
🚰 borne – 1 🗉 28 €

To visit a town or region, use the MICHELIN Green Guides.

In the middle of an oak forest; pitches beside a stream. Choose those furthest away from the road.

Surroundings : ⌨ 〰〰
Leisure activities : ▼ ✕ 🏛 🏃 ⛹ 🎿 ♨
multi-sports ground
Facilities : 🚿 ⚡ 🚻 🍽 launderette
🏊 🐕

GPS Longitude : -1.68461
Latitude : 43.33405

⚠ Larrouleta

☎ 05 59 47 37 84, www.larrouleta.com

Address : Socoa quartier, 210 route de Socoa (3km to the south)

Opening times : Permanent

5 ha (327 pitches) flat, grassy

Tariff : 29€ ✝✝ 🚗 📺 (10A) – Extra per person 8€
🚐 borne – 50 📺 23,50€

A very pleasant site surrounding a small lake (swimming). Choose the pitches away from the road.

Surroundings : 〰〰
Leisure activities : ▼ ✕ 🏛 ⛹ 🎿 🖼 (open air in season) ≋ (beach) 🚣 pedalos
Facilities : 🚿 ⚡ 🛁 🍽 launderette
🏊 🐕

GPS Longitude : -1.6859
Latitude : 43.37036

URT

64240 – Michelin map **342** E2 – pop. 2 183 – alt. 41
▶ Paris 757 – Bayonne 17 – Biarritz 24 – Cambo-les-Bains 28

⚠ Etche Zahar

☎ 05 59 56 27 36, www.etche-zahar.fr

Address : 175 allée de Mesplès (located 1km west along the D 257, towards Urcuit and take the turning to the left)

Opening times : from beginning March to mid Nov.

1,5 ha (47 pitches)

Tariff : ✝ 4,60€ 🚗 3,20€ 📺 12,40€
– (10A) 3,85€ – Reservation fee 13€

Rental rates : (from beginning March to mid Nov.) 🚿 (2 chalets) 9 🚐 – 9 🏠 – 5 canvas bungalows – 4 tent lodges. Per night from 27 to 71€ – Per week from 189 to 665 € – Reservation fee 13€
🚐 2 📺 17€

In a green setting with a variety of rental options.

Surroundings : ≋ ⌨ 〰〰
Leisure activities : 🖼 ⛹ 🚲 🎿
Facilities : 🚿 ⚡ 🍽 launderette

GPS Longitude : -1.2973
Latitude : 43.4919

VENDAYS-MONTALIVET

33930 – Michelin map **335** E2 – pop. 2 288 – alt. 9
▶ Paris 535 – Bordeaux 82 – Lesparre-Médoc 14 – Soulac-sur-Mer 21

⚠ La Chesnays

☎ 05 56 41 72 74, www.camping-montalivet.com

Address : 8 route de Soulac, at Mayan

Opening times : from beginning May to end Sept.

1,5 ha (59 pitches) flat, grassy

Tariff : 27,80€ ✝✝ 🚗 📺 (10A) – Extra per person 5,90€
Reservation fee 15€

Rental rates : (from end April to end Sept.) 🚿 (from end June to end Aug) – 4 🚐 – 3 🏠 – 2 canvas bungalows – 2 tent lodges. Per night from 38 to 111€ – Per week from 240 to 780€
Reservation fee 15€

Surroundings : ⌨ 〰〰
Leisure activities : 🖼 ⛹ 🚲 🎿
Facilities : 🚿 ⚡ 🛁 🍽 🖼

GPS Longitude : -1.08262
Latitude : 45.37602

⚠ Le Mérin

☎ 05 56 41 78 64, www.campinglemerin.com

Address : 7 route du Mérin (3.7km northwest along the D 102, follow the signs for Montalivet and take road to the left)

Opening times : from beginning April to end Oct.

3,5 ha (165 pitches)

Tariff : ✝ 3,80€ 🚗 📺 5,90€ – (10A) 9,30€ – Reservation fee 20€

Rental rates : (from beginning April to end Oct.) 🚿 – 9 🚐 3 🏠 – (without sanitary facilities). Per night from 45€ – Per week from 210 to 460€ – Reservation fee 20€

Surroundings : ≋ ⌨ 〰〰
Leisure activities : ⛹
Facilities : ⚡ 🚻 🍽 🖼

GPS Longitude : -1.09932
Latitude : 45.36703

VENSAC

33590 – Michelin map **335** E2 – pop. 854 – alt. 5
▶ Paris 528 – Bordeaux 82 – Lesparre-Médoc 14 – Soulac-sur-Mer 18

⚠ Les Acacias

☎ 05 56 09 58 81, www.les-acacias-du-medoc.fr

Address : 44 route de St-Vivien (located 1.5km northeast along the N 215, follow the signs for Verdon-sur-Mer and take the road to the right)

3,5 ha (175 pitches)

Rental rates : – 57 🚐 .

Surroundings : ⌨ 〰〰
Leisure activities : ✕ 🖼 🕐 nighttime ⛹ 🏖 🎿
Facilities : 🚿 ⚡ 🛁 🍽 launderette 🐕

GPS Longitude : -1.03252
Latitude : 45.40887

LE-VERDON-SUR-MER

33123 – Michelin map **335** E2 – pop. 1 334 – alt. 3
▶ Paris 514 – Bordeaux 100 – La Rochelle 80

⚠ Sunêlia La Pointe du Médoc 🛆👥

☎ 05 56 73 39 99, www.camping-lapointedumedoc.com

Address : 18 rue Ausone (follow signs for the Pointe de Grave along the D 1215 and turn right)

Opening times : from mid April to mid Sept.

6,5 ha (260 pitches)

Tariff : (2013 Price) 18€ ✝✝ 🚗 📺 (10A) – Extra per person 6€
Reservation fee 10€

Rental rates : (from mid April to mid Sept.) 🚿 (1 mobile home) – 114 🚐 – 31 🏠. Per night from 46 to 157€ – Per week from 423 to 1 099€ – Reservation fee 30€
🚐 58 📺 32€ – 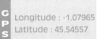 12€

Surroundings : 〰
Leisure activities : ▼ ✕ 🖼 🕐 🏃 ⛹ 🚲 🏖
🖼 🎿 multi-sports ground, entertainment room
Facilities : 🚿 ⚡ 🛁 🍽 launderette
🏊 🐕

GPS Longitude : -1.07965
Latitude : 45.54557

VÉZAC

24220 – Michelin map **329** I6 – pop. 617 – alt. 90
▶ Paris 535 – Bergerac 65 – Brive-la-Gaillarde 60 – Fumel 53

△ Les Deux Vallées

✆ 05 53 29 53 55, www.campingles2vallees.com

Address : at La Gare (to the west, behind the old station; beside a little lake)

Opening times : from mid Feb. to mid Nov.

2,5 ha (100 pitches) flat, grassy

Tariff : ♣ 7,10€ ⇌ 回 9,30€ – 図 (10A) 4,10€ – Reservation fee 15€

Rental rates : (from end March to mid Oct.) – 18 ⬛ – 10 canvas bungalows – 2 gîtes. Per night from 26 to 59€ – Per week from 159 to 889€ – Reservation fee 15€

Uninterrupted view of the Château de Beynac from some pitches.

Surroundings : ⬠ ⟨ ▭ 𝕈𝕈
Leisure activities : ⟟ ✗ 🎱 🏊 🚴 🛶
Facilities : ♿ 🏢 🚿 launderette 🍴 refrigerators

G P S Longitude : 1.15844
Latitude : 44.83542

---

*The classification (1 to 5 tents, **black** or **red**) that we award to selected sites in this guide is our own system. It should not be confused with the classification (1 to 5 stars) of official organisations.*

VIELLE-SAINT-GIRONS

40560 – Michelin map **335** D11 – pop. 1 160 – alt. 27
▶ Paris 719 – Castets 16 – Dax 37 – Mimizan 32

△△△ Sunêlia Le Col Vert ♣♣

✆ 08 90 71 00 01, www.colvert.com

Address : 1548 route de l'Étang (5.5km south along the D 652; beside the Étang de Léon)

Opening times : from mid April to end Sept.

24 ha (800 pitches)

Tariff : 45€ ♣♣ ⇌ 回 図 (6A) Extra per person 7,20€ – Reservation fee 30€

Rental rates : (from mid April to end Sept.) ♿ (1 mobile home) 311 ⬛ – 34 🏠 – 27 canvas bungalows – 18 tent lodges. Per night from 21 to 197€ – Per week from 147 to 1379€ – Reservation fee 33,50€

🚐 borne – 25 回 12€ – 💧 12€

A free shuttle service to St-Girons-Plage beach.

Surroundings : 𝕈𝕈 ⛰
Leisure activities : ⟟ ✗ 🎱 🎣 🏓 🎮 📺 hammam, jacuzzi 🏊 🚴 🎳 🛶 ⛷ multi-sports ground
Facilities : ♿ 🚿 🚿 – 6 individual sanitary facilities (🚽 🚿 wc) 🧺 🚿 launderette 🛒 🍴 refrigerated food storage facilities
Nearby : 🏕 🐎 🚤 boats to hire

G P S Longitude : -1.30946
Latitude : 43.90416

△△ L'Océane

✆ 05 58 42 94 37, www.camping-oceane.fr – limited spaces for one-night stay

Address : route des Lacs (located 1km to the north)

Opening times : from mid June to mid Sept.

3 ha (99 pitches)

Tariff : 28€ ♣♣ ⇌ 回 図 (16A) – Extra per person 9,50€ – Reservation fee 15€

Rental rates : (from beginning May to end Sept.) – 58 ⬛. Per night from 38 to 110€ – Per week from 260 to 750€ Reservation fee 15€

Pleasant pine grove.

Surroundings : 𝕈𝕈𝕈
Leisure activities : ⟟ ✗ 🎱 🏊 🚴 🛶
Facilities : 🚿 (July–Aug.) 🍴 launderette 🛒

G P S Longitude : -1.30611
Latitude : 43.92278

VIEUX-BOUCAU-LES-BAINS

40480 – Michelin map **335** C12 – pop. 1 577 – alt. 5
▶ Paris 740 – Bayonne 41 – Biarritz 48 – Castets 28

△ Municipal les Sablères

✆ 05 58 48 12 29, www.camping-les-sableres.com

Address : boulevard du Marensin (to the northwest, 250m from the beach (direct access)

Opening times : from beginning April to mid Oct.

11 ha (517 pitches)

Tariff : 24,70€ ♣♣ ⇌ 回 図 (10A) – Extra per person 4,60€ Reservation fee 20€

Rental rates : (from beginning April to mid Oct.) – 7 ⬛ – 11 🏠 3 canvas bungalows. Per night from 38 to 80€ – Per week from 190 to 882€ – Reservation fee 20€

Surroundings : 𝕈
Leisure activities : 🏊 multi-sports ground
Facilities : ♿ 🚿 🚿 🍴 launderette refrigerated food storage facilities
Nearby : 🏊 ⟟ ✗ 🍴

G P S Longitude : -1.40596
Latitude : 43.79326

Some campsites benefit from proximity to a municipal leisure centre.

VILLERÉAL

47210 – Michelin map **336** G2 – pop. 1 286 – alt. 103
▶ Paris 566 – Agen 61 – Bergerac 35 – Cahors 76

△△△ Yelloh! Village Le Château de Fonrives ♣♣

✆ 05 53 36 63 38, www.campingchateaufonrives.com

Address : route d'Issigeac, at Rives (2.2km northwest along the D 207 and take the turning to the left, by the château)

20 ha/10 for camping (370 pitches)

Rental rates : 124 ⬛ – 38 🏠.

🚐 borne

Surroundings : ⬠ ▭ 𝕈𝕈
Leisure activities : ⟟ ✗ 🎱 🎣 🏓 📺 jacuzzi 🏊 🚴 🎮 🎳 🛶 ⛷ sports trail
Facilities : ♿ 🚿 🚿 🍴 launderette 🛒

G P S Longitude : 0.7314
Latitude : 44.65739

⛺ Sites et Paysages Fontaine du Roc

☏ 0553360816, www.fontaineduroc.com

Address : at Dévillac (7.5km southeast along the D 255 and take the turning to the left)

Opening times : from beginning April to end Sept.

2 ha (60 pitches) flat, grassy

Tariff : ★ 6€ ⇌ 🅔 8€ – (½) (10A) 4,50€

Rental rates : (from beginning April to end Sept.) – 4 🚐 – 3 🏠.
Per night from 50 to 120€ – Per week from 350 to 630€

🚐 borne – 🔧 (½)11€

Surroundings : 🏞 ♒♒
Leisure activities : 🎱 ⛵ jacuzzi 🚣 🏊
Facilities : ♿ ☎ 🚿 🍴 launderette

G P S Longitude : 0.8187
Latitude : 44.61414

VITRAC

24200 – Michelin map **329** I7 – pop. 870 – alt. 150
▶ Paris 541 – Brive-la-Gaillarde 64 – Cahors 54 – Gourdon 23

⛰ Domaine Soleil Plage 👥

☏ 0553283333, www.soleilplage.fr

Address : at Caudon (beside the Dordogne river)

Opening times : from mid April to end Sept.

8 ha/5 for camping (199 pitches) flat, grassy

Tariff : 37,50€ 👥 ⇌ 🅔 (½) (16A) – Extra per person 7,90€
Reservation fee 39€

Rental rates : (from mid April to end Sept.) 🅟 – 52 🚐 – 27 🏠.
Per night from 48 to 107€ – Per week from 310 to 1260€
Reservation fee 39€

🚐 borne 3€ – 10 🅔 21€

Small but luxurious chalet village, rather pretty.

Surroundings : 🏞 ≤ 🏠 ♒♒
Leisure activities : 🍷 ✗ 🎱 📺 🏓 🏇 🚣 ✂ 🎮 🏊 🏖 (beach) ⛏ 🎣 multi-sports ground
Facilities : ♿ ☎ 🚿 🍽 🏖 🍴 launderette 🧺 🔧

G P S Longitude : 1.25374
Latitude : 44.82387

⛰ La Bouysse de Caudon

☏ 0553283305, www.labouysse.com

Address : at Caudon (2.5km east, near the Dordogne river)

Opening times : from mid April to end Sept.

6 ha/3 for camping (160 pitches) flat, grassy, walnut trees

Tariff : 26,50€ 👥 ⇌ 🅔 (½) (10A) – Extra per person 6,60€
Reservation fee 20€

Rental rates : (from mid April to end Sept.) 🎿 (from mid April to end June) 🅟 – 4 🚐 – 9 🏠 – 5 apartments – 2 gîtes. Per night 810€ – Per week 780€ – Reservation fee 20€

🚐 borne 5€

Surroundings : 🏞 🏠 ♒♒
Leisure activities : 🍷 🚣 ✂ 🏊 🏖 (beach) 🎣
Facilities : ♿ ☎ 🏖 🍴 launderette 🧺 🔧 refrigerators

G P S Longitude : 1.25063
Latitude : 44.82357

AUVERGNE

G. Labriet / Photononstop

Shhh! Don't wake the volcanoes. They are the giant sleeping beauties of the Auvergne, a stunning region at the heart of France. Dormant for several millennia, they form a natural barrier that keeps them secure from any encroachment by man. If you listen very carefully, you may just make out a distant rumble from Vulcania, the interactive and educational European Park of Volcanism, where you can learn all you could possibly want to know about volcanoes. The region's domes and peaks, sculpted by volcanic fire, are the source of countless mountain springs that cascade down the steep slopes into brooks, rivers and crystal-clear lakes. Renowned for the therapeutic qualities of its waters, the Auvergne has long played host to well-heeled visitors at its elegant spa resorts, but many find it simply impossible to follow doctor's orders when faced with the tempting aroma of an Auvergne country stew, a savoury *Pounti* cake or a full-bodied Cantal cheese!

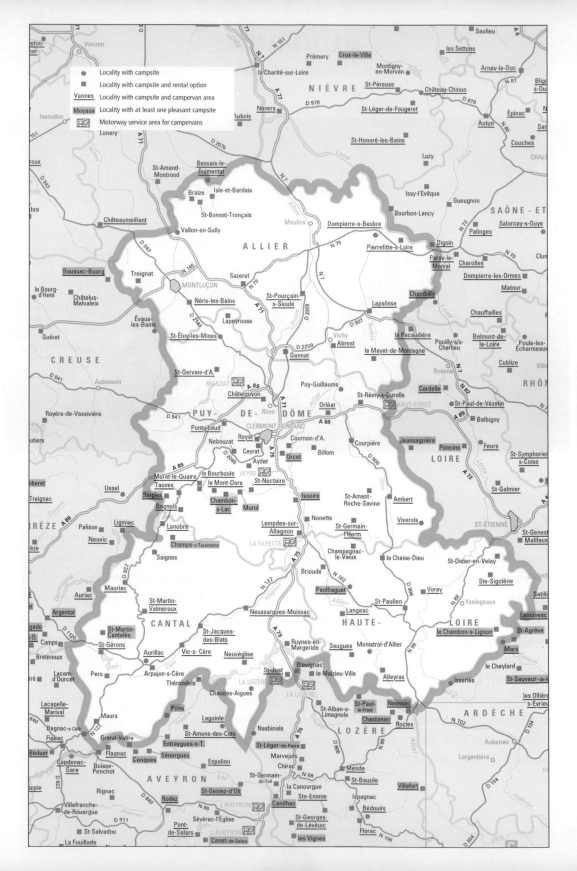

ABREST

03200 – Michelin map **326** H6 – pop. 2 696 – alt. 290
▶ Paris 361 – Clermont-Ferrand 70 – Moulins 63 – Montluçon 94

🏔 La Croix St-Martin

𝒫 0470326774, www.camping-vichy.com

Address : 99 avenue des Graviers (to the north, near the Allier)

Opening times : from beginning April to mid Oct.

3 ha (100 pitches) flat, grassy

Tariff : ✷ 5€ ⇦ 🔲 6€ – ⚡ (10A) 3,50€

Rental rates : (from beginning April to mid Oct.) – 18 🚐.
Per night from 39 to 67€ – Per week from 330 to 640€
🔖 borne 5€ – 🚐 ⚡ 12€

Surroundings : ♀
Leisure activities : 🏊
Facilities : ♿ ☛ ᵀ launderette
Nearby : 🍴 🔲 🎣 casino

G P S Longitude : 3.44012
Latitude : 46.10819

ALLEYRAS

43580 – Michelin map **331** E4 – pop. 173 – alt. 779
▶ Paris 549 – Brioude 71 – Langogne 43 – Le Puy-en-Velay 32

🏔 Municipal Au Fil de l'Eau

𝒫 0471575686, camping-municipal.alleyras.fr – alt. 660

Address : Le Pont-d'Alleyras (2.5km to the northwest, direct access
to the Allier)

Opening times : from mid April to mid Oct.

0,9 ha (60 pitches) flat and relatively flat

Tariff : (2013 Price) 12,20€ ✷✷ ⇦ 🔲 ⚡ (6A) – Extra per person 4,20€
Rental rates : (from mid April to mid Oct.) – 6 huts (without
sanitary facilities). Per night from 22 to 41€ – Per week
from 102 to 285€
🔖 borne 3€

Surroundings : 🏞 ≼
Leisure activities : 🛶
Facilities : ♿ ☛ (July–Aug.) launderette
Nearby : 🏊 🎣

G P S Longitude : 3.67005
Latitude : 44.91786

AMBERT

63600 – Michelin map **326** J9 – pop. 6 962 – alt. 535
▶ Paris 438 – Brioude 63 – Clermont-Ferrand 77 – Montbrison 47

🏔 Municipal Les Trois Chênes

𝒫 0473823468, www.camping-ambert.com

Address : route du Puy (located 1.5km south along the D 906, follow
the signs for La Chaise-Dieu; near the Dore river)

Opening times : from end April to end Sept.

3 ha (120 pitches) flat, grassy

Tariff : 19,95€ ✷✷ ⇦ 🔲 ⚡ (10A) – Extra per person 4,60€
Rental rates : Permanent – 18 🏠. Per night from 60 to 119€
Per week from 265 to 690€
🔖 borne 2€ – 🚐 ⚡ 15,15€
In a pleasant leafy setting.

Surroundings : ≼ 🏞 ♀♀
Leisure activities : 🏓 🔲 ⛷
Facilities : ♿ ☛ 🏊 ⚡ ᵀ launderette
At the river : 🏊 🍴 🍴 🛶 🎣 🏞
fitness trail

G P S Longitude : 3.7291
Latitude : 45.53953

ARNAC

15150 – Michelin map **330** B4 – pop. 148 – alt. 620
▶ Paris 541 – Argentat 38 – Aurillac 35 – Mauriac 36

🏔 Village Vacances La Gineste

(rental of mobile homes and chalets only)

𝒫 0471629190, www.village-vacances-cantal.com

Address : at La Gineste (3km northwest along the D 61, follow the
signs for Pleaux then continue 1.2km along the road to the right)

Opening times : Permanent

3 ha terraced

Rental rates : 🅿 – 60 🚐 – 40 🏠. Per week from 395 to 600€
Reservation fee 13€
🔖 borne 2€ – 2 🔲

A pleasant location on a peninsula in the Lac de Enchanet.

Surroundings : 🏞 ≼ 🏠 ♀
Leisure activities : 🍷 🍴 🏠 ⚡ 🛶 🎣 ⛷
🏖 (beach) 🎣 🐴
Facilities : ☛ ᵀ 🔲 🏊 🚿
Nearby : watersports centre

G P S Longitude : 2.2121
Latitude : 45.08285

ARPAJON-SUR-CÈRE

15130 – Michelin map **330** C5 – pop. 6 009 – alt. 613
▶ Paris 559 – Argentat 56 – Aurillac 5 – Maurs 44

🏔 La Cère

𝒫 0471645507, www.camping.caba.fr

Address : south of the town, access via the D 920, opposite the Esso
service station; beside the river

Opening times : from beginning June to end Sept.

2 ha (78 pitches) flat, grassy

Tariff : (2013 Price) 15,70€ ✷✷ ⇦ 🔲 ⚡ (10A) –
Extra per person 4,50€
Rental rates : (from beginning April to end Oct.) – 10 🚐.
Per week from 252 to 476€
A wooded setting and a well-kept site.

Surroundings : 🏞 ♀
Leisure activities : 🏓 🛶 🚲 ⛷
Facilities : ♿ ☛ ᵀ 🔲
Nearby : 🍴

G P S Longitude : 2.46246
Latitude : 44.89858

AURILLAC

15000 – Michelin map **330** C5 – pop. 28 207 – alt. 610
▶ Paris 557 – Brive-la-Gaillarde 98 – Clermont-Ferrand 158
– Montauban 174

🏔 Municipal l'Ombrade

𝒫 0471482887, www.camping.caba.fr

Address : head 1km north along the D 17 and take r. du Gué-Bouliaga
to the right; on both sides of the Jordanne

Opening times : from mid June to mid Sept.

7,5 ha (200 pitches) flat

Tariff : (2013 Price) 13,20€ ✷✷ ⇦ 🔲 ⚡ (10A)
Extra per person 4,50€
🔖 borne – 35 🔲 10,50€

Surroundings : ♀♀
Leisure activities : 🏓 🚲
Facilities : ♿ ☛ 🏊 🚿 ᵀ 🔲

G P S Longitude : 2.4559
Latitude : 44.93562

AYDAT

63970 – Michelin map **326** E9 – pop. 2 122 – alt. 850
▶ Paris 438 – La Bourboule 33 – Clermont-Ferrand 21 – Issoire 38

⚠ Lac d'Aydat

✆ 04 73 79 38 09, www.camping-lac-aydat.com

Address : beside the lake, Foret du lot (head 2km northeast along the D 90 and take the road to the right; near the lake)

Opening times :

7 ha (150 pitches) very uneven, terraced, flat, grassy, stony

Tariff : ✻ 5€ ⟷ 2,50€ 🖳 10€ – ⚡ (15A) 5€ – Reservation fee 20€
Rental rates : Permanent – 55 🚐 – 17 🏠. Per night from 70 to 135€ – Per week from 280 to 735€ – Reservation fee 20€

In a pleasant pine wood.

Surroundings : ♤♤
Leisure activities : ♟✗ 🏠 🛶
Facilities : ♿ ⌒ 🕸 ♨♨ launderette
Nearby : 🎣 🛝 🚣 🚲 🏊 (beach) 🐟 ⛵ 🐎 forest trail

Longitude : 2.98907
Latitude : 45.66903

BAGNOLS

63810 – Michelin map **326** C9 – pop. 496 – alt. 862
▶ Paris 483 – Bort-les-Orgues 19 – La Bourboule 23 – Bourg-Lastic 38

⚠ Municipal la Thialle

✆ 04 73 22 28 00, www.bagnols63.fr

Address : route de St-Donat (take southeastern exit along the D 25; beside the Thialle river)

Opening times : from beginning April to beginning Nov.

2,8 ha (70 pitches)

Tariff : ✻ 4,20€ ⟷ 2,20€ 🖳 2,20€ – ⚡ (6A) 3€
Rental rates : Permanent – 8 🏠. Per night 62€ – Per week 554€ Reservation fee 35€
🚐 borne – 5 🖳 16€

Surroundings : ♤
Leisure activities : 🏠 🛶 🎯 🚣 (small swimming pool) 🐟
Facilities : ♿ ⌒ (season) 🚿 🕸 launderette
Nearby : 🏊 ♟✗

Longitude : 2.63466
Latitude : 45.49758

BILLOM

63160 – Michelin map **326** H8 – pop. 4 637 – alt. 340
▶ Paris 437 – Clermont-Ferrand 28 – Cunlhat 30 – Issoire 31

⚠ Municipal le Colombier

✆ 04 73 68 91 50, www.billom.fr

Address : rue Carnot (To the northeast of the town, follow the signs for Lezoux)

1 ha (40 pitches)
Rentals : 12 🏠.

Surroundings : 🗖 ♤
Leisure activities : ♿ 🛶
Facilities : ♿ ⌒ ♨ 🖳
Nearby : 🏊 🎾 🚣 🚣 🐎

Longitude : 3.3459
Latitude : 45.72839

LA BOURBOULE

63150 – Michelin map **326** D9 – pop. 1 961 – alt. 880 – 🌡
▶ Paris 469 – Aubusson 82 – Clermont-Ferrand 50 – Mauriac 71

⚠ Les Clarines

✆ 04 73 81 02 30, www.camping-les-clarines.com

Address : 1424 avenue du Mar. Leclerc

Opening times : from mid Dec. to mid Oct.

3,75 ha (194 pitches)

Tariff : 21,10€ ✻✻ ⟷ 🖳 ⚡ (10A) – Extra per person 4,85€
Rental rates : (from mid Dec. to mid Oct.) – 31 🚐 – 1 gîte. Per night from 37 to 78€ – Per week from 259 to 707€
🚐 borne 5€ – 10 🖳 9,30€

Surroundings : ♤♤
Leisure activities : ♟ 🏠 ⚄daytime 🛶 🚣
Facilities : ♿ ⌒ 🏕 🧺 ♨♨ ♨ launderette
Nearby : 🏊

Longitude : 2.76222
Latitude : 45.59463

⚠ Les Vernières

✆ 04 73 81 10 20, www.camping-la-bourboule.fr

Address : avenue du Mar. de Lattre-de-Tassigny (take the eastern exit along the D 130, follow the signs for Le Mont-Dore; near the Dordogne)

Opening times : from end April to end Sept.

1,5 ha (165 pitches)

Tariff : (2013 Price) 17,50€ ✻✻ ⟷ 🖳 ⚡ (10A)
Extra per person 3,85€
Rental rates : (2013 Price) (from end April to end Sept.) – 2 🏠 1 yurt. Per night from 35 to 80€ – Per week from 245 to 580€
🚐 borne – 🔋 10€

Surroundings : ⛰ ♤ ♀
Leisure activities : ♟ ✗ 🏠 🛶 🐟
Facilities : ♿ ⌒ 🕸 ♨ 🖳 🚣
Nearby : 🎿 🚣 🚣

Longitude : 2.75285
Latitude : 45.58943

To visit a town or region, use the MICHELIN Green Guides.

BRAIZE

03360 – Michelin map **326** C2 – pop. 290 – alt. 240
▶ Paris 297 – Dun-sur-Auron 30 – Cérilly 16 – Culan 35

⚠ Le Champ de la Chapelle

✆ 04 70 06 15 45, www.champdelachapelle.com

Address : Champ de la Chapelle (5.7km south along the D 28, follow the signs for Meaulnes and turn left onto D 978a, follow the signs for Tronçais then continue 1km along the gravel road to the left)

Opening times : from mid April to mid Oct.

5,6 ha (80 pitches)

Tariff : 19€ ✻✻ ⟷ 🖳 ⚡ (10A) – Extra per person 3,25€
Rental rates : (from mid April to mid Oct.) 🛶 – 2 🚐. Per week from 320 to 400€

An attractive location in the woods.

Surroundings : 🌲 ♤♤
Leisure activities : 🛶 🚣 (beach)
Facilities : ♿ ⌒ ♨ ♨ 🖳
At the Étang de St-Bonnet : ♟ ✗ 🎾 🎯 🐟 watersports centre

Longitude : 2.65558
Latitude : 46.64304

BRIOUDE

43100 – Michelin map **331** C2 – pop. 6 688 – alt. 427
▶ Paris 487 – Clermont-Ferrand 71 – Le Puy-en-Velay 59 – Aurillac 105

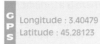 Aquadis Loisirs La Bageasse

📞 0471500770, www.aquadis-loisirs.com

2,5 ha (49 pitches) terraced, flat, grassy
Rentals : ♿ (1 chalet) – 4 🚐 – 15 🏠.
A pleasant site near the river.

Surroundings : 🗔 ⚏
Leisure activities : ♟ ✕
Facilities : ♿ 🗑 ⚐ launderette
Nearby : 🏊

GPS Longitude : 3.40479
Latitude : 45.28123

CEYRAT

63122 – Michelin map **326** F8 – pop. 5 371 – alt. 560
▶ Paris 423 – Clermont-Ferrand 6 – Issoire 36 – Le Mont-Dore 42

Le Chanset

📞 0473613073, www.campingdeceyrat63.com – alt. 600

Address : rue du Camping (av. J.-B.-Marrou)

5 ha (140 pitches)
Rentals : 20 🚐 – 14 🏠 – 1 tent lodge.

Surroundings : ⚏
Leisure activities : ♟ ✕ 🗔 ⚏ 🏊
Facilities : ♿ 🏛 ⚐ ⚑ ⚐ launderette 🏊 ⚑

GPS Longitude : 3.06196
Latitude : 45.73852

LA CHAISE-DIEU

43160 – Michelin map **331** E2 – pop. 730 – alt. 1 080
▶ Paris 503 – Ambert 29 – Brioude 35 – Issoire 59

⛰ Municipal les Prades

📞 0471000788, andre.brivadis@orange.fr

Address : situated 2km northeast along the D 906, follow the signs for Ambert, near the small lake at La Tour (direct access)

Opening times : from beginning June to end Sept.

3 ha (100 pitches) relatively flat

Tariff : (2013 Price) ♟ 3,10€ – 🚗 🅿 3,10€ – 🔌 3,30€
Rental rates : (2013 Price) (from beginning June to end Sept.) chalets (without sanitary facilities). Per night from 22 to 64€ Per week from 102 to 321€
🚐 borne – 3 🅿 13,70€

Surroundings : ⚏
Leisure activities : ⚑
Facilities : ♿ ⚐ ⚑ ⚑
Nearby : ⚑ 🏊 🐎

GPS Longitude : 3.70496
Latitude : 45.33321

The Michelin classification (⛰⛰⛰… ⛰) is totally independent of the official star classification system awarded by the local prefecture or other official organisation.

CHAMBON-SUR-LAC

63790 – Michelin map **326** E9 – pop. 352 – alt. 885 – Winter sports : 1 150/1 760m
▶ Paris 456 – Clermont-Ferrand 37 – Condat 39 – Issoire 32

 Le Pré Bas ♟♟

📞 0473886304, www.campingauvergne.com

Address : near the lake (direct access)

Opening times : from mid April to mid Sept.

3,8 ha (180 pitches)

Tariff : 31,90€ ♟♟ 🚗 🅿 🔌 (6A) – Extra per person 7,20€
Reservation fee 19€

Rental rates : (from mid April to mid Sept.) ⚑ – 106 🚐 1 gîte. Per night from 47 to 87€ – Per week from 282 to 1082€
Reservation fee 19€
🚐 30 🅿 27,10€

Beautiful flowers and shrubs decorate a large, partially covered water park.

Surroundings : ⚑ 🗔 ⚏
Leisure activities : ♟ ✕ 🗔 ⚐ ⚑ ⚑ hammam, jacuzzi ⚑ 🗔 🏊 ⚑ multi-sports ground, spa centre, entertainment room
Facilities : ♿ ⚑ ⚐ ⚑ launderette ⚑
Nearby : 🏊 🚣 ⚑ 🐎 quad biking

GPS Longitude : 2.91427
Latitude : 45.57516

⛰ Les Bombes

📞 0473886403, www.camping-les-bombes.com

Address : chemin de Pétary (east of Chambon-sur-Lac, head towards Murol and take a right turn; beside the Couze de Chambon river)

Opening times : from beginning May to mid Sept.

5 ha (150 pitches) flat, grassy

Tariff : ♟ 5,10€ 🚗 🅿 9,50€ – 🔌 (16A) 4,60€ – Reservation fee 12€
Rental rates : (from beginning May to mid Sept.) – 2 caravans 15 🚐 – 3 canvas bungalows. Per night from 35 to 65€ Per week from 190 to 700€ – Reservation fee 12€
🚐 borne 3€ – 30 🅿 6€

Surroundings : ⚑ ⚑ Vallée de Chaudefour ⚏
Leisure activities : ♟ ✕ 🗔 ⚑ 🚴 🏊 ⚑
Facilities : ♿ ⚑ ⚐ ⚑ launderette ⚑
At the lake : ⚑ 🚣 (beach) ⚑ 🐎

GPS Longitude : 2.90188
Latitude : 45.56994

⛰ Serrette

📞 0473886767, www.campingdeserrette.com – alt. 1 000

Address : Serrette (2.5km west along the D 996, follow the signs for Le Mont-Dore and take the D 636 (to the left), follow the signs for Chambon-des-Neiges)

Opening times : from beginning May to mid Sept.

2 ha (75 pitches)

Tariff : (2013 Price) ♟ 5€ 🚗 🅿 8,60€ – 🔌 (10A) 5,40€ – Reservation fee 12€
Rental rates : (2013 Price) (from beginning May to mid Sept.) 8 🚐 – 3 🏠. Per night 60€ – Per week 725€ – Reservation fee 12€

A magnificent view over the lake and the surrounding area.

Surroundings : ⚑ ⚑ Lac Chambon and mountains ⚏
Leisure activities : ♟ 🗔 🏊 (open air in season)
Facilities : ♿ ⚑ ⚑ ⚑
At the lake : ⚑ ⚑ 🚣 (beach) 🐎

GPS Longitude : 2.89105
Latitude : 45.57099

LE CHAMBON-SUR-LIGNON

43400 – Michelin map **331** H3 – pop. 2 690 – alt. 967
▶ Paris 573 – Annonay 48 – Lamastre 32 – Le Puy-en-Velay 45

⚠️ Les Hirondelles

🔗 0471597384, www.campingleshirondelles.fr – alt. 1 000

Address : route de la Suchère (located 1km south along the D 151 and turn left onto D 7)

Opening times : from mid June to end Aug.

1 ha (45 pitches) flat

Tariff : 17,95€ ✚✚ 🚐 🗉 🔌 (6A) – Extra per person 4,20€
Rental rates : (from mid April to end Oct.) 🚫 – 3 🏠. Per night from 40 to 70€ – Per week from 230 to 460€
🚰 borne 10€
In a pleasant setting overlooking the town.

Surroundings : 🏞 ⟨ 🏕 ⚓
Leisure activities : 🍷 🎪 🏇
Facilities : ♿ 🔌 🚿🚻 🗉 🧺
At the river : 🍴 📺 🏊 🐴 sports trail

GPS	Longitude : 4.2986	Latitude : 45.05436

⚠️ Le Lignon

🔗 0471597286, contact@campingdulignon.com – alt. 1 000

Address : route du Stade (take the southwestern exit along the D 15, follow the signs for Mazet-sur-Voy and take a right turn before the bridge, near the river)

Opening times : from mid April to end Sept.

2 ha (130 pitches) flat, grassy

Tariff : 19,50€ ✚✚ 🚐 🗉 🔌 (10A) – Extra per person 6,20€
Rental rates : (from end April to end Sept.) – 3 🚐. Per night from 55 to 90€ – Per week 510€

Surroundings : ⚓ ⛰
Leisure activities : 🎪 🏇 🚲
Facilities : ♿ 🔌 🚿🚻 🗉
At the river : 🍴 📺 🏊 🐴 sports trail

GPS	Longitude : 4.29686	Latitude : 45.05944

CHAMPAGNAC-LE-VIEUX

43440 – Michelin map **331** D1 – pop. 234 – alt. 880
▶ Paris 486 – Brioude 16 – La Chaise-Dieu 25 – Clermont-Ferrand 76

⚠️ Le Chanterelle

🔗 0471763400, www.champagnac.com

Address : Le Prat Barrat (1.4km north along the D 5, follow the signs for Auzon, and take the road to the right)

Opening times : from mid April to mid Oct.

4 ha (90 pitches) terraced

Tariff : 20,60€ ✚✚ 🚐 🗉 🔌 (10A) – Extra per person 4€
Rental rates : (from mid April to mid Oct.) – 4 🚐 – 20 🏠 10 canvas bungalows. Per night from 40 to 114€ – Per week from 240 to 798€ – Reservation fee 15€
A lush, green site near a small lake.

Surroundings : 🏞 ⛰
Leisure activities : 🎪 🏇 🚲
Facilities : ♿ 🔌 🚿🚻 🧺 🚿 🍴 launderette
Nearby : 🎪 🍴 🏊 (beach) 🐴 🏃 fitness trail

GPS	Longitude : 3.50575	Latitude : 45.3657

CHAMPS-SUR-TARENTAINE

15270 – Michelin map **330** D2 – pop. 1 035 – alt. 450
▶ Paris 500 – Aurillac 90 – Clermont-Ferrand 82 – Condat 24

⚠️ Les Chalets de l'Eau Verte (rental of chalets only)

🔗 0471787878, www.auvergne-chalets.fr

Address : Le Jagounet

Opening times : Permanent

8 ha relatively flat

Rental rates : 🅿 – 10 🏠. Per night from 39 to 110€ – Per week from 273 to 798€ – Reservation fee 10€
There is a 2-night minimum stay in low season.

Surroundings : 🏞
Leisure activities : 🏕
Facilities : 🔌 🍴 📷
Nearby : 🍴 🏊 🎣 🐴

GPS	Longitude : 2.63853	Latitude : 45.40595

*The classification (1 to 5 tents, **black** or **red**) that we award to selected sites in this guide is our own system. It should not be confused with the classification (1 to 5 stars) of official organisations.*

CHÂTELGUYON

63140 – Michelin map **326** F7 – pop. 6 223 – alt. 430 – ⚕
▶ Paris 411 – Aubusson 93 – Clermont-Ferrand 21 – Gannat 31

⚠️ Le Ranch des Volcans 👥

🔗 0473860247, www.ranchdesvolcans.com

Address : route de la Piscine (take southeastern exit along the D 985, follow the signs for Riom)

Opening times : from end March to end Oct.

4 ha (285 pitches)

Tariff : ✚ 4,50€ 🚐 2,50€ 🗉 4,50€ – 🔌 (10A) 3,50€
Rental rates : (from end March to end Oct.) – 2 caravans 30 🚐 – 3 🏠 – 3 tipis. Per night from 60 to 112€ – Per week from 250 to 500€
🚰 borne – 21 🗉 8€ – 🚐 🔌20,82€

Surroundings : ⛰
Leisure activities : 🍷 🍴 🎪 🎯 🎿 🏇 🚲 🏃 🏊
Facilities : ♿ 🔌 🚿 🚿 🍴 launderette 🧺

GPS	Longitude : 3.07732	Latitude : 45.91491

⚠️ La Croze

🔗 0473860827, www.campingcroze.com

Address : at St-Hippolyte, route de Mozac (located 1km southeast along the D 227, follow the signs for Riom)

Opening times : from beginning April to end Oct.

3,7 ha (100 pitches)

Tariff : ✚ 3,20€ 🚐 1,60€ 🗉 3,60€ – 🔌 (10A) 3,60€
Rental rates : (from beginning April to end Oct.) ♿ (1 chalet) 17 🚐 – 9 🏠. Per night from 40 to 70€ – Per week from 320 to 530€
🚰 10 🗉 5,20€

Surroundings : 🏞 ⛰
Leisure activities : 🍴 🏇 🎿
Facilities : ♿ 🔌 🚿 🍴 launderette

GPS	Longitude : 3.06083	Latitude : 45.90589

CHAUDES-AIGUES

15110 – Michelin map **330** G5 – pop. 940 – alt. 750 – ⚓
▶ Paris 538 – Aurillac 94 – Entraygues-sur-Truyère 62 – Espalion 54

⛺ Le Château du Couffour

✆ 0471235708, www.camping-chaudes-aigues.fr – alt. 900

Address : at the stadium (situated 2km south along the D 921, follow the signs for Laguiole then take the road to the right)

2,5 ha (90 pitches) flat, grassy

Located in the heart of the countryside.

Surroundings : 🌳 ≤ ♀
Leisure activities : 🏠 ⛴
Facilities : 🚿 ⚲ 🏛 🍴 🖥
Nearby : 🚴 🏇 climbing, casino

GPS Longitude : 3.00071
Latitude : 44.8449

COURNON-D'AUVERGNE

63800 – Michelin map **326** G8 – pop. 19 494 – alt. 380
▶ Paris 422 – Clermont-Ferrand 12 – Issoire 31 – Le Mont-Dore 54

⛺ Municipal le Pré des Laveuses

✆ 0473848130, www.cournon-auvergne.fr/camping

Address : rue des Laveuses (head 1.5km east via road to Billom and take the beach road to the left)

5 ha (150 pitches)

Rentals : 12 🚐 – 18 🏠 – 12 canvas bungalows.

Situated between a small landscaped lake and the Allier river.

Surroundings : ♀♀
Leisure activities : 🍷 ✕ 🏠 ⛴ 🏊
Facilities : 🚿 ⚲ 🏛 🍴 launderette
Nearby : 🏇 🏄 🚣

GPS Longitude : 3.22271
Latitude : 45.74029

COURPIÈRE

63120 – Michelin map **326** I8 – pop. 4 514 – alt. 320
▶ Paris 399 – Ambert 40 – Clermont-Ferrand 50 – Issoire 53

⛺ Municipal les Taillades

✆ 0473530121, www.ville-courpiere.fr

Address : Les Taillades (take the southern exit along the D 906, follow the signs for Ambert, take the D 7 to the left, follow the signs for Aubusson-d'Auvergne and take the road to the right; by the swimming pool and near a stream)

Opening times : from mid June to end Aug.

0,5 ha (40 pitches) flat, grassy

Tariff : (2013 Price) 🚶 2,50€ ⛺ 🚗 📧 4€ – [⚡] (10A) 4,70€ – Reservation fee 10€

Rental rates : (2013 Price) (from mid June to end Aug.) 4 🚐. Per night from 40 to 49€ – Per week from 275 to 337€ Reservation fee 10€

Surroundings : 🌳 🗆
Leisure activities : 🏃 🏊
Facilities : 🚿 ⚲ 🏛 🍴 🖥
Nearby : 🚴 🏇 🏄 🚣

GPS Longitude : 3.5487
Latitude : 45.75354

We have selected the best campsites in France with our usual care, listing those with the best facilities in the most pleasant surroundings.

DOMPIERRE-SUR-BESBRE

03290 – Michelin map **326** J3 – pop. 3 184 – alt. 234
▶ Paris 324 – Bourbon-Lancy 19 – Decize 46 – Digoin 27

⛺ Municipal Les Bords de Bresbe

✆ 0470345557, camping@mairie-dsb.fr

Address : La Madeleine (take the southeastern exit along the N 79, follow the signs for Digoin; near the Besbre river and not far from a lake)

Opening times : from mid May to mid Sept.

2 ha (70 pitches) flat, grassy

Tariff : 🚶 2,60€ ⛺ 🚗 📧 2,10€ – [⚡] (10A) 2,40€

🚐 borne 2€

Pretty shrubs and flowers decorate the site.

Surroundings : 🌳 🗆 ♀
Leisure activities : ⛴ 🚴 🎯
Facilities : ⚲ 🏛 🛁 🍴 🖥
Nearby : 🏊 wildlife park

GPS Longitude : 3.68289
Latitude : 46.51373

GANNAT

03800 – Michelin map **326** G6 – pop. 5 853 – alt. 345
▶ Paris 383 – Clermont-Ferrand 49 – Montluçon 78 – Moulins 58

⛺ Municipal Le Mont Libre

✆ 0470901216, www.camping-gannat.fr

Address : 10 route de la Batisse (located 1km south along the N 9 and take turning to the right)

Opening times : from beginning April to end Oct.

1,5 ha (70 pitches)

Tariff : 15,30€ 🚶🚶 ⛺ 🚗 📧 [⚡] (10A) – Extra per person 2,90€

Rental rates : (from beginning April to end Oct.) – 13 🏠. Per week from 245 to 523€

🚐 borne 4,20€ – 🔌 [⚡]14,90€

Surroundings : ≤ 🗆 ♀
Leisure activities : 🏠 ⛴ 🏊 (small swimming pool)
Facilities : 🚿 ⚲ 🍴 🖥
Nearby : 🎯 🎣 🏊

GPS Longitude : 3.19403
Latitude : 46.0916

ISLE-ET-BARDAIS

03360 – Michelin map **326** D2 – pop. 275 – alt. 285
▶ Paris 280 – Bourges 60 – Cérilly 9 – Montluçon 52

⛺ Les Écossais

✆ 0470666257, www.campingstroncais.com

Address : located 1km south via road to Les Chamignoux

Opening times : from beginning April to end Sept.

2 ha (70 pitches)

Tariff : (2013 Price) 🚶 2,90€ ⛺ 🚗 1,35€ 📧 2,45€ – [⚡] (10A) 3,30€ Reservation fee 15€

Rental rates : (2013 Price) (from beginning April to end Sept.) 2 🚐 – 7 gîtes. Per night 64€ – Per week 459€ – Reservation fee 15€

Beside the Étang de Pirot (lake) and at the edge of the Tronçais forest.

Surroundings : 🌳 🗆 ♀♀
Leisure activities : 🍷 🏠 🎯 🏄 🚣 (beach)
Facilities : ⚲ 🍴 launderette
Nearby : ⛴ 🚣

GPS Longitude : 2.78814
Latitude : 46.68278

ISSOIRE

63500 – Michelin map **326** G9 – pop. 13 949 – alt. 400
▶ Paris 446 – Aurillac 121 – Clermont-Ferrand 36 – Le Puy-en-Velay 94

⚲ Château La Grange Fort

✆ 0473710243, www.lagrangefort.eu

Address : 4km southeast along the D 996, follow the signs for la Chaise-Dieu then take a right turn, 3km along the D 34, follow the signs for Auzat-sur-Allier, from the A 75, take exit 13 towards Parentignat

Opening times : from mid April to end Oct.

23 ha/4 for camping (120 pitches) relatively flat, flat, grassy

Tariff : 26,75€ ♣ ♣ ⟺ 🅴 🔌 (6A) – Extra per person 6,25€
Reservation fee 15€

Rental rates : (from mid April to end Oct.) – 24 🛖 – 8 🏠 – 5 ⛺
2 apartments – 8 canvas bungalows – 2 tent lodges – 1 gîte.
Per night from 50 to 105€ – Per week 810€ – Reservation fee 15€
🚐 borne – 8 🅴 26,75€ – 🚌 🔌 18€

Based around a picturesque medieval château overlooking the Allier river.

Surroundings : ⸜ ⟜ ▱ ♀
Leisure activities : 🍷 🍴 🍱 ⟺ jacuzzi ⟝⟞
🚲 ✗ 🎱 🏊
Facilities : 🚿 ⚷ 🅿 🏛 🚽 🍽 launderette ✂

G P S   Longitude : 3.28501
Latitude : 45.50859

⚲ Municipal du Mas

✆ 0473890359, www.camping-issoire.com

Address : rue du Dr Bienfait (2.5km east along the D 9, follow the signs for Orbeil and take a right turn, 50m from a lake and 300m from the Allier river; from A 75 take exit 12)

Opening times : from beginning April to mid Nov.

3 ha (138 pitches) flat, grassy

Tariff : 19,90€ ♣ ♣ ⟺ 🅴 🔌 (10A) – Extra per person 5,30€
Rental rates : (from beginning April to mid Nov.) – 4 🛖 – 6 🏠.
Per night from 42 to 84€ – Per week from 266 to 537€
🚐 borne 3,55€ – 10 🅴 19,90€

Surroundings : ⸜ ♀
Leisure activities : 🍱 ⟺ daytime ⟝⟞ 🎣
Facilities : ⚷ 🏛 🚽 ✂ 🍽 launderette
Nearby : ✗ 🚲 ✗ ⟝ bowling

G P S   Longitude : 3.27397
Latitude : 45.55108

LANGEAC

43300 – Michelin map **331** C3 – pop. 4 004 – alt. 505
▶ Paris 513 – Clermont-Ferrand 97 – Le Puy-en-Velay 44
– Aurillac 134

⚲ Les Gorges de l'Allier

✆ 0471770501, www.campinglangeac.com

Address : Domaine Le Pradeau

14 ha (214 pitches) flat, grassy

Rentals : ⚷ (2 chalets) – 10 🛖 – 21 🏠.
🚐 borne

Surroundings : ⸜ ⟜ ♀
Leisure activities : 🍷 🍴 🍱 ⟝⟞ 🏊 🎣
multi-sports ground, entertainment room
Facilities : ⚷ ⚷ 🚿 ✂ launderette
Nearby : 🛶 🚲 ✗ ⟝

G P S   Longitude : 3.50069
Latitude : 45.10389

LANOBRE

15270 – Michelin map **330** D2 – pop. 1 400 – alt. 650
▶ Paris 493 – Bort-les-Orgues 7 – La Bourboule 33 – Condat 30

⚲ Le Lac de la Siauve

✆ 0471403185, www.camping-lac-siauve.fr – alt. 660

Address : rue du Camping (3km southwest along the D 922, follow the signs for Bort-les-Orgues and take turning to the right, 200m from the lake (direct access)

8 ha (220 pitches) terraced, flat, grassy

Rentals : 14 🛖 – 19 🏠 – mini-chalets (without sanitary facilities).
🚐 borne

Surroundings : ⸜ ⟜ ▱ ♀
Leisure activities : 🍷 🍱 ⟺ daytime ⟝⟞
🚲 🏊
Facilities : ⚷ ⚷ ✂ 🍽 launderette
Nearby : ≋ (beach) watersports centre

G P S   Longitude : 2.50407
Latitude : 45.4306

LAPALISSE

03120 – Michelin map **326** I5 – pop. 3 162 – alt. 280
▶ Paris 346 – Digoin 45 – Mâcon 122 – Moulins 50

⚲ Camping Communautaire

✆ 0470992631, www.lapalisse-tourisme.com

Address : rue des Vignes (take the southeastern exit along the N 7; beside the Besbre river, pedestrian path linking campsite to town centre)

Opening times : from beginning April to end Sept.

0,8 ha (66 pitches) flat, grassy

Tariff : ♣ 2,40€ ⟺ 1,80€ 🅴 1,85€ – 🔌 (0A) 2,40€
Rental rates : (from beginning April to end Sept.) ✗ – 2 🛖
6 🏠. Per night from 30 to 60€ – Per week from 150 to 370€
🚐 🚌 9€

Surroundings : ♀
Leisure activities : ⟝⟞ ✗ ⟝ fitness trail
Facilities : ⚷ ⚷ ✂ 🍽 🅿

G P S   Longitude : 3.6395
Latitude : 46.2433

LAPEYROUSE

63700 – Michelin map **326** E5 – pop. 561 – alt. 510
▶ Paris 350 – Clermont-Ferrand 74 – Commentry 15
– Montmarault 14

⚲ Municipal les Marins

✆ 04.73.93.60.00, www.63lapeyrouse.free.fr

Address : Etang de La Loge (lake) (situated 2km southeast along the D 998, follow the signs for Echassières and turn right onto D 100, follow the signs for Durmignat)

Opening times : Permanent

2 ha (68 pitches) flat, grassy

Tariff : 12€ ♣ ♣ ⟺ 🅴 🔌 (10A) – Extra per person 3€
Rental rates : Permanent – 6 🏠. Per week from 230 to 460€

Ornamental trees and shrubs around the pitches; near a small lake.

Surroundings : ⸜ ▱
Leisure activities : 🍱 ⟝⟞ 🚲 ≋ (beach) ⟝
Facilities : ⚷ ⚷ 🏧 ✂ 🍽 🅿
Nearby : 🍷 ✗

G P S   Longitude : 2.8837
Latitude : 46.22125

LEMPDES-SUR-ALLAGNON

43410 – Michelin map **331** B1
▶ Paris 472 – Clermont-Ferrand 56 – Le Puy-en-Velay 73 – Aurillac 102

🏔 Pont d'Allagnon

📞 0471765369, www.campingenauvergne.com

Address : rue René Filiol

Opening times :

2 ha (60 pitches) flat, grassy

Tariff : 19,20€ ♦♦ ⇌ 🔲 🚽 (10A) – Extra per person 4€

Rental rates : Permanent ♿ (1 chalet) – 2 🚐 – 6 🏠. Per night from 37 to 60€ – Per week from 215 to 500€

🚰 borne 2€

Direct access to the village via the small footbridge over the Allagnon river.

Surroundings : 🏕 🛏 🌳
Leisure activities : 🍴✕ 🎪 🏊 🎯 🎣 🛶 🏐
multi-sports ground
Facilities : ♿ 🚿 🚻 🚮 🧺 launderette
Nearby : 🚤

G P S Longitude : 3.26624
Latitude : 45.38697

MAURIAC

15200 – Michelin map **330** B3 – pop. 3 854 – alt. 722
▶ Paris 490 – Aurillac 53 – Le Mont-Dore 77 – Riom-és-Montagnes 37

🏔 Val St-Jean

📞 0471673113, www.tourismevalsaintjean.fr

Address : Base de Loisirs (2.2km west along the D 681, follow the signs for Pleaux and turn right onto D 682, direct access to a small lake)

Opening times : from beginning May to mid Sept.

3,5 ha (100 pitches) terraced, flat, grassy

Tariff : 24,70€ ♦♦ ⇌ 🔲 🚽 (10A) – Extra per person 6€

Rental rates : Permanent ♿ (1 chalet) – 20 🏠 – 10 cabins in the trees – 5 tipis. Per night from 24 to 65€ – Per week from 105 to 595€

🚰 borne 2€ – 🚽 🚽12€

Beside a lake and close to the historic city.

Surroundings : 🏕 🌲 🌳
Leisure activities : 🎪 ⏰daytime 🏃
Facilities : ♿ 🚿 🔲 🚮 🧺 launderette
Nearby : ✕ 🏊 🚲 🎣 🛶 🏖 (beach) 🏔 🎣
🐴 pedalos

G P S Longitude : 2.31657
Latitude : 45.21835

MAURS

15600 – Michelin map **330** B6 – pop. 2 213 – alt. 290
▶ Paris 568 – Aurillac 43 – Entraygues-sur-Truyère 50 – Figeac 22

🏔 Municipal le Vert

📞 0471490415, www.campinglevert-maurs.fr

Address : avenue du stade (800m southeast along the D 663, follow the signs for Décazeville; beside the Rance)

Opening times : from beginning May to end Sept.

1,2 ha (44 pitches) flat, grassy

Tariff : (2013 Price) ♦ 3,25€ ⇌ 1,60€ 🔲 6,30€ 🚽 (10A)

Rental rates : (2013 Price) Permanent – 4 🏠. Per week from 125 to 490€

Surroundings : 🛏 🌳🌳
Leisure activities : 🎪 🏊 🛶
Facilities : ♿ 🚿 🚮 🚻 🚮 🧺 🚾
Nearby : 🐴 🐴

G P S Longitude : 2.2064
Latitude : 44.70507

LE MAYET-DE-MONTAGNE

03250 – Michelin map **326** J6 – pop. 1 555 – alt. 535
▶ Paris 369 – Clermont-Ferrand 81 – Lapalisse 23 – Moulins 73

🏔 Municipal du Lac

📞 0470597052, www.lemayetdemontagne.planet-allier.com

Address : chemin de Fumouse (1.2km south along the D 7, follow the signs for Laprugne)

Opening times : from mid March to end Oct.

1 ha (50 pitches)

Tariff : ♦ 1,90€ ⇌ 🔲 2,10€ – 🚽 (10A) 1,90€

🚰 borne

Near the Lac des Moines.

Surroundings : 🏕 🌳 🌳
Leisure activities : 🎪 🏊 🎯
Facilities : ♿ 🚿 (July–Aug.) 🚮 🔲
Nearby : 🎣 🛶

G P S Longitude : 3.66854
Latitude : 46.06104

MONISTROL-D'ALLIER

43580 Michelin map **331** D4   pop. 210   alt. 500
▶ Paris 535 – Brioude 58 – Langogne 56 – Le Puy-en-Velay 28

🏔 Municipal le Vivier

📞 0471572414, www.monistroldallier.com

Address : to the south, near the Allier (direct access)

Opening times : from beginning April to mid Sept.

1 ha (48 pitches)

Tariff : (2013 Price) 14,40€ ♦♦ ⇌ 🔲 🚽 (8A) – Extra per person 3,40€

Surroundings : 🌲🌳
Leisure activities : 🎪
Facilities : ♿ 🚿 🚮
Nearby : ✕ 🏊 🎯 🎣 🛶 rafting and canyoning

G P S Longitude : 3.65348
Latitude : 44.96923

LE MONT-DORE

63240 – Michelin map **326** D9 – pop. 1 391 – alt. 1 050 – ⛷ – Winter sports : 1 050/1 850m
▶ Paris 462 – Aubusson 87 – Clermont-Ferrand 43 – Issoire 49

🏔 Municipal l'Esquiladou

📞 0473652374, www.mairie-mont-dore.fr

Address : at Queureuilh, route des Cascades (head along the D 996, following signs for Murat-le-Quaire and take turning to the right)

Opening times : from mid April to end Oct.

1,8 ha (100 pitches)

Tariff : ♦ 3,75€ ⇌ 🔲 3,85€ – 🚽 (16A) 4€

Rental rates : (from mid Dec. to end Oct.) – 17 🚐. Per night from 51 to 89€ – Per week from 270 to 540€

🚰 borne

In a mountainous setting, green and wooded.

Surroundings : 🏕 🌲 🛏
Leisure activities : 🎪 jacuzzi 🏊 🔲
Facilities : ♿ 🚿 🚾 🧺 launderette
Nearby : 🎯 🎣 🐴

G P S Longitude : 2.80162
Latitude : 45.58706

Some campsites benefit from proximity to a municipal leisure centre.

MURAT-LE-QUAIRE

63150 – Michelin map **326** D9 – pop. 476 – alt. 1 050
▷ Paris 478 – Clermont-Ferrand 45 – Aurillac 120 – Cournon d'Auvergne 60

⛰ Le Panoramique

✆ 04 73 81 18 79, www.campingpanoramique.fr/
Address : 1.4km east along the D 219, follow the signs for Le Mont-Dore and take road to the left
Opening times : from end Dec. to end Oct.
3 ha (85 pitches)
Tariff : ♦ ⇌ 🔲 17,30€ – (₦) (10A) 6,10€
Rental rates : (from end Dec. to end Oct.) – 1 ⬚ – 4 🏠.
Per week from 310 to 739€
🚐 borne 4,50€
In an attractive, elevated location.

Surroundings : ⑆ ⩽ Les Monts Dore and Dordogne valley	**GPS**	Longitude : 2.74779
Leisure activities : 🍽 ✗ 🏤 🚴 🏊		Latitude : 45.596
Facilities : ⛔ ☎ 🏧 🛁 ☁ 🗑 🍴 🔲		

🏕 Municipal les Couderts

✆ 04 73 65 54 81, www.camping-couderts.e-monsite.com/
Address : Les Couderts (take the northern exit; beside a stream)
Opening times : from beginning April to mid Oct.
1,7 ha (58 pitches)
Tariff : (2013 Price) 9,10€ ♦♦ ⇌ 🔲 (₦) (10A) – Extra per person 2,95€
Rental rates : (2013 Price) Permanent – 3 ⬚ – 6 🏠. Per night 80€ – Per week 515€
🚐 borne 8€

Surroundings : ⑆ ⩽ ⌷ ♀	**GPS**	Longitude : 2.73511
Leisure activities : 🚴		Latitude : 45.59937
Facilities : ⛔ ☎ 🏧 🏤 🛁 🍴 launderette		

To make the best possible use of this guide, please read pages 2–15 carefully.

MUROL

63790 – Michelin map **326** E9 – pop. 546 – alt. 830
▷ Paris 456 – Besse-en-Chandesse 10 – Clermont-Ferrand 37 – Condat 37

🏕 Sunêlia La Ribeyre 👥

POMMIER

✆ 04 73 88 64 29, www.laribeyre.com
Address : at Jassat (1.2km to the south, follow the signs for Jassat; beside a stream)
Opening times : from beginning May to mid Sept.
10 ha (460 pitches)
Tariff : 41,45€ ♦♦ ⇌ 🔲 (₦) (10A) Extra per person 7,90€ – Reservation fee 30€
Rental rates : (from beginning May to mid Sept.) ⛔ – 97 ⬚.
Per night from 36 to 203€ – Per week from 252 to 1 421 € – Reservation fee 30€
The site has an excellent water park.

Surroundings : ⑆ ⩽ ♀♀	**GPS**	Longitude : 2.93719
Leisure activities : 🍽 ✗ 🏤 🗗 🏃 jacuzzi 🚴 🎿 🔲 🛶 (lake) 🏊		Latitude : 45.56232
Facilities : ⛔ ☎ 🛁 🍴 🗑 launderette 🏊 🛁		
Nearby : 🎣		

⛰ Le Repos du Baladin

✆ 04 73 88 61 93, www.camping-auvergne-france.com
Address : Groire (located 1.5km east along the D 146, follow the signs for St-Diéry)
Opening times : from end April to mid Sept.
1,6 ha (88 pitches)
Tariff : (2013 Price) ♦ 5,10€ ⇌ 🔲 13,60€ – (₦) (10A) 6€ – Reservation fee 13€
Rental rates : (2013 Price) (from end April to mid Sept.) – 22 ⬚ 2 🏠. Per night from 45 to 62€ – Per week from 220 to 695€ Reservation fee 13€

Surroundings : ⩽ ⌷ ♀♀	**GPS**	Longitude : 2.95728
Leisure activities : 🍽 ✗ 🏤 ⛲ 🚴 🎿		Latitude : 45.57379
Facilities : ⛔ ☎ 🛁 🍴 🔲 🛁		

NÉBOUZAT

63210 – Michelin map **326** E8 – pop. 774 – alt. 860
▷ Paris 434 – La Bourboule 34 – Clermont-Ferrand 20 – Pontgibaud 19

⛰ Les Dômes

✆ 04 73 87 14 06, www.les-domes.com – alt. 815
Address : Les Quatre Routes de Nébouzat (along the D 216, follow the signs for Rochefort-Montagne)
1 ha (65 pitches) flat, grassy
Rentals : 8 ⬚ – 5 🏠 – 5 canvas bungalows.
Boasts an entrance surrounded by flowers in a well-kept, green setting.

Surroundings : ⩽ ♀	**GPS**	Longitude : 2.89028
Leisure activities : 🏤 🔲 (open air in season)		Latitude : 45.72538
Facilities : ☎ 🛁 🗑 🍴 🔲		
Nearby : 🍽 ✗ 🚲 🐎		

NÉRIS-LES-BAINS

03310 – Michelin map **326** C5 – pop. 2 705 – alt. 364 – ⚓
▷ Paris 336 – Clermont-Ferrand 86 – Montluçon 9 – Moulins 73

⛰ Municipal du Lac

✆ 04 70 03 24 70, www.ville-neris-les-bains.fr
Opening times : from end March to beginning Nov.
3,5 ha (129 pitches)
Tariff : (2013 Price) 10,80€ ♦♦ ⇌ 🔲 (₦) (6A) – Extra per person 4,20€
Rental rates : (2013 Price) Permanent – 21 🏠 – 7 apartments. Per night from 31 to 44€ – Per week from 390 to 545€
🚐 borne 7€ – 5 🔲
A pleasant location near the old station and a lake. A tariff including spa entry is available.

Surroundings : ⑆ ⌷ ♀	**GPS**	Longitude : 2.65174
Leisure activities : 🍽 ✗ 🏤 🏃 🚴 🎿		Latitude : 46.28702
Facilities : ⛔ ☎ 🗗 🛁 🍴 launderette		
Nearby : 🚲 ✗ 🔲 🏊 fitness trail		

NEUSSARGUES-MOISSAC

15170 – Michelin map **330** F4 – pop. 959 – alt. 834
▶ Paris 509 – Aurillac 58 – Brioude 49 – Issoire 64

⚠ Municipal de la Prade

✆ 0471205021, www.neussargues-moissac.fr

Address : route de Murat (take the western exit along the D 304,
follow the signs for Murat; beside the Alagnon river)

Opening times : from beginning June to end Aug.

2 ha (22 pitches) terraced, small wood

Tariff : 11,10€ ♦♦ ⬅ ▣ ⵑ (10A) – Extra per person 1,95€
Rental rates : Permanent 🅿 – 8 🛏 – 6 🏠. Per week
from 234 to 494€
Situated on the banks of the river.

Surroundings : 🏞 ⬳ ▱ 🌳	G	Longitude : 2.96695
Leisure activities : 🏛 🛶 🏊	P	Latitude : 45.12923
Facilities : ♿ ⚡ 🚻 ♨ ⛴ 🧺 ⛽ 🛒	S	

NEUVÉGLISE

15260 – Michelin map **330** F5 – pop. 1 130 – alt. 938
▶ Paris 528 – Aurillac 78 – Entraygues-sur-Truyère 70 – Espalion 66

⚠ Flower Le Belvédère

✆ 0471235050, www.campinglebelvedere.com – pitches accessed
via steep slope, help moving caravans onto and off pitches available
on request – alt. 670

Address : Lanau (6.5km south along the D 48, D 921, follow the signs
for Chaudes-Aigues and take the Chemin de Gros to the right)

Opening times : from mid April to end Sept.

5 ha (116 pitches) terraced

Tariff : 29€ ♦♦ ⬅ ▣ ⵑ (15A) – Extra per person 6€ – Reservation
fee 13€
Rental rates : (from mid April to end Sept.) – 29 🛏 – 7 🏠
4 canvas bungalows – 2 tent lodges. Per night from 30 to 127€ –
Per week from 180 to 889€ – Reservation fee 13€
🚐 borne
In an attractive elevated location.

Surroundings : ⬳ Gorges de la Truyère ▱ 🌳	G	Longitude : 3.00045
Leisure activities : 🍴 🍽 🏛 🕑 🚴 🚎 🖼	P	Latitude : 44.89534
Facilities : ♿ ⚡ ♨ ⛴ ⛽ 🧺 launderette 🚿	S	

To visit a town or region, use the MICHELIN Green Guides.

NONETTE

63340 – Michelin map **326** G10 – pop. 322 – alt. 480
▶ Paris 467 – Clermont-Ferrand 51 – Cournon-d'Auvergne 47 –
Riom 66

⚠ Les Loges

✆ 0473716582, www.lesloges.com

Address : situated 2km south along the D 722, follow the signs for
Le Breuil-sur-Couze then continue 1km along the road near the
bridge; beside the Allier river

4 ha (126 pitches) flat, grassy
Rentals : 25 🛏.

Surroundings : 🏞 ▱ 🌳	G	Longitude : 3.27158
Leisure activities : 🍴 🍽 🛶 ♨ 🚣 🛝	P	Latitude : 45.47367
Facilities : ♿ ⚡ ♨ ⛴ 🛒	S	

ORCET

63670 – Michelin map **326** G8 – pop. 2 729 – alt. 400
▶ Paris 424 – Billom 16 – Clermont-Ferrand 14 – Issoire 25

⚠ Clos Auroy

✆ 0473842697, www.camping-le-clos-auroy.com

Address : 15 rue de la Narse (200m south of the town, near the
Auzon river)

Opening times : Permanent

3 ha (91 pitches)

Tariff : ♦ 6,30€ ⬅ ▣ 14,18€ – ⵑ (10A) 5€ – Reservation fee 20€
Rental rates : (from beginning April to mid Oct.) 🛶 (April to
July) – 9 🛏 – 2 canvas bungalows. Per night from 50 to 75€ –
Per week from 250 to 750€ – Reservation fee 20€
🚐 borne 4€
Attractive shrubs surround the pitches.

Surroundings : ▱	G	Longitude : 3.16912
Leisure activities : 🍽 🏛 🕑daytime 🛁 jacuzzi 🛶 🏊	P	Latitude : 45.70029
Facilities : ♿ ⚡ 🚻 ♨ ⛴ 🛒 🍴 launderette	S	
Nearby : ✂		

ORLÉAT

63190 – Michelin map **326** H7 – pop. 2 010 – alt. 380
▶ Paris 440 – Clermont-Ferrand 34 – Roanne 76 – Vichy 38

⚠ Le Pont-Astier

✆ 0473536440, www.camping-lepont-astier.fr

Address : base de loisirs (leisure centre) (5km east along the D 85,
D 224 and take road to the left; beside the Dore river)

Opening times : from beginning March to end Nov.

2 ha (90 pitches) flat, grassy

Tariff : 16,50€ ♦♦ ⬅ ▣ ⵑ (16A) – Extra per person 4€
Rental rates : (from beginning March to end Nov.) – 7 🛏.
Per night from 60€ – Per week from 260 to 390€ – Reservation
fee 8€
🚐 borne

Surroundings : ⬳ ▱	G	Longitude : 3.47664
Leisure activities : 🍴 🍽 🛶 ✂ 🚣 🛶	P	Latitude : 45.86813
Facilities : ♿ ⚡ ⛽ 🛒	S	
Nearby : 🎣		

PAULHAGUET

43230 – Michelin map **331** D2 – pop. 959 – alt. 562
▶ Paris 495 – Brioude 18 – La Chaise-Dieu 24 – Langeac 15

⚠ La Fridière

✆ 0471766554, www.campingfr.nl

Address : 6 route d'Esfacy (located to the southeast along the D 4;
beside the Senouire river)

Opening times : from beginning April to beginning Oct.

3 ha (45 pitches) flat, grassy

Tariff : 17,90€ ♦♦ ⬅ ▣ ⵑ (16A) – Extra per person 3,50 €
🚐 borne

Surroundings : 🏞 ▱	G	Longitude : 3.52
Leisure activities : 🍴 🏛 🛶 🏊	P	Latitude : 45.199
Facilities : ♿ ⚡ 🚻 ▨ 🎢 ⛴ 🍴 🛒	S	

PERS

15290 – Michelin map **330** B5 – pop. 303 – alt. 570
▶ Paris 547 – Argentat 45 – Aurillac 25 – Maurs 24

Le Viaduc

📞 0471647008, www.camping-cantal.com

Address : Le Ribeyrès (5km northeast along the D 32 and take the D 61; beside the lake at St-Etienne-Cantalès)

1 ha (54 pitches) terraced

Rentals : 8 🚐 – 1 🏠.

In a pleasant location.

Surroundings : ⛱ ⇜ ⌂ ♀
Leisure activities : ⛵ ⛱ 🏊 🎣 ⛷
Facilities : & 🚿 🕈 launderette 🧹
Nearby : watersports centre

G P S Longitude : 2.2556
Latitude : 44.90602

PIERREFITTE-SUR-LOIRE

03470 – Michelin map **326** J3 – pop. 518 – alt. 228
▶ Paris 324 – Bourbon-Lancy 20 – Lapalisse 50 – Moulins 42

⛺ Municipal le Vernay

📞 0670505036, www.pierrefitte03.fr

Address : Le Vernay (Take the northwestern exit along the N 79, follow the signs for Dompierre, left onto D 295, follow the signs for Saligny-sur-Roudon then continue 900m along the road to the right after the bridge, 200m from the canal)

Opening times : from beginning April to end Sept.

2 ha (35 pitches) flat, grassy

Tariff : ♣ 2,50€ 🚐 🔲 3,50€ – 🔌 (6A) 2€

Rental rates : (from beginning April to end Sept.) – 12 🚐 1 gîte. Per night from 50 to 60€ – Per week from 200 to 300€ Reservation fee 15€

🚐 borne

Situated near a small lake.

Surroundings : ⇜ ⌂
Facilities : & 🚿 (July-Aug.) 🚮 🚻 🕈 🔲
Nearby : ⛵ ✕ 🏊 🎾 ⛱ (beach) 🎣 fitness trail

G P S Longitude : 3.80334
Latitude : 46.51734

PONTGIBAUD

63230 – Michelin map **326** E8 – pop. 745 – alt. 735
▶ Paris 432 – Aubusson 68 – Clermont-Ferrand 23 – Le Mont-Dore 37

⛺ Municipal de la Palle

📞 0473889699, campongibaud.free.fr

Address : route de la Miouze (500m southwest along the D 986, follow the signs for Rochefort-Montagne; beside the Sioule river)

Opening times : from mid April to end Sept.

4,5 ha (85 pitches) flat, grassy

Tariff : (2013 Price) 15,60€ ♣♣ 🚐 🔲 🔌 (16A) Extra per person 4,20€

Rental rates : (from mid April to mid Oct.) & (1 chalet) – 6 🏠. Per night from 60€ – Per week from 250 to 470€

🚐 borne 2,50€

Surroundings : ⌂
Leisure activities : 🏠 🏊 🎣
Facilities : & 🚿 🕈 launderette
Nearby : ⛵ ✕

G P S Longitude : 2.84516
Latitude : 45.82982

PUY-GUILLAUME

63290 – Michelin map **326** H7 – pop. 2 631 – alt. 285
▶ Paris 374 – Clermont-Ferrand 53 – Lezoux 27 – Riom 35

⛰ Municipal de la Dore

📞 0473947851, www.puy-guillaume.com

Address : 86 rue Joseph-Claussat (take the western exit along the D 63, follow the signs for Randan and take a right turn before the bridge, near the river)

Opening times : from mid June to end Aug.

3 ha (100 pitches) flat, grassy

Tariff : ♣ 3,90€ 🚐 🔲 4,60€ – 🔌 (6A) 3,90€

Surroundings : ♀
Leisure activities : 🏠 🏊 🎣 🎣
Facilities : & 🚿 🚮 🔲
Nearby : ⛵ ✕ 🎾 fitness trail

G P S Longitude : 3.46623
Latitude : 45.96223

A chambre d'hôte is a guesthouse or B & B-style accommodation.

ROYAT

63130 – Michelin map **326** F8 – pop. 4 431 – alt. 450 – ♨
▶ Paris 423 – Aubusson 89 – La Bourboule 47 – Clermont-Ferrand 5

⛰ Indigo Royat ♣♣

HUTTOPIA

📞 0473359705, www.camping-indigo.com

Address : route de Gravenoire (situated 2km southeast along the D 941c, follow the signs for Le Mont-Dore and take a right turn D 5, follow the signs for Charade)

Opening times : from end March to beginning Nov.

7 ha (200 pitches)

Tariff : (2013 Price) 29,80€ ♣♣ 🚐 🔲 🔌 (10A) – Extra per person 6,10€ – Reservation fee 22€

Rental rates : (from end March to beginning Nov.) – 2 caravans 31 🚐 – 6 🏠 – 9 tent lodges. Per night from 48 to 129€ – Per week from 235 to 903€ – Reservation fee 22€

🚐 borne 7€

Pleasantly leafy setting with plenty of shade.

Surroundings : ⌂ ♀
Leisure activities : ⛵ ✕ 🏠 🎮 🏃 🏊 🚲 🎾 🎣
Facilities : & 🚿 🔲 🚻 🚮 🕈 🔲

G P S Longitude : 3.05452
Latitude : 45.75868

RUYNES-EN-MARGERIDE

15320 – Michelin map **330** H4 – pop. 640 – alt. 920
▶ Paris 527 – Clermont-Ferrand 111 – Aurillac 86 – Le Puy-en-Velay 88

⛺ Révéa Le Petit Bois

📞 0471234226, www.revea-camping.fr

Address : at Lesparot

4 ha (90 pitches) relatively flat, flat, grassy

Rentals : 20 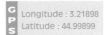 – 20 huts (without sanitary facilities).
Located in a pleasant pine forest

Surroundings : ⚓ ≤ ♨♨
Facilities : ♿ ⊶ launderette
Nearby : 🌳 forest trail

GPS
Longitude : 3.21898
Latitude : 44.99899

SAIGNES

15240 – Michelin map **330** C2 – pop. 892 – alt. 480
▶ Paris 483 – Aurillac 78 – Clermont-Ferrand 91 – Mauriac 26

⚠ Municipal Bellevue

☎ 0471406840, www.saignes-mairie.fr

Address : take the northwestern exit, by the stadium

Opening times : from beginning July to end Aug.

1 ha (42 pitches) flat, grassy

Tariff : (2013 Price) 🧍 2,24€ ⛺ 1,17€ 🔲 1,38€ – 🔌 (16A) 2,45€
Rental rates : (2013 Price) (from beginning June to end Aug.)
3 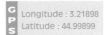. Per night from 40 to 50€ – Per week from 250 to 310€

Surroundings : ≤ ▱ ♨
Leisure activities : 🎱 ⛱
Facilities : ♿ ⊶ 🧺 📷
Nearby : 🍴 🏊

GPS
Longitude : 2.47416
Latitude : 45.33678

ST-AMANT-ROCHE-SAVINE

63890 – Michelin map **326** I9 – pop. 539 – alt. 950
▶ Paris 474 – Ambert 12 – La Chaise-Dieu 39 – Clermont-Ferrand 65

⚠ Municipal Saviloisirs

☎ 0473957360, www.saviloisirs.com

Address : 7 place de la Liberté (east of the town)

1,3 ha (19 pitches)

Rentals : 30 🏠.

Surroundings : ≤ ▱
Leisure activities : 🎱 ⛹ ⛱
Facilities : ♿ ▥ ⛲ ⚒ launderette
Nearby : 🌳 🍷 🍴 🏊

GPS
Longitude : 3.63389
Latitude : 45.64347

ST-BONNET-TRONÇAIS

03360 – Michelin map **326** D3 – pop. 751 – alt. 224
▶ Paris 301 – Bourges 57 – Cérilly 12 – Montluçon 44

⛰ Centre de Tourisme de Champ Fossé

☎ 0470061130, www.campingstroncais.com

Address : place du Champ de Foire (700m southwest)

Opening times : from beginning April to end Sept.

3 ha (110 pitches)

Tariff : 🧍 4,45€ ⛺ 1,35€ 🔲 4,45€ – 🔌 (10A) 3,50€ – Reservation fee 15€
Rental rates : (from beginning April to end Sept.) – 12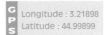
10 gîtes. Per night 120€ – Per week 520€ – Reservation fee 15€
An attractive location beside the Étang de St-Bonnet (lake).

Surroundings : ⚓ ≤ ♨
Leisure activities : 🍷 🎱 🏇
Facilities : ⊶ ⚒ launderette
Nearby : ⛱ 🚲 🍴 ⚲ 🏖 (beach) ⛷ 🎣
pedalos

GPS
Longitude : 2.68841
Latitude : 46.65687

ST-DIDIER-EN-VELAY

43140 – Michelin map **331** H2 – pop. 3 313 – alt. 830
▶ Paris 538 – Annonay 49 – Monistrol-sur-Loire 11 – Le Puy-en-Velay 58

⚠ La Fressange

☎ 0471662528, www.saint-didier.com/camping

Address : 800m southeast along the D 45, follow the signs for St-Romain-Lachalm and take the turning to the left; beside a stream

Opening times : from end April to end Sept.

1,5 ha (72 pitches) sloping

Tariff : 17,55€ 🧍🧍 ⛺ 🔲 🔌 (16A) – Extra per person 4,75€
Rental rates : (from mid April to mid Oct.) – 11 🏠. Per night from 78 to 115€ – Per week from 190 to 480€
A sunny site, on the side of a hill.

Surroundings : ♨
Leisure activities : ⛱
Facilities : ♿ ⊶ 🍴 📷
Nearby : ⚲ 🏊 🎣 sports trail

GPS
Longitude : 4.28302
Latitude : 45.30119

ST-ÉLOY-LES-MINES

63700 – Michelin map **326** E6 – pop. 3 703 – alt. 490
▶ Paris 358 – Clermont-Ferrand 64 – Guéret 86 – Montluçon 31

⚠ Municipal la Poule d'Eau

☎ 0473854547, selm.maire@wanadoo.fr – ₣₮

Address : rue de la Poule d'Eau (southern exit from the N144, signs for Clermont, then right turn, 1.3km on the D110, rte de Pionsat)

Opening times : from mid June to mid Sept.

1,8 ha (50 pitches)

Tariff : (2013 Price) 11,40€ 🧍🧍 ⛺ 🔲 🔌 (8A) – Extra per person 2,50€
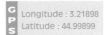 6 🔲 6,90€
In a green setting beside two lakes.

Surroundings : ≤ ▱ ♨ ⛰
Leisure activities : ⛱ 🎣
Facilities : ♿ ⊶ 🧺
Nearby : 🍷 🍴 ⚲ 🎿 🏖 🏊 (beach) fitness trail

GPS
Longitude : 2.83057
Latitude : 46.15064

ST-GERMAIN-L'HERM

63630 – Michelin map **326** I10 – pop. 508 – alt. 1 050
▶ Paris 476 – Ambert 27 – Brioude 33 – Clermont-Ferrand 66

⛰ St-Éloy

☎ 0473720513, www.camping-le-saint-eloy.fr

Address : route de la Chaise-Dieu (take the southeastern exit, on the D 999)

Opening times : from beginning May to end Sept.

3 ha (63 pitches)

Tariff : 19,10€ 🧍🧍 ⛺ 🔲 🔌 (10A) – Extra per person 4,50€
Rental rates : Permanent – 13 🏠. Per week from 220 to 700€
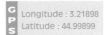 borne 15€ – 4 🔲 15€

Surroundings : ≤
Leisure activities : ✗ 🎱 ⛱ 🚲 🏊
Facilities : ♿ ⊶ 🍴 📷
Nearby : 🌳 🍴 🏊

GPS
Longitude : 3.54781
Latitude : 45.45653

ST-GÉRONS

15150 – Michelin map **330** B5 – pop. 209 – alt. 526
▶ Paris 538 – Argentat 35 – Aurillac 24 – Maurs 33

⛰ Les Rives du Lac

✆ 06 25 34 62 89, www.lesrivesdulac.fr

Address : 8.5km southeast along the follow the signs for Espinet; 300m from the lake at St-Étienne-Cantalès

Opening times : from mid March to mid Nov.

3 ha (100 pitches) relatively flat

Tariff : 19€ � ✦ ⬛ 🔌 (10A) – Extra per person 4,50€ – Reservation fee 10€

Rental rates : (from mid March to mid Nov.) – 20 🛖. Per night from 60 to 75€ – Per week from 220 to 550€ – Reservation fee 16€

🚐 borne 2€ – 🚿 🔌12€

In a pleasant setting.

Surroundings : 🚣 🛶 〰
Leisure activities : 🍸 🛶 🏖 🔥 🛶
Facilities : ♿ ⛱ 🚿 🛖 launderette 🚮
Nearby : ✗ 🍴 🛶 (beach) 🚣

GPS Longitude : 2.23057
Latitude : 44.93523

ST-GERVAIS-D'AUVERGNE

63390 – Michelin map **326** D6 – pop. 1 304 – alt. 725
▶ Paris 377 – Aubusson 72 – Clermont-Ferrand 55 – Gannat 41

⛰ Municipal de l'Étang Philippe

✆ 04 73 85 74 84, www.ville-stgervais-auvergne.fr

Address : Mazières (take the northern exit along the D 987, follow the signs for St-Éloy-les-Mines; near a small lake)

Opening times : from beginning April to end Sept.

3 ha (130 pitches)

Tariff : 10€ ✦ ✦ ⬛ 🔌 (10A) – Extra per person 1,50€ – Reservation fee 20€

Rental rates : Permanent – 6 🏠 – 4 tent lodges. Per night 40€ Per week from 180 to 390€ – Reservation fee 45€

🚐 borne 2€

Surroundings : 🛶 🌳 ⛰
Leisure activities : 🏛
Facilities : ♿ ⛱ 🚿 🛖 📶
Nearby : 🛶 🛶 🔥 🛶 (beach) 🚣 🐎

In order for the guide to remain wholly objective, the selection of campsites is made on an entirely independent basis.

ST-JACQUES-DES BLATS

15800 – Michelin map **330** E4 – pop. 325 – alt. 990
▶ Paris 536 – Aurillac 32 – Brioude 76 – Issoire 91

⛰ des Blats

✆ 04 71 47 06 00, www.camping-des-blats.fr

Address : east of the village, follow the signs for Nierevèze, beside the Cère river

Opening times : from mid Dec. to mid March and from beginning May to mid Sept.

1,5 ha (50 pitches) flat, grassy

Tariff : 16,80€ ✦ ✦ ⬛ 🔌 (10A) – Extra per person 4,60€ Reservation fee 4€

Rental rates : Permanent ♿ (1 chalet) – 4 🏠 – 1 tipi – 3 mini-chalets (without sanitary facilities). Per night from 30 to 45€ Per week from 210 to 550€ – Reservation fee 8€

🚐 borne 2€

Surroundings : ⟨ 🛶 〰
Leisure activities : ✗ 🏛 🛶 🚲 🚣
Facilities : ♿ ⛱ 🎱 🛶 🚿 launderette
Nearby : 🛶 🔥

GPS Longitude : 2.71345
Latitude : 45.05182

ST-JUST

15320 – Michelin map **330** H5 – pop. 206 – alt. 950
▶ Paris 531 – Chaudes-Aigues 29 – Ruynes-en-Margeride 22 – St-Chély-d'Apcher 16

⛰ Municipal

✆ 04 71 73 70 48, www.saintjust.com

Address : in the village (southeast; beside a stream - follow A 75: take exit 31 ou 32)

Opening times : from end April to end Sept.

2 ha (60 pitches) flat and relatively flat

Tariff : 12€ ✦ ✦ ⬛ 🔌 (10A) – Extra per person 2,10€

Rental rates : Permanent ♿ (1 mobile home) – 7 🛖 – 5 🏠 7 gîtes. Per night from 59 to 133€ – Per week from 195 to 442€

🚐 borne 2€ – 6 ⬛ 9,50€ – 🚿 🔌9,50€

In the heart of the mountains, the site is crossed by a stream.

Surroundings : 🛶 🌿
Leisure activities : 🏛
Facilities : ♿ ⛱ 🚐 🛖 launderette
Nearby : 🚮 🍸 ✗ 🛶 🔥 🛶

GPS Longitude : 3.20938
Latitude : 44.88993

ST-MARTIN-CANTALES

15140 – Michelin map **330** B4 – pop. 177 – alt. 630
▶ Paris 546 – Clermont-Ferrand 135 – Le Puy-en-Velay 180 – Aurillac 34

⛰ Pont du Rouffet

✆ 04 71 69 42 76, www.campingpontdurouffet.com

Address : Pont du Rouffet

1 ha (30 pitches) terraced, flat, grassy

Rentals : 4 🛖.

Surroundings : 🛶 ⟨ 🛶 〰
Leisure activities : 🏛 🛶 🚣
Facilities : ♿ ⛱ 🚿 🛶 📶

GPS Longitude : 2.2585
Latitude : 45.072

ST-MARTIN-VALMEROUX

15140 – Michelin map **330** C4 – pop. 856 – alt. 646
▶ Paris 510 – Aurillac 33 – Mauriac 21 – Murat 53

⛰ Municipal Le Moulin du Teinturier

✆ 04 71 69 43 12, campingdestmartinvalmeroux15140@wanadoo.fr

Address : 9 rue de Montjoly (take the western exit, on the D 37, follow the signs for Ste-Eulalie-Nozières; beside the Maronne)

Opening times : from mid June to mid Sept.

3 ha (100 pitches) flat, grassy

Tariff : (2013 Price) 12,40€ ✦ ✦ ⬛ 🔌 (20A)
Extra per person 3,50€ – Reservation fee 30€

Rental rates : (2013 Price) (from mid April to mid Nov.) 20 🏠. Per night from 33 to 72€ – Per week from 230 to 505€ Reservation fee 30€

🚐 borne 6€

Surroundings : ≤ ⌂
Leisure activities : 🏛 🛶 🎣
Facilities : 🚹 ⚭ 🍴 ⛱ 🏕 ♨ 🎱
Nearby : ✗ 🏇 ⛷

Longitude : 2.42336
Latitude : 45.11619

ST-NECTAIRE

63710 – Michelin map **326** E9 – pop. 732 – alt. 700 – ⚐
▶ Paris 453 – Clermont-Ferrand 43 – Issoire 27 – Le Mont-Dore 24

🏔 Le Viginet

☎ 04 73 88 53 80, www.camping-viginet.com

Address : take southeastern exit along the D 996 then continue 600m along the road to the left (opposite the Ford garage)

Opening times : from beginning April to end Sept.

2 ha (61 pitches)

Tariff : 24€ ✶✶ 🚐 🔲 🔌 (10A) – Extra per person 4,80€ – Reservation fee 7€

Rental rates : Permanent – 12 🏠 – 14 canvas bungalows. Per night from 25 to 80€ – Per week from 150 to 900€ Reservation fee 7€

There are fine views of the surrounding countryside from the site.

Surroundings : 🐿 ≤ ⌂ ♨
Leisure activities : 🏛 🛶 ⛷
Facilities : 🚹 ⚭ 🍴 🎱
Nearby : ✗ 🏇 fitness trail

Longitude : 3.00269
Latitude : 45.57945

🏔 La Clé des Champs

☎ 04 73 88 52 33, www.campingcledeschamps.com

Address : take southeastern exit along the D 996 and take D 642, follow the signs for Les Granges; beside a stream and 200m from the Couze de Chambon

Opening times : from beginning April to end Sept.

1 ha (84 pitches)

Tariff : 19,50€ ✶✶ 🚐 🔲 🔌 (6A) – Extra per person 5,50€ Reservation fee 10€

Rental rates : Permanent – 18 🚐 – 9 🏠. Per night from 28 to 70€ – Per week from 160 to 810€ – Reservation fee 10€

🚐 borne 4€ – 3 🔲 11,50€

Surroundings : ⌂ ♨
Leisure activities : ▼ ✗ 🏛 🛶 ⛷ 🎣
Facilities : 🚹 ⚭ 🏕 ♨ 🍴 🎱 ⛱

Longitude : 2.99934
Latitude : 45.57602

ST-PAULIEN

43350 – Michelin map **331** E3 – pop. 2 398 – alt. 795
▶ Paris 529 – La Chaise-Dieu 28 – Craponne-sur-Arzon 25 – Le Puy-en-Velay 14

🏔 La Rochelambert

☎ 04 71 00 54 02, www.camping-rochelambert.com

Address : route de Lanthenas (head 2.7km southwest along the D 13, follow the signs for Allègre and turn left onto D 25, follow the signs for Loudes; near the Borne (direct access)

Opening times : from beginning April to end Sept.

---

3 ha (100 pitches) flat, grassy

Tariff : 21,90€ ✶✶ 🚐 🔲 🔌 (16A)
Extra per person 4,70€ – Reservation fee 9€

Rental rates : (2013 Price) (from beginning April to end Sept.) 2 caravans – 12 🏠. Per night from 62€ – Per week from 249 to 610€ Reservation fee 9€

🚐 borne 3€ – 🛒 11€

Surroundings : ⌂
Leisure activities : ▼ ✗ 🛶 ✗ 🎣
Facilities : 🚹 ⚭ ⛱ 🍴 launderette

Longitude : 3.81192
Latitude : 45.13547

ST-POURÇAIN-SUR-SIOULE

03500 – Michelin map **326** G5 – pop. 5 030 – alt. 234
▶ Paris 325 – Montluçon 66 – Moulins 33 – Riom 61

🏔 L'Ile de la Ronde

☎ 04 70 45 45 43, www.campingiledelaronde.fr

Address : quai de la Ronde

Opening times :

1,5 ha (58 pitches) flat, grassy

Tariff : (2013 Price) 13,05€ ✶✶ 🚐 🔲 🔌 (10A)
Extra per person 2,50€

Rental rates : (2013 Price) (from beginning April to beginning Oct.) 6 🚐. Per night from 40 to 55€ – Per week from 200 to 380€

🚐 borne

In a public park, beside the Sioule river.

Surroundings : ⌂ ♨
Leisure activities : 🛶 🚲 🎣
Facilities : 🚹 ⚭ 🏕 🎱
Nearby : ✗ ⛷

Longitude : 3.29265
Latitude : 46.30605

There are several different types of sani-station ('borne' in French) – sanitation points providing fresh water and disposal points for grey water. See page 12 for further details.

ST-RÉMY-SUR-DUROLLE

63550 – Michelin map **326** I7 – pop. 1 847 – alt. 620
▶ Paris 395 – Chabreloche 13 – Clermont-Ferrand 55 – Thiers 7

🏔 Révéa Les Chanterelles

☎ 04 73 94 31 71, www.revea-camping.fr/fr/accueil-camping-les-chanterelles.ht

Address : 3km northeast along the D 201 and take the road to the right – take A 72: exit 3

Opening times : from end April to mid Sept.

5 ha (150 pitches)

Tariff : (2013 Price) 16,60€ ✶✶ 🚐 🔲 🔌 (10A)
Extra per person 4,10€ – Reservation fee 10€

Rental rates : (from end April to mid Sept.) – 8 🏠. Per night from 100€ – Per week from 225 to 550€ – Reservation fee 25€

A pleasant location in the highlands near a small lake.

Surroundings : ≤ ♨
Leisure activities : 🏛 🛶
Facilities : 🚹 ⚭ 🔲 🎱
At the lake : 🛶 ▼ ✗ ✗ 🖼 🏇 ⛷ 🛥 (beach) ⛵, squash

Longitude : 3.59918
Latitude : 45.90308

STE-SIGOLÈNE

43600 – Michelin map **331** H2 – pop. 5 900 – alt. 808
▶ Paris 551 – Annonay 50 – Monistrol-sur-Loire 8 – Montfaucon-en-Velay 14

⚠ Kawan Village de Vaubarlet ♣

📞 0471666495, www.vaubarlet.com – alt. 600

Address : head 6km southwest along the D 43, follow the signs for Grazac

Opening times : from beginning May to end Sept.

15 ha/3 for camping (131 pitches) flat, grassy

Tariff : 28€ ★★ ⇔ 圓 ▣ (16A) – Extra per person 4€ – Reservation fee 15€

Rental rates : (from beginning May to end Sept.) ⅙ (2 chalets) 1 caravan – 18 🚐 – 5 🏠 – 5 canvas bungalows – 2 tent lodges. Per night from 40 to 65€ – Per week from 305 to 685€ Reservation fee 30€

🚐 borne 17€ – 💧▣14€

In a green valley crossed by the Dunière river.

Surroundings : 🏞 ⋖ ⬤
Leisure activities : 🍴 ✗ 🎯 ☉daytime 🏃
🚣 🚲 🎿
Facilities : ⅙ ⌁ 🛆 – 2 individual sanitary facilities (🚿 ⚿ wc) 🍴 launderette 🚿

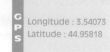

G
P
S
Longitude : 4.21254
Latitude : 45.21634

SAUGUES

43170 – Michelin map **331** D4 – pop. 1 873 – alt. 960
▶ Paris 529 – Brioude 51 – Mende 72 – Le Puy-en-Velay 43

⚠ Municipal Sporting de la Seuge

📞 0471778062, www.saugues.fr/tourisme/hebergements/camping

Address : avenue du Gévaudan (take the western exit along the D 589, follow the signs for Le Malzieu-Ville and take a right turn; beside the Seuge river and near two lakes and a pine forest)

Opening times : from mid April to mid Oct.

3 ha (92 pitches) flat, grassy

Tariff : (2013 Price) 13,50€ ★★ ⇔ 圓 ▣ (16A) – Extra per person 3€
Rental rates : Permanent – 15 🏠 – 5 ⛺ – 1 gîte. Per week 459€
🚐 borne – 3 圓 6,30€

A natural pool (clean and filtered but no chemicals).

Surroundings : ⋖ ⬤
Leisure activities : 🎯 🚣 ✗ 🏊(fresh water) 🎿 multi-sports ground, entertainment room
Facilities : ⅙ ⌁ 🛆 🍴 launderette
Nearby : 🏊 🎿 🐎 sports trail, pedalos

G
P
S
Longitude : 3.54073
Latitude : 44.95818

SAZERET

03390 – Michelin map **326** E4 – pop. 157 – alt. 370
▶ Paris 348 – Gannat 44 – Montluçon 34 – Montmarault 4

⚠ La Petite Valette

📞 0470076457, www.valette.nl – access difficult in some places (track)

Address : 5.5km to the northeast, access via rte Les Deux-Chaises parallel to the N 79 and Chemin des Prugnes on the left – from the A 71, take exit 11.

4 ha (55 pitches) flat

Rentals : 🏕 – 8 🚐 – 2 🏠.
Pretty shrubs and flowers decorate the site based around an old farm.

Surroundings : 🏞 🗔 ⬤
Leisure activities : ✗ 🚲 🎿 🎣
Facilities : ⅙ ⌁ 🚿 🍴 🛆
Nearby : 🎿 🐎

G
P
S
Longitude : 2.99231
Latitude : 46.3596

SINGLES

63690 – Michelin map **326** C9 – pop. 170 – alt. 737
▶ Paris 484 – Bort-les-Orgues 27 – La Bourboule 23 – Bourg-Lastic 20

⚠ Le Moulin de Serre ♣

📞 0473211606, www.moulindeserre.com

Address : 1.7km south of the Guinguette, along the D 73, follow the signs for Bort-les-Orgues; beside the Burande river

Opening times : from mid April to mid Sept.

7 ha/2,6 for camping (90 pitches) flat, grassy

Tariff : 24€ ★★ ⇔ 圓 ▣ (10A) – Extra per person 4,65€ – Reservation fee 15€

Rental rates : (from mid April to mid Sept.) – 23 🚐 – 12 canvas bungalows. Per night from 30 to 57€ – Per week from 175 to 686€ – Reservation fee 15€

🚐 borne 4€

In a green setting in a small valley.

Surroundings : 🏞 ⋖ 🗔 ⬤
Leisure activities : 🍴 ✗ 🎯 ☉ 🏃 jacuzzi
🚣 🚲 🎿 🎣 🏊
Facilities : ⅙ ⌁ 🛆 🍴 launderette 🚿

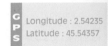

G
P
S
Longitude : 2.54235
Latitude : 45.54357

TAUVES

63690 – Michelin map **326** C9 – pop. 768 – alt. 820
▶ Paris 474 – Bort-les-Orgues 27 – La Bourboule 13 – Bourg-Lastic 29

⚠ Les Aurandeix

📞 0473211406, www.camping-les-aurandeix.fr

Address : at the stadium (east of the town)

Opening times : from beginning April to end Sept.

2 ha (50 pitches)

Tariff : 23€ ★★ ⇔ 圓 ▣ (10A) – Extra per person 4,85€ – Reservation fee 10€

Rental rates : (from beginning April to end Sept.) – 11 🚐.
Per night from 29 to 95€ – Per week from 135 to 635€ Reservation fee 19€

🚐 borne 5€ – 💧▣15€

Surroundings : 🗔 ⬤
Leisure activities : 🎯 🚣 ✗ 🎿
Facilities : ⅙ ⌁ 🛆 🍴 launderette
Nearby : 🏊 🗔 🏊 fitness trail, at the lake at La Tour d'Auvergne

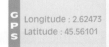

G
P
S
Longitude : 2.62473
Latitude : 45.56101

The prices listed were supplied by the campsite owners in 2013 (if prices were not available, those from the previous year are given). The fees should be regarded as basic charges and may fluctuate with inflation.

TREIGNAT

03380 – Michelin map **326** B4 – pop. 443 – alt. 450
▶ Paris 342 – Boussac 11 – Culan 27 – Gouzon 25

⛺ Municipal de l'Étang d'Herculat

🖉 0470070389, mairie-treignat@pays-allier.com

Address : 2.3km to the northeast, access via the road to the left, after the church

Opening times : from mid April to end Sept.

1,6 ha (35 pitches)

Tariff : (2013 Price) 8,85€ ♟ ♟ ⊜ ▣ ⚡ (24A) – Extra per person 1,65€
Rental rates : (2013 Price) (from mid April to end Sept.) – 2 🏠.
Per night from 55 to 60 € – Per week from 183 to 310 €

In a pleasant location beside the Étang d'Herculat (lake).

Surroundings : ⛱ ⊡ ⛰
Leisure activities : 🎏 🏇 ⟋
Facilities : ♿ ⟞ (July–Aug.) ⟐ ⊠ ⟑ ⟟

Longitude : 2.3673
Latitude : 46.35611

*We value your opinion and welcome your feedback.
Do email us at campingfrance@tp.michelin.com*

VALLON-EN-SULLY

03190 – Michelin map **326** C3 – pop. 1 693 – alt. 192
▶ Paris 313 – La Châtre 55 – Cosne-d'Allier 23 – Montluçon 25

⛺ Municipal les Soupirs

🖉 0630659258, monclocher.com

Address : head 1km southeast along the D 11, between the Cher river and the Canal du Berry, take the road to the right

2 ha (50 pitches)

Surroundings : ⛱ ⟗
Leisure activities : ⟟ ⟋
Facilities : ⟟

Nearby : ♟ ✗ 🏇 ✗

Longitude : 2.61437
Latitude : 46.53032

VIC-SUR-CÈRE

15800 – Michelin map **330** D5 – pop. 1 988 – alt. 678
▶ Paris 549 – Aurillac 19 – Murat 29

⛰ La Pommeraie

🖉 0471475418, www.camping-la-pommeraie.com – alt. 750

Address : at Daïsses (2.5km southeast along the D 54, D 154 and take the road to the right)

Opening times : from end May to end Aug.

2,8 ha (100 pitches) terraced

Tariff : 18€ ♟ ♟ ⊜ ▣ ⚡ (10A) – Extra per person 5€ – Reservation fee 18€
Rental rates : (from end May to end Aug.) – 40 . Per night from 55 to 130€ – Per week from 330 to 990€ – Reservation fee 18€

In an attractive elevated location.

Surroundings : ⛱ ⟜mountain peaks, Vallée de la Cère and small town of Vic-sur-Cère ⊡ ⟗
Leisure activities : ♟ ✗ 🎏 ⟟nighttime ⟟
✗ ⟅ ⟂ ⟍walking trails
Facilities : ♿ ⟞ ⟐ ⟂ ⟟ launderette
⟂ ⟋

Longitude : 2.63307
Latitude : 44.9711

⛺ Vic'Nature

🖉 0471475418, www.camping-la-pommeraie.com

Address : route de Salvanhac (beside the Cère river)

3 ha (200 pitches) flat, grassy
Rentals : 5 .

Surroundings : ⟜ ⟗
Leisure activities : 🎏 🏇
Facilities : ♿ ⟞ ⟟ launderette
Nearby : ⟂ ✗ ⟟ ⟂ ⟍

Longitude : 2.62492
Latitude : 44.97986

VIVEROLS

63840 – Michelin map **326** K10 – pop. 396 – alt. 860
▶ Paris 463 – Ambert 25 – Clermont-Ferrand 103 – Montbrison 38

⛺ Municipal le Pradoux

🖉 0473953431, viverols@wanadoo.fr – limited spaces for one-night stay

Address : Le Ruisseau quartier (to the southwest of the village along the D 111, follow the signs for Medeyrolles, near the Ligonne river)

Opening times : from beginning April to end Oct.

1,2 ha (49 pitches) flat, grassy

Tariff : (2013 Price) ♟ 1,70€ ⊜ 1,70€ ▣ 1,70€ – ⚡ (6A) 3€
⟠ borne 2€ – 5 ▣

Leisure activities : 🎏 🏇
Facilities : ♿ ⟐ ⟂ ⟟
Nearby : ✗ ⟋

Longitude : 3.88224
Latitude : 45.43159

VOREY

43800 – Michelin map **331** F2 – pop. 1 428 – alt. 540
▶ Paris 544 – Ambert 53 – Craponne-sur-Arzon 18 – Le Puy en Velay 23

⛰ Pra de Mars

🖉 0471034086, http://www.leprademars.com

Address : le Chambon de Vorey

Opening times :

3,6 ha (100 pitches) flat, grassy

Tariff : (2013 Price) 18€ ♟ ♟ ⊜ ▣ ⚡ (5A) – Extra per person 3,70€
Rental rates : (2013 Price) (from beginning April to end Sept.)
6 ⟦. Per night from 35 to 60€ – Per week from 250 to 400€
⟠ borne 3€

Surroundings : ⛱ ⟜ ⊡ ⟗
Leisure activities : ♟ ✗ 🎏 🏇 ⟟ ✗ ⟟ ⟂
⟂ ⟋
Facilities : ♿ ⟞ ⟐ ⟂ ⟟ launderette ⟋

Longitude : 3.9429
Latitude : 45.20352

⛰ Les Moulettes

🖉 0471037048, www.camping-les-moulettes.fr

Address : chemin de Félines (to the west of the town centre; beside the Arzon river)

Opening times : from beginning May to mid Sept.

1,3 ha (45 pitches) flat, grassy

Tariff : ♟ 5,50€ ⊜ ▣ 7€ – ⚡ (10A) 3,50€
Rental rates : (from beginning April to end Oct.) – 6 ⟦ – 6 🏠.
Per week from 250 to 580€
⟠ borne 3€ – 5 ▣ 2€

Surroundings : ⛱ ⊡ ⟗
Leisure activities : ♟ ✗ 🎏 🏇 ⟂ ⟍
Facilities : ♿ ⟞ ⟐ ⟂ ⟟ ⟟ ▣
Nearby : ✗ ⟋

Longitude : 3.90363
Latitude : 45.18637

BRITTANY

Brittany, or Breizh, as it is known to those lucky enough to live there, is a region of harsh granite coastlines, mysterious dolmens and menhirs, enchanted forests and pretty ports, dotted with colourful fishing boats. Its charm lies in its sea breeze, seafood and sea-faring history; in its varied landscapes, extensive coastline and delightful islands; in its gastronomy, music and traditional festivals. Its inhabitants were born – or so they claim – with a drop of salt water in their blood. Proud of the language handed down from their Celtic ancestors, today's Bretons nurture their identity with lively celebrations of folklore and customs. Naturally, such devotion to culture demands plenty of delicious and wholesome nourishment: sweet and savoury pancakes, thick slices of butter cake and mugs of cold cider. However, Brittany's gastronomic reputation doesn't end there and gourmets can feast on the oysters, lobster and crab for which it is famous. A visit to Brittany is a jigsaw of wonderful experiences.

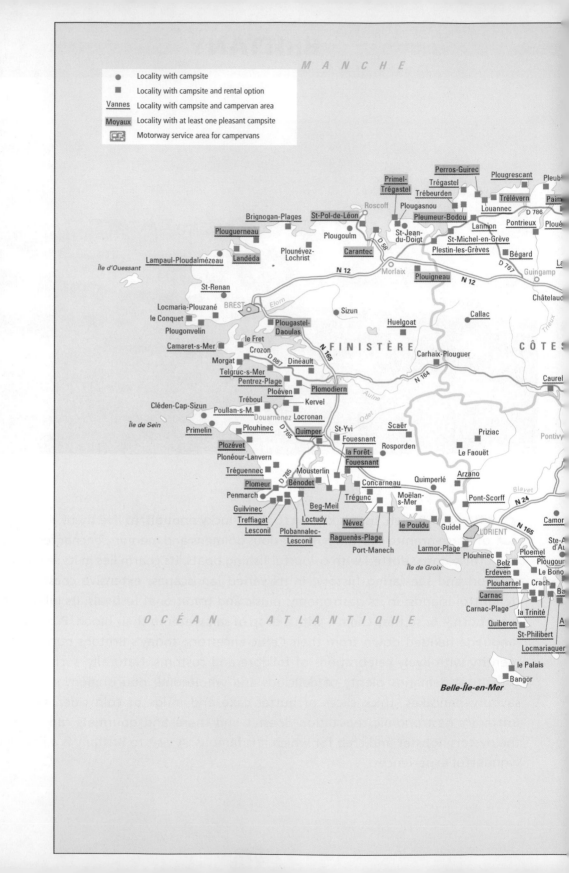

MANCHE

Locality with campsite
Locality with campsite and rental option
Vannes   Locality with campsite and campervan area
Moyaux   Locality with at least one pleasant campsite
Motorway service area for campervans

Île d'Ouessant

Brignogan-Plages
Plouguerneau
Lampaul-Ploudalmézeau   Landéda

Plounévez-Lochrist

St-Pol-de-Léon
Roscoff
Plougoulm
Carantec

Primel-Trégastel
Plougasnou
St-Jean-du-Doigt
Pleumeur-Bodou

Perros-Guirec
Trégastel
Trébeurden
Louannec
Lannion

Plougrescant
Trélévern
Pontrieux
St-Michel-en-Grève
Plestin-les-Grèves   Bégard
D 786
Ploué

Pleub
Paim
Paim

N 12   Morlaix
Plouigneau   N 12
D 767   Guingamp
La

St-Renan
Locmaria-Plouzané
le Conquet
Plougonvelin

BREST   Elorn

Sizun

Plougastel-Daoulas

Huelgoat

Callac

FINISTÈRE

Carhaix-Plouguer

N 165

N 164

Châtelaud

CÔTES

Caurel

Camaret-s-Mer
Crozon
Morgat
Telgruc-s-Mer
Pentrez-Plage
Ploéven

le Fret
D 887   Dinéault

Plomodiern

Aune

Odet

Scaër
Priziac
Le Faouët

Pontivy

Cléden-Cap-Sizun
Poullan-s-M.
Primelin
Plouhinec
Plozévet
Plonéour-Lanvern
Tréguennec
Plomeur
Penmarch
Guilvinec
Treffiagat
Lescanil
Plobannalec-Lesconil

Tréboul
Douarnenez   Kervel
Locronan

Quimper
St-Yvi
Fouesnant
la Forêt-Fouesnant

Rosporden
Rosporden

Arzano

D 765
D 765   Mousterlin
Bénodet
Beg-Meil
Loctudy

Concarneau
Trégunc
Moëlan-s-Mer
Quimperlé

Port-Scorff
N 24

Camor

Névez
le Pouldu
Guidel
LORIENT
N 165

Ste-A
d'Au

Raguenès-Plage
Port-Manech
Larmor-Plage
Île de Groix

Plouhinec
Belz
Erdeven
Plouharnel
Carnac
Carnac-Plage
Quiberon
St-Philibert

Ploemel
Crach

la Trinité

Plougour
Le Bono

Ba

A
Locmariaquer

le Palais
Bangor
Belle-Île-en-Mer

OCÉAN   ATLANTIQUE

Île de Sein

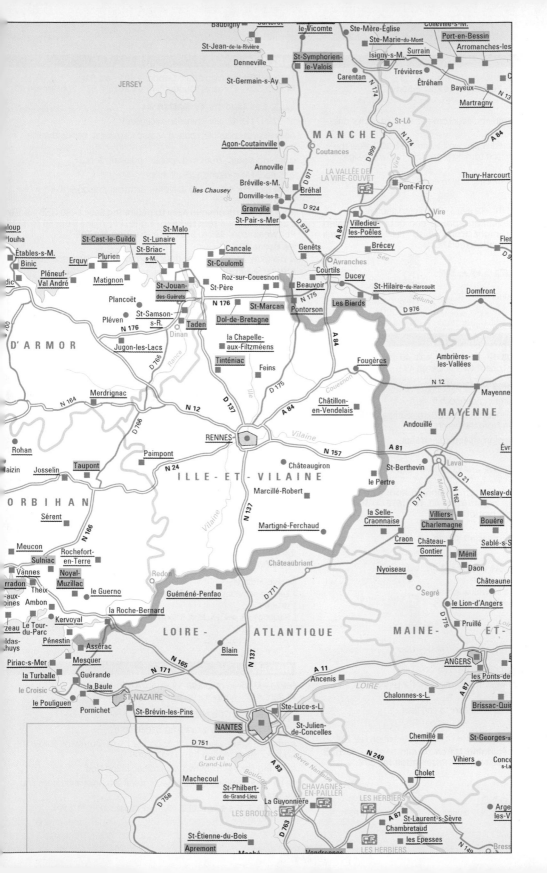

AMBON

56190 – Michelin map **308** P9 – pop. 1 676 – alt. 30
▶ Paris 465 – Muzillac 7 – Redon 42 – La Roche-Bernard 22

D'Arvor

02 97 41 16 69, www.campingdarvor.com – limited spaces for one-night stay

Address : 18 Brouel (located 1.5km west along the D 20, follow the signs for Sarzeau and take the turning to the left, follow the signs for Brouel)

Opening times : from beginning May to end Sept.

4 ha (140 pitches)

Tariff : ✤ 5,50€ ⟵ 🔲 9,50€ – (½) (6A) 3,60€ – Reservation fee 6€

Rental rates : (from beginning April to end Oct.) ♿ (1 chalet) 60 🚐 – 1 🏠. Per night from 48 to 111€ – Per week from 179 to 779€ – Reservation fee 17€

Surroundings : ♀
Leisure activities : 🍴✕ 🏠 🎣🏃‍♂️🏄‍♀️🚴
🏊🏄
Facilities : ♿ ⟿ 🚰 launderette

GPS Longitude : -2.57221
Latitude : 47.55654

ARRADON

56610 – Michelin map **308** O9 – pop. 5 301 – alt. 40
▶ Paris 467 – Auray 18 – Lorient 62 – Quiberon 49

Sites et Paysages Penboch ♣♣

02 97 44 71 29, www.camping-penboch.fr

Address : 9 chemin de Penboch (situated 2km southeast following signs for Roguedas, 200m from the beach)

Opening times : from beginning April to end Sept.

4 ha (175 pitches)

Tariff : (2013 Price) 39,30€ ✤✤ ⟵ 🔲 (½) (10A) – Extra per person 6,20€

Rental rates : (2013 Price) (from beginning April to end Sept.) 45 🚐 – 3 🏠. Per night from 40 to 165€ – Per week from 266 to 1 050€ – Reservation fee 20€

🚰 borne 5€ – 🚿 14€
In a leafy location with pleasant shade.

Surroundings : 🏞 🗺 ♀♀
Leisure activities : 🍴 🏠 🏃‍♂️ jacuzzi 🏄‍♀️ m
🏄 🏊 multi-sports ground
Facilities : ♿ ⟿ ▥ 🚿 – 4 individual sanitary facilities (🚿 🚾 wc) 🧺 🚰 launderette 🧊 refrigerators
Nearby : 🏖 🐎

GPS Longitude : -2.80085
Latitude : 47.62217

L'Allée

02 97 44 01 98, www.camping-allee.com

Address : located 1.5km west, follow the signs for Le Moustoir and take the turning to the left

Opening times : from beginning April to end Sept.

3 ha (148 pitches)

Tariff : ✤ 4,95€ ⟵ 🔲 9,25€ – (½) (10A) 4,60€ – Reservation fee 20€

Rental rates : (from beginning March to mid Sept.) – 28 🚐 2 gîtes. Per week from 195 to 610€ – Reservation fee 20€

🚰 borne

Surroundings : 🏞 🗺 ♀
Leisure activities : 🏠 🏄‍♀️ 🏊
Facilities : ♿ ⟿ (July–Aug.) 🚿 launderette
Nearby : 🍴

GPS Longitude : -2.84025
Latitude : 47.62109

ARZANO

29300 – Michelin map **308** K7 – pop. 1 403 – alt. 91
▶ Paris 508 – Carhaix-Plouguer 54 – Châteaulin 82 – Concarneau 40

Les Castels Ty Nadan ♣♣

02 98 71 75 47, www.tynadan-vacances.fr

Address : at Locunolé, route d'Arzano (3km west; beside the Ellé river)

Opening times : from mid April to beginning Sept.

20,5 ha/5 for camping (325 pitches)

Tariff : 52,85€ ✤✤ ⟵ 🔲 (½) (10A) – Extra per person 9,10€ Reservation fee 25€

Rental rates : (from mid April to beginning Sept.) – 80 🚐 – 9 🏠 2 apartments – 5 tent lodges – 1 gîte. Per night from 56 to 119€ Per week from 336 to 833€ – Reservation fee 30€

🚰 borne 12€

A partially indoor water park with lots of sports activities and lesiure facillities.

Surroundings : 🏞 🗺 ♀♀ 🌲
Leisure activities : 🍴✕ 🏠 🎣🏃‍♂️ jacuzzi
🏄‍♀️🚴🎾 🏊 🏖 (beach) 🏊🐎 climbing wall 🎭 entertainment room
Facilities : ♿ ⟿ ▥ 🚿 🧺 🚰 launderette 🧊 🚿

GPS Longitude : -3.47461
Latitude : 47.90476

ARZON

56640 – Michelin map **308** N9 – pop. 2 132 – alt. 9
▶ Paris 487 – Auray 52 – Lorient 94 – Quiberon 81

Municipal le Tindio

02 97 53 75 59, www.camping-arzon.fr

Address : 2 rue du Bilouris, at Kermers (800m to the northeast)

Opening times : from beginning April to beginning Nov.

5 ha (220 pitches)

Tariff : (2013 Price) ✤ 4,10€ ⟵ 🔲 8,10€ – (½) (10A) 3,25€

Rental rates : (2013 Price) (from beginning April to beginning Nov.) ♿ (3 chalets) – 18 🏠. Per week from 260 to 665€

🚰 borne 2€ – 19 🔲 10€ – 🚿 10€
The site is beside the sea.

Surroundings : ♀
Leisure activities : 🏠 🏄‍♀️ 🐎 multi-sports ground
Facilities : ♿ ⟿ 🚿 🧺 🚰 launderette

GPS Longitude : -2.8828
Latitude : 47.55562

BADEN

56870 – Michelin map **308** N9 – pop. 4 077 – alt. 28
▶ Paris 473 – Auray 9 – Lorient 52 – Quiberon 40

Mané Guernehué ♣♣

02 97 57 02 06, www.camping-baden.com

Address : 52 rue Mané Er Groëz (located 1km southwest, follow the signs for Mériadec and take a right turn)

Opening times : from mid April to beginning Nov.

18 ha/8 for camping (377 pitches) natural setting among trees and bushes

Tariff : 43,90€ ✤✤ ⟵ 🔲 (½) (10A) – Extra per person 7,90€ Reservation fee 20€

Rental rates : (from mid April to beginning Nov.) ৬ – 4 caravans
161 ⛺ – 19 🚐 – 2 tent lodges – 6 gîtes. Per night from 35 to
202€ – Per week from 238 to 1 414 €– Reservation fee 20 €
🚰 borne 6,50€ – 🛢14€

*Attractive indoor spa area and riding centre with ponies and
horses.*

Surroundings : 🐟 🗐 ⚲
Leisure activities : ♟ ✗ 🏛 🎱 🚣 🏓 🎣 🎿 🔥
hammam, jacuzzi 🚴 🏊 🎿 🏄
zip wire, multi-sports ground, spa centre,
water park, entertainment room
Facilities : ৬ ⛗ 🖃 🎞 🍴 🚿 🚻 launderette
🛁
Nearby : ✗

Longitude : -2.92531
Latitude : 47.61418

BÉGARD

22140 – Michelin map **309** C3 – pop. 4 652 – alt. 142
▶ Paris 499 – Rennes 147 – St-Brieuc 51 – Quimper 132

🔺 Donant

📞 02 96 45 46 46, www.camping-donant-bretagne.com

Address : at Gwénézhan

Opening times : from beginning April to end Sept.

3 ha (91 pitches)

Tariff : (2013 Price) ♦ 3,30€ 🚗 2€ 🗉 3,40€ – 🗲 (10A) 3€
Rental rates : Permanent ৬ (1 chalet) – 15 🚐 – 12 🛏 – 5 canvas
bungalows. Per night from 78 to 147€ – Per week from 149 to 609€
🚰 borne 4€ – 🛢11€

Surroundings : 🗐
Leisure activities : 🎱 🗐 🚴 entertainment
room
Facilities : ৬ ⛗ (July–Aug.) 🚻 launderette
Nearby : ♟ 🏊 🎿 🏄 leisure park

Longitude : -3.2837
Latitude : 48.61807

BEG-MEIL

29170 – Michelin map **308** H7
▶ Paris 562 – Rennes 211 – Quimper 23 – Brest 95

🔺 La Piscine ♣

📞 02 98 56 56 06, www.campingdelapiscine.com

Address : 51 Hent Kerleya (4km to the northwest)

Opening times : from mid April to mid Sept.

3,8 ha (185 pitches) flat, grassy, small lake

Tariff : 37,40€ ♦♦ 🚗 🗉 🗲 (10A) – Extra per person 7,60€

Reservation fee 20€

Rental rates : (from mid April to mid Sept.) 🐾 – 30 🚐 – 4 🚐.
Per week from 200 to 650 € – Reservation fee 20€
🚰 borne 5€

Surroundings : 🐟 🗐 ⚲
Leisure activities : 🎱 🏓 🚣 hammam,
jacuzzi 🚴 🎿 🏊 🏄 mountain biking
Facilities : ৬ ⛗ 🚿 🚻 launderette 🛁
🛁

Longitude : -4.01579
Latitude : 47.86671

🔺 La Roche Percée ♣ (rental of mobile homes only)

📞 02 98 94 94 15, www.camping-larochepercee.com

Address : 30 Hent Kerveltrec (located 1.5km north along the D 45,
follow the signs for Fouesnant, 500m from the beach at Kerveltrec)

Opening times : from beginning April to end Sept.

2 ha

Rental rates : 65 🚐. Per night from 90 to 150€ – Per week
from 310 to 940 € – Reservation fee 16€

Surroundings : 🐟 🗐
Leisure activities : ♟ 🏓 🚣 🚴🏻 🎿 🏄
Facilities : ⛗ 🛁 🚻 launderette
Nearby : ✗ 🎿 🐎

Longitude : -3.98981
Latitude : 47.87074

🔺 Le Kervastard

📞 02 98 94 91 52, www.campinglekervastard.com

Address : 56 chemin de Kervastard (150m from the town)

Opening times : from beginning April to end Sept.

2 ha (128 pitches) flat, grassy

Tariff : 32,50€ ♦♦ 🚗 🗉 🗲 (10A) – Extra per person 6,10€
Reservation fee 15€

Rental rates : (from beginning April to end Oct.) – 23 🚐.
Per night from 45 to 105€ – Per week from 290 to 720€ –
Reservation fee 15€
🚰 borne 6€ – 5 🗉 22,50€ – 🛢 🗲13€

Surroundings : 🗐 ⚲
Leisure activities : 🎱 🚴 🎿
Facilities : ৬ ⛗ 🛁 🚻 launderette
Nearby : 🛁 ♟ ✗

Longitude : -3.98825
Latitude : 47.86015

BELLE-ÎLE

56360 – Michelin map **308** – pop. 2 457 – alt. 7

Bangor 56360 – Michelin map **308** L11 – pop. 926 – alt. 45
▶ Paris 513 – Rennes 162 – Vannes 53

🔺 Municipal de Bangor

📞 02 97 31 89 75, camping.bangor@orange.fr

Address : 18 rue Pierre Cadre (to the west of the town)

0,8 ha (75 pitches)

Rentals : 6 🚐 – 16 🛏.

Surroundings : 🐟 🗐
Leisure activities : 🚴
Facilities : ৬ ⛗
Nearby : 🎿 🐎

Longitude : -3.19103
Latitude : 47.31453

Le Palais 56360 – Michelin map **308** M10 – pop. 2 545 – alt. 7
▶ Paris 508 – Rennes 157 – Vannes 48

🔺 Bordenéo

📞 02 97 31 88 96, www.bordeneo.com

Address : 1.7km northwest following signs for Port Fouquet, 500m
from the sea

Opening times : from mid April to end Sept.

5,5 ha (202 pitches) flat, grassy

Tariff : ♦ 7,10€ 🚗 2,60€ 🗉 11€ – 🗲 (5A) 3,50€ – Reservation
fee 15€

Rental rates : (from mid April to end Sept.) – 58 🚐 – 12 🚐
4 studios – 10 canvas bungalows. Per night from 55 to 120€
Per week from 290 to 820€ – Reservation fee 15€

Ornamental flowers and shrubs adorn the site.

Surroundings : 🐟 🗐 ⚲⚲
Leisure activities : ♟ 🎱 🚴nighttime 🚴
🚴 🎿 🏊 🏄
Facilities : ৬ ⛗ 🛁 🚻 launderette 🛁
Nearby : 🐎 scuba diving

Longitude : -3.16711
Latitude : 47.35532

▲▲ L'Océan

📞 0297318386, www.camping-ocean-belle-ile.com

Address : at Rosboscer (to the southwest of the town, 500m from the port)

Opening times : from beginning April to end Oct.

2,8 ha (125 pitches)

Tariff : (2013 Price) ♦ 5,30€ 🚗 📧 8,50€ – ⚡ (10A) 3,85€ – Reservation fee 5€

Rental rates : (from beginning March to mid Nov.) ♿ – 24 🚐 32 🏠. Per night from 45 to 90€ – Per week from 218 to 748€ Reservation fee 10€

Surroundings : 🌿 🗭 👯
Leisure activities : ♈ ✖ ⚓ 🛶
Facilities : ♿ ⛽ 🏕 🛁 ♨ 🚰 💧 launderette 🐾
Nearby : 🐎 scuba diving

Longitude : -3.13996
Latitude : 47.53473

BELZ

56550 – Michelin map **308** L8 – pop. 3 476 – alt. 12
▶ Paris 494 – Rennes 143 – Vannes 34 – Lorient 25

▲▲ Le Moulin des Oies

📞 0297555326, www.lemoulindesoies.com

Address : 21 rue de la Côte

Opening times : from beginning April to end Sept.

1,9 ha (90 pitches) flat, grassy

Tariff : 18,25€ ♦♦ 🚗 📧 ⚡ (6A) – Extra per person 4,85€ Reservation fee 12€

Rental rates : (from beginning April to end Sept.) – 18 🚐. Per night from 53 to 89€ – Per week from 236 to 633€ Reservation fee 12€ – 🚐 borne – 🔌 ⚡13€

Beside the Ria d'Étel river.

Surroundings : 🌿 🗭 💧
Leisure activities : 🍽 ⚓ 🌊 (seawater pool), multi-sports ground
Facilities : ♿ ⛽ 💧 launderette

Longitude : -3.17603
Latitude : 47.68045

BÉNODET

29950 – Michelin map **308** G7 – pop. 3 271
▶ Paris 563 – Concarneau 19 – Fouesnant 8 – Pont-l'Abbé 13

▲▲▲▲ Sunêlia L'Escale St-Gilles ♣♣

📞 0298570537, www.stgilles.fr – limited spaces for one-night stay

Address : corniche de la mer (located at La Pointe St-Gilles (headland)

Opening times : from end April to end Sept.

11 ha/7 for camping (480 pitches) flat, grassy

Tariff : 44€ ♦♦ 🚗 📧 ⚡ (10A) – Extra per person 9€ – Reservation fee 35€

Rental rates : (from end April to end Sept.) 🚫 – 160 🚐 – 2 tent lodges. Per night from 37 to 174€ – Per week from 207 to 1218€ Reservation fee 35€

🚐 🔌 ⚡13€

An attractive location opposite the ocean, near the beach. Option for full- and half-board stays.

Surroundings : 🌿 🗭 👯
Leisure activities : 🍽 ✖ 🎬 🌋 🎣 🔥 🈀 hammam, jacuzzi ⚓ 🎾 🏊 🏊 🏄 spa centre, water park, entertainment room
Facilities : ♿ ⛽ 💧 🛁 🚰 💧 launderette 🐾
Nearby : 💧 🐎

Longitude : -4.09669
Latitude : 47.86325

▲▲▲ Le Letty ♣♣

📞 0298570469, www.campingduletty-benodet.com

Address : impasse de Creisanguer

Opening times : from mid June to beginning Sept.

10 ha (493 pitches) flat, grassy

Tariff : 43€ ♦♦ 🚗 📧 ⚡ (10A) – Extra per person 10€ – Reservation fee 12€

Rental rates : (from mid June to beginning Sept.) 🚫 – 9 tent lodges. Per week from 405 to 650€ – Reservation fee 12€ 🚐 borne

An attractive location close to the beach with plenty of pitches for tents and caravans.

Surroundings : 🌿 👯 ⛰
Leisure activities : 🍽 🎬 🌋 🎣 🔥 🈀 hammam, jacuzzi ⚓ 🎾 🏊 🏊 🏄 🏄 entertainment room
Facilities : ♿ ⛽ 🛁 ♨ 🚰 💧 launderette 🐾 🐾
Nearby : 🎣 🚵 ⛵, squash

Longitude : -4.08995
Latitude : 47.86537

▲▲ Le Poulquer

📞 0298570419, www.campingdupoulquer.com

Address : 23 rue du Poulquer (150m from the sea)

Opening times : from beginning May to end Sept.

3 ha (215 pitches)

Tariff : ♦ 7,20€ 🚗 3,20€ 📧 7,50€ – ⚡ (10A) 5,30€ – Reservation fee 20€

Rental rates : Permanent 🚫 – 32 🚐. Per night from 60 to 120€ Per week from 250 to 800€ – Reservation fee 20€

In a green setting with plenty of shade.

Surroundings : 🗭 👯
Leisure activities : 🍽 ✖ 🎬 ⚓ 🏊 🏄 entertainment room
Facilities : ♿ ⛽ 💧 launderette
Nearby : 🎾 🎣 🚵 ⛵

Longitude : -4.09844
Latitude : 47.86794

BINIC

22520 – Michelin map **309** F3 – pop. 3 602 – alt. 35
▶ Paris 463 – Guingamp 37 – Lannion 69 – Paimpol 31

▲▲ Le Panoramic

📞 0296736043, www.lepanoramic.net

Address : rue Gasselin

Opening times : from end March to end Sept.

4 ha (150 pitches) terrace, relatively flat, flat, grassy

Tariff : 28€ ♦♦ 🚗 📧 ⚡ (10A) – Extra per person 6,50€ – Reservation fee 10€

Rental rates : (from end March to end Sept.) – 1 caravan – 42 🚐 8 🏠. Per night from 48 to 85€ – Per week from 240 to 870€ Reservation fee 10€

Surroundings : 🗭 👯
Leisure activities : 🍽 ✖ 🎬 ⚓ 🌋 (open air in season)
Facilities : ♿ ⛽ 🏕 🛁 💧 launderette

Longitude : -2.82304
Latitude : 48.59098

To visit a town or region, use the MICHELIN Green Guides.

⌂ Municipal des Fauvettes

📞 02 96 73 60 83, www.ville-binic.fr

Address : rue des Fauvettes

Opening times : from beginning April to end Sept.

1 ha (83 pitches) terraced, flat and relatively flat, grassy

Tariff : 19,40€ ♣♣ ⌁ ▤ ⴵ (6A) Extra per person 5€

Rental rates : (from beginning April to end Sept.) 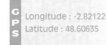 – 4 ⛟ – 3 studios. Per week 405€

🚐 borne – ⛽ ⴵ 13,40€

Rentals reserved for the Gendarmerie during July and August (beach patrol).

Surroundings : ⋙ ≼ of the Baie de St-Brieuc ♀
Leisure activities : ⛵⛷
Facilities : ♿ ☞ ⁌ 🏠

GPS Longitude : -2.82122
Latitude : 48.60635

BONO

56400 – Michelin map **308** N9 – pop. 2 198 – alt. 10
▶ Paris 475 – Auray 6 – Lorient 49 – Quiberon 37

⌂ Parc-Lann

📞 02 97 57 93 93, www.campingduparclann.fr

Address : 52 rue Thiers (1.2km northeast along the D 101e, follow the signs for Plougoumelen)

Opening times :

2 ha (60 pitches) flat, grassy

Tariff : 17,90€ ♣♣ ⌁ ▤ ⴵ (6A) – Extra per person 4,60€

Rental rates : Permanent – 5 caravans – 2 ⛟ – 1 gîte. Per night from 65 to 100€ – Per week from 220 to 750€

Surroundings : ⋙ ▭ ♀♀
Leisure activities : 🛶 ⛷
Facilities : ♿ ☞ (July–Aug.) ♨ ⁌ launderette
Nearby : ✂

GPS Longitude : -2.93746
Latitude : 47.64411

BRIGNOGAN-PLAGES

29890 – Michelin map **308** F3 – pop. 848 – alt. 17
▶ Paris 585 – Brest 41 – Carhaix-Plouguer 83 – Landerneau 27

⩕ La Côte des Légendes

📞 02 98 83 41 65, www.campingcotedeslegendes.com

Address : rue Douar ar Pont (situated 2km to the northwest)

Opening times : from end March to mid Nov.

3,5 ha (150 pitches)

Tariff : (2013 Price) 18€ ♣♣ ⌁ ▤ ⴵ (10A) – Extra per person 4,60€

Rental rates : (2013 Price) (from end March to mid Nov.) – 11 ⛟ 4 ⛟ – 4 canvas bungalows. Per night from 33 to 93€ – Per week from 231 to 649€

🚐 borne 2,80€ – 4 ▤ 7€ – ⛽ ⴵ 9,90€

Beside La Plage Des Crapauds (beach).

Surroundings : ⋙ ▭ ♀ ⛰
Leisure activities : 🛶 ⛷
Facilities : ♿ ☞ (July–Aug.) ♨ ⁌ 🏠
Nearby : ◗

GPS Longitude : -4.32928
Latitude : 48.67284

CALLAC

22160 – Michelin map **309** B4 – pop. 2 359 – alt. 172
▶ Paris 510 – Carhaix-Plouguer 22 – Guingamp 28 – Morlaix 41

⌂ Municipal Verte Vallée

📞 02 96 45 58 50, commune@mairie-callac.fr

Address : place Jean Auffret (take the western exit along the D 28, follow the signs for Morlaix and turn left onto av. Ernest-Renan; 50m from a small lake)

Opening times : from mid June to mid Sept.

1 ha (60 pitches)

Tariff : ♣ 2,65€ ⌁ 1,30€ ▤ 2€ – ⴵ (32A) 2€

🚐 borne 2€ – 8 ▤

Surroundings : ⋙ ▭ ♀♀
Leisure activities : ✂ ⊼ ⛷
Facilities : ♿ ☞ (July–Aug.) ↝

GPS Longitude : -3.43765
Latitude : 48.40174

CAMARET-SUR-MER

29570 – Michelin map **308** D5 – pop. 2 576 – alt. 4
▶ Paris 597 – Brest 4 – Châteaulin 45 – Crozon 11

⩕ Le Grand Large

📞 02 98 27 91 41, www.campinglegrandlarge.com

Address : at Lambézen (3km northeast along the D 355 and take turning to the right; 400m from the beach)

Opening times : from beginning April to end Sept.

2,8 ha (123 pitches)

Tariff : 27,30€ ♣♣ ⌁ ▤ ⴵ (10A) – Extra per person 4,90€ Reservation fee 16€

Rental rates : Permanent – 27 ⛟ – 3 ⛟. Per night from 35 to 80€ – Per week from 245 to 750€ – Reservation fee 16€

🚐 borne

Surroundings : ⋙ ≼ ▭
Leisure activities : ♥ 🛶 ⛷ ⊼ ♨ ↗
Facilities : ♿ ☞ ⌗ ♨ ♨ ⁌ launderette ♨ ⛷

GPS Longitude : -4.56472
Latitude : 48.28083

This guide is updated regularly, so buy your new copy every year!

CAMORS

56330 – Michelin map **308** M7 – pop. 2 788 – alt. 113
▶ Paris 472 – Auray 24 – Lorient 39 – Pontivy 31

⌂ Municipal du Petit Bois

📞 02 97 39 18 36, www.camors56.fr

Address : rue des Mésanges (located 1km west along the D 189, follow the signs for Lambel-Camors)

Opening times : from beginning July to end Aug.

1 ha (30 pitches)

Tariff : (2013 Price) ♣ 2,70€ ⌁ 2,30€ ▤ 2,30€ – ⴵ (10A) 2,60€

🚐 borne 3,30€

Near lakes and a national forest.

Surroundings : ⋙ ♀
Facilities : ♿ ↝ ♨ ♨ ⛷ 🏠
Nearby : ⛷ ⛷ sports trail

GPS Longitude : -3.01304
Latitude : 47.84613

CANCALE

35260 – Michelin map **309** K2 – pop. 5 374 – alt. 50
▶ Paris 398 – Avranches 61 – Dinan 35 – Fougères 73

🏕 Le Bois Pastel

📞 02 99 89 66 10, www.campingboispastel.fr

Address : 13 rue de la Corgnais (7km northwest along the D 201 coast road and take the turning to the left)

Opening times : from beginning April to end Sept.

5,2 ha (250 pitches) flat, grassy

Tariff : (2013 Price) 🧍 4,70€ 🚗 2€ 🔲 11€ – ⚡ (6A) 4€ – Reservation fee 15€

Rental rates : (2013 Price) (from beginning April to end Sept.) 20 🚐. Per week from 290 to 690€ – Reservation fee 15€

🚐 borne 4,50€

Surroundings : 🏞 ♨
Leisure activities : 🍸 🚣 🏊 (open air in season)
Facilities : 👤 🚿 🍴 launderette 🧺 🚗

GPS Longitude : -1.86861 Latitude : 48.68875

CARANTEC

29660 – Michelin map **308** H2 – pop. 3 249 – alt. 37
▶ Paris 552 – Brest 71 – Lannion 53 – Morlaix 14

🏕 Yelloh! Village Les Mouettes 👥

📞 02 98 67 02 46, www.les-mouettes.com – limited spaces for one-night stay

Address : 50 route de la Grande Grève (located 1.5km southwest following the signs for St-Pol-de-Léon and take right turn.)

Opening times : from mid April to beginning Sept.

14 ha (434 pitches)

Tariff : 49€ 🧍🧍 🚗 🔲 ⚡ (10A) – Extra per person 9€

Rental rates : (from mid April to beginning Sept.) 👤 🅿 – 223 🚐 34 🏠. Per night from 39 to 234€ – Per week from 238 to 1638€

🚐 borne

A landscaped water park with giant water slides and a village of upmarket rental options.

Surroundings : 🏞 🚐 ♨
Leisure activities : 🍸 🍴 🏠 🎣 🏊 library, spa centre, entertainment room
Facilities : 👤 🚿 🧺 🍴 launderette 🧺 🚗

GPS Longitude : -3.92802 Latitude : 48.65922

CARHAIX-PLOUGUER

29270 – Michelin map **308** J5 – pop. 7 717 – alt. 138
▶ Paris 506 – Brest 86 – Concarneau 66 – Guingamp 49

🏕 Municipal de la Vallée de l'Hyères

📞 02 98 99 10 58, www.ville-carhaix.com

Address : route de Kerniguez (head 2.3km west towards Morlaix and take turning in front of the police station; beside the Hyères river)

1 ha (62 pitches) flat, grassy

Rentals : 3 🚐.

Decorative trees and shrubs, near some lakes.

Surroundings : 🏞 ♨
Leisure activities : 🍸
Facilities : 🚿 launderette
Nearby : 🐎 forest trail, golf

GPS Longitude : -3.60202 Latitude : 48.27758

CARNAC

56340 – Michelin map **308** M9 – pop. 4 362 – alt. 16
▶ Paris 490 – Auray 13 – Lorient 49 – Quiberon 19

🏕 Les Castels La Grande Métairie 👥

Cie Bel Air

📞 02 97 52 24 01, www.lagrandemetairie.com – limited spaces for one-night stay

Address : route de Kerlescan (2.5km to the northeast)

Opening times : from beginning April to mid Sept.

15 ha/11 for camping (575 pitches)

Tariff : 🧍 8€ 🚗 🔲 28€ ⚡ (10A)

Rental rates : (from beginning April to mid Sept.) 👤 – 8 caravans – 187 🚐 – 2 cabins in the trees. Per night from 70 to 175€ – Per week from 255 to 910€

🚐 borne 6,50€ – 💧 ⚡18€

The site is beside the Étang de Kerloquet (lake) with a range of good-quality rental options.

Surroundings : 🚐 ♨
Leisure activities : 🍸 🍴 🏠 🎣 (open-air theatre) 🏃 jacuzzi 🚣 🚴 🎯 🎱 🏊 🏄 zip wire, skate park
Facilities : 👤 🚿 🏧 🧺 🚗 🍴 launderette 🧺 🚗

GPS Longitude : -3.05975 Latitude : 47.59647

🏕 Le Moustoir 👥

📞 02 97 52 16 18, www.lemoustoir.com

Address : 71 route du Moustoir (situated 3km to the northeast)

Opening times : from mid April to mid Sept.

5 ha (165 pitches)

Tariff : 🧍 6,30€ 🚗 🔲 22€ – ⚡ (10A) 5,60€ – Reservation fee 8€

Rental rates : (from end April to mid Sept.) – 85 🚐 – 15 🏠 65 🛏. Per night from 89 to 149€ – Per week from 252 to 889€ Reservation fee 8€ – 🚐 borne

Surroundings : 🏞 ♨
Leisure activities : 🍸 🍴 🏠 🎣 🏃 🚣 🎱 🏊 🏄
Facilities : 👤 🚿 🏧 🧺 🚗 🍴 launderette 🧺 🚗

GPS Longitude : -3.06689 Latitude : 47.60829

🏕 Moulin de Kermaux 👥

📞 02 97 52 15 90, www.camping-moulinkermaux.com

Address : route de Kerlescan (2.5km to the northeast)

Opening times : from mid April to mid Sept.

3 ha (150 pitches)

Tariff : 🧍 5,30€ 🚗 🔲 22,50€ ⚡ (15A) – Reservation fee 18€

Rental rates : (from mid April to mid Sept.) 👤 🏠 (from beginning July to end Aug) – 55 🚐 – 5 🏠 – 3 canvas bungalows 3 gîtes. Per night from 60 to 120€ – Per week from 210 to 890€ Reservation fee 20€

🚐 borne 4€ – 💧 ⚡14€

Surroundings : 🏞 🚐 ♨
Leisure activities : 🍸 🍴 🏠 🎣 🏃 ♨ jacuzzi 🚣 🏊 (open air in season) 🏄 multi-sports ground
Facilities : 👤 🚿 🧺 🍴 launderette 🚗
Nearby : 🐎

GPS Longitude : -3.06523 Latitude : 47.59512

⚴ Flower Le Lac

☎ 0297557878, www.lelac-carnac.com

Address : Passage du Lac (6.3km to the northeast; beside the lake)

Opening times : from beginning May to end Sept.

2,5 ha (140 pitches)

Tariff : ♦ 5,20€ ⇌ 🅿 13,60€ – (⚡) (6A) 5€ – Reservation fee 8€

Rental rates : (from end May to end Sept.) – 25 ⬚ – 65 🛏. Per week from 196 to 693€ – Reservation fee 8€

🚰 borne

Surroundings : ⚲ ≺ 🗔 ᵭᵭ

Leisure activities : multi-sports ground

Facilities : �🔒 🅾 🖉 🔥 ♨ ¶ launderette 🛁

Nearby : 🐎 🦆

G P S	Longitude : -3.02912 Latitude : 47.61117

⚴ Kérabus

☎ 0297522490, www.camping-kerabus.com

Address : 13 allée des Alouettes (situated 2km to the northeast)

Opening times : from beginning May to mid Sept.

1,4 ha (86 pitches) flat, grassy

Tariff : ♦ 5,15€ ⇌ 🅿 9€ – (⚡) (6A) 3,55€

Rental rates : (from beginning April to end Sept.) – 7 ⬚. Per night from 44 to 147€ – Per week from 205 to 680€

🚰 borne 3,50€ – 🚰 8,50€

Surroundings : ⚲ 🗔 ᵭᵭ

Leisure activities : 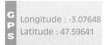 🛝 multi-sports ground

Facilities : 🅾 🖉 ¶ launderette

G P S	Longitude : -3.07648 Latitude : 47.59641

⚴ VivaCamp les Bruyères

☎ 0297523057, www.camping-lesbruyeres.com

Address : at Kérogile (3km to the north)

Opening times : from beginning April to end Sept.

2 ha (115 pitches) flat, grassy

Tariff : (2013 Price) ♦ 6€ ⇌ 🅿 10,20€ – (⚡) (10A) 3,70€ – Reservation fee 10€

Rental rates : (from beginning April to end Sept.) – 30 ⬚. 3 canvas bungalows. Per night from 28 to 120€ – Per week from 196 to 840€ – Reservation fee 15€ – 🚰 borne

Surroundings : ⚲ ᵭᵭ

Leisure activities : 🖼 🛝 🛝 🖥 (open air in season), zip wire

Facilities : 🅾 🖉 ¶ 🖥

Nearby : bowling

G P S	Longitude : -3.08884 Latitude : 47.60437

⚴ L'Étang

☎ 0297521406, www.camping-etang.fr

Address : at Kerlann (head 2km north along the D 119 towards Auray then take left turning, 50m from a lake)

Opening times : from beginning April to mid Oct.

2,5 ha (165 pitches) flat, grassy

Tariff : (2013 Price) 21,30€ ♦♦ ⇌ 🅿 (⚡) (6A) – Extra per person 5,50€

Rental rates : (2013 Price) – 10 ⬚ – 5 mobile homes (without sanitary facilities). Per night from 45 to 60€ – Per week from 220 to 550€ – 🚰 borne

Surroundings : ⚲ 🗔 ᵭ

Leisure activities : ¶ 🛝 🛝 🖥 ♨

Facilities : 🅾 (summer) 🛁 🖉 launderette

Nearby : 🛶

G P S	Longitude : -3.08137 Latitude : 47.60107

⚴ Vacances Directes Le Domaine de Kermario

(mobile home and gîte rentals only)

☎ 0825133400, www.campingkermario.com

Address : 1 chemin de Kerluir (situated 2km to the northeast)

Opening times : from mid April to end Sept.

4 ha

Rental rates : (🅿) – 79 ⬚ – 9 gîtes. Per night from 30 to 105€ – Per week from 210 to 735€ – Reservation fee 30€

Furnished gîtes in old farm buildings that have been beautifully restored.

Surroundings : ⚲ ᵭᵭ

Leisure activities : ✗ 🖼 🔥 🛝 🛝 🖥 entertainment room

Facilities : 🅾 ¶ launderette 🖉

G P S	Longitude : -3.06636 Latitude : 47.59521

CARNAC-PLAGE

56340 – Michelin map **308** M9

▶ Paris 494 – Rennes 143 – Vannes 34

⚴ Les Menhirs ♟

☎ 0297529467, www.lesmenhirs.com – limited spaces for one-night stay

Address : allée Saint-Michel

Opening times : from mid April to end Sept.

6 ha (360 pitches) flat, grassy

Tariff : ♦ 8,55€ ⇌ 🅿 31,40€ – (⚡) (10A) 4,80€ – Reservation fee 20€

Rental rates : (from mid April to end Sept.) ᴙ (1 mobile home) 🦽 – 61 ⬚ – 1 🏠. Per night from 90 to 152€ – Per week from 309 to 1119€ – Reservation fee 20€

🚰 borne

400m from the beach and the town centre.

Surroundings : ⚲ 🗔 ᵭ

Leisure activities : ¶ 🖼 🔥 🛝 ♨ jacuzzi 🛝 ✗ 🖥 🛝 ♨ multi-sports ground, spa centre, entertainment room

Facilities : 🅾 🖉 🔥 ♨ ¶ launderette 🛁 🖉

Nearby : 🚲

G P S	Longitude : -3.06979 Latitude : 47.57683

⚴ Les Druides

☎ 0297520818, www.camping-les-druides.com

Address : 55 chemin de Beaumer (To the east, in part of town called Beaumer, 500m from the beach)

Opening times : from mid April to beginning Sept.

2,5 ha (110 pitches)

Tariff : 40,30€ ♦♦ ⇌ 🅿 (⚡) (10A) – Extra per person 6,80€ Reservation fee 20€

Rental rates : (from beginning April to beginning Sept.) ᴙ 17 ⬚ – 3 apartments. Per night from 140 to 210€ – Per week from 225 to 800€ – Reservation fee 20€

🚰 borne

Surroundings : ᵭᵭ

Leisure activities : 🖼 🔥 🛝 multi-sports ground

Facilities : 🅾 🖉 🔥 ♨ ¶ launderette

G P S	Longitude : -3.05689 Latitude : 47.58012

To make the best possible use of this guide, please read pages 2–15 carefully.

⚠ Le Men-Du

🔗 0297520423, www.camping-mendu.com

Address : 22bis chemin de Beaumer (in suburb called Le Men-Du, 300m from the beach)

Opening times : from beginning April to beginning Oct.

1,5 ha (100 pitches)

Tariff : 28,40€ ⚫⚫ 🚐 🔲 🚿 (15A) – Extra per person 5,20€
Reservation fee 15€

Rental rates : (from beginning April to beginning Oct.) 👤 (1 mobile home) – 19 🚐. Per week from 250 to 650€
Reservation fee 15€

Surroundings : 🌳 ⚲
Leisure activities : ✕
Facilities : 👤 🅾 🚿 🔆 launderette
Nearby : ✕ ♨ 🐎

G P S Longitude : -3.05522
Latitude : 47.57941

⚠ L'Océan

🔗 0631650075, www.camping-delocean.com – limited spaces for one-night stay

Address : Quartier le Men-Du, impasse des Gabelous (head along the D 186 towards La Trinité sur Mer and take the Chemin de Beaumer; 250m from the beach)

Opening times : from beginning April to mid Nov.

0,5 ha (50 pitches)

Tariff : 23,50€ ⚫⚫ 🚐 🔲 🚿 (10A) – Extra per person 5€ – Reservation fee 15€

Rental rates : (from beginning April to mid Nov.) – 17 🚐. Per night from 50 to 70€ – Per week from 230 to 630€
Reservation fee 15€

🚐 borne 4€

Surroundings : ⚲
Leisure activities : 🐎
Facilities : 👤 🅾 🔆 🚿 🖼
Nearby : ✕ ♨ 🐎

G P S Longitude : -3.05327
Latitude : 47.57849

CAUREL

22530 – Michelin map **309** D5 – pop. 381 – alt. 188
▶ Paris 461 – Carhaix-Plouguer 45 – Guingamp 48 – Loudéac 24

🏔 Sites et Paysage Nautic International

🔗 0296285794, www.campingnautic.fr

Address : route de Beau Rivage (situated 2km southwest along the D 111; beside the lake at Guerlédan)

Opening times : from mid May to end Sept.

3,6 ha (100 pitches)

Tariff : 30,50€ ⚫⚫ 🚐 🔲 🚿 (10A) – Extra per person 6,50€
Reservation fee 15€

Rental rates : (from mid May to end Sept.) – 5 🚐. Per week from 290 to 610€ – Reservation fee 22,90€

🚐 🚐23€

In a green setting with lots of trees.

Surroundings : 🏞 🌳 ⚲⚲ 🏔
Leisure activities : 🏊 🐎 ✕ 🛶 🚣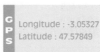
Facilities : 👤 🅾 🚿 launderette 🏖
Nearby : 🍴 ✕ ⚓ water skiing

G P S Longitude : -3.04847
Latitude : 48.2069

LA CHAPELLE-AUX-FILTZMEENS

35190 – Michelin map **309** L4 – pop. 726 – alt. 40
▶ Paris 388 – Rennes 39 – Saint-Malo 42 – Fougères 83

🏔 Le Domaine du Logis

🔗 0299452545, www.domainedulogis.com

Address : Le Logis (located 1.5km west on the D 13, follow the signs for St-Domineuc)

Opening times : from end March to beginning Nov.

20 ha/6 for camping (180 pitches) flat, grassy

Tariff : 35€ ⚫⚫ 🚐 🔲 🚿 (16A) – Extra per person 6€

Rental rates : (from end March to beginning Nov.) 🏠 – 17 🚐. Per night from 75 to 100€ – Per week from 300 to 850€
Reservation fee 10€

Surroundings : 🌳 ⚲
Leisure activities : 🍴 ✕ 🏠 🎣 🛶 🚣 🏊 mountain biking
Facilities : 👤 🅾 🖼 🔆 launderette 🐎
Nearby : 🎣

G P S Longitude : -1.83566
Latitude : 48.38306

Some information or pricing may have changed since the guide went to press. We recommend you check the price list online in advance or at the entrance to the campsite and enquire about possible restrictions.

CHÂTEAUGIRON

35410 – Michelin map **309** M6 – pop. 6 450 – alt. 45
▶ Paris 336 – Angers 114 – Châteaubriant 45 – Fougères 56

⚠ Les Grands Bosquets

🔗 0299378902, www.tourisme-payschateaugiron.fr

Address : route d'Ossé (take the eastern exit along the D 34)

Opening times : from beginning April to end Sept.

0,6 ha (33 pitches) flat, grassy

Tariff : 6,60€ ⚫⚫ 🚐 🔲 🚿 (6A) – Extra per person 2,20€

The site is beside a lake.

Surroundings : ⚲⚲
Leisure activities : 🏖 (beach) 🎣
Facilities : 🚿
Nearby : 🐎 ✕

G P S Longitude : -1.49734
Latitude : 48.04983

CHÂTELAUDREN

22170 – Michelin map **309** E3 – pop. 1 047 – alt. 105
▶ Paris 469 – Guingamp 17 – Lannion 49 – St-Brieuc 18

⚠ Municipal de l'Étang

🔗 0296741038, www.chatelaudren.fr – 🏕

Address : rue de la Gare (in the town; beside a large, beautiful lake)

Opening times : from beginning May to end Sept.

0,2 ha (17 pitches)

Tariff : (2013 Price) ⚫ 3€ 🚐 1€ 🔲 4,20€ – 🚿 (10A) 3€

Surroundings : 🌳 ⚲
Leisure activities : 🎣
Facilities : 🚿
Nearby : 🐎

G P S Longitude : -2.9709
Latitude : 48.53883

CHÂTILLON-EN-VENDELAIS

35210 – Michelin map **309** O5 – pop. 1 698 – alt. 133
▶ Paris 311 – Fougères 17 – Rennes 49 – Vitré 13

⚠ Municipal du Lac

☏ 02 99 76 06 32, www.chatillon-en-vendelais.fr

Address : route de Parce, l'Épine (500m north along the D 108; beside the Étang de Châtillon)

Opening times : from beginning May to end Sept.

0,6 ha (61 pitches)

Tariff : ✱ 2,64€ ⏚ 1,28€ 🅴 1,98€ – 🔌 (5A) 3,61€
Rental rates : Permanent – 1 🏠. Per night from 44€ – Per week from 221€
🚰 borne
In a pleasant location and green setting.

Surroundings : 🏞 ← 🏕 ⛳ ⛰
Leisure activities : 🎣
Facilities : 🚽 🏛
Nearby : 🍷 ✖ 🍴 pedalos

| | Longitude : -1.18026 |
| G P S | Latitude : 48.22909 |

CLÉDEN-CAP-SIZUN

29770 – Michelin map **308** D6 – pop. 1 003 – alt. 30
▶ Paris 608 – Audierne 11 – Douarnenez 27 – Quimper 46

⚠ La Baie

☏ 02 98 70 64 28 – 🚩

Address : at Lescleden (2.5km west)

Opening times : Permanent

0,4 ha (27 pitches)

Tariff : 15€ ✱✱ ⏚ 🅴 🔌 (8A) – Extra per person 3,40€

Surroundings : 🏞 ←
Leisure activities : 🍷 ✖
Facilities : 🔑 🚽 🏛

| | Longitude : -4.68312 |
| G P S | Latitude : 48.04842 |

CONCARNEAU

29900 – Michelin map **308** H7 – pop. 19 352 – alt. 4
▶ Paris 546 – Brest 96 – Lorient 49 – Quimper 22

⚠ Les Sables Blancs 👥

☏ 02 98 97 16 44, www.camping-lessablesblancs.com

Address : rue des Fleurs (100m from the beach)

Opening times : from beginning April to end Oct.

3 ha (149 pitches)

Tariff : 26€ ✱✱ ⏚ 🅴 🔌 (10A) – Extra per person 7€
Rental rates : (from beginning April to end Oct.) – 34 🚐.
Per night from 45 to 115€ – Per week from 220 to 784€
🚰 borne 5€
Some pitches have a view of the sea.

Surroundings : 🏞 🏕 ⛰
Leisure activities : 🍷 ✖ 🏸 jacuzzi
🏊 🛶
Facilities : 🔑 🚽 ⛺ launderette 🚿
Nearby : 🎣

| | Longitude : -3.92836 |
| G P S | Latitude : 47.88203 |

⚠ Les Prés Verts

☏ 02 98 97 09 74, www.presverts.com

Address : Kernous-Plage (3km northwest along the coast road and take a left turn; 250m from the beach (direct access)

Opening times : from beginning May to end Sept.

3 ha (150 pitches)

Tariff : 29€ ✱✱ ⏚ 🅴 🔌 (10A) – Extra per person 6,20€
Rental rates : (from beginning May to end Sept.) 🏊 – 2 🚐
4 🏠. Per week from 230 to 640€
Some pitches have a sea view.

Surroundings : 🏞
Leisure activities : 🏠 🏊 ⛰ 🛶
Facilities : 🔑 🚽 ⛺ launderette

| | Longitude : -3.93333 |
| G P S | Latitude : 47.88333 |

LE CONQUET

29217 – Michelin map **308** C4 – pop. 2 635 – alt. 30
▶ Paris 619 – Brest 24 – Brignogan-Plages 59 – St-Pol-de-Léon 85

⚠ Les Blancs Sablons

☏ 02 98 36 07 91, www.les-blancs-sablons.com

Address : Le Théven (5km northeast along the D 67 and take D 28, follow the signs for the beach at Les Blancs Sablons, 400m from the beach – passenger walkway to town)

Opening times : from beginning April to end Sept.

12 ha (360 pitches)

Tariff : (2013 Price) 19,50€ ✱✱ ⏚ 🅴 🔌 (16A)
Extra per person 4,50€
Rental rates : (2013 Price) (from beginning April to beginning Nov.) – 8 🚐 – 3 🏠. Per night from 55 to 75€
Per week from 250 to 650€
In a natural setting, bordering on the wild.

Surroundings : 🏞 🏕
Leisure activities : 🍷 ✖ 🏸 🛶
Facilities : 🔑 🚽 ⛺ launderette

| | Longitude : -4.76071 |
| G P S | Latitude : 48.36687 |

*The classification (1 to 5 tents, **black** or **red**) that we award to selected sites in this guide is our own system. It should not be confused with the classification (1 to 5 stars) of official organisations.*

CRACH

56950 – Michelin map **308** M9 – pop. 3 276 – alt. 35
▶ Paris 482 – Auray 6 – Lorient 46 – Quiberon 29

⚠ Le Fort Espagnol

☏ 02 97 55 14 88, www.fort-espagnol.com

Address : route du Fort Espagnol (800m east, follow the signs for La Rivière d'Auray)

5 ha (190 pitches)

Rentals : 3 caravans – 83 🚐 – 4 🏠 – 4 tent lodges.

Surroundings : 🏞 🏕 ⛰
Leisure activities : 🍷 ✖ 🏠 🏊 🛶
Facilities : 🔑 🚽 ⛺ launderette 🚿
Nearby : 🏸 🎣

| | Longitude : -2.98988 |
| G P S | Latitude : 47.61539 |

CROZON

29160 – Michelin map **308** E5 – pop. 7 697 – alt. 85
▶ Paris 587 – Brest 60 – Châteaulin 35 – Douarnenez 40

⚠ Les Pins

✆ 06 60 54 40 09, www.camping-crozon-lespins.com

Address : route de Dinan (situated 2km southwest along the D 308 follow the signs for La Pointe de Dinan (headland)

Opening times : from beginning April to mid Sept.

4 ha (155 pitches)

Tariff : ♣ 5€ 🚐 📺 9,50€ – [½] (16A) 3,75€

Rental rates : (from beginning April to mid Nov.) ♿ – 12 🚐 13 🏠. Per night from 65€ – Per week from 330 to 680€

Surroundings : 🔾🔾
Leisure activities : 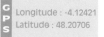 🖼 (small swimming pool)
Facilities : ♿ ⚬🔫 🚿 🛁🍴
Nearby : forest trail

G P S	Longitude : -4.51462 Latitude : 48.24153

Some campsites benefit from proximity to a municipal leisure centre.

DINÉAULT

29150 – Michelin map **308** G5 – pop. 1 739 – alt. 160
▶ Paris 560 – Rennes 208 – Quimper 36 – Brest 54

⚠ Ty Provost

✆ 02 98 86 29 23, www.typrovost.com

Address : 4km southeast along the C 1, follow the signs for Châteaulin and take road to the left

Opening times : from beginning June to mid Sept.

1,2 ha (44 pitches)

Tariff : ♣ 12,90€ 🚐 📺 – [½] (10A) 3,50€

Rental rates : Permanent ♿ (2 chalets) – 5 🚐 – 7 🏠 – 2 gîtes. Per night from 49 to 79€ – Per week from 297 to 497€

🚐 borne – 4 📺 16,80€
A pleasant site and setting.

Surroundings : ≤ ♀
Leisure activities : 🍴 🖼 🚣
Facilities : ♿ ⚬🔫 🛁🍴 launderette

G P S	Longitude : -4.12421 Latitude : 48.20706

DOL-DE-BRETAGNE

35120 – Michelin map **309** L3 – pop. 5 163 – alt. 20
▶ Paris 378 – Alençon 154 – Dinan 26 – Fougères 54

⚠⚠⚠ Les Castels Domaine des Ormes

✆ 02 99 73 53 00, www.lesormes.com – limited spaces for one-night stay

Address : Épiniac (7.5km south along the D 795, follow the signs for Combourg then take the road to the left)

Opening times : from mid April to mid Sept.

200 ha/40 for camping (750 pitches) forest

Tariff : (2013 Price) 61€ ♣♣ 🚐 📺 [½] (16A) – Extra per person 8€ Reservation fee 20€

Rental rates : Permanent – 1 caravan – 81 🚐 – 28 🏠 – 45 🛏 11 studios – 25 apartments – 30 cabins in the trees – 4 gîtes. Per night 185€ – Per week 1 795€ – Reservation fee 20€

🚐 borne

In the grounds of a 16th-century château, with wide open spaces and plenty of activities, including a partially covered water park.

Surroundings : 🐾 ≤ 🔾🔾
Leisure activities : 🍴 ✗ 🖼 🎣 ♦🏇 🎿 ♒ 🚣 🚴 ✗ 🖼 🎱 🚣 🏊 🎿 🐎 disco, climbing wall, golf course, driving range, multi-sports ground, water park, entertainment room
Facilities : ♿ ⚬🔫 🍴 launderette 🛒 🛁

G P S	Longitude : -1.72722 Latitude : 48.49139

⚠⚠⚠ Le Vieux Chêne

✆ 02 99 48 09 55, www.camping-vieuxchene.fr

Address : route de Pontorson (5km east, along the N 176, follow the signs for Pontorson, east of Baguer-Pican on the D 57 - Advised route via the diversion, take exit Dol-de-Bretagne-Est and take D 80, D 576)

Opening times : from mid May to mid Sept.

4 ha/2 for camping (199 pitches)

Tariff : 31€ ♣♣ 🚐 📺 [½] (10A) – Extra per person 10€

Rental rates : (from beginning April to mid Sept.) – 18 🚐 18 🏠. Per night from 69 to 113€ – Per week from 273 to 791€ 🚐 borne 8€

Pleasant location around some lakes.

Surroundings : 🐾 🚃 🔾🔾
Leisure activities : 🍴 ✗ 🖼 🚣 ✗ 🎣 🖼 🎱 🚣
Facilities : ♿ ⚬🔫 🛁🍴 🚿 🛁 🗑 🍴 launderette 🛁 🛒

G P S	Longitude : -1.68361 Latitude : 48.54945

We value your opinion and welcome your feedback.
Do email us at campingfrance@tp.michelin.com

ERDEVEN

56410 – Michelin map **308** M9 – pop. 3 402 – alt. 18
▶ Paris 492 – Auray 15 – Carnac 10 – Lorient 28

⚠ La Croëz-Villieu

✆ 02 97 55 90 43, www.la-croez-villieu.com – limited spaces for one-night stay

Address :
Kernogan, route de Kerhillio (located 1km southwest along the beach road at Kerhillio)

Opening times : from beginning May to end Sept.

3 ha (158 pitches) flat, grassy

Tariff : ♣ 6,60€ 🚐 📺 12,30€ – [½] (6A) 4,20€

Rental rates : (from beginning April to mid Oct.) – 27 🚐 – 2 tent lodges. Per week from 185 to 790€

Partially indoor water park.

Surroundings : 🐾 🚃 ♀
Leisure activities : 🍴 🏊 hammam, jacuzzi 🚣 🖼 🎱 🏊
Facilities : ⚬🔫 🛁🍴 launderette

G P S	Longitude : -3.15838 Latitude : 47.63199

⚠ L' Idéal

✆ 02 97 55 67 66, www.camping-l-ideal.com – limited spaces for one-night stay

Address : route de la plage

Opening times : from beginning April to end Sept.

0,6 ha (30 pitches) flat, grassy

Tariff : 32€ ♣♣ 🚐 📺 [½] (10A) – Extra per person 6€

Rental rates : (from beginning April to end Sept.) – 16  – 3 🏠
5 apartments. Per week from 200 to 740€ – Reservation fee 20€
🚐 2 ▣ 18€

Surroundings : 🌳 ♀
Leisure activities : 🍸 🏛 🖾
Facilities : 🚿 🚻 🍴 launderette

GPS	Longitude : -3.16317
	Latitude : 47.62115

The prices listed were supplied by the campsite owners in 2013 (if prices were not available, those from the previous year are given). The fees should be regarded as basic charges and may fluctuate with inflation.

ERQUY

22430 – Michelin map **309** H3 – pop. 3 802 – alt. 12
▶ Paris 451 – Dinan 46 – Dinard 39 – Lamballe 21

🏕 Le Vieux Moulin 👥

📞 02 96 72 34 23, www.camping-vieux-moulin.com

Address : 14 rue des Moulins (situated 2km east)

Opening times : from mid April to beginning Sept.

2,5 ha (173 pitches) flat, grassy

Tariff : ★ 6€ 🚗 4€ ▣ 11€ – 🔌 (10A) 6€

Rental rates : (from mid April to beginning Sept.) – 70 .
Per night from 49 to 147€ – Per week from 257 to 1 029€

A well-kept, green setting.

Surroundings : 🔲 ♀♀
Leisure activities : 🍸 ✕ 🏛 🚶 🐎 🖾 🎣 multi-sports ground
Facilities : 🚿 🚻 🚱 📋 🍴 launderette 🖾 🚿
Nearby : ✕ 🖾 🏕

GPS	Longitude : -2.44249
	Latitude : 48.63828

🏕 Yelloh! Village Les Pins 👥

📞 02 96 72 31 12, www.yellohvillage.fr/camping/les_pins.com

Address : Le Guen, 88 rue des Moulins (located 1km to the north, on the corner of r. des Moulins and r. Léon Hamonet)

Opening times : from end April to mid Sept.

10 ha (488 pitches)

Tariff : 36€ ★★ 🚗 ▣ 🔌 (6A) – Extra per person 7€

Rental rates : (from end April to mid Sept.) 🚿 – 155
11 🏠 – 11 tent lodges. Per night from 35 to 283€ – Per week from 245 to 1 981€

Surroundings : 🌳 🔲 ♀♀
Leisure activities : 🍸 ✕ 🏛 🖐 🚶 🐎 🚣 hammam, jacuzzi 🎣 ✕ 🖾 🎣 spa centre
Facilities : 🚿 🚻 📋 🍴 launderette 🖾 🚿
Nearby : 🏕

GPS	Longitude : -2.45573
	Latitude : 48.63802

🏕 Sites et Paysages Bellevue 👥

📞 02 96 72 33 04, http://campingbellevue.fr

Address : route de la Libération (5.5km southwest)

Opening times : from mid April to mid Sept.

3,5 ha (160 pitches) flat, grassy

Tariff : 29€ ★★ 🚗 ▣ 🔌 (10A) – Extra per person 5,70€

Rental rates : (from beginning April to end Sept.) 🚿 (1 chalet) 24 – 3 🏠 – 4 tent lodges. Per night from 60 to 120€
Per week from 280 to 790€
🚐 borne – 60 ▣ 17,50€ – 🚐 🔌 16€

The entrance is surrounded by flowers, the pitches are surrounded by trees and shrubs.

Surroundings : 🔲 ♀♀
Leisure activities : 🍸 🏛 🚶 🐎 🏕 🖾 (open air in season), multi-sports ground
Facilities : 🚿 🚻 📋 🍴 launderette 🚿
Nearby : 🖾

GPS	Longitude : -2.48486
	Latitude : 48.59377

🏕 St-Pabu

📞 02 96 72 24 65, www.saintpabu.com

Address : St-Pabu (at the beach at Saint-Pabu, 4km southwest)

Opening times : from beginning April to mid Oct.

5,5 ha (409 pitches)

Tariff : 26,30€ ★★ 🚗 ▣ 🔌 (10A) – Extra per person 5,60€
Reservation fee 20€

Rental rates : (from beginning April to mid Oct.) – 39 .
Per night from 40 to 106€ – Per week from 280 to 740€
Reservation fee 20€
🚐 borne 6€

Opposite the Baie d'Erquy.

Surroundings : 🌳 🔲 ⛰
Leisure activities : 🍸 🏛 🚶
Facilities : 🚿 🚻 📋 🍴 launderette 🖾
Nearby : 🤿 scuba diving

GPS	Longitude : -2.49459
	Latitude : 48.60878

🏕 Les Roches

📞 02 96 72 32 90, www.camping-les-roches.com

Address : rue Pierre Vergos (3km southwest)

Opening times : from beginning April to beginning Nov.

3 ha (160 pitches)

Tariff : (2013 Price) 20,20€ ★★ 🚗 ▣ 🔌 (10A)
Extra per person 3,90€ – Reservation fee 8€

Rental rates : (2013 Price) (from beginning April to beginning Nov.) – 18 . Per night from 44 to 59€ – Per week from 250 to 640€ – Reservation fee 8€
🚐 borne

On the slopes of Caroual Village.

Surroundings : 🌳 ♀
Leisure activities : 🏛 🚶 🐎 🏕
Facilities : 🚿 🚻 📋 🍴 launderette 🖾

GPS	Longitude : -2.4769
	Latitude : 48.6094

🏕 Des Hautes Grées

📞 02 96 72 34 78, www.camping-hautes-grees.com

Address : 123 rue St Michel, Les Hopitaux (3.5km to the northeast, 400m from the St-Michel beach)

Opening times : from mid April to end Sept.

3 ha (177 pitches) flat, grassy

Tariff : 26,40€ ★★ 🚗 ▣ 🔌 (10A) – Extra per person 5,60€
Reservation fee 15€

Rental rates : (from mid April to end Sept.) – 32 . Per night from 45 to 64€– Per week from 290 to 680€ – Reservation fee 15€
🚐 borne 3,50€ – 🚐 🔌 14,50€

Surroundings : 🌳 🔲
Leisure activities : 🏛 🚶 🐎 🎣 🖾
Facilities : 🚿 🚻 📋 🍴 launderette

GPS	Longitude : -2.42491
	Latitude : 48.64254

ÉTABLES-SUR-MER

22680 – Michelin map **309** E3 – pop. 3 091 – alt. 65
▶ Paris 467 – Guingamp 31 – Lannion 56 – St-Brieuc 19

⚲ L'Abri-Côtier

✆ 02 96 70 61 57, www.camping-abricotier.fr

Address : 12 rue De Robien (located 1km north following signs for St-Quay-Portrieux and take the turning to the left)

Opening times : from beginning May to mid Sept.

2 ha (140 pitches)

Tariff : ♟ 5,20€ ⇚ 🅿 7,90€ – ⚡ (10A) 4€

Rental rates : (from beginning May to mid Sept.) – 15 🏠 5 canvas bungalows. Per night from 40 to 70€ – Per week from 220 to 610€

🖭 borne 2€

Surroundings : ⛵
Leisure activities : ▼ jacuzzi ⤬
Facilities : ⚙ ⚬═ ▥ ♨ ⚱ ⟲ ❝ launderette ⚿ ⚲
Nearby : ✂ ⚲ ⚞

Longitude : -2.83529
Latitude : 48.6354

LE FAOUËT

56320 – Michelin map **308** J6 – pop. 2 893 – alt. 68
▶ Paris 516 – Carhaix-Plouguer 35 – Lorient 40 – Pontivy 47

⚲ Municipal Beg er Roch

✆ 02 97 23 15 11, http://campingbegerroch.jimdo.com

Address : route de Lorient (situated 2km southeast along the D 769, follow the signs for Lorient)

Opening times : from mid March to end Sept.

3 ha (65 pitches) flat, grassy

Tariff : ♟ 4€ ⇚ 2,40€ 🅿 3,60€ – ⚡ (10A) 3€ – Reservation fee 9€

Rental rates : (from mid March to end Sept.) – 8 🏠. Per night from 56 to 75€ – Per week from 216 to 425€ – Reservation fee 15€

Pleasant setting beside the Ellé river.

Surroundings : ⚲
Leisure activities : ⚞ ⚞ ⚲ ⛵
Facilities : ⚙ ⚬═ ▥ ⚱ launderette

Longitude : -3.46973
Latitude : 48.01794

FEINS

35440 – Michelin map **309** M5 – pop. 798 – alt. 104
▶ Paris 369 – Avranches 55 – Fougères 44 – Rennes 30

⚲ Municipal La Bijouterie

✆ 02 99 69 63 23, www.pays-aubigne.fr/camping

Address : at Domaine de Boulet (situated 2km northeast along the D 91, follow the signs for Marcillé-Raoul and take road to the left)

Opening times : from mid April to end Sept.

1,5 ha (62 pitches) flat, grassy

Tariff : 11€ ♥♥ ⇚ 🅿 ⚡ (10A) – Extra per person 3,50€

Rental rates : (from mid April to end Sept.) – 6 🏠. Per night from 44 to 60€ – Per week from 200 to 556€

In a pleasant location beside the lake.

Surroundings : ⛵ ⛄ ⚲ ⚲ ⛰
Leisure activities :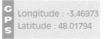
Facilities : ⚙ ⚬═ (July-Aug.) ⚱ ⟲ ❝ launderette, refrigerated food storage facilities
Nearby : ≋ ⚲ ⚞ watersports centre

Longitude : -1.63863
Latitude : 48.33845

LA FORÊT-FOUESNANT

29940 – Michelin map **308** H7 – pop. 3 299 – alt. 19
▶ Paris 553 – Rennes 202 – Quimper 18 – Brest 94

⚲ Kerleven ⚲⚲

✆ 02 98 56 98 83, www.campingdekerleven.com

Address : at Kerleven, 4 route de Port La Forêt, (situated 2km southeast, 200m from the beach)

Opening times : from mid April to end Sept.

4 ha (235 pitches)

Tariff : (2013 Price) 32,60€ ♥♥ ⇚ 🅿 ⚡ (10A) Extra per person 7,50€ Reservation fee 9€

Rental rates : (2013 Price) (from mid April to end Sept.) ⚲ – 37 🏠 – 1 gîte. Per night from 60 to 80€ – Per week from 240 to 790€ – Reservation fee 9€

🖭 borne 2€

Surroundings : ⛏ ⚲⚲
Leisure activities : ▼ ✗ ⚞ ⚑ ⚲ ⚲ ⚲ ⛰ ⛲ ⤬ ⤬
Facilities : ⚙ ⚬═ ⚱ ❝ launderette ⚿ ⚲
Nearby : ⚲

Longitude : -3.96788
Latitude : 47.89807

⚲ Club Airotel Kérantérec ⚲⚲

✆ 02 98 56 98 11, www.camping-keranterec.com

Address : at Kerleven (2.8km southeast)

Opening times : from mid April to mid Sept.

6,5 ha (265 pitches)

Tariff : 35€ ♥♥ ⇚ 🅿 ⚡ (10A) – Extra per person 8,50€

Rental rates : Permanent – 52 🏠. Per night from 60 to 100€ Per week from 230 to 950€ – Reservation fee 30€

🖭 borne 4€

Based around an old renovated farmhouse beside the ocean.

Surroundings : ⛵ ⛏ ⚲ ⛰
Leisure activities : ▼ ✗ ⚞ ⚑ ⚲ ⚲ ⤬ ⤬  entertainment room
Facilities : ⚙ ⚬═ ⚱ ⟲ ❝ launderette

Longitude : -3.95538
Latitude : 47.89903

⚲ Les Saules ⚲⚲

✆ 02 98 56 98 57, www.camping-les-saules.com

Address : at Kerléven, 54 route de la Plage (2.5km southeast; beside the beach at Kerléven (direct access)

Opening times : from beginning May to mid Sept.

4 ha (242 pitches)

Tariff : (2013 Price) 31,30€ ♥♥ ⇚ 🅿 ⚡ (6A) – Extra per person 6,65€ Reservation fee 18€

Rental rates : (2013 Price) (from mid April to end Sept.) ⚙ (1 mobile home) – 36 🏠. Per night from 80 to 150€ – Per week from 199 to 899€ – Reservation fee 18€

Dvided into 2 separate campsites.

Surroundings : ⛏ ⚲ ⛰
Leisure activities : ▼ ✗ ⚞ ⚲ ⚲ ⤬ ⤬ ⛰
Facilities : ⚬═ ⚱ ❝ launderette ⚿ ⚲
Nearby : ⚲

Longitude : -3.9611
Latitude : 47.899

There are several different types of sani-station ('borne' in French) – sanitation points providing fresh water and disposal points for grey water. See page 12 for further details.

⛰ Manoir de Penn ar Ster

✆ 02 98 56 97 75, www.camping-pennarster.com

Address : 2 chemin de Penn-Ar-Ster (take the northeastern exit, follow the signs for Quimper and take the turning to the left)

Opening times : from beginning March to mid Nov.

3 ha (105 pitches)

Tariff : 28,50€ ♣♣ ⇦ 回 ⑭ (10A) – Extra per person 7€ – Reservation fee 15€

Rental rates : (from beginning March to mid Nov.) ♿ – 6 🚐 2 🏠. Per night from 45 to 100€ – Per week from 250 to 680€ Reservation fee 15€

⛽ borne 5€

A pretty stone manor house with adjacent garden.

Surroundings : ⥷ ☞ ♉♉
Leisure activities : 🎮 ✗ ⌁
Facilities : ♿ ⚲ 🎭 🛁 ⚱ ⚙ 🍴 launderette

GPS Longitude : -3.97977
Latitude : 47.91215

⛰ FranceLoc Domaine du St-Laurent

✆ 02 98 56 97 65, www.campings-franceloc.fr

Address : at Kerleven (3km southeast, 500m from the large beach at Kerleven)

5,4 ha (260 pitches)

Rentals : ♿ (1 mobile home) – 203 🚐.

Some pitches have a view of the sea and the Glénan islands.

Surroundings : ⥷ ☞ ♉♉ ⚠
Leisure activities : 🍷 🎮 🏃 🛶 🚣 🚴 ✗ ⌁ 🎣 🏊 🏐 multi-sports ground
Facilities : ♿ ⚲ ⚱ 🍴 launderette 🍖
Nearby : ♨

GPS Longitude : -3.9547
Latitude : 47.89623

The information in the guide may have changed since going to press.

FOUESNANT

29170 – Michelin map **308** G7 – pop. 9 356 – alt. 30
▶ Paris 555 – Carhaix-Plouguer 69 – Concarneau 11 – Quimper 16

⛰ Sunêlia L'Atlantique ♣♣

✆ 02 98 56 14 44, www.latlantique.fr – limited spaces for one-night stay ✗

Address : 4.5km to the south, towards La Chapelle de Kerbader, 400m from the beach (direct access)

Opening times : from end April to beginning Sept.

10 ha (432 pitches) flat, grassy

Tariff : 42€ ♣♣ ⇦ 回 ⑭ (6A) – Extra per person 8€ – Reservation fee 35€

Rental rates : (from end April to beginning Sept.) ♿ ✗ 176 🚐 – 2 yurts – 10 tent lodges. Per night from 30 to 191€ Per week from 210 to 1 337€ – Reservation fee 35€

⛽ borne – 12 回 53€ – 🚐 ⑭14€

A pretty swimming area and spa.

Surroundings : ⥷ ☞ ♉♉
Leisure activities : 🍷 🎮 🎭 🏃 ⚽ 🚣 hammam, jacuzzi 🛶 🚴 ✗ ⌁ 🏊 🏐 ⚱ spa centre, entertainment room
Facilities : ♿ ⚲ 📺 🛁 ⚱ ⚙ 🍴 launderette 🍖 🍖

GPS Longitude : -4.01854
Latitude : 47.85487

FOUGÈRES

35300 – Michelin map **309** O4 – pop. 19 820 – alt. 115
▶ Paris 326 – Caen 148 – Le Mans 132 – Nantes 158

⛰ Municipal de Paron

✆ 02 99 99 40 81, campingmunicipal35@orange.fr

Address : route de la Chapelle-Janson (located 1.5km east along the D 17, access recommended via the eastern bypass (rocade)

2,5 ha (90 pitches) relatively flat, flat, grassy

⛽ borne

In a pleasant setting among trees.

Surroundings : ⥷ ☞ ♉♉
Leisure activities : 🏃
Facilities : ⚲ launderette
Nearby : ✗ 🎣 ⌁ 🐴

GPS Longitude : -1.18193
Latitude : 48.35371

LE FRET

29160 – Michelin map **308** D5
▶ Paris 591 – Rennes 239 – Quimper 56 – Brest 10

⛰ Gwel Kaër

✆ 02 98 27 61 06, www.camping-gwel-kaer.com

Address : 40 rue de Pen-An-Ero (take the southeastern exit along the D 55, follow the signs for Crozon; beside the sea)

Opening times : from beginning April to end Sept.

2,2 ha (98 pitches)

Tariff : ♣ 4,35€ ⇦ 2,30€ 回 4,20€ – ⑭ (6A) 3,20€

Rental rates : (from beginning April to end Sept.) ✗ – 7 🚐. Per night from 40 to 65€ – Per week from 240 to 515€

Surroundings : ⥷ ≤ ♉ ⚠
Leisure activities : 🏃
Facilities : ♿ ⚲ (from mid June to mid Sept) 🛁 🍴 🖼

GPS Longitude : -4.50237
Latitude : 48.28132

LE GUERNO

56190 – Michelin map **308** Q9 – pop. 818 – alt. 60
▶ Paris 460 – Muzillac 8 – Redon 30 – La Roche-Bernard 17

⛰ Municipal de Borg-Néhué

✆ 02 97 42 94 76, www.leguerno.fr

Address : rue du Borg Nehué (500m northwest following signs for Noyal-Muzillac)

Opening times : from beginning April to end Sept.

1,4 ha (50 pitches) flat, grassy

Tariff : (2013 Price) 11,60€ ♣♣ ⇦ 回 ⑭ (6A) – Extra per person 2,90€

⛽ borne

Surroundings : ⥷ ☞ ♉♉
Leisure activities : 🏃
Facilities : ♿ 🍳 🛁 🍴 🖼
Nearby : ✗

GPS Longitude : -2.41557
Latitude : 47.58251

The Michelin classification (⛰⛰⛰... ⛰) is totally independent of the official star classification system awarded by the local prefecture or other official organisation.

GUIDEL

56520 – Michelin map **308** K8 – pop. 10 174 – alt. 38
▶ Paris 511 – Nantes 178 – Quimper 60 – Rennes 162

⚠️ Les Jardins de Kergal

☎ 02 97 05 98 18, www.camping-lorient.com

Address : route des Plages (3km southwest along the D 306, follow the signs for Guidel-Plages and take road to the left)

5 ha (153 pitches) flat, grassy
Rentals : ♿ (1 chalet) – 78 🚐 – 41 🏠.
A pleasant wooded site.

Surroundings : 🏞️ ♨️
Leisure activities : 🍽️ 🏛️ ♣️ 🚲 🎯 🏊 🎣 🏊
♒ multi-sports ground
Facilities : ♿ ⚏ ♨️ 🍴 launderette, refrigerators
Nearby : 🛶 🏇 sports trail

G P S Longitude : -3.50734
Latitude : 47.77464

GUILVINEC

29730 – Michelin map **308** F8 – pop. 2 945 – alt. 5
▶ Paris 584 – Douarnenez 44 – Pont-l'Abbé 10 – Quimper 30

⚠️ Yelloh! Village La Plage 👥

☎ 02 98 58 61 90, www.villagelaplage.com

Address : route des Fusillés de Poulguen (situated 2km west, follow the signs for La pointe de Penmarc'h (headland), 100m from the beach (direct access)

Opening times : from mid April to mid Sept.

14 ha (410 pitches)

Tariff : 46€ 🏕️🏕️ 🚐 🔲 ⚡ (10A) – Extra per person 8€
Rental rates : (from mid April to mid Sept.) – 200 🚐 – 2 cabins in the trees – 8 tent lodges. Per night from 39 to 232€ – Per week from 273 to 1 624€
🚐 borne 10€

Surroundings : ♀️
Leisure activities : 🍽️ 🏛️ 🛁 🏇 🛶 🚤
♣️ 🚲 🎯 🏊 🎣 🏊 ♒ pedal go-carts, multi-sports ground
Facilities : ♿ ⚏ ♨️ 🍴 launderette ♨️
Nearby : 🛶

G P S Longitude : -4.31194
Latitude : 47.8035

HUELGOAT

29690 – Michelin map **308** I4 – pop. 1 604 – alt. 149
▶ Paris 523 – Brest 66 – Carhaix-Plouguer 18 – Châteaulin 36

⚠️ La Rivière d'Argent

☎ 02 98 99 72 50, www.larivieredargent.com

Address : La Coudraie (3.4km east along the D 769a, follow the signs for Locmaria-Berrien and take the road to the right)

Opening times : from mid March to mid Oct.

5 ha (90 pitches) flat, grassy

Tariff : 🏕️ 4,60€ 🚐 1,90€ 🔲 5,90€ – ⚡ (10A) 4,30€ – Reservation fee 15€
Rental rates : (from mid March to mid Oct.) – 11 🚐 – 1 tipi 1 canvas bungalow. Per night from 25 to 80€ – Per week from 140 to 610€ – Reservation fee 15€
🚐 borne 3,20€
Attractive location beside a river on the edge of a forest.

Surroundings : 🏞️ 🏕️ ♨️
Leisure activities : 🍽️ 🛁 🏊 🐟
Facilities : ♿ ⚏ ♨️ ♨️ 🍴 🔲 🏊

G P S Longitude : -3.71681
Latitude : 48.36428

ÎLE-AUX-MOINES

56780 – Michelin map **308** N9 – pop. 601 – alt. 16
▶ Paris 483 – Rennes 132 – Vannes 15 – Lorient 59

⚠️ Municipal du Vieux Moulin

☎ 02 97 26 30 68, www.mairie-ileauxmoines.fr ♨️

Address : Le Vieux Moulin (take southeastern exit from town, follow the signs for La Pointe de Brouel (headland)

Opening times : from beginning April to end Sept.

1 ha (44 pitches)

Tariff : 🏕️ 7€ 🚐
Rental rates : Permanent ♨️ – 2 tent lodges – 2 tents. Per night from 45 to 75€ – Per week from 180 to 420€ – Reservation fee 5€
Site with no electricity supply and reserved for tents.

Surroundings : 🏞️
Leisure activities : 🏇
Facilities : ⚏
Nearby : 🏖️

G P S Longitude : -2.84514
Latitude : 47.59292

JOSSELIN

56120 – Michelin map **308** P7 – pop. 2 533 – alt. 58
▶ Paris 428 – Dinan 86 – Lorient 76 – Pontivy 35

⚠️ Domaine de Kerelly

☎ 02 97 22 22 20, www.camping-josselin.com

Address : Le Bas de la Lande (situated 2km west along the D 778 and take the D 724, follow the signs for Guégon to the left, 50m from the Oust river, take the western exit Guégon along the dual carriageway)

Opening times : from beginning April to end Oct.

2 ha (60 pitches) adjacent pine trees

Tariff : (2013 Price) 19,50€ 🏕️🏕️ 🚐 🔲 ⚡ (10A)
Extra per person 3,50€
Rental rates : (2013 Price) (from beginning April to end Oct.) – 8 🚐 – 3 canvas bungalows. Per night from 45 to 90 € – Per week from 270 to 540 €
🚐 borne
Cyclists are welcome.

Surroundings : 🏞️ ♀️
Leisure activities : 🍽️ 🏛️ 🏇 🚲
Facilities : ♿ ⚏ ♨️ 🍴 launderette
Nearby : 🏊 🐟

G P S Longitude : -2.57352
Latitude : 47.95239

JUGON-LES-LACS

22270 – Michelin map **309** I4 – pop. 1 683 – alt. 29
▶ Paris 417 – Lamballe 22 – Plancoët 16 – St-Brieuc 59

⚠️ Au Bocage du Lac

☎ 02 96 31 60 16, www.camping-location-bretagne.com

Address : rue du Bocage (located 1km southeast along the D 52, follow the signs for Mégrit)

Opening times : from mid April to mid Sept.

4 ha (180 pitches)

Tariff : (2013 Price) 🏕️ 3,90€ 🚐 🔲 6€ – ⚡ (10A) 3,50€ – Reservation fee 17€
Rental rates : (2013 Price) (from mid April to end Sept.) – 7 🚐 40 🏠 – 1 cabin in the trees. Per night from 77 to 164 € – Per week from 277 to 1 148 € – Reservation fee 17€
🚐 borne 2,50€ – 2 🔲 5€

Beside the large Étang deJugon (lake).

Surroundings : 🔲 🎣
Leisure activities : 🍴 🏛 🛝 🚣 🏊 🎿 wildlife park
Facilities : 👤 🚿 🔥 🍴 launderette
Nearby : 🚴 🎣 ⚓

GPS Longitude : -2.31663
Latitude : 48.40165

KERVEL

29550 – Michelin map **308** F6
▶ Paris 586 – Rennes 234 – Quimper 24 – Brest 67

🏔 FranceLoc Domaine de Kervel 👥

📞 02 98 92 51 54, www.franceloc.fr

Address : at Kervel

Opening times : from mid April to mid Sept.

7 ha (300 pitches) flat, grassy

Tariff : 👤 12 € 🚗 🔲 – 🔌 (10A) 8 € – Reservation fee 27 €
Rental rates : (from mid April to mid Sept.) 👤 – 147 🏕 – 3 🏠.
Per night from 37 to 89 € – Per week from 147 to 987 €
Reservation fee 27 €

Surroundings : 🎣
Leisure activities : 🍴 🏛 🛝 🏃 🎿 🚴 🎣
🎯 🎱 🏊 🏓 multi-sports ground
Facilities : 👤 🚿 🔥 🍴 launderette
🛝

GPS Longitude : -4.26737
Latitude : 48.11617

KERVOYAL

56750 – Michelin map **308** P9
▶ Paris 471 – Rennes 124 – Vannes 30 – Lorient 87

⛰ Oasis

📞 02 97 41 10 52, www.campingloasis.com

Address : rue Port Lestre (100m from the beach)

Opening times : from beginning April to end Sept.

3 ha (150 pitches) flat, grassy

Tariff : 21,90 € 👥 🚗 🔲 🔌 (6A) – Extra per person 3,60 €
🚗 borne

Surroundings : 🌊 🎣
Leisure activities : 🚣
Facilities : 🚿 🍴 launderette

GPS Longitude : -2.55013
Latitude : 47.51897

LAMPAUL-PLOUDALMEZEAU

29830 – Michelin map **308** D3 – pop. 753 – alt. 24
▶ Paris 613 – Brest 27 – Brignogan-Plages 36 – Ploudalmézeau 4

⛰ Municipal des Dunes

📞 02 98 48 14 29, lampaul-ploudalmezeau.mairie@wanadoo.fr – 🅿

Address : Le Vourc'h (700m north of the town, beside the sports field and 100m from the beach (direct access)

Opening times : from mid June to mid Sept.

1,5 ha (150 pitches) dunes

Tariff : 👤 4,60 € 🚗 🔲 – 🔌 (12A) 2,55 €
🚗 borne 2,45 €

Surroundings : 🌊
Leisure activities : 🏛
Facilities : 👤 🚿 (July–Aug.) 🛝 launderette

GPS Longitude : -4.65639
Latitude : 48.56785

LANDÉDA

29870 – Michelin map **308** D3 – pop. 3 620 – alt. 52
▶ Paris 604 – Brest 28 – Brignogan-Plages 25 – Ploudalmézeau 17

🏔 Les Abers 👥

📞 02 98 04 93 35, www.camping-des-abers.com

Address : 51 Toull Tréaz (2.5km to the northwest; by the dunes at Ste-Marguerite)

Opening times : from beginning May to end Sept.

4,5 ha (180 pitches) dunes

Tariff : 20 € 👥 🚗 🔲 🔌 (10A) – Extra per person 4 €
Rental rates : (from beginning May to end Sept.) – 22 🏕
1 studio – 1 apartment. Per night 90 € – Per week 630 €
🚗 borne – 🔋 🔌 20 €
A pleasant location close to the beach, information and map table on site.

Surroundings : 🌊 🌲 ⛰
Leisure activities : 🏛 🛝 🏃 🚣 🚴
Facilities : 👤 🚿 🔥 🍴 launderette 🛝
Nearby : 🍴 🍴

GPS Longitude : -4.60306
Latitude : 48.59306

LANLOUP

22580 – Michelin map **309** E2 – pop. 272 – alt. 58
▶ Paris 484 – Guingamp 29 – Lannion 44 – St-Brieuc 36

🏔 Le Neptune

📞 02 96 22 33 35, www.leneptune.com

Opening times : from beginning April to mid Oct.

2 ha (84 pitches)

Tariff : (2013 Price) 👤 6 € 🚗 🔲 12 € – 🔌 (10A) 4 € – Reservation fee 9 €
Rental rates : (2013 Price) (from beginning April to mid Oct.)
16 🏕 – 4 🏠. Per night from 26 to 109 € – Per week from 235 to 813 € – Reservation fee 9 €
🚗 borne 8 € – 5 🔲 14 €
Set among pleasant trees.

Surroundings : 🔲 🎣
Leisure activities : 🍴 🏛 🚣 🚴 🎯 🎱
(open air in season), multi-sports ground
Facilities : 👤 🚿 🆑 🔥 🍴 launderette 🛝
Nearby : 🍴

GPS Longitude : -2.96704
Latitude : 48.71372

LANNION

22300 – Michelin map **309** B2 – pop. 19 847 – alt. 12
▶ Paris 516 – Brest 96 – Morlaix 42 – St-Brieuc 65

🏔 Les Plages de Beg-Léguer

📞 02 96 47 25 00, www.campingdesplages.com

Address : route de la Côte (6km west following signs for Trébeurden and take the turning to the left, 500m from the beach)

Opening times : from mid April to beginning Nov.

5 ha (240 pitches)

Tariff : 👤 7,50 € 🚗 🔲 8,50 € – 🔌 (6A) 3,80 €
Rental rates : (from mid April to beginning Nov.) 🅿 – 30 🏕
7 🏠 – 6 canvas bungalows. Per night from 33 to 97 € – Per week from 231 to 679 €
🚗 borne

Surroundings : 🌊 🔲 🎣
Leisure activities : 🍴 🍴 🏛 🚣 🚴 🎣 🎯
🏊 🎱 multi-sports ground
Facilities : 👤 🚿 🔥 🍴 launderette 🛝

GPS Longitude : -3.545
Latitude : 48.73834

▲ Municipal des 2 Rives

🖉 02 96 46 31 40, www.ville-lannion.fr

Address : rue du Moulin du Duc (situated 2km southeast along the D 767, follow the signs for Guingamp and take the turning to the right after the Leclerc commercial centre)

Opening times : Permanent

2,3 ha (116 pitches) flat, grassy

Tariff : 🛉 3,65 € 🚗 2,25 € 🔳 5,30 € – 🔌 (10A) 2,65 €

Rental rates : Permanent ♿ (1 chalet) – 14 🏠 – 4 canvas bungalows. Per night from 34 to 71 € – Per week from 227 to 472 €

🚐 borne 6,10 €

Attractive trees and shrubs on both banks of the Léguer river.

Surroundings : 🌳 ⚲	**G** Longitude : -3.44584
Leisure activities : 🍸 🏄 🎣	**P** Latitude : 48.72293
Facilities : ♿ ⌕ 🚿 ♨ 🚾 🚰 launderette	**S**
Nearby : walking trails	

LANTIC

22410 – Michelin map **309** E3 – pop. 1 483 – alt. 50
▶ Paris 466 – Brest 139 – Lorient 133 – Rennes 116

▲ Les Étangs

🖉 02 96 71 95 47, www.campinglesetangs.com

Address : rue des Terres Neuvas, Le Pont de la Motte (situated 2km east along the D 4, follow the signs for Binic, near two lakes)

Opening times : from mid April to end Sept.

1,5 ha (110 pitches)

Tariff : 20,50 € 🛉🛉 🚗 🔳 🔌 (10A) – Extra per person 4,50 €

Rental rates : (from beginning April to end Sept.) – 10 🚐 – 1 🏠 2 canvas bungalows. Per night from 35 to 100 € – Per week from 180 to 640 €

🚐 borne 10 € – 🔌 10 €

Surroundings : 🌳 ⚲⚲	**G** Longitude : -2.86254
Leisure activities : 🍽 🏄 🎿	**P** Latitude : 48.6068
Facilities : ♿ ⌕ 🚿🚾 🔲	**S**
Nearby : 🎣	

LARMOR-PLAGE

56260 – Michelin map **308** K8 – pop. 8 423 – alt. 4
▶ Paris 510 – Lorient 7 – Quimper 74 – Vannes 66

▲ La Fontaine

🖉 02 97 33 71 28, www.campingdelafontaine.fr

Address : Kerdeff, rue de Quéhello (to the west of the resort, 300m from the D 152 (recommended route)

Opening times : from beginning Jan.yy to end Dec.

4 ha (130 pitches) relatively flat, flat, grassy

Tariff : (2013 Price) 16,10 € 🛉🛉 🚗 🔳 🔌 (16A)
Extra per person 4,90 €

Rental rates : (2013 Price) Permanent – 11 🚐. Per night from 50 to 60 € – Per week from 265 to 543 €

🚐 borne – 3 🔳 11,50 € – 🔌 11,50 €

Surroundings : 🌳 🛖 ⚲⚲	**G** Longitude : -3.39212
Leisure activities : 🍽 🏃 🏄	**P** Latitude : 47.70912
Facilities : ♿ ⌕ ▥ 🚿 🚰 launderette	**S**

LESCONIL

29740 – Michelin map **308** F8
▶ Paris 581 – Douarnenez 41 – Guilvinec 6 – Loctudy 7

▲ La Grande Plage

🖉 02 98 87 88 27, www.campinggrandeplage.com

Address : 71 rue Paul Langevin (located 1km west, follow the signs for Guilvinec, 300m from the beach (direct access)

Opening times : from mid April to end Sept.

2,5 ha (120 pitches)

Tariff : 26,80 € 🛉🛉 🚗 🔳 🔌 (10A) – Extra per person 5,50 €

Rental rates : Permanent – 15 🚐 – 5 canvas bungalows. Per night from 42 to 68 € – Per week from 262 to 855 €

🚐 borne 2 €

Surroundings : 🛖 ⚲⚲	**G** Longitude : -4.22897
Leisure activities : 🍽 🏄	**P** Latitude : 47.79804
Facilities : ♿ ⌕ 🚿 🚰 launderette	**S**

▲ Les Dunes

🖉 02 98 87 81 78, http://www.camping-desdunes.com

Address : 67 rue Paul-Langevin (located 1km west, follow the signs for Guilvinec; 150m from the beach (direct access)

Opening times : from beginning April to mid Oct.

2,8 ha (120 pitches) flat, grassy

Tariff : 25,18 € 🛉🛉 🚗 🔳 🔌 (10A) – Extra per person 4,80 €

Rental rates : Permanent – 4 🚐. Per night from 50 to 95 € Per week from 350 to 685 €

🚐 borne – 🔌 10 €

Surroundings : 🛖 ⚲	**G** Longitude : -4.22856
Leisure activities : 🍽 🏄	**P** Latitude : 47.79716
Facilities : ♿ ⌕ 🚿 🚰 launderette	**S**

▲ Keralouet

🖉 02 98 82 23 05, www.campingkeralouet.com

Address : 11 rue Eric Tabarly (located 1km east on the Loctudy road)

Opening times : from beginning April to end Sept.

1 ha (64 pitches) flat, grassy

Tariff : (2013 Price) 20,15 € 🛉🛉 🚗 🔳 🔌 (10A)
Extra per person 4,20 €

Rental rates : (2013 Price) (from beginning April to end Sept.) ♿ (2 chalets) – 6 🚐 – 13 🏠 – 4 canvas bungalows – 2 tent lodges. Per night from 39 to 90 € – Per week from 205 to 635 €

A well-kept, pleasant site.

Surroundings : ⚲⚲	**G** Longitude : -4.20595
Leisure activities : 🏄 🎿	**P** Latitude : 47.80424
Facilities : ♿ ⌕ 🚿 🚰 🔲	**S**
Nearby : 🛶	

LOCMARIA-PLOUZANÉ

29280 – Michelin map **308** D4 – pop. 4 837 – alt. 65
▶ Paris 610 – Brest 15 – Brignogan-Plages 50 – Ploudalmézeau 23

▲ Municipal de Portez

🖉 02 98 48 49 85, camping-portez@locmaria-plouzane.fr

Address : Portez (3.5km southwest along the D 789 and follow the signs for the beach at Trégana; 200m from the beach)

2 ha (110 pitches)

Rentals : 4 🏠 .

Surroundings : ⛵ ⬚ ♨
Leisure activities : 🏓 🏖
Facilities : ♿ ⚷ ☕ launderette
Nearby : 🍷 ✗

G P S Longitude : -4.66344
Latitude : 48.3582

LOCMARIAQUER

56740 – Michelin map **308** N9 – pop. 1 692 – alt. 5
▶ Paris 488 – Auray 13 – Quiberon 31 – La Trinité-sur-Mer 10

🏕 Lann-Brick

✆ 02 97 57 32 79, www.camping-lannbrick.com

Address : Lann Brick – route de Kérinis (2.5km northwest following signs for Kérinis, 200m from the beach)

Opening times : from beginning April to end Sept.

1,2 ha (98 pitches) flat, grassy

Tariff : 24,60€ 🚹🚹 🚗 🔲 🔌 (10A) – Extra per person 4,80€
Reservation fee 15€

Rental rates : (from end March to mid Oct.) – 20 🏠 – 2 canvas bungalows. Per night from 40 to 100€ – Per week from 170 to 680€ – Reservation fee 15€

🚐 borne – 🚰 🔌15€

Surroundings : ⬚ ♨
Leisure activities : 🍷 🏖 🏖 🚲 ⛵
Facilities : ♿ ⚷ ☕ launderette
Nearby : ✗ ♨

G P S Longitude : -2.97436
Latitude : 47.57838

LOCRONAN

29180 – Michelin map **308** F6 – pop. 798 – alt. 105
▶ Paris 580 – Rennes 229 – Quimper 17

🏕 Le Locronan

✆ 02 98 91 87 76, www.camping-locronan.fr

Address : rue de la Troménie

Opening times : from mid April to beginning Nov.

2,6 ha (103 pitches)

Tariff : 23,30€ 🚹🚹 🚗 🔲 🔌 (10A) – Extra per person 5,40€
Reservation fee 5€

Rental rates : (from mid April to beginning Nov.) – 20 🏠 2 canvas bungalows. Per night from 40 to 78€ – Per week from 220 to 530€ – Reservation fee 15€

🚐 borne – 10 🔲 15€

Surroundings : ⛵ ⬚ ♨
Leisure activities : 🏖 🔲
Facilities : ♿ ⚷ ☕ launderette

G P S Longitude : -4.19918
Latitude : 48.09582

LOCTUDY

29750 – Michelin map **308** F8 – pop. 4 207 – alt. 8
▶ Paris 578 – Bénodet 18 – Concarneau 35 – Pont-l'Abbé 6

🏕 Les Hortensias

✆ 02 98 87 46 64, www.camping-loctudy.com

Address : 38 rue des Tulipes (3km southwest following signs for Larvor, 500m from the beach at Lodonnec)

Opening times : from beginning April to end Sept.

1,5 ha (100 pitches) flat, grassy

Tariff : 24,60€ 🚹🚹 🚗 🔲 🔌 (10A) – Extra per person 4,70€

Rental rates : (from beginning April to end Sept.) – 1 caravan 21 🏠. Per night from 45 to 110€ – Per week from 242 to 756€
🚐 borne 7€ – 🚰 🔌14,80€

Surroundings : ♨♨
Leisure activities : 🏖 ⛰ ⛵ ⛵
Facilities : ♿ ⚷ ☕ launderette
Nearby : 🍷 ✗

G P S Longitude : -4.1823
Latitude : 47.81259

Key to rentals symbols :

12 🏠	*Number of mobile homes*
20 🏡	*Number of chalets*
6 🛏	*Number of rooms to rent*
Per night 30–50€	*Minimum/maximum rate per night*
Per week 300–1,000€	*Minimum/maximum rate per week*

LOUANNEC

22700 – Michelin map **309** B2 – pop. 2 946 – alt. 53
▶ Paris 527 – Rennes 175 – St-Brieuc 77 – Lannion 10

🏕 Municipal Ernest Renan

✆ 02 96 23 11 78, www.camping-louannec.fr

Address : located 1km west; beside the sea

Opening times : from beginning May to end Sept.

4 ha (265 pitches) flat, grassy

Tariff : (2013 Price) 17,75€ 🚹🚹 🚗 🔲 🔌 (16A)

Extra per person 3,70€

Rental rates : (from beginning April to end Sept.) 🏖 – 8 🏠 2 canvas bungalows. Per night from 42 to 78€ – Per week from 190 to 630€

🚐 borne 4,20€ – 11 🔲 9,90€

Surroundings : ⛵ ⛰
Leisure activities : 🍷 🏖 ☀daytime 🏖 ⛵ ♨
Facilities : ♿ ⚷ ☕ ☂ ⚿ ☕ launderette 🏖 ⚒
Nearby : 🐎 🏇

G P S Longitude : -3.42723
Latitude : 48.79666

MARCILLÉ-ROBERT

35240 – Michelin map **309** N7 – pop. 929 – alt. 65
▶ Paris 333 – Bain-de-Bretagne 33 – Châteaubriant 30 – La Guerche-de-Bretagne 11

🏕 Municipal de l'Étang

✆ 06 02 08 60 22, camping.marcillerobert@yahoo.fr

Address : rue des Bas Gasts (take the southern exit along the D 32, follow the signs for Arbrissel)

Opening times : Permanent

0,5 ha (22 pitches) pond

Tariff : 10,60€ 🚹🚹 🚗 🔲 🔌 (10A) – Extra per person 3€

Rental rates : Permanent – 1 🏠 – 1 🏡. Per night from 23 to 32€
Per week from 160 to 230€

A pleasant setting looking out over a lake.

Surroundings : ⛰ ⬚ ♨♨
Facilities : ♿ ⚒
Nearby : 🏖 ✗ 🎣 pedalos

G P S Longitude : -1.36471
Latitude : 47.94768

MARTIGNÉ-FERCHAUD

35640 – Michelin map **309** O8 – pop. 2 650 – alt. 90
▶ Paris 340 – Bain-de-Bretagne 31 – Châteaubriant 15 – La Guerche-de-Bretagne 16

⚠ Municipal du Bois Feuillet

☎ 02 99 47 84 38, www.ville-martigne-ferchaud.fr

Address : Étang de la Forge (to the northwest of the town)

Opening times : from beginning June to end Sept.

1,7 ha (50 pitches)

Tariff : (2013 Price) ✦ 3 € ⟷ 🚐 🅿 2 € – 🔌 (10A) 2 €

🚐 borne – 1 🅿

| Surroundings : ⟸ 🗗 ♀♀ |
| Leisure activities : 🖼 |
| Facilities : ⚅ ☞ (July-Aug.) 🚿 ⚐ 🔲 |
| Nearby : 🛝 ✗ ⟐ (beach) 🚣 🛶 pedalos |

GPS
Longitude : -1.31599
Latitude : 47.83385

MATIGNON

22550 – Michelin map **309** I3 – pop. 1 647 – alt. 70
▶ Paris 425 – Dinan 30 – Dinard 23 – Lamballe 23

⚠ Le Vallon aux Merlettes

☎ 02 96 80 37 99, www.campingdematignon.com

Address : 43 rue du Dr-Jobert (to the southwest along the D 13, follow the signs for Lamballe, by the stadium)

Opening times : from beginning April to mid Oct.

3 ha (100 pitches)

Tariff : (2013 Price) 17,50 € ✦✦ ⟷ 🚐 🅿 🔌 (10A) – Extra per person 4 €

Rental rates : (2013 Price) (from beginning April to mid Oct.) 3 🛖 – 3 tent lodges. Per night from 30 to 70 € – Per week from 210 to 490 €

🚐 borne 3 € – 3 🅿 17,50 €

| Surroundings : 🌳 ♀ |
| Leisure activities : 🖼 ✗ 🔲 |
| Facilities : ⚅ ☞ 🚿 ⚐ launderette |

GPS
Longitude : -2.29607
Latitude : 48.59168

MERDRIGNAC

22230 – Michelin map **309** H5 – pop. 2 916 – alt. 140
▶ Paris 411 – Dinan 47 – Josselin 33 – Lamballe 40

⚠ Val de Landrouet

☎ 02 96 28 47 98, www.valdelandrouet.com

Address : 14 rue du Gouède (0.8km to the north, near the swimming pool and two lakes; at the leisure and activity park)

Opening times : from beginning May to end Sept.

15 ha/2 for camping (50 pitches)

Tariff : ✦ 4 € ⟷ 🚐 3 € 🅿 5 € – 🔌 (5A) 3 €

Rental rates : (from beginning Jan.yy to mid Dec.) – 5 🛖. Per night from 62 to 86 € – Per week from 260 to 540 €
Reservation fee 15 €

🚐 borne 3 € – 5 🅿 – 🚿 🔌 10 €

| Surroundings : 🌳 🗗 ♀♀ |
| Leisure activities : ✗ 🖰 |
| Facilities : ⚅ ☞ 🚿 ⚐ 🔲 |
| Nearby : 🛝 ✗ 🔲 🚣 🛶 |

GPS
Longitude : -2.41525
Latitude : 48.19843

MEUCON

56890 – Michelin map **308** O8 – pop. 2 131 – alt. 80
▶ Paris 467 – Rennes 116 – Vannes 8 – Lorient 62

⛰ Le Haras

DANARD

☎ 0033(0)297446606, www.campingvannes.com

Address : at Kersimon (from Vannes, head north along the D 767 then take the D 778 E, behind Vannes-Meucon-Bretagne-Sud flying club)

Opening times : from mid March to mid Nov.

14 ha/2,5 for camping (140 pitches)

Tariff : 22 € ✦✦ ⟷ 🚐 🅿 🔌 (16A)

Extra per person 4 € – Reservation fee 30 €

Rental rates : (from mid March to mid Nov.) ⚅ (1 chalet) – 46 🛖 7 🏠. Per night from 50 to 160 € – Per week from 248 to 1 118 € Reservation fee 30 €

🚐 borne 14 € – 8 🅿 14 €

| Surroundings : 🌳 🗗 ♀♀ |
| Leisure activities : 🍷 ✗ ⏲ daytime 🎐 hammam, jacuzzi 🛝 🚴 ✗ 🛷 🏊 🚣 wildlife park, multi-sports ground, spa centre |
| Facilities : ⚅ ☞ ▥ 🚿 ⚐ 🍴 launderette |
| Nearby : 🐴 |

GPS
Longitude : -2.72795
Latitude : 47.73035

MOËLAN-SUR-MER

29350 – Michelin map **308** J8 – pop. 6 956 – alt. 58
▶ Paris 523 – Carhaix-Plouguer 66 – Concarneau 27 – Lorient 27

⚠ L'Île Percée

☎ 02 98 71 16 25, www.camping-ile-percee.fr

Address : plage de Trenez (5.8km west along the D 116, follow the signs for Kerfany-les-Pins, then continue 1.7km along the turning to the left)

Opening times : from mid March to end Sept.

1 ha (65 pitches) flat, grassy

Tariff : 20,40 € ✦✦ ⟷ 🚐 🅿 🔌 (6A) – Extra per person 4,40 € Reservation fee 8 €

Rental rates : (from mid March to end Sept.) – 4 🛖. Per night from 36 to 60 € – Per week from 248 to 529 € – Reservation fee 8 €

A pleasant, natural site looking out over the ocean.

| Surroundings : 🌳 ⟸ ♀ 🏔 |
| Leisure activities : 🍷 ⚑ |
| Facilities : ⚅ ☞ 🚿 🍴 🔲 |
| Nearby : ✗ 🐴 walking trails |

GPS
Longitude : -3.70241
Latitude : 47.78872

MORGAT

29160 – Michelin map **308** E5 – pop. 7 535
▶ Paris 590 – Rennes 238 – Quimper 55 – Brest 15

⚠ Les Bruyères

☎ 02 98 26 14 87, www.camping-bruyeres-crozon.com

Address : Le Bouis (located 1.5km along the D 255, follow the signs for Le Cap de la Chèvre and take road to the right)

Opening times : from beginning May to mid Sept.

4 ha (130 pitches)

Tariff : ✦ 5,20 € ⟷ 🚐 🅿 7,90 € – 🔌 (5A) 3,45 €

Rental rates : (from beginning April to end Sept.) ✂ – 17 ⊞. Per night from 50 to 70€ – Per week from 295 to 655€
Natural setting with access to Morgat via a pedestrian path.

Surroundings : ♨ ♀
Leisure activities : 🏕
Facilities : ⊶ 🔥 ⚒ launderette

G P S Longitude : -4.53183
Latitude : 48.22293

MOUSTERLIN

29170 – Michelin map **308** G7
▶ Paris 563 – Rennes 212 – Quimper 22 – Brest 94

⚠⚠⚠ FranceLoc Le Grand Large 👥♦

📞 02 98 56 04 06, www.campings-franceloc.fr – limited spaces for one-night stay

Address : 48 route du Grand Large (near the beach)

Opening times : from beginning April to beginning Sept.

5,8 ha (287 pitches) flat, grassy

Tariff : 29€ ♟♟ 🚐 ▤ ⚡ (6A) – Extra per person 7€ – Reservation fee 27€

Rental rates : (from beginning April to beginning Sept.) ♿ 211 ⊞ . Per night from 33 to 112€ – Per week from 133 to 1 085€ Reservation fee 27€

Surroundings : ♨ ♀

Leisure activities : ♟ 🏠 🎣 ⛹ ⛵ jacuzzi 🚗 🚲 🏌 🏊 (open air in season) ☂ multi-sports ground
Facilities : ♿ ⊶ 🔥 ⚒ launderette 🚿
Nearby : 🍴

G P S Longitude : -4.0367
Latitude : 47.84809

⚠⚠ Kost-Ar-Moor

📞 02 98 56 04 16, www.camping-fouesnant.com

Address : 17 route du Grand Large (500m from the beach)

Opening times : from beginning May to mid Sept.

3,5 ha (177 pitches) flat, grassy

Tariff : (2013 Price) 27,50€ ♟♟ 🚐 ▤ ⚡ (10A) Extra per person 5,70€ – Reservation fee 15€

Rental rates : (2013 Price) (from mid April to mid Sept.) 25 ⊞ – 5 apartments. Per night from 31 to 102€ – Per week from 220 to 715€ – Reservation fee 15€

Surroundings : ♨ ♀♀
Leisure activities : ♟ 🏠 🚗 🚲 🏊
Facilities : ♿ ⊶ 🔥 ⚒ launderette
Nearby : ⚓

G P S Longitude : -4.03421
Latitude : 47.85106

NAIZIN

56500 – Michelin map **308** O7 – pop. 1 695 – alt. 106
▶ Paris 454 – Ploërmel 40 – Pontivy 16 – Rennes 106

⚠ Municipal de Coetdan

📞 02 97 27 43 27, naizin.fr

Address : rue des Peupliers (600m east along the D 17 and take D 203 towards Réguiny)

Opening times : from beginning June to end Sept.

0,7 ha (28 pitches)

Tariff : (2013 Price) ♟ 3€ 🚐 2€ ▤ 2€ – ⚡ (3A) 3€

A pleasant setting near a small lake.

Surroundings : ⛰ ♀♀
Leisure activities : 🎣
Facilities : ♿ 🚿
Nearby : 🚗 🏃 fitness trail

G P S Longitude : -2.82616
Latitude : 47.99336

NÉVEZ

29920 – Michelin map **308** I8 – pop. 2 718 – alt. 40
▶ Paris 541 – Concarneau 14 – Pont-Aven 8 – Quimper 40

⚠ Les Chaumières

📞 02 98 06 73 06, www.camping-des-chaumieres.com

Address : 24 hamlet de Kerascoët (head 3km south along the D 77 towards Port Manec'h then take the turning to the right)

Opening times : from mid May to mid Sept.

3 ha (110 pitches) flat, grassy

Tariff : 21,90€ ♟♟ 🚐 ▤ ⚡ (10A) – Extra per person 5,25€

Rental rates : (from beginning April to mid Sept.) – 6 ⊞. Per night from 35 to 55€ – Per week from 200 to 580€ Reservation fee 10€

🚉 borne 13,50€

Surroundings : ♨ ⛰ ♀
Leisure activities : 🚗
Facilities : ♿ ⊶ (July-Aug.) ⚒ launderette
Nearby : 🍴 🍴

G P S Longitude : -3.77433
Latitude : 47.79598

NOYAL-MUZILLAC

56190 – Michelin map **308** Q9 – pop. 2 410 – alt. 52
▶ Paris 468 – Rennes 108 – Vannes 31 – Lorient 88

⚠⚠⚠ Moulin de Cadillac

📞 02 97 67 03 47, www.camping-moulin-cadillac.com

Address : 4.5km northwest following signs for Berric

Opening times : from mid April to mid Sept.

7 ha (192 pitches) adjacent wood

Tariff : ♟ 6,20€ 🚐 ▤ 13€ – ⚡ (10A) 3,80€ – Reservation fee 10€

Rental rates : (from mid April to mid Sept.) – 60 ⊞ – 9 🏠 4 canvas bungalows. Per night 160€ – Per week from 240 to 770€ Reservation fee 10€

🚉 borne

Pleasant setting laid out around an indoor water park; beside the Kervily.

Surroundings : ♨ ⛰ ♀
Leisure activities : 🍴 🏠 🎣 🚗 ⛹ 🏌 🏊 ☂ 🎣 wildlife park, multi-sports ground, entertainment room
Facilities : ♿ ⊶ 🔥 ⚒ launderette

G P S Longitude : -2.50199
Latitude : 47.61412

These symbols are used for a campsite that is exceptional in its category:

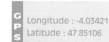 *Particularly pleasant setting, quality and range of services available*

♨♨ *Tranquil, isolated site – quiet site, particularly at night*

⇐⇐ *Exceptional view – interesting or panoramic view*

PAIMPOL

22500 – Michelin map **309** D2 – pop. 7 828 – alt. 15
▶ Paris 494 – Guingamp 29 – Lannion 33 – St-Brieuc 46

⚠ Municipal de Cruckin-Kérity

🔌 02 96 20 78 47, www.camping-paimpol.com

Address : Kérity (head 2km southeast along the D 786, follow the signs for St-Quay-Portrieux, next to the stadium, 100m from the beach at Cruckin)

Opening times : from beginning April to beginning Oct.

2 ha (130 pitches) flat, grassyTariff : ⚡ 4,30€ ⇌ 🅿 8,55€ ⚡ (10A) 3,90€

Rental rates : (from beginning April to beginning Oct.) – 5 canvas bungalows. Per night from 43€ – Per week from 220 to 360€
🚐 10 🅿 12,50€

Surroundings : 🐾 ⌒ �‿
Leisure activities : 🎣 🚣
Facilities : ♿ ⛟ 🚿🍴 launderette
Nearby : ✕ 🏃 fitness trail

GPS Longitude : -3.02224
Latitude : 48.76972

The pitches of many campsites are marked out with low hedges of attractive bushes and shrubs.

PAIMPONT

35380 – Michelin map **309** I6 – pop. 1 641 – alt. 159
▶ Paris 390 – Dinan 60 – Ploërmel 26 – Redon 47

⚠ Municipal Paimpont Brocéliande

🔌 02 99 07 89 16, www.camping-paimpont-broceliande.com

Address : 2 rue du Chevalier Lancelot du Lac (take the northern exit along the D 773, near the lake)

Opening times : from beginning April to end Sept.

1,5 ha (90 pitches) flat, grassy

Tariff : (2013 Price) ⚡ 3,30€ ⇌ 1,60€ 🅿 3€ – ⚡ (32A) 3,20€
Rental rates : (2013 Price) Permanent ♿ (1 chalet) – 6 🚐. Per week from 260 to 490€
🚐 borne 3,50€

Surroundings : ⌒
Leisure activities : 🎣 🚣
Facilities : ♿ ⛟ (July–Aug.) 🍴 launderette
Nearby : 🍴

GPS Longitude : -2.17248
Latitude : 48.02404

PÉNESTIN

56760 – Michelin map **308** Q10 – pop. 1 867 – alt. 20
▶ Paris 458 – La Baule 29 – Nantes 84 – La Roche-Bernard 18

🏕 Le Cénic 👥

🔌 02 99 90 45 65, www.lecenic.com

Address : route de La Roche-Bernard (located 1.5km east along the D 34; beside a lake)

Opening times : from mid April to mid Sept.

5,5 ha (310 pitches)

Tariff : 19€ ⚡ ⚡ ⇌ 🅿 ⚡ (6A) – Extra per person 5€ – Reservation fee 15€

Rental rates : (from mid April to mid Sept.) – 60 🚐 – 8 🏠. Per night from 100 to 160€ – Per week from 250 to 780€
Reservation fee 15€
🚐 borne 3€ – 7 🅿 19€

Partially open-air water park.

Surroundings : ⌒ �‿�‿
Leisure activities : 🍷 🎣 ♿ 🏓 🏊 hammam 🏋 📺 🏸 🎮 🎱 🏐 entertainment room
Facilities : ♿ ⛟ 🚿🍴 launderette

GPS Longitude : -2.45547
Latitude : 47.47889

🏕 Les Îles 👥

🔌 02 99 90 30 24, www.camping-des-iles.fr

Address : at La Pointe du Bile, 119 route des Trois Îles (4.5km south along the D 201 to the right)

Opening times : from mid April to end Sept.

3,5 ha (184 pitches)

Tariff : 43€ ⚡ ⚡ ⇌ 🅿 (10A) – Extra per person 5,80€
Rental rates : (from mid April to end Sept.) ♿ (1 chalet) – 65 🚐 8 🏠 – 2 tent lodges – 10 gîtes. Per night 120 € – Per week from 250 to 1 300€
🚐 borne 4€ – ⚡🔋16€
Close to the beach.

Surroundings : ⌒ �‿⚿ ⛺
Leisure activities : 🍷 ✕ 🎣 ♿ 🌙 nighttime 🏃 🏊 🏋 🚴 🎱 🏓 🏐 multi-sports ground
Facilities : ♿ ⛟ 📇 🚿🍴 launderette 🚿 ♨
Nearby : 🐎

GPS Longitude : -2.48426
Latitude : 47.44561

🏕 Yelloh! Village Le Domaine d'Inly 👥

YELLOH

🔌 02 99 90 35 09, www.camping-inly.com – limited spaces for one-night stay

Address : route de Couarne (situated 2km southeast along the D 201 and take turning to the left)

Opening times : from mid April to mid Sept.

30 ha/12 for camping (500 pitches)

Tariff : 42€ ⚡ ⚡ ⇌ 🅿 ⚡ (10A) Extra per person 7€

Rental rates : (from mid April to mid Sept.) – 110 🚐. Per night from 39 to 194€ – Per week from 273 to 1 358€
🚐 borne 2,50€

Surroundings : 🐾 ⌒ ⚿⚿
Leisure activities : 🍷 ✕ 🎣 ♿ 🏃 🏊 🚴 🏐 📺 🏓 ⛵ ⛺ pedalos 🎣
Facilities : ⛟ 🚿 🏧 🛒 🍴 launderette 🚿 ♨

GPS Longitude : -2.46694
Latitude : 47.47138

🏕 Les Parcs

🔌 02 99 90 30 59, www.camping-lesparcs.com

Address : route de la Roche-Bernard (500m east along the D 34)

Opening times : from beginning April to mid Oct.

3 ha (100 pitches)

Tariff : 24,70€ ⚡ ⚡ ⇌ 🅿 ⚡ (6A) – Extra per person 5,60€ Reservation fee 15€
Rental rates : (from beginning April to mid Oct.) – 20 🚐. Per week from 190 to 610€ – Reservation fee 15€

Surroundings : ⌒ ⚿⚿
Leisure activities : 🍷 🏊 (open air in season)
Facilities : ♿ ⛟ 🚿🍴 launderette

GPS Longitude : -2.46583
Latitude : 47.48166

PENMARCH

29760 – Michelin map **308** E8 – pop. 5 749 – alt. 7
▶ Paris 585 – Audierne 40 – Douarnenez 45 – Pont-l'Abbé 12

⌂ **Municipal de Toul ar Ster**

℘ 02 98 58 86 88, www.penmarch.fr/Office-de-Tourisme

Address : 110 rue Edmond Michelet (1.4km southeast following signs for Guilvinec along the coast and take turning to the right, 100m from the beach (direct access)

Opening times : from mid June to mid Sept.

3 ha (202 pitches)

Tariff : ♣ 3,45€ ⇔ 2,30€ 圓 3,30€ – ⚡ (16A) 3€

Surroundings : ⌇
Leisure activities : 🎱
Facilities : 🚿 ☎ (July–Aug.) ♨ ⛲ launderette
Nearby : ⌘

G P S Longitude : -4.33726
Latitude : 47.81246

PENTREZ-PLAGE

29550 – Michelin map **308** F5
▶ Paris 566 – Brest 55 – Châteaulin 18 – Crozon 18

⛰ **Homair Vacances Le Ker'Ys** 👥

℘ 08 20 20 12 07, www.homair.com/camping/le-domaine-de-ker-ys – limited spaces for one-night stay

Address : chemin des Dunes (opposite the beach)

Opening times : from mid April to beginning Sept.

3 ha (190 pitches)

Tariff : 15,50€ ♣♣ ⇔ 圓 ⚡ (8A) – Reservation fee 10€
Rental rates : (from mid April to mid Sept.) – 136 🏠. Per night from 15 to 60€ – Per week from 105 to 420€ – Reservation fee 49€

🏠 borne 9,50€ – 8 圓 9,50€

Surroundings : ⌇ ⌘
Leisure activities : 🎱 🕐daytime ⛹ 🐎
🏊 ⛵
Facilities : & ☎ 🅲 ♨ ⛲ launderette
Nearby : ♟ ✗

G P S Longitude : -4.30137
Latitude : 48.19249

PERROS-GUIREC

22700 – Michelin map **309** B2 – pop. 7 375 – alt. 60
▶ Paris 527 – Lannion 12 – St-Brieuc 76 – Tréguier 19

⛰ **Yelloh! Village Le Ranolien** 👥

℘ 02 96 91 65 65, www.leranolien.fr

Address : at Ploumanac'h, boulevard du Sémaphore (located 1km southeast along the D 788, 200m from the sea)

15 ha (525 pitches)

Rentals : 5 caravans – 330 🏠.
🏠 borne

A very pleasant spa centre (open all year round).

Surroundings : ⇐ ⌇ ⌘
Leisure activities : ♟ ✗ 🎱 🕐⛹ ♫ ⛵
hammam, jacuzzi 🎣 🏊 🏓 ⛷ disco,
multi-sports ground, spa centre, entertainment room
Facilities : & ☎ 🏛 ♨ ⛲ launderette 🛒 🔧

G P S Longitude : -3.4747
Latitude : 48.82677

⌂ Claire Fontaine

℘ 02 96 23 03 55, www.camping-claire-fontaine.com

Address : rue de Toul al Lann (2.6km southwest along the r. des Frères-Mantrier, follow the signs for Pleumeur-Bodou and take turning to the right)

3 ha (180 pitches)

Rentals : 2 🏡 – 6 🛏 – 1 gîte.

A pleasant setting; the site is based around an old renovated farmhouse of great character.

Surroundings :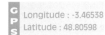
Leisure activities : 🎱
Facilities : ☎ ♨ ⛲ launderette

G P S Longitude : -3.46538
Latitude : 48.80598

LE PERTRE

35370 – Michelin map **309** P6 – pop. 1 434 – alt. 174
▶ Paris 303 – Châteaubriant 55 – Laval 25 – Redon 116

⌂ **Municipal le Chardonneret**

℘ 06 79 50 41 77, www.lepertre.fr – 🅁 ✗

Address : rue du Chardonneret (take the southwestern exit along the D 43, follow the signs for Brielles and take turning to the right)

Opening times : from beginng April to end Sept.

1 ha (31 pitches)

Tariff : ♣ 2,90€ ⇔ 圓 1,95€ – ⚡ (15A) 1,95€
Rental rates : Permanent ✗ – 2 🏠. Per week from 190 to 341€
Near a small lake.

Surroundings : ⌇ ⌘ ⌘
Facilities : & ⛲ 🏛
Nearby : 🎣 ✗ 🎱 🏓 ⛱ (beach) ⛵

G P S Longitude : -1.03943
Latitude : 48.03286

Michelin classification:
⛰⛰ *Extremely comfortable, equipped to a very high standard*
⛰⛰ *Very comfortable, equipped to a high standard*
⛰ *Comfortable and well equipped*
⌂ *Reasonably comfortable*
⌂ *Satisfactory*

PLANCOËT

22130 – Michelin map **309** I3 – pop. 3 079 – alt. 41
▶ Paris 417 – Dinan 17 – Dinard 20 – St-Brieuc 46

⌂ Municipal Les Vergers

℘ 02 96 84 03 42, mairie-plancoet@wanadoo.fr

Address : rue du Verger (Continue towards southeastern exit, follow the signs for Dinan, behind the fire station; beside the Arguenon river and a small lake)

1,2 ha (100 pitches) flat, grassy

Surroundings : ⇐ the village of Plancoët
⌇ ⌘
Leisure activities : ⛵
Facilities : & ☎ launderette
Nearby : 🎣

G P S Longitude : -2.23366
Latitude : 48.52041

PLÉNEUF-VAL-ANDRÉ

22370 – Michelin map **309** G3 – pop. 3 942 – alt. 52
▶ Paris 446 – Dinan 43 – Erquy 9 – Lamballe 16

⚠ Campéole Les Monts Colleux ♣♣

✆ 02 96 72 95 10, www.camping-montscolleux.com

Address : 26 rue Jean Lebrun

Opening times : from end March to end April

5 ha/200 for camping

Tariff : 15,70€ ♣♣ ⇔ 🗉 ⏚ (10A) – Extra per person 4,20€
Reservation fee 25€

Rental rates : (from end March to end Sept.) ♿ (1 mobile home) – 43 ⏚ – 23 ⏚. Per night from 41 to 95€ – Per week from 299 to 665€ – Reservation fee 25€

🚰 borne

| Surroundings : ➘ ⬳ |
| Leisure activities : ⛷ ⛵ ⛵ |
| Facilities : ⚬ 🛁 🚰 launderette ⚓ |
| Nearby : 🏊 |

G P S Longitude : -2.5508
       Latitude : 48.5898

*We value your opinion and welcome your feedback.
Do email us at campingfrance@tp.michelin.com*

PLESTIN-LES-GRÈVES

22310 – Michelin map **309** A3 – pop. 3 644 – alt. 45
▶ Paris 528 – Brest 79 – Guingamp 46 – Lannion 18

⚠ Municipal St-Efflam

✆ 02 96 35 62 15, www.camping-municipal-bretagne.com

Address : at St-Efflam, place de Lan-Carré (3.5km to the northeast, follow the signs for St-Michel-en-Grève; 200m from the sea)

Opening times : from beginning April to beginning Oct.

4 ha (190 pitches) terraced, relatively flat, flat, grassy

Tariff : 17€ ♣♣ ⇔ 🗉 ⏚ (10A) – Extra per person 3,50€ – Reservation fee 31€

Rental rates : (from beginning April to beginning Oct.) ♿ (1 mobile home) – 11 ⏚ – 8 ⏚. Per night from 40 to 65€ Per week from 200 to 550€ – Reservation fee 55€

🚰 borne 3€ – 10 🗉 12€ – ⚡ ⏚ 15€

| Surroundings : ⬳ ♨ |
| Leisure activities : 🍷 🏠 ⛵ 🏊 |
| Facilities : ♿ ⚬ (July-Aug.) 🛁 🚰 launderette |
| Nearby : 🍴 🛶 |

G P S Longitude : -3.60108
       Latitude : 48.66834

⚠ Aire Naturelle Ker-Rolland

✆ 02 96 35 08 37, www.camping-ker-rolland.com

Address : Ker Rolland (2.2km southwest along the D 786, follow the signs for Morlaix and take the turning to the left, following signs for Plouégat-Guérand)

Opening times : from mid June to beginning Sept.

1,6 ha (22 pitches) flat, grassy

Tariff : 11,60€ ♣♣ ⇔ 🗉 ⏚ (13A) – Extra per person 2,80€
Rental rates : Permanent – 4 ⏚. Per night from 35€ – Per week from 200 to 370€

A farm campsite (market garden).

| Surroundings : ⬳ |
| Leisure activities : 🏊 |
| Facilities : ♿ ⚬ 🚰 ☑ 🚰 📷 |

G P S Longitude : -3.64337
       Latitude : 48.64338

PLEUBIAN

22610 – Michelin map **309** D1 – pop. 2 577 – alt. 48
▶ Paris 506 – Lannion 31 – Paimpol 13 – St-Brieuc 58

⚠ Port la Chaîne

SUQUET

✆ 02 96 22 92 38, www.portlachaine.com

Address : situated 2km north along the D 20, follow the signs for Larmor-Pleubian and take turning to the left

Opening times : from beginning April to end Sept.

4,9 ha (200 pitches)

Tariff : 27,90€ ♣♣ ⇔ 🗉 ⏚ (6A)
Extra per person 6,90€ – Reservation fee 4,50€

Rental rates : (from beginning April to end Sept.) – 42 ⏚ – 3 canvas bungalows. Per night from 37 to 106€ – Per week from 232 to 854€ – Reservation fee 16,50€

Plenty of shade from centuries-old maritime pines; beside the sea.

| Surroundings : ⬳ ♨ ⛰ |
| Leisure activities : 🍷 🏠 ⛵ 🏊 🏊 |
| Facilities : ♿ ⚬ 🛁 🚰 🚰 launderette |

G P S Longitude : -3.13284
       Latitude : 48.85545

PLEUMEUR-BODOU

22560 – Michelin map **309** A2 – pop. 4 039 – alt. 94
▶ Paris 523 – Lannion 8 – Perros-Guirec 10 – St-Brieuc 72

⚠ Le Port

✆ 02 96 23 87 79, www.camping-du-port-22.com

Address : 3 chemin des Douaniers (6km to the north, to the south of Trégastel-Plage)

Opening times : from end March to mid Oct.

2 ha (80 pitches)

Tariff : 18,20€ ♣♣ ⇔ 🗉 ⏚ (15A) – Extra per person 4,50€
Reservation fee 15€

Rental rates : (from end March to mid Oct.) – 27 ⏚ – 6 ⏚ 5 canvas bungalows. Per night from 40 to 85€ – Per week from 150 to 770€ – Reservation fee 15€

🚰 borne

Beside the sea, some pitches are 'almost on top of the water'.

| Surroundings : ⬳ ⬳ ⛰ |
| Leisure activities : 🍷 🍴 ⛵ ⛷ 🚴 |
| Facilities : ♿ ⚬ 🛁 🚰 launderette |

G P S Longitude : -3.54278
       Latitude : 48.81029

PLÉVEN

22130 – Michelin map **309** I4 – pop. 587 – alt. 80
▶ Paris 431 – Dinan 24 – Dinard 28 – St-Brieuc 38

⚠ Municipal

✆ 02 96 84 46 71, www.pleven.fr

Address : in the village (in the grounds of the town hall)

1 ha (40 pitches)

| Surroundings : ♨ |
| Facilities : ♿ ⚬ 🚰 |
| Nearby : 🍴 |

G P S Longitude : -2.31911
       Latitude : 48.48914

PLOBANNALEC-LESCONIL

29740 – Michelin map **308** F8 – pop. 3 326 – alt. 16
▶ Paris 578 – Audierne 38 – Douarnenez 38 – Pont-l'Abbé 6

⚠ Yelloh! Village L'Océan Breton ♣♨

✆ 02 98 82 23 89, www.camping-bretagne-oceanbreton.fr – limited spaces for one-night stay

Address : route de Plobannalec, Le Manoir de Kerlut (1.6km south along the D 102, follow the signs for Lesconil and take the road to the left)

Opening times : from mid April to mid Sept.

12 ha/8 for camping (240 pitches) flat, grassy

Tariff : 44€ ♣♣ ⊶ 🔲 (10A) – Extra per person 8€
Rental rates : Permanent – 207 ▦ – 8 🏠 – 5 canvas bungalows. Per night from 33 to 231€ – Per week from 231 to 1 659€
🚻 borne 10€

Access to the beach via a free shuttle service.

Surroundings : 🗆 🎗
Leisure activities : ♈ 🍽 🎗 🎣 🎿 🎻 🛶
🚴 🎿 🔲 🎿 🌊 forest trail
Facilities : ♿ ⊶ 🚿 launderette 🚮 🚿

GPS Longitude : -4.22574
Latitude : 47.81167

PLOEMEL

56400 – Michelin map **308** M9 – pop. 2 508 – alt. 46
▶ Paris 485 – Auray 8 – Lorient 34 – Quiberon 23

⚠ Municipal St-Laurent ♣♨

✆ 02 97 56 85 90, www.campingdesaintlaurent.com

Address : Kergonvo (2.5km to the northwest, follow the signs for Belz, near D 22 junction, take D 186)

Opening times : from mid April to end Oct.

3 ha (90 pitches)

Tariff : 21,60€ ♣♣ ⊶ 🔲 🔲 (10A) – Extra per person 5,20€
Reservation fee 10€
Rental rates : (from mid April to end Oct.) – 23 ▦ – 2 canvas bungalows – 6 tent lodges. Per night from 46 to 114 € – Per week from 322 to 798€ – Reservation fee 10€
🚻 borne – 🚿 12€

Surroundings : 🗆 🎗🎗
Leisure activities : ✘ 🎣 🛶 🔲
Facilities : ⊶ 🚿 🔲 🚿

GPS Longitude : -3.10013
Latitude : 47.66369

⚠ Kergo

✆ 02 97 56 80 66, www.campingkergo.com

Address : situated 2km southeast along the D 186, follow the signs for La Trinité-sur-Mer and take the turning to the left

Opening times : from beginning May to beginning Oct.

2,5 ha (135 pitches)

Tariff : 19€ ♣♣ ⊶ 🔲 🔲 (10A) – Extra per person 4,20€
Rental rates : (from beginning April to end Oct.) – 12 ▦. Per night from 40 to 85€ – Per week from 235 to 590€
🚻 borne 6€

Surroundings : 🌳 🎗
Leisure activities : 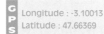 🏊s jacuzzi 🛶 🚴
Facilities : ♿ ⊶ 🚿 🔲

GPS Longitude : -3.05362
Latitude : 47.64403

The guide covers all 22 regions of France – see the map and list of regions on pages 4–5.

PLOÉVEN

29550 – Michelin map **308** F6 – pop. 505 – alt. 60
▶ Paris 585 – Brest 64 – Châteaulin 15 – Crozon 25

⚠ La Mer

✆ 02 98 81 29 19, www.campingdelamer29.fr

Address : Ty Anquer Plage (3km southwest, 300m from the beach)

Opening times : from beginning June to end Sept.

1 ha (54 pitches) flat, grassy

Tariff : ♣ 4,20€ ⊶ 2,50€ 🔲 4,20€ – 🔲 (10A) 4,30€
Rental rates : (from beginning June to end Sept.) 🚫 – 1 ▦ 6 canvas bungalows. Per night from 50 to 90€ – Per week from 180 to 500€
🚻 🚿 🔲 21,50€

Surroundings : 🎗
Facilities : ⊶ 🎿 🚿 🔲

GPS Longitude : -4.26796
Latitude : 48.14806

Using the traditional Michelin classification method, the guide provides you with an easy, speedy reference for assessing the category of each site : 1 to 5 tents (see page 10).

PLOMEUR

29120 – Michelin map **308** F7 – pop. 3 634 – alt. 33
▶ Paris 579 – Douarnenez 39 – Pont-l'Abbé 6 – Quimper 26

⚠ Aire Naturelle Kéraluic

✆ 02 98 82 10 22, www.keraluic.fr

Address : Keraluic (4.3km northeast along the D 57, follow the signs for Plonéour-Lanvern)

Opening times : from mid April to mid Oct.

1 ha (25 pitches) flat, grassy

Tariff : 20,90€ ♣♣ ⊶ 🔲 🔲 (10A) – Extra per person 4,50€
Rental rates : Permanent 🚫 – 3 studios – 1 apartment – 2 canvas bungalows. Per week from 395 to 495€
Old farmhouse buildings that have undergone attractive renovations.

Surroundings : 🌳 🎗
Leisure activities : 🔲 🛶
Facilities : ♿ ⊶ 🚿 🔲

GPS Longitude : -4.26624
Latitude : 47.86148

⚠ Lanven

✆ 02 98 82 00 75, www.campinglanven.com

Address : La Chapelle de Beuzec (3.5km northwest along the D 57, follow the signs for Plonéour-Lanvern then take the road to the left)

Opening times : from beginning April to end Sept.

3,7 ha (159 pitches) flat, grassy

Tariff : 20,20€ ♣♣ ⊶ 🔲 🔲 (8A) – Extra per person 4,20€
Rental rates : (from beginning April to end Sept.) – 6 ▦. Per night from 45 to 60€ – Per week from 200 to 530€
🚻 borne
Summer camps are held here.

Surroundings : 🌳 🗆 🎗
Leisure activities : ♈ ✘ 🛶
Facilities : ⊶ 🚿 launderette

GPS Longitude : -4.30663
Latitude : 47.8505

PLOMODIERN

29550 – Michelin map **308** F5 – pop. 2 182 – alt. 60
▶ Paris 559 – Brest 60 – Châteaulin 12 – Crozon 25

🏕 La Mer d'Iroise

✆ 02 98 81 52 72, www.camping-iroise.fr

Address : plage de Pors-Ar-Vag (5km southwest, 100m from the beach)

Opening times : from mid April to beginning Oct.

2,5 ha (132 pitches)

Tariff : 28,10€ ✶✶ ⇌ 🔲 🈸 (10A) – Extra per person 4,40€
Reservation fee 16€

Rental rates : Permanent – 16 🚐 – 15 🏠. Per night from 56 to 92€ – Per week from 250 to 730€– Reservation fee 16€
🚐 borne

Surroundings : ⅏ ≼ Baie de Douarnenez ♀
Leisure activities : 🍸 🎱 jacuzzi 🎣 ☝
🏊 ⛷
Facilities : ⅋ ⊶ 🛁 🔥 🚰 🍽 launderette 🧺
Nearby : ✗ watersports centre

The information in the guide may have changed since going to press.

PLONÉOUR-LANVERN

29720 – Michelin map **308** F7 – pop. 5 725 – alt. 71
▶ Paris 578 – Douarnenez 25 – Guilvinec 14 – Plouhinec 21

⛰ Municipal de Mariano

✆ 02 98 87 74 80, www.ploneour-lanvern.fr

Address : impasse du Plateau (to the north along the D 57)

1 ha (59 pitches) flat, grassy
Rentals : 3 🏠.

Surroundings : ⅏ ▱ ♀♀
Leisure activities : 🎱 🎣 ✗
Facilities : ⅋ ⊶ launderette

PLOUÉZEC

22470 – Michelin map **309** E2 – pop. 3 368 – alt. 100
▶ Paris 489 – Guingamp 28 – Lannion 39 – Paimpol 6

🏕 Domaine du Launay

✆ 02 96 20 63 15, www.domaine-du-launay.com

Address : 11 route de Toul Veign (3.1km southwest along the D 77, follow the signs for Yvias and take turning to the right)

Opening times : from beginning April to mid Oct.

4 ha (90 pitches) terraced, flat, grassy

Tariff : ✶ 3€ ⇌ 🔲 5€ – 🈸 (16A) 3€ – Reservation fee 10€

Rental rates : (from beginning April to mid Oct.) – 10 🚐 2 canvas bungalows. Per night 85€ – Per week from 180 to 650€
Reservation fee 10€
🚐 borne 3€ – 8 🔲 10€ – 🚐 🈸 10€
Ornamental trees and shrubs decorate the site.

Surroundings : ⅏ ≼ ▱ ♀
Leisure activities : 🍸 🎱 🎣 🚲 ☝ ⛷
entertainment room
Facilities : ⅋ ⊶ 🍽 launderette
Nearby : ✗ ♫ 🐎

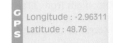
Longitude : -3.00286
Latitude : 48.73523

🏔 Le Cap Horn Cap des Îles

✆ 02 96 20 64 28, www.lecaphorn.com

Address : rue de Port Lazo (2.3km northeast along the D 77, direct access to the beach)

Opening times : from beginning April to end Sept.

4 ha (149 pitches) terraced, relatively flat, stony, grassy

Tariff : 22,50€ ✶✶ ⇌ 🔲 🈸 (16A) – Extra per person 5,50€
Reservation fee 15€

Rental rates : (from beginning April to end Sept.) – 40 🚐 1 cabin in the trees. Per night from 37 to 143€ – Per week from 259 to 1 001€ – Reservation fee 15€

The site overlooks the Anse de Paimpol (bay) and the Île de Bréhat.

Surroundings : ⅏ ≼ ▱
Leisure activities : 🍸 🎱 🎣 🚲 🏊 ⛷
Facilities : ⅋ ⊶ 🛁 🍽 launderette 🧺
Nearby : ✗ ☝ ♫ 🐎

Longitude : -2.96311
Latitude : 48.76

PLOUGASNOU

29630 – Michelin map **308** I2 – pop. 3 268 – alt. 55
▶ Paris 545 – Brest 76 – Guingamp 62 – Lannion 34

🏕 Flower Domaine de Mesqueau

✆ 02 98 67 37 45, www.domaine-de-mesqueau.com

Address : 870 route de Mesqueau (3.5km south along the D 46, follow the signs for Morlaix then continue 800m along the turning to the left, 100m from a small lake (direct access)

Opening times : from end March to end Sept.

7,5 ha (100 pitches) flat, grassy

Tariff : 25€ ✶✶ ⇌ 🔲 🈸 (10A) – Extra per person 4,50€ – Reservation fee 10€

Rental rates : (from end March to end Sept.) ℗ – 30 🚐 4 canvas bungalows – 4 tent lodges. Per night from 29 to 97€ – Per week from 203 to 679€ – Reservation fee 10€

Surroundings : ⅏ ♀♀
Leisure activities : 🎱 🎣 ✗ ⛷
multi-sports ground
Facilities : ⅋ ⊶ 🛁 🍽 📷
Nearby : ✗ 🧺 ⚓

Longitude : -3.78101
Latitude : 48.66462

PLOUGASTEL-DAOULAS

29470 – Michelin map **308** E4 – pop. 13 304 – alt. 113
▶ Paris 596 – Brest 12 – Morlaix 60 – Quimper 64

🏕 St-Jean 👥

✆ 02 98 40 32 90, www.campingsaintjean.com

Address : Saint-Jean (4.6km northeast along the D 29 and N 165, take the exit for the Leclerc commercial centre)

Opening times : from mid April to mid Sept.

203 ha (125 pitches)

Tariff : ✶ 5,10€ ⇌ 2,50€ 🔲 15,30€ – 🈸 (10A) 3,10€ – Reservation fee 20€

Rental rates : (from mid April to mid Sept.) – 44 🚐. Per night from 48 to 73€ – Per week from 224 to 714€ – Reservation fee 20€

Pleasant location and setting beside the estuary of the Elorn river.

Surroundings : ⅏ ▱ ♀ ⛰
Leisure activities : 🍸 ✗ 🎱 🌙 nighttime 🎣
🎣 🚲 🏊 ⛷ multi-sports ground
Facilities : ⅋ ⊶ 🔲🏧 🛁 🍽 launderette 🧺

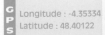
Longitude : -4.35334
Latitude : 48.40122

PLOUGONVELIN

29217 – Michelin map **308** C4 – pop. 3 693 – alt. 44
▶ Paris 616 – Brest 21 – Brignogan-Plages 56 – Quimper 95

� Les Terrasses de Bertheaume

(mobile home rentals only)

✆ 02 98 48 32 37, www.camping-brest.com – traditional camp. spaces also available

Address : route de Perzel

Opening times : Permanent

2 ha, terraced, grassy

Rental rates : 33 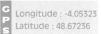. Per night from 38 to 100€ – Per week from 167 to 620€

Surroundings : 🐟 ≼
Leisure activities : 🛶 ♒ ⚓ (small swimming pool)
Facilities : ⚷ 🍴 launderette
Nearby : scuba diving

G P S Longitude : -4.70303
Latitude : 48.33989

PLOUGOULM

29250 – Michelin map **308** G3 – pop. 1 805 – alt. 60
▶ Paris 560 – Brest 58 – Brignogan-Plages 27 – Morlaix 24

⚐ Municipal du Bois de la Palud

✆ 02 98 29 81 82, www.plougoulm.fr

Address : Creach ar Feunteun (900m west of the D 10-D 69 junction (Criossant de Plougoulm), following signs for Plouescat and take the road to the right)

0,7 ha (34 pitches)

Surroundings : 🐟 ≼ ⌂ ♤♤
Facilities : ⚷ ⚷ ⚓
Nearby : ♒⚓

G P S Longitude : -4.05323
Latitude : 48.67236

PLOUGOUMELEN

56400 – Michelin map **308** N9 – pop. 2 378 – alt. 27
▶ Paris 471 – Auray 10 – Lorient 51 – Quiberon 39

⚐ La Via Natura Fontaine du Hallate

✆ 06 16 30 08 33, www.camping-en-morbihan.fr

Address : 8 chemin de Poul Fetan (3.2km southeast towards Ploeren and follow the signs for Baden to the right; at Hallate)

Opening times : from beginning April to end Oct.

3 ha (94 pitches)

Tariff : 19,50€ ♟ ♟ ⚗ 🅴 ⚡ (6A) – Extra per person 3€
Rental rates : (from beginning April to end Oct.) – 12 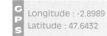 1 yurt. Per night from 60 to 70€ – Per week from 195 to 599€ Reservation fee 20€

Surroundings : 🐟 ≼ ⌂ ♀
Leisure activities : ♒⚓
Facilities : ⚷ ⚷ ⊞ ☂ 🍴 launderette

G P S Longitude : -2.8989
Latitude : 47.6432

For more information on visiting particular towns or regions, consult the relevant regional MICHELIN Green Guide. We also recommend you use the appropriate Michelin regional map to locate your selected campsite, to calculate distances and to work out the best route.

PLOUGRESCANT

22820 – Michelin map **309** C1 – pop. 1 347 – alt. 53
▶ Paris 516 – Lannion 26 – Perros-Guirec 23 – St-Brieuc 68

⚐ Le Gouffre

✆ 02 96 92 02 95, www.camping-gouffre.com – limited spaces for one-night stay

Address : Hent Crec'h Kermorvant (2.7km north following signs for La Pointe du Château (headland)

Opening times : from beginning April to end Sept.

3 ha (130 pitches)

Tariff : 12€ ♟ ♟ ⚗ 🅴 ⚡ (6A) – Extra per person 4€
Rental rates : (from beginning April to end Sept.) – 12 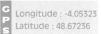. Per night from 48 to 162€ – Per week from 175 to 500€
🚐 borne – ⚡ ⚡ 12€

Surroundings : 🐟 ⌂
Facilities : ⚷ ⚷ (July-Aug.) 🍴 ▦

G P S Longitude : -3.22749
Latitude : 48.86081

⚐ Le Varlen

✆ 02 96 92 52 15, www.levarlen.com

Address : 4. Pors Hir (2km to the northeast, follow the signs for Pors Hir, 200m from the sea)

1 ha (60 pitches) flat, grassy

Rentals : 14 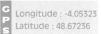 – 2 studios – 1 canvas bungalow.

Surroundings : 🐟 ⌂
Leisure activities : 🍴 🛶 ♒⚓
Facilities : ⚷ ⚷ ⚷ 🍴 launderette ⚓
Nearby : ✗

G P S Longitude : -3.21873
Latitude : 48.86078

Key to rentals symbols:

12 🚐	*Number of mobile homes*
20 🏠	*Number of chalets*
6 🛏	*Number of rooms to rent*
Per night 30–50€	*Minimum/maximum rate per night*
Per week 300–1,000€	*Minimum/maximum rate per week*

PLOUGUERNEAU

29880 – Michelin map **308** D3 – pop. 6 411 – alt. 60
▶ Paris 604 – Brest 27 – Landerneau 33 – Morlaix 68

⚐⚐ La Grève Blanche

✆ 02 98 04 70 35, www.campinggreveblanche.com

Address : St-Michel (4km north along the D 32, follow the signs for Le Mont-St-Michel and take the turning to the left; beside beach)

Opening times : from beginning April to mid Oct.

2,5 ha (100 pitches)

Tariff : ♟ 3,60€ ⚗ 1,70€ 🅴 3,60€ – ⚡ (10A) 2,95€
Rental rates : Permanent ⚐ – 2 caravans – 2 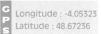 – 2 cottages on stilts (without sanitary facilities). Per night from 37 to 125€ Per week from 210 to 530€
🚐 borne – 15 🅴 14,25€ – ⚡ 9€
A natural setting among rocks overlooking the beach.

Surroundings : ≼ ⛰
Leisure activities : 🍴 ♒⚓
Facilities : ⚷ ⚷ ⚷ 🍴

G P S Longitude : -4.523
Latitude : 48.6305

⚠ Du Vougot

𝒫 0298256151, www.campingplageduvougot.com

Address : route de Prat Ledan (7.4km northeast along the D 13 and the D 10, follow the signs for Guisseny, then take the D 52; along the bank of the Vougot, 250m from the sea)

Opening times : from end March to end Oct.

2,5 ha (55 pitches)

Tariff : ★ 3,70€ ⇔ 1,80€ 圓 5,90€ – (½) (10A) 3,30€
Rental rates : (from end March to end Oct.) – 15 🛏 – 1 tent lodge. Per night from 49 to 80€ – Per week from 190 to 592€
🛢 borne 4,50€ – 🛒 8€

Surroundings : 🏖 🖵 🎡
Leisure activities : 🏊
Facilities : 🚿 🍴 launderette
Nearby : watersports centre

Longitude : -4.45
Latitude : 48.63132

PLOUHA

22580 – Michelin map **309** E2 – pop. 4 582 – alt. 96
▶ Paris 479 – Guingamp 24 – Lannion 49 – St-Brieuc 31

🏔 Les Castels Le Domaine de Keravel 🔒

𝒫 0296224913, www.keravel.com

Address : La Trinité (situated 2km to the northeast, near the chapel)

Opening times : from beginning June to mid Sept.

5 ha/2 for camping (116 pitches) terraced, relatively flat, flat, grassy

Tariff : (2013 Price) 30,50€ ★★ ⇔ 圓 (½) (10A)
Extra per person 7,40€

Rental rates : (2013 Price) Permanent – 6 🛏 – 4 apartments 3 gîtes. Per night 89€ – Per week from 304 to 1202€

Located in the pleasant grounds of a manor house, with an option for half-board stays.

Surroundings : 🏖 🖵 🎡🎡
Leisure activities : 🍷 ✕ 🏛 ⑨ 🧗 🏄 jacuzzi
🏊 🚲 🎯 🎱 💆 ⛷
Facilities : ♿ 🚿 🛁 ♨ 🍴 launderette
Nearby : 🛶 🐎

Longitude : -2.9092
Latitude : 48.68936

PLOUHARNEL

56340 – Michelin map **308** M9 – pop. 2 000 – alt. 21
▶ Paris 490 – Auray 13 – Lorient 33 – Quiberon 15

⚠ Kersily

𝒫 0297523965, www.camping-kersily.com

Address : Ste-Barbe (2.5km northwest along the D 781, follow the signs for Lorient)

Opening times : from beginning April to end Oct.

2,5 ha (120 pitches)

Tariff : ★ 5,60€ ⇔ 圓 9,20€ – (½) (10A) 4€ – Reservation fee 10€
Rental rates : (from beginning April to end Oct.) – 25 🛏 . Per night from 50 to 70€ – Per week from 195 to 670€
Reservation fee 10€
🛢 borne 2€ – 🛒 10€

Surroundings : 🏖 🎡🎡
Leisure activities : 🍷 ✕ 🏛 ⑨ nighttime 🏄 ✂ 🎱 💆 entertainment room
Facilities : ♿ 🚿 🛁 ♨ ⛲ 🍴 launderette

Longitude : -3.1316
Latitude : 47.61107

⚠ Les Goélands

𝒫 0297523192, www.camping-lesgoelands.com

Address : Kergonan (located 1.5km east along the D 781, follow the signs for Carnac then continue 500m along the turning to the left)

1,6 ha (80 pitches) flat, grassy
Rentals : 🏕 – 3 🛏 – 2 🏠 .

Surroundings : 🏖 🎡
Leisure activities : 🏄 🏊
Facilities : 🚿 🛁 🖂
Nearby : ✕

Longitude : -3.09657
Latitude : 47.59461

PLOUHINEC

29780 – Michelin map **308** E6 – pop. 4 217 – alt. 101
▶ Paris 594 – Audierne 5 – Douarnenez 18 – Pont-l'Abbé 27

⚠ Kersiny-Plage

𝒫 0298708244, www.kersinyplage.com

Address : 1 rue Nominoé (take the western exit along the D 784, follow the signs for Audierne then continue 1km south following signs for Kersiny, 100m from the beach (direct access)

Opening times : from mid May to mid Sept.

2 ha (70 pitches)

Tariff : 18,80€ ★★ ⇔ 圓 (½) (8A) – Extra per person 5,70€
Reservation fee 10€
Rental rates : (from mid May to mid Sept.) 🏕 – 4 🛏 – 3 🏠 . Per night from 38 to 76€ – Per week from 260 to 530€
Reservation fee 10€
🛢 borne
The site is in an attractive location.

Surroundings : 🏖 ≤ sea 🖵
Facilities : 🚿 🍴 🖂
Nearby : ✕

Longitude : -4.50819
Latitude : 48.00719

PLOUHINEC

56680 – Michelin map **308** L8 – pop. 4 922 – alt. 10
▶ Paris 503 – Auray 22 – Lorient 18 – Quiberon 30

🏔 Moténo 🔒

𝒫 0297367663, www.camping-le-moteno.com

Address : rue du Passage d'Étel (4.5km southeast along the D 781 and take a right turn, follow the signs for Le Magouër)

4 ha (256 pitches) flat, grassy
Rentals : 90 🛏 – 22 🏠 .

Surroundings : 🖵 🎡
Leisure activities : 🍷 ✕ 🏛 ⑨ 🧗 🏄 jacuzzi 🏊 🚲🎱 💆 ⛷ multi-sports ground, entertainment room
Facilities : ♿ 🚿 🛁 🍴 launderette 🖳 🛒

Longitude : -3.22127
Latitude : 47.66492

Michelin classification:

🏔🏔🏔🏔🏔 *Extremely comfortable, equipped to a very high standard*

🏔🏔🏔🏔 *Very comfortable, equipped to a high standard*

🏔🏔🏔 *Comfortable and well equipped*

🏔🏔 *Reasonably comfortable*

🏔 *Satisfactory*

PLOUIGNEAU

29610 – Michelin map **308** I3 – pop. 4 685 – alt. 156
▶ Paris 526 – Brest 72 – Carhaix-Plouguer 43 – Guingamp 44

⛰ Aire Naturelle la Ferme de Croas Men

✆ 02 98 79 11 50, http://ferme-de-croasmen.com

Address : Croas Men (2.5km northwest along the D 712 and the D 64, follow the signs for Lanmeur then continue 4.7km following signs for Lanleya to the left, then follow the signs for Garlan)

Opening times : from beginning April to end Oct.

1 ha (25 pitches) flat, grassy, fruit trees

Tariff : (2013 Price) 17,94€ ✦✦ ⬛ 🔲 ⚡ (6A) – Extra per person 2,80€
Rental rates : (2013 Price) Permanent – 2 caravans – 4 🏠 – 2 tent lodges. Per night from 60 to 85€ – Per week from 350 to 520€
🚐 borne 8€ – 🚐8€
A working educational farm, with a museum of agricultural tools.

Surroundings : 🌲 🌿
Leisure activities :
Facilities : ♿ ⚟ 🚿 🍴 launderette
Nearby : 🐎

G P S	Longitude : -3.73792
	Latitude : 48.60465

PLOUNÉVEZ-LOCHRIST

29430 – Michelin map **308** F3 – pop. 2 398 – alt. 70
▶ Paris 576 – Brest 41 – Landerneau 24 – Landivisiau 22

⛰ Municipal Odé-Vras

✆ 02 98 61 65 17, www.plounevez-lochrist.fr

Address : Ode Vras (4.5km to the north, along the D 10, 300m from the Baie de Kernic (direct access)

3 ha (135 pitches)
Rentals : 1 🚍.

Surroundings : 🌳 🌿
Leisure activities :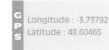
Facilities : ⚟ 🛉launderette

G P S	Longitude : -4.23942
	Latitude : 48.64564

PLOZÉVET

29710 – Michelin map **308** E7 – pop. 2 988 – alt. 70
▶ Paris 588 – Audierne 11 – Douarnenez 19 – Pont-l'Abbé 22

⛰ La Corniche

✆ 02 98 91 33 94, www.campinglacorniche.com

Address : chemin de la Corniche (take the southern exit along the coast road)

Opening times : from beginning March to end Sept.

2 ha (120 pitches) flat, grassy

Tariff : 23,30€ ✦✦ ⬛ 🔲 ⚡ (10A) – Extra per person 4,80€
Rental rates : Permanent – 13 🚍 – 9 🏠 – 5 tent lodges. Per night from 40 to 100€ – Per week from 200 to 700€
Reservation fee 10€
🚐 borne 4€ – 6 🔲 12€ – 🚐⚡8€

Surroundings : 🌲
Leisure activities : 🍴 🏛 🏌 🏊
Facilities : ♿ ⚟ 🛉 🏖 🚽 🍴 launderette

G P S	Longitude : -4.4287
	Latitude : 47.98237

This guide is updated regularly, so buy your new copy every year!

PLURIEN

22240 – Michelin map **309** H3 – pop. 1 396 – alt. 48
▶ Paris 436 – Dinard 34 – Lamballe 25 – Plancoët 23

⛰ Municipal la Saline

✆ 02 96 72 17 40, http://campinglessalines.fr

Address : rue du Lac, Sables d'or-Les Pins (1.2km northwest along the D 34, follow the signs for Sables-d'Or-les-Pins; 500m from the sea)

Opening times : from beginning April to end Oct.

3 ha (150 pitches)

Tariff : 14,20€ ✦✦ ⬛ 🔲 ⚡ (6A) – Extra per person 3,15€
Rental rates : Permanent – 6 🚍 – 2 tent lodges. Per night from 35 to 80€ – Per week from 200 to 500€
🚐 borne 2€ – 4 🔲 8€

Surroundings : ≤ 🌿
Leisure activities : 🏌
Facilities : ♿ ⚟ launderette

G P S	Longitude : -2.41396
	Latitude : 48.63281

PONTRIEUX

22260 – Michelin map **309** D2 – pop. 1 053 – alt. 13
▶ Paris 491 – Guingamp 18 – Lannion 27 – Morlaix 67

⛰ Traou-Mélédern

✆ 02 96 95 69 27, www.camping-pontrieux.com

Address : 400m south of the town; beside the Trieux river

Opening times : Permanent

1 ha (50 pitches)

Tariff : ✦ 4€ ⬛ 🔲 5€ – ⚡ (10A) 3,20€
Rental rates : Permanent – 1 🚍 – 2 gîtes. Per night 50€ Per week 360€
🚐 5 🔲 11€

Surroundings : 🌳 🌿🌿
Leisure activities : 🏌
Facilities : ♿ ⚟ (from mid June to mid Sept.) 🚿 🍴 🖼
Nearby : marina

G P S	Longitude : -3.16355
	Latitude : 48.6951

We have selected the best campsites in France with our usual care, listing those with the best facilities in the most pleasant surroundings.

PONT-SCORFF

56620 – Michelin map **308** K8 – pop. 3 167 – alt. 42
▶ Paris 509 – Auray 47 – Lorient 11 – Quiberon 56

⛰ Ty Nénez

✆ 02 97 32 51 16, www.lorient-camping.com

Address : route de Lorient (1.8km southwest along the D 6)

Opening times : Permanent

2,5 ha (93 pitches)

Tariff : (2013 Price) ✦ 4,60€ ⬛ 🔲 7€ – ⚡ (16A) 3€
Rental rates : (2013 Price) Permanent ♿ (1 mobile home) 12 🚍. Per night from 43 to 99€ – Per week from 258 to 693€
🚐 borne 2€ – 5 🔲 – 🚐11€

Surroundings : 🌳 🌿
Leisure activities : 🍴 🏌
Facilities : ♿ ⚟ 🏛 🛉 🍴 launderette

G P S	Longitude : -3.40664
	Latitude : 47.82081

PORDIC

22590 – Michelin map **309** F3 – pop. 5 923 – alt. 97
▶ Paris 459 – Guingamp 33 – Lannion 65 – St-Brieuc 11

🏕 Les Madières

📞 02 96 79 02 48, www.campinglesmadieres.com

Address : Le Vau Madec (situated 2km northeast following signs for Binic and take a right turn)

Opening times : from beginning April to end Oct.

1,6 ha (93 pitches)

Tariff : (2013 Price) 23€ 🚿🚿 ⛺ 🔲 🔌 (10A) – Extra per person 5,50€
Rental rates : (2013 Price) (from beginning April to end Oct.) 9 🚐. Per week from 310 to 580€ – Reservation fee 10€
🚗 8 🔲 17€ – 🚗15€
A pleasant, leafy setting, attractively shady; some pitches with a view of the sea and the port at St-Quay-Portrieux.

Surroundings : 🌳 🗺 ♀♀
Leisure activities : 🍴 🍽 ⛵
Facilities : 🔧 ⛽ 🏪 🚰 launderette

G P S Longitude : -2.80475
Latitude : 48.58266

🏕 Le Roc de l'Hervieu

📞 02 96 79 30 12, www.campinglerocdelhervieu.fr – limited spaces for one-night stay

Address : 19 rue d'Estienne d'Orves (3km northeast following signs for La Pointe de Pordic (headland) and take the road to the right)

2,5 ha (166 pitches) flat, grassy
Rentals : 20 🚐.

Surroundings : 🌳 🗺
Leisure activities : 🍽 ⛵
Facilities : 🔧 ⛽ 🚰 🔲

G P S Longitude : -2.7811
Latitude : 48.58188

The Michelin classification (🏕🏕🏕 … 🏕) is totally independent of the official star classification system awarded by the local prefecture or other official organisation.

PORT-MANECH

29920 – Michelin map **308** I8
▶ Paris 545 – Carhaix-Plouguer 73 – Concarneau 18 – Pont-Aven 12

🏕 St-Nicolas

📞 02 98 06 89 75, www.campinglesaintnicolas.com

Address : at Port-Manech, 8 Kergouliou (north of the town, 200m from the beach)

Opening times : from beginning May to mid Sept.

3 ha (180 pitches)

Tariff : (2013 Price) 32,30€ 🚿🚿 ⛺ 🔲 🔌 (10A)
Extra per person 6,20€ – Reservation fee 7€
Rental rates : (2013 Price) (from mid April to end Sept.) 🚫 – 14 🚐. Per week from 210 to 806€ – Reservation fee 7€
Pretty shrubs and flowers.

Surroundings : 🗺 ♀♀
Leisure activities : 🍽 ⛵ 🔲 ⛵ ⛷
Facilities : 🔧 ⛽ 🚰 launderette
Nearby : 🍴 🛶

G P S Longitude : -3.74541
Latitude : 47.80512

LE POULDU

29360 – Michelin map **308** J8
▶ Paris 521 – Concarneau 37 – Lorient 25 – Moëlan-sur-Mer 10

🏕 Les Embruns

📞 02 98 39 91 07, www.camping-les-embruns.com

Address : rue du Philosophe-Alain (in the town, 350m from the beach)

Opening times : from mid April to mid Sept.

5,5 ha (180 pitches) fruit trees

Tariff : 35,50€ 🚿🚿 ⛺ 🔲 🔌 (16A) – Extra per person 7€ – Reservation fee 20€
Rental rates : (from mid April to mid Sept.) – 34 🚐. Per night from 50 to 150€ – Per week from 265 to 935€ – Reservation fee 20€
🚗 borne 5,50€ – 14 🔲 16,50€
Pretty shrubs and flowers decorate the site.

Surroundings : 🗺 ♀♀
Leisure activities : 🍴 🏠 🎣 🛁 🏊 hammam 🔲 (open air in season) ⛷ wildlife park
Facilities : 🔧 ⛽ 🏪 🚿 ⛷ 🚰 🏪 launderette
Nearby : 🏊 🍴 🛶 🎿 🛶

G P S Longitude : -3.54696
Latitude : 47.76947

🏕 Keranquernat

📞 02 98 39 92 32, www.camping.keranquernat.com

Address : Keranquernat (at the roundabout, take northeastern exit)

Opening times : from end April to mid Sept.

1,5 ha (100 pitches)

Tariff : 21€ 🚿🚿 ⛺ 🔲 🔌 (10A) – Extra per person 4€
Rental rates : (from end April to mid Sept.) 🚫 – 10 🚐. Per night from 40 to 45€ – Per week from 199 to 490€
🚗 borne
A pleasant setting shaded by apple trees and surrounded by flowers.

Surroundings : 🌳 🗺 ♀♀
Leisure activities : 🍽 🎣 ⛵ ⛷
Facilities : 🔧 ⛽ (July–Aug.) 🚿 ⛷ 🏪 launderette
Nearby : 🏊 🍴 🎿 🛶

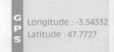

G P S Longitude : -3.54332
Latitude : 47.7727

🏕 Locouarn

📞 02 98 39 91 79, www.camping-locouarn.com

Address : situated 2km north along the D 49, follow the signs for Quimperlé

Opening times : from beginning June to mid Sept.

2,5 ha (100 pitches)

Tariff : 18,10€ 🚿🚿 ⛺ 🔲 🔌 (10A) – Extra per person 3,50€
Rental rates : (from beginning May to mid Sept.) – 14 🚐. Per night from 50€ – Per week from 160 to 490€ – Reservation fee 5€

Surroundings : ♀
Leisure activities : ⛷
Facilities : 🔧 ⛽ 🚿 ⛷ 🚰 🏪 launderette
Nearby : 🏊 🍴 🍴 🐎

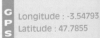

G P S Longitude : -3.54793
Latitude : 47.7855

Do not confuse:
🏕 *to* 🏕🏕🏕 *: MICHELIN classification with*
★ *to* ★★★★★ *: official classification*

⛺ Les Grands Sables

☎ 02 98 39 94 43, www.camping-lesgrandssables.com

Address : 22 rue Philosophe Alain (in the town, 200m from the beach)

Opening times : from beginning April to mid Sept.

2,4 ha (133 pitches)

Tariff : 20,10€ ♥♥ ⚑ 🔲 ⚡ (10A) – Extra per person 4,75€
Reservation fee 9€

Rental rates : (from beginning April to mid Sept.) – 17 🚐.
Per night from 43 to 61€ – Per week from 203 to 580€
Reservation fee 9€

🚐 ♨ 8,50€

In a leafy location with plenty of shade and a view of the pretty chapel of Notre-Dame-de-la-Paix.

Surroundings : ♨	**G**
Leisure activities : 🎣	**P** Longitude : -3.54716
Facilities : ⚊ 🚽 ♨ 🍴 launderette	**S** Latitude : 47.7683
Nearby : 🏖 ✗ ✗ 🐾 ◊	

⛺ Croas An Ter

☎ 02 98 39 94 19, www.campingcroasanter.com

Address : Quelvez (located 1.5km north along the D49, follow the signs for Quimperlé)

Opening times : from beginning May to mid Sept.

3,5 ha (90 pitches)

Tariff : (2013 Price) 15,70€ ♥♥ ⚑ 🔲 ⚡ (6A) – Extra per person 3,60€
Rental rates : (2013 Price) Permanent – 2 🚐 – 2 tent lodges.
Per night from 51 to 63€ – Per week from 360 to 440€

Surroundings : ♨ 🚐 ♨♨	**G**
Leisure activities : ✗ 🎣	**P** Longitude : -3.54104
Facilities : ♿ ⚊ 🚽 ♨ 🍴 🔲	**S** Latitude : 47.78515
Nearby : 🏖 🚤	

Routes nationales are main roads and their identifying numbers begin with N or RN. Routes départementales are generally quieter roads and begin with D or DN.

29100 – Michelin map **308** E6 – pop. 1 499 – alt. 79
▶ Paris 596 – Rennes 244 – Quimper 30 – Brest 80

⛰ Flower La Baie de Douarnenez

☎ 02 98 74 26 39, www.camping-douarnenez.com

Address : 30 rue Luc Robet (600m east of the town along the D7)

Opening times : from mid April to mid Sept.

5,7 ha (190 pitches) flat, grassy

Tariff : 16€ ♥♥ ⚑ 🔲 ⚡ (10A) – Extra per person 3,60€

Rental rates : (from mid April to mid Sept.) – 73 🚐 – 20 🏠 3 canvas bungalows – 6 tent lodges. Per night from 44 to 142€
Per week from 196 to 994€

🚐 borne 2€ – ♨ ⚡ 12€

Surroundings : ♨ 🚐 ♨♨	
Leisure activities : 🏴 ✗ 🔲 📺 nighttime 🎣 🚴 🏓 🎳 🎯 🔲 🏊 ⛱ multi-sports ground	**G** Longitude : -4.40634
Facilities : ♿ ⚊ ♨ ⛲ 🍴 launderette	**P** Latitude : 48.08162
🚿 🚾	**S**

29630 – Michelin map **308** I2
▶ Paris 554 – Rennes 198 – Quimper 105 – Brest 79

⛺ Municipal de la Mer

☎ 02 98 72 37 06, www.campingprimel.jimdo.com

Address : 15 route de Karreg An Ty (4km north along the D 46)

Opening times : from beginning May to end Sept.

1 ha (63 pitches)

Tariff : (2013 Price) 14,20€ ♥♥ ⚑ 🔲 ⚡ (8A) – Extra per person 3,70€
Rental rates : (2013 Price) Permanent – 2 canvas bungalows.
Per night from 40 to 60€ – Per week from 250 to 350€

🚐 borne 3,30€

Exceptional location on a site beside the sea.

Surroundings : 🚤 ⟵ Île de Batz and Roscoff ⛰	
Leisure activities : 🔲 🎣	**G** Longitude : -3.81527
Facilities : ♿ ⚊ (July-Aug.) 🍴 launderette	**P** Latitude : 48.71477
Nearby : 🍽 ✗	**S**

29770 – Michelin map **308** D6 – pop. 742 – alt. 78
▶ Paris 605 – Audierne 7 – Douarnenez 28 – Quimper 44

⛰ Municipal de Kermalero

☎ 02 98 74 84 75, www.primelin.fr

Address : route de l'Océan (take the western exit towards the port)

Opening times : from beginning March to end Oct.

1 ha (75 pitches)

Tariff : (2013 Price) 15€ ♥♥ ⚑ 🔲 ⚡ (6A) – Extra per person 3,50€
Reservation fee 10€

🚐 borne 2€ – 6 🔲 3€

Surroundings : ♨ 🚐	
Leisure activities : 🔲 🎣	**G** Longitude : -4.61067
Facilities : ♿ ⚊ (July-Aug.) ♨ 🚾 launderette	**P** Latitude : 48.02544
Nearby : ✗	**S**

56320 – Michelin map **308** K6 – pop. 1 046 – alt. 163
▶ Paris 498 – Concarneau 55 – Lorient 42 – Pontivy 39

⛺ Municipal Bel Air

☎ 02 97 34 63 55, priziac.com

Address : at l'Etang du Bel Air (500m north along the D 109 and take the turning to the left)

1,5 ha (60 pitches) flat, grassy

Rentals : 4 🚐 .

Green setting and plenty of shade, near a small lake.

Surroundings : ♨ ♨♨ ⛰	
Leisure activities : 🔲	**G** Longitude : -3.41418
Facilities : ♿ launderette	**P** Latitude : 48.06155
Nearby : 🍽 🎣 ✗ 🚤 (beach) 🐾 ◊	**S**
watersports centre	

QUIBERON

56170 – Michelin map **308** M10 – pop. 5 027 – alt. 10
▶ Paris 505 – Auray 28 – Concarneau 98 – Lorient 47

⚠ Flower Le Bois d'Amour ♣♣

℘ 02 97 50 13 52, www.quiberon-camping.com

Address : rue Saint-Clément (located 1.5km southeast, 300m from the sea and sea spa centre)

Opening times : from beginning April to end Sept.

4,6 ha (272 pitches)

Tariff : 40€ ♦♦ ⇔ 🔳 🔌 (6A) – Extra per person 6,40€ – Reservation fee 15€

Rental rates : (from beginning April to end Sept.) – 84 🚐 10 tent lodges – 10 huts on stilts. Per night from 44 to 143€ Per week from 220 to 1022€ – Reservation fee 20€

Surroundings : 🔲 ⚘
Leisure activities : ⛲ ✕ 🏠 ⅁ 🏃 🚣 🚲 🏖
Facilities : 🛁 🔑 🍴 launderette 🚰
Nearby : 🍴 🏕 ⌂ 🏇

Longitude : -3.10427
Latitude : 47.47632

⚠ Do.Mi.Si.La.Mi. ♣♣

℘ 02 97 50 22 52, www.domisilami.com

Address : St-Julien-Plage, 31 rue de la Vierge (600m to the north, 100m from the beach)

4,4 ha (350 pitches)

Rentals : 🚫 – 80 🚐.

🚐 borne – 2 🔳

A free shuttle service to Quiberon.

Surroundings : 🔲 ⚘
Leisure activities : ⛲ ✕ 🏠 🏃 🚣 🚲 multi-sports ground
Facilities : 🛁 🔑 🍴 🚰 launderette 🚰 🚰

Longitude : -3.12045
Latitude : 47.49937

⚠ Les Joncs du Roch

℘ 02 97 50 24 37, www.lesjoncsduroch.com

Address : rue de l'Aérodrome (situated 2km southeast, 500m from the sea)

Opening times : from mid April to end Sept.

2,3 ha (163 pitches) flat, grassy

Tariff : (2013 Price) 34,50€ ♦♦ ⇔ 🔳 🔌 (10A) – Extra per person 7€ Reservation fee 15€

Rental rates : (2013 Price) (from mid April to end Sept.) 🚫 26 🚐 – 2 canvas bungalows. Per night from 30 to 130€ Per week from 180 to 780€ – Reservation fee 15€

Surroundings : 🔲 ⚘
Leisure activities : 🏠 🚣 🔳 (open air in season), multi-sports ground, entertainment room
Facilities : 🛁 🔑 🍴 🚰 launderette
Nearby : 🏕 ⌂ 🏇

Longitude : -3.10098
Latitude : 47.47946

We value your opinion and welcome your feedback.
Do email us at campingfrance@tp.michelin.com

⚠ Beauséjour

℘ 02 97 30 44 93, www.campingbeausejour.com

Address : boulevard du Parco (800m to the north, 50m from the beach)

Opening times : from beginning April to end Sept.

2,4 ha (160 pitches)

Tariff : ♦ 4€ ⇔ 🔳 15€ – 🔌 (10A) 5,20€

Rental rates : (from beginning April to end Sept.) – 15 🚐. Per night from 60 to 100€ – Per week from 310 to 690€ Reservation fee 18€

🚐 borne 4€

Leisure activities : 🏠 🚣 multi-sports ground
Facilities : 🛁 🔑 (July–Aug.) 🚰 🚰 🍴 launderette
Nearby : 🍴 ✕ 🚣

Longitude : -3.12027
Latitude : 47.5003

QUIMPER

29000 – Michelin map **308** G7 – pop. 63 387 – alt. 41
▶ Paris 564 – Brest 73 – Lorient 67 – Rennes 215

⚠ Les Castels L'Orangerie de Lanniron ♣♣

℘ 02 98 90 62 02, www.lanniron.com

Address : allée de Lanniron (3km south along the ring road (périphérique), then take the exit towards Bénodet and a right turn; near the leisure centre at Creac'h Gwen)

Opening times : from mid May to mid Sept.

38 ha/6,5 for camping (235 pitches) flat, grassy

Tariff : 44,60€ ♦♦ ⇔ 🔳 🔌 (10A) – Extra per person 8,50€

Rental rates : Permanent 🚫 – 40 🚐 – 11 studios – 1 apartment 6 gîtes. Per night from 83 to 146€ – Per week from 463 to 1213€ Reservation fee 20€

🚐 borne 4,50€

Situated in the magnificent park and grounds of a 15th-century manor house; beside the Odet river, with a pretty water park.

Surroundings : 🔲 ⚘⚘
Leisure activities : ⛲ ✕ 🏠 ⅁ 🏃 jacuzzi 🚣 🚲 🏕 ⌂ 🔲 🚰 🚣 9-hole golf course 🚫
Facilities : 🛁 🔑 🚰 🚰 🍴 launderette 🚰 🚰

Longitude : -4.10338
Latitude : 47.97923

QUIMPERLÉ

29300 – Michelin map **308** J7 – pop. 11 384 – alt. 30
▶ Paris 517 – Carhaix-Plouguer 57 – Concarneau 32 – Pontivy 76

⚠ Municipal de Kerbertrand

℘ 02 98 39 31 30, www.quimperle-tourisme.com

Address : 2 rue de Kermaria (located 1.5km west along the D 783, follow the signs for Concarneau and take the road to the right, after the stadium, opposite the Leclerc commercial centre)

1 ha (40 pitches) flat, grassy

Surroundings : 🐟 ⚘⚘
Leisure activities : 🏠 🚣
Facilities : 🔑 🚰
Nearby : 🏕 🔲 🔳

Longitude : -3.57044
Latitude : 47.872

RAGUENÈS-PLAGE

29920 – Michelin map **308** I8
▶ Paris 545 – Carhaix-Plouguer 73 – Concarneau 17 – Pont-Aven 12

⚠️ Les Deux Fontaines ♦♣

✆ 02 98 06 81 91, www.les2fontaines.com

Address : Feunten Vihan (1.3km north following signs for Névez and Trémorvezen)

Opening times : from end April to beginning Sept.

9 ha (270 pitches) flat, grassy

Tariff : 37,80€ ♦♦ 🚗 🔲 ⚡ (10A) – Extra per person 6,70€
Reservation fee 15€

Rental rates : (from end April to beginning Sept.) – 50 🏚
11 🏠. Per night from 46 to 160€– Per week from 203 to 1120€
Reservation fee 15€

🚐 borne 5€ – 🛁 ⚡15€

A partially open-air water park with good facilities for children.

Surroundings : 🏞 ☁ 🌳🌳
Leisure activities : 🍴✖🎣 🎱🎿 🏇 🎠 🚴 ✂
🔲 🛶 🏊 pool scuba diving
Facilities : 🚿 o🔑 ⌨ 🏕 🚿 🚽 launderette
🛁 🚰
Longitude : -3.79129
Latitude : 47.7992

⚠️ Club Airotel Le Raguenès-Plage ♦♣

✆ 02 98 06 80 69, www.camping-le-raguenes-plage.com

Address : 19 rue des Îles (400m from the beach, direct access)

Opening times : from mid April to end Sept.

6 ha (287 pitches) flat, grassy

Tariff : 41,30€ ♦♦ 🚗 🔲 ⚡ (15A) – Extra per person 6,20€
Rental rates : (from mid April to end Sept.) – 60 🏚. Per night from 85 to 150€ – Per week from 265 to 890€

🚐 borne

Surroundings : 🌳🌳
Leisure activities : 🍴✖🎣 🎱🎿 🏇 🚤
🏇 🛶 🏊
Facilities : 🚿 o🔑 🏕 🚿 🚽 launderette
🛁 🚰
Longitude : -3.80085
Latitude : 47.79373

⚠️ Le Vieux Verger - Ty Noul

✆ 02 98 06 86 08, www.campingduvieuxverger.com

Address : 20 Kéroren (take the northern exit, follow the signs for Névez)

Opening times : from mid April to end Sept.

2,5 ha (110 pitches) flat, grassy

Tariff : 22,50€ ♦♦ 🚗 🔲 ⚡ (10A) – Extra per person 5€ – Reservation fee 10€

Rental rates : (from mid March to end Sept.) 🏠 – 10 🏚
1 apartment. Per night from 30 to 40€ – Per week from 185 to 570€ – Reservation fee 10€

In two separate sections with a small but attractive water park.

Surroundings : 🌳
Leisure activities : 🏇 🚴 🛶 🏊
Facilities : 🚿 o🔑 🚽 📷
Longitude : -3.79777
Latitude : 47.79663

This guide is updated regularly, so buy your new copy every year!

⚠️ L'Océan

✆ 02 98 06 87 13, www.camping-ocean.fr

Address : 15 impasse des Mouettes, at Kéroren (take the northern exit, follow the signs for Névez and take a right turn, 350m from the beach (direct access)

2,2 ha (150 pitches)
Rentals : 🏠 – 8 🏚 .

Surroundings : 🏞 ☁ ☁ 🌳
Leisure activities : 🎣 🏇 🔲 (open air in season)
Facilities : 🚿 o🔑 🏕 🚽 launderette
Nearby : ✂ 🛶
Longitude : -3.79789
Latitude : 47.79471

RENNES

35000 – Michelin map **309** L6 – pop. 206 604 – alt. 40
▶ Paris 349 – Angers 129 – Brest 246 – Caen 185

⚠️ Municipal des Gayeulles

✆ 02 99 36 91 22, www.camping-rennes.com

Address : rue Professeur Maurice-Audin (take the northeastern exit towards the N 12, follow the signs for Fougères then take the av. des Gayeulles near a small lake)

Opening times : Permanent

3 ha (179 pitches) flat, grassy

Tariff : (2013 Price) ♦ 4€ 🚗 1,70€ 🔲 6,80€ – ⚡ (16A) 3,50€
🚐 borne 2€

In the middle of the immense wooded park at Les Gayeulles.

Surroundings : 🏞 ☁ 🌳🌳
Leisure activities : 🏇
Facilities : 🚿 o🔑 (July-Aug.) ⌨ 🏕 🚿 🚽
launderette
Nearby : ✂ 🎯 🛶 🔲 (open air in season)
skating rink, wildlife park
Longitude : -1.64772
Latitude : 48.13455

LA ROCHE-BERNARD

56130 – Michelin map **308** R9 – pop. 757 – alt. 38
▶ Paris 444 – Nantes 70 – Ploërmel 55 – Redon 28

⚠️ Municipal le Pâtis

✆ 02 99 90 60 13, www.camping-larochebernard.com

Address : 3 chemin du Pâtis (to the west of the town towards the marina)

Opening times : from beginning April to mid Oct.

1 ha (58 pitches) flat, grassy

Tariff : (2013 Price) 21,50€ ♦♦ 🚗 🔲 ⚡ (6A) – Extra per person 4,10€
Rental rates : (2013 Price) (from beginning April to mid Oct.)
2 🏚. Per night from 39 to 110€ – Per week from 231 to 641€
🚐 borne 2€ – 18 🔲 10,90€

Beside the Vilaine river, opposite the port.

Surroundings : ☁ 🌳
Leisure activities : 🎣 🚴
Facilities : 🚿 o🔑 (July-Aug.) ⌨ 🏕 🚽
launderette
Nearby : 🏇 🛶
Longitude : -2.30523
Latitude : 47.51923

ROCHEFORT-EN-TERRE

56220 – Michelin map **308** Q8 – pop. 662 – alt. 40
▶ Paris 431 – Ploërmel 34 – Redon 26 – Rennes 82

⚠ Sites et Paysages Au Gré des Vents

📞 02 97 43 37 52, www.campingaugredesvents.com

Address : 2 chemin de Bogeais (located 1km southwest along the D 774, follow the signs for Péaule and take the road to the right; 500m from a small lake)

Opening times : from beginning April to end Sept.

2,5 ha (60 pitches)

Tariff : (2013 Price) 25€ ♥♥ ⬅ 🔲 ⚡ (10A) – Extra per person 5,50€
Rental rates : (2013 Price) (from beginning April to end Sept.) 6 🛖 – 2 tent lodges. Per night from 47 to 95€ – Per week from 195 to 625€
🚐 borne 2,50€ – 🔋 ⚡11€

Surroundings : 🏞
Leisure activities : 🚣 🎿 🖼 (open air in season)
Facilities : 🔥 ⚡ 🖥 ⛺ 🍴 launderette
Nearby : 🍴 ⛵ (beach) 🎣

ROHAN

56580 – Michelin map **308** O6 – pop. 1 637 – alt. 55
▶ Paris 451 – Lorient 72 – Pontivy 17 – Quimperlé 86

⚠ Municipal le Val d'Oust

📞 02 97 51 57 58, rohan.fr

Address : rue de St-Gouvry (take the northwestern exit)

Opening times : from beginning May to mid Sept.

1 ha (45 pitches) flat, grassy

Tariff : ♥ 3,40€ ⬅ 1,50€ 🔲 1,90€ – ⚡ (15A) 3,30€
🚐 borne
Beside the Nantes-Brest canal and near a small lake.

Surroundings : 🌳🌳
Leisure activities : 🚣 🎣
Facilities : 🔥 🖥 🖼
Nearby : 🍴 🍴 ⛵ (beach) ⚓ sports trail

ROSPORDEN

29140 – Michelin map **308** I7 – pop. 7 126 – alt. 125
▶ Paris 544 – Carhaix-Plouguer 51 – Châteaulin 50 – Concarneau 15

⚠ Municipal Roz-an-Duc

📞 02 98 59 99 00, www.rosporden.fr

Address : rue de Coray (located 1km north along the D 36, follow the signs for Châteauneuf-du-Faou and take a right turn; by the swimming pool, 100m from a lake)

Opening times : from beginning July to end Aug.

1 ha (49 pitches)

Tariff : ♥ 2,65€ ⬅ 1,45€ 🔲 2,55€ – ⚡ (6A) 2,50€
Pleasant wooded setting beside the Aven river.

Surroundings : 🏞 🌳🌳
Facilities : 🔥 🖥 launderette
Nearby : 🎿 🖼 🎣 sports trail

ROZ-SUR-COUESNON

35610 – Michelin map **309** M3 – pop. 1 034 – alt. 65
▶ Paris 365 – Rennes 82 – Caen 134 – St-Lô 99

⚠ Les Couesnons

📞 02 99 80 26 86, www.lescouesnons.com

Address : l'Hopital (situated 2km southeast on the D 797)

Opening times : from beginning April to beginning Nov.

1 ha (57 pitches) flat, grassy

Tariff : 20€ ♥♥ ⬅ 🔲 ⚡ (10A) – Extra per person 5€
Rental rates : (from beginning April to beginning Nov.) – 1 caravan 8 🛖. Per night from 65 to 129€ – Per week from 129 to 660€

Surroundings : 🏕 🌳🌳
Leisure activities : 🍴 🍴 🏊
Facilities : 🔥 ⚡ 🖥 ⛺ 🍴 🖼

ST-BRIAC-SUR-MER

35800 – Michelin map **309** J3 – pop. 1 955 – alt. 30
▶ Paris 411 – Dinan 24 – Dol-de-Bretagne 34 – Lamballe 41

⛰ Émeraude

📞 02 99 88 34 55, www.campingemeraude.com

Address : 7 chemin de la Souris

Opening times : from mid April to mid Sept.

3,2 ha (194 pitches)

Tariff : ♥ 5,50€ ⬅ 🔲 8€ – ⚡ (6A) 4€
Rental rates : (from mid April to mid Sept.) 🔥 – 66 🛖 – 14 🏠. Per night from 43 to 102€ – Per week from 298 to 714€ Reservation fee 16€
🚐 borne 2,50€ – 🔋 15€
An attractive swimming area.

Surroundings : 🏞 🏕 ♀
Leisure activities : 🍴 🍴 🏊 🚣 🚴 🎿 🏐 entertainment room
Facilities : 🔥 ⚡ ⛺ 🍴 launderette 🛒

ST-CAST-LE-GUILDO

22380 – Michelin map **309** I3 – pop. 3 500 – alt. 52
▶ Paris 427 – Avranches 91 – Dinan 32 – St-Brieuc 50

⛰ Les Castels Le Château de la Galinée 🧍‍♂️🧍

📞 02 96 41 10 56, www.chateaudegalinee.com

Address : rue de Galinée (7km to the south, access via the D 786, near the crossroads with the road to St-Cast-le-Guildo)

Opening times : from mid May to beginning Sept.

14 ha (272 pitches) flat, grassy

Tariff : ♥ 7,10€ ⬅ 🔲 20,50€ – ⚡ (10A) 6€ – Reservation fee 23€
Rental rates : (from mid April to beginning Sept.) 🔥 – 2 caravans 50 🛖 – 10 🏠 – 6 canvas bungalows. Per night from 37 to 106€ Per week from 266 to 602€ – Reservation fee 23€
🚐 borne

Surroundings : 🏞 🏕 🌳🌳
Leisure activities : 🍴 🖼 🏊 ⛲ 🚣 🎿 🏓 🖼 🏊 🏐 🎣 multi-sports ground, entertainment room
Facilities : 🔥 ⚡ ♿ 🖥 ⛺ – 4 individual sanitary facilities (🍴 ⛺ 🚿 WC) 🔥 🛒 🍴 launderette 🔲 🛒

🗻🗻🗻 Le Châtelet ♣♣

📞 02 96 41 96 33, www.lechatelet.com – limited spaces for one-night stay

Address : rue des Nouettes (located 1km west, 250m from the beach (direct access)

Opening times : from mid April to mid Sept.

9 ha/3,9 for camping (216 pitches) small lake

Tariff : 🛉 7,20€ 🚗 🅴 22,50€ – 🔌 (8A) 6,20€ – Reservation fee 23€

Rental rates : (from mid April to mid Sept.) – 52 🚐 – 1 tipi – 6 tent lodges. Per night from 48 to 135€ – Per week from 335 to 1290€ Reservation fee 23€

🚰 borne

The site overlooks the bay at La Frênaye.

Surroundings : 🐃 ⇇ 🛏 ♀
Leisure activities : 🍷 🎮 🎯 🎿 🚴 🏊 (open air in season) 🐃
Facilities : ♿ 🔑 🛁 ⛺ 🍴 launderette 🏧 🚿
Nearby : ✗ 🚲

Longitude : -2.26959
Latitude : 48.63773

🗻🗻 Vert-Bleu Les Mielles

📞 02 96 41 87 60, www.campings-vert-bleu.com

Address : boulevard de la Vieux-Ville (take the southern exit along the D 19, follow the signs for St-Malo, right next to the stadium and 200m from the beach)

Opening times : from mid March to mid Nov.

3,5 ha (160 pitches) flat, grassy

Tariff : 🛉 5,90€ 🚗 2,95€ 🅴 10,25€ – 🔌 (10A) 6,25€ – Reservation fee 20€

Rental rates : (from mid March to mid Nov.) – 15 🚐. Per night from 120 to 170€ – Per week from 420 to 840€ – Reservation fee 20€

🚰 borne – 🛢 12,70€

Surroundings : 🛏 ♀
Leisure activities : 🎮 🎿 🏊
Facilities : ♿ 🔑 ⛺ 🍴 launderette
Nearby : ✗ 🎮 🚿

Longitude : -2.25402
Latitude : 48.62694

The pitches of many campsites are marked out with low hedges of attractive bushes and shrubs.

ST-COULOMB

35350 – Michelin map **309** K2 – pop. 2 454 – alt. 35
▶ Paris 398 – Cancale 6 – Dinard 18 – Dol-de-Bretagne 21

🗻🗻 Le Tannée

📞 02 99 89 41 20, www.campingdetannee.com – limited spaces for one-night stay

Address : rue de Tannée

Opening times : from beginning April to end Sept.

0,6 ha (30 pitches) flat and relatively flat

Tariff : (2013 Price) 21,50€ 🛉🛉 🚗 🅴 🔌 (10A) Extra per person 4,15€ Reservation fee 15€

Rental rates : (2013 Price) (from beginning April to end Sept.) 13 🚐. Per week from 230 to 670€ – Reservation fee 15€

Surroundings : 🐃 ⇇ 🛏
Leisure activities : 🚲 🖼 (open air in season)
Facilities : ♿ 🔑 🛁 ⛺ 🍴 launderette

Longitude : -1.889
Latitude : 48.68655

🗻 Du Guesclin

📞 02 99 89 03 24, www.camping-duguesclin.com – limited spaces for one-night stay

Address : rue de Tannée (2.5km northeast along the D 355, follow the signs for Cancale and take turning to the left)

Opening times : from beginning April to end Oct.

0,9 ha (43 pitches)

Tariff : 20,50€ 🛉🛉 🚗 🅴 🔌 (10A) – Extra per person 4,50€

Rental rates : (from beginning April to end Oct.) – 15 🚐. Per week from 240 to 645€ – Reservation fee 15€

Surroundings : 🐃 ⇇ 🛏 ♀
Leisure activities : 🎮 🎿 🚴
Facilities : ♿ 🔑 ⛺ 🍴 🍴 🏧

Longitude : -1.89027
Latitude : 48.68628

ST-GILDAS-DE-RHUYS

56730 – Michelin map **308** N9 – pop. 1 647 – alt. 10
▶ Paris 483 – Arzon 9 – Auray 48 – Sarzeau 7

🗻🗻🗻 Le Menhir ♣♣

📞 02 97 45 22 88, www.camping-bretagnesud.com

Address : route de Clos er Bé (3.5km north - recommended route via the D 780, follow the signs for Port-Navalo)

5 ha/3 for camping (176 pitches)

Rentals : 🏚 – 49 🚐.

🚰 borne

Surroundings : 🛏 ♀♀
Leisure activities : 🍷 🎮 🎯 🎿 🚴 🏊 🖼
Facilities : ♿ 🔑 🛁 ⛺ 🍴 launderette 🏧 🚿

Longitude : -2.84781
Latitude : 47.52874

🗻 Goh'Velin

📞 02 97 45 21 67, www.camping-gohvelin.fr

Address : 89 rue Guernevé (located 1.5km to the north, 300m from the beach)

Opening times : from beginning April to end Sept.

1 ha (93 pitches) flat, grassy

Tariff : 26,50€ 🛉🛉 🚗 🅴 🔌 (16A) – Extra per person 5,50€ Reservation fee 10€

Rental rates : (from beginning April to end Sept.) 🏚 – 17 🚐. Per night from 100 to 150€ – Per week from 240 to 750€ Reservation fee 10€

Surroundings : 🛏 ♀
Leisure activities : 🎮 🎿 🏊
Facilities : 🔑 🍴 🏧
Nearby : 🎿 🚿

Longitude : -2.84515
Latitude : 47.51204

These symbols are used for a campsite that is exceptional in its category:

🗻🗻🗻....🗻 *Particularly pleasant setting, quality and range of services available*

🐃🐃 *Tranquil, isolated site – quiet site, particularly at night*

⇇⇇ *Exceptional view – interesting or panoramic view*

ST-JEAN-DU-DOIGT

29630 – Michelin map **308** I2 – pop. 623 – alt. 15
▶ Paris 544 – Brest 77 – Guingamp 61 – Lannion 33

⚠ Municipal du Pont Ar Gler

🖉 02 98 67 32 15, st-jean-du-doigt-mairie@wanadoo.fr

Address : Pont ar Gler (in the town)

Opening times : from end June to end Aug.

1 ha (34 pitches)

Tariff : (2013 Price) ♦ 3,25€ ⇌ 1,70€ 🔲 3€ – ⚡ (6A) 2,80€

Surroundings : 🐾 🗗 ♀
Leisure activities : 🖼 🎿 🏊
Facilities : 🚿 🔓 🗑 ♨ 🔥

GPS Longitude : -3.77487
Latitude : 48.69405

ST-JOUAN-DES-GUÉRETS

35430 – Michelin map **309** K3 – pop. 2 699 – alt. 31
▶ Paris 396 – Rennes 63 – St-Helier 10 – St-Brieuc 85

🏔 Le P'tit Bois 🔒👤

🖉 02 99 21 14 30, www.ptitbois.com

Address : La Chalandouze (access via the N 137)

Opening times : from mid April to mid Sept.

6 ha (274 pitches) flat, grassy

Tariff : ♦ 9€ ⇌ 🔲 20€ – ⚡ (10A) 6,50€ – Reservation fee 10€

Rental rates : (from mid April to mid Sept.) – 168 🏚. Per night from 39 to 216€ – Per week from 273 to 1512€ – Reservation fee 10€

🛒 borne 7€

In a pleasant rural setting.

Surroundings : 🗗 ♀
Leisure activities : ♦ 🖼 🎣 🏃 hammam, jacuzzi 🎿 🚴 ⛏ 🏓 🔲 🏊 🏄 multi-sports ground, entertainment room
Facilities : 🚿 🔓 🗑 🔥 ♨ 🍽 launderette 🏊 🚿

GPS Longitude : -1.9869
Latitude : 48.60966

ST-LUNAIRE

35800 – Michelin map **309** J3 – pop. 2 309 – alt. 20
▶ Paris 410 – Rennes 76 – St-Helier 16 – St-Brieuc 83

🏔 La Touesse

🖉 02 99 46 61 13, www.campinglatouesse.com

Address : 171 rue Ville Géhan (situated 2km east along the D 786, follow the signs for Dinard; 400m from the beach)

Opening times : from beginning April to end Sept.

2,5 ha (141 pitches) flat, grassy

Tariff : ♦ 5,50€ ⇌ 3,10€ 🔲 7,90€ – ⚡ (5A) 3,30€ – Reservation fee 16€

Rental rates : (from beginning April to end Sept.) – 50 🏚 3 studios – 6 apartments – 4 gîtes. Per night from 33 to 98€ Per week from 231 to 686€ – Reservation fee 16€

🛒 borne 6€ – 🔋 ⚡19,50€ 22,20€

Surroundings : ♀ ♀
Leisure activities : ♦ ✗ 🖼 📺 🎿
Facilities : 🚿 🔓 🏛 🗑 🔥 ♨ 🍽 launderette 🏊 🚿
Nearby : 🏇

GPS Longitude : -2.08425
Latitude : 48.63086

ST-MALO

35400 – Michelin map **309** J3 – pop. 47 045 – alt. 5
▶ Paris 404 – Alençon 180 – Avranches 68 – Dinan 32

🏔 Domaine de la Ville Huchet 🔒👤

DU JONCHAY

🖉 02 99 81 11 83, www.lavillehuchet.com

Address : route de la Passagère, Quelmer (5km south along the D 301, follow the signs for Dinard and take turning for La Grassinais to the left in front of the Mercedes showroom)

Opening times : from beginning April to end Sept.

6 ha (198 pitches) flat, grassy

Tariff : ♦ 7,10€ ⇌ 🔲 16,90€ ⚡ (6A) 6€ – Reservation fee 18€

Rental rates : (from beginning April to end Sept.) 🚿 (1 mobile home) – 85 🏚 – 6 🏠 – 3 studios. Per night from 37 to 144€ – Per week from 259 to 1008€ – Reservation fee 18€

🛒 borne – 🔋 ⚡19,50€

A pleasant site spread out around a small but pretty château.

Surroundings : 🗗 ♀ ♀
Leisure activities : ♦ ✗ 🖼 🏃 🎿 🚴 🏓 🔲 🎿 🏄 multi-sports ground
Facilities : 🚿 🔓 🗑 🍽 launderette 🏊 🚿

GPS Longitude : -1.98704
Latitude : 48.61545

ST-MARCAN

35120 – Michelin map **309** M3 – pop. 455 – alt. 60
▶ Paris 370 – Dinan 42 – Dol-de-Bretagne 14 – Le Mont-St-Michel 17

🏔 Le Balcon de la Baie

🖉 02 99 80 22 95, www.lebalcondelabaie.com

Address : Le Verger (500m southeast along the D 89, follow the signs for Pleine-Fougères and turn left after the cemetery)

Opening times : from beginning April to end Oct.

2,8 ha (66 pitches) flat, grassy

Tariff : (2013 Price) ♦ 5€ ⇌ 🔲 6,50€ – ⚡ (6A) 4€

Rental rates : Permanent – 11 🏚. Per week from 250 to 690€

Surroundings : 🐾 ≤ Baie du Mont-St-Michel 🗗 ♀ ♀
Leisure activities : 🖼 🎿 🏊
Facilities : 🚿 🔓 🗑 🍽 launderette

GPS Longitude : -1.62929
Latitude : 48.58942

ST-MICHEL-EN-GRÈVE

22300 – Michelin map **309** A2 – pop. 480 – alt. 12
▶ Paris 526 – Guingamp 43 – Lannion 11 – Morlaix 31

🏔 Sites et Paysages Les Capucines

🖉 02 96 35 72 28, www.lescapucines.fr

Address : ancienne Voie Romaine, at Kervourdon (located 1.5km north following signs for Lannion and take road to the left)

Opening times : from beginning April to end Sept.

4 ha (100 pitches)

Tariff : 28,20€ ♦♦ ⇌ 🔲 ⚡ (10A) – Extra per person 5,75€

Rental rates : (from beginning April to end Sept.) ⟨wheelchair⟩ (1 chalet) 12 ⟨mobile home⟩ – 5 ⟨chalet⟩ . Per night from 50 to 170€ – Per week from 230 to 1190€ – Reservation fee 15€
⟨borne⟩ borne – ⟨⟩14€

Surroundings : ⟨icons⟩
Leisure activities : ⟨icons⟩ (open air in season), multi-sports ground
Facilities : ⟨icons⟩ launderette ⟨⟩

G P S Longitude : -3.55694
Latitude : 48.69278

ST-PÈRE

35430 – Michelin map **309** K3 – pop. 2 289 – alt. 50
▶ Paris 392 – Cancale 14 – Dinard 15 – Dol-de-Bretagne 16

⟨M⟩ Bel Évent

☎ 02 99 58 83 79, www.camping-bel-event.com

Address : Bellevent (located 1.5km southeast along the D 74, follow the signs for Châteauneuf and take the road to the right)

Opening times : from beginning April to end Sept.

2,5 ha (115 pitches) flat, grassy

Tariff : (2013 Price) 23,30€ ⟨icons⟩ (10A)
Extra per person 3,60€

Rental rates : (2013 Price) (from beginning April to end Sept.) 17 ⟨mobile home⟩ – 1 ⟨chalet⟩. Per week from 240 to 730€

Surroundings : ⟨icons⟩
Leisure activities : ⟨icons⟩ multi-sports ground
Facilities : ⟨icons⟩ launderette

G P S Longitude : -1.91838
Latitude : 48.57347

ST-PHILIBERT

56470 – Michelin map **308** N9 – pop. 1 520 – alt. 15
▶ Paris 486 – Auray 11 – Locmariaquer 7 – Quiberon 27

⟨M⟩ Les Palmiers

☎ 02 97 55 01 17, www.campinglespalmiers.com

Address : Kernivilit (situated 2km west, 500m from the river at Crach (sea)

Opening times : from beginning April to mid Oct.

3 ha (115 pitches)

Tariff : 24,70€ ⟨icons⟩ (10A) – Extra per person 5,70€
Reservation fee 19,50€

Rental rates : (from beginning April to mid Oct.) – 48 ⟨mobile home⟩. Per night from 50 to 90€ – Per week from 190 to 850€ Reservation fee 19,50€
⟨borne⟩ borne 7€ – ⟨⟩13,50€
The site is based around an old renovated farmhouse.

Surroundings : ⟨icons⟩
Leisure activities : ⟨icons⟩ entertainment room
Facilities : ⟨icons⟩ launderette
Nearby : ⟨icon⟩

G P S Longitude : -3.01504
Latitude : 47.58831

⟨M⟩ Le Chat Noir

☎ 02 97 55 04 90, www.campinglechatnoir.com

Address : le Congre (located 1km to the north)

Opening times : from beginning April to end Oct.

1,7 ha (98 pitches)

Tariff : (2013 Price) 24,10€ ⟨icons⟩ (10A)
Extra per person 2,50€ – Reservation fee 20€

Rental rates : (from beginning April to end Oct.) – 35 ⟨mobile home⟩ 2 canvas bungalows. Per night from 35 to 85€ – Per week from 170 to 650€ – Reservation fee 20€

Surroundings : ⟨icons⟩
Leisure activities : ⟨icons⟩
Facilities : ⟨icons⟩ launderette
Nearby : ⟨icons⟩

G P S Longitude : -2.99778
Latitude : 47.59591

ST-POL-DE-LÉON

29250 – Michelin map **308** H2 – pop. 7 043 – alt. 60
▶ Paris 557 – Brest 62 – Brignogan-Plages 31 – Morlaix 21

⟨M⟩ Ar Kleguer ⟨icons⟩

KER3RAT

☎ 02 98 69 18 81, www.camping-ar-kleguer.com

Address : plage Ste-Anne (east of the town)

Opening times : from beginning April to end Sept.

5 ha (173 pitches)

Tariff : (2013 Price) 28,60€ ⟨icons⟩ (10A) – Extra per person 6,20€
Reservation fee 18€

Rental rates : (2013 Price) (from beginning April to end Sept.) 45 ⟨mobile home⟩ – 4 ⟨chalet⟩ – 3 gîtes. Per week from 280 to 800€ – Reservation fee 18€
⟨borne⟩ borne
A pleasant wildlife park with lovely scenery.

Surroundings : ⟨icons⟩
Leisure activities : ⟨icons⟩ multi-sports ground
Facilities : ⟨icons⟩ launderette

G P S Longitude : -3.9677
Latitude : 48.6907

⟨M⟩ Le Trologot

☎ 02 98 69 06 26, www.camping-trologot.com

Address : Grève du Man (To the east, follow the signs for Îlot St-Anne; near the beach)

Opening times : from beginning May to end Sept.

2 ha (100 pitches) flat, grassy

Tariff : ⟨icon⟩ 4,80€ ⟨icon⟩ 2,10€ ⟨icon⟩ 6,80€ – (10A) 3,65€ – Reservation fee 10€

Rental rates : (from mid April to end Sept.) – 15 ⟨mobile home⟩. Per night from 43 to 70€ – Per week from 260 to 660€ – Reservation fee 15€
⟨borne⟩ borne

Surroundings : ⟨icons⟩
Leisure activities : ⟨icons⟩
Facilities : ⟨icons⟩ launderette

G P S Longitude : -3.9698
Latitude : 48.6935

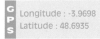

Michelin classification:

⟨icon⟩ *Extremely comfortable, equipped to a very high standard*

⟨icon⟩ *Very comfortable, equipped to a high standard*

⟨icon⟩ *Comfortable and well equipped*

⟨icon⟩ *Reasonably comfortable*

⟨icon⟩ *Satisfactory*

ST-RENAN

29290 – Michelin map **308** D4 – pop. 7 468 – alt. 50
▶ Paris 605 – Brest 14 – Brignogan-Plages 43 – Ploudalmézeau 14

⚠ Municipal de Lokournan

✆ 02 98 84 37 67, www.saint-renan.com

Address : route de l'Aber (take northwestern exit along the D 27 and take the road to the right; near the stadium)

Opening times : from beginning June to mid Sept.

0,8 ha (30 pitches) flat, grassy, sandy

Tariff : (2013 Price) ♦ 3,20 € ⬅ 🅴 3,20 € – 🔌 (6A) 3,40 €
🚐 borne
Near a small lake.

Surroundings : 🎣 🏕 ♤♤
Leisure activities : 🎮
Facilities : ♿ 🚿🖼 launderette
Nearby : 🍽

Longitude : -4.62929
Latitude : 48.43991

ST-SAMSON-SUR-RANCE

22100 – Michelin map **309** J4 – pop. 1 514 – alt. 64
▶ Paris 401 – Rennes 57 – St-Brieuc 64 – St-Helier 34

🏕 Municipal Beauséjour

✆ 02 96 39 53 27, www.beausejour-camping.com

Address : La Hisse (3km east, along the D 57 and take the D 12 to the right, 200m from the port - access via steep slope)

Opening times : from mid May to end Sept.

3 ha (120 pitches) flat, grassy

Tariff : (2013 Price) ♦ 3,95 € ⬅ 🅴 5 € – 🔌 (10A) 3,45 €
Rental rates : Permanent 🏕 – 6 🛖 – 12 🛏 – 3 gîtes. Per night from 41 to 61 € – Per week from 213 to 508 €
🚐 borne 3 €
Pretty gîtes in the local stone.

Surroundings : 🎣
Leisure activities : 🎮 🏊
Facilities : ♿ 🚿 🍽 launderette
Nearby : 🍽 🚴 🎣

Longitude : -2.00889
Latitude : 48.48889

ST-YVI

29140 – Michelin map **308** H7 – pop. 2 755 – alt. 105
▶ Paris 563 – Rennes 212 – Quimper 17 – Vannes 119

🏕 Village Center Le Bois de Pleuven

Interaview Production

✆ 08 25 00 20 30, www.village-center.fr

Address : Kerancolven

Opening times : from mid April to end Sept.

17 ha/10 for camping (280 pitches) flat, grassy

Tariff : (2013 Price) 16 € ♦♦ ⬅ 🅴 🔌 (12A) – Extra per person 4 €

Rental rates : (2013 Price) (from mid April to end Sept.) – 65 🛖 – 15 🏠 – Per night from 25 to 111 € Per week from 175 to 777 €

In a natural, wild setting among trees and bushes.

Surroundings : 🎣 🏕 ♫♫♫
Leisure activities : 🍽 🎮 🏊 🚴 🎯 🍽 🎣 🏓 🖼
🏊 🏊
Facilities : ♿ 🚿 🅲 🏊 launderette

Longitude : -3.97056
Latitude : 47.95028

STE-ANNE-D'AURAY

56400 – Michelin map **308** N8 – pop. 2 347 – alt. 42
▶ Paris 475 – Auray 7 – Hennebont 33 – Locminé 27

⚠ Municipal du Motten

✆ 02 97 57 60 27, contact@sainte-anne-auray.com

Address : allée des Pins (located 1km southwest along the D 17, follow the signs for Auray and take r. du Parc to the right)

1,5 ha (115 pitches) flat, grassy

Surroundings : ♤♤
Leisure activities : 🎮 🏊 🎯
Facilities : ♿ 🚿 🖼
Nearby : 🏊

Longitude : -2.96251
Latitude : 47.69831

SARZEAU

56370 – Michelin map **308** O9 – pop. 7 659 – alt. 30
▶ Paris 478 – Nantes 111 – Redon 62 – Vannes 23

🏕 FranceLoc Domaine An Trest 🧑‍🤝‍🧑

✆ 02 97 41 79 60, www.an-trest.com

Address : 1 chemin du Treste (2.5km to the south, follow the signs for Le Roaligen)

Opening times : from mid April to mid Sept.

5 ha (225 pitches) terraced, flat, grassy

Tariff : 35 € ♦♦ ⬅ 🅴 🔌 (10A) – Extra per person 7 € – Reservation fee 11 €

Rental rates : (from mid April to mid Sept.) ♿ (1 mobile home) 124 🛖. Per night from 33 to 103 € – Per week from 133 to 1 022 € Reservation fee 27 €

A partially covered water park, with some impressive slides.

Surroundings : ♤
Leisure activities : 🍽 🍽 🎮 🎯 🚴 🎯 🚴 🍽
🏊 🏊 🏊
Facilities : ♿ 🚿 🍽 🍽 launderette
Nearby : 🐎

Longitude : -2.77208
Latitude : 47.50612

🏕 Lodge Club Presqu'île de Rhuys 🧑‍🤝‍🧑

✆ 02 97 41 29 93, www.lodgeclub.fr

Address : Le Bas Bohat (2.8km west)

Opening times : from beginning April to end Sept.

15 ha/10 for camping (250 pitches) flat, grassy, adjacent forest

Tariff : 34,30 € ♦♦ ⬅ 🅴 🔌 (10A) – Extra per person 5,20 € Reservation fee 18 €

Rental rates : (from beginning April to beginning Nov.) 18 🛖 – 6 tent lodges. Per night from 34 to 140 € – Per week from 238 to 980 € – Reservation fee 18 €

Surroundings : 🎣 ♤
Leisure activities : 🍽 🍽 🎮 🎯 🚴 🎯 🖼
🏊 🏊 🏊 multi-sports ground
Facilities : ♿ 🚿 🍽 🍽 launderette 🍽

Longitude : -2.79722
Latitude : 47.5225

🏕 Ferme de Lann Hoedic

✆ 02 97 48 01 73, www.camping-lannhoedic.fr

Address : rue Jean de La Fontaine

Opening times : from beginning April to end Oct.

3,6 ha (128 pitches)

Tariff : (2013 Price) 21,90 € ♦♦ ⬅ 🅴 🔌 (10A) Extra per person 4,90 € Reservation fee 10 €

Rental rates : (2013 Price) (from beginning April to end Oct.) ⚡ 12 ⛟. Per night from 70 to 100€ – Per week from 250 to 690€ Reservation fee 13€

🚐 borne 12€ – 🚐 11€

Surroundings : 🏖 ⚲
Leisure activities : 🛶 🚣 🚲
Facilities : 🚿 ☎ 🗑 ♿ 🚽 🚰 ⛽ launderette

| G P S | Longitude : -2.76249
Latitude : 47.5068 |

⛺ La Grée Penvins

📞 02 97 67 33 96, www.campinglagreepenvins.com

Address : 8 route de la Chapelle (9km southeast along the D 198)

Opening times : from beginning April to end Sept.

2,5 ha (125 pitches)

Tariff : 16,45€ ✝✝ 🚐 🔲 ⚡ (6A) – Extra per person 3,80€
Rental rates : (from beginning April to end Sept.) ⚡ – 12 ⛟. Per night from 80 to 114€ – Per week from 167 to 585€
Direct access to the beach at La Pointe de Penvins.

Surroundings : 🚣 ⚲ ⛰
Facilities : 🚿 ☎ 🗑 🚽 🚰 📷
Nearby : 🍷 🍴 🍺

| G P S | Longitude : -2.68242
Latitude : 47.49665 |

This guide is not intended as a list of all the camping sites in France; its aim is to provide a selection of the best sites in each category.

SCAËR

29390 – Michelin map **308** I6 – pop. 5 244 – alt. 190
▶ Paris 544 – Carhaix-Plouguer 38 – Concarneau 29 – Quimper 35

⛺ Municipal de Kérisole

📞 02 98 57 60 91, www.ville-scaer.fr

Address : rue Louis Pasteur (take the eastern exit following signs for Le Faouët)

Opening times : from beginning June to end Aug.

4 ha/2,3 for camping (83 pitches)

Tariff : ✝ 2,65€ 🚐 1,85€ 🔲 3,15€ – ⚡ (10A) 2,75€
Rental rates : Permanent – 3 ⛟. Per night from 52 to 62€ Per week from 290 to 345€
🚐 borne

Surroundings : 🚣 ⚲
Leisure activities : 🚣
Facilities : 🚿 🚰 launderette
Nearby : 🍴 🛶 fitness trail

| G P S | Longitude : -3.69756
Latitude : 48.0278 |

SÉRENT

56460 – Michelin map **308** P8 – pop. 2 985 – alt. 80
▶ Paris 432 – Josselin 17 – Locminé 31 – Ploërmel 19

⛺ Municipal du Pont Salmon

📞 02 97 75 91 98, www.serent.fr

Address : 29 rue du Général de Gaulle (in the town, follow the signs for Ploërmel)

Opening times : from mid June to end Aug.

1 ha (30 pitches) flat, grassy

Tariff : (2013 Price) ✝ 2,50€ 🚐 🔲 4,70€ – ⚡ (10A) 3€
Rental rates : Permanent 🚿 (1 chalet) – 4 🏠. Per night from 36 to 76€ – Per week from 245 to 430€
🚐 borne – 8 🔲

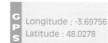

Free use of the municipal swimming pool

Surroundings : ⚲⚲
Leisure activities : 🚣
Facilities : 🚿 🚰 🗑 launderette
Nearby : 🍴 🛶

| G P S | Longitude : -2.50191
Latitude : 47.82506 |

SIZUN

29450 – Michelin map **308** G4 – pop. 2 221 – alt. 112
▶ Paris 572 – Brest 37 – Carhaix-Plouguer 44 – Châteaulin 36

⛺ Municipal du Gollen

📞 02 98 24 11 43, www.mairie-sizun.fr

Address : Le Gollen (located 1km south along the D 30, follow the signs for St-Cadou and take the turning to the left; beside the Elorn river)

0,6 ha (30 pitches)

Surroundings : 🚣 ⚲
Leisure activities : 🚣
Facilities : 🚿 🚰
Nearby : 🍴 🛶

| G P S | Longitude : -4.07659
Latitude : 48.4 |

SULNIAC

56250 – Michelin map **308** P8 – pop. 3 133 – alt. 125
▶ Paris 457 – Rennes 106 – Vannes 21 – Nantes 112

⛰ Village Vacances La Lande du Moulin

(rental of chalets, gîtes and mobile homes only)

📞 02 97 53 29 39, www.la-lande-du-moulin.com

Address : Le Nounène (located 1.5km east along the D 104 and follow the signs for Theix)

12 ha

Rentals : 🚿 (3 chalets) – 2 ⛟ – 50 🏠 – 17 gîtes.
Option for full- or half-board accommodation available.

Surroundings : 🚣 ⚲
Leisure activities : 🍷 🍴 🏛 🎮 🚣 🛶 🚣 🚲
🍴 🎱 🛶 🏊 🚣
Facilities : ☎ 🗑 🚰 launderette 🚗

| G P S | Longitude : -2.56557
Latitude : 47.66686 |

TADEN

22100 – Michelin map **309** J4 – pop. 2 340 – alt. 46
▶ Paris 404 – Rennes 71 – St-Brieuc 64 – St-Helier 34

⛰ Municipal de la Hallerais

📞 02 96 39 15 93, http://www.camping-lahallerais.com

Address : 4 rue de la Robardais (to the southwest of the town)

Opening times : from mid March to mid Nov.

7 ha (225 pitches)

Tariff : 21,34€ ✝✝ 🚐 🔲 ⚡ (10A) – Extra per person 3,96€
Rental rates : (from mid March to mid Nov.) – 9 ⛟ – 11 🏠. Per night from 33 to 68€ – Per week from 172 to 463€
🚐 borne – 15 🔲 21,34€

Surroundings : 🚣 🚐 ⚲⚲
Leisure activities : 🍷 🍴 🏛 🚣 🚣 🎱 🏃 🛶
multi-sports ground
Facilities : 🚿 ☎ ♿ 🗑 🚽 🚰 ⛽ launderette 🚗 ♨
Nearby : 📷 🛶 🍺

| G P S | Longitude : -2.0232
Latitude : 48.47181 |

TAUPONT

56800 – Michelin map **308** Q7 – pop. 2 140 – alt. 81
▶ Paris 422 – Josselin 16 – Ploërmel 5 – Rohan 37

⛰ La Vallée du Ninian

📞 02 97 93 53 01, www.camping-ninian.fr

Address : Ville Bonne, le Rocher (take the northern exit along the D 8, follow the signs for la Trinité-Phoët, then continue 2.5km along the turning to the left, direct access to the river)

Opening times : from beginning April to end Sept.

2,7 ha (100 pitches) flat, grassy, fruit trees

Tariff : (2013 Price) ⚹ 4,50€ 🚗 📧 6,50€ – 🔌 (10A) 4,60€
Reservation fee 10€

Rental rates : (2013 prices) (from beginning April to end Sept.) 10 🚐 – 2 canvas bungalows – 3 tent lodges. Per night from 32 to 67€ – Per week from 155 to 610€ – Reservation fee 10€

🚐 borne – 🚐 🔌16€

Evening events organised, gathering around the bread oven or the apple press.

Surroundings : 🌿 🚏 🏊‍♀️
Leisure activities : 🍽 🏛 🏇 🛶 ⛵
Facilities : ♿ 🔌 🅿 🚿 🚽 🚰 launderette 🚿

GPS Longitude : -2.47
Latitude : 47.96928

TELGRUC-SUR-MER

29560 – Michelin map **308** E5 – pop. 2 088 – alt. 90
▶ Paris 572 – Châteaulin 25 – Douarnenez 29 – Quimper 39

⛰ Armorique

📞 02 98 27 77 33, www.campingarmorique.com

Address : 112 rue de la Plage (1.2km southwest following signs for Trez-Bellec-Plage)

Opening times : from beginning April to end Sept.

2,5 ha (100 pitches) Tariff : ⚹ 5€ 🚗 📧 9€ – 🔌 (10A) 3,90€
Reservation fee 16€

Rental rates : (from beginning April to end Sept.) – 25 🚐 4 🏠. Per night from 92 to 142€ – Per week from 240 to 710€
Reservation fee 16€

🚐 borne – 🚐 🔌14€

Surroundings : 🌿 ⛰ 🚏 🏊‍♀️
Leisure activities : 🍽 🍴 🏛 🏇 🛶 🏊
Facilities : ♿ 🔌 🅿 🚿 🚰 launderette 🚿

GPS Longitude : -4.37085
Latitude : 48.22531

*The classification (1 to 5 tents, **black** or **red**) that we award to selected sites in this guide is our own system. It should not be confused with the classification (1 to 5 stars) of official organisations.*

THEIX

56450 – Michelin map **308** P9 – pop. 6 765 – alt. 5
▶ Paris 464 – Ploërmel 51 – Redon 58 – La Roche-Bernard 33

⛰ Rhuys

📞 02 97 54 14 77, http://campingderhuys.free.fr

Address : rue Dugay Trouin, Le Poteau Rouge (3.5km to the northwest, along the N 165; if coming from Vannes, take the exit for Sarzeau)

2 ha (66 pitches)

Rentals : 6 🚐 – 2 🏠.

Surroundings : 🏊‍♀️
Leisure activities : 🏇 🛶 (small swimming pool)
Facilities : ♿ 🔌 🅿 🚿 🚽 🚰 📧
Nearby : 🍽 🍴 🎿

GPS Longitude : -2.69413
Latitude : 47.64108

TINTÉNIAC

35190 – Michelin map **309** K5 – pop. 3 304 – alt. 40
▶ Paris 377 – Avranches 70 – Dinan 28 – Dol-de-Bretagne 30

⛰ Domaine Les Peupliers

📞 02 99 45 49 75, www.domainelespeupliers.fr

Address : at the Domaine de la Besnelais (situated 2km southeast along the old road to Rennes; near lakes, along the N 137, take the exit for Tinténiac Sud)

Opening times : from beginning April to end Sept.

4 ha (100 pitches) flat, grassy

Tariff : 22€ ⚹⚹ 🚗 📧 🔌 (10A) – Extra per person 5,70€
Rental rates : (from mid March to beginning Nov.) – 6 🚐 – 2 🏠 1 gite. Per night from 40 to 67€ – Per week from 250 to 610€
🚐 4 📧 21€

Surroundings : 🚏 🏊‍♀️
Leisure activities : 🍽 🏛 🏇 🚲 🏓 🛶 ⛵
Facilities : ♿ 🔌 🅿 🚰 🚽 launderette

GPS Longitude : -1.82167
Latitude : 48.30917

LE TOUR-DU-PARC

56370 – Michelin map **308** P9 – pop. 1 105
▶ Paris 476 – La Baule 62 – Redon 57 – St-Nazaire 81

⛰ Le Cadran Solaire

📞 02 97 67 30 40, www.campingcadransolaire.fr

Address : rue de Banastère (situated 2km south along the D 324, follow the signs for Sarzeau)

Opening times : from beginning April to end Oct.

2 ha (115 pitches) flat, grassy

Tariff : ⚹ 4,60€ 🚗 📧 9,50€ – 🔌 (10A) 3,50€
Rental rates : (from beginning April to end Oct.) 🏓 – 10 🚐. Per week from 200 to 600€

Surroundings : 🚏 🏊‍♀️
Leisure activities : 🏛 🏇 🏓
Facilities : ♿ 🔌 🅿 🚽 launderette

GPS Longitude : -2.65748
Latitude : 47.5208

TRÉBEURDEN

22560 – Michelin map **309** A2 – pop. 3 714 – alt. 81
▶ Paris 525 – Lannion 10 – Perros-Guirec 14 – St-Brieuc 74

⛰ L'Espérance

📞 07 86 17 48 08, www.camping-esperance.com

Address : rue de Kéralégan (5km northwest along the D 788, follow the signs for Trégastel; near the sea)

Opening times : from beginning April to end Sept.

1 ha (70 pitches)

Tariff : ⚹ 4,70€ 🚗 2,90€ 📧 4,90€ – 🔌 (10A) 3,60€ – Reservation fee 15€

Rental rates : (from beginning April to end Oct.) – 6 🚐. Per night from 60€ – Per week from 270 to 570€ – Reservation fee 20€

🚰 borne

Surroundings : ⩽ ⌂ 🌳🌳
Leisure activities : 🏋 🎱
Facilities : 🚿 ⊶ 🚿 launderette

G P S	Longitude : -3.55743 Latitude : 48.79096

The Michelin classification (ᐃᐃᐃ ... ᐃ) is totally independent of the official star classification system awarded by the local prefecture or other official organisation.

TRÉBOUL

29100 – Michelin map **308** E6
▶ Paris 591 – Rennes 239 – Quimper 29 – Brest 75

ᐃ Kerleyou

✆ 02 98 74 13 03, www.camping-kerleyou.com

Address : 15 chemin de Kerleyou (located 1km to the west)

Opening times : from mid April to mid Sept.

3,5 ha (100 pitches)

Tariff : 22,78€ 🏋🏋 🚗 🔲 ⚡ (10A) – Extra per person 4,45€
Reservation fee 12€

Rental rates : (from mid April to mid Sept.) – 38 🚐 – 4 🏠. Per night from 40 to 107€ – Per week from 201 to 840€
Reservation fee 15€

Surroundings : 🐟 ⩽ 🌳🌳
Leisure activities : 🏋 🎱 🏄 🛶
Facilities : 🚿 ⊶ 🚿 launderette 🛒

G P S	Longitude : -4.36198 Latitude : 48.09842

ᐃ Trézulien

✆ 02 98 74 12 30, www.camping-trezulien.com

Address : 14 route de Trézulien (via the r. Frédéric-Le-Guyader)

Opening times : from beginning April to end Sept.

5 ha (199 pitches) uneven

Tariff : 🏋 4,40€ 🚗 2,80€ 🔲 5,50€ – ⚡ (10A) 3,60€

Rental rates : (from beginning April to mid Oct.) – 12 🚐 4 🏠 – 1 gîte. Per night from 42 to 80€ – Per week from 170 to 680€ – Reservation fee 13€

Surroundings : 🐟 ⩽ 🌳
Leisure activities : 🏋 🎱 🏄 🛶 ⛷
Facilities : 🚿 ⊶ (season) 🚿 launderette

G P S	Longitude : -4.34931 Latitude : 48.09311

TREFFIAGAT

29730 – Michelin map **308** F8 – pop. 2 343 – alt. 20
▶ Paris 582 – Audierne 39 – Douarnenez 41 – Pont-l'Abbé 8

ᐃ Les Ormes

✆ 02 98 58 21 27, www.campingdesormesleguilvinec.fr

Address : Kerlay (situated 2km to the south, follow the signs for Lesconil and take the turning to the right 400m from the beach) (direct access)

Opening times : from beginning May to end Sept.

2 ha (76 pitches) flat, grassy

Tariff : (2013 Price) 🏋 4,10€ 🚗 2,50€ 🔲 4,20€ – ⚡ (6A) 3,50€
Reservation fee 6,25€

Rental rates : (2013 Price) (from beginning April to end Sept.) 🚲 – 2 🚐 – 2 🛏. Per night from 65€ – Per week from 450€ – Reservation fee 6,25€

🚰 borne 5€ – 4 🔲 14,90€

Surroundings : 🐟 ⌂ 🌳
Leisure activities : 🏄
Facilities : ⊶ 🚿 launderette
Nearby : 🎣

G P S	Longitude : -4.25518 Latitude : 47.79666

TRÉGASTEL

22730 – Michelin map **309** B2 – pop. 2 435 – alt. 58
▶ Paris 526 – Lannion 11 – Perros-Guirec 9 – St-Brieuc 75

ᐃ Tourony-Camping

✆ 02 96 23 86 61, www.camping-tourony.com

Address : 105 rue de Poul Palud (1.8km east along the D 788, follow the signs for Perros-Guirec; 500m from the beach)

Opening times : from mid April to mid Sept.

2 ha (100 pitches) flat, grassy

Tariff : (2013 Price) 22€ 🏋🏋 🚗 🔲 ⚡ (10A) – Extra per person 5,40€

Rental rates : (2013 Price) (from mid April to mid Sept.) – 17 🚐 2 🏠. Per night from 46 to 90€ – Per week from 225 to 620€
Reservation fee 14€

🚰 borne – 10 🔲 10,40€

Opposite the marina.

Surroundings : 🌳
Leisure activities : 🏋 ✕ 🏄
Facilities : 🚿 ⊶ 🛁 🛒 🚿 launderette
Nearby : ✂ 🏇

G P S	Longitude : -3.49131 Latitude : 48.82565

TRÉGUENNEC

29720 – Michelin map **308** F7 – pop. 348 – alt. 31
▶ Paris 582 – Audierne 27 – Douarnenez 27 – Pont-l'Abbé 11

ᐃ Kerlaz

✆ 02 98 87 76 79, www.kerlaz.com

Address : route de la mer (in the village, along the D 156)

Opening times : from beginning April to end Sept.

1,25 ha (80 pitches) flat, grassy

Tariff : (2013 Price) 🏋 4€ 🚗 2,25€ 🔲 5,50€ – ⚡ (10A) 3,65€
Reservation fee 10€

Rental rates : (from beginning April to end Sept.) – 10 🚐 5 🏠. Per night from 61 to 90€ – Per week from 249 to 624€
Reservation fee 10€

🚰 borne 12,50€

Surroundings : 🌳
Leisure activities : 🏋 🏄 🚲 🖼 (open air in season)
Facilities : 🚿 ⊶ (July-Aug.) 🚿 launderette
Nearby : 🏊 ✕ 🏇

G P S	Longitude : -4.32848 Latitude : 47.89457

Using the traditional Michelin classification method, the guide provides you with an easy, speedy reference for assessing the category of each site: 1 to 5 tents (see page 10).

TRÉGUNC

29910 – Michelin map **308** H7 – pop. 6 785 – alt. 45
▶ Paris 543 – Concarneau 7 – Pont-Aven 9 – Quimper 29

ᴧᴧᴧ Le Domaine de Pendruc

✆ 02 98 97 66 28, www.domainedependruc.com – limited spaces for one-night stay

Address : Roz Pennanguer (2.8km southwest, follow the signs for Pendruc and take the turning to the left)

Opening times : from mid June to end Sept.

6 ha (200 pitches) flat, grassy

Tariff : ♦ 5,50€ ⇔ 2,50€ 🅴 8€ – [⚡] (6A) 4€ – Reservation fee 10€
Rental rates : (from mid April to end Sept.) ⚸ – 43 🚐. Per night from 30 to 50€ – Per week from € 200 to 790 – Reservation fee 20€
🚐 borne – 4 🅴 15€ – 🚿 15€

Surroundings : 🛶 🔀 ♀
Leisure activities : ♟ ✗ 🏠 🖥 🕴 🏊 🚲 🎱 ⛷ multi-sports ground
Facilities : ⚲ 🍴 launderette 🐕
Nearby : ⛵

GPS
Longitude : -3.88093
Latitude : 47.84086

ᴧᴧᴧ La Pommeraie ♣♠

✆ 02 98 50 02 73, www.campingdelapomeraie.com

Address : Kerdalidec (6km south along the D 1, follow the signs for La Pointe de Trévignon (headland) and take the turning to the left following signs for St-Philibert)

7 ha (198 pitches) flat, grassy

Rental rates : – 34 🚐 .

Surroundings : 🔀 ♀
Leisure activities : ♟ 🏠 🖥 🕴 jacuzzi ⛷ 🚲 🎱 ⛷ multi-sports ground, entertainment room
Facilities : ♿ 🍴 🚿 ⛺ launderette 🐕

GPS
Longitude : -3.83698
Latitude : 47.80786

There are several different types of sani-station ('borne' in French) – sanitation points providing fresh water and disposal points for grey water. See page 12 for further details.

TRÉLÉVERN

22660 – Michelin map **309** B2 – pop. 1 390 – alt. 76
▶ Paris 524 – Lannion 13 – Perros-Guirec 9 – St-Brieuc 73

ᴧᴧ RNC Port-l'Épine

✆ 02 96 23 71 94, www.rcn.fr

Address : 10 Venelle de Pors Garo (1.5km northwest then take a road to the left; at Port-l'Épine)

Opening times : from mid April to mid Sept.

3 ha (160 pitches)

Tariff : 15,50€ ♦♦ ⇔ 🅴 [⚡] (6A) – Extra per person 2,50€
Reservation fee 19,95€
Rental rates : (from mid April to mid Sept.) – 45 🚐. Per night from 29 to 137€ – Per week from 203 to 959€ – Reservation fee 19,95€

Surroundings : 🛶 ∠ Baie de Perros-Guirec
🔀 ♀ ⛰
Leisure activities : ♟ ✗ ⛷ 🚲 🎱
Facilities : ♿ 🍴 🚿 ⛺ launderette 🐕

GPS
Longitude : -3.38594
Latitude : 48.8128

LA TRINITÉ-SUR-MER

56470 – Michelin map **308** M9 – pop. 1 622 – alt. 20
▶ Paris 488 – Auray 13 – Carnac 4 – Lorient 52

ᴧᴧᴧ La Plage ♣♠

✆ 02 97 55 73 28, www.camping-plage.com

Address : plage de Kervillen (located 1km to the south, direct access to the beach)

Opening times : from beginning May to mid Sept.

3 ha (200 pitches)

Tariff : 45,30€ ♦♦ ⇔ 🅴 [⚡] (10A)
Extra per person 6,20€

Reservation fee 15€

Rental rates : (from beginning May to mid Sept.) – 32 🚐
6 canvas bungalows. Per week from 199 to 920€ – Reservation fee 15€

🚐 borne 4€

Surroundings : 🔀 ♀ ⛰
Leisure activities : 🏠 🖥 🕴 jacuzzi ⛷ 🚲 🎱 ⛷ 🏊
Facilities : ♿ 🍴 🚿 ⛺ launderette
Nearby : 🏊 ♟ ✗ 🐕 ⛷ 🎿

GPS
Longitude : -3.02869
Latitude : 47.57562

ᴧᴧᴧ Kervilor

✆ 02 97 55 76 75, www.camping-kervilor.com

Address : route du Latz (1.6km to the north)

Opening times :

5 ha (230 pitches)

Tariff : (2013 Price) 34,65€ ♦♦ ⇔ 🅴 [⚡] (10A)
Extra per person 5,55€ – Reservation fee 18€
Rental rates : Permanent – 68 🚐 . Per night from 108 to 190€ – Per week from 270 to 947€ – Reservation fee 18€

Surroundings : 🛶 🔀 ♀ ♀
Leisure activities : ♟ 🏠 🏌 jacuzzi ⛷ 🚲 🎿 🏊 🎱 ⛷ multi-sports ground
Facilities : ♿ 🍴 ⛺ launderette 🏊 🐕 refrigerators

GPS
Longitude : -3.03588
Latitude : 47.60168

ᴧᴧ La Baie ♣♠

✆ 02 97 55 73 42, www.campingdelabaie.com – limited spaces for one-night stay

Address : plage de Kervillen (located 1.5km to the south, 100m from the beach)

Opening times : from mid May to mid Sept.

2,2 ha (170 pitches)

Tariff : (2013 Price) ♦ 8,20€ ⇔ 🅴 27,20€ – [⚡] (10A) 5,20€

Reservation fee 22€

Rental rates : (from mid May to mid Sept.) – 40 🚐. Per week from 259 to 917€ – Reservation fee 22€

Surroundings : 🛶 🔀 ♀
Leisure activities : 🏠 🖥 🕴 ⛷ 🚲 🎱 ⛷
Facilities : ♿ 🍴 🚿 ⛺ launderette
Nearby : 🏊 ♟ ✗ 🐕 🎿 🎿

GPS
Longitude : -3.02789
Latitude : 47.57375

APV Plijadur ▲▲ 👥

📞 02 97 55 72 05, www.camping-apv.com

Address : 94 route de Carnac (1.3km northwest on the D 781)

Opening times : from beginning April to end Sept.

5 ha (198 pitches)

Tariff : 26,82€ ♣♣ 🚗 🔲 [⚡] (10A) – Extra per person 7,24€
Reservation fee 27€

Rental rates : (from beginning April to end Sept.) – 116 🛏.
Per night from 58 to 84€ – Per week from 224 to 994€
Reservation fee 27€

🚐 borne 14,79€

Choose pitches away from the road in preference.

Surroundings : ⌂ 👥👥
Leisure activities : 🍷 🏛 🎣 🏕 🏇 ⛳ 🏊
hammam, jacuzzi 🚴 🐴 ⛺ 🎿 🛶
Facilities : 👦 ⊶ ⛺ 🍴 launderette 🧺

GPS — Longitude : -3.04394
Latitude : 47.60464

· *Some campsites benefit from proximity to a municipal leisure centre.*

56000 – Michelin map **308** 09 – pop. 52 683 – alt. 20
▶ Paris 459 – Quimper 122 – Rennes 110 – St-Brieuc 107

Flower Le Conleau

📞 02 97 63 13 88, www.vannes-camping.com

Address : at la Pointe de Conleau (to the south, towards the Parc du Golfe (leisure park), on the Avenue du Maréchal Juin)

Opening times : from beginning April to end Sept.

5 ha (260 pitches)

Tariff : 24,50€ ♣♣ 🚗 🔲 [⚡] (6A) – Extra per person 5€ – Reservation fee 15€

Rental rates : (from beginning April to end Sept.) – 57 🛏.
6 canvas bungalows. Per night from 42 to 103€ – Per week from 210 to 721€ – Reservation fee 20€

🚐 borne 5,50€ – 14 🔲 16,50€

Pleasant location opposite the Golfe du Morbihan (gulf).

Surroundings : ⊲ 👥👥
Leisure activities : 🍷 🏛 🎣 🏕 🏇 🚴
Facilities : 👦 ⊶ ⛺ 🗑 🍴 launderette,
refrigerated food storage facilities

GPS — Longitude : -2.77994
Latitude : 47.63326

BURGUNDY

H. Lenain / hemis.fr

A visit to Burgundy takes you back in time to an era when the influence of the mighty Burgundian dukes rivalled that of the kings of France. Stately castles and imposing abbeys still bear witness to a past golden age of ostentation and power. It is hard now to reproach the dukes too much for a flamboyance that has today made Dijon a world-renowned city of art, endowed with an exceptional architectural heritage. And who would dispute their claim to be the lords of the best wines in Christendom when wine lovers still flock to the region in search of the finest cellars and vintages? A dedication to time-honoured traditions remains at the heart of the cuisine of the region, from the pungent *Époisses* cheese to the delicious local gingerbread dripping with honey. After indulging yourself in such gourmet delights, what could be better than a delightful barge trip along the canals and rivers of the region to relax in peace amid the gloriously unspoilt countryside?

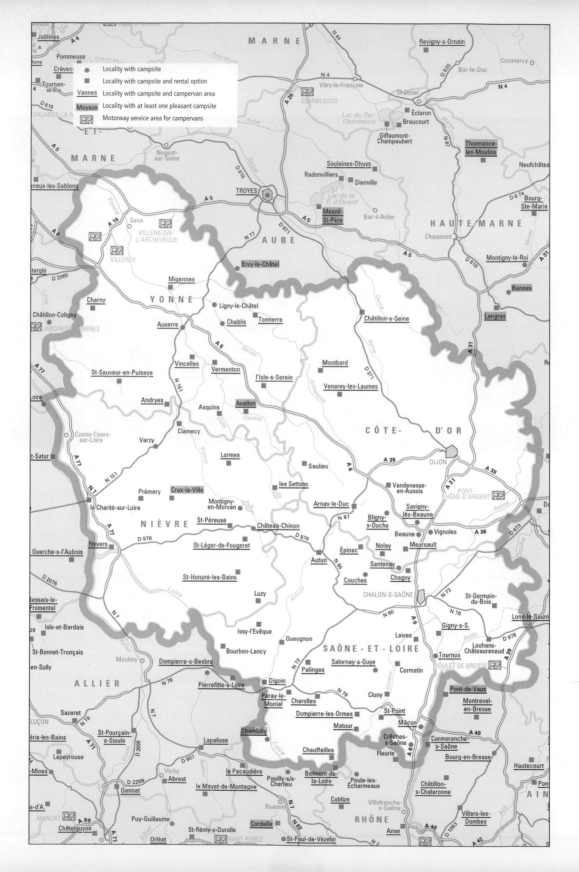

ANDRYES

89480 – Michelin map **319** D6 – pop. 471 – alt. 162
▶ Paris 204 – Auxerre 39 – Avallon 44 – Clamecy 10

🏔 Sites et Paysages Au Bois Joli

☎ 03 86 81 70 48, www.campingauboisjoli.fr

Address : 2 route de Villeprenoy (800m southwest)

Opening times : from beginning April to end Oct.

5 ha (100 pitches) sloping

Tariff : 29 € ♦♦ 🚗 🖪 ⚡ (10A) – Extra per person 6 € – Reservation fee 9 €

Rental rates : (from beginning April to end Oct.) 🚲 – 6 🚐.
Per night from 75 to 110 € – Per week from 270 to 690 €
Reservation fee 9 €

🚾 borne 8 € – 1 🖪 18 € – 🌙 10 €

A wooded site.

Surroundings : 🌿 ♨♨ Leisure activities : 🏓 ⚽ 🚴 🏊 Facilities : ♿ ⚲ 🏛 ⚒ 🚿 🚽 🖻 Nearby : 🎣 ✕	**G P S** Longitude : 3.47969 Latitude : 47.51655

ARNAY-LE-DUC

21230 – Michelin map **320** G7 – pop. 1 674 – alt. 375
▶ Paris 285 – Autun 28 – Beaune 36 – Chagny 38

🏔 VivaCamp l'Étang de Fouché

☎ 03 80 90 02 23, www.campingfouche.com

Address : rue du 8 mai 1945 (700m east along the D 17c, follow the signs for Longecourt)

Opening times : from mid April to mid Oct.

8 ha (209 pitches) flat

Tariff : 27 € ♦♦ 🚗 🖪 ⚡ (10A) – Extra per person 6 € – Reservation fee 15 €

Rental rates : (from mid April to mid Oct.) – 20 🚐 – 19 🏠 – 6 tent lodges. Per night from 40 to 120 € – Per week from 240 to 840 €
Reservation fee 30 €

🚾 borne

In a pleasant location beside a lake.

Surroundings : 🌿 ⛰ ⌂ ♨ ⛰ Leisure activities : 🍴 ✕ 🎬 ⊙daytime ⛹ ⚽ 🎣 🚣 pedalos Facilities : ♿ ⚲ ⚒ 🚿 🚽 🎯 launderette 🏧 🚙 Nearby : ✕ ≅ (beach) ⛷	**G P S** Longitude : 4.49802 Latitude : 47.13414

ASQUINS

89450 – Michelin map **319** F7 – pop. 324 – alt. 146
▶ Paris 219 – Dijon 123 – Auxerre 49 – Avallon 17

🏔 Municipal le Patis

☎ 03 86 33 30 80, www.asquins-sous-vezelay-camping-roulottes.com

Address : route de Givry (500m, after the bridge on the left)

Opening times : from end April to end Sept.

1 ha (33 pitches) flat, grassy

Tariff : ♦ 2 € 🚗 2 € 🖪 2 € – ⚡ (16A) 3 €

Rental rates : Permanent – 2 caravans. Per night from 75 to 95 €
Per week from 375 to 475 €

Surroundings : ♨ Leisure activities : 🎬 ⚽ Facilities : ♿ ⚗ 🏛 🖻 Nearby : ≅	**G P S** Longitude : 3.75899 Latitude : 47.48293

AUTUN

71400 – Michelin map **320** F8 – pop. 14 496 – alt. 326
▶ Paris 287 – Auxerre 128 – Avallon 78 – Chalon-sur-Saône 51

🏔 Aquadis Loisirs La Porte d'Arroux

☎ 03 85 52 10 82, www.aquadis-loisirs.com

Address : rue du Traité d'Anvers, at Les Chaumottes (take the northern exit along the D 980, follow the signs for Saulieu, Arroux suburb; beside the Ternin river)

Opening times : from beginning April to end Oct.

2,8 ha (81 pitches) flat, grassy

Tariff : 16,50 € ♦♦ 🚗 🖪 ⚡ (10A) – Extra per person 3,50 € – Reservation fee 9,90 €

Rental rates : (from beginning April to end Oct.) – 6 🚐.
Per night from 62 € – Per week from 162 to 499 € – Reservation fee 19,80 €

🚾 borne 5,50 € – 🌙 11 €

Pretty, shady pitches beside the Ternin river.

Surroundings : ⌂ ♨♨ Leisure activities : 🍴 ✕ 🎬 ⚽ 🚴 🚣 ⛹ Facilities : ♿ ⚲ 🆒 🚿 🖻 🚙	**G P S** Longitude : 4.29358 Latitude : 46.96447

To visit a town or region, use the MICHELIN Green Guides.

AUXERRE

89000 – Michelin map **319** E5 – pop. 36 702 – alt. 130
▶ Paris 166 – Bourges 144 – Chalon-sur-Saône 176 – Chaumont 143

🏔 Municipal

☎ 03 86 52 11 15, camping.mairie@auxerre.com

Address : 8 route de Vaux (to the southeast of the town, near the stadium, 150m from the Yonne river)

Opening times : from mid April to mid Sept.

4,5 ha (164 pitches) flat, grassy

Tariff : ♦ 3,90 € 🚗 🖪 3,40 € – ⚡ (5A) 3,20 €

🚾 borne 3 €

Surroundings : ♨ Leisure activities : 🎬 ⚽ 🚴 🚣 Facilities : ♿ ⚲ 🏛 ⚒ launderette 🏧 Nearby : ✕ 🎿 🎱 🏊	**G P S** Longitude : 3.58703 Latitude : 47.7865

AVALLON

89200 – Michelin map **319** G7 – pop. 7 252 – alt. 250
▶ Paris 220 – Dijon 106 – Auxerre 55 – Autun 80

🏔 Municipal Sous Roches

☎ 03 86 34 10 39, www.campingsousroches.com

Address : route de Méluzien

Opening times : from beginning April to mid Oct.

2,7 ha (98 pitches) terraced, flat, grassy

Tariff : 16,40 € ♦♦ 🚗 🖪 ⚡ (10A) – Extra per person 3,60 €

Rental rates : (from beginning March to mid Nov.) ♿ (1 chalet)
🚲 – 4 🏠 – 4 tent lodges. Per night from 30 to 85 € – Per week from 190 to 540 € – Reservation fee 30 €

🚾 borne 5 €

Surroundings : 🌿 Leisure activities : 🎬 ⚽ 🚣 Facilities : ♿ ⚲ 🚽 launderette 🏧	**G P S** Longitude : 3.91293 Latitude : 47.47993

BEAUNE

21200 – Michelin map **320** I7 – pop. 22 516 – alt. 220
▶ Paris 308 – Autun 49 – Auxerre 149 – Chalon-sur-Saône 29

⚠ Municipal les Cent Vignes

📞 03 80 22 03 91, campinglescentvignes@mairie-beaune.fr

Address : 10 rue Auguste Dubois (take the northern exit along the r. du Faubourg-St-Nicolas and take D 18 to the left)

Opening times : from mid March to end Oct.

2 ha (116 pitches) flat, grassy

Tariff : ♠ 4,30€ ⟷ 🅿 6€ – 🔌 4,10€

Pitches attractively marked out and an entrance surrounded by flowers.

Surroundings : ⌱ ♀
Leisure activities : ☂ ✗ 🏠 🚣 multi-sports ground
Facilities : ♿ ⊶ 🚿 🛁 ▥ 🚾 🚽 launderette 🍴

G P S Longitude : 4.8386
Latitude : 47.03285

BLIGNY-SUR-OUCHE

21360 – Michelin map **320** I7 – pop. 863 – alt. 360
▶ Paris 295 – Dijon 63 – Chalon-sur-Saône 48 – Le Creusot 62

⚠ Les Isles

📞 03 80 20 00 64, www.camping-des-isles.fr

Address : 2 allée de la Gare

1,2 ha (70 pitches) flat, grassy

🚐 borne

Surroundings : ♀♀
Leisure activities : 🚣
Facilities : ♿ ⊶ 🚽 launderette
Nearby : ✗

G P S Longitude : 4.66019
Latitude : 47.10864

BOURBON-LANCY

71140 – Michelin map **320** C10 – pop. 5 275 – alt. 240 – ♨
▶ Paris 308 – Autun 62 – Mâcon 110 – Montceau-les-Mines 55

⚠ Aquadis Loisirs Les Chalets du Breuil

📞 03 85 89 20 98, www.aquadis-loisirs.com

Address : 11 rue des Eurimants (towards the southwestern exit, follow the signs for Digoin; by the swimming pool)

Opening times : from beginning April to end Oct.

2 ha (63 pitches) flat

Tariff : 18,30€ ♠♠ ⟷ 🅿 🔌 (10A) – Extra per person 4,75€ – Reservation fee 9,90€

Rental rates : (from beginning April to end Oct.) ♿ (1 chalet) 4 🚐 – 22 🏠. Per night from 89€ – Per week from 223 to 595€ Reservation fee 19,80€

Camping piches around 200m from a small lake.

Surroundings : ⌱ ♀
Leisure activities : 🏠 🐎
Facilities : ⊶ ▥ ▥ 🛁 🚾 🚽 📶
Nearby : ✗ 🚣 ✗ 🛶 🚤 (beach) 🎣

G P S Longitude : 3.76646
Latitude : 46.62086

We value your opinion and welcome your feedback. Do email us at campingfrance@tp.michelin.com

CHABLIS

89800 – Michelin map **319** F5 – pop. 2 383 – alt. 135
▶ Paris 181 – Dijon 138 – Orléans 172 – Troyes 76

⚠ Municipal du Serein

📞 03 86 42 44 39, www.chablis.net

Address : quai Paul Louis Courier (600m west along the D 956, follow the signs for Tonnerre and take the road to the right after the bridge; beside the Serein river)

Opening times : from beginning June to beginning Sept.

2 ha (43 pitches) flat, grassy

Tariff : ♠ 3€ ⟷ 🅿 6€ – 🔌 (10A) 2€

🚐 borne

A green setting beside the Serein river.

Surroundings : ⌱ ♀
Leisure activities : 🚣
Facilities : ♿ ⊶ 🚿 🚽
Nearby : 🚴

G P S Longitude : 3.80596
Latitude : 47.81368

A 'quartier' is a district or area of a town or village.

CHAGNY

71150 – Michelin map **320** I8 – pop. 5 525 – alt. 215
▶ Paris 327 – Autun 44 – Beaune 15 – Chalon-sur-Saône 20

⚠ Le Pâquier Fané

📞 03 85 87 21 42, www.camping-chagny.com

Address : rue du Pâquier fané (to the west; beside the Dheune river)

Opening times : from beginning April to end Oct.

1,8 ha (85 pitches) flat, grassy

Tariff : 18,50€ ♠♠ ⟷ 🅿 🔌 (16A) – Extra per person 4€

Rental rates : (from beginning April to end Oct.) 6 🚐 4 🏠. Per night from 50 to 120€ – Per week from 350 to 840€– Reservation fee 15€

🚐 borne

in a pleasant setting beside the Dheune river.

Surroundings : ⌱ ♀
Leisure activities : 🚣
Facilities : ♿ ⊶ 🚽 launderette 📶
Nearby : 🚴 ✗ 🛶

G P S Longitude : 4.74574
Latitude : 46.91193

CHAMBILLY

71110 – Michelin map **320** E12 – pop. 523 – alt. 249
▶ Paris 363 – Chauffailles 28 – Digoin 27 – Dompierre-sur-Besbre 55

⚠ La Motte aux Merles

📞 03 85 25 37 67, campingpicard@yahoo.fr

Address : route de la Palisse (5km southwest along the D 990 and take road to the left)

Opening times : from beginning April to end Oct.

1 ha (25 pitches) flat

Tariff : ♠ 3€ ⟷ 🅿 4€ – 🔌 (6A) 6€

🚐 borne – 3 🅿 10€

Surroundings : 🐟 🚣
Leisure activities : 🚣 🛶 (small swimming pool)
Facilities : ♿ ⊶ 🚿 🚽 📶

G P S Longitude : 3.95755
Latitude : 46.26443

LA CHARITÉ-SUR-LOIRE

58400 – Michelin map **319** B8 – pop. 5 203 – alt. 170
▶ Paris 212 – Bourges 51 – Clamecy 54 – Cosne-sur-Loire 30

▲ Municipal la Saulaie

☎ 03 86 70 00 83, www.lacharitesurloire-tourisme.com

Address : quai de La Saulaie (southwestern exit)

Opening times : from end April to end Sept.

1,7 ha (90 pitches) flat, grassy

Tariff : (2013 Price) 17,60€ ★★ ⇔ 🔲 (16A) –
Extra per person 4,20€

Rental rates : (2013 Price) (from end April to end Sept.) ⑤
(1 'gypsy' caravan) – 2 caravans. Per night from 49 to 89€
Per week from 309 to 560€

On the Île de la Saulaie, near the beach.

Surroundings : ♀
Leisure activities : 🏠 🎣
Facilities : ⑤ ⚿ 🚻 🗑 ♨ 🚾 🍴
Nearby : ✄ 🏯

GPS Longitude : 3.00927
Latitude : 47.17879

CHARNY

89120 – Michelin map **319** B4 – pop. 1 689 – alt. 139
▶ Paris 151 – Dijon 193 – Auxerre 47 – Orléans 105

▲▲ Flower Les Platanes

☎ 03 86 91 83 60, www.campingdesplatanes.com

Address : 41 route de la Mothe

Opening times : from beginning April to end Oct.

2 ha (82 pitches) flat, grassy

Tariff : 21€ ★★ ⇔ 🔲 (16A) – Extra per person 4,20€ – Reservation fee 7€

Rental rates : (from beginning April to end Oct.) ⑤ (1 mobile home) – 12 🚐. Per night from 40 to 97€ – Per week from 196 to 679€ – Reservation fee 7€

🔲 borne 3,50€ – 6 🔲 17,50€

Surroundings : 🌅 ♀
Leisure activities : 🏠 🎣 ⛵
Facilities : ⑤ ⚿ 🚻 ♨ 🚾 🍴 launderette ⛲
Nearby : 🏊 🚲 ✄ 🎣

GPS Longitude : 3.09392
Latitude : 47.89097

CHAROLLES

71120 – Michelin map **320** F11 – pop. 2 807 – alt. 279
▶ Paris 374 – Autun 80 – Chalon-sur-Saône 67 – Mâcon 55

▲ Municipal 👥

☎ 03 85 24 04 90, www.ville-charolles.fr

Address : route de Viry (take the northeastern exit, follow the signs for Mâcon and turn left onto D 33)

Opening times : from beginning April to beginning Oct.

1 ha (50 pitches) flat, grassy

Tariff : ★ 2,50€ ⇔ 2€ 🔲 4,20€ – (16A) 2,50€

Rental rates : (from beginning April to end Sept.) ⑤ (1 mobile home) ✄ – 6 🚐. Per week from 220 to 360€

🔲 borne 3€ – 15 🔲 3€

A pleasant setting beside the Arconce river.

Surroundings : 🌅 ♀
Leisure activities : ⛾ 🏃 🎣 🚲
Facilities : ⑤ ⚿ ♨ 🚾 🍴 🏠
Nearby : 🏠 🏀 🎣

GPS Longitude : 4.28209
Latitude : 46.43959

CHÂTEAU-CHINON

58120 – Michelin map **319** G9 – pop. 2 137 – alt. 510
▶ Paris 281 – Autun 39 – Avallon 60 – Clamecy 65

▲ Municipal du Perthuy d'Oiseau

☎ 03 86 85 08 17, mairiechateauchinonville@wanadoo.fr

Address : rue du Perthuy d'Oiseau (take the southern exit along the D 27, follow the signs for Luzy and take a right turn)

Opening times : from beginning May to end Sept.

1 ha (50 pitches) relatively flat to hilly, grassy

Tariff : ★ 2€ ⇔ 2,50€ 🔲 1,50€ – (10A) 2,50€
🔲 borne

At the edge of a forest.

Surroundings : 🌅 ← ♀
Leisure activities : 🏠
Facilities : 🚾 ♨

GPS Longitude : 3.92613
Latitude : 47.05518

CHÂTILLON-SUR-SEINE

21400 – Michelin map **320** H2 – pop. 5 613 – alt. 219
▶ Paris 233 – Auxerre 85 – Avallon 75 – Chaumont 60

▲ Municipal Louis-Rigoly

☎ 03 80 91 03 05, www.mairie-chatillon-sur-seine.fr

Address : esplanade St-Vorles (follow the signs for Langres)

Opening times : from beginning April to end Sept.

0,8 ha (46 pitches) flat and relatively flat, grassy, hard surface areas

Tariff : (2013 Price) 16,50€ ★★ ⇔ 🔲 (6A) – Extra per person 4,20€

Rental rates : (from beginning April to end Sept.) – 2 🚐. Per night from 45 to 60€ – Per week from 240 to 350€

🔲 borne 4€

On the shaded slopes above the town, near the town swimming pool.

Surroundings : 🌅 ♀
Leisure activities : 🏠
Facilities : ⑤ ♨ 🚾 🍴 🏠
Nearby : 🍴 ✕ 🏊 🎣

GPS Longitude : 4.56969
Latitude : 47.87051

CHAUFFAILLES

71170 – Michelin map **320** G12 – pop. 3 939 – alt. 405
▶ Paris 404 – Charolles 32 – Lyon 77 – Mâcon 64

▲▲ Municipal les Feuilles

☎ 03 85 26 48 12, www.chauffailles.com

Address : 18 rue de Châtillon (to the southwest along the r. du Chatillon)

Opening times : from beginning May to end Sept.

4 ha (67 pitches) flat and relatively flat

Tariff : (2013 Price) 16€ ★★ ⇔ 🔲 (10A) – Extra per person 4,30€

Rental rates : (from beginning May to end Sept.) – 2 🏠 14 canvas bungalows. Per night from 36 to 80€ – Per week from 141 to 450€ – Reservation fee 32€

🔲 🛶 13€

In a green setting beside the Botoret river.

Surroundings : 🌅 ♀
Leisure activities : 🏠 🏃 ✄ 🎣
Facilities : ⑤ ⚿ ♨ 🍴 🏠
Nearby : ⛵

GPS Longitude : 4.33817
Latitude : 46.20004

CLAMECY

58500 – Michelin map **319** E7 – pop. 4 238 – alt. 144
▶ Paris 208 – Auxerre 42 – Avallon 38 – Bourges 105

⚠ Le Pont Picot

☎ 03 86 27 05 97, clamecycamping@orange.fr

Address : rue de Chevroches (to the south; beside the Yonne and the Nivernais canal, recommended route via Beaugy)

Opening times : from beginning April to end Sept.

1 ha (90 pitches) flat, grassy

Tariff : (2013 Price) 9 € ♣ ♣ ⇌ 🗐 🖪 (60A) – Extra per person 3 €
Rental rates : (from beginning April to end Sept.) – 6 🚐. Per night from 45 to 70 € – Per week from 270 to 400 €

A pleasant location on a small island.

Surroundings : 🏞 ≤ ♀
Leisure activities : 🎣
Facilities : 🕭 ⚭ 🕎 launderette

GPS Longitude : 3.52784
Latitude : 47.45203

CLUNY

71250 – Michelin map **320** H11 – pop. 4 624 – alt. 248
▶ Paris 384 – Chalon-sur-Saône 49 – Charolles 43 – Mâcon 25

⚠ Municipal St-Vital

☎ 03 85 59 08 34, www.cluny-camping.blogspot.com

Address : 30 rue des Griottons (take the eastern exit along the D 15, follow the signs for Azé)

Opening times : from end April to mid Oct.

3 ha (174 pitches) flat, grassy

Tariff : (2013 Price) ♣ 3,90 € ⇌ 2,50 € 🗐 2,50 € – 🖪 (6A) 4,70 €
Rental rates : (from end April to mid Oct.) ⚡ – 2 🏠. Per night from 60 to 95 € – Per week from 320 to 500 €

The site has views of the old town of Cluny.

Surroundings : ≤ ♀
Leisure activities : 🚲
Facilities : 🕭 ⚭ 🕮 🖪
Nearby : ✗ 🏊 🛶 🐎

GPS Longitude : 4.66778
Latitude : 46.43088

CORMATIN

71460 – Michelin map **320** I10 – pop. 544 – alt. 212
▶ Paris 371 – Chalon-sur-Saône 37 – Mâcon 36 – Montceau-les-Mines 41

⚠ Le Hameau des Champs

☎ 03 85 50 76 71, www.le-hameau-des-champs.com

Address : take the northern exit along the D 981, follow the signs for Chalon-sur-Saône

Opening times : from beginning April to end Sept.

5,2 ha (50 pitches) flat, grassy

Tariff : ♣ 4 € ⇌ 🗐 6 € – 🖪 (13A) 3,50 €
Rental rates : Permanent 🕭 (1) – 10 🏠. Per night from 65 to 88 € Per week from 415 to 503 €

150m from a small lake and the Givry-Cluny Voie Verte (Green Trail).

Surroundings : 🏞
Leisure activities : 🍴 🛶 🚲
Facilities : 🕭 ⚭ 🧺 🕎 🖪
Nearby : 🏊 ✗ ✂ 🎣

GPS Longitude : 4.68391
Latitude : 46.54868

COUCHES

71490 – Michelin map **320** H8 – pop. 1 493 – alt. 320
▶ Paris 328 – Autun 26 – Beaune 31 – Le Creusot 16

⚠ La Gabrelle

☎ 03 85 45 59 49, www.lagabrelle.com

Address : 1.7km northwest along the D 978, follow the signs for Autun, near a small lake

Opening times : from mid June to mid Sept.

1 ha (50 pitches) terraced, flat, grassy

Tariff : ♣ 3 € ⇌ 3 € 🗐 3,50 € – 🖪 (6A) 3 €
🚐 borne 4 €

Surroundings : ▱
Leisure activities : 🍴 ✗ 🎱 🛶
Facilities : 🕭 ⚭ ☑ 🕎

GPS Longitude : 4.5588
Latitude : 46.87586

This guide is updated regularly, so buy your new copy every year!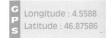

CRÊCHES-SUR-SAÔNE

71680 – Michelin map **320** I12 – pop. 2 838 – alt. 180
▶ Paris 398 – Bourg-en-Bresse 45 – Mâcon 9 – Villefranche-sur-Saône 30

⚠ Municipal Port d'Arciat

☎ 03 85 37 11 83, http://pagesperso-orange.fr/campingduportdarciat

Address : route du Port d'Arciat (located 1.5km east along the D 31, follow the signs for Pont de Veyle)

Opening times : from mid May to mid Sept.

5 ha (160 pitches) flat, grassy

Tariff : (2013 Price) 15,60 € ♣ ♣ ⇌ 🗐 🖪 (6A) – Extra per person 4,10 €

Beside the Saône river and near a small lake, direct access.

Surroundings : ♀
Leisure activities : 🛶 🎣
Facilities : 🕭 ⚭ 🕎 🖪
Nearby : 🍴 🛥 🏊 🛶

GPS Longitude : 4.80581
Latitude : 46.24037

CRUX-LA-VILLE

58330 – Michelin map **319** E9 – pop. 410 – alt. 319
▶ Paris 248 – Autun 85 – Avallon 138 – La Charité-sur-Loire 45

⚠ Aquadis Loisirs Le Merle

☎ 03 86 58 38 42, www.aquadis-loisirs.com

Address : at Le Merle (4.5km southwest along the D 34, follow the signs for St-Saulge and turn right onto D 181, follow the signs for Ste-Marie; beside the lake)

Opening times : from beginning April to end Oct.

2,6 ha (43 pitches) flat

Tariff : 17,30 € ♣ ♣ ⇌ 🗐 🖪 (10A) – Extra per person 4,80 €
Reservation fee 9,90 €

Rental rates : (from beginning April to end Oct.) – 11 🚐 5 🏠. Per night from 62 to 68 € – Per week from 167 to 599 €
Reservation fee 19,80 €

Surroundings : 🏞 ♀♀ ⛰
Leisure activities : 🍴 🛶 🛥 🛶 🎣
Facilities : 🕭 ⚭ ☑ 🕎 🖪
Nearby : pedalos

GPS Longitude : 3.52478
Latitude : 47.1624

DIGOIN

71160 – Michelin map **320** D11 – pop. 8 460 – alt. 232
▶ Paris 337 – Autun 69 – Charolles 26 – Moulins 57

⚠ Flower La Chevrette

✆ 03 85 53 11 49, www.lachevrette.com

Address : rue de la Chevrette (take the western exit towards Moulins, towards the municipal swimming pool; near the Loire river)

Opening times : from beginning April to mid Oct.

1,6 ha (81 pitches) flat

Tariff : 19,90€ ♣♣ ⇌ ▤ ⚡ (10A) – Extra per person 4€
Rental rates : (from beginning April to mid Oct.) ⚙ – 2 ⊡
2 ⌂. Per night from 49 to 81€ – Per week from 196 to 567€
⊞ borne

Surroundings : ⌂ ⚘
Leisure activities : ✗ ⌂ ⚘ (small swimming pool)
Facilities : ♿ ⚓ ⬛ ⚘ ⚘ ♈ launderette
Nearby : ♨ ⚓

GPS Longitude : 3.96768
Latitude : 46.47983

A chambre d'hôte is a guesthouse or B & B-style accommodation.

DOMPIERRE-LES-ORMES

71520 – Michelin map **320** G11 – pop. 922 – alt. 480
▶ Paris 405 – Chauffailles 28 – Cluny 23 – Mâcon 35

⚠ Le Village des Meuniers

✆ 03 85 50 36 60, www.villagedesmeuniers.com

Address : 344 rue du Stade (take the northwestern exit along the D 41, follow the signs for La Clayette and take the road to the right, near the stadium)

Opening times : from beginning April to end Oct.

3 ha (113 pitches) terraced

Tariff : 30,50€ ♣♣ ⇌ ▤ ⚡ (10A) – Extra per person 7,50€
Reservation fee 15€
Rental rates : (from mid March to end Oct.) ♿ (1) – 16 ⊡
8 ⌂ – 2 canvas bungalows – 3 gîtes. Per night from 31 to 130€
Per week from 145 to 840€ – Reservation fee 15€
⊞ ♨ ⚡14€
Elevated panoramic location.

Surroundings : ⌂ ⬅ ⌂
Leisure activities : ♈ ✗ ⌂ ⧖nighttime ⚘ ⚓ ⚘
Facilities : ♿ ⚓ ⚘ ♈ ▤
Nearby : 🚲 ⚘

GPS Longitude : 4.47468
Latitude : 46.36393

ÉPINAC

71360 – Michelin map **320** H8 – pop. 2 357 – alt. 340
▶ Paris 304 – Arnay-le-Duc 20 – Autun 19 – Chagny 29

⚠ Municipal le Pont Vert

✆ 03 85 82 00 26, www.campingdupontvert.com

Address : rue de la Piscine (take the southern exit along the D 43 and take the road to the right; beside the Drée river)

Opening times : from beginning April to end Oct.

2,9 ha (71 pitches) flat, grassy

Tariff : (2013 Price) 17,90€ ♣♣ ⇌ ▤ ⚡ (10A)
Extra per person 3,20€ – Reservation fee 10€

Rental rates : (from beginning April to end Oct.) – 1 ⊡. Per night from 25 to 59€ – Per week from 102 to 395€ – Reservation fee 10€
⊞ borne 2€ – 3 ▤

Surroundings : ⚘ ⌂ ⚘
Leisure activities : ⌂
Facilities : ♿ ⚓ ♈ ▤
Nearby : ♈ ✗ ⚓ ⚘ ⚓

GPS Longitude : 4.50617
Latitude : 46.98577

GIGNY-SUR-SAÔNE

71240 – Michelin map **320** J10 – pop. 522 – alt. 178
▶ Paris 355 – Chalon-sur-Saône 29 – Le Creusot 51 – Louhans 30

⚠⚠ Les Castels Château de l'Épervière ⚐

✆ 03 85 94 16 90, www.domaine-eperviere.com – limited spaces for one-night stay

Address : 6 rue du Château (located 1km to the south; at Épervière)

Opening times : from beginning April to end Sept.

7 ha (100 pitches) flat, grassy

Tariff : 38,90€ ♣♣ ⇌ ▤ ⚡ (10A) – Extra per person 8,90€
Reservation fee 10€
Rental rates : (from beginning April to end Sept.) ⚙ – 5 ⊡
3 gîtes. Per week from 439 to 879€ – Reservation fee 20€
⊞ borne 5€
A pleasant wooded park beside a lake. Burgundy wines can be tasted in the château's vaulted cellar.

Surroundings : ⚘ ⌂ ⚘⚘
Leisure activities : ♈ ✗ ⌂ ⚓ ⬅ jacuzzi ⚓ 🚲 ⚘ ⚘ ⚓ (pool) ⚘ paddling pool
Facilities : ♿ ⚓ ⚘ ♈ ▤ ⚘ ⚘ ⚘
Nearby : ⚘

GPS Longitude : 4.94386
Latitude : 46.65446

Key to rentals symbols:

12 ⊡   *Number of mobile homes*
20 ⌂   *Number of chalets*
6 ⊨   *Number of rooms to rent*
Per night   *Minimum/maximum rate per night*
30–50€
Per week   *Minimum/maximum rate per week*
300–1,000€

GUEUGNON

71130 – Michelin map **320** E10 – pop. 7 638 – alt. 243
▶ Paris 335 – Autun 53 – Bourbon-Lancy 27 – Digoin 16

⚠ Municipal de Chazey

✆ 03 85 85 23 11, www.ccpaysgueugnon.fr

Address : zone de Chazey (4km south along the D 994, follow the signs for Digoin and take the road to the right)

1 ha (20 pitches) flat, grassy

Rentals : 3 ⌂ – 6 tent lodges – chalets (without sanitary facilities).
Near a small canal and two lakes.

Surroundings : ⚘ ⌂
Leisure activities : ⌂ ⚓
Facilities : ♿ ⚓ ⚘ ▤
Nearby : ⚓

GPS Longitude : 4.05386
Latitude : 46.57077

L'ISLE-SUR-SEREIN

89440 – Michelin map **319** H6 – pop. 747 – alt. 190
▶ Paris 209 – Auxerre 50 – Avallon 17 – Montbard 36

▲ Municipal le Parc du Château

📞 03 86 33 93 50, www.isle-sur-serein.fr

Address : route d'Avallon (800m south along the D 86; by the stadium, 150m from the Serein river)

Opening times : from mid April to end Sept.

1 ha (30 pitches) flat, grassyTariff : 10,10€ ✚✚ 🚐 🗐 ⚡ (6A)
Extra per person 2,20€

Rental rates : (from mid April to end Sept.) – 4 🛏. Per night from 40€ – Per week from 150 to 200€

🚰 borne 3€

Surroundings : 🌳	**G P S** Longitude : 4.00542
Facilities : ⚷ 🚽 🏛 ⚐ 🍴	
Nearby : 🏊 🎿 sports trail	Latitude : 47.58119

ISSY-L'EVÊQUE

71760 – Michelin map **320** D9 – pop. 842 – alt. 310
▶ Paris 325 – Bourbon-Lancy 25 – Gueugnon 17 – Luzy 12

▲▲ L'Etang Neuf

📞 03 85 24 96 05, camping-etangneuf@orange.fr

Address : rue de l'Étang (located 1km west along the D 42, follow the signs for Grury and take the road to the right)

6 ha/3 for camping (71 pitches) flat

Rentals : 2 🛏 – 6 🏠.

A pleasant location beside a lake and a wood.

Surroundings : 🌳 ⟨ 🏞	**G P S** Longitude : 3.9602
Leisure activities : 🍴 🍽 🏛 🏊 🎿	
Facilities : 🚿 ⚷ 🍴 🗑	Latitude : 46.7078
Nearby : 🧗 🛶 🐎	

LAIVES

71240 – Michelin map **320** J10 – pop. 997 – alt. 198
▶ Paris 355 – Chalon-sur-Saône 20 – Mâcon 48 – Montceau-les-Mines 49

▲▲ Les Lacs de Laives - la Héronnière

📞 03 85 44 98 85, www.camping-laheronniere.com

Address : route de la Ferté (4.2km north along the D 18, follow the signs for Buxy and take right turn)

1,5 ha (80 pitches) flat, grassy

Rentals : 1 caravan – 2 🛏 – 2 🏠.

Close to the lakes at Laives.

Surroundings : 🌳 🏞 🌳	**G P S** Longitude : 4.83426
Leisure activities : 🚲 🎿	
Facilities : 🚿 ⚷ 🍴 🗑	Latitude : 46.67448
Nearby : 🍴 🍽 🛶	

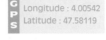
LIGNY-LE-CHÂTEL

89144 – Michelin map **319** F4 – pop. 1 334 – alt. 130
▶ Paris 178 – Auxerre 22 – Sens 60 – Tonnerre 28

▲ Municipal Parc de la Noue Marrou

📞 03 86 47 56 99, www.tourisme-camping-municipal-de-la-noue-marrou.fr

Address : avenue de la Noue Marrou (take the southwestern exit along the D 8, follow the signs for Auxerre and take road to the left; beside the Serein)

Opening times : from beginning May to end Sept.

2 ha (50 pitches) flat, grassy

Tariff : 12€ ✚✚ 🚐 🗐 ⚡ (16A) – Extra per person 2,50€

On the edge of the Othe forest and the Serein river.

Surroundings : 🍃	**G P S** Longitude : 3.75274
Leisure activities : 🍴 🍽	
Facilities : 🚿 ⚷ ⚐ 🍴 🗑	Latitude : 47.89597
Nearby : 🧗 🍽 🛶	

Routes nationales are main roads and their identifying numbers begin with N or RN. Routes départementales are generally quieter roads and begin with D or DN.

LORMES

58140 – Michelin map **319** F8 – pop. 1 389 – alt. 420
▶ Paris 255 – Dijon 135 – Nevers 73 – Auxerre 76

▲ L'Étang du Goulot

📞 03 86 22 82 37, www.etangdugoulot.com

Address : 2 rue des Campeurs

2,5 ha (64 pitches) flat, grassy

Rentals : 1 caravan – 2 yurts – 1 tipi – 1 chalet (without sanitary facilities).

🚰 borne – 2 🗐

Surroundings : 🍃 🏞 🌳	**G P S** Longitude : 3.82297
Leisure activities : 🍴 🍽 🏛 🏊 🧗 🛶 🍽	
Facilities : 🚿 ⚷	Latitude : 47.28268
Nearby : 🛶 🚲 🍽	

LOUHANS

71500 – Michelin map **320** L10 – pop. 6 451 – alt. 179
▶ Paris 373 – Bourg-en-Bresse 61 – Chalon-sur-Saône 38 – Dijon 85

▲ Municipal

📞 03 85 75 19 02, www.louhans-chateaurenaud.fr

Address : 10 chemin de La Chapellerie (located 1km southwest along the D 971, follow the signs for Tournus and take the D 12, following signs for Romenay, turn left after the stadium)

Opening times : from beginning April to end Sept.

1 ha (60 pitches) flat, grassy

Tariff : 15€ ✚✚ 🚐 🗐 ⚡ (10A) – Extra per person 2,50€

Rental rates : (from beginning April to end Sept.) – 2 🛏. Per night from 70 to 90€ – Per week from 280 to 380€

In a green setting beside a river.

Surroundings : 🏞 🌳🌳	**G P S** Longitude : 5.21714
Facilities : 🚿 ⚷ (July–Aug.) 🚽 🍴	
Nearby : 🍽 🎿 🏊	Latitude : 46.62436

LUZY

58170 – Michelin map **319** G11 – pop. 2 018 – alt. 275
▶ Paris 314 – Autun 34 – Château-Chinon 39 – Moulins 62

⚑ Club Airotel Château de Chigy ♣♣

✆ 03 86 30 10 80, www.chateaudechigy.com.fr

Address : at Tazilly (4km southwest along the D 973, follow the signs for Bourbon-Lancy then take the road to the left)

Opening times : from end April to end Sept.

70 ha/15 for camping (135 pitches) flat

Tariff : ★ 5€ 🚗 ▣ 20€ – ⚡ (6A) 6€

Rental rates : (from end April to mid Oct.) – 6 🚐 – 29 🏠 3 apartments – 6 gîtes. Per night from 59 to 120€ – Per week from 295 to 840€ – Reservation fee 15€

A spacious site laid out around a château, with meadows, woods and lakes.

Surroundings : 🏊 ≤
Leisure activities : 🍴 ✗ 🎪 ☺ 🏃 ♞ ⚓ ⛳ 🎯
⛵ 🏖 🐎 multi-sports ground
Facilities : & ⚙ 🏕 🗄 🚿

G P S Longitude : 3.94445
Latitude : 46.75716

MACON

71000 – Michelin map **320** I12 – pop. 34 000 – alt. 175
▶ Paris 398 – Dijon 128 – Lyon 72 – Bourg-en-Bresse 37

⚑ Municipal

✆ 03 85 38 16 22, www.macon.fr/tourisme/camping

Address : at Sancé, 1 rue des Grandes Varennes

5 ha (266 pitches) flat, grassy

🚐 borne

Surroundings : 🌲 🏞
Leisure activities : 🍴 ✗ 🎪 ♞ ⛵
Facilities : & ⚙ 🏕 🚿 launderette 🗄 🚿
Nearby : ⚓ marina

G P S Longitude : 4.84372
Latitude : 46.3301

MATOUR

71520 – Michelin map **320** G12 – pop. 1 095 – alt. 500
▶ Paris 405 – Chauffailles 22 – Cluny 24 – Mâcon 36

⚑ Flower Le Paluet

✆ 03 85 59 70 92, www.matour.com

Address : 2 rue de la Piscine (located to the west; follow the signs for la Clayette and take a left turn)

Opening times : from beginning May to end Sept.

3 ha (73 pitches) flat and relatively flat

Tariff : 20,30€ ♣♣ 🚗 ▣ ⚡ (3A) – Extra per person 5,10€ Reservation fee 12€

Rental rates : (from mid March to mid Nov.) – 10 🏠 4 canvas bungalows. Per night from 42 to 100€ – Per week from 294 to 700€ – Reservation fee 25€

🚐 borne – 🚐 ⚡ 18,30€

Beside a lake and near a leisure centre.

Surroundings : 🏊 🌲 🏞
Leisure activities : 🎪 ☀daytime ♞ ⛳ ⛵
🏖 🐎 multi-sports ground
Facilities : & ⚙ (season) 🚿 🏕 launderette

G P S Longitude : 4.48232
Latitude : 46.30677

MEURSAULT

21190 – Michelin map **320** I8 – pop. 1 542 – alt. 243
▶ Paris 326 – Dijon 56 – Chalon-sur-Saône 28 – Le Creusot 40

⚑ La Grappe d'Or

✆ 03 80 21 22 48, www.camping-meursault.com

Address : 2 route de Volnay

Opening times : from beginning April to mid Oct.

4,5 ha (130 pitches) terraced, flat, grassy

Tariff : (2013 Price) 22€ ♣♣ 🚗 ▣ ⚡ (10A) – Extra per person 3,80€ Reservation fee 10€

Rental rates : (from end April to beginning Oct.) – 20 🚐 1 gîte. Per night from 45 to 89€ – Per week from 315 to 623€ Reservation fee 15€

🚐 borne 4€

The site overlooks the old town of Mersault and the vineyards.

Surroundings : ≤ 🏞
Leisure activities : ✗ ♞ 🚴 ⛳ 🏖 ♨
Facilities : & ⚙ 📼 🏕 🗄 🚿

G P S Longitude : 4.76987
Latitude : 46.98655

MIGENNES

89400 – Michelin map **319** E4 – pop. 7 360 – alt. 87
▶ Paris 162 – Dijon 169 – Auxerre 22 – Sens 46

⚑ Les Confluents

✆ 03 86 80 94 55, www.les-confluents.com

Address : allée Léo Lagrange (near the stadium)

Opening times : from beginning April to end Oct.

1,5 ha (61 pitches) flat, grassy

Tariff : ★ 4,50€ 🚗 ▣ 5,55€ – ⚡ (10A) 4,30€

Rental rates : (from beginning April to end Oct.) ⛳ – 12 🚐. Per night from 40 to 73€ – Per week from 234 to 470€

🚐 borne 3,50€ – 8 ▣ 16€ – 🚐 ⚡ 14€

On the banks of the Yonne river.

Surroundings : 🌲 🏞
Leisure activities : 🎪 ♞ 🚴 ⛵
Facilities : ⚙ 🏛 🗄 🚿 🏕 🚿 🗄 🚿
Nearby : ✗ ⛳ 🐎 watersports centre

G P S Longitude : 3.5095
Latitude : 47.95613

MONTBARD

21500 – Michelin map **320** G4 – pop. 5 527 – alt. 221
▶ Paris 240 – Autun 87 – Auxerre 81 – Dijon 81

⚑ Municipal les Treilles

✆ 03 80 92 69 50, www.montbard.com

Address : rue Michel Servet (along the D 980 diversion northwest of the town, near the swimming complex)

Opening times : from beginning March to end Oct.

2,5 ha (80 pitches) flat, grassy

Tariff : 19,30€ ♣♣ 🚗 ▣ ⚡ (16A) – Extra per person 5,10€

Rental rates : (from beginning April to end Oct.) – 2 🚐. Per night from 35 to 85€ – Per week from 255 to 555€

🚐 borne 3,10€ – 5 ▣ 19,30€

Attractive trees and shrubs surround some pitches.

Surroundings : ≤ 🌲 🏞
Leisure activities : 🎪 ☀daytime ♞
multi-sports ground
Facilities : & ⚙ 🏛 🏕 🚿 🏕 🗄
Nearby : ♨ hammam 🎯 🏖 🐎 ⛳

G P S Longitude : 4.33129
Latitude : 47.63111

MONTIGNY-EN-MORVAN

58120 – Michelin map **319** G9 – pop. 319 – alt. 350
▶ Paris 269 – Château-Chinon 13 – Corbigny 26 – Nevers 64

⚠ Municipal du Lac

✆ 03 86 84 71 77, www.montigny-en-morvan.fr – 🏠

Address : Continue 2.3km northeast along the D 944, D 303 towards the dam at Pannecière-Chaumard and take the road to the right.

Opening times : from beginning May to end Sept.

2 ha (59 pitches) undulating

Tariff : 🚶 2,50€ – 🚗 1,70€ – 🔌 (30A) 1,90€

In a pleasant location near a lake.

Surroundings : 🏞 🎣
Leisure activities : 🚣 🎣
Facilities : ♿ 🚿 🚮
Nearby : 🛶

G P S	Longitude : 3.8735
	Latitude : 47.15573

NEVERS

58000 – Michelin map **319** B10 – pop. 36 762 – alt. 194
▶ Paris 247 – Dijon 187 – Bourges 68 – Moulins 57

⚠ Nevers

✆ 06 84 98 69 79, www.campingnevers.com

Address : rue de la Jonction

Opening times : from mid April to mid Oct.

1,6 ha (73 pitches) terraced, flat, grassy

Tariff : 20,80€ 🚶🚶 🚗 🏠 🔌 (6A) – Extra per person 3,30€

Rental rates : (from mid April to mid Oct.) – 2 🚐. Per night from 56€ – Per week from 335 to 495€ – Reservation fee 10€

🚰 borne 2,50€

On the banks of the Loire river with a view of the cathedral, Ducal Palace and the stone bridge.

Surroundings : 🌅 🎣
Leisure activities : 🍴 🍽 🏠 🚣 🎣
Facilities : ♿ 🚿 🚮 🚽 🚿 🚱 launderette 🚿
Nearby : 🛶 🚲

G P S	Longitude : 3.16095
	Latitude : 46.98222

NOLAY

21340 – Michelin map **320** H8 – pop. 1 510 – alt. 299
▶ Paris 316 – Autun 30 – Beaune 20 – Chalon-sur-Saône 34

⚠ Municipal les Chaumes du Mont

✆ 03 45 63 40 01, campingleschaumes@sfr.fr

Address : 0.8km southwest along the D 33A, follow the signs for Couches

1,5 ha (70 pitches) terraced, relatively flat, flat, grassy

The site is near a lake.

Surroundings : 🌅 🎣 🏔
Leisure activities : 🚣 🎾
Facilities : ♿ 🚿 🚮

G P S	Longitude : 4.62457
	Latitude : 46.94682

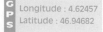

*The classification (1 to 5 tents, **black** or red) that we award to selected sites in this guide is our own system. It should not be confused with the classification (1 to 5 stars) of official organisations.*

⚠ La Bruyère

✆ 03 80 21 87 59, www.bourgogne-sante-services.com

Address : rue de Moulin Larché (1.2km west along the D 973, follow the signs for Autun and take road to the left)

Opening times : Permanent

1,2 ha (22 pitches) flat, grassy

Tariff : (2013 Price) 18,10€ 🚶🚶 🚗 🏠 🔌 (16A)
Extra per person 2,35€

Rentals : (2013 Price) Permanent – 3 🏠. Per week from 253 to 337 €

🚰 borne

Surroundings : 🐟 🌅
Leisure activities : 🏠
Facilities : ♿ 🚿 🚮 🍴 launderette

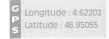

G P S	Longitude : 4.62202
	Latitude : 46.95055

PALINGES

71430 – Michelin map **320** F10 – pop. 1 512 – alt. 274
▶ Paris 352 – Charolles 16 – Lapalisse 70 – Lyon 136

⚠ Le Lac

✆ 03 85 88 14 49, www.campingdulac.eu

Address : at Lac du Fourneau (located 1km northeast along the D 128, rte de Génelard)

Opening times : from beginning April to end Oct.

1,5 ha (44 pitches) terraced

Tariff : (2013 Price) 21,70€ 🚶🚶 🚗 🏠 🔌 (10A) –
Extra per person 3,90€

Rental rates : (from beginning April to end Oct.) ♿ (1) – 6 🏠. Per night 200€ – Per week 670€

🚰 borne – 8 🏠 21,70€

Situated near a small lake.

Surroundings : 🏠
Leisure activities : 🏠 🚣
Facilities : ♿ 🚿 🚮 🚿 🍴 📶 refrigerators
Nearby : 🏖 🎾 🛶 (beach) 🎣

G P S	Longitude : 4.22521
	Latitude : 46.56106

Some information or pricing may have changed since the guide went to press. We recommend you check the price list online in advance or at the entrance to the campsite and enquire about possible restrictions.

PARAY LE MONIAL

71600 – Michelin map **320** E11 – pop. 9 115 – alt. 245
▶ Paris 377 – Dijon 149 – Mâcon 66 – Moulins 69

⚠ Mambre

✆ 03 85 88 89 20, www.campingdemambre.com

Address : 19 rue du Gué Léger

6 ha (161 pitches) flat, grassy

Rentals : 20 🚐.

🚰 borne

Surroundings : 🎣🎣
Leisure activities : 🍴 🚣 🚴 🛝
Facilities : ♿ 🚿 🚮 🍴 launderette 🛒
Nearby : 🍴

G P S	Longitude : 4.10479
	Latitude : 46.45743

PRÉMERY

58700 – Michelin map **319** C8 – pop. 2 031 – alt. 237
◻ Paris 231 – La Charité-sur-Loire 28 – Château-Chinon 57
– Clamecy 41

⚠ Municipal

📞 0965216556, www.mairie-premery.fr rubrique camping

Address : chemin des Prés de la Ville (take the northeastern exit along the D 977, follow the signs for Clamecy and take the road to the right)

Opening times : from mid April to end Sept.

1,6 ha (50 pitches) flat and relatively flat

Tariff : 9,80€ ✤ ✤ ⇌ 🔲 🔌 (13A) – Extra per person 3,25€
Rental rates : (from mid April to beginning Nov.) – 10 🏠.
Per night from 35 to 42€ – Per week from 154 to 378€
Near the Nièvre river and a small lake.

Leisure activities : 🚲 🏊 multi-sports ground Facilities : ♿ ⚡ (July–Aug.) 🛁 🚰 🔲 Nearby : 🏖 🎣 🍴 🛶	**GPS** Longitude : 3.33683 Latitude : 47.1781

ST-GERMAIN-DU-BOIS

71330 – Michelin map **320** L9 – pop. 1 935 – alt. 210
◻ Paris 367 – Chalon-sur-Saône 33 – Dole 58 – Lons-le-Saunier 29

⚠ Municipal de l'Étang Titard

📞 0385720615, www.st-germaindubois.fr

Address : route de Louhans (take the southern exit along the D 13)

Opening times : from beginning May to mid Sept.

1 ha (40 pitches) flat

Tariff : ✤ 2,30€ ⇌ 1,50€ 🔲 1,20€ – 🔌 (16A) 2,50€
Rental rates : Permanent ♿ (1) 🍴 – 5 🏠. Per night from 42 to 60€ – Per week from 294 to 420€
Situated near a lake.

Surroundings : ♀ Leisure activities : 🎱 Facilities : ♿ ⚡ 🛁 🚰 🔲 Nearby : 🍴 🔲 🛶 🏖 sports trail	**GPS** Longitude : 5.24617 Latitude : 46.74635

ST-HONORÉ-LES-BAINS

58360 – Michelin map **319** G10 – pop. 841 – alt. 300 – ♨
◻ Paris 303 – Château-Chinon 28 – Luzy 22 – Moulins 69

⚠ Camping et Gîtes des Bains

📞 0386307344, www.campinglesbains.com

Address : 15 avenue Jean Mermoz (take the western exit, follow the signs for Vandenesse)

Opening times : from end March to end Oct.

4,5 ha (130 pitches) flat, grassy

Tariff : 20€ ✤ ✤ ⇌ 🔲 🔌 (6A) – Extra per person 4,60€ – Reservation fee 8€
Rental rates : (from end March to end Oct.) – 4  – 3 apartments 20 gîtes – 1 hut. Per night from 33 to 80€ – Per week from 195 to 565€ – Reservation fee 8€
🚐 borne

Surroundings : 🏕 ♀ Leisure activities : 🍴 🍽 🎣 🛶 🛥 🛶 🏖 Facilities : ♿ ⚡ 🛁 🚰 launderette Nearby : 🍴 🛶	**GPS** Longitude : 3.82832 Latitude : 46.90684

⚠ Municipal Plateau du Gué

📞 0386307600, http://st-honore-les-bains.com

Address : 13 rue Eugène-Collin (in the town, 150m from the post office)

Opening times : from beginning April to end Oct.

1,2 ha (73 pitches) flat and relatively flat, grassy

Tariff : (2013 Price) ✤ 2,50€ ⇌ 1,80€ 🔲 1,80€ – 🔌 (15A) 2,90€
🚐 borne 2€ – 10 🔲 1,80€

Surroundings : ♀ Leisure activities : 🎱 🎣 Facilities : ♿ ⚡ 🚰 🔲	**GPS** Longitude : 3.83918 Latitude : 46.90376

ST-LÉGER-DE-FOUGERET

58120 – Michelin map **319** G9 – pop. 289 – alt. 500
◻ Paris 308 – Dijon 122 – Nevers 65 – Le Creusot 69

⚠ Sites et Paysages Étang de la Fougeraie

📞 0386851185, www.campingfougeraie.com 🚿

Address : at Hameau de champs (2.4km southeast along the D 157, follow the signs for Onlay)

Opening times : from beginning April to end Sept.

7 ha (60 pitches) flat

Tariff : 23,50€ ✤ ✤ ⇌ 🔲 🔌 (10A) – Extra per person 6,50€ – Reservation fee 8€
Rental rates : Permanent – 5 🏠 – 3 canvas bungalows. Per night from 40 to 70€ – Per week from 280 to 555€ – Reservation fee 15€
🚐 borne – 10 🔲 20€ – 🚐 11€
In a rural setting around a lake.

Surroundings : 🏞 ⛰ Leisure activities : 🍴 🍽 🚲 🛶 🎣 🛶 Facilities : ♿ ⚡ 🛁 🚰 launderette 🛒 refrigerators	**GPS** Longitude : 3.90492 Latitude : 47.00616

In order for the guide to remain wholly objective, the selection of campsites is made on an entirely independent basis.

ST-PÉREUSE

58110 – Michelin map **319** F9 – pop. 280 – alt. 355
◻ Paris 289 – Autun 54 – Château-Chinon 15 – Clamecy 57

⛰ Le Manoir de Bezolle

📞 0386844255, www.camping-bezolle.com 🚿

Address : to the southeast along the D 11, 300m from the D 978, follow the signs for Château-Chinon

Opening times : Permanent

8 ha/5 for camping (140 pitches) terraced, small lakes

Tariff : (2013 Price) 28€ ✤ ✤ ⇌ 🔲 🔌 (10A) – Extra per person 5,50€ – Reservation fee 5€
Rental rates : (2013 Price) Permanent – 2 caravans – 4  12 🏠 – 2 yurts – 4 canvas bungalows. Per night from 35 to 85€ – Per week from 245 to 610€ – Reservation fee 5€
🚐 borne 5€ – 🚐 🔌 28€
In the grounds of the manor house.

Surroundings : 🏞 ⛰ ♀♀ Leisure activities : 🍴 🍽 🎱 🎣 🛶 🛶 🏖 🐴 Facilities : ♿ ⚡ 🔲 🛁 🛁 🚰 launderette 🏖 🛒	**GPS** Longitude : 3.8158 Latitude : 47.05732

ST-POINT

71520 – Michelin map **320** H11 – pop. 341 – alt. 335
▶ Paris 396 – Beaune 90 – Cluny 14 – Mâcon 26

⚠ Lac de St-Point-Lamartine

🔗 03 85 50 52 31, www.campingsaintpoint.com

Address : take the southern exit along the D 22, follow the signs for Tramayes; beside a lake

Opening times : from beginning April to end Oct.

3 ha (102 pitches) flat and relatively flat

Tariff : 12,50€ ♦♦ ⇔ 🔲 🗓 (13A) – Extra per person 5€
Rental rates : (from beginning April to end Oct.) – 3 🚐 – 11 🏠.
Per night from 50 to 60€ – Per week from 190 to 350€
Reservation fee 20€
🚰 borne – 10 🔲 10€ – 🔌 🗓 11€
On the edge of a lake.

Surroundings : 🌳 ⇐ 🏞
Leisure activities : 🎣 🏊 ♣ 🎿
Facilities : ♿ ⚡ 🏢 🚿 🔲
Nearby : 🍷 ✗ 🚤 🎣 pedalos

GPS Longitude : 4.61175
Latitude : 46.33703

ST-SAUVEUR-EN-PUISAYE

89520 – Michelin map **319** C6 – pop. 946 – alt. 259
▶ Paris 174 – Dijon 184 – Moulins 146 – Tours 242

⚠ Parc des Joumiers

🔗 03 86 45 66 28, www.camping-motel-joumiers.com

Address : 2.3km northwest along the D 7 and take the road to the right

Opening times : from end March to mid Oct.

21 ha/7 for camping (100 pitches) flat and relatively flat

Tariff : 17,85€ ♦♦ ⇔ 🔲 🗓 (10A) – Extra per person 4€
Rental rates : Permanent – 13 🚐 – 3 🏠 – 10 🏕. Per night from 75 to 145€ – Per week from 138 to 750€
🚰 borne 5€ – 10 🔲 14€ – 🔌 🗓 16€
Situated beside a lake.

Surroundings : 🌳 🏞 ⚠
Leisure activities : ✗ 🏊 🎿 🎣
Facilities : ♿ ⚡ 🏢 🚿 🚽 🔲
Nearby : boats to hire

GPS Longitude : 3.19357
Latitude : 47.63082

SALORNAY-SUR-GUYE

71250 – Michelin map **320** H10 – pop. 826 – alt. 210
▶ Paris 377 – Chalon-sur-Saône 51 – Cluny 12 – Paray-le-Monial 44

⚠ Municipal de la Clochette

🔗 03 85 59 90 11, www.salornay-sur-guye.fr

Address : place de la Clochette (in the village, access via the road in front of the post office)

Opening times : from end May to beginning Sept.

1 ha (60 pitches) flat

Tariff : ♦ 3,50€ ⇔ 🔲 3€ – 🗓 (10A) 3€ – Reservation fee 5€
🚰 borne 5€
Beside the Gande river.

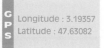

Surroundings : 🏞 🌿
Leisure activities : 🎣
Facilities : ♿ 🚻 🔲
Nearby : 🏊 ✗

GPS Longitude : 4.59907
Latitude : 46.51659

SANTENAY

21590 – Michelin map **320** I8 – pop. 827 – alt. 225
▶ Paris 330 – Autun 39 – Beaune 18 – Chalon-sur-Saône 25

⛰ Aquadis Les Sources

🔗 03 80 20 66 55, www.aquadis-loisirs.com

Address : avenue des Sources (head 1km southwest following signs for Cheilly-les-Maranges, near the spa centre)

Opening times : from mid April to mid Oct.

3,1 ha (150 pitches) flat and relatively flat

Tariff : 18€ ♦♦ ⇔ 🔲 🗓 (6A) – Extra per person 3€ – Reservation fee 9,90€
🚰 borne 5,20€

Surroundings : ⇐ 🌿
Leisure activities : 🏊 🎿
Facilities : ♿ ⚡ 🚿 🔲 🏊 🚲
Nearby : ✗ 🎿

GPS Longitude : 4.6857
Latitude : 46.90716

There are several different types of sani-station ('borne' in French) – sanitation points providing fresh water and disposal points for grey water. See page 12 for further details.

SAULIEU

21210 – Michelin map **320** F6 – pop. 2 574 – alt. 535
▶ Paris 248 – Autun 40 – Avallon 39 – Beaune 65

⛰ Aquadis Loisirs Saulieu

🔗 03 80 64 16 19, www.aquadis-loisirs.com

Address : located 1km northwest along the N 6, follow the signs for Paris; near a lake

Opening times : from beginning March to beginning Nov.

6 ha (100 pitches) flat and relatively flat, grassy

Tariff : 16€ ♦♦ ⇔ 🔲 🗓 (10A) – Extra per person 3,45€ – Reservation fee 9,90€
Rental rates : (from beginning March to beginning Nov.) – 6 🚐 6 🏠 – 20 chalets (without sanitary facilities). Per night from 28 to 85€ – Per week from 116 to 636€ – Reservation fee 19,80€

Leisure activities : 🍷 🎣 🏊 ♣ ✗ 🎿 🎿
Facilities : ♿ ⚡ 🆑 🚿 🚽 🔲

GPS Longitude : 4.22373
Latitude : 47.28934

SAVIGNY-LÈS-BEAUNE

21420 – Michelin map **320** I7 – pop. 1 371 – alt. 237
▶ Paris 314 – Dijon 39 – Mâcon 93 – Lons-le-Saunier 109

⚠ Les Premiers Prés

🔗 03 80 26 15 06, www.camping-savigny-les-beaune.fr

Address : route de Bouilland (located 1km northwest along the D 2)

1,5 ha (88 pitches) flat and relatively flat
🚰 borne
In a green setting beside a stream.

Surroundings : 🌿
Leisure activities : 🍷 🏊
Facilities : ♿ ⚡ 🔲 🚲

GPS Longitude : 4.82192
Latitude : 47.06246

LES SETTONS

58230 – Michelin map **319** H8
▶ Paris 259 – Autun 41 – Avallon 44 – Château-Chinon 25

⚠ Les Mésanges

📞 03 86 84 55 77, www.campinglesmesanges.fr

Address : rive gauche, L'Huis-Gaumont (4km south along the D193, D 520, follow the signs for Planchez and turn left towards Chevigny, 200m from the lake)

Opening times : from mid May to mid Sept.

5 ha (100 pitches) relatively flat

Tariff : 19,90€ ♛♛ ⬅ 🅴 (10A) – Extra per person 5€
🚐 borne – 🚐11€
In a pleasant location beside a lake.

Surroundings : 🌳 ⌂ ♀ ⛰	G	
Leisure activities : 🏊⬈ 🎣	P	Longitude : 4.05385
Facilities : 🚿 ⛟ 🏖 🚮 🕜 🍴 launderette	S	Latitude : 47.18077
Nearby : 🚣		

⚠ Plage du Midi

📞 03 86 84 51 97, www.settons-camping.com

Address : rive droite Lac des Settons, Les Branlasses (2.5km southeast along the D 193 and take turning to the right)

Opening times : from mid April to beginning Oct.

4 ha (110 pitches) relatively flat

Tariff : ♛ 4,50€ ⬅ 2,50€ 🅴 3,20€ – (10A) 4€ – Reservation fee 15€

Rental rates : (from mid April to beginning Oct.) 🚿 (1) 27 🏠. Per night from 52 to 87€ – Per week from 350 to 725€ Reservation fee 15€
🚐 borne – 🚐 🚰10€
Situated beside a lake.

Surroundings : 🌳 ≤♀⛰	G	
Leisure activities : 🍴 🏊⬈ 🖼 (open air in	P	Longitude : 4.07056
season)		Latitude : 47.18578
Facilities : 🚿 ⛟ 🆑 🏖 🍴 launderette 🚗	S	
Nearby : 🗡 🍴 ♪ pedalos		

⚠ La Plage des Settons

📞 03 86 84 51 99, www.camping-chalets-settons.com

Address : rive gauche - Lac des Settons (300m south of the dam)

2,6 ha (60 pitches) terraced, flat, grassy

Rentals : 🚿 (2 chalets) – 14 🏠.

Pleasant pitches set on terraces, opposite the lake.

Surroundings : 🌳 ≤⌂	G	
Leisure activities : 🖼 🏊⬈ pedalos	P	Longitude : 4.06132
Facilities : 🚿 ⛟ 🚮 🍴 🖼	S	Latitude : 47.18958
Nearby : 🍴🗡 🚣		

For more information on visiting particular towns or regions, consult the relevant regional MICHELIN Green Guide. We also recommend you use the appropriate Michelin regional map to locate your selected campsite, to calculate distances and to work out the best route.

TONNERRE

89700 – Michelin map **319** G4 – pop. 5 246 – alt. 156
▶ Paris 199 – Auxerre 38 – Montbard 45 – Troyes 60

⚠ La Cascade

📞 03 86 55 15 44, http://www.revea-camping.fr/fr/accueil-camping-la-cascade.html

Address : avenue Aristide-Briand (take the northern exit along the D 905, follow the signs for Troyes and take D 944, towards the town centre; beside the Yonne canal)

Opening times : from mid April to end Sept.

3 ha (107 pitches) flat, grassy

Tariff : (2013 Price) 13,60€ ♛♛ ⬅ 🅴 (10A)
Extra per person 3,60€ – Reservation fee 10€

Rental rates : (from mid April to end Sept.) – 6 🏠. Per night from 90 to 100€ – Per week from 190 to 460€ – Reservation fee 25€
🚐 3 🅴 13,60€

Surroundings : ♀	G	
Leisure activities : 🖼 🚲	P	Longitude : 3.98415
Facilities : 🚿 ⛟ 🆑 🚮 🍴 🖼	S	Latitude : 47.8603
Nearby : 🚣 🎣		

TOURNUS

71700 – Michelin map **320** J10 – pop. 5 884 – alt. 193
▶ Paris 360 – Bourg-en-Bresse 70 – Chalon-sur-Saône 28 – Lons-le-Saunier 58

⚠ Camping de Tournus

📞 03 85 51 16 58, www.camping-tournus.com

Address : 14 rue des Canes (located 1km north of the town; take the r. St-Laurent opposite the station. situated right next to the swimming pool and 150m from the Saône (direct access)

Opening times : from beginning April to end Sept.

2 ha (90 pitches) flat, grassy

Tariff : 26,80€ ♛♛ ⬅ 🅴 (10A) – Extra per person 6,20€
Reservation fee 5€
🚐 borne 5€ – 20 🅴 26,80€

Leisure activities : 🖼	G	
Facilities : 🚿 ⛟ 🆑 🏖 🍴 🖼	P	Longitude : 4.90932
Nearby : 🗡 🍴 🖼 🏊	S	Latitude : 46.57375

VANDENESSE-EN-AUXOIS

21320 – Michelin map **320** H6 – pop. 279 – alt. 360
▶ Paris 275 – Arnay-le-Duc 16 – Autun 42 – Châteauneuf 3

⚠ Sunêlia Le Lac de Panthier 🚶🚶

📞 03 80 49 21 94, www.lac-de-panthier.com

Address : situated 2.5km northeast along the D 977bis; follow the road to Commarin and take turning to the left; near the lake

Opening times : from beginning April to beginning Oct.

5,2 ha (210 pitches) terraced

Tariff : 28€ ♛♛ ⬅ 🅴 (6A) – Extra per person 7€ – Reservation fee 15€

Rental rates : (from beginning April to beginning Oct.) – 45
14 🏠. Per night from 43 to 148€ – Per week from 181 to 1036€
Reservation fee 15€

Surroundings : 🌳 ≤⌂♀⛰	G	
Leisure activities : 🍴🗡 🖼 🏃 ♪ 🛶 🏊⬈	P	Longitude : 4.62507
🚲🖼 🏊 🏓		Latitude : 47.24935
Facilities : 🚿 ⛟ 🏖 🍴 🖼 🚗 🚣	S	
Nearby : 🚣 ♪		

VARZY

58210 – Michelin map **319** D7 – pop. 1 329 – alt. 249
▶ Paris 224 – La Charité-sur-Loire 37 – Clamecy 17 – Cosne-sur-Loire 43

⛺ Municipal du Moulin Naudin

✆ 03 86 29 43 12, mairievarzy@wanadoo.fr

Address : route de Corvol (located 1.5km north along the D 977)

Opening times : from mid May to end Sept.

3 ha (50 pitches) flat

Tariff : (2013 Price) 12€ ✶✶ ⇌ 🅴 ⒂ (5A) – Extra per person 2,90€

Situated near a small lake.

Surroundings : ▭ ♀	
Leisure activities : 🏊	**GPS** Longitude : 3.38312
Facilities : 🚿🚻♿🚮	Latitude : 47.3722
Nearby : 🍴 🏖	

VENAREY-LES-LAUMES

21150 – Michelin map **320** G4 – pop. 2 981 – alt. 235
▶ Paris 259 – Avallon 54 – Dijon 66 – Montbard 15

⛺ Municipal Alésia

✆ 03 80 96 07 76, www.venareyleslaumes.fr

Address : rue du Dct Roux (take the western exit along the D 954, follow the signs for Semur-en-Auxois and take a right turn before the bridge; beside the Brenne and near a small lake)

Opening times : from beginning April to mid Oct.

1,5 ha (67 pitches) flat, grassy

Tariff : (2013 Price) ✶ 3,50€ ⇌ 🅴 3,80€ – ⒂ (16A) 3€

Rental rates : (from beginning April to mid Oct.) ♿ (1 chalet) – 5 🏠 – 1 🛏. Per night from 50 to 70€ – Per week from 270 to 395€

🚰 borne 3€ – 5 🅴 14,70€ – 🔌⒂14,70€

Surroundings : ▭ ♀	
Leisure activities : 🏊 ⛵ 🏊	**GPS** Longitude : 4.45151
Facilities : ♿ 🚻🚿♿🚮	Latitude : 47.54425
Nearby : 🍴 🏖 (beach)	

VERMENTON

89270 – Michelin map **319** F6 – pop. 1 183 – alt. 125
▶ Paris 190 – Auxerre 24 – Avallon 28 – Vézelay 28

⛺ Municipal les Coullemières

✆ 03 86 81 53 02, www.camping-vermenton.com

Address : at Les Coullemières (to the southwest of the town, behind the station)

Opening times : from beginning April to end Sept.

1 ha (53 pitches) flat, grassy

Tariff : (2013 Price) 16,20€ ✶✶ ⇌ 🅴 ⒂ (6A) – Extra per person 3,60€

Rental rates : (2013 Price) (from beginning April to end Sept.)
♿ (1) 🛏 – 6 🚐 . Per night from 62 to 72€ – Per week from 360 to 407€

🚰 4 🅴 16,20€

A pleasant setting near a wide stretch of the Cure river.

Surroundings : ♀♀ ⛰	
Leisure activities : 🏊 ⛵ 🚴 🍴	**GPS** Longitude : 3.73123
Facilities : ♿ 🚻 (season) 🚿 🚮	Latitude : 47.65843
Nearby : 🏖 (beach) sports trail	

Using the traditional Michelin classification method, the guide provides you with an easy, speedy reference for assessing the category of each site: 1 to 5 tents (see page 10).

VIGNOLES

21200 – Michelin map **320** J7 – pop. 810 – alt. 202
▶ Paris 317 – Dijon 40 – Chalon-sur-Saône 34 – Le Creusot 51

⛺ Les Bouleaux

✆ 03 80 22 26 88, camping-les-bouleaux@hotmail.fr

Address : 11 rue Jaune (located at Chevignerot; beside a stream)

Opening times : Permanent

1,6 ha (46 pitches) flat, grassy

Tariff : (2013 Price) 17,40€ ✶✶ ⇌ 🅴 ⒂ (6A) – Extra per person 4€

Surroundings : ▭ ♀♀	
Leisure activities : 🏊	**GPS** Longitude : 4.88298
Facilities : ♿ 🚿 🚻♿🚮	Latitude : 47.02668
Nearby : 🏇	

VINCELLES

89290 – Michelin map **319** E5 – pop. 841 – alt. 110
▶ Paris 180 – Auxerre 14 – Avallon 38 – Clamecy 39

⛺ Les Ceriselles ⛺👥

✆ 03 86 42 50 47, www.campingceriselles.com

Address : route de Vincelottes (north of the village, along the D 38)

1,5 ha (80 pitches) flat, grassy

Rental rates : ♿ (1 chalet) – 16 🚐 – 2 🏠 .

🚰 borne

Beside the Nivernais canal and 150m from the Yonne river.

Surroundings : ♀ ♀	
Leisure activities : 🍴🍴 🏊 🏊 ⛵ 🚴🏊 (open air in season) 🏊	**GPS** Longitude : 3.63536
Facilities : ♿ 🚿🚻 🚿 🚮 launderette	Latitude : 47.70705
Nearby : 🏊 🍴 ⚓ 🎣	

Ph. Body / hemis.fr

Sleeping Beauty is said to slumber still within the thick stone walls of one of the Loire's fairy-tale castles. Does she await that kiss in Chambord, Azay-le-Rideau, Chenonceau, or perhaps one of the many other wonderful châteaux that lie in wait for you? To list all the Centre's architectural wonders set in the most glorious of gardens would take far too long, but visitors can appreciate some of the Loire's treasures during a season of spectacular *son et lumière* (sound and light) shows. The landscape of the region has inspired a host of writers, from Pierre de Ronsard, the 16th-century 'Prince of Poets', to Balzac and Georges Sand. All succumbed to the charm and beauty of this valley of kings, with its untamed river and atmospheric woodlands. In order to savour the region's twin talents for storytelling and culinary arts to the full, enjoy a plate of delicious chicken stew before settling down to listen to your host's tales of werewolves and other local legends!

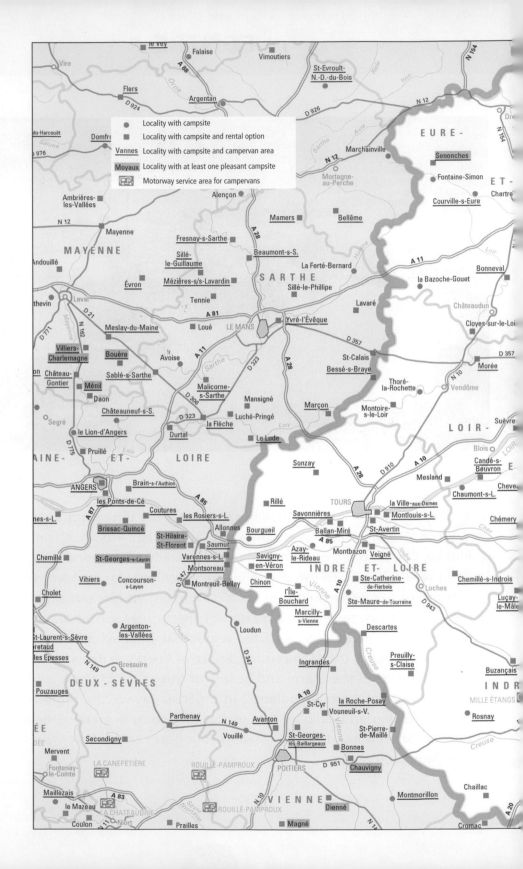

Locality with campsite
Locality with campsite and rental option
Vannes Locality with campsite and campervan area
Moyaux Locality with at least one pleasant campsite
Motorway service area for campervans

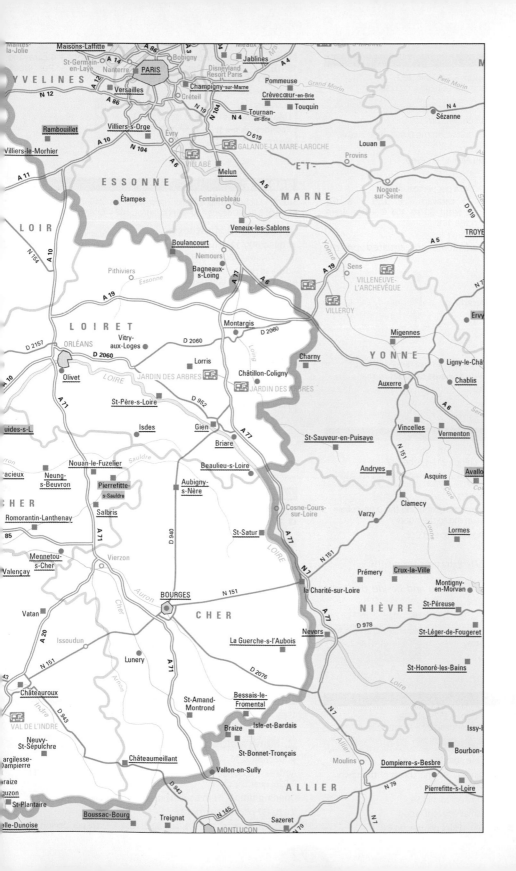

AUBIGNY-SUR-NÈRE

18700 – Michelin map **323** K2 – pop. 5 879 – alt. 180
▶ Paris 180 – Bourges 48 – Cosne-sur-Loire 41 – Gien 30

Flower Les Étangs

✆ 02 48 58 02 37, www.camping-aubigny.com

Address : route de Oizon (1.4km east along the D 923, near a lake (direct access)

Opening times : from beginning April to end Sept.

3 ha (100 pitches) flat, grassy

Tariff : 22 € ♦♦ ⇔ ▣ 🗲 (10A) – Extra per person 4,50 €
Rental rates : Permanent – 1 caravan – 8 �🚐 – 6 🏠 2 canvas bungalows. Per night from 30 to 105 € – Per week from 150 to 735 € – Reservation fee 15 €
🚗 borne 🔋 12 €

The pitches are well shaded, some are situated on the lakeshore.

Surroundings : 🗂 ♀♀
Leisure activities : 🎣 🛶 🛷
Facilities : ⚙ ⚡ 🚿 🚰 launderette 🧺
Nearby : 🍴 🏖 🎣

We have selected the best campsites in France with our usual care, listing those with the best facilities in the most pleasant surroundings.

AZAY-LE-RIDEAU

37190 – Michelin map **317** L5 – pop. 3 418 – alt. 51
▶ Paris 265 – Châtellerault 61 – Chinon 21 – Loches 58

▲ Municipal le Sabot

✆ 02 47 45 42 72, www.azaylerideau.fr

Address : rue du Stade (take the eastern exit along the D 84, follow the signs for Artannes and take turning to the right)

Opening times : from beginning April to end Oct.

6 ha (256 pitches) flat, grassy

Tariff : 16,80 € ♦♦ ⇔ ▣ 🗲 (10A) – Extra per person 3,10 €
🚗 borne 3 € – 🔋 16 €

A pleasant location close to a château and beside the Indre river.

Surroundings : 🌿 ♀
Leisure activities : 🎣 🛶 🚲 🛷
Facilities : ⚙ ⚡ 🚿 🚰 launderette
Nearby : 🍴 🎣 🛷

GPS Longitude : 0.46963
Latitude : 47.25863

BALLAN-MIRÉ

37510 – Michelin map **317** M4 – pop. 8 152 – alt. 88
▶ Paris 251 – Azay-le-Rideau 17 – Langeais 20 – Montbazon 13

⚶ Club Airotel la Mignardière

✆ 02 47 73 31 00, www.mignardiere.com

Address : 22 avenue des Aubépines (2.5km northeast of the town, not far from the small lake at Joué-Ballan)

Opening times : from beginning April to mid Sept.

2,5 ha (177 pitches) flat, grassy, small adjacent wood

Tariff : 25,50 € ♦♦ ⇔ ▣ 🗲 (10A) – Extra per person 6 €

Rental rates : (from beginning April to mid Sept.) – 4 caravans 15 🚐 – 23 🏠. Per night from 39 to 85 €) – Per week from 273 to 763 € – Reservation fee 15 €
🚗 borne 4 €

Surroundings : 🗂 ♀
Leisure activities : 🏊 🛶 🚲 🍴 🏖 🏊
Facilities : ⚙ ⚡ 🚿 🚰 🍴 🔋 🚰
Nearby : 🍴 🍴 🎣 🏇

GPS Longitude : 0.63402
Latitude : 47.35524

BARAIZE

36270 – Michelin map **323** F8 – pop. 313 – alt. 240
▶ Paris 318 – Orléans 192 – Châteauroux 47 – Guéret 86

▲ Municipal Montcocu

✆ 02 54 25 34 28, syndicat.laceguzon@wanadoo.fr – for caravans – from the 'Montcocu' locality, 12% gradient for 1km

Address : at Montcocu (4.8km southeast along the D 913, follow the signs for Éguzon and take D 72, take left turn for Pont-de-Piles)

Opening times : from beginning May to end Sept.

1 ha (26 pitches)

Tariff : (2013 Price) ♦ 2,20 € ⇔ ▣ 2,70 € – 🗲 (8A) 3,10 €
Rental rates : (2013 Price) (from beginning April to end Oct.) 4 🏠 – 5 canvas bungalows. Per week from 138 to 433 €

In a pleasant location and setting in the Creuse valley.

Surroundings : 🌿 🗂 ♀ ⛰
Leisure activities : 🍴 🎣 🛶 🛷 ✈
Facilities : ⚙ ⚡ 🚽 🍴

GPS Longitude : 1.60023
Latitude : 46.47159

This guide is updated regularly, so buy your new copy every year!

LA BAZOCHE-GOUET

28330 – Michelin map **311** B7 – pop. 1 314 – alt. 185
▶ Paris 146 – Brou 18 – Chartres 61 – Châteaudun 33

▲ Municipal la Rivière

✆ 02 37 49 36 49, commune-bazoche-gouet-28330@wanadoo.fr

Address : located 1.5km southwest along the D 927, follow the signs for la Chapelle-Guillaume and take road to the left

1,8 ha (30 pitches) flat, grassy

Beside the Yerre river and close to some lakes.

Leisure activities : 🛶 🚲 🛷
Facilities : ⚙ ▣
Nearby : 🍴

GPS Longitude : 0.9689
Latitude : 48.129

BEAULIEU-SUR-LOIRE

45630 – Michelin map **318** N6 – pop. 1 779 – alt. 156
▶ Paris 170 – Aubigny-sur-Nère 36 – Briare 15 – Gien 27

▲ Municipal Touristique du Canal

✆ 02 38 35 32 16, www.beaulieu-sur-loire.fr

Address : route de Bonny-sur-Loire (take the eastern exit along the D 926, near the canal)

Opening times : from beginning April to end Oct.

0,6 ha (37 pitches) flat, grassy

Tariff : (2013 Price) 10 € ♦♦ ⇔ ▣ 🗲 (10A) – Extra per person 2,65 €

borne
Surroundings :
Facilities :
Nearby :

GPS Longitude : 2.8176
Latitude : 47.5435

BESSAIS-LE-FROMENTAL

18210 – Michelin map **323** M6 – pop. 313 – alt. 210
▶ Paris 300 – Orléans 172 – Bourges 51 – Moulins 66

⚲ Le Village de Goule

✆ 02 48 60 82 66, www.levillagedegoule.com

Address : 1 route de Goule (4.7km southeast along the D 110 and D 110E)

120 ha/2 for camping (75 pitches) flat, grassy

Rentals : (1 chalet) – 15 – 1 yurt – 5 tipis – 5 canvas bungalows.

borne – 4

A green setting around a lake, offering various rental options.

Surroundings :
Leisure activities : pedalos
Facilities : launderette

GPS Longitude : 2.79853
Latitude : 46.73515

BONNEVAL

28800 – Michelin map **311** E6 – pop. 4 565 – alt. 128
▶ Paris 117 – Ablis 61 – Chartres 31 – Châteaudun 14

⚲ Le Bois Chièvre

✆ 02 37 47 54 01, www.camping-bonneval-28.fr

Address : route de Vouvray (located 1.5km south following signs for Conie and take turning to the right; beside the Loir)

Opening times : from beginning April to mid Oct.

4,5 ha/2,5 for camping (104 pitches) adjacent wood

Tariff : 17€ (10A) – Extra per person 5€

Rental rates : (from beginning April to mid Oct.) – 3
1 studio. Per night from 58 to 80€ – Per week from 310 to 417€

borne

In a pleasant oak wood overlooking the Loir river.

Surroundings :
Leisure activities :
Facilities : launderette
Nearby :

GPS Longitude : 1.3864
Latitude : 48.1708

BOURGES

18000 – Michelin map **323** K4 – pop. 66 786 – alt. 153
▶ Paris 244 – Châteauroux 65 – Dijon 254 – Nevers 69

⚲ Municipal Robinson

✆ 02 48 20 16 85, www.ville.bourges.fr –

Address : 26 boulevard de l'Industrie (head towards the southern exit along the N 144, follow the signs for Montluçon and take the turning to the left, near the Lac d'Auron, take exit A 71 and follow the signs for Bourges Centre)

Opening times : from mid March to mid Nov.

2,2 ha (107 pitches)

Tariff : 4,40€ 5,60€ – (16A) 8,60€

borne

Not far from the town centre (1.2km), in a green setting, but choose the pitches away from the road.

Surroundings :
Leisure activities :
Facilities : launderette
Nearby :

GPS Longitude : 2.39488
Latitude : 47.07232

BOURGUEIL

37140 – Michelin map **317** J5 – pop. 3 924 – alt. 42
▶ Paris 281 – Angers 81 – Chinon 16 – Saumur 23

⚲ Municipal Parc Capitaine

✆ 02 47 97 85 62, www.bourgueil.fr

Address : 31 avenue du Général de Gaulle (1.5 km south along the D 749, follow the signs for Chinon)

Opening times : from mid May to mid Sept.

2 ha (87 pitches) flat, grassy

Tariff : 2,20€ 6,50€ – (7A) 2,45€

borne – 2 6,50€

In a green setting with plenty of shade, near a lake.

Surroundings :
Leisure activities :
Facilities :
Nearby : pedalos

GPS Longitude : 0.16684
Latitude : 47.27381

Using the traditional Michelin classification method, the guide provides you with an easy, speedy reference for assessing the category of each site: 1 to 5 tents (see page 10).

BRACIEUX

41250 – Michelin map **318** G6 – pop. 1 256 – alt. 70
▶ Paris 185 – Blois 19 – Montrichard 39 – Orléans 64

⚲ Indigo Les Châteaux

✆ 02 54 46 41 84, www.camping-indigo.com

Address : 11 rue Roger-Brun (take the northern exit, follow the signs for Blois; beside the Beuvron)

Opening times : from end March to beginning Nov.

8 ha (350 pitches) flat, grassy

Tariff : 28,60€ (10A) Extra per person 6€ – Reservation fee 22€

Rental rates : (from end March to beginning Nov.) (1 chalet) 6 caravans – 20 – 10 – 26 tent lodges. Per night from 40 to 114€ Per week from 196 to 798€

Reservation fee 22€

borne 7€

In a wooded setting with a variety of tree species.

HUTTOPIA

Surroundings :
Leisure activities :
Facilities : launderette

GPS Longitude : 1.53821
Latitude : 47.55117

BRIARE

45250 – Michelin map **318** N6 – pop. 5 688 – alt. 135
▶ Paris 160 – Orléans 85 – Gien 11 – Montargis 50

⛺ Onlycamp Le Martinet

✆ 02 38 31 24 50, campinglemartinet.fr

Address : at Val Martinet (located 1km north via town centre, between the Loire river and the canal)

Opening times : from beginning April to end Sept.

4,5 ha (160 pitches) flat, grassy

Tariff : 17,80€ ✶✶ 🚗 ▣ 🔌 (10A) – Extra per person 3,80€

🚰 borne 3€

Surroundings : ⛰ 🟢🟢	**G** Longitude : 2.72441
Leisure activities : ⛺	**P** Latitude : 47.64226
Facilities : ♿ ⚡ ▥ 🚿 ♨ 🚻 🗑	**S**
Nearby : 🏊 🎣	

BUZANÇAIS

36500 – Michelin map **323** E5 – pop. 4 501 – alt. 111
▶ Paris 286 – Le Blanc 47 – Châteauroux 25 – Châtellerault 78

⛰ Aquadis Loisirs La Tête Noire

✆ 02 54 84 17 27, www.aquadis-loisirs.com

Address : to the northwest along the r. des Ponts; beside the Indre river, near the stadium

Opening times : from end April to end Sept.

2,5 ha (134 pitches) flat, grassy

Tariff : ✶ 3,70€ 🚗 2,10€ ▣ 3,70€ – 🔌 (6A) 3,70€ – Reservation fee 9,90€

Rental rates : (from end April to end Sept.) – 4 🚐. Per night from 36 to 52€ – Per week from 204 to 265€ – Reservation fee 19,80€

🚰 🔋11€

Surroundings : 🟢🟢	**G** Longitude : 1.41805
Leisure activities : 🏛 🏋 🛶	**P** Latitude : 46.89285
Facilities : ♿ ⚡ ▣ 🚿 🚻 🗑	**S**
Nearby : 🍴 🛝 skateboarding	

CANDÉ-SUR-BEUVRON

41120 – Michelin map **318** E7 – pop. 1 462 – alt. 70
▶ Paris 199 – Blois 15 – Chaumont-sur-Loire 7 – Montrichard 21

⛰ Kawan Village La Grande Tortue

✆ 02 54 44 15 20, www.la-grande-tortue.com

Address : 3 route de Pontlevoy (500m south along the D 751, follow the signs for Chaumont-sus-Loire and take the turning to the left, follow the signs for La Pieuse, not far from the Beuvron river)

Opening times : from beginning April to mid Sept.

5 ha (208 pitches)

Tariff : 42€ ✶✶ 🚗 ▣ 🔌 (10A) – Extra per person 10,50€ Reservation fee 12€

Rental rates : (from beginning April to end Sept.) – 28 🚐 8 🏠. Per night from 52 to 115€ – Per week from 268 to 987€ Reservation fee 12€

🚰 borne

Surroundings : ⛰ 🚗 🟢🟢	**G** Longitude : 1.2583
Leisure activities : 🍴✗ 🏛 🏋 🎱 (open air in season)	**P** Latitude : 47.48992
Facilities : ♿ ⚡ cc 🚿 🚻 ♨ 🗑 🚰	**S**

CHAILLAC

36310 – Michelin map **323** D8 – pop. 1 136 – alt. 180
▶ Paris 333 – Argenton-sur-Creuse 35 – Le Blanc 34 – Magnac-Laval 34

⛺ Municipal les Vieux Chênes

✆ 02 54 25 61 39, chaillac36.fr

Address : allée des Vieux Chênes (southwest of the town, 500m from a lake)

Opening times : Permanent

2 ha (40 pitches)

Tariff : (2013 Price) ✶ 2,10€ 🚗 ▣ 2,60€ – 🔌 (0A) 3,30€

Rental rates : Permanent – 3 🏠. Per night from 42 to 66€ Per week from 213 to 331€

A green, well-kept site with flowers, close to the stadium and beside a lake.

Surroundings : 🏊 🚗 🟢🟢	**G** Longitude : 1.29539
Leisure activities : 🏋 🛶 fitness trail	**P** Latitude : 46.43224
Facilities : ⚡ 🚿 ▥ ♨ 🗑	**S**
Nearby : 🍴 🎣 🏊 pedalos	

To visit a town or region, use the MICHELIN Green Guides.

CHARTRES

28000 – Michelin map **311** E5 – pop. 39 122 – alt. 142
▶ Paris 92 – Orléans 84 – Dreux 38 – Rambouillet 45

⛰ Les Bords de l'Eure

✆ 02 37 28 79 43, www.auxbordsdeleure.com

Address : 9 rue de Launay

4 ha (110 pitches) flat, grassy

Rentals : 2 caravans – 1 🚐.

In a pleasant wooded setting near the river.

Surroundings : 🟢🟢	**G** Longitude : 1.4951
Leisure activities : 🏛 🏋 ⛺ pedalos	**P** Latitude : 48.43265
Facilities : ♿ ⚡ ▥ ♨ ♨ 🗑	**S**
Nearby : 🍴 🛶 sports trail	

CHÂTEAUMEILLANT

18370 – Michelin map **323** J7 – pop. 2 082 – alt. 247
▶ Paris 313 – Aubusson 79 – Bourges 66 – La Châtre 19

⛰ Municipal l'Étang Merlin

✆ 02 48 61 31 38, http://ot.chateaumeillant.free.fr

Address : route de Vicq (located 1km northwest along the D 70, follow the signs for Beddes and take D 80 to the left)

Opening times : from beginning May to end Sept.

1,5 ha (30 pitches) flat, grassy

Tariff : ✶ 2,80€ 🚗 ▣ 3,30€ – 🔌 (5A) 2,25€

Rental rates : Permanent ♿ 🚳 – 2 🚐 – 6 🏠. Per night from 27 to 49€ – Per week from 157 to 293€

🚰 borne 10,70€

The chalets are in a pleasant setting beside the lake.

Surroundings : 🚗 🟢	**G** Longitude : 2.19034
Leisure activities : 🏛 🏋 🚲 🛶	**P** Latitude : 46.56818
Facilities : ♿ ⚡ 🚿 ♨ 🚻 🗑	**S**
Nearby : 🍴 🏊	

CHÂTEAUROUX

36000 – Michelin map **323** G6 – pop. 46 386 – alt. 155
▶ Paris 265 – Blois 101 – Bourges 65 – Châtellerault 98

⛰ Aquadis Loisirs Le Rochat Belle-Isle

☎ 02 54 08 96 29, www.aquadis-loisirs.com

Address : 17 avenue du Parc de Loisirs (continue north along the av. de Paris and take turning to the left; beside the Indre river and 100m from a small lake)

Opening times : from beginning April to end Oct.

4 ha (205 pitches) flat, grassy

Tariff : (2013 Price) 19,30€ ♦♦ ⇔ 🅴 🅷 (10A) –
Extra per person 4,30€ – Reservation fee 9,90€

Rental rates : (from beginning April to end Oct.) – 8 🚐.
Per night from 68€ – Per week from 166 to 525€ – Reservation fee 19,80€

🚰 🛒11€

There's a free bus service nearby to the town centre.

Surroundings : 🌲 ♤♤
Leisure activities : 🏛 ♣♠
Facilities : ♿ ⌂ 🎦 ♨♠♡ 🚽 launderette
Nearby : ♥ ✖ 🔲 ♨ ⚓ ♤ bowling, fitness trail
Longitude : 1.69472
Latitude : 46.8236

CHÂTILLON-COLIGNY

45230 – Michelin map **318** O5 – pop. 1 962 – alt. 130
▶ Paris 140 – Auxerre 70 – Gien 26 – Joigny 48

⛺ Municipal de la Lancière

☎ 06 16 09 30 26, lalanciere@wanadoo.fr – limited spaces for one-night stay

Address : route de la Lancière (south of the town, between the Loing river and the Briare canal)

1,9 ha (55 pitches) flat, grassy

Surroundings : 🌲 ♤♤
Leisure activities : ♣♠ ♨ (small swimming pool)
Facilities : ⌂ launderette, refrigerated food storage facilities
Nearby : ⚓
Longitude : 2.84394
Latitude : 47.81816

CHAUMONT-SUR-LOIRE

41150 – Michelin map **318** E7 – pop. 1 037 – alt. 69
▶ Paris 201 – Amboise 21 – Blois 18 – Contres 24

⛺ Municipal Grosse Grève

☎ 02 54 20 95 22, www.chaumont-sur-loire.fr – ♨

Address : 81 rue de Marue de Lattre-de-Tassigny (take the eastern exit along the D 751, follow the signs for Blois and take the turning to the left, before the bridge; beside the Loire river)

Opening times : from end April to end Sept.

4 ha (150 pitches)

Tariff : (2013 Price) ♦ 3€ ⇔ 1€ 🅴 2€ – 🅷 (10A) 2€
🚰 borne 2€

Leisure activities : ♣♠ ♥
Facilities : ♿ ⌂ 🎦 ♡ launderette
Nearby : 🚲
Longitude : 1.1999
Latitude : 47.48579

CHÉMERY

41700 – Michelin map **318** F7 – pop. 940 – alt. 90
▶ Paris 213 – Blois 32 – Montrichard 29 – Romorantin-Lanthenay 29

⛺ Municipal le Gué

☎ 02 54 32 97 40, www.camping-le-gue.com – ♨

Address : route de Couddes (to the west of the village; beside a stream)

Opening times : Permanent

1,2 ha (50 pitches) flat, grassy

Tariff : 17€ ♦♦ ⇔ 🅴 🅷 (16A) – Extra per person 3,80€

Rental rates : Permanent ♨ (from beginning Jan to end Dec) 2 🚐. Per night from 95 to 135€ – Per week from 299 to 690€
🚰 borne 3,50€ – 🛒11€

Surroundings : ♨ ♤
Leisure activities : ♨
Facilities : ⌂ 🎦 ♡ 🅰
Nearby : ♥
Longitude : 1.47388
Latitude : 47.34562

CHEMILLÉ-SUR-INDROIS

37460 – Michelin map **317** P6 – pop. 221 – alt. 97
▶ Paris 244 – Châtillon-sur-Indre 25 – Loches 16 – Montrichard 27

⛰ Les Coteaux du Lac

☎ 02 47 92 77 83, www.lescoteauxdulac.com

Address : at Leisure base (to the southwest of the town)

Opening times : from end March to beginning Oct.

1 ha (72 pitches)

Tariff : 26,90€ ♦♦ ⇔ 🅴 🅷 (16A) – Extra per person 5,90€ – Reservation fee 14€

Rental rates : (from end March to beginning Oct.) – 29 🏠 4 canvas bungalows. Per night from 55 to 151 € – Per week from 195 to 1057€ – Reservation fee 14€
🚰 borne – 4 🅴 14€ – 🛒10€

An attractive location near a lake.

Surroundings : ≼
Facilities : ⌂ ♡
Nearby : ♥ ✖ ♣♠ ♨ ♨ ⚓ ♢ pedalos
Longitude : 1.15889
Latitude : 47.15772

CHEVERNY

41700 – Michelin map **318** F7 – pop. 939 – alt. 110
▶ Paris 194 – Blois 14 – Châteauroux 88 – Orléans 73

⛰ Sites et Paysages Les Saules ♠♠

CHERRIER

☎ 02 54 79 90 01, www.camping-cheverny.com

Address : route de Contres (3km southeast along the D 102)

Opening times : from beginning April to mid Sept.

8 ha (164 pitches) flat, grassy

Tariff : 33,50€ ♦♦ ⇔ 🅴 🅷 (10A) – Extra per person 4,50€

Rental rates : (from beginning April to mid Sept.) ♿ (1 chalet) ♨ – 11 🏠 – 4 tent lodges. Per night from 40 to 94€ – Per week from 245 to 658€
🚰 borne – 🛒14€

Surroundings : ♤♤
Leisure activities : ♥ ✖ 🔲 ♣ ♠♠ 🚲 ♨ ♢ sports trail
Facilities : ♿ ⌂ 🎦 ♨ ♡ launderette ♨ ♢
Longitude : 1.45184
Latitude : 47.47871

CHINON

37500 – Michelin map **317** K6 – pop. 7 986 – alt. 40
▶ Paris 285 – Châtellerault 51 – Poitiers 80 – Saumur 29

⚠ Intercommunal de l'île Auger

📞 02 47 93 08 35, www.camping-chinon.com

Address : quai Danton

Opening times : from beginning April to end Oct.

4,5 ha (277 pitches) flat, grassy

Tariff : (2013 Price) 14,50€ ★★ ⊕ 🔲 (12A)
Extra per person 2,75€

Rental rates : (2013 Price) (from mid May to end Sept.) 🐾
4 canvas bungalows. Per night from 35 to 42€ – Per week
from 210 to 252€

🚐 borne 4,50€ – 🛒 9€

*In a pleasant location opposite a château and beside the
Vienne river.*

| Surroundings : ≤ town and Château de Chinon ♀ Leisure activities : 🛶🏄 🤿 Facilities : ⅙ ☞ (summer) 🔥🍳 🔥 Nearby : 🍴 🔲 🏊 | GPS | Longitude : 0.23654 Latitude : 47.16379 |

CLOYES-SUR-LE-LOIR

28220 – Michelin map **311** D8 – pop. 2 692 – alt. 97
▶ Paris 143 – Blois 54 – Chartres 57 – Châteaudun 13

⚠ Parc de Loisirs - Le Val Fleuri

📞 02 37 98 50 53, www.val-fleuri.fr – limited spaces for one-night stay

Address : route de Montigny (take the northern exit along the N 10,
follow the signs for Chartres then turn left onto D 23)

Opening times : from mid March to mid Nov.

5 ha (196 pitches) flat, grassy

Tariff : 26,90€ ★★ ⊕ 🔲 (6A) – Extra per person 6,40€
Reservation fee 10€

Rental rates : (from mid March to mid Nov.) – 10 🚐. Per week
from 295 to 735€ – Reservation fee 22€

In a pleasant location beside the Loir river.

| Surroundings : 🚪 ♀ Leisure activities : 🍴🍴 🏠 🛶🏄 🚴 🏊 🏊 🛶 pedalos 🐾 Facilities : ⅙ ☞ 🔥 🍳 🍴 launderette 🏖 🗑 Nearby : 🍴 ♪ | GPS | Longitude : 1.2333 Latitude : 48.0024 |

COURVILLE-SUR-EURE

28190 – Michelin map **311** D5 – pop. 2 776 – alt. 170
▶ Paris 111 – Bonneval 47 – Chartres 20 – Dreux 37

⚠ Municipal les Bords de l'Eure

📞 02 37 23 76 38, www.courville-sur-eure.fr

Address : rue Thiers (take the southern exit along the D 114)

1,5 ha (56 pitches) flat, grassy

🚐 borne – 12 🔲

A wooded setting on the banks of the river.

| Surroundings : 🚪 ♀ Leisure activities : 🤿 Facilities : ⅙ ☞ 🔥 Nearby : 🛶🏄 🏊 | GPS | Longitude : 1.2414 Latitude : 48.4462 |

DESCARTES

37160 – Michelin map **317** N7 – pop. 3 817 – alt. 50
▶ Paris 292 – Châteauroux 94 – Châtellerault 24 – Chinon 51

⚠ Municipal la Grosse Motte

📞 02 47 59 85 90, www.ville-descartes.fr

Address : allée Léo Lagrange (take the southern exit along the D 750,
follow the signs for Le Blanc and take boulevard to the right; beside
the Creuse river)

Opening times : from beginning May to end Sept.

1 ha (50 pitches)

Tariff : 9,20€ ★★ ⊕ 🔲 (15A) – Extra per person 2,40€

Rental rates : Permanent 🐾 – 8 🛖 – 1 gîte. Per week
from 250 to 390€

🚐 7 🔲 9,20€

*In a shady park next to a leisure centre and the municipal
gardens.*

| Surroundings : 🏖 🚪 ♀♀ Leisure activities : 🤿 Facilities : ☞ 🔥🍳 Nearby : 🛶🏄 🍴 🚵 🏊 🏊 | GPS | Longitude : 0.69715 Latitude : 46.96961 |

ÉGUZON

36270 – Michelin map **323** F8 – pop. 1 362 – alt. 243
▶ Paris 319 – Argenton-sur-Creuse 20 – La Châtre 47 – Guéret 50

⚠ Municipal du Lac Les Nugiras

📞 02 54 47 45 22, www.campingmunicipal-eguzon.com

Address : route de Messant (3km southeast along the D 36, follow
the signs for the Lac de Chambon then continue 500m along the
turning to the right; 450m from the lake)

Opening times : Permanent

4 ha (180 pitches)

Tariff : 12,80€ ★★ ⊕ 🔲 (10A) – Extra per person 3,26€

Rental rates : (from beginning March to end Nov.) – 7 🛖
5 canvas bungalows. Per night from 32 to 125€ – Per week
from 143 to 452€

🚐 borne 4,96€

*A peaceful site laid out on terraces, near a well-equipped
boating centre.*

| Surroundings : ≤ ♀ Leisure activities : 🍴 🏠 🛶🏄 multi-sports ground Facilities : ⅙ ☞ 🔥🍳 🔥🍳 🔥 🏖 Nearby : 🚴 🚣 (beach) 🏊 🤿 ♪ water skiing | GPS | Longitude : 1.604 Latitude : 46.433 |

FONTAINE-SIMON

28240 – Michelin map **311** C4 – pop. 870 – alt. 200
▶ Paris 117 – Chartres 40 – Dreux 40 – Évreux 66

⚠ Du Perche

📞 02 37 81 88 11, www.campingduperche.com

Address : rue de la Ferrière (1.2km north following signs for
Senonches and take turning to the left)

Opening times : Permanent

5 ha (115 pitches) flat, grassy

Tariff : (2013 Price) 20€ ★★ ⊕ 🔲 (6A) – Extra per person 4€

Rental rates : (2013 Price) Permanent 🚐 – 2 🛏 – 2 🏠.
Per night from 65 to 75€ – Per week from 360 to 455€
🚐 borne – 7 ▣
Beside the Eure river and a small lake.

Leisure activities : 🏊 🎣
Facilities : 🚿 🕯 (July–Aug.) 🅿 🔌 📶 🗐
Nearby : ✕ 🖼 🛶 🎣

GPS	Longitude : 1.0194
	Latitude : 48.5132

GARGILESSE-DAMPIERRE

36190 – Michelin map **323** F7 – pop. 326 – alt. 220
▶ Paris 310 – Châteauroux 45 – Guéret 59 – Poitiers 113

⚠ La Chaumerette

🖊 02 54 47 84 22, www.gargilesse.fr – ⛟

Address : at Le Moulin (1.4km southwest along the D 39, follow the signs for Argenton-sur-Creuse and take the road to the left leading to the Barrage de La Roche au Moine (dam)

Opening times : from beginning May to end Sept.

2,6 ha (72 pitches) flat, grassy

Tariff · (2013 Price) 👤 1,60€ – 🚗 6,20€ – ▣ 3,10€ – [⚡] (10A) 4,50€
Rental rates : (2013 Price) (from beginning March to end Nov.)
8 🏠. Per night from 25 to 41€ – Per week from 172 to 284€

In a picturesque setting, part of the site is on an island in the Creuse river.

Surroundings : 🌿 💧💧
Leisure activities : 🍴 ✕ 🎣
Facilities : 🚿 🕯 🅿

GPS	Longitude : 1.58346
	Latitude : 46.5077

GIEN

45500 – Michelin map **318** M5 – pop. 15 161 – alt. 162
▶ Paris 149 – Auxerre 85 – Bourges 77 – Cosne-sur-Loire 46

🏕 Kawan Village Les Bois du Bardelet 👥

🖊 02 38 67 47 39, www.bardelet.com

Address : at Le Petit Bardelet, route de Bourges (5km southwest along the D 940 et 2km along the turning to the left – recommended route for vehicles coming from Gien, take the D 53, follow the signs for Poilly-lez-Gien and take first turning to the right)

Opening times : from mid April to end Sept.

15 ha/8 for camping (260 pitches)

Tariff : 28,20€ 👤👤 🚗 ▣ [⚡] (10A)
Extra per person 7€ – Reservation fee 9€

Rental rates : (from mid April to end Sept.) 🅿 – 33 🛏 – 45 🏠.
Per night from 57 to 156€ – Per week from 399 to 1092€ – Reservation fee 9€

🚐 borne – 25 ▣ 26,30€ – 🚐 [⚡]12€

Surroundings : 🌿 💧💧
Leisure activities : 🍴 ✕ 🎮 🏊 💆 ♨ jacuzzi 🚲 🎯 🏓 🖼 🛶 🎣
Facilities : 🚿 🕯 🔌 📼 👶 – 4 individual sanitary facilities (🏠 🚽 wc) 🚿 📶 launderette 🗐 🔧

GPS	Longitude : 2.61619
	Latitude : 47.64116

LA GUERCHE-SUR-L'AUBOIS

18150 – Michelin map **323** N5 – pop. 3 395 – alt. 184
▶ Paris 242 – Bourges 48 – La Charité-sur-Loire 31 – Nevers 22

⚠ Municipal le Robinson

🖊 02 48 74 18 86, www.laguerche-aubois.fr

Address : 2 rue de Couvache (1.4km southeast along the D 200, follow the signs for Apremont then take a right turn, 600m along the D 218 and take road to the left)

Opening times : from end April to beginning Oct.

1,5 ha (33 pitches)

Tariff : (2013 Price) 14€ 👤👤 🚗 ▣ [⚡] (6A) – Extra per person 2,50€
Rental rates : (2013 Price) (from end April to beginning Oct.)
6 🏠. Per night from 48 to 60€ – Per week from 310 to 405€
🚐 borne

A pleasant location beside a small lake with rather old chalets, some adjacent to each other.

Surroundings : 🌿 💧💧
Leisure activities : 🎮 🚲 🎣
Facilities : 🚿 🅿 🔌 📶 🗐
Nearby : 🍷 🏊 🛶 pedalos

GPS	Longitude : 2.95872
	Latitude : 46.94029

The guide covers all 22 regions of France – see the map and list of regions on pages 4–5.

L'ÎLE-BOUCHARD

37220 – Michelin map **317** L6 – pop. 1 754 – alt. 41
▶ Paris 284 – Châteauroux 118 – Châtellerault 49 – Chinon 16

⚠ Les Bords de Vienne

🖊 02 47 95 23 59, http://www.campingbordsdevienne.com

Address : 4 allée du camping (near the quartier St-Gilles, upstream of the bridge over the Vienne, near the river)

Opening times : from mid March to end Oct.

1 ha (90 pitches) flat, grassy

Tariff : 21€ 👤👤 🚗 ▣ [⚡] (16A) – Extra per person 5€
Rental rates : Permanent – 4 🛏 – 1 gîte. Per night from 60 to 75€
Per week from 223 to 510€ – Reservation fee 20€
🚐 borne 2€

Surroundings : 💧💧
Leisure activities : 🏊 🎣
Facilities : 🚿 🕯 📶 🗐
Nearby : 🍴 🛶

GPS	Longitude : 0.42833
	Latitude : 47.12139

ISDES

45620 – Michelin map **318** K5 – pop. 612 – alt. 152
▶ Paris 174 – Bourges 75 – Gien 35 – Orléans 40

⚠ Municipal les Prés Bas

🖊 06 78 43 46 28, www.isdes.fr

Address : take the northeastern exit along the D 59, near a lake

Opening times : from beginning April to end Oct.

0,5 ha (20 pitches) flat, grassy

Tariff : 👤 3€ 🚗 1,50€ ▣ 3,50€ [⚡] (15A)

Surroundings : 🌿
Leisure activities : 🎣
Facilities : 🚿 🅿 🚿 🔧
Nearby : 🏊

GPS	Longitude : 2.2565
	Latitude : 47.6744

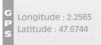

LORRIS

45260 – Michelin map **318** M4 – pop. 2 941 – alt. 126
▶ Paris 132 – Gien 27 – Montargis 23 – Orléans 55

⚠ L'Étang des Bois

✆ 02 38 92 32 00, www.canal-orleans.fr

Address : 6km west along the D 88, follow the signs for Châteauneuf-sur-Loire, near the lake at Les Bois

Opening times : from beginning April to end Sept.

3 ha (150 pitches) grassy

Tariff : 👤 3,60€ 🚗 🅟 5,90€ – 🔌 (10A) 4,50€

Rental rates : (from beginning April to end Sept.) – 4 🚐
Per night from 52 to 67€ – Per week from 310 to 420€
A wooded setting in a pleasant location.

Surroundings : 🏕 🎣
Leisure activities : 🏖 🔥
Facilities : 🚿 🚮 ♨ 🧺 🚰 🛗
Nearby : 🍴 🏊 🏖 (beach) 🎣 🏇

G P S	Longitude : 2.44454
	Latitude : 47.87393

LUÇAY-LE-MÂLE

36360 – Michelin map **323** E4 – pop. 1 496 – alt. 160
▶ Paris 240 – Le Blanc 73 – Blois 60 – Châteauroux 43

⚠ Municipal la Foulquetière

✆ 02 54 40 43 31, www.lucaylemale.fr

Address : at La Foulquetière (3.8km southwest along the D 960, follow the signs for Loches, D 13, follow the signs for Ecueillé to the left and take the road to the right)

Opening times : from beginning April to mid Oct.

1,5 ha (30 pitches) flat and relatively flat, grassy

Tariff : 👤 2€ 🚗 🅟 2,50€ – 🔌 (6A) 1,50€

Rental rates : Permanent 🚭 – 3 🏠 – 2 gîtes. Per night from 88€
Per week from 263 to 330€
🚐 borne 3€
80m from a small lake that is very popular with anglers.

Surroundings : 🏕 🎣
Leisure activities : 🏖 🔥
Facilities : 🛗 ♿ 🚮 ♨ 🛠
Nearby : 🍴 🍴 🎣 🏖 🔥 🏖 (beach) 🎣 pedalos

G P S	Longitude : 1.40417
	Latitude : 47.1109

LUNERY

18400 – Michelin map **323** J5 – pop. 1 449 – alt. 150
▶ Paris 256 – Bourges 23 – Châteauroux 51 – Issoudun 28

⚠ Intercommunal de Lunery

✆ 02 48 68 07 38, www.cc-fercher.fr – 🏕

Address : 6 rue de l'Abreuvoir (in the town, near the church)

Opening times : from mid May to mid Sept.

0,5 ha (37 pitches) flat, grassy

Tariff : (2013 Price) 👤 4€ 🚗 🅟 6€ – 🔌 (10A) 2€

Based around the remains of an old windmill near the Cher river.

Surroundings : 🌿 🏕 🎣
Leisure activities : 🏖 🔥
Facilities : 🛗 🚿 🚮 🛠
Nearby : 🍴 🍴 🍴

G P S	Longitude : 2.27038
	Latitude : 46.93658

MARCILLY-SUR-VIENNE

37800 – Michelin map **317** M6 – pop. 559 – alt. 60
▶ Paris 280 – Azay-le-Rideau 32 – Chinon 30 – Châtellerault 29

⚠ Intercommunal la Croix de la Motte

✆ 02 47 65 20 38, www.cc-saintemauredetouraine.fr

Address : 1.2km north along the D 18, follow the signs for L'Ile-Bouchard and take turning to the right

Opening times : from mid June to mid Sept.

1,5 ha (61 pitches) flat, grassy

Tariff : (2013 Price) 👤 2,50€ 🚗 🅟 3€ – 🔌 (16A) 3€

Rental rates : (2013 Price) (from mid June to mid Sept.) 🚭
2 🚐 – 1 tent lodge . Per night 31 € – Per week from 150 to 315€
🚐 borne 4,10€
In pleasant, shaded surroundings near the Vienne river.

Surroundings : 🌿 🏕 🎣
Leisure activities : 🏖 🔥
Facilities : ♿ 🚿 🚮 ♨ 🛠

G P S	Longitude : 0.54337
	Latitude : 47.05075

MENNETOU-SUR-CHER

41320 – Michelin map **318** I8 – pop. 878 – alt. 100
▶ Paris 209 – Bourges 56 – Romorantin-Lanthenay 18 – Selles-sur-Cher 27

⚠ Municipal Val Rose

✆ 02 54 98 11 02, mairie.mennetou@wanadoo.fr

Address : rue de Val Rose (south of the town, to the right after the bridge over the canal, 100m from the Cher river)

Opening times : from beginning May to beginning Sept.

0,8 ha (50 pitches) flat, grassy

Tariff : 👤 2€ 🚗 🅟 3€ – 🔌 (2A) 2,50€

🚐 borne 2€ – 🚿 🔌 8€

Surroundings : 🏕 🎣
Leisure activities : 🏖 🔥
Facilities : ♿ 🚿 🚮
Nearby : 🍴 🏊 🎣 💧

G P S	Longitude : 1.86173
	Latitude : 47.26937

Some campsites benefit from proximity to a municipal leisure centre.

MESLAND

41150 – Michelin map **318** D6 – pop. 547 – alt. 79
▶ Paris 205 – Amboise 19 – Blois 23 – Château-Renault 20

⚠ Yelloh! Village Le Parc du Val de Loire 👥

✆ 02 54 70 27 18, www.parcduvaldeloire.com

Address : 155 route de Fleuray (located 1.5km west)

Opening times : from beginning April to end Sept.

15 ha (300 pitches)

Tariff : 18€ 👥 🚗 🅟 🔌 (10A) – Extra per person 6€

Rental rates : (from beginning April to end Sept.) 🚭 – 130 🚐
20 🏠. Per night from 39 to 97€ – Per week from 234 to 582€
In a wooded setting opposite a vineyard.

Surroundings : 🌿 🏕 🎣
Leisure activities : 🍴 🍴 🏖 🏀 🔥 🚴 🏊
🔥 🏊 🎿 ⛷
Facilities : ♿ 🚿 🚮 ♨ 🧺 🚰 🛠 🛠 🛠

G P S	Longitude : 1.10477
	Latitude : 47.51001

MONTARGIS

45200 – Michelin map **318** N4 – pop. 15 020 – alt. 95
▶ Paris 109 – Auxerre 252 – Nemours 36 – Nevers 126

⚐ Municipal de la Forêt

☏ 02 38 98 00 20, camping@agglo-montargoise.fr

Address : 38 avenue Louis-Maurice Chautemps (take the northern exit along the D 943 and continue 1km along the D 815, follow the signs for Paucourt)

Opening times : from beginning Feb. to end Nov.

5,5 ha (100 pitches) flat, grassy, stony, sandy

Tariff : ♀ 3,10€ 🚗 2,40€ 📧 3,10€ – ⚡ (10A) 7,80€
🚐 borne – 🚐 ⚡8,30€

Surroundings : ♨♨♨
Leisure activities : 🏊 ⛵
Facilities : 🚿 ⚐ 🏢 ♨ 🚰 🍴
Nearby : ✂ 🏊

G P S Longitude : 2.75102
Latitude : 48.00827

MONTBAZON

37250 – Michelin map **317** N5 – pop. 3 904 – alt. 59
▶ Paris 247 – Châtellerault 59 – Chinon 41 – Loches 33

⚑ La Grange Rouge

☏ 02 47 26 06 43, www.camping-montbazon.com

Address : route de Tours, road RD 910 (after the bridge over the Indre; behind the tourist office and near the stadium)

2 ha (108 pitches) flat, grassy

Rentals : 15 🏠 .

In a pleasant location beside a river and near the town centre.

Surroundings : ♨♨
Leisure activities : ✗ 🏊 🏊
Facilities : 🚿 ⚐ ♨ 🍴 🏢
Nearby : ✂ 🎣 🏃 sports trail

G P S Longitude : 0.7159
Latitude : 47.29049

MONTLOUIS-SUR-LOIRE

37270 – Michelin map **317** N4 – pop. 10 448 – alt. 60
▶ Paris 235 – Amboise 14 – Blois 49 – Château-Renault 32

⚑ Aquadis Loisirs Les Peupliers

☏ 02 47 50 81 90, www.aquadis-loisirs.com

Address : located 1.5km west along the D 751, follow the signs for Tours, 100m from the Loire river

Opening times : from beginning April to end Oct.

6 ha (252 pitches) flat, grassy

Tariff : 17,20€ ♀♀ 🚗 📧 ⚡ (10A) – Extra per person 3,85€ – Reservation fee 9,90€

Rental rates : (from beginning April to end Oct.) – 8 🏠 . Per night from 84 to 94€ – Per week from 215 to 454€ – Reservation fee 19,80€

🚐 borne 5,90€ – 🚐 11€
A pleasant wooded site.

Surroundings : 🏞 ♨♨
Leisure activities : 🍴 🏊 ⛵
Facilities : 🚿 ⚐ 🏧 ♨ 🍴 🏢 🚰
Nearby : ✂ 🏊 🏊

G P S Longitude : 0.81144
Latitude : 47.39437

MONTOIRE-SUR-LE-LOIR

41800 – Michelin map **318** C5 – pop. 4 081 – alt. 65
▶ Paris 186 – Blois 52 – Château-Renault 21 – La Flèche 81

⚑ Municipal les Reclusages

☏ 02 54 85 02 53, www.mairie-montoire.fr

Address : at Les Reclusages (southwestern exit, follow the signs for Tours and follow the signs for Lavardin to the left after the bridge)

Opening times : from beginning May to end Sept.

2 ha (133 pitches) flat, grassy

Tariff : ♀ 3,67€ 🚗 📧 2€ – ⚡ (10A) 3,85€

Rental rates : (from beginning May to end Sept.) – 4 🏠. Per night from 61€ – Per week from 209 to 335€

Beside the Loir river.

Surroundings : ♨♨
Leisure activities : 🍴 🏊 ⛵
Facilities : 🚿 ⚐ 🍴 🏢
Nearby : ⛵ 🏃 🏊 🏊

G P S Longitude : 0.86289
Latitude : 47.74788

Michelin classification:

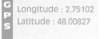

⚑⚑⚑⚑	*Extremely comfortable, equipped to a very high standard*
⚑⚑⚑	*Very comfortable, equipped to a high standard*
⚑⚑⚑	*Comfortable and well equipped*
⚑⚑	*Reasonably comfortable*
⚑	*Satisfactory*

MORÉE

41160 – Michelin map **318** E4 – pop. 1 117 – alt. 96
▶ Paris 154 – Blois 42 – Châteaudun 24 – Orléans 58

⚐ Municipal de la Varenne

☏ 02 54 89 15 15, mairie-de-moree@wanadoo.fr

Address : chemin de la Varenne (to the west of the town; beside a small lake, recommended route via the D 19, follow the signs for St-Hilaire-la-Gravelle and take road to the left)

Opening times : from Easter to end Sept.

0,8 ha (43 pitches) flat, grassy

Tariff : ♀ 4€ 🚗 📧 3,50€ – ⚡ (10A) 3€

Rental rates : Permanent – 2 🏠 – 2 🏡. Per night from 32 to 50€ Per week from 300 to 400€

🚐 borne 3€ – 🚐 9€

Surroundings : 🏞
Leisure activities : 🏖 (beach) 🏊
Facilities : 🚿 ⚐ 🏕 ♨ 🍴
Nearby : 🏊

G P S Longitude : 1.23424
Latitude : 47.9031

The Michelin classification (⚑⚑⚑⚑ ... ⚑) is totally independent of the official star classification system awarded by the local prefecture or other official organisation.

MUIDES-SUR-LOIRE

41500 – Michelin map **318** G5 – pop. 1 350 – alt. 82
▶ Paris 169 – Beaugency 17 – Blois 20 – Chambord 9

🔺 Château des Marais ▲▲

📞 02 54 87 05 42, www.camping-marais.com

Address : 27 rue de Chambord (to the southeast along the D 103, follow the signs for Crouy-sur-Cosson - for caravans, access via the D 112 and take D 103 to the right)

Opening times : from beginning May to end Sept.

8 ha (299 pitches) flat, grassy

Tariff : 32 € 🕴🕴 🚐 🔲 🔣 (10A) – Extra per person 8 € – Reservation fee 15 €

Rental rates : (from mid April to beginning Nov.) 🐾 – 21 🚐 19 🏠 – 1 cabin in the trees. Per night from 68 to 182 € – Per week from 476 to 1274 € – Reservation fee 15 €

🚰 borne 6 € – 4 🔲 32 € – 🚰 🔣 32 €
In the pleasantly wooded grounds of a 17th-century château.

Surroundings : 🏞 🛖 🌳🌳
Leisure activities : 🍷 🍴 🎮 🌙 nighttime 🎯
🛶 hammam 🔥 🚴 ✂ 🎱 🔲 🏊 🐾
Facilities : 🚿 🔌 🚽 🏄 ✈ 🚰 🛆 launderette 🐾🦎

GPS Longitude : 1.52897
Latitude : 47.66585

🔺 Municipal Bellevue

📞 02 54 87 01 56, mairie.muides@wanadoo.fr – 🎌

Address : avenue de la Loire (north of the town along the D 112, follow the signs for Mer and take the turning to the left before the bridge; near the Loire)

2,5 ha (100 pitches)

🚰 borne

Facilities : 🚿 🔌 🚽 🔳
Nearby : 🏊 ✂

GPS Longitude : 1.52607
Latitude : 47.67178

NEUNG-SUR-BEUVRON

41210 – Michelin map **318** H6 – pop. 1 223 – alt. 102
▶ Paris 183 – Beaugency 33 – Blois 39 – Lamotte-Beuvron 20

🔺 Municipal de la Varenne

📞 02 54 83 68 52, www.neung-sur-beuvron.fr

Address : 34 rue de Veillas (located 1km to the northeast, access via the turning to the left of the church; near the Beuvron)

Opening times : from mid April to mid Oct.

4 ha (73 pitches) relatively flat, flat, grassy, sandy

Tariff : 12,20 € 🕴🕴 🚐 🔲 🔣 (10A) – Extra per person 2,70 €
Rental rates : (from mid April to mid Nov.) – 4 🚐. Per night from 57 € – Per week from 267 to 412 €
🚰 borne – 🚰 🔣 12,20 €
A pleasant wooded site.

Surroundings : 🏞 🛖 🌳🌳
Leisure activities : 🎮 🕷 ✂ 🐾
Facilities : 🚿 🔌 🚽 🔳

GPS Longitude : 1.81507
Latitude : 47.53849

NEUVY-ST-SÉPULCHRE

36230 – Michelin map **323** G7 – pop. 1 690 – alt. 186
▶ Paris 295 – Argenton-sur-Creuse 24 – Châteauroux 29 – La Châtre 16

🔺 Municipal les Frênes

📞 02 54 30 82 51, www.campingdeneuvy.new.fr

Address : route de l'Augère (take the western exit along the D 927, follow the signs for Argenton-sur-Creuse then continue 600m along the turning to the left and take the road to the right, 100m from a lake and the Bouzanne river)

Opening times : from mid June to mid Sept.

1 ha (35 pitches) flat, grassy

Tariff : (2013 Price) 11,50 € 🕴🕴 🚐 🔲 🔣 (9A) – Extra per person 2 €
Rental rates : (2013 Price) Permanent 🐾 – 2 🏠. Per night 90 € Per week from 240 to 270 €

Surroundings : 🏞 🕷 🌳
Leisure activities : 🔥 🐾 🎱
Facilities : 🔌 🏄 ✈ 🚽 launderette
Nearby : 🍷 🍴 🕷 🐾

GPS Longitude : 1.7828
Latitude : 46.5903

The pitches of many campsites are marked out with low hedges of attractive bushes and shrubs.

NOUAN-LE-FUZELIER

41600 – Michelin map **318** J6 – pop. 2 439 – alt. 113
▶ Paris 177 – Blois 59 – Cosne-sur-Loire 74 – Gien 56

🔺 La Grande Sologne

📞 02 54 88 70 22, www.campinggrandesologne.com

Address : rue des Peupliers (take the southern exit along the D 2020, then the road to the left opposite the station)

Opening times : from beginning April to mid Oct.

10 ha/4 for camping (180 pitches) flat, grassy

Tariff : (2013 Price) 🕴 5,80 € 🚐 🔲 8,20 € – 🔣 (10A) 3 €
Rental rates : (2013 Price) (from beginning April to mid Oct.) 8 🚐 – 4 canvas bungalows. Per night from 25 to 76 €
Per week 670 €
🚰 borne
In a wooded setting beside a lake.

Surroundings : 🌳🌳
Leisure activities : 🍴 🎮 🔥 🚴 🕷 🐾
Facilities : 🚿 🔌 🏄 🚽 🔳 🏊
Nearby : 🍷 ✂ 🏊

GPS Longitude : 2.03631
Latitude : 47.53337

OLIVET

45160 – Michelin map **318** I4 – pop. 19 806 – alt. 100
▶ Paris 137 – Orléans 4 – Blois 70 – Chartres 78

🔺 Municipal

📞 02 38 63 53 94, www.camping-olivet.org

Address : rue du Pont Bouchet (situated 2km southeast along the D 14, follow the signs for St-Cyr-en-Val)

Opening times : from beginning April to mid Oct.

1 ha (46 pitches) flat, grassy

Tariff : 21,60 € 🕴🕴 🚐 🔲 🔣 (16A) – Extra per person 4,50 €

This guide is not intended as a list of all the camping sites in France; its aim is to provide a selection of the best sites in each category.

borne 5,50€ – 6 ⊞ 21,60€

A pleasant location where the Loiret and Dhuy rivers meet.

Surroundings : ☐ ⁰⁰
Leisure activities : ⬍
Facilities : ⬍ ⊶ ▥ ⚏ ⤳ ⛊ ⊞
Nearby : ⬈ ⬍

G P S Longitude : 1.92543
Latitude : 47.85601

PIERREFITTE-SUR-SAULDRE

41300 – Michelin map **318** J6 – pop. 848 – alt. 125
▶ Paris 185 – Aubigny-sur-Nère 23 – Blois 73 – Bourges 55

⚿ Les Alicourts ⚏

ℰ 0254886334, www.lesalicourts.com ⬊

Address : au Domaine des Alicourts (6km northeast along the D 126 and take the D 126b; beside a small lake)

Opening times : from end April to beginning Sept.

21 ha/10 for camping (420 pitches)

Tariff : 49€ ⚣ ⬅ ⊞ ⚡ (6A) – Extra per person 12€

Rental rates : (from end April to beginning Sept.) ⬍ (3 chalets) ⬊ – 180 ▥ – 90 ⌂ – 8 cabins in the trees – 3 tent lodges. Per night from 44 to 314€ – Per week from 308 to 2198€

A pretty, partially enclosed swimming area, upmarket spa centre and good quality rental options.

Surroundings : ⬊ ☐ ⁰⁰
Leisure activities : ⚿ ✗ ⛱ ⚐ ⚲ ⭄ ⛷ ⛲ hammam, jacuzzi ⚙ ⚲ ⚙ ⚲ ⬈ ⊞ ⬍ ⩲ (beach) ⬈ ⬍ pedalos ⚘ spa centre, entertainment room, skate park
Facilities : ⬍ ⊶ ⚏ ⤳ ⛊ ⊞ launderette ⬈⬍

G P S Longitude : 2.191
Latitude : 47.54482

PREUILLY-SUR-CLAISE

37290 – Michelin map **317** O7 – pop. 1 075 – alt. 80
▶ Paris 299 – Le Blanc 31 – Châteauroux 64 – Châtellerault 35

⚠ Municipal

ℰ 0247945004, www.preuillysurclaise.fr

Address : to the southwest of the town; near the swimming pool, the Claise river and a small lake

Opening times : from beginning June to end Sept.

0,7 ha (37 pitches) flat, grassy

Tariff : ⚣ 2,50€ ⬅ ⊞ 3€ – ⚡ (16A) 4€

Rental rates : Permanent – 2 ▥ – 4 gîtes. Per night from 50 to 60€ – Per week from 200 to 250€

borne 10€

A green setting In the middle of a leisure centre.

Surroundings : ☐ ⁰
Leisure activities : ⬍
Facilities : ⊶ ⤳ ⛊ ⊞
Nearby : ⚙ ⚲ ⬈ ⬍ sports trail

G P S Longitude : 0.92618
Latitude : 46.85305

The Michelin classification (⚿⚿⚿⚿... ⚠) is totally independent of the official star classification system awarded by the local prefecture or other official organisation.

RILLÉ

37340 – Michelin map **317** K4 – pop. 300 – alt. 82
▶ Paris 282 – Orléans 158 – Tours 47 – Nantes 160

⚿ Huttopia Rillé

HUTTOPIA

ℰ 0247246297, www.huttopia.com

Address : at the lake Rillé (situated 2km to the east along the D49)

Opening times : from mid April to beginning Nov.

5 ha (120 pitches) flat, grassy

Tariff : 33,50€ ⚣ ⬅ ⊞ ⚡ (10A) Extra per person 7,80€ – Reservation fee 22€

Rental rates : (from mid April to beginning Nov.) – 10 caravans 22 ⌂ – 10 tent lodges. Per night from 63 to 160€ – Per week from 330 to 1120€ – Reservation fee 22€

borne 7€

Surroundings : ⁰⁰
Leisure activities : ⚿ ✗ ⛱ ⚐ daytime ⚙ ⚲ ⬈ ⬍ ⚑ ⚙
Facilities : ⬍ ⊶ Ⓟ ⬈ launderette ⬈ ⬍
Nearby : ⚘

G P S Longitude : 0.33278
Latitude : 47.44584

Key to rentals symbols:

12 ▥	*Number of mobile homes*
20 ⌂	*Number of chalets*
6 ⏚	*Number of rooms to rent*
Per night 30–50€	*Minimum/maximum rate per night*
Per week 300–1,000€	*Minimum/maximum rate per week*

ROMORANTIN-LANTHENAY

41200 – Michelin map **318** H7 – pop. 17 092 – alt. 93
▶ Paris 202 – Blois 42 – Bourges 74 – Châteauroux 72

⚿ Tournefeuille

ℰ 0254761660, www.campingtournefeuille-sologne.com

Address : 32 rue des Lices (take the eastern exit, follow the signs for Salbris and then Long-Eaton; beside the Sauldre river)

Opening times : from beginning April to end Sept.

1,5 ha (103 pitches) flat, grassy

Tariff : 19,30€ ⚣ ⬅ ⊞ ⚡ (10A) – Extra per person 7,10€ Reservation fee 5€

Rental rates : Permanent – 6 ⌂ . Per night from 69 to 137€ – Per week from 339 to 492€ – Reservation fee 5€

borne 3,10€ – 15 ⊞ 10,80€ – ⬍ 10,80€

Surroundings : ⬊ ⁰
Leisure activities : ✗ ⛱ ⚙ ⚲ ⚲
Facilities : ⬍ ⊶ ▥ ⚏ ⤳ ⛊ ⊞
Nearby : ⚲ ⌸ ⬍

G P S Longitude : 1.75586
Latitude : 47.35503

ROSNAY

36300 – Michelin map **323** D6 – pop. 615 – alt. 112
▶ Paris 307 – Argenton-sur-Creuse 31 – Le Blanc 16 – Châteauroux 44

⚠ Municipal

🔗 02 54 37 80 17, rosnay-mairie@wanadoo.fr

Address : route de St-Michel-en-Brenne (500m north along the D 44)

Opening times : from mid Feb. to mid Nov.

2 ha (36 pitches) flat, grassy

Tariff : ♦ 2€ ⇔ 2€ ▣ 2,50€ – ⓖ (6A) 2€
borne – 15 ▣ 2,50€
A small, pleasant site near a lake.

Surroundings : 🌳 ♤♤
Leisure activities : ⚓ ✗ 🐟
Facilities : 🚽 ⑂ ♨ ♨ 🔲
Longitude : 1.21172
Latitude : 46.70645

ST-AMAND-MONTROND

18200 – Michelin map **323** L6 – pop. 10 952 – alt. 160
▶ Paris 282 – Bourges 52 – Châteauroux 65 – Montluçon 56

⚠ Municipal de la Roche

🔗 02 48 96 09 36, www.entreprisefrery.com

Address : chemin de La Roche (take the southwestern exit along the D 2144, follow the signs for Montluçon, take the Chemin de la Roche to the right before the canal; near the Cher river)

Opening times : from beginning April to end Sept.

4 ha (100 pitches)

Tariff : (2013 Price) ♦ 3,30€ ⇔ ▣ 4,50€ – ⓖ (6A) 3,10€
Rental rates : (2013 Price) (from beginning April to end Sept.) 3 canvas bungalows. Per week from 115 to 310 €

Attractive pitches in a green setting between a canal and the Cher river, but basic and rather old sanitary facilities.

Surroundings : 🌳 ⌂♤♤
Leisure activities : ⚓ ✗
Facilities : ⑂ ♨ ♨ ♨ ♨ launderette
Nearby : 🐟
Longitude : 2.49108
Latitude : 46.71816

ST-AVERTIN

37550 – Michelin map **317** N4 – pop. 13 946 – alt. 49
▶ Paris 245 – Orléans 121 – Tours 7 – Blois 70

⚠ Onlycamp Les Rives du Cher

🔗 02 47 27 87 47, www.camping-lesrivesducher.com

Address : 61 rue de Rochepinard (to the north along the left bank of the Cher river)

Opening times : from mid March to mid Nov.

2 ha (90 pitches) flat, grassy

Tariff : (2013 Price) 19,20€ ♦♦ ⇔ ▣ ⓖ (10A) – Extra per person 4,20€
Rental rates : (2013 Price) (from mid March to mid Nov.) – 12 🏠. Per night from 59 to 99€ – Per week from 389 to 589€
borne 5€
Near a small lake.

Surroundings : ⌂ ♤
Facilities : ⑂ ♨ ♨ launderette
Nearby : ⚓ ✗ 🎣 🐟 ♨
Longitude : 0.72296
Latitude : 47.37064

ST-PÈRE-SUR-LOIRE

45600 – Michelin map **318** L5 – pop. 1 056 – alt. 115
▶ Paris 147 – Aubigny-sur-Nère 38 – Châteauneuf-sur-Loire 40 – Gien 25

⚠ Le Jardin de Sully

🔗 02 38 67 10 84, www.camping-lejardindesully.fr

Address : 1 route de St-Benoit (to the west along the D 60, follow the signs for Châteauneuf-sur-Loire; near the river)

Opening times : Permanent

2,7 ha (80 pitches)

Tariff : 19€ ♦♦ ⇔ ▣ ⓖ (10A) – Extra per person 3€ – Reservation fee 5€

Rental rates : Permanent – 14 🚐 – 6 canvas bungalows. Per night from 20 to 90€ – Per week from 193 to 330€ Reservation fee 10€
borne 4€

Leisure activities : 🏠 ⚓
Facilities : ⑂ ♨ ♨ ♨ ♨ launderette
Nearby : ✗ ♨
Longitude : 2.36229
Latitude : 47.7718

ST-PLANTAIRE

36190 – Michelin map **323** G8 – pop. 549 – alt. 300
▶ Paris 339 – Orléans 214 – Châteauroux 68 – Limoges 95

⚠ Municipal de Fougères

🔗 02 54 47 20 01, www.www.saint-plantaire.fr

Address : 19 plage de Fougères

Opening times : from beginning April to end Oct.

4,5 ha (150 pitches) flat, grassy

Tariff : (2013 Price) 14,80€ ♦♦ ⇔ ▣ ⓖ (10A) – Extra per person 4€
Rental rates : (2013 Price) (from beginning March to end Dec.) 7 🚐 – 13 🏠 – 4 canvas bungalows. Per night from 36 to 110€ Per week from 142 to 580€

In a pleasant location beside the Lac de Chambon

Surroundings : ≤ ♤
Leisure activities : 🏠 ⚓ ✗ 🎣 ♨ 🐟
Facilities : ⑂ ♨ ♨ launderette ♨
Nearby : ✗ ♨ pedalos
Longitude : 1.61952
Latitude : 46.42756

ST-SATUR

18300 – Michelin map **323** N2 – pop. 1 627 – alt. 155
▶ Paris 194 – Aubigny-sur-Nère 42 – Bourges 50 – Cosne-sur-Loire 12

⚠ Flower Les Portes de Sancerre

🔗 02 48 72 10 88, www.camping-cher-sancerre.com

Address : quai de Loire (located 1km east along the D 2)

Opening times : from end March to mid Oct.

1 ha (87 pitches) flat, grassy

Tariff : (2013 Price) 20,50€ ♦♦ ⇔ ▣ ⓖ (6A) – Extra per person 4€ Reservation fee 15€

Rental rates : (2013 Price) (from end March to mid Oct.) ♨ (1 mobile home) – 16 🚐 – 3 tent lodges. Per night from 41 to 100€ – Per week from 280 to 750€ – Reservation fee 20€
borne 4€ – 4 ▣ 15,50€ – 🚐 ⓖ 15,50€

Well-shaded pitches and rental options beside the Loire river near a small leisure centre.

Surroundings : 🦢 ➞ ♨♨
Leisure activities : 🏚 🎿
Facilities : ♿ ⚡ 🧺 🚿 ♨ 🍴 🔥
Nearby : 🍸 🚲 🛶 🛷 🦢 🐎

GPS Longitude : 2.86671
Latitude : 47.34251

STE-CATHERINE-DE-FIERBOIS

37800 – Michelin map **317** M6 – pop. 657 – alt. 114
▶ Paris 263 – Azay-le-Rideau 25 – Chinon 37 – Liguiel 19

⛰ Les Castels Parc de Fierbois 👥

📞 02 47 65 43 35, www.fierbois.com

Address : 1.2km to the south

Opening times : from mid May to beginning Sept.

30 ha/12 for camping (420 pitches)

Tariff : 50€ 👥👥 🚐 🔲 ⚡ (6A) – Extra per person 9€
Rental rates : (from mid May to beginning Sept.) – 130 🚐
35 🏚 – 8 cabins in the trees – 8 gîtes. Per night from 45 to 165€
Per week from 315 to 1155€
🚽 borne – 🚰 14€
A pleasant and spacious site with woods, lake and a water park.

Surroundings : ➞ ♨♨♨ ⛰
Leisure activities : 🍸 🍴 🏚 🎣 🚣 🏄
🚲 🎿 🛝 🛶 🏊 (beach) ⛵ 🦢
Facilities : ♿ ⚡ 🧺 🚿 ♨ 🍴 launderette 🚿
🚰 refrigerated food storage facilities
Nearby : adventure park

GPS Longitude : 0.6549
Latitude : 47.1486

STE-MAURE-DE-TOURAINE

37800 – Michelin map **317** M6 – pop. 4 072 – alt. 85
▶ Paris 273 – Le Blanc 71 – Châtellerault 39 – Chinon 32

⛰ Municipal de Marans

📞 02 47 65 44 93, camping@sainte-maure-de-touraine.fr

Address : rue de Toizelet (located 1.5km southeast along the D 760, follow the signs for Loches, and take the turning to the left; 150m from a small lake)

1 ha (66 pitches)

🚽 borne

Leisure activities : 🎿 sports trail
Facilities : ♿ ⚡ 🚿 🍴
Nearby : 🛶 🦢

GPS Longitude : 0.6252
Latitude : 47.10509

SALBRIS

41300 – Michelin map **318** J7 – pop. 5 682 – alt. 104
▶ Paris 187 – Aubigny-sur-Nère 32 – Blois 65 – Lamotte-Beuvron 21

⛰ Le Sologne

📞 02 54 97 06 38, www.campingdesologne.fr

Address : 8 allée de la Sauldre (take northeastern exit along the D 55, follow the signs for Pierrefitte-sur-Sauldre; beside a lake and near the Sauldre river)

Opening times : from beginning April to end Sept.

2 ha (81 pitches) flat, grassy

Tariff : 18,50€ 👥👥 🚐 🔲 ⚡ (10A) – Extra per person 4,50€

Rental rates : (from beginning April to end Sept.) 🎿 – 5 🚐
1 🏚. Per night from 55 to 88€ – Per week from 225 to 498€
🚽 borne 7,50€

Surroundings : ➞ ♨
Leisure activities : 🏚 🦢
Facilities : ♿ ⚡ 🚿 ♨ 🍴 🔥
Nearby : 🎿 🏞 🛶 🛷

GPS Longitude : 2.05522
Latitude : 47.43026

SAVIGNY-EN-VÉRON

37420 – Michelin map **317** J5 – pop. 1 447 – alt. 40
▶ Paris 292 – Chinon 9 – Langeais 27 – Saumur 20

⛰ La Fritillaire

📞 02 47 58 03 79, www.camping-la-fritillaire.fr

Address : rue Basse (to the west of the town centre; 100m from a lake)

Opening times : Permanent

2,5 ha (100 pitches) flat, grassy, adjacent wood

Tariff : (2013 Price) 16,80€ 👥👥 🚐 🔲 ⚡ (10A)
Extra per person 2,80€ – Reservation fee 9€
Rental rates : (2013 Price) Permanent – 6 canvas bungalows
1 tent lodge. Per night from 40 to 60€ – Per week from 195 to
440€ – Reservation fee 9€
🚽 borne 4,20€ – 🚰 ⚡ 16,80€

Surroundings : 🦢 ➞
Leisure activities : 🚣
Facilities : ♿ ⚡ 🧺 🚿 ♨ 🍴 🔥
Nearby : 🎿 🛷 ⛵ 🦢 🐎

GPS Longitude : 0.13937
Latitude : 47.20039

These symbols are used for a campsite that is exceptional in its category:

⛰⛰⛰…⛰ *Particularly pleasant setting, quality and range of services available*

🦢 🦢 *Tranquil, isolated site – quiet site, particularly at night*

≪ ≪ *Exceptional view – interesting or panoramic view*

SAVONNIÈRES

37510 – Michelin map **317** M4 – pop. 3 041 – alt. 47
▶ Paris 263 – Orléans 139 – Tours 17 – Blois 88

⛰ Onlycamp Confluence

📞 02 47 50 00 25, www.onlycamp.fr

Address : route du Bray (take the northern exit from the town; beside Cher)

flat, grassy

Rentals : 2 canvas bungalows – 2 tents.

🚽 borne

Beside the Cher river and a cycle path.

Surroundings : ➞ ♨
Leisure activities : 🚣 🎿 🦢 🎣
Facilities : ♿ ⚡ 🚿 🍴
Nearby : 🍸 🎿

GPS Longitude : 0.55006
Latitude : 47.34887

SENONCHES

28250 – Michelin map **311** C4 – pop. 3 186 – alt. 223
▶ Paris 115 – Chartres 38 – Dreux 38 – Mortagne-au-Perche 42

🏔 Huttopia Senonches ♣♣

🖉 02 37 37 81 40, www.huttopia.com

Address : Etang de Badouleau

Opening times : from mid April to beginning Nov.

10,5 ha (126 pitches)

Tariff : (2013 Price) 31€ ♣♣ ⟵ 🔲 🔲 (10A) – Extra per person 6,50€
Reservation fee 22€

Rental rates : (2013 Price) (from mid April to beginning Nov.) 🅿 10 🏠 – 10 tent lodges. Per night from 79 to 142€ – Per week from 497 to 994€ – Reservation fee 22€

🚐 borne 7€

Beside a lake and on the edge of the national forest at Senonches.

Surroundings : ♒♒ 🛆
Leisure activities : 🏠 🕙daytime 🏃 🏇
🏊 🛶
Facilities : 🔑 🅿 🎦 🛁launderette 🧺
Nearby : ✕ 🎣 🐎

GPS Longitude : 1.0435
Latitude : 48.553

SONZAY

37360 – Michelin map **317** L3 – pop. 1 298 – alt. 94
▶ Paris 257 – Château-la-Vallière 39 – Langeais 26 – Tours 25

🏔 L'Arada Parc ♣♣

🖉 02 47 24 72 69, www.laradaparc.com

Address : rue de la Baratière (take the western exit along the D 68, follow the signs for Souvigné and take a right turn)

Opening times : from beginning April to mid Oct.

1,7 ha (94 pitches)

Tariff : 30€ ♣♣ ⟵ 🔲 🔲 (10A) – Extra per person 5,80€ – Reservation fee 10€

Rental rates : (from beginning April to mid Oct.) – 21 🔲 3 🏠 – 5 tent lodges. Per night from 62 to 105€ – Per week from 227 to 784€ – Reservation fee 10€

🚐 borne 5€

Surroundings : 🦕 ⟋
Leisure activities : 🍽 ✕ 🏠 🏃 🛝 hammam
jacuzzi 🚣 🚲 🎣 🏊 🛶
Facilities : ♿ 🔑 🎦 🛁 🚿 🚰 🍴 launderette
Nearby : 🎣 🐟

GPS Longitude : 0.45069
Latitude : 47.52615

For more information on visiting particular towns or regions, consult the relevant regional MICHELIN Green Guide. We also recommend you use the appropriate Michelin regional map to locate your selected campsite, to calculate distances and to work out the best route.

SUÈVRES

41500 – Michelin map **318** F5 – pop. 1 481 – alt. 83
▶ Paris 170 – Beaugency 18 – Blois 15 – Chambord 16

🏔 Les Castels Le Château de la Grenouillère ♣♣

🖉 02 54 87 80 37, www.camping-loire.com 🦅

Address : 3km northeast on the D 2152

Opening times : from mid April to mid Sept.

11 ha (250 pitches) flat, grassy

Tariff : 22€ ♣♣ ⟵ 🔲 🔲 (10A) – Extra per person 8€ – Reservation fee 10€

Rental rates : Permanent 🦅 – 140 🔲 – 20 🏠. Per night from 50 to 130€ – Per week from 300 to 990€ – Reservation fee 15€

A wooded park and a pleasant orchard.

Surroundings : ⟋ 🎵
Leisure activities : 🍽 ✕ 🏠 🕙 🏃 jacuzzi
🚣 🚲 🎣 🏊 🛶
Facilities : ♿ 🔑 🛁 🚿 🚰 🍴 launderette 🧺
🚿

GPS Longitude : 1.48512
Latitude : 47.68688

The prices listed were supplied by the campsite owners in 2013 (if prices were not available, those from the previous year are given). The fees should be regarded as basic charges and may fluctuate with inflation.

THORÉ-LA-ROCHETTE

41100 – Michelin map **318** C5 – pop. 899 – alt. 75
▶ Paris 176 – Blois 42 – Château-Renault 25 – La Ferté-Bernard 58

🔺 Intercommunal la Bonne Aventure

🖉 02 54 72 00 59, www.vendome.eu

Address : route de la Cunaille (head 1.7km north along the D 82, follow the signs for Lunay and take turning to the right; near the stadium; beside the Loir)

2 ha (60 pitches) flat, grassy

Surroundings : 🦕 ♀ 🛆
Leisure activities : 🏠 🚣 🚲 🎣 🐟
Facilities : ♿ 🔑 🎦
Nearby : 🏊

GPS Longitude : 0.95855
Latitude : 47.80504

VALENÇAY

36600 – Michelin map **323** F4 – pop. 2 617 – alt. 140
▶ Paris 233 – Blois 59 – Bourges 73 – Châteauroux 42

🏔 Municipal les Chênes

🖉 02 54 00 03 92, commune@mairie-valencay.fr

Address : located 1km west on the D 960, follow the signs for Luçay-le-Mâle

Opening times : from beginning May to mid Sept.

5 ha (50 pitches) relatively flat

Tariff : ♣ 3,90€ ⟵ 🔲 4,50€ – 🔲 (10A) 4,60€

🚐 borne 4,10€

In a pleasant green site beside a lake.

Surroundings : ⟋ ♒♒
Leisure activities : 🚣 🏊 🛶
Facilities : ♿ 🔑 🎦

GPS Longitude : 1.55542
Latitude : 47.15808

VATAN

36150 – Michelin map **323** G4 – pop. 2 059 – alt. 140
▶ Paris 235 – Blois 78 – Bourges 50 – Châteauroux 31

⚠ Municipal

📞 02 54 49 91 37, www.vatan-en-berry.com

Address : rue du Collège (take the western exit along the D 2, follow the signs for Guilly and take the turning to the left)

Opening times : from mid April to mid Sept.

2,4 ha (55 pitches) flat, grassy

Tariff : 12€ ✦✦ ⊕ ▤ ⚡ (12A) – Extra per person 4,50€
Rental rates : (from beginning April to end Sept.) – 3 ⌂. Per week from 200 to 250€

Beside a delightful lake.

Surroundings : ⌒ ♀♀
Leisure activities : ▲ ⚓
Facilities : ⚷ 🚮 ⚒ 🐎 🍴 ▣
Nearby : ✗ 🚣

G P S Longitude : 1.80601
Latitude : 47.07146

VEIGNÉ

37250 – Michelin map **317** N5 – pop. 6 055 – alt. 58
▶ Paris 252 – Orléans 128 – Tours 16 – Joué-lès-Tours 11

⚠ Onlycamp La Plage

📞 02 47 34 95 39, www.onlycamp.fr

Address : route de Tours (take the northern exit along the D 50)

Opening times :

2 ha (110 pitches) flat, grassy

Tariff : (2013 Price) 17,80€ ✦✦ ⊕ ▤ ⚡ (10A)
Extra per person 3,80€
Rental rates : (2013 Price) (from beginning May to end Sept.)
10 canvas bungalows. Per night from 42 to 62€ – Per week from 265 to 390€

🚐 borne 5€

Surroundings : ♀
Leisure activities : ▾✗ ▣ ⚹ 🚲 🛶 🚣 🎣
Facilities : ⚷ 🚰 (season) ⛺ 🍴 launderette

G P S Longitude : 0.73464
Latitude : 47.28929

LA VILLE-AUX-DAMES

37700 – Michelin map **317** N4 – pop. 4 889 – alt. 50
▶ Paris 244 – Orléans 120 – Tours 7 – Blois 53

⚠ Les Acacias

📞 02 47 44 08 16, www.camplvad.com

Address : rue Berthe Morisot (to the northeast of the town, near the D 751)

Opening times : Permanent

2,6 ha (90 pitches) flat, grassy

Tariff : 20€ ✦✦ ⊕ ▤ ⚡ (10A) – Extra per person 3,50€

Rental rates : Permanent – 15 🛏 . Per night from 42 to 110€
Per week from 290 to 560€
🚐 borne 6€ – 5 ▤ 15,50€

Surroundings : ♀♀
Leisure activities : ✗ ⚓
Facilities : ⚷ 🚰 ⚒ 🍴 launderette
Nearby : ▾ ✗ 🎿 fitness trail

G P S Longitude : 0.7772
Latitude : 47.40224

VILLIERS-LE-MORHIER

28130 – Michelin map **311** F4 – pop. 1 338 – alt. 99
▶ Paris 83 – Orléans 108 – Chartres 24 – Versailles 61

⛰ Les Ilots de St-Val

📞 02 37 82 71 30, www.campinglesilotsdestval.com – limited spaces for one-night stay

Address : at Le Haut Bourray (4.5km northwest along the D 983, follow the signs for Nogent-le-Roi then continue 1km along the D 1013, follow the signs for Neron to the left)

Opening times : from beginning Feb. to mid Dec.

10 ha/6 for camping (153 pitches)

Tariff : 24,40€ ✦✦ ⊕ ▤ ⚡ (10A) – Extra per person 5,80€
Rental rates : Permanent ⚒ – 15 🛏 – 4 ⌂. Per week from 260 to 500€
🚐 borne 5,80€

Surroundings : ⚒
Leisure activities : ▣ ⚓ ✗
Facilities : ⚷ 🚰 ⚒ ⛺ 🍴 ▣
Nearby : 🚣 🐎

G P S Longitude : 1.5476
Latitude : 48.6089

Some campsites benefit from proximity to a municipal leisure centre.

VITRY-AUX-LOGES

45530 – Michelin map **318** K4 – pop. 1 826 – alt. 120
▶ Paris 111 – Bellegarde 17 – Châteauneuf-sur-Loire 11
– Malesherbes 48

⛰ Étang de la Vallée

📞 06 10 53 35 37, www.campingdeletangdelavallee.fr

Address : at the base de loisirs (leisure centre) (3.3km to the northwest, 100m from the lake)

Opening times : Permanent

3,7 ha (180 pitches) flat, grassy

Tariff : (2013 Price) 19,50€ ✦✦ ⊕ ▤ ⚡ (16A) – Extra per person 5€

In a pleasant wooded setting near a leisure and activity centre.

Surroundings : ⌒ ♀
Leisure activities : ⚓ 🎿
Facilities : ⚷ 🚰 📮 ⚒ 🍴 ▣
Nearby : ▾ ✗ 🎿 (beach) 🚣 pedalos

G P S Longitude : 2.28162
Latitude : 47.95868

CHAMPAGNE-ARDENNE

G. Labriet / Photononstop

It's easy to spot visitors heading to the Champagne-Ardenne region by the sparkle in their eyes and the look of pure anticipation and delight on their faces as they gaze out at endless vineyards. They are already picturing themselves sipping the famous delicacy that was once known as 'devil's wine' before a monk discovered the secret of its divine bubbles. As those lucky enough to taste the delights of Champagne continue their voyage, they will see the beautiful cathedral of Reims rise up ahead. They will drink in the sight of the delightful half-timbered houses of Troyes and savour the taste of *andouillettes* (chitterling sausages). Visitors can then explore the Ardennes forest by bike or by walking along its hiking trails. This ancient woodland paradise, bordered by the gentle river Meuse, has other delights as well: watch the graceful flight of the crane over a lake as smooth as glass, or succumb to the temptation of a plate of local wild boar.

BELGIQUE

LUXEMBE

SENTINELLE

Valenciennes

A 2

D 64

Cambrai

D 64

le Nouvion-
en-Thiérache

A 26

ST-QUENTIN

D 1029

Oise

N 2

Vervins

la Fère

AISNE

A 26

N 51

Rethel

D 8043

CHARLEVILLE-MÉZIÈRES

Signy-l'Abbaye

A 34

A 203

D 8043

ARDENNES

Buzancy

Vouziers

Meuse

Semois

Longwy

D 618

N 52

LU

A 31

D 843

Briey

D 603

N 55

Aire

VERDUN-ST-NICOLAS

Verdun

A 4

MEUSE

Jaulny

Lac de
Madine

A 31

rny-Rivière

ns-
g

Soissons

Aisne

REIMS

Vesle

N 31

A 4

A 4

Ste-Menehould

A 4

Ourcq

Charly-s-M.

Château-
Thierry

Épernay

CHÂLONS-EN-
CHAMPAGNE

N 44

Revigny-s-Ornain

Commercy

Toul

A 31

Villey-le-Se

OSSY-S-MARNE

Marne

MARNE

Petit Morin

D 635

Bar-le-Duc

N 4

N 4

Sézanne

N 4

Vitry-le-François

St-Dizier

A 26

SOMMESOUS

Lac du Der-
Chantecoq

Éclaron

Braucourt

Marne

N 67

Thonnance-
les-Moulins

Neufchâteau

D 674

Bulgnéville

Vittel

Contrexéville

Louan

Provins

Nogent-
sur-Seine

D 619

Seine

Giffaumont-
Champaubert

Soulaines-Dhuys

Radonvilliers

Dienville

Lac de la
Fl. d'Orient

Bourg-
Ste-Marie

HAUTE-MARNE

A 5

TROYES

D 671

A 5

Mesnil-
St-Père

Bar-s-Aube

Chaumont

Meuse

Montigny-le-Roi

A 31

Sens

A 19

VILLENEUVE-
L'ARCHEVÊQUE

N 77

AUBE

Ervy-le-Châtel

A 5

D 619

Bannes

Bourbonne-
les-Bains

VILLEROY

Migennes

YONNE

Ligny-le-Châtel

Langres

N 19

Auxerre

Chablis

Tonnerre

Châtillon-s-Seine

Ource

Seine

A 31

Renaucourt

HAUT

A 6

Sèrein

N 151

veur-en-Puisaye

Vincelles

Vermenton

l'Isle-s-Serein

Montbard

D 971

Venarey-les-Laumes

Armançon

Aube

Saône

Andryes

Asquins

Avallon

Cousin

Clamecy

Varzy

CÔTE-
D'OR

BESANÇON-CHA

BANNES

52360 – Michelin map **313** M6 – pop. 401 – alt. 388
▶ Paris 291 – Chaumont 35 – Dijon 86 – Langres 9

⚠ Hautoreille

✆ 03 25 84 83 40, www.campinghautoreille.com –

Address : 6 rue du Boutonnier (take the southwestern exit along the D 74, follow the signs for Langres then continue 700m along the road to the left)

Opening times : from beginning Jan. to end Nov.

3,5 ha (100 pitches)

Tariff : ♦ 5€ 🚗 🅿 5,50€ – 🔌 (10A) 4€

Surroundings : 🏊 ♨♨
Leisure activities : ♟ ✕ 🖼
Facilities : ♿ ☕🗝 ✉ Ⅲ 🚿 🍴 🏠

G P S Longitude : 5.39519
Latitude : 47.89508

BOURBONNE-LES-BAINS

52400 – Michelin map **313** O6 – pop. 2 255 – alt. 290 – ♨
▶ Paris 313 – Chaumont 55 – Dijon 124 – Langres 39

⚠ Le Montmorency

✆ 03 25 90 08 64, www.camping-montmorency.com

Address : rue du Stade (take the western exit following signs for Chaumont and take turning to the right; 100m from the stadium)

Opening times : from end March to end Oct.

2 ha (74 pitches)

Tariff : (2013 Price) ♦ 4,30€ 🚗 🅿 4,90€ – 🔌 (10A) 3,90€

Rental rates : (2013 Price) (from end March to end Oct.) – 11 🛖. Per night from 37 to 43 € – Per week from 249 to 291€

🚐 borne 5€ – 6 🅿 16,90€

Surroundings : 🏊 ♨♨
Facilities : ☕🗝 Ⅲ 🚿 🍴 launderette
Nearby : ✂ 🖼 (open air in season)

G P S Longitude : 5.74027
Latitude : 47.95742

In order for the guide to remain wholly objective, the selection of campsites is made on an entirely independent basis.

BOURG-STE-MARIE

52150 – Michelin map **313** N4 – pop. 94 – alt. 329
▶ Paris 330 – Châlons-en-Champagne 153 – Chaumont 50 – Metz 142

⚠ Les Hirondelles

✆ 03 10 20 61 64, www.camping-les-hirondelles.eu

Address : at Romain-sur-Meuse, rue du Moulin de Dona (located 1.5km to the south, along the D 74, follow the signs for Montigny-le-Roi)

Opening times : Permanent

4,6 ha (54 pitches)

Tariff : ♦ 4€ 🚗 🅿 5€ – 🔌 (10A) 3,50€

Rental rates : Permanent – 8 🛖. Per night from 25 to 85€ Per week from 203 to 595€

🚐 borne 4€ – 15 🅿 14€ – 🔌14€

Surroundings : 🏊 ♨ ♨
Leisure activities : 🖼 🏃 🚴
Facilities : ♿ ☕🗝 Ⅲ 🚿 🍴 launderette

G P S Longitude : 5.55533
Latitude : 48.17234

BRAUCOURT

52290 – Michelin map **313** I2
▶ Paris 220 – Bar-sur-Aube 39 – Brienne-le-Château 29 – Châlons-en-Champagne 69

🏔 La Presqu'île de Champaubert 🏕

✆ 03 25 04 13 20, www.lescampingsduder.com

Address : 3km northwest along the D 153

Opening times : from beginning April to mid Nov.

3,6 ha (200 pitches)

Tariff : (2013 Price) 36€ ♦♦ 🚗 🅿 🔌 (10A) – Extra per person 7€

Rental rates : (from mid April to mid Nov.) – 50 🛖. Per night from 29 to 142€ – Per week from 203 to 994€

A pleasant location beside the Lac du Der-Chantecoq.

Surroundings : 🏊 ← ♨♨ ≈
Leisure activities : ♟ ✕ 🖼 ♠ ♣ 🏊 ✂ 🐟
Facilities : ♿ ☕🗝 🚿 🍴 launderette
Nearby : ≈ 🚣 pedalos

G P S Longitude : 4.562
Latitude : 48.55413

Michelin classification:

🏔🏔🏔🏔 *Extremely comfortable, equipped to a very high standard*

🏔🏔🏔 *Very comfortable, equipped to a high standard*

🏔🏔 *Comfortable and well equipped*

🏔 *Reasonably comfortable*

⚠ *Satisfactory*

BUZANCY

08240 – Michelin map **306** L6 – pop. 372 – alt. 176
▶ Paris 228 – Châlons-en-Champagne 86 – Charleville-Mézières 58 – Metz 130

⚠ La Samaritaine

✆ 03 24 30 08 88, www.campinglasamaritaine.com

Address : 3 rue des Étangs (1.4km southwest along the road to the right near the leisure and activity park)

Opening times : from mid April to mid Sept.

2 ha (110 pitches)

Tariff : ♦ 3,50€ 🚗 2,50€ 🅿 6€ – 🔌 (10A) 3,60€

Rental rates : (from mid April to mid Sept.) – 6 🛖 – 9 🛖. Per night from 48 to 66€ – Per week from 320 to 595€ Reservation fee 5€

🚐 borne 3€ – 9 🅿 6€

Surroundings : 🏊 ♨ 🚣
Leisure activities : 🖼
Facilities : ♿ ☕🗝 🚿 🍴 🏠
Nearby : ≈ (lake)

G P S Longitude : 4.9402
Latitude : 49.42365

For more information on visiting particular towns or regions, consult the relevant regional MICHELIN Green Guide. We also recommend you use the appropriate Michelin regional map to locate your selected campsite, to calculate distances and to work out the best route.

CHÂLONS-EN-CHAMPAGNE

51000 – Michelin map **306** I9 – pop. 46 236 – alt. 83
▶ Paris 188 – Charleville-Mézières 101 – Metz 157 – Nancy 162

⛰ Aquadis Loisirs Châlons en Champagne

✆ 03 26 68 38 00, www.aquadis-loisirs.com

Address : rue de Plaisance (take the southeastern exit along the N 44, follow the signs for Vitry-le François and take D 60, following signs for Sarry)

Opening times : from beginning March to beginning Nov.

3,5 ha (148 pitches)

Tariff : 🚶 5,30€ 🚗 3,50€ ▣ 5,40€ – (⚡) (10A) 4€ – Reservation fee 9,90€

Rental rates : (from beginning March to beginning Nov.) – 8 🛖. Per night from 70€ – Per week from 165 to 515€ – Reservation fee 19,80€

🚐 borne 7,20€ – 🚐14€

An entrance decorated with flowers and a pleasant setting beside a lake.

Surroundings : 🏞 ♤♤
Leisure activities : ✕ 🎮 🏊 🎯 🛶
Facilities : 🚿 ⌐ 🈲 🏖 🛁 🚽 🍴 launderette

Longitude : 4.38309
Latitude : 48.98582

CHARLEVILLE-MÉZIÈRES

08000 – Michelin map **306** K4 – pop. 49 975 – alt. 145
▶ Paris 233 – Châlons-en-Champagne 130 – Namur 149 – Arlon 120

⛺ Municipal du Mont Olympe

✆ 03 24 33 23 60, camping-charlevillemezieres@wanadoo.fr

Address : 174 rue des Paquis (in the town centre)

Opening times : from beginning April to beginning Oct.

2,7 ha (100 pitches) flat, grassy

Tariff : (2013 Price) 🚶 4,40€ 🚗 ▣ 11€ (⚡) (10A)

In a bend of the Meuse river with pedestrian access to the town centre and the Rimbaud museum via a walkway.

Surroundings : 🏞 🏞 ♤♤
Leisure activities : 🎮 🏊
Facilities : 🚿 ⌐ 🈲 🏖 🛁 🚽 🍴 launderette
Nearby : 🍴 ✕ 🏊 🚢 hammam, jacuzzi 🎿 🏊
⚓ marina

Longitude : 4.72091
Latitude : 49.77914

DIENVILLE

10500 – Michelin map **313** H3 – pop. 828 – alt. 128
▶ Paris 209 – Bar-sur-Aube 20 – Bar-sur-Seine 33 – Brienne-le-Château 8

⛰ Le Tertre

✆ 03 25 92 26 50, www.campingdutertre.fr

Address : 1 route de Radonvilliers (take the western exit on the D 11)

Opening times : from end March to mid Oct.

3,5 ha (155 pitches)

Tariff : 🚶 4,90€ 🚗 ▣ 9,90€ – (⚡) (6A) 4€ – Reservation fee 12€

Rental rates : Permanent – 13 🛖. Per week from 195 to 530€ Reservation fee 12€

Opposite the sailing centre of the leisure and activity park.

Surroundings : 🏞
Leisure activities : 🍴 ✕ 🏊 🎿
Facilities : 🚿 ⌐ 🏖 🛁 🚽 🍴 🔲
Nearby : 🎿 🚢 🚢 water skiing

Longitude : 4.52737
Latitude : 48.34888

ÉCLARON

52290 – Michelin map **313** J2 – pop. 1 991 – alt. 132
▶ Paris 255 – Châlons-en-Champagne 71 – Chaumont 83 – Bar-le-Duc 37

⛰ Yelloh! Village en Champagne-Les Sources du Lac 👥

✆ 03 25 06 34 24, www.yellohvillage.com – limited spaces for one-night stay

Address : RD 384 (situated 2km to the south, follow the signs for Montier-en-Der; beside the Lac du Der)

Opening times : from beginning April to end Nov.

3 ha (120 pitches)

Tariff : 36€ 🚶🚶 🚗 ▣ (⚡) (10A) – Extra per person 7€

Rental rates : (from beginning April to end Sept.) – 50 🛖. Per night from 35 to 142€ – Per week from 245 to 994€

Choose the pitches away from the road.

Surroundings : 🏞 ♤♤ 🏔
Leisure activities : 🍴 🎮 🏊 🏊 🚲 🎿 🚣
(beach) 🏊 multi-sports ground
Facilities : 🚿 ⌐ 🏖 🛁 🍴 launderette 🚿

Longitude : 4.84798
Latitude : 48.57179

ÉPERNAY

51200 – Michelin map **306** F8 – pop. 24 317 – alt. 75
▶ Paris 143 – Amiens 199 – Charleville-Mézières 113 – Meaux 96

⛺ Municipal

✆ 03 26 55 32 14, www.epernay.fr

Address : allée de Cumières (located 1.5km north along the D 301; beside the Marne river)

2 ha (109 pitches) flat, grassy

🚐 borne

Surroundings : 🏞 ♤♤
Leisure activities : 🏊 🚲
Facilities : 🚿 ⌐ 🔲 🍴 launderette
Nearby : ⚓

Longitude : 3.95026
Latitude : 49.05784

Using the traditional Michelin classification method, the guide provides you with an easy, speedy reference for assessing the category of each site: 1 to 5 tents (see page 10).

ERVY-LE-CHÂTEL

10130 – Michelin map **313** D5 – pop. 1 224 – alt. 160
▶ Paris 169 – Auxerre 48 – St-Florentin 18 – Sens 62

⛺ Municipal les Mottes

✆ 03 25 70 07 96, www.ervy-le-chatel.reseaudescommunes.fr/communes

Address : chemin des Mottes (1.8km east along the D 374, follow the signs for Auxon, D 92 and take the road to the right after the level crossing)

Opening times : from beginning May to mid Sept.

0,7 ha (53 pitches) flat, grassy

Tariff : (2013 Price) 🚶 3,50€ 🚗 3€ ▣ 3€ – (⚡) (6A) 3,50€

Beside a small river and a wood.

Surroundings : 🏞
Leisure activities : 🚣
Facilities : 🚿 🚻 🔲

Longitude : 3.91827
Latitude : 48.04069

GIFFAUMONT-CHAMPAUBERT

51290 – Michelin map **306** K11 – pop. 261 – alt. 130
▶ Paris 213 – Châlons-en-Champagne 67 – St-Dizier 25 – Bar-le-Duc 52

🏠 Village Vacances Marina-Holyder

(rental of small houses only)

📞 03 26 72 99 90, www.marina-holyder.com

Address : rue de Champaubert (Presqu'Île de Rougemer (peninsula)

Opening times : Permanent

2 ha flat

Rental rates : (2013 Price) **P** – 67 🏠. Per night from 95 to 150€
Per week from 220 to 945 €

Surroundings : 🏊
Leisure activities : ▼ ✕ 🎮 👬 🎿 🛶 hammam, jacuzzi 🚣 🎣 🎯 🏹 🎣 forest trail
Facilities : ⚡ 🚻 🗑 ▥ 🔧 launderette 🔧
Nearby : 🚲

G P S — Longitude : 4.77328
Latitude : 48.54987

LANGRES

52200 – Michelin map **313** L6 – pop. 8 066 – alt. 466
▶ Paris 295 – Châlons-en-Champagne 197 – Chaumont 36 – Dijon 79

🏠 Kawan Village Le Lac de la Liez 👥

📞 03 25 90 27 79, www.campingliez.com

Address : at Peigney, at la base nautique (5km east along the D 284)

Opening times : from beginning April to end Sept.

4,5 ha (190 pitches)

Tariff : 34€ 👫 🚗 ▣ (10A) – Extra per person 8€ – Reservation fee 15€

Rental rates : (from end March to end Sept.) – 2 caravans – 2 🚐 24 🏠. Per night from 39 to 114€ – Per week from 273 to 798€
Reservation fee 30€

🚐 borne 6€ – 6 ▣ – 🚐 (10€

Surroundings : 🏊 ◁ lake, countryside and the town of Langres 🌳 🏊
Leisure activities : ▼ ✕ 🏠 👬 🎿 🚣 🎯 🛶 🏹 🎣
Facilities : ⚡ 🚻 ▥ 🔧 – 16 individual sanitary facilities (🚿 🔧 🚽 wc) 🔧 🏹 🎣 launderette 🔧 🔧
Nearby : 🚲 🏊 (beach) 🏹 🎣 water skiing

G P S — Longitude : 5.3807
Latitude : 47.87146

MESNIL-ST-PERE

10140 – Michelin map **313** G4 – pop. 415 – alt. 131
▶ Paris 209 – Châlons-en-Champagne 98 – Troyes 25 – Chaumont 79

🏠 Kawan Le Lac d'Orient 👥

📞 03 25 40 61 85, www.camping-lacdorient.com

Address : route du Lac

Opening times : from beginning April to end Sept.

4 ha (199 pitches) flat, grassy

Tariff : 35€ 👫 🚗 ▣ (10A) – Extra per person 8,20€ – Reservation fee 20€

We value your opinion and welcome your feedback.
Do email us at campingfrance@tp.michelin.com

Rental rates : (from beginning April to end Sept.) 🚐 – 2 caravans 18 🚐 – 2 🏠. Per night from 51 to 130€ – Per week from 306 to 910€ – Reservation fee 20€
🚐 borne – 9 ▣ 26€

Surroundings : 🏊 🌳
Leisure activities : ▼ 🏠 👬 🚣 🖼 🛶 🎿 multi-sports ground
Facilities : ⚡ 🚻 [CC] ▥ 🔧 🔧 🏹 🎣 launderette 🔧 🔧
Nearby : 🏹 🐎 🚴

G P S — Longitude : 4.34624
Latitude : 48.26297

MONTIGNY-LE-ROI

52140 – Michelin map **313** M6 – pop. 2 168 – alt. 404
▶ Paris 296 – Bourbonne-les-Bains 21 – Chaumont 35 – Langres 23

⛺ Municipal du Château

📞 03 25 87 38 93, www.campingduchateau.com

Address : rue Hubert Collot (access via the town centre and take the pedestrian path to the village)

Opening times : from mid April to end Sept.

6 ha/2 for camping (75 pitches)

Tariff : 👤 5,60€ 🚗 5,60€ ▣ 5,60€ – (10A) 4,60€
🚐 borne 2€

In a wooded park overlooking the Vallée de la Meuse.

Surroundings : ◁ 🌳
Leisure activities : 🚣 🎯 🎣
Facilities : ⚡ 🚻 ▥ 🔧 🎣
Nearby : ✕

G P S — Longitude : 5.4965
Latitude : 48.00068

Key to rentals symbols:

12 🚐	*Number of mobile homes*
20 🏠	*Number of chalets*
6 🛏	*Number of rooms to rent*
Per night 30–50€	*Minimum/maximum rate per night*
Per week 300–1,000€	*Minimum/maximum rate per week*

RADONVILLIERS

10500 – Michelin map **313** H3 – pop. 384 – alt. 130
▶ Paris 206 – Bar-sur-Aube 22 – Bar-sur-Seine 35 – Brienne-le-Château 6

⛺ Le Garillon

📞 03 25 92 21 46, www.campinglegarillon.fr

Address : take the southwestern exit along the D 11, follow the signs for Piney and take turning to the right; beside a stream and 250m from the lake, (top of dike via steps)

Opening times : from beginning April to mid Oct.

1 ha (55 pitches) flat, grassy

Tariff : (2013 Price) 21€ 👫 🚗 ▣ (16A) – Extra per person 4€
Rental rates : (2013 Price) (from beginning April to mid Oct.) 11 🚐. Per night from 32 to 83 € – Per week from 192 to 498€

Leisure activities : 🛶
Facilities : ⚡ 🚻 🔧
Nearby : ✕

G P S — Longitude : 4.50206
Latitude : 48.3586

SÉZANNE

51120 – Michelin map **306** E10 – pop. 5 268 – alt. 137
▶ Paris 116 – Châlons-en-Champagne 59 – Meaux 78 – Melun 89

⚠ Municipal

✆ 03 26 80 57 00, campingdesezanne@wanadoo.fr

Address : route de Launat (take the western exit along the D 373, follow the signs for Paris (near N 4) then continue 700m along the road to the left and take turning to the right)

1 ha (79 pitches)

Surroundings : ♀
Leisure activities : 🛶 🎿 ⛷
Facilities : ⚹ ⚏ 🛜 📷
Nearby : ✕

GPS Longitude : 3.70212
Latitude : 48.72154

SIGNY-L'ABBAYE

08460 – Michelin map **306** I4 – pop. 1 365 – alt. 240
▶ Paris 208 – Charleville-Mézières 31 – Hirson 41 – Laon 74

⚠ Municipal l'Abbaye

✆ 03 24 52 87 73, www.signy-abbaye.fr

Address : route de l'Abbaye (situated north, near the stadium, beside the Vaux river)

Opening times : from beginning May to end Sept.

1,2 ha (60 pitches) flat, grassy, fine gravel

Tariff : ⚹ 2€ ⇔ 1,50€ 🔲 1,70€ – 🔋 (5A) 3,20€
🚐 10 🔲 1,70€

Surroundings : 🌲 ♀
Facilities : 🛜 📷 🏢
Nearby : ✕

GPS Longitude : 4.41967
Latitude : 49.70134

SOULAINES-DHUYS

10200 – Michelin map **313** I3 – pop. 311 – alt. 153
▶ Paris 228 – Bar-sur-Aube 18 – Brienne-le-Château 17 – Chaumont 48

⚠ La Croix Badeau

✆ 03 25 27 05 43, www.croix-badeau.com

Address : 6 rue de La Croix Badeau (to the northeast of the town, near the church)

Opening times : from beginning April to end Sept.

1 ha (39 pitches)

Tariff : (2013 Price) 17,50€ ⚹⚹ ⇔ 🔲 🔋 (10A) – Extra per person 3,50€

Rental rates : Permanent – 1 🚐. Per night 70€ – Per week 470€
🚐 borne 3€ – 🚿 9,50€

Surroundings : 🏕
Leisure activities : ♟ 🏠 🎿
Facilities : ⚹ ⚏ 🏢 ⛺ 🛜
Nearby : 🛶 ✕

GPS Longitude : 4.73846
Latitude : 48.37672

THONNANCE-LES-MOULINS

52230 – Michelin map **313** L3 – pop. 120 – alt. 282
▶ Paris 254 – Bar-le-Duc 64 – Chaumont 48 – Commercy 55

⚠⚠ Les Castels La Forge de Sainte Marie

✆ 03 25 94 42 00, www.laforgedesaintemarie.com

Address : route de Joinville (1.7km west along the D 427; beside the Rongeant river)

Opening times : from end April to beginning Sept.

32 ha/3 for camping (133 pitches) terraced, relatively flat, flat, grassy, pond

Tariff : ⚹ 9€ ⇔ 🔲 18€ 🔋 (6A)

Rental rates : (from end April to beginning Sept.) – 39 🚐 15 gîtes. Per night from 60 to 150€ – Per week from 240 to 950€ Reservation fee 12€

🚐 borne

In a pleasant green setting based around an old restored forge.

Surroundings : 🌲 🏞 ♀
Leisure activities : ♟ ✕ 🏠 🎣 🎣 🛶 🚴 🎿 🏊
Facilities : ⚹ ⚏ 🔲 🏖 ⛺ 🛜 launderette 🏊 🚿

GPS Longitude : 5.27097
Latitude : 48.40629

TROYES

10000 – Michelin map **313** E4 – pop. 61 188 – alt. 113
▶ Paris 170 – Dijon 185 – Nancy 186

⚠ Municipal

✆ 03 25 81 02 64, www.troyescamping.net

Address : at Pont Sainte-Marie, 7 rue Roger Salengro (situated 2km to the northeast, follow the signs for Nancy)

Opening times : from beginning April to mid Oct.

3,8 ha (150 pitches) flat, grassy

Tariff : 25€ ⚹⚹ ⇔ 🔲 🔋 (10A) – Extra per person 6,20€
🚐 borne 3,50€ – 15 🔲 17,80€

Close to the bus stop for Troyes town centre and factory outlets at Pont Sainte-Marie.

Surroundings : ♀
Leisure activities : 🏠 🛶 🎣 🛝 🎿
Facilities : ⚹ ⚏ 🏢 🛜 launderette
Nearby : 🏊 🚿

GPS Longitude : 4.09682
Latitude : 48.31112

These symbols are used for a campsite that is exceptional in its category:

⚠⚠⚠...⚠ *Particularly pleasant setting, quality and range of services available*

🌲🌲 *Tranquil, isolated site – quiet site, particularly at night*

≪≪ *Exceptional view – interesting or panoramic view*

M. Rock / Cephas / Photononstop

Corsica emerges from the Mediterranean like a glinting jewel. It is indeed the 'Isle of Beauty'. Follow its twisting roads to ancient citadels, perched on the island's rocky flanks in spectacular cliff-top settings, and your efforts will be more than rewarded. Enjoy panoramic views and inhale the fragrance of wild rosemary as you make your way up the rugged hills, clad in *maquis* (Mediterranean shrubs and herbs). The sudden sight of a secluded chapel or timeless village, or indeed an unscheduled encounter with a herd of mountain sheep, are among the many lasting memories that those discovering Corsica on foot, by bike or in their cars take home with them. After exploring the wild interior of the island, plunge into the impossibly clear turquoise waters that surround it and recharge your solar batteries on its warm sandy beaches, dreaming of an *assiette de charcuterie* (pork platter) and traditional cheese. Corsica seduces the eyes and taste buds of every visitor.

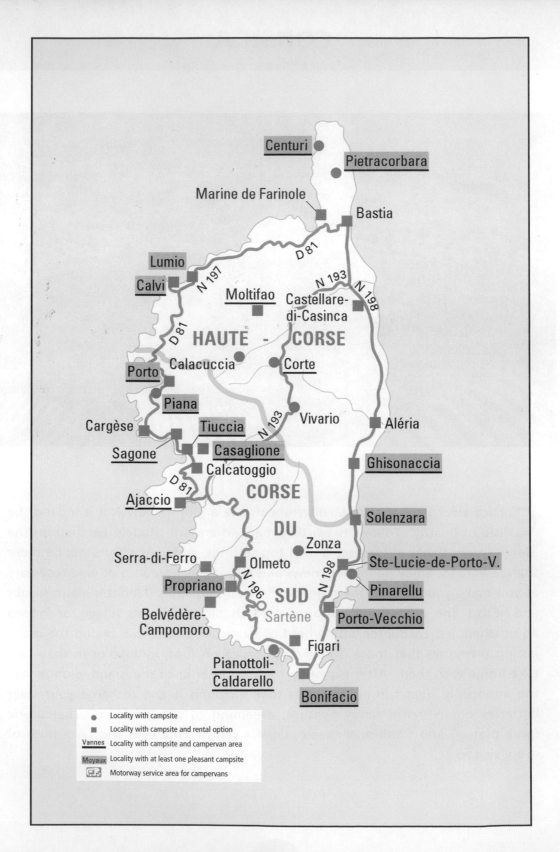

Centuri

Pietracorbara

Marine de Farinole

Bastia

D 81

Lumio

N 197

N 193

N 198

Calvi

Moltifao

Castellare-
di-Casinca

D 81

HAUTE - CORSE

Porto

Calacuccia

Corte

Piana

Cargèse

Tiuccia

Vivario

N 193

Aléria

Sagone

Casaglione

Calcatoggio

Ghisonaccia

D 81

CORSE

Ajaccio

DU

Solenzara

Zonza

Serra-di-Ferro

Olmeto

Ste-Lucie-de-Porto-V.

N 198

Propriano

N 196

Pinarellu

Belvédère-
Campomoro

SUD

Sartène

Porto-Vecchio

Figari

Pianottoli-
Caldarello

Bonifacio

● Locality with campsite

■ Locality with campsite and rental option

Vannes Locality with campsite and campervan area

Moyaux Locality with at least one pleasant campsite

Motorway service area for campervans

AJACCIO

20000 – Michelin map **345** B8 – pop. 64 306
▶ Bastia 147 – Bonifacio 131 – Calvi 166 – Corte 80

⚐ Les Mimosas

✆ 04 95 20 99 85, www.camping-lesmimosas.com – ℝ ✲

Address : route d'Alata (5km, take the northern exit along the D 61 and take the turning to the left, follow the signs for Les Milelli)

Opening times : from mid April to beginning Oct.

2,5 ha (70 pitches)

Tariff : ✚ 6€ ⇦ 3€ ▣ 3€ – (∮) (6A) 2,80€
Rental rates : Permanent ✲ – 12 ⎘ – 5 ⌂ – 1 studio. Per week from 280 to 580€
⛽ borne 8€
Rental mobile homes and chalets with pleasant shade from eucalyptus trees.

Surroundings : ⅏ ♨♨
Facilities : ⅊ ⛲ ⬗ ⬦¶ launderette , refrigerators

G P S Longitude : 8.73069
Latitude : 41.94066

ALÉRIA

20270 – Michelin map **345** G7 – pop. 1 996 – alt. 20
▶ Bastia 71 – Corte 50 – Vescovato 52

⚐ Marina d'Aléria ♟♟

✆ 04 95 57 01 42, www.marina-aleria.com

Address : plage de Padulone (3km east of Cateraggio along the N 200; beside the Tavignano river)

Opening times : from end April to beginning Oct.

17 ha/7 for camping (335 pitches)

Tariff : (2013 Price) 38€ ✚✚ ⇦ ▣ (∮) (9A) – Extra per person 6,95€
Reservation fee 20€

Rental rates : (from end April to beginning Oct.) ✲ Ⓟ (mobile homes) – 151 ⎘ – 31 ⌂. Per night from 30 to 140€ – Per week from 200 to 980€ – Reservation fee 20€

Shady and sunny pitches laid out along the beach.

Surroundings : ⅏ ≤ sea and mountain ♨♨ ⌂
Leisure activities : ¶ ✕ ⛛ ◷ daytime ⚡
⬗⬦ ⚡ ⚲
Facilities : ⅊ ⛲ ⬗¶ launderette ⬗ ⬦
refrigerated food storage facilities

G P S Longitude : 9.55
Latitude : 42.11139

BASTIA

20200 – Michelin map **345** F3 – pop. 43 545
▶ Ajaccio 148 – Bonifacio 171 – Calvi 92 – Corte 69

⚐ San Damiano

✆ 04 95 33 68 02, www.campingsandamiano.com

Address : Lido de la Marana (9km southeast along the N 193 and turn left onto D 107)

Opening times : from beginning April to end Oct.

12 ha (320 pitches)

Tariff : (2013 Price) ✚ 8,30€ ⇦ ▣ 8€ – (∮) (6A) 5€

Rental rates : (2013 Price) (from beginning April to end Oct.)
✲ – 8 ⎘ – 53 ⌂. Per night from 49 to 141€ – Per week from 343 to 987€

Some luxury chalets, some with with a sea view, and a bar-restaurant right next to the water.

Surroundings : ⅏ ⛺ ♨♨ ⌂
Leisure activities : ¶ ✕ ⛛ ⬗⬦ ⚡ ⚲ ⌇ ⚓
Facilities : ⅊ ⛲ ⬗¶ launderette ⇫⬗
Nearby : ◔ ⚞

G P S Longitude : 9.46718
Latitude : 42.63114

BELVÉDÈRE-CAMPOMORO

20110 – Michelin map **345** B10 – pop. 135 – alt. 5
▶ Ajaccio 88 – Bonifacio 72 – Porto 82 – Sartène 24

⚐ La Vallée

✆ 04 95 74 21 20, www.campomoro-lavallee.com ✲

Address : at Campomoro (on the D 121, 400m from the beach)

Opening times : from beginning May to end Sept.

3,5 ha (199 pitches)

Tariff : (2013 Price) ✚ 9€ ⇦ 5€ ▣ 5€ – (∮) (12A) 12€

Rental rates : (2013 Price) (from beginning May to end Sept.)
✲ Ⓟ – 12 ⌂ – 3 apartments. Per week from 700 to 950€
Reservation fee 40€

A view of the sea and the Genoese tower from some pitches and chalets.

Surroundings : ⅏ ♨♨
Facilities : ⅊ ⛲ ⬗ ▣ ▣
Nearby : ⚞

G P S Longitude : 8.81625
Latitude : 41.62815

Using the traditional Michelin classification method, the guide provides you with an easy, speedy reference for assessing the category of each site: 1 to 5 tents (see page 10).

BONIFACIO

20169 – Michelin map **345** D11 – pop. 2 919 – alt. 55
▶ Ajaccio 132 – Corte 150 – Sartène 50

⚐ Pertamina Village - U-Farniente ♟♟

✆ 04 95 73 05 47, www.camping-pertamina.com

Address : at Canelli (5km northeast along the N 198, follow the signs for Porto-Vecchio - Bastia)

Opening times : from mid April to mid Nov.

20 ha/8 for camping (150 pitches)

Tariff : 43€ ✚✚ ⇦ ▣ (∮) (6A) – Extra per person 12€ – Reservation fee 24€

Rental rates : (from mid April to mid Nov.) ⅊ (1 mobile home) 18 ⎘ – 54 ⌂ – 6 apartments – 10 canvas bungalows. Per night from 50 to 180€ – Per week from 350 to 1 200€ – Reservation fee 26€

A pleasant, undulating site with plenty of shade and a variety of rental options, some of which are quite luxurious.

Surroundings : ⅏ ⛺ ♨♨
Leisure activities : ¶ ✕ ⛛ ◷ ⚡ ⚲ jacuzzi
⬗⬦ ⚲ ⚲ ⚲
Facilities : ⅊ ⛲ ▣▥ ⬗¶ launderette ⬗
⬗ refrigerated food storage facilities

G P S Longitude : 9.17905
Latitude : 41.41825

Rondinara

📞 04 95 70 43 15, www.rondinara.fr 🏊

Address : at Suartone (18km northeast along the N 198, follow the signs for Porto-Vecchio and take D 158 to the right, follow the signs for La Pointe de la Rondinara (headland); 400m from the beach)

5 ha (120 pitches) terraced, relatively flat, flat, grassy, stony

Rentals : 🛖 – 36 🚐.

Situated in the heart of the maquis (typical shrubland), with a swimming pool, a restaurant and a panoramic view of the sea and Sardinia.

Surroundings : 🏖 ⬅ ♀
Leisure activities : 🍷 ✕ 🏠 🚣 🛶
Facilities : ♿ ⚲ 🍴 🔥 🗑 🚿 refrigerated food storage facilities
Nearby : pedalos, bar-restaurant on the beach

G P S Longitude : 9.26289
Latitude : 41.47322

Les Îles

📞 04 95 73 11 89, www.camping-desiles.com 🏊

Address : route de Piantarella (4.5km east, follow the signs for Piantarella, towards the landing stage at Cavallo)

8 ha (150 pitches) undulating, relatively flat, flat, grassy, stony

Rentals : ♿ (1 mobile home) 🏊 – 17 🚐 – 20 🛖.
🚻 borne

There's a panoramic view over to Sardinia and nearby islands from some pitches.

Surroundings : 🏖 ⬅ 🛖 ♀♀
Leisure activities : ✕ 🏠 🚣 ✕ 🛶
Facilities : ♿ ⚲ 🔥 🗑 🚿 🚰

G P S Longitude : 9.21034
Latitude : 41.37818

Campo-di-Liccia

📞 04 95 73 03 09, www.campingdiliccia.com

Address : at Parmentil (5.2km northeast along the N 198, follow the signs for Porto-Vecchio)

Opening times : from beginning April to end Sept.

5 ha (161 pitches)

Tariff : 🧍 7,90€ 🚗 3,50€ 🅿 – 🔌 (10A) 4€ – Reservation fee 16€
Rental rates : (from beginning April to end Sept.) 🏊 – 25 🚐 10 🛖. Per night from 47 to 90€ – Per week from 295 to 930€ Reservation fee 16€
🚻 borne 5€

Centuries-old Holm oaks, eucalyptus and olive trees provide generous amounts of shade; a mobile home park of a good standard.

Surroundings : 🏖 ♀♀
Leisure activities : 🍷 ✕ 🚣 🛶
Facilities : ♿ ⚲ (July-Aug.) 🔥 🗑 🚿 🚰 refrigerated food storage facilities

G P S Longitude : 9.17893
Latitude : 41.41943

Pian del Fosse

📞 04 95 73 16 34, www.piandelfosse.com

Address : 3.8 km northeast along the D 58 - or 5km along the N 198 following the signs for Porto-Vecchio and take the D 60 following signs for Santa-Manza

Opening times : from mid April to mid Oct.

5,5 ha (100 pitches)

Tariff : 32,80€ 🧍🧍 🚗 🅿 🔌 (10A) – Extra per person 8,40€ Reservation fee 15€

Rental rates : (from mid April to mid Oct.) 🏊 – 1 🚐 – 5 🛖
6 apartments – 12 canvas bungalows. Per night from 60 to 155€
Per week from 300 to 1000€ – Reservation fee 15€
🚻 borne

Pitches shaded by mulberry trees, plane trees, pines and four-hundred-year old olive trees.

Surroundings : 🏖 🛖 ♀♀
Leisure activities : ✕ 🚣
Facilities : ♿ ⚲ 🅿 🔥 🍴 launderette
Nearby : 🐎

G P S Longitude : 9.20083
Latitude : 41.39972

CALACUCCIA

20224 – Michelin map **345** D5 – pop. 316 – alt. 830
▶ Ajaccio 107 – Bastia 76 – Porto-Vecchio 146 – Corte 27

Acquaviva

📞 04 95 48 00 08, www.acquaviva-fr.com

Address : 500m southwest along the D 84 and take road to the left, opposite the service station

Opening times : from mid April to mid Oct.

4 ha (50 pitches)

Tariff : 🧍 7€ 🚗 4€ 🅿 7€ – 🔌 (16A) 5€

The site looks out over the lake with some shade; hotel-restaurant services are provided by the site owner.

Surroundings : 🏖 ⬅ Lake and mountains ♀
Leisure activities : 🚣 🛶
Facilities : ♿ 🚿 🔥 🗑
Nearby : 🍷 ✕ 🚢 🛶

G P S Longitude : 9.01049
Latitude : 42.33341

A 'quartier' is a district or area of a town or village.

CALCATOGGIO

20111 – Michelin map **345** B7 – pop. 522 – alt. 250
▶ Ajaccio 23 – Bastia 156

La Liscia

📞 04 95 52 20 65, www.la-liscia.com

Address : route de Tiuccia (5km northwest along the D 81; beside the river, in the Golfe de La Liscia (bay), 500m from the beach)

3 ha (100 pitches)

Rentals : 🏊 – 7 🚐 – 1 🛖 – 3 studios.

Partly laid out in well-shaded terraces, but choose the pitches furthest away from the road. Basic sanitary facilities.

Surroundings : ♀♀
Leisure activities : 🍷 ✕ 🏠 🚣 🚲 🎣
Facilities : ♿ ⚲ 🔥 🍴 launderette 🚰 refrigerators

G P S Longitude : 8.75526
Latitude : 42.04678

CALVI

20260 – Michelin map **345** B4 – pop. 5 377
▶ Bastia 92 – Corte 88 – L'Ile-Rousse 25 – Porto 73

La Pinède 👥

📞 04 95 65 17 80, www.camping-calvi.com

Address : route de la Pinède (300m from the beach)

5 ha (262 pitches)

Rentals : ☂ – 14 caravans – 20 📷 – 80 🏠 .
Choose the pitches away from the road in preference.

Surroundings : 🌳🌳
Leisure activities : ♟✕🏠🚴🚣✂🎣🏊
multi-sports ground
Facilities : ☂ ☕ 🚿🚻 launderette ♨ 🚰
refrigerated food storage facilities
G P S Longitude : 8.76795
Latitude : 42.55318

🏔 Les Castors

📞 0495651330, www.camping-castors.fr ✂

Address : route de Piétramaggiore (located 1km south along the N 197 towards L'Île Rousse and follow the signs for Pietra-Major to the right)

Opening times : from beginning April to beginning Nov.

2 ha (105 pitches)

Tariff : ♟ 7€ 🚗 2€ 🔲 3€ – 🔌 (15A) 4,50€ – Reservation fee 10€
Rental rates : (from beginning April to beginning Nov.) ✂ 36 📷 – 38 studios. Per night 147€ – Per week 1025€ Reservation fee 10€
🚰 borne 7€ – 10 🔲 26€
Well shaded, in many cases by eucalyptus trees; many different rental options.

Surroundings : 🌿🌳🌳
Leisure activities : ♟✕🚣🏊🏄
Facilities : ☂ ☕ 🚿🚻 🔲
G P S Longitude : 8.7561
Latitude : 42.55735

🏔 Bella Vista

📞 0495651176, www.camping-bellavista.com – 🏪

Address : route de Pietramaggiore (head 1.5km south along the N 197 towards l'Île Rousse and follow the signs for Pietra-Major to the right)

Opening times : from beginning April to beginning Oct.

6 ha/4 for camping (152 pitches)

Tariff : ♟ 8€ 🚗 4,50€ 🔲 4,50€ – 🔌 (10A) 4€
Rental rates : (from beginning April to beginning Oct.) ✂ (from beginning April to beginning June) – 21 🏠. Per week from 250 to 980€ – Reservation fee 15€
In the shade of pine and eucalyptus trees and oleanders.

Surroundings : 🌿🌳🌳
Leisure activities : ✕ 🚣
Facilities : ☂ ☕ 🅿 🚿🏊🚽🚻 🔲 ♨ 🚰
G P S Longitude : 8.75334
Latitude : 42.55068

🏔 Paradella

📞 0495650097, www.camping-paradella.fr ✉ 20214 Calenzana

Address : route de la forêt de Bonifato (9.5km southeast along the N 197, follow the signs for l'Île-Rousse and take D 81 to the right, follow the signs for the airport and Bonifato)

Opening times : from beginning April to end Sept.

5 ha (150 pitches)

Tariff : 27,80€ ♟♟ 🚗 🔲🔌 (8A) – Extra per person 8,40€ Reservation fee 10€
Rental rates : (from beginning April to end Sept.) ✂ (July–Aug.) 3 📷 – 18 🏠. Per week from 290 to 780€ – Reservation fee 10€
🚰 borne 5€ – 8 🔲

There are several different types of sani-station ('borne' in French) – sanitation points providing fresh water and disposal points for grey water. See page 12 for further details.

Choose the pitches away from the road in preference, sheltered by pines and eucalyptus trees.

Surroundings : 🏞🌳🌳
Leisure activities : 🚣🏊🏄
Facilities : ☂ ☕ 🚿🚻 🔲 🚰
Nearby : 🐎
G P S Longitude : 8.79166
Latitude : 42.50237

🏔 Paduella

📞 0495650616, www.campingpaduella.com – 🏪

Address : route de Bastia (1.8km southeast along the N 197, follow the signs for l'Ile-Rousse; 400m from the beach)

Opening times : from beginning May to beginning Oct.

4,5 ha (160 pitches)

Tariff : ♟ 8,20€ 🚗 3,50€ 🔲 3,50€ – 🔌 (10A) 3,80€
Rental rates : (from beginning May to beginning Oct.) – 35 canvas bungalows. Per night from 53 to 82€ – Per week from 371 to 574€
Some pitches are well marked out in the shade of a beautiful pine wood.

Surroundings : 🌳🌳
Leisure activities : ♟ 🚣
Facilities : ☂ ☕ 🚐 🚿🚲🚻 🔲 🚰
G P S Longitude : 8.76429
Latitude : 42.55219

🏔 Dolce Vita

📞 0495650599, www.dolce-vita.fr ✂

Address : 4.5km southeast along the N 197, follow the signs for l'Ile-Rousse; at the mouth of the Figarella river, 200m from the sea

Opening times : from mid May to mid Sept.

6 ha (200 pitches)

Tariff : 22€ ♟♟ 🚗 🔲 🔌 (10A) – Extra per person 8€
Choose the pitches near the sea, away from the road and the Calvi-l'Île Rousse railway line.

Surroundings : 🌊🌳
Leisure activities : ✕ 🏄 🚣🏊🎣
Facilities : ☂ ☕ 🎣 🚻 launderette ♨ 🚰
Nearby : ⚓
G P S Longitude : 8.78972
Latitude : 42.55582

20130 – Michelin map **345** A7 – pop. 1 117 – alt. 75
▶ Ajaccio 51 – Calvi 106 – Corte 119 – Piana 21

🏔 Torraccia

📞 0495264239, www.camping-torraccia.com

Address : at Bagghiuccia (4.5km north along the D 81, follow the signs for Porto)

Opening times : from end April to end Sept.

3 ha (90 pitches)

Tariff : ♟ 9,50€ 🚗 4€ 🔲 4,50€ – 🔌 (10A) 4,50€ – Reservation fee 18,50€
Rental rates : (from end April to end Sept.) – 25 📷. Per night from 60 to 120€ – Per week from 335 to 900€ – Reservation fee 18,50€
Choose the pitches furthest away from the road. Good sanitary facilities and some chalets have a panoramic view.

Surroundings : 🌄🌳🌳
Leisure activities : ♟ jacuzzi 🚣🏊
Facilities : ☂ ☕ 🚿🚻 🔲 🚰
G P S Longitude : 8.59797
Latitude : 42.16258

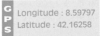

CASAGLIONE

20111 – Michelin map **345** B7 – pop. 365 – alt. 150
▶ Ajaccio 33 – Bastia 166

⚠️ U Sommalu

🔗 04 95 52 24 21, www.usommalu-camping.fr

Address : route de Casaglione (3km northeast along the D 81, then right onto the D 25, 600m from La plage de Liamone (beach)

Opening times : from end March to end Sept.

4 ha (123 pitches)

Tariff : ♣ 8,50€ ⇌ 4€ 🔲 6€ – (16A) 4,50€

Rental rates : (from end March to end Sept.) – 15 🏠 – 11 🏠.
Per night from 85 to 155€ – Per week from 385 to 840€
Reservation fee 4€

🔲 borne

Shady pitches laid out on terraces, some of which have a sea view.

Surroundings : ≋ ♨♨
Leisure activities : 🍷 🏖 ⛵ 🛶
Facilities : ♿ ⚡ 🚿 laundrette

G P S Longitude : 8.73126
Latitude : 42.07027

CASTELLARE-DI-CASINCA

20213 – Michelin map **345** F5 – pop. 557 – alt. 140
▶ Paris 943 – Ajaccio 136 – Bastia 31

⛰️ Village Center Domaine d'Anghione 👥

Interaview Production

(rental of mobile homes and gîtes only)

🔗 04 95 36 50 22, www.village-center.fr

Address : at Anghione (6km along the D 106)

Opening times : from beginning March to end Oct.

40 ha/26 for camping flat

Rental rates : (2013 Price) – 95 🏠
155 gîtes. Per week from 357 to 1 036€

Reservation fee 10€

A holiday village close to the beach with plenty of green spaces.

Surroundings : ≋ ♨♨ ⛰️
Leisure activities : 🍷 🍴 🏠 📺 ⛲ 🏖 ⛵ 🎾 🎣
🏊 🛶 multi-sports ground
Facilities : ♿ ⚡ 🍽️ 🏖 laundrette 🚿
Nearby : 🏇

G P S Longitude : 9.52707
Latitude : 42.47547

CENTURI

20238 – Michelin map **345** F2 – pop. 221 – alt. 228
▶ Ajaccio 202 – Bastia 55

⚠️ Isulottu

🔗 04 95 35 62 81, www.isulottu.fr

Address : at Marine de Mute (head along the D 35 following the signs for Morsiglia, 200m from the beach)

Opening times : from beginning May to end Sept.

2,3 ha (150 pitches)

Tariff : ♣ 7,50€ ⇌ 3,50€ 🔲 3,80€ – (20A) 3,50€

🔲 borne 7€

Well-shaded pitches laid out across a series of small terraces, some of which have a view of the sea or the village.

Surroundings : ≋ ≤ ♨♨
Leisure activities : 🍷 🏖
Facilities : ♿ ⚡ 🚿 🍽️ 🔲 🚿
Nearby : scuba diving

G P S Longitude : 9.3515
Latitude : 42.96048

CORTE

20250 – Michelin map **345** D6 – pop. 6 744 – alt. 396
▶ Ajaccio 81 – Bastia 68

⚠️ Aire Naturelle St-Pancrace

🔗 04 95 46 09 22, www.campingsaintpancrace.fr

Address : Saint-Pancrace quartier (located 1.5km north along the Cours Paoli and take road to the left after the Sous-Préfecture)

Opening times : from mid April to mid Oct.

12 ha/1 campable (25 pitches)

Tariff : ♣ 6€ ⇌ 3€ – (45A) 4€

🔲 borne 4€

A farm campsite with produce for sale: ewe's milk, Tomme cheese and a range of jams.

Surroundings : ≋ ≤ ♨♨
Leisure activities : 🏠
Facilities : ⚡ 🚿 🔲 🏖

The information in the guide may have changed since going to press.

FARINOLE (MARINA DE)

20253 – Michelin map **345** F3 – pop. 224 – alt. 250
▶ Bastia 20 – Rogliano 61 – St-Florent 13

⚠️ A Stella

🔗 04 95 37 14 37, www.campingastella.com

Address : along the D 80; beside the sea

Opening times : from beginning June to end Sept.

3 ha (100 pitches) terraced, relatively flat, flat, grassy, stony

Tariff : (2013 Price) ♣ 7€ ⇌ 3,50€ 🔲 7€ – (4) 4,50€

Rental rates : (2013 Price) (from beginning June to end Sept.)
2 apartments. Per week 850€

Some sunny pitches with a sea view; close to a pebble beach.

Surroundings : ≋ ≤ ♨♨ ⛰️
Leisure activities : 🏠
Facilities : ⚡ 🔲 🏖 🚿

G P S Longitude : 9.34259
Latitude : 42.72911

FIGARI

20114 – Michelin map **345** D11 – pop. 1 217 – alt. 80
▶ Ajaccio 122 – Bonifacio 18 – Porto-Vecchio 20 – Sartène 39

⚠️ U Moru

🔗 04 95 71 23 40, www.u-moru.com

Address : 5km northeast along the D 859

Opening times : from mid June to mid Sept.

6 ha/4 for camping (100 pitches)

Tariff : ♣ 8€ ⇌ 3,50€ 🔲 4,10€ – (6A) 4,20€

Rental rates : (from mid June to mid Sept.) – 12 ⌐••⌐. Per week from 560 to 940€

Well-shaded pitches and well-equipped mobile home terraces.

Surroundings : ⌐⌐ ♨♨♨
Leisure activities : 🛶 🚣 🏊 (small swimming pool)
Facilities : ⚷ 🚰 🖼 🧺 refrigerators

GPS Longitude : 9.16564
Latitude : 41.53096

GHISONACCIA

20240 – Michelin map **345** F7 – pop. 3 669 – alt. 25
▶ Bastia 85 – Aléria 14 – Ghisoni 27 – Venaco 56

🅰 Arinella-Bianca ♣♠

📞 04 95 56 04 78, www.arinellabianca.com

Address : route de la mer (3.5km east along the D 144 then continue 700m along the road to the right)

Opening times : from mid April to beginning Oct.

10 ha (416 pitches)

Tariff : 53€ ♣♣ 🚗 🔲 🔌 (10A) – Extra per person 15€ – Reservation fee 50€
Rental rates : (from mid April to beginning Oct.) ♿ – 227 ⌐••⌐ 56 🏠. Per week from 302 to 1472€ – Reservation fee 50€
🚽 borne 10€

A pretty seaside area with a pleasant 'zen' water park, several luxurious rental options and a relaxation area close to the beach.

Surroundings : ♨♨ ⌂
Leisure activities : 🍽 🍴 🛶 🎣 🏃 🎣 🎱 hammam, jacuzzi 🚣 🎾 🏊 tourist information, multi-sports ground, spa centre, water park
Facilities : ♿ ⚷ 🖼 🚿 🚰 launderette 🧺 🚰 refrigerated food storage facilities
Nearby : 🚤

GPS Longitude : 9.44331
Latitude : 41.9972

🅰 Homair Vacances Marina d'Erba Rossa ♣♠

📞 04 95 56 25 14, www.marina-erbarossa.com

Address : route de la Mer (4km east along the D 144; beside the beach)

Opening times : from April to Oct.

12 ha/8 for camping (588 pitches) flat, grassy

Tariff : (2013 Price) ♣ 10€ 🚗 🔲 26€ – 🔌 5,70€ – Reservation fee 25€
Rental rates : (2013 Price) (from beginning April to mid Oct.) ♿ – 350 ⌐••⌐ – 90 🏠 – 25 gîtes. Per night from 29 to 202€ Per week from 203 to 1414€ – Reservation fee 25€

A green setting with plenty of pleasant shade and a relaxation area close to the beach. Option for full-board or half-board stays.

Surroundings : ⌐⌐ ♨♨ ⌂
Leisure activities : 🍽 🍴 🛶 🎣 🏃 🎱 jacuzzi 🚣 🎾 🏊 wildlife park, spa centre
Facilities : ♿ ⚷ 🚿 🚰 launderette 🧺 🚰 refrigerated food storage facilities
Nearby : 🚤 scuba diving

GPS Longitude : 9.44339
Latitude : 42.00211

We have selected the best campsites in France with our usual care, listing those with the best facilities in the most pleasant surroundings.

🅰 Sunêlia Perla Di Mare

Bertran

(rental of mobile homes, gîtes and apartments only)
📞 04 95 56 53 10, www.perla.di.mare.fr
Address : plage de Vignale
Opening times : Permanent
10 ha (174 pitches) undulating
Rental rates : ♿ (2 mobile homes) ♿ 100 ⌐••⌐ – 4 studios – 50 apartments. Per night from 41 to 178€ – Per week from 287 to 1246€ – Reservation fee 30€

A range of rental options with a relaxation area close to the beach.

Surroundings : 🏖 ♨ ⌂
Leisure activities : 🍽 🍴 🛶 🎮 🏃 hammam, jacuzzi 🚣 🚴 🏊 🎯 archery, spa centre
Facilities : ⊙ 🚿 🖼 🚰 launderette 🚰

GPS Longitude : 9.4558
Latitude : 42.00647

LUMIO

20260 – Michelin map **345** B4 – pop. 1 250 – alt. 150
▶ Ajaccio 158 – Bastia 83 – Corte 77 – Calvi 10

🅰 Le Panoramic

📞 04 95 60 73 13, www.le-panoramic.com

Address : route de Lavatoggio (situated 2km northeast on the D 71, follow the signs for Belgodère)

6 ha (108 pitches)

Rentals : ♿ – 7 ⌐••⌐.

A panoramic view of the sea from some pitches.

Surroundings : 🏖 ⋞ ♨♨
Leisure activities : 🍴 🏊
Facilities : ⚷ 🖼 🚰

GPS Longitude : 8.84805
Latitude : 42.58973

The guide covers all 22 regions of France – see the map and list of regions on pages 4–5.

MOLTIFAO

20218 – Michelin map **345** D5 – pop. 724 – alt. 420
▶ Ajaccio 113 – Bastia 58

🅰 E Canicce

📞 04 95 35 16 75, www.campingecanicce.com

Address : Vallée de l'Asco (3km south on the D 47; beside the Asco river)

Opening times : from beginning March to end Oct.

1 ha (25 pitches)

Tariff : 21€ ♣♣ 🚗 🔲 🔌 (10A) – Extra per person 6€
Rental rates : Permanent ♿ – 3 apartments. Per night from 40 to 72€ – Per week from 280 to 500€
🚽 5 🔲 21€

In the heart of the maquis (typical shrubland), at the foot of mountains and beside a stream.

Surroundings : 🏖 ⋞ Monte Cinto and Scala di Santa Régina (gorge) ♨♨
Leisure activities : 🚤
Facilities : ⚷ 🚰 🚿 🖼

GPS Longitude : 9.13444
Latitude : 42.47573

OLMETO

20113 – Michelin map **345** C9 – pop. 1 230 – alt. 320
▶ Ajaccio 64 – Propriano 8 – Sartène 20
à la Plage SW : 7 km via D 157

▲ L'Esplanade

𝒫 04 95 76 05 03, www.camping-esplanade.com

Address : at Olmeto-plage (1.6km along the D 157, 100m from the beach - direct access)

4,5 ha (100 pitches) extremely uneven
Rentals : 🚫 🅿 (chalets) – 8 caravans – 53 🏠 – 6 tipis – 2 tent lodges.

Choose the pitches furthest away from the road. There's a panoramic view from some chalets, a swimming pool and a restaurant.

Surroundings : 🏕 ♨♨♨	**G** Longitude : 8.88868
Leisure activities : ✗ 🏠 ⛵ ⛷	**P**
Facilities : ♿ ⚡ 🔦 🛁 🚿	**S** Latitude : 41.69562

PIANA

20115 – Michelin map **345** A6 – pop. 450 – alt. 420
▶ Ajaccio 72 – Calvi 85 – Évisa 33 – Porto 13

▲ Plage d'Arone

𝒫 04 95 20 64 54

Address : route Danièle Casanova (11.5km southwest along the D 824; 500m from the beach - direct access)

3,8 ha (125 pitches) terraced, open site, flat, grassy, stony
🚰 borne

Situated 500m from the beach in the maquis (typical shrubland), shaded by olive, eucalyptus, bay and other trees and Mediterranean shrubs.

Surroundings : 🏞 < ♨♨	**G** Longitude : 8.58092
Facilities : ♿ ⚡ 🛁 🔦 🚿	**P**
	S Latitude : 42.20843

PIANOTTOLI-CALDARELLO

20131 – Michelin map **345** D11 – pop. 864 – alt. 60
▶ Ajaccio 113 – Bonifacio 19 – Porto-Vecchio 29 – Sartène 31

▲ Kévano Plage

𝒫 04 95 71 83 22, campingkevano.com

Address : route de la plage (3.3km southeast along the D 122 and take right turning; 500m from the beach)

Opening times : from mid April to mid Oct.

6 ha (100 pitches)

Tariff : 30€ 🚶🚶 🚗 📧 🔌 (3A) – Extra per person 9€ – Reservation fee 30€
🚰 borne

In a natural setting in the middle of the maquis (typical shrubland) and granite rocks. .

Surroundings : 🏞 🏕 ♨♨	**G** Longitude : 9.04294
Leisure activities : ✗ ⛵	**P**
Facilities : ♿ ⚡ 🌳 🛁 🍴 🔦 🚿 🚿	**S** Latitude : 41.47111

To visit a town or region, use the MICHELIN Green Guides.

PIETRACORBARA

20233 – Michelin map **345** F2 – pop. 573 – alt. 150
▶ Paris 967 – Ajaccio 170 – Bastia 21 – Biguglia 31

⛰ La Pietra

𝒫 04 95 35 27 49, www.la-pietra.com – ℞

Address : head 4km southeast along the D 232 and take road to the left; 500m from the beach

Opening times : from mid March to beginning Nov.

3 ha (80 pitches)

Tariff : (2013 Price) 🚶 9,95€ 🚗 3,80€ – 🔌 (6A) 3,50€
🚰 borne

A well-maintained setting with marked-out, shaded pitches and a sunny meadow.

Surroundings : 🏞 < 🏕 ♨♨	**G** Longitude : 9.4739
Leisure activities : ✗ 🏠 ⛵ ✂ ⛷	**P**
Facilities : ♿ ⚡ 🔦 🛁 🍴 🔦 🚿	**S** Latitude : 42.83939
refrigerated food storage facilities	
Nearby : 🐎	

This guide is not intended as a list of all the camping sites in France; its aim is to provide a selection of the best sites in each category.

PINARELLU

20124 – Michelin map **345** F9
▶ Ajaccio 146 – Bonifacio 44 – Porto-Vecchio 16

▲ California

𝒫 04 95 71 49 24, www.camping-california.net ✉ 20144 Ste-Lucie-de-Porto-Vecchio 🚫 (July–Aug.)

Address : 800m south along the D 468 and 1.5km along the road to the left; beside the beach

Opening times : from beginning June to end Sept.

7 ha/5 for camping (100 pitches)

Tariff : (2013 Price) 🚶 10€ 🚗 📧 11€ – 🔌 3€

Situated near lakes and the sea, an exclusive location in an unspoilt setting.

Surroundings : 🏞 ♨♨ ⛰	**G** Longitude : 9.38084
Leisure activities : ✗ ⛵ ✂	**P**
Facilities : ♿ ⚡ 🅿 🌳 🔦 🍴 🔦 🚿 🚿	**S** Latitude : 41.66591

PORTO

20150 – Michelin map **345** B6 – pop. 544
▶ Ajaccio 84 – Calvi 73 – Corte 93 – Évisa 23

⛰ Les Oliviers 👥

𝒫 04 95 26 14 49, www.camping-oliviers-porto.com ✉ 20150 Ota 🚫

Address : at the bridge (along the D 81, beside the Porto river, 100m from the town)

Opening times : from end March to mid Nov.

5,4 ha (216 pitches) extremely uneven

Tariff : 🚶 10,80€ 🚗 4,20€ 📧 4€ – 🔌 (10A) 4,50€ – Reservation fee 15€

Rental rates : (from end March to mid Nov.) 🚫 – 6 caravans 46 🏠. Per night from 79 to 148€ – Per week from 474 to 1 165€ Reservation fee 16€
🚰 borne

An attractive swimming pool area, spa and camping area in a natural wooded setting.

Surroundings :
Leisure activities : ▼ ✕ ⚓ ♨ ⛵ hammam 🚣 🏊 ⚓ diving (sub aqua) school, spa centre
Facilities : ♿ ⚡ Ⓟ 🍽 ☕ launderette ⚒ refrigerated food storage facilities
Nearby : 🚲 ⚓

G P S Longitude : 8.71005
Latitude : 42.26242

⛺ Sole e Vista

📞 04 95 26 15 71, www.camping-sole-e-vista.com ✉ 20150 Ota

Address : at the town (main access via the supermarket car park – secondary access: head 1km east along the D 124, follow the signs for Ota, 150m from the Porto and the town)

Opening times : from mid March to mid Nov.

4 ha (170 pitches) extremely uneven

Tariff : 30€ ♥♥ ⚓ 🔲 (20A) – Extra per person 9€
Rental rates : Permanent ✂ – 34 🚐. Per night from 45 to 10 € Per week from 300 to 1 350€ – 🔌 borne

A natural, wooded setting with an array of small terraces for pitches. A panoramic view of the sea and the mountains from the swimming pool and restaurant.

Surroundings : ⚓ 🚐 ♨
Leisure activities : 🚣 🏊
Facilities : ⚒ ☕ launderette, refrigerators
Nearby : ⚓ ⚓

G P S Longitude : 8.71114
Latitude : 42.26313

⛺ Funtana a l'Ora

📞 04 95 26 11 65, www.funtanaalora.com ✉ 20150 Ota

Address : route d'Évisa (1.4km southeast along the D 84, 200m from the Porto)

Opening times : from beginning April to end Oct.

2 ha (70 pitches)

Tariff : ♥ 9,40€ ⚓ 4€ 🔲 7€ – 🔌 (5A) 4€ – Reservation fee 15€
Rental rates : (from beginning April to end Oct.) – 7 🏠. Per night from 48 to 131 € – Per week from 300 to 830 € – Reservation fee 15€
🔌 borne 5€ – 20 🔲 8€

Well-shaded pitches on small terraces in a wild setting.

Surroundings : ⚓ 🚐 ♨
Leisure activities : 🎱 🏊 multi-sports ground
Facilities : ♿ ☕ ✉ ☕ launderette ⚒ refrigerated food storage facilities

G P S Longitude : 8.71528
Latitude : 42.25887

⛺ Casa del Torrente (rental of chalets only)

📞 04 95 22 45 14, www.casadeltorrente.com ✉ 20150 Ota

Address : route Evisa (located 1km southeast along the D 84; beside the Porto river (direct access)

Opening times : from beginning April to mid Nov.

1,5 ha terraced

Rental rates : ✂ –12 🏠 –2 apartments. Per night from 48 to 131€ Per week from 300 to 830€ – Reservation fee 15€

Gîtes for large families and free use of the leisure facilities and services at the Funtana a l'Ora campsite 200m on the other side of the road.

Surroundings : ⚓ ♨
Leisure activities : ⚓
Facilities : ☕ ✉ 🍽 ☕ 🔳
Nearby : 🏊

G P S Longitude : 8.70824
Latitude : 42.26209

⛺ Le Porto

📞 06 85 41 50 74, www.camping-le-porto.com ✉ 20150 Ota

Address : take the western exit along the D 81, follow the signs for Piana; 200m from Le Porto and 300m from town

Opening times : from beginning June to end Sept.

2 ha (60 pitches) extremely uneven

Tariff : 26€ ♥♥ ⚓ 🔲 🔌 (20A) – Extra per person 7€

Lovely terraces with plenty of shade, but choose the pitches furthest away from the road.

Surroundings : ♨ ⚓
Facilities : ♿ ☕ ✉ ☕ 🔳
Nearby : ⚓

G P S Longitude : 8.7055
Latitude : 42.26645

Key to rentals symbols:

12 🚐	*Number of mobile homes*
20 🏠	*Number of chalets*
6 🛏	*Number of rooms to rent*
Per night 30–50€	*Minimum/maximum rate per night*
Per week 300–1,000€	*Minimum/maximum rate per week*

PORTO-VECCHIO

20137 – Michelin map **345** E10 – pop. 11 005 – alt. 40
▶ Ajaccio 141 – Bonifacio 28 – Corte 121 – Sartène 59

⛺ Golfo di Sogno

📞 04 95 70 08 98, www.golfo-di-sogno.fr

Address : route de Cala-Rossa (6km northeast along the D 468)

Opening times : from beginning May to end Sept.

22 ha (650 pitches)

Tariff : 30€ ♥♥ ⚓ 🔲 – Extra per person 9,90€
Rental rates : (2013 Price) (from beginning May to end Sept.) ✂ 12 🚐 – 61 🏠 – 12 gîtes – 138 bungalows without sanitary facilities. Per week from 290 to 1 540€

A very pleasant pine forest beside the sea, plenty of space with a range of rental options of varying degrees of comfort.

Surroundings : 🚐 ♨ ⚓
Leisure activities : ▼ ✕ 🚣 ✂ ⚓ ♦ watersports centre, multi-sports ground
Facilities : ☕ ✉ ☕ launderette 🛒 ⚒
Nearby : ⚓

G P S Longitude : 9.31297
Latitude : 41.62975

⛺ Pitrera

📞 04 95 70 20 10, www.pitrera.com

Address : at La Trinite (head 5.8km north along the N 198, follow the signs for Bastia and take road to the right)

4 ha (95 pitches)

Rentals : 1 🚐 – 56 🏠 – 1 yurt.

Well-shaded pitches, a lovely swimming pool area and a panoramic sea view from some chalets.

Surroundings : ♨
Leisure activities : ✕ 🚣 🏊 ✂
Facilities : ♿ ☕ ☕ 🍽 🔳 ⚒

G P S Longitude : 9.29535
Latitude : 41.63461

▲ U Pirellu

℘ 0495702344, www.u-pirellu.com – acces to some pitches via steep slope – ⋈

Address : route de Palombaggia (located 9km to the east, at Piccovagia)

Opening times : from mid April to end Sept.

5 ha (150 pitches) extremely uneven

Tariff : ♦ 9,80€ 🚗 4€ 🅴 4,50€ – ⊌ (6A) 3,80€

Rental rates : (from mid April to end Sept.) 🚿 – 17 🏠. Per week from 400 to 1280€ – Reservation fee 10€

Some chalets have a panoramic view of the sea and La Pointe de la Chiappa (headland).

Surroundings : 🌊 � ♤♤
Leisure activities : ♟ ✗ ⛵ 🛝
Facilities : ♿ ⊶ 🅿 🚿 🚽 🖼 🛒 🚿
Nearby : 🐎

Longitude : 9.3322
Latitude : 41.58962

▲ La Vetta

℘ 0495700986, www.campinglavetta.com – ⋈

Address : at La Trinité (5.5km north on N 198, follow the signs for Bastia)

Opening times : from beginning June to end Sept.

8 ha (100 pitches)

Tariff : ♦ 9€ 🚗 3,50€ 🅴 5,50€ – ⊌ (10A) 3,50€

Rental rates : (from mid May to end Sept.) 🚿 – 41 🚐 – 6 🏠. Per night from 52 to 205€ – Per week from 392 to 1435€ Reservation fee 15€

A wild and natural setting with some luxurious rental options, but choose the pitches away from the road.

Surroundings : ♤♤
Leisure activities : ✗ ⛵ 🛝
Facilities : ♿ ⊶ 🚿 🖼

Longitude : 9.29356
Latitude : 41.63285

▲ Arutoli

℘ 0495701273, www.arutoli.com

Address : route de l'Ospédale (situated 2km northwest along the D 368)

Opening times : from beginning April to end Oct.

4 ha (150 pitches)

Tariff : 22,65€ ♦♦ 🚗 🅴 ⊌ (6A) – Extra per person 7€

Rental rates : (from beginning April to end Oct.) – 28 🏠. Per night from 52 to 150€ – Per week from 301 to 965€ Reservation fee 12€

🚐 borne – 10 🅴 5,95€

Well-shaded pitches with a variety of rental options.

Surroundings : ♤♤
Leisure activities : ✗ ⛱ 🛝
Facilities : ♿ ⊶ 🚿 🖼 🛒 🚿
Nearby : 🐎

Longitude : 9.26556
Latitude : 41.60186

▲ Bella Vista

℘ 0495705801, www.bella-vista.cc 🚿

Address : route de Palombaggia (located 9.3km to the east, at Piccovagia)

Opening times : from mid May to mid Sept.

2,5 ha (100 pitches) very uneven

Tariff : ♦ 8€ 🚗 4€ 🅴 4€ – ⊌ (6A) 4€

Rental rates : (from beginning April to end Sept.) 🚿 – 8 🏠 . Per week from 450 to 1500€ – Reservation fee 15€

Some chalets have a panoramic view of the sea and La Pointe de la Chiappa (headland).

Surroundings : 🌊 ≼ ♤♤
Leisure activities : ✗ 🛝
Facilities : ♿ ⊶ 🚿 🚽 🖼

Longitude : 9.3367
Latitude : 41.58672

▲ Les Ilots d'Or

℘ 0495700130, www.campinglesilotsdor.com

Address : route Pezza Cardo (head 6km northeast along the D 568 or the N 198, follow the signs for Bastia and take a right turn along the D 468 b before La Trinité)

Opening times : from beginning May to end Sept.

4 ha (176 pitches)

Tariff : (2013 Price) ♦ 7€ 🚗 3€ 🅴 5€ – ⊌ (6A) 3,50€

Rental rates : (2013 Price) (from beginning May to end Sept.) 🚿 – 3 🚐 – 23 🏠. Per night from 50 to 110€ – Per week from 350 to 770 €

Some pitches are virtually on top of the water!

Surroundings : 🌊 🚐 ♤♤ ≜
Leisure activities : ✗ ≜
Facilities : ♿ ⊶ 🚿 🚽 🖼
Nearby : 🤿

Longitude : 9.30819
Latitude : 41.6275

▲ Les Jardins du Golfe

℘ 0495704692, www.a-stella.org – ⋈

Address : route de Palombaggia (5.2km to the south)

Opening times : from beginning June to end Sept.

4 ha (200 pitches) sloping, flat, grassy, sandy

Tariff : (2013 Price) ♦ 7€ 🚗 3,20€ 🅴 3,50€ – ⊌ (5A) 3,20€

Rental rates : (from beginning April to end Oct.) – 9 🏠. Per night from 50 to 105 € – Per week from 330 to 780 €

🚐 borne 5€

Surroundings : ♤♤
Leisure activities : ♟ 🛝 (small swimming pool)
Facilities : ⊶ 🚽 🖼
Nearby : 🛝

Longitude : 9.2905
Latitude : 41.57353

20110 – Michelin map **345** C9 – pop. 3 292 – alt. 5
▶ Ajaccio 70 – Bastia 202 – Olbia 126 – Sassari 32

▲▲▲ Village Vacances U Livanti (rental of chalets only)

℘ 0495760806, www.ulivanti.com

Address : at Portigliolo - route de Campomoro (8km south along the RN 196 and take D 121; in the Gulf of Le Valinco)

Opening times : from beginning April to beginning Nov.

6 ha terraced

Rental rates : 🚿 🅿 – 89 🏠. Per night from 52 to 129€ Per week from 310 to 1850€ – Reservation fee 10€

A village of chalets ranging from basic to luxurious, with pretty, well-kept terraces and a restaurant right beside the water.

Surroundings : 🌊 ♤ ≜
Leisure activities : ♟ ✗ 🏃
Facilities : ⊶ 🚽 🖼
Nearby : 🤿 water skiing

Longitude : 8.86912
Latitude : 41.64491

SAGONE

20118 – Michelin map **345** B7
▶ Ajaccio 38 – Calvi 119 – Corte 106 – Sartène 110

🏔 Le Sagone 👥

☎ 04 95 28 04 15, www.camping-sagone.com

Address : route de Vico (2km north along the D 70)

Opening times :

30 ha/9 for camping (300 pitches) flat, grassy

Tariff : 🧍 9,25€ 🚗 5,75€ 🔲 9,80€ – 🔌 5€ – Reservation fee 20€

Rental rates : (from mid Jan. to mid Dec.) ♿ (2 mobile homes) 20 🏠 – 30 🏠 – 8 tent lodges. Per week from 245 to 1785€ Reservation fee 20€

🔌 borne

In the middle of olive, orange, mandarin and lemon trees; some luxurious rental options; themed stays possible.

Surroundings : 🌿 🗒 🎿
Leisure activities : ✕ 🏛 🎣 🏃 🛶 🚵 🚴
🍴 🏊 (open air in season), sports trail, use of golf buggies, multi-sports ground, entertainment room
Facilities : ♿ 🚿 🥘 🧺 launderette 🚰 refrigerated food storage facilities

GPS Longitude : 8.70553
Latitude : 42.1311

STE-LUCIE-DE-PORTO-VECCHIO

20144 – Michelin map **345** F9
▶ Ajaccio 142 – Porto-Vecchio 16

🏔 Homair Vacances Acqua E Sole 👥

(rental of mobile homes and chalets only)

☎ 04 95 50 15 75, www.homair.com

Address : at Pianu Di Conca (located 1km northeast along the N 198; follow the signs for Solenzara and take road to the left)

5 ha

Rental rates : ♿ – 117 🏠 – 28 🏠 – 7 🏠.

A selection of mobile homes and chalets of a good standard.

Surroundings : 🌿 🎣
Leisure activities : 🍴 ✕ 🏛 🏃 🛶 🎿
Facilities : 🚿 🍴 🥘 launderette 🚰
Nearby : 🐎

GPS Longitude : 9.35129
Latitude : 41.70328

🏔 Santa-Lucia 👥

☎ 04 95 71 45 28, www.campingsantalucia.com

Address : road RN 198 (in the village)

Opening times : from beginning April to beginning Oct.

3 ha (160 pitches)

Tariff : 🧍 9,50€ 🚗 3,70€ 🔲 6,85€ – 🔌 (6A) 2,90€ – Reservation fee 10€

Rental rates : (from beginning April to beginning Oct.) 🏠 21 🏠 – 22 canvas bungalows. Per week from 185 to 940€ Reservation fee 15€

Well-shaded pitches with good sanitary facilities and a charming small chalet village.

Surroundings : 🗒 🎿
Leisure activities : ✕ 🏃 🛶 🎿
Facilities : ♿ 🚿 🥘 🍴 🏛 🚰

GPS Longitude : 9.3434
Latitude : 41.6966

🏔 Fautea

☎ 04 95 71 41 51 – 🏪 🏠

Address : at Fautea, to the seaside (5km northeast on the N 198, follow the signs for Solenzara)

Opening times : from beginning May to end Sept.

5 ha (100 pitches)

Tariff : (2013 Price) 🧍 9,70€ 🚗 2,10€ 🔲 5,10€ – 🔌 (3A) 4€

Choose the pitches on the small terraces with a sea view, further away from the road.

Surroundings : 🌿 🗒 🎣 🏖
Leisure activities : 🛶
Facilities : ♿ 🚿 🧺🗒 🥘 🏛 🚰
Nearby : ✕

GPS Longitude : 9.40191
Latitude : 41.71557

SERRA-DI-FERRO

20140 – Michelin map **345** B9 – pop. 458 – alt. 140
▶ Ajaccio 47 – Propriano 20 – Sartène 32

🏔 U Casellu

☎ 04 95 74 01 80 🏠

Address : at Porto-Pollo (head 5km south along the D 155, follow the signs for Propriano and take D 757 to the right)

3,5 ha (100 pitches)

Rentals : 4 gîtes.

In a very pleasant location beside the sea, but with somewhat poor sanitary facilities.

Surroundings : 🌿 🎣 🏖
Leisure activities : 🍴 ✕
Facilities : ♿ 🚿 🏛
Nearby : ⚓

GPS Longitude : 8.80413
Latitude : 41.71234

The Michelin classification (🏔🏔🏔 ... 🏔) is totally independent of the official star classification system awarded by the local prefecture or other official organisation.

SOLENZARA

20145 – Michelin map **345** F8 – pop. 1 169
▶ Paris 1017 – Ajaccio 131 – Bastia 105

🏔 Homair Vacances Sole di Sari 👥

(rental of mobile homes, chalets and canvas bungalows only)

☎ 04 95 57 07 70, www.soledisari.com

Address : route de Bavella (1.5km northwest along the D 268)

Opening times : from beginning April to mid Oct.

4 ha terraced

Rental rates : ♿ (1 mobile home) 🏠 – 50 🏠 – 44 🏠 – 16 tent lodges. Per night from 39 to 199€ – Per week from 273 to 1393€ Reservation fee 25€

An attractive site with rental options, some equipped to a high level of comfort.

Surroundings : 🌿
Leisure activities : ✕ 🗒 daytime 🏃 🛶 🎿 🏊 🎣
Facilities : ♿ 🚿 🔲 🏛 🥘 🍴 launderette 🚰

GPS Longitude : 9.38396
Latitude : 41.86493

TIUCCIA

20111 – Michelin map **345** B7
▶ Ajaccio 30 – Cargèse 22 – Vico 22

▲ Les Couchants

☎ 04 95 52 26 60, http://camping-lescouchants.fr
✉ 20111 Casaglione

Address : route de Casaglione (4.9km north along the D 81 and turn right onto the D 25)

Opening times : from mid June to mid Sept.

5 ha (120 pitches)

Tariff : (2013 Price) ★ 7€ ⇦ 4€ – ⚡ (6A) 5€

Rental rates : (from mid June to mid Sept.) – 8 ⌂. Per week from 674 to 1 406€ – Reservation fee 20€

🚐 22 ▣ 9€

Pitches surrounded by colourful olive, eucalyptus and laurel trees.

Surroundings : ⌂ ≤ 🟢🟢
Leisure activities : 🍷 ✗ 🛶 🛝
Facilities : ♿ ⊶ 🚿 🟢 ⚘ 🍴 📷 🚰

GPS Longitude : 8.74894
Latitude : 42.08114

VIVARIO

20219 – Michelin map **345** E6 – pop. 532 – alt. 850
▶ Bastia 89 – Aléria 49 – Corte 22 – Bocognano 22

▲ Aire Naturelle le Soleil

☎ 04 95 47 21 16, camping-lesoleil@orange.fr – alt. 800

Address : at Tattone (6km southwest along the N 193, follow the signs for Ajaccio, near the small Tattone railway station)

Opening times : from beginning May to end Sept.

1 ha (25 pitches)

Tariff : (2013 Price) ★ 7€ ⇦ 2€ ▣ 2€ – ⚡ (15A) 20€

Partly shaded by fruit trees looking out over the mountains.

Surroundings : ⌂ ≤ 🟢🟢
Leisure activities : 🍷 ✗ 🏠
Facilities : ⊶ 🟢 🍴
Nearby : 🎣

GPS Longitude : 9.15186
Latitude : 42.1532

ZONZA

20124 – Michelin map **345** E9 – pop. 1 802 – alt. 780
▶ Ajaccio 93 – Porto-Vecchio 40 – Sartène 38 – Solenzara 40

▲ Municipal

☎ 04 95 78 62 74, campingmunzonza@voila.fr

Address : route de Porto-Vecchio (3km southeast along the D 368)

Opening times : from beginning April to end Sept.

2 ha (120 pitches) undulating, terraced, flat, stony

Tariff : (2013 Price) ★ 6€ ⇦ ▣

🚐 borne 6€

In the shade of some pine trees, beside the river.

Surroundings : ⌂ 🌊
Leisure activities : 🎣
Facilities : ♿ 🚿 🟢

GPS Longitude : 9.19563
Latitude : 41.7504

These symbols are used for a campsite that is exceptional in its category:

▲▲▲ ... ▲ *Particularly pleasant setting, quality and range of services available*

⌂ ⌂ *Tranquil, isolated site – quiet site, particularly at night*

≤ ≤ *Exceptional view – interesting or panoramic view*

FRANCHE-COMTÉ

H. Hughes / hemis.fr

Once upon a time in a land called Franche-Comté . . . many of France's tales and legends begin in the secret wilderness of this secluded region on the Swiss border. The high peaks and protected valleys of Jura, cloaked in fragrant conifers, cast a gentle charm over all who explore them. And an irresistible magic spell is woven by its cascading waterfalls, fascinating grottoes and mysterious lakes. The dark blue waters reflect the hills around them while forming a dramatic contrast with the lush green pastures. Nimble-fingered craftsmen transform the local wood into clocks, toys and pipes to the delight of all those who love and appreciate fine craftsmanship. Hungry travellers may want to savour the lovely hazelnut tang of Comté cheese but should beware the region's powerful gastronomic spell. The delicate smoked and salted meats, in which you can almost taste the pine and juniper, along with Franche-Comté's subtle but fruity wines, will have you coming back for more!

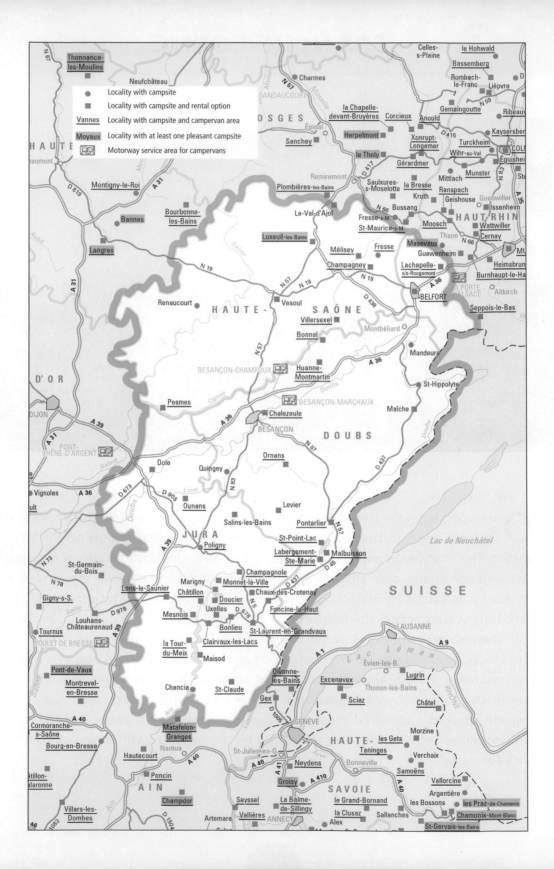

BELFORT

90000 – Michelin map **315** F11 – pop. 50 199 – alt. 360
▶ Paris 422 – Lure 33 – Luxeuil-les-Bains 52 – Montbéliard 23

⚔ L'Étang des Forges

✆ 03 84 22 54 92, www.camping-belfort.com

Address : rue du Général Béthouart (located 1.5km north along the D 13, follow the signs for Offemont and take a right turn – from the A 36, take exit 13)

Opening times : from mid April to end Sept.

3,4 ha (90 pitches)

Tariff : 21,50€ ♦♦ ⚍ 国 ⚡ (10A) – Extra per person 4,50€

Rental rates : (from mid April to end Sept.) ♿ (1 chalet) 5 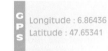 – 9 ⌂ – 1 canvas bungalow. Per night from 40 to 120€ Per week from 217 to 588€

⛽ borne

A smart and well-maintained establishment with a great variety of trees.

Surroundings : ⚘ ♀
Leisure activities : ♟ ⌂ ⚔ ⚓
Facilities : ♿ ⚡ cc ▦ ⚑ ♨ launderette
Nearby : ⚲

GPS Longitude : 6.86436
Latitude : 47.65341

Key to rentals symbols:

12 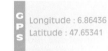		*Number of mobile homes*
20 ⌂		*Number of chalets*
6 🛏		*Number of rooms to rent*
Per night 30–50€		*Minimum/maximum rate per night*
Per week 300–1,000€		*Minimum/maximum rate per week*

BONLIEU

39130 – Michelin map **321** F7 – pop. 253 – alt. 785
▶ Paris 439 – Champagnole 23 – Lons-le-Saunier 32 – Morez 24

⚔ L'Abbaye

✆ 03 84 25 57 04, www.camping-abbaye.com

Address : 2 route du Lac (located 1.5km east along the N 78, follow the signs for St-Laurent-en-Grandvaux)

Opening times : from beginning May to end Sept.

3 ha (88 pitches)

Tariff : 19,90€ ♦♦ ⚍ 国 ⚡ (10A) – Extra per person 4,80€

Rental rates : (from beginning May to mid Oct.) ♿ – 4  1 🛏 – 1 studio – 1 apartment. Per night from 48 to 72€ Per week from 295 to 525€

⛽ borne 5€ – 4 国 9€

On a pretty site at the base of the cliffs, not far from the Le Hérisson waterfall.

Surroundings : ⚘ ⚘ ⌂
Leisure activities : ♟ ✗ ⚔
Facilities : ♿ ⚡ ♨ launderette ⚓
Nearby : 🐎 canoeing

GPS Longitude : 5.87562
Latitude : 46.59199

BONNAL

25680 – Michelin map **321** I1 – pop. 21 – alt. 270
▶ Paris 392 – Besançon 47 – Belfort 51 – Épinal 106

⚔ Les Castels Le Val de Bonnal ♟♟

✆ 03 81 86 90 87, www.camping-valdebonnal.com

Address : 1 chemin du Moulin

Opening times : from beginning May to beginning Sept.

140 ha/15 for camping (280 pitches) flat, grassy

Tariff : (2013 Price) 47,70€ ♦♦ ⚍ 国 ⚡ (10A)
Extra per person 13,50€ – Reservation fee 20€

Rental rates : (2013 Price) (from beginning May to beginning Sept.) ♿ – 12 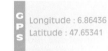 – 6 ⌂ – 6 tent lodges. Per week from 350 to 1 250€ – Reservation fee 20€

⛽ borne

In a pleasant location beside the Ognon river and near a lake.

Surroundings : ⚘ ⌂ ♀
Leisure activities : ♟ ✗ ⌂ ⚑ nighttime ⚔ ⚔ ⚴ ⚓ ⚓
Facilities : ♿ ⚡ ⚑ ♨ launderette ⚓ ⚓
Nearby : ⚹ forest trail

GPS Longitude : 6.35619
Latitude : 47.50734

CHALEZEULE

25220 – Michelin map **321** G3 – pop. 1 180 – alt. 252
▶ Paris 410 – Dijon 96 – Lyon 229 – Nancy 209

⚔ Municipal de la Plage

✆ 03 81 88 04 26, www.campingdebesancon.com

Address : 12 route de Belfort (4.5km northeast along the N 83; beside the Doubs river)

Opening times : from beginning April to end Sept.

2,5 ha (152 pitches)

Tariff : ♦ 5,15€ ⚍ 国 6,75€ – ⚡ (16A) 3,95€

Rental rates : (from beginning April to end Sept.) – 8 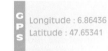 2 canvas bungalows. Per night from 35 to 91€ – Per week from 240 to 645€

⛽ borne 4€ – 10 国 12,25€

Particular attention has been paid to the floral decoration, but rather old sanitary facilities.

Surroundings : ♀♀
Leisure activities : ✗ ⚔
Facilities : ♿ ⚡ ▦ ♨ launderette
Nearby : ⚹ ⚴ ⚓ ⚓

GPS Longitude : 6.07103
Latitude : 47.26445

For more information on visiting particular towns or regions, consult the relevant regional MICHELIN Green Guide. We also recommend you use the appropriate Michelin regional map to locate your selected campsite, to calculate distances and to work out the best route.

CHAMPAGNEY

70290 – Michelin map **314** H6 – pop. 3 728 – alt. 370
▶ Paris 413 – Besançon 115 – Vesoul 48

⚐ Domaine Des Ballastières

✆ 03 84 23 11 22, www.campingdesballastieres.com

Address : 20 rue du Pâquis

Opening times : from beginning April to end Oct.

5 ha (110 pitches)

Tariff : 20€ ✶✶ ⇌ 🔲 🔋 (6A) – Extra per person 8€

Rental rates : (from beginning April to end Oct.) 🔥 (1 mobile home) – 10 🚐. Per night from 60 to 75€ – Per week from 410 to 640€ – Reservation fee 10€

🚐 borne 3,50€ – 10 🔲 10,50€

Beside a small lake.

Leisure activities : 🛶 🏃 🚴 🏊
Facilities : 🔥 ⚷ 🔲 🍴 launderette
Nearby : 🏊 🚣 🐎 pedalos

GPS	Longitude : 6.67414 Latitude : 47.70615

CHAMPAGNOLE

39300 – Michelin map **321** F6 – pop. 8 088 – alt. 541
▶ Paris 420 – Besançon 66 – Dole 68 – Genève 86

⚐ Municipal de Boyse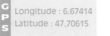

✆ 03 84 52 00 32, www.camping-boyse.com

Address : 20 rue Georges Vallerey (take the northwestern exit along the D 5, follow the signs for Lons-le-Saunier and take turning to the left)

Opening times : from beginning June to mid Sept.

9 ha/7 for camping (240 pitches)

Tariff : 23,10€ ✶✶ ⇌ 🔲 🔋 (10A) – Extra per person 6€

Rental rates : (from beginning April to end Sept.) 🔥 (2 chalets) 25 🏠. Per night from 65 to 75€ – Per week from 240 to 575€

🚐 borne 3,80€ – 7 🔲 6€

A pretty site on a hillside looking out over the Ain river from an elevation of 30m. Direct access along a road to the river.

Surroundings : 🌳 ♀♀
Leisure activities : ✗ 🎣 🏃 🚴 🏐 🏊
Facilities : 🔥 ⚷ 🏠 🍴 launderette 🔧
Nearby : 🍴 🎯 🚣 sports trail

GPS	Longitude : 5.89741 Latitude : 46.74643

CHÂTILLON

39130 – Michelin map **321** E7 – pop. 131 – alt. 500
▶ Paris 421 – Champagnole 24 – Clairvaux-les-Lacs 15 – Lons-le-Saunier 19

⚐ Kawan Village Domaine de l'Épinette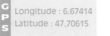

✆ 03 84 25 71 44, www.domaine-epinette.com

Address : 15 rue de l'Épinette (1.3km south along the D 151)

7 ha (150 pitches)

Rentals : 71 🚐 – 2 🏠 – 4 canvas bungalows.

🚐 borne

Laid out on terraces on the side of a valley overlooking a river.

Surroundings : 🌳 ≤
Leisure activities : 🛶 🏃 🚴 🏊 🏐 🏊 🐬
Facilities : 🔥 ⚷ 🏠 launderette 🏊 🔧

GPS	Longitude : 5.72218 Latitude : 46.6513

CHAUX DES CROTENAY

39150 – pop. 412 – alt. 735
▶ Paris 440 – Besançon 88 – Lons-le-Saunier 48

⚐ Municipal du Bois Joli

✆ 03 84 51 50 82, www.chaletsalesiajura.com 🚭

Address : 8 route de la Piscine

Opening times : from beginning July to end Aug.

1 ha (42 pitches) flat, grassy

Tariff : (2013 Price) ✶ 3,50€ ⇌ 🔲 6€

Rental rates : (2013 Price) Permanent 🔥 (1 chalet) 🚭 – 8 🏠. Per week from 370 to 480€

A pretty view of the surrounding hills.

Surroundings : ≤ mountains
Leisure activities : 🛶 🏃
Facilities : 🔥 🏠 launderette
Nearby : 🏊 🍴 🚴 🍴 🏊

GPS	Longitude : 5.96072 Latitude : 46.66307

We have selected the best campsites in France with our usual care, listing those with the best facilities in the most pleasant surroundings.

CLAIRVAUX-LES-LACS

39130 – Michelin map **321** E7 – pop. 1 454 – alt. 540
▶ Paris 428 – Bourg-en-Bresse 94 – Champagnole 34 – Lons-le-Saunier 22

⚐ Yelloh! Village Le Fayolan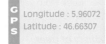

✆ 03 84 25 88 52, www.campinglefayolan.fr

Address : rue du Langard (1.2km southeast along the D 118)

17 ha/13 for camping (516 pitches) pine trees

Rentals : 112 🚐 – 10 tent lodges.

Beside a lake, with numerous services and leisure facilities.

Surroundings : ≤ 🏠 ♀ ⚠
Leisure activities : 🍴 ✗ 🛶 🎮 🏃 🚴 hammam 🏋 🏐 🏊 🏊 🎿 entertainment room
Facilities : 🔥 ⚷ 🏠 🏊 🔧 🍴 launderette 🏊 🔧
Nearby : 🚣 fitness trail

GPS	Longitude : 5.75 Latitude : 46.56667

⚐ Flower Le Grand Lac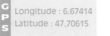

✆ 03 84 25 22 14, www.odesia-clairvaux.com

Address : chemin du Langard (800m southeast along the D 118, follow the signs for Châtel-de-Joux and take the road to the right)

Opening times : from beginning June to end Sept.

2,5 ha (191 pitches)

Tariff : (2013 Price) 26,50€ ✶✶ ⇌ 🔲 🔋 (10A) – Extra per person 5€ Reservation fee 12€

🚐 borne 17€

Beside the lake with a beautiful beach and an impressive diving board!

Surroundings : ≤ ♀ ⚠
Leisure activities : 🎮 🏃 🏋 🏊 🏊 (beach) 🚣 pedalos
Facilities : 🔥 ⚷ 🏠 launderette
Nearby : 🍴

GPS	Longitude : 5.75507 Latitude : 46.56823

DOLE

39100 – Michelin map **321** C4 – pop. 24 906 – alt. 220
▶ Paris 363 – Besançon 55 – Chalon-sur-Saône 67 – Dijon 50

🏔 Le Pasquier

✆ 03 84 72 02 61, www.camping-le-pasquier.com

Address : 18 chemin Victor et Georges Thévenot (to the southeast along the av. Jean-Jaurès)

2 ha (120 pitches)

Rentals : 10 🏚 – 4 canvas bungalows.

In a lush, green setting near the Doubs river, with a view of the Dole collegiate church.

Surroundings : ♀
Leisure activities : 🍴 ✗ 🎮 daytime 🚣 🏊 ⛷
(small swimming pool)
Facilities : ♿ ⚷ 🛁 🚿 ♨ 🍴 launderette
Nearby : 🏊 🎣

G P S	Longitude : 5.50357 Latitude : 47.08982

DOUCIER

39130 – Michelin map **321** E7 – pop. 296 – alt. 526
▶ Paris 427 – Champagnole 21 – Lons-le-Saunier 25

🏔 Domaine de Chalain 🛖🧑

✆ 03 84 25 78 78, www.chalain.com

Address : 3km to the northeast

Opening times : from end April to mid Sept.

30 ha/18 for camping (712 pitches)

Tariff : (2013 Price) 38€ 🧑🧑 🚐 🔲 ⚡(10A) – Extra per person 7€

Rental rates : (from end April to mid Sept.) 🛖 – 48 🏚 – 35 🏡.
Per night from 42 to 151€ – Per week from 294 to 1057€

🚽 borne 2€

An attractive location ringed by cliffs, situated between forest and the Lac de Chalain.

Surroundings : ≤ ♀ ⛰
Leisure activities : 🍴 ✗ 🚣 🎮 🏹 🎣 ⛵
jacuzzi 🚣🚴 ✂ ♨ 🔲 🏊 🏊 🎿 🎣
Facilities : ♿ ⚷ 🍴 🛁 🚿 ♨ 🍴 launderette
🏊 🍴 refrigerated food storage facilities

G P S	Longitude : 5.81395 Latitude : 46.66422

To visit a town or region, use the MICHELIN Green Guides.

FONCINE-LE-HAUT

39460 – Michelin map **321** G7 – pop. 1 027 – alt. 790
▶ Paris 444 – Champagnole 24 – Clairvaux-les-Lacs 34 – Lons-le-Saunier 62

🏔 Les Chalets du Val de Saine (rental of chalets only)

✆ 03 84 51 93 11, www.camping-haut-jura.com – alt. 900 – traditional camp. spaces also available

Address : take the southwestern exit along the D437, follow the signs for St-Laurent-en-Grandvaux and take the turning to the left, by the stadium; beside the Saine river

Opening times : Permanent

1,2 ha flat

Rental rates : (2013 Price) 🅿 – 13 🏡. Per week from 250 to 450€
🚽 borne 2€

Surroundings : 🏊
Leisure activities : 🎣
Facilities : launderette
Nearby : 🏊 🍴 ✗ ✂ 🎣

G P S	Longitude : 6.07253 Latitude : 46.65888

Michelin classification:

🏔🏔🏔🏔 *Extremely comfortable, equipped to a very high standard*

🏔🏔🏔 *Very comfortable, equipped to a high standard*

🏔🏔🏔 *Comfortable and well equipped*

🏔🏔 *Reasonably comfortable*

🏔 *Satisfactory*

FRESSE

70270 – Michelin map **314** IG – pop. 725 – alt. 472
▶ Paris 405 – Belfort 31 – Épinal 71 – Luxeuil-les-Bains 30

🏔 La Broche

✆ 03 84 63 31 40, www.camping-broche.com

Address : at Le Volvet (take the western exit, follow the signs for Melesey and then take road to the left)

Opening times : from mid April to mid Oct.

2 ha (50 pitches)

Tariff : 12€ 🧑🧑 🚐 🔲 ⚡(10A) – Extra per person 3€
🚽 borne 3€ – 🚐12€

An undulating, wooded site beside a lake.

Surroundings : 🏊 ≤ ♀
Leisure activities : 🎣
Facilities : ♿ ⚷ 🚿 🍴

G P S	Longitude : 6.65269 Latitude : 47.75587

HUANNE-MONTMARTIN

25680 – Michelin map **321** I2 – pop. 83 – alt. 310
▶ Paris 392 – Baume-les-Dames 14 – Besançon 37 – Montbéliard 52

🏔 Le Bois de Reveuge

✆ 03 81 84 38 60, www.campingduboisdereveuge.com

Address : route de Rougemont (1.1km north along the D 113)

Opening times : from end April to beginning Sept.

24 ha/15 for camping (320 pitches)

Tariff : 34€ 🧑🧑 🚐 🔲 ⚡(10A) – Extra per person 8€ – Reservation fee 25€

Rental rates : (from end April to beginning Sept.) – 118 🏚 34 🏡. Per night from 45 to 146€ – Per week from 270 to 1022€ Reservation fee 25€

🚽 borne – 20 🔲 20€

The site is laid out around two large lakes on the edge of a wood.

Surroundings : 🏊 🚤 ♀♀
Leisure activities : 🍴 ✗ 🚣 🎮 🏹 🎣 🚣
🚴 🎣 🔲 🎿 🎣 🐎
Facilities : ♿ ⚷ 🛁 🚿 ♨ 🍴 launderette 🏊

G P S	Longitude : 6.3447 Latitude : 47.44346

LABERGEMENT-STE-MARIE

25160 – Michelin map **321** H6 – pop. 1 040 – alt. 859
▶ Paris 454 – Champagnole 41 – Pontarlier 17 – St-Laurent-en-Grandvaux 41

⚠ Le Lac

☎ 03 81 69 31 24, www.camping-lac-remoray.com

Address : 10 rue du Lac (take the southwestern exit along the D 437, follow the signs for Mouthe and take turning to the right)

Opening times : from beginning May to end Sept.

1,8 ha (80 pitches)

Tariff : 21,70€ ✝✝ ⬟ 🔲 (6A) – Extra per person 4,80€ – Reservation fee 5€

Rental rates : (from beginning May to end Sept.) – 8 🚐. Per night 79€ – Per week from 198 to 650€ – Reservation fee 5€

🚐 borne

300m from the Lac de Remoray.

Surroundings : ≤
Leisure activities : ♟ ✕ 🖼 🚲
Facilities : ♿ ⚡ 🍽 launderette ♨
Nearby : ✗ 🛶 🐎

GPS Longitude : 6.27563
     Latitude : 46.77134

LACHAPELLE-SOUS-ROUGEMONT

90360 – Michelin map **315** G10 – pop. 549 – alt. 400
▶ Paris 442 – Belfort 16 – Basel 66 – Colmar 55

⚠ Le Lac de la Seigneurie

☎ 03 84 23 00 13, www.camping-lac-seigneurie.com

Address : 3 rue de la Seigneurie (3.2km north along the D 11, follow the signs for Lauw)

Opening times : from beginning April to end Oct.

4 ha (110 pitches) flat, grassy

Tariff : 17€ ✝✝ ⬟ 🔲 (6A) – Extra per person 4,20€

Rental rates : (from beginning April to end Oct.) ✂ – 2 🚐. Per night from 120 to 160€ – Per week from 300 to 550€ Reservation fee 15€

🚐 borne –

In a quiet location, at the edge of a forest and near a lake.

Surroundings : 🌳 ⌁ ♀
Leisure activities : 🖼 🐎 🛶
Facilities : ♿ ⚡ 🍽 launderette
Nearby : ✗ 🛶

A 'quartier' is a district or area of a town or village.

LEVIER

25270 – Michelin map **321** G5 – pop. 1 949 – alt. 719
▶ Paris 443 – Besançon 45 – Champagnole 37 – Pontarlier 22

⚠ La Forêt

☎ 03 81 89 53 46, www.camping-dela-foret.com

Address : route de Septfontaines (located 1km northeast along the D 41)

Opening times : from beginning May to mid Sept.

4 ha/2,5 for camping (70 pitches)

Tariff : (2013 Price) 22,70€ ✝✝ ⬟ 🔲 (10A)
Extra per person 4,20€ – Reservation fee 10€

Rental rates : Permanent – 2 🚐 – 8 🏠. Per night from 66 to 146€ Per week from 317 to 709€ – Reservation fee 10€

Nestling at the edge of a forest in a very beautiful setting of fine trees and rocky outcrops.

Surroundings : 🌳 ♀♀
Leisure activities : 🖼 🐎 🚲 🛶
Facilities : ♿ ⚡ 🍽 🔥 launderette
Nearby : sports trail

GPS Longitude : 6.13308
     Latitude : 46.95915

We value your opinion and welcome your feedback. Do email us at campingfrance@tp.michelin.com

LONS-LE-SAUNIER

39000 – Michelin map **321** D6 – pop. 17 907 – alt. 255 – ⚕
▶ Paris 408 – Besançon 84 – Bourg-en-Bresse 73 – Chalon-sur-Saône 61

⛰ La Marjorie

☎ 03 84 24 26 94, www.camping-marjorie.com

Address : 640 boulevard de l'Europe (to the northeast towards Besançon along the bd de Ceinture)

Opening times : from end March to mid Oct.

9 ha/3 for camping (193 pitches) hard surface areas

Tariff : 23€ ✝✝ ⬟ 🔲 (10A) – Extra per person 5,30€ – Reservation fee 15€

Rental rates : (from end March to mid Oct.) ♿ (1 chalet) – 4 🚐 15 🏠. Per night from 50 to 90€ – Per week from 225 to 660€ Reservation fee 15€

🚐 borne 4,50€ – 39 🔲 16,35€

Attractive trees and shrubs decorate the site; beside a stream.

Surroundings : ⌁ ♀♀
Leisure activities : ♟ 🖼 🌙 nighttime 🏃
Facilities : ♿ ⚡ 🍽 🔥 launderette 🏊 ♨
Nearby : ✗ 🛶 🛶

GPS Longitude : 5.56855
     Latitude : 46.68422

LUXEUIL-LES-BAINS

70300 – Michelin map **314** G6 – pop. 7 370 – alt. 305
▶ Paris 380 – Besançon 88 – Vesoul 35

⛰ Domaine du Chatigny

☎ 03 84 93 97 97, www.camping.luxeuil.fr

Address : 14 rue Grammont

Opening times : from mid March to end Oct.

4,5 ha (98 pitches) flat, grassy

Tariff : (2013 Price) ✝ 17€ ⬟ 🔲 16,50€ – (16A) 3,50€ – Reservation fee 8€

Rental rates : (from mid March to end Oct.) ♿ (2 chalets) – 20 🚐 20 🏠. Per night from 68 to 138€ – Per week from 256 to 558€ Reservation fee 8€

🚐 borne 2€ – 10 🔲 12,50€ – 🚰 10€

In the town centre, a pleasant, well-maintained green setting.

Surroundings : 🌳 ♀
Leisure activities : ♟ ✕ 🖼 🐎 🚲 ✂ 🛶
multi-sports ground
Facilities : ⚡ 🍽 🔥 launderette

GPS Longitude : 6.37876
     Latitude : 47.82259

MAICHE

25120 – Michelin map **321** K3 – pop. 4 282 – alt. 777
▶ Paris 501 – Baume-les-Dames 69 – Besançon 74 – Montbéliard 43

⚠ Municipal St-Michel

✆ 03 81 64 12 56, www.mairie-maiche.fr

Address : 23 rue Saint-Michel (head 1.3km south on the D 422 before joining the D 464, follow the signs for Charquemont and take the D 437 heading for Pontarlier - recommended route via the D 437, follow the signs for Pontarlier)

Opening times : from beginning Dec. to mid Nov.

2 ha (70 pitches)

Tariff : (2013 Price) ✦ 3,35 € ⇌ 🖃 4,46 € – ⚡ (10A) 4,46 €
Rental rates : (from beginning Dec. to mid Nov.) – 5 ⌂ – 3 ⊨.
Per night from 51 to 75 € – Per week from 225 to 300 €
Near an indoor water park.

Surroundings : ♀
Leisure activities : 🛶
Facilities : ♿ ☕ ▥ ▦
Nearby : ≋ hammam, jacuzzi 🏊 ⛷ 🚣

GPS	Longitude : 6.80109 Latitude : 47.24749

MAISOD

39260 – Michelin map **321** E8 – pop. 316 – alt. 520
▶ Paris 436 – Lons-le-Saunier 30 – Oyonnax 34 – St-Claude 29

⚠ Trelachaume

✆ 03 84 42 03 26, www.trelachaume.fr

Address : 50 route du Mont du Cerf (2.2km south along the D 301 and take turning to the right)

Opening times : from mid April to beginning Sept.

3 ha (180 pitches)

Tariff : (2013 Price) 19,10 € ✦✦ ⇌ 🖃 ⚡ (10A) – Extra per person 3,95 €
Rental rates : (from mid April to beginning Sept.) 🏄 – 3 caravans 10 🚐 – 6 ⌂ – 5 canvas bungalows. Per night from 29 to 92 € Per week from 199 to 642 €
Nestling in woods looking down over the Lac de Vouglans.

Surroundings : 🌲 ♀♀
Leisure activities : 🏛 🎣 🛶 cinema
Facilities : ♿ ☕ ▥ laundrette

GPS	Longitude : 5.68875 Latitude : 46.46873

The pitches of many campsites are marked out with low hedges of attractive bushes and shrubs.

MALBUISSON

25160 – Michelin map **321** H6 – pop. 687 – alt. 900
▶ Paris 456 – Besançon 74 – Champagnole 42 – Pontarlier 16

⚠ Les Fuvettes ♣♣

✆ 03 81 69 31 50, www.camping-fuvettes.com

Address : 24 route de la Plage et des Perrières (located 1km southwest)

Opening times : from beginning April to beginning Oct.

6 ha (306 pitches)

Tariff : (2013 Price) 26,30 € ✦✦ ⇌ 🖃 ⚡ (6A) – Extra per person 5 € Reservation fee 10 €

Rental rates : (from beginning April to beginning Oct.) ♿ (1 mobile home) – 31 🚐 – 8 ⌂ – 3 canvas bungalows. Per night from 35 to 90 € – Per week from 240 to 890 € – Reservation fee 15 €
🚐 borne 3 €
Beside the Lac de St-Point, near a mini water activity park.

Surroundings : ⇐ ♀ ▲
Leisure activities : ♀ ✗ 🏛 🎣 🏃 🛶 🏊 ≋ 🚣 🛶 mini farm with ponies and alpacas
Facilities : ♿ ☕ laundrette 🚿 ⚙
Nearby : canoeing, pedalos

GPS	Longitude : 6.29391 Latitude : 46.79232

MANDEURE

25350 – Michelin map **321** K2 – pop. 4 959 – alt. 336
▶ Paris 473 – Baume-les-Dames 41 – Maïche 34 – Sochaux 15

⚠ Municipal les Grands Ansanges

✆ 03 81 35 23 79, www.ville-mandeure.com

Address : rue de l'Église (located to the northwest, take exit towards Pont-de-Roide; beside the Doubs)

1,7 ha (96 pitches) flat, grassy
A fairly simple site, but perfect for a one-night stay.

Surroundings : ♀
Leisure activities : ♀ 🏛 🎣 🛶
Facilities : launderette

GPS	Longitude : 6.80556 Latitude : 47.45557

MARIGNY

39130 – Michelin map **321** E6 – pop. 177 – alt. 519
▶ Paris 426 – Arbois 32 – Champagnole 17 – Doucier 5

🏔 Les Castels La Pergola ♣♣

✆ 03 84 25 70 03, www.lapergola.com

Address : 1 rue des Vernois (800m to the south)

Opening times : from beginning May to beginning Sept.

10 ha (350 pitches)

Tariff : 45 € ✦✦ ⇌ 🖃 ⚡ (10A) – Extra per person 8 €
Rental rates : (from beginning May to beginning Sept.) – 154 🚐.
Per night from 113 to 185 € – Per week from 791 to 1 295 €
Attractive layout of swimming pools overlooking the Lac de Chalain; some luxurious mobile homes.

Surroundings : ⇐ ♀ ▲
Leisure activities : ♀ ✗ 🏛 🎣 🏃 🛶 🚲 🏊 ≋ 🚣 💧
Facilities : ♿ ☕ 🚾 ▦ 🚿 ⚙ ♨ launderette 🚐 ⚙

GPS	Longitude : 5.77984 Latitude : 46.67737

These symbols are used for a campsite that is exceptional in its category:

🏔🏔...⚠ *Particularly pleasant setting, quality and range of services available*

🌲🌲 *Tranquil, isolated site – quiet site, particularly at night*

⇐⇐ *Exceptional view – interesting or panoramic view*

MÉLISEY

70270 – Michelin map **314** H6 – pop. 1 699 – alt. 330
▶ Paris 397 – Belfort 33 – Épinal 63 – Luxeuil-les-Bains 22

⚑ La Pierre

✆ 03 84 20 84 38, mairie.melisey@wanadoo.fr – limited spaces for one-night stay – ℟

Address : at Les Granges Baverey (2.7km north on the D 293, follow the signs for Mélay)

Opening times : from beginning May to end Sept.

1,5 ha (58 pitches)

Tariff : ♀ 3€ ⇔ 1,30€ 🅴 3€ – (⚡) (6A) 2,20€

Rental rates : Permanent – 4 ⌂. Per night from 80 to 100€ Per week from 220 to 354€ – Reservation fee 13€

🚐 borne 6€ – 8 🅴 6€ – 🚰 (⚡)12,20€

In a picturesque setting on a wooded site.

Surroundings : 🌲 ⌂ ♀		
Leisure activities : 🏠 🏊	**G**	Longitude : 6.58101
Facilities : ⚹ 🚿 🏠	**P** **S**	Latitude : 47.77552

MESNOIS

39130 – Michelin map **321** E7 – pop. 202 – alt. 460
▶ Paris 431 – Besançon 90 – Lons 18 – Chalon 77

🏔 Sites et Paysages Beauregard

✆ 03 84 48 32 51, www.juracampingbeauregard.com

Address : 2 Grande-Rue (take the southern exit)

Opening times : from beginning April to end Sept.

6 ha/4,5 for camping (192 pitches)

Tariff : (2013 Price) 29,80€ ♀♀ ⇔ 🅴 (⚡) (6A) – Extra per person 5,50€ Reservation fee 10€

Rental rates : (from beginning April to end Sept.) – 43 5 canvas bungalows – 1 gîte. Per night from 40 to 112€ – Per week from 280 to 784€ – Reservation fee 10€

🚐 borne – 🚰 (⚡)14€

A partially open-air water park.

Surroundings : ≮ ⌂ ♀		
Leisure activities : ♀ ✗ 🏠 ⛵ hammam, jacuzzi 🏊 🎯 🏓 🎱 🛝	**G**	Longitude : 5.68878
Facilities : ⚹ 🚿 🏠 🍴 launderette 🚿	**P** **S**	Latitude : 46.60036

MONNET-LA-VILLE

39300 – Michelin map **321** E6 – pop. 372 – alt. 550
▶ Paris 421 – Arbois 28 – Champagnole 11 – Doucier 10

🏔 Sous Doriat

TOURNIER

✆ 03 84 51 21 43, www.camping-sous-doriat.com

Address : 34 rue Marcel Hugon (take the northern exit along the D 27e, follow the signs for Ney)

Opening times : from beginning May to end Sept.

3 ha (110 pitches) flat, grassy

Tariff : 19,50€ ♀♀ ⇔ 🅴 (⚡) (10A)

Extra per person 4€ – Reservation fee 10€

Rental rates : (from beginning May to end Sept.) – 16 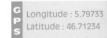 5 ⌂. Per night from 30 to 105€ – Per week from 210 to 735€ Reservation fee 10€

🚐 borne 12€

A simple campsite with an unrestricted view of the Jura mountains.

Surroundings : ≮ ♀		
Leisure activities : 🏠 🏊 🛷 multi-sports area	**G**	Longitude : 5.79779
Facilities : ⚹ 🚿 🍴 launderette	**P** **S**	Latitude : 46.72143
Nearby : 🏊 ♀ ✗		

⚑ Du Gît

✆ 03 84 51 21 17, www.campingdugit.com

Address : 7 chemin du Gît (located 1km southeast along the D 40, follow the signs for Mont-sur-Monnet and take the road to the right)

Opening times : from beginning June to end Aug.

6 ha (60 pitches)

Tariff : 16€ ♀♀ ⇔ 🅴 (⚡) (5A) – Extra per person 4€

Rental rates : (from beginning June to end Aug.) – 2 . Per week from 250 to 400€

🚐 borne 3€ – 🚰 12€

A very simple campsite with poor sanitary facilities.

Surroundings : 🌲 ≮		
Leisure activities : 🏠 🏊	**G**	Longitude : 5.79733
Facilities : ⚹ 🚿 🍴 🏠	**P** **S**	Latitude : 46.71234

There are several different types of sani-station ('borne' in French) – sanitation points providing fresh water and disposal points for grey water. See page 12 for further details.

ORNANS

25290 – Michelin map **321** G4 – pop. 4 152 – alt. 355
▶ Paris 428 – Baume-les-Dames 42 – Besançon 26 – Morteau 48

🏔 Domaine Le Chanet ♟♟

✆ 03 81 62 23 44, www.lechanet.com

Address : 9 chemin du Chanet (located 1.5km southwest along the D 241, follow the signs for Chassagne-St-Denis and take the road to the right; 100m from the Loue)

Opening times : from beginning April to beginning Oct.

1,4 ha (95 pitches)

Tariff : 31€ ♀♀ ⇔ 🅴 (⚡) (10A) – Extra per person 6,20€ – Reservation fee 7,50€

Rental rates : (from beginning April to beginning Oct.) – 21 [⬜] 4 ⌂ – 1 studio – 1 apartment – 2 tipis – 7 canvas bungalows 1 gîte. Per night from 45 to 111€ – Per week from 220 to 810€ Reservation fee 15€

🚐 borne 3€ – 5 🅴 16,50€

In the hills above the town, features an eco (no chemicals) swimming pool.

Surroundings : 🌲 ≮ ♀♀		
Leisure activities : ♀ ✗ 🏠 🎯 🚴 ⛵ 🏊 🛷	**G**	Longitude : 6.12779
Facilities : ⚹ 🚿 🏛 🏠 🍴 launderette	**P** **S**	Latitude : 47.10164
Nearby : 🚴 ✗ 🚣		

Sites et Paysages La Roche d'Ully

📞 03 81 57 17 79, www.camping-ornans.com

Address : allée de la Tour de Peilz

Opening times : from beginning April to mid Oct.

2 ha (125 pitches) flat, grassy

Tariff : 34€ ♀♀ ⇐ ▣ ⚡ (10A) – Extra per person 6,70€ – Reservation fee 7,50€

Rental rates : (from beginning April to mid Oct.) – 10 🛖 5 tipis – 5 tent lodges. Per night from 47 to 155€ – Per week from 220 to 980€ – Reservation fee 15€

🚐 borne 3€ – 🚽 ⚡14€

Surroundings : 🏕
Leisure activities : ♀ ✕ 🏃 🚴 🚲
Facilities : ♿ 🚰 🔌 ✉ 🧺 ⛱ 🍽 🚿
Nearby : ♨ hammam, jacuzzi 🏊 🛶 🏖

G P S Longitude : 6.15807
Latitude : 47.10286

OUNANS

39380 – Michelin map **321** D5 – pop. 371 – alt. 230
▶ Paris 383 – Arbois 16 – Arc-et-Senans 13 – Dole 23

La Plage Blanche 👥

📞 03 84 37 69 63, www.la-plage-blanche.com

Address : 3 rue de la Plage (located 1.5km north along the D 71, follow the signs for Montbarey and take road to the left)

Opening times : from beginning May to end Sept.

7 ha (218 pitches) flat, grassy

Tariff : 29,50€ ♀♀ ⇐ ▣ ⚡ (10A) – Extra per person 5,50€

Rental rates : (from beginning May to end Sept.) – 6 🚐 4 canvas bungalows. Per night from 40 to 106€ – Per week from 280 to 740€

🚐 borne

The site is on the banks of the Loue river.

Surroundings : 🏞 ♀
Leisure activities : ♀ ✕ 🎬 nighttime 🏃 ♨ jacuzzi 🛶 🏊 🐎 multi-sports ground
Facilities : ♿ 🚰 🛏 ⛱ 🍽 launderette 🛒 🚿
Nearby : 🚴

G P S Longitude : 5.66333
Latitude : 47.00276

Le Val d'Amour

📞 03 84 37 61 89, www.levaldamour.com

Address : 1 rue du Val d'Amour (take the eastern exit along the D 472, towards Chamblay)

Opening times : from beginning April to end Sept.

3,7 ha (97 pitches) flat, grassy, fruit trees

Tariff : 24€ ♀♀ ⇐ ▣ ⚡ (10A) – Extra per person 6€ – Reservation fee 10€

Rental rates : (from mid March to mid Oct.) – 14 🚐 – 6 🛖 3 canvas bungalows – 6 tent lodges. Per night from 40 to 55€ Per week from 280 to 670€ – Reservation fee 10€

🚐 borne 3€

Pretty floral decoration.

Surroundings : 🏞 ♀♀
Leisure activities : ✕ 🎯 🛶 🚴 🏊 🏖 mountain biking
Facilities : ♿ 🚰 ⛱ 🍽 launderette
Nearby : 🏊

G P S Longitude : 5.6733
Latitude : 46.99103

PESMES

70140 – Michelin map **314** B9 – pop. 1 111 – alt. 205
▶ Paris 387 – Besançon 52 – Vesoul 64 – Dijon 69

La Colombière

📞 03 84 31 20 15, mairie-pesmes@wanadoo.fr

Address : take the southern exit along the D 475, follow the signs for Dole; beside the Ognon river

Opening times : from beginning May to end Oct.

1 ha (70 pitches) flat, grassy

Tariff : (2013 Price) 18,60€ ♀♀ ⇐ ▣ ⚡ (16A) – Extra per person 3€ Reservation fee 5€

Rental rates : (2013 Price) (from beginning May to end Oct.) 5 🚐 – 1 gîte. Per night from 35 to 90€ – Per week from 240 to 450€ – Reservation fee 5€

🚐 borne 6€ – 8 ▣ 6€

Beside the river, not far from the village centre.

Surroundings : ♀
Leisure activities : 🛶 🏖
Facilities : ♿ 🚰 🔌 ✉ 🛏 ⛱
Nearby : ♀ ✕ 🚴

G P S Longitude : 5.56392
Latitude : 47.27403

POLIGNY

39800 – Michelin map **321** E5 – pop. 4 229 – alt. 373
▶ Paris 397 – Besançon 57 – Dole 45 – Lons-le-Saunier 30

La Croix du Dan

📞 03 84 73 77 58, contact@ccgrimont.fr

Address : route de Lons-le-Saunier (located 1km southwest along the N 83 towards Lons-le-Saunier)

Opening times : from mid May to mid Sept.

1,5 ha (87 pitches) flat, grassy

Tariff : (2013 Price) ♀ 2,20€ ⇐ 2,30€ ▣ 2,80€ – ⚡ (10A) 8€

🚐 borne

Situated at the exit from the town, ideal for a stopover.

Surroundings : ≼ ♀
Leisure activities : 🛶
Facilities : ♿ 🚰 ⛱ 🍽

G P S Longitude : 5.70078
Latitude : 46.83424

PONTARLIER

25300 – Michelin map **321** I5 – pop. 18 267 – alt. 838
▶ Paris 462 – Basel 180 – Beaune 164 – Belfort 126

Le Larmont

📞 03 81 46 23 33, www.camping-pontarlier.fr – alt. 880

Address : 2 chemin du Toulombief (to the southeast towards Lausanne, near the riding centre)

Opening times : Permanent

4 ha (75 pitches)

Tariff : (2013 Price) ♀ 4€ ⇐ ▣ 9€ – ⚡ (10A) 4€

Rental rates : (2013 Price) Permanent – 7 🛖. Per night from 50 to 112€ – Per week from 296 to 643€

🚐 borne – 🚽 10€

On a hillside with well-marked out pitches.

Surroundings : 🏞 ≼ 🏕
Leisure activities : 🎬 🛶
Facilities : ♿ 🚰 ✉ 🛏 ⛱ 🍽 🧺 launderette
Nearby : 🐎 sports trail

G P S Longitude : 6.37349
Latitude : 46.90013

QUINGEY

25440 – Michelin map **321** F4 – pop. 1 300 – alt. 275
▶ Paris 397 – Baume-les-Dames 40 – Besançon 23 – Morteau 78

▲ Municipal Les Promenades

✆ 03 81 63 74 01, www.campingquingey.fr

Address : at Les Promenades (take the southern exit, follow the signs for Lons-le-Saunier and take road to the right after the bridge)

Opening times : from beginning May to end Sept.

1,5 ha (75 pitches)

Tariff : ✝ 4€ ⟷ 3€ 📖 – ⚡ (15A) 3€

The site is on the bank of the Loue river, near the village centre and a water sports centre.

Surroundings : 🞗 ♋♋
Leisure activities : 🛶 ✂ 🎣
Facilities : ♿ ⚬━ (July–Aug.) 🏖 🚾 🚰 launderette
Nearby : 🏊 ✕ 🚲

GPS Longitude : 5.88928
Latitude : 47.10454

RENAUCOURT

70120 – Michelin map **314** C7 – pop. 107 – alt. 209
▶ Paris 338 – Besançon 58 – Bourbonne-les-Bains 49 – Épinal 98

▲ Municipal la Fontaine aux Fées

✆ 03 84 92 06 22

Address : rte de Volon (1.3km southwest, follow the signs for Volon)

2 ha (23 pitches) flat, grassy

On the edge of a wood, near a lake.

Surroundings : 🞗 ♋
Facilities : ⚬━ 🏖
Nearby : 🏊

GPS Longitude : 5.75707
Latitude : 47.63468

ST-CLAUDE

39200 – Michelin map **321** F8 – pop. 11 355 – alt. 450
▶ Paris 465 – Annecy 88 – Bourg-en-Bresse 90 – Genève 60

⛰ Flower Le Martinet

✆ 03 84 45 00 40, www.camping-saint-claude.fr

Address : 14 route du Martinet (situated 2km southeast following signs for Genève and take the D 290 to the right, where the Flumen and the Tacon rivers meet)

Opening times : from beginning April to end Sept.

2,9 ha (112 pitches)

Tariff : 19€ ✝✝ ⟷ 📖 ⚡ (10A) – Extra per person 4€

Rental rates : (from beginning April to end Sept.) – 8 🏠 1 tipi – 2 tent lodges. Per night from 41 to 96€ – Per week from 287 to 672€

🚐 21 📖 19€

Nestling in a pleasant mountain setting beside a river.

Surroundings : ≤ ♋♋
Leisure activities : 🍽 ✕ 🎪 🛶
Facilities : ♿ ⚬━ (July–Aug.) 🚰 launderette 🏊
Nearby : ✕ 🎣 🏊 🎣

GPS Longitude : 5.86953
Latitude : 46.37309

ST-HIPPOLYTE

25190 – Michelin map **321** K3 – pop. 917 – alt. 380
▶ Paris 490 – Basel 93 – Belfort 48 – Besançon 89

▲ Les Grands Champs

✆ 03 81 96 54 53, www.ville.saint-hippolyte.fr

Address : located 1km northeast along the D 121, follow the signs for Montécheroux and take the road to the right, near the Doubs (direct access)

2,2 ha (65 pitches)

A linear site with pitches spread out down a slope beside the Doubs river.

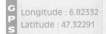

Surroundings : 🞗 ≤ ♋
Leisure activities : 🎣
Facilities : ♿ ⚬━ 🏖

GPS Longitude : 6.82332
Latitude : 47.32291

ST-LAURENT-EN-GRANDVAUX

39150 – Michelin map **321** F7 – pop. 1 779 – alt. 904
▶ Paris 442 – Champagnole 22 – Lons-le-Saunier 45 – Morez 11

▲ Municipal Champ de Mars

✆ 03 84 60 19 30, www.st-laurent39.fr

Address : 8 rue du Camping (take the eastern exit along the N 5)

Opening times : from mid Dec. to end Sept.

3 ha (133 pitches)

Tariff : 12,40€ ✝✝ ⟷ 📖 ⚡ (10A) – Extra per person 3,40€
Rental rates : (from mid Dec. to end Sept.) ♿ (2 chalets) – 10 🏠. Per night 120 € – Per week from 308 to 504€

🚐 borne 6,25€ – 12 📖 12,40€

Close to the snowshoe hiking trails and cross-country skiing pistes. Higher rates in winter (not given in this guide).

Surroundings : ❄ ≤
Leisure activities : 🎪 🛶
Facilities : ♿ ⚬━ 🏛 🏖 🚰 launderette

GPS Longitude : 5.96294
Latitude : 46.57616

ST-POINT-LAC

25160 – Michelin map **321** H6 – pop. 269 – alt. 860
▶ Paris 453 – Champagnole 39 – Pontarlier 13 – St-Laurent-en-Grandvaux 45

▲ Municipal

✆ 03 81 69 61 64, www.campingsaintpointlac.com

Address : 8 rue du Port (in the town)

Opening times : Permanent

1,8 ha (84 pitches)

Tariff : (2013 Price) 18€ ✝✝ ⟷ 📖 ⚡ (16A) – Extra per person 3,30€

🚐 62 📖 12,50€

The campervan pitches are close to the campsite.

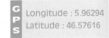

Surroundings : ≤ 🏔
Leisure activities : 🎪 🛶 🚲
Facilities : ♿ ⚬━ 🏛 🚰 launderette 🏊
Nearby : 🏖 🎣 watersports centre

GPS Longitude : 6.30336
Latitude : 46.81209

SALINS-LES-BAINS

39110 – Michelin map **321** F5 – pop. 2 987 – alt. 340 – ⚓ (beg Mar-end Oct)
▶ Paris 419 – Besançon 41 – Dole 43 – Lons-le-Saunier 52

⚠ Municipal

☎ 03 84 37 92 70, www.salinscamping.com

Address : place de la Gare (take the northern exit, following signs for Besançon)

Opening times : from beginning April to end Sept.

1 ha (44 pitches)

Tariff : ♦ 4€ – 🚗 2,60€ – 🅴 5,80€ – 🔌 (10A) 3,20€ – Reservation fee 5€
Rental rates : (from beginning April to end Sept.) – 2 🚐.
Per week from 200 to 350€ – Reservation fee 5€

In a valley with a superb view of the citadel and surrounding mountains.

Surroundings : ⟨ 🏠
Leisure activities : 🏠 🏌 🛶 (small swimming pool)
Facilities : ♿ 🗝 🚿 🍴 🎠

GPS Longitude : 5.87919
Latitude : 46.94625

LA TOUR-DU-MEIX

39270 – Michelin map **321** D7 – pop. 226 – alt. 470
▶ Paris 430 – Champagnole 42 – Lons-le-Saunier 24 – St-Claude 36

⚠ Surchauffant

☎ 03 84 25 41 08, www.camping-surchauffant.fr

Address : at Le Pont de la Pyle (located 1km southeast along the D 470 and take road to the left, 150m from the Lac de Vouglans - direct access)

Opening times : from end April to mid Sept.

2,5 ha (200 pitches)

Tariff : 24€ ♦♦ 🚗 🅴 🔌 (10A)

Extra per person 6€

Rental rates : (from end April to mid Sept.) – 24 🚐 – 24 🏠.
Per night from 29 to 97€ – Per week from 203 to 679€

🚐 borne 2€ – 10 🅴 9€

Surroundings : 🛶 ⟨ ♨
Leisure activities : ✗ 🏠 🏌 🚲 🛶
Facilities : ♿ 🗝 (July-Aug.) 🚿 🍴 launderette 🎠 refrigerated food storage facilities
Nearby : ♟ 🛶 (beach) 🎣

GPS Longitude : 5.6742
Latitude : 46.52298

UXELLES

39130 – Michelin map **321** I2 – pop. 49 – alt. 598
▶ Paris 440 – Besançon 93 – Genève 86 – Lausanne 102

🏠 Village Vacances Odesia Les Crozats

(rental of chalets and rooms only)

☎ 03 84 25 51 43, www.odesia-lacs.com

Address : 1 rue Principale

Opening times : Permanent

2 ha

Rental rates : (2013 Price) 🚿 🅿 – 15 🏠 – 28 🛏. Per week from 299 to 816€

A small but pretty chalet village in the lake valley with an option for half-board accommodation.

Surroundings : ❄ 🛶
Leisure activities : ♟ ✗ 🏠 🎠 🎯 🛶 hammam 🚲 📺 cinema/activity centre
Facilities : 🗝 🚿 🍴 launderette 🎠

GPS Longitude : 5.78836
Latitude : 46.60277

The prices listed were supplied by the campsite owners in 2013 (if prices were not available, those from the previous year are given). The fees should be regarded as basic charges and may fluctuate with inflation.

VESOUL

70000 – Michelin map **314** E7 – pop. 15 920 – alt. 221
▶ Paris 360 – Belfort 68 – Besançon 47 – Épinal 91

🏠 International du Lac

☎ 03 84 76 22 86, www.camping-vesoul.com

Address : at Vaivre-et-Montoille, avenue des Rives du Lac (2.5km west)

Opening times : Permanent

4 ha (183 pitches) flat, grassy

Tariff : (2013 Price) ♦ 4€ 🚗 3€ 🅴 4€ – 🔌 (10A) 3€
Rental rates : Permanent ♿ (1 mobile home) 🚿 – 7 🚐 18 🏠. Per night from 23 to 38€ – Per week from 138 to 539€

Beside a wide lake.

Surroundings : 🛶 🏠 ♨
Leisure activities : 🏠 🎠 🏌 🛶 🎣
Facilities : ♿ 🗝 🚿 🎪 🚿 🍴 launderette
Nearby : ♟ ✗ 🍴 🛶

GPS Longitude : 6.13084
Latitude : 47.63121

VILLERSEXEL

70110 – Michelin map **314** G7 – pop. 1 472 – alt. 287
▶ Paris 386 – Belfort 41 – Besançon 59 – Lure 18

⚠ Le Chapeau Chinois

☎ 03 84 63 40 60, www.camping-villersexel.com

Address : 92 rue du Chapeau Chinois (located 1km north along the D 486, follow the signs for Lure and take the road to the right after the bridge)

Opening times : from mid March to beginning Oct.

2 ha (80 pitches) flat, grassy

Tariff : (2013 Price) ♦ 3,20€ 🚗 2€ 🅴 4,30€ – 🔌 (10A) 3,10€
Rental rates : (2013 Price) (from mid March to beginning Oct.) 🚿 – 6 🚐 – 1 gîte. Per night from 40 to 60€ – Per week from 320 to 440€

🚐 borne 3€ – 3 🅴 14,60€

Beside the Ognon river.

Surroundings : 🛶 ♨
Leisure activities : 🏠 🏌 🎯 🛶 🎣
Facilities : ♿ 🗝 🚿 🍴 launderette
Nearby : ✗ 🛶

GPS Longitude : 6.436
Latitude : 47.55814

ÎLE-DE-FRANCE

Paris, the 'City of Light' on the River Seine, lies at the heart of the Île-de-France. A chic and cosmopolitan capital, it is dominated by the iconic silhouette of the Eiffel Tower. Its former royal palace is now adorned with glass pyramids, a former railway station has been transformed into a magnificent museum and narrow streets lined with bohemian houses branch off from wide, formal, tree-lined boulevards. This is a city of endless contrasts: from busy department stores to elegant cafés, from the *bateaux-mouches* (restaurant boats) that glide along the majestic river at night to the sophisticated glamour of Parisian cabarets. But the region that lies beyond Paris has no intention of remaining in the capital's shadow; it is home to secluded châteaux, the magical world of Disneyland and the relaxed ambience of the summer cafés on the banks of the River Marne. And who could forget the magnificent splendour of Versailles, the most beautiful palace in the world?

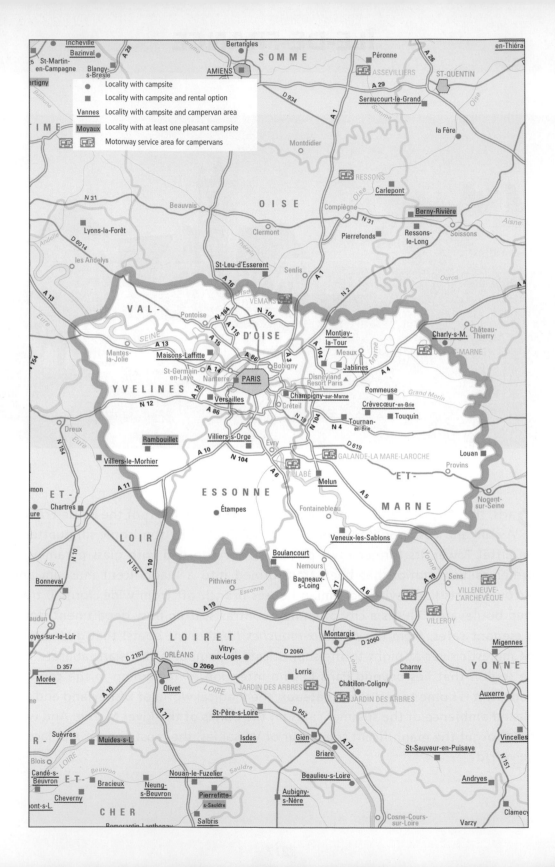

Legend:
- ● Locality with campsite
- ■ Locality with campsite and rental option
- <u>Vannes</u> Locality with campsite and campervan area
- <u>Moyaux</u> Locality with at least one pleasant campsite
- 🚐 Motorway service area for campervans

BAGNEAUX-SUR-LOING

77167 – Michelin map **312** F6 – pop. 1 686 – alt. 45

▶ Paris 84 – Fontainebleau 21 – Melun 39 – Montargis 30

⛰ Municipal de Pierre le Sault

📞 01 64 29 97 51, www.camping-bagneaux-sur-loing.fr – limited spaces for one-night stay

Address : chemin des Grèves (to the northeast of the town, near the sports field, between the canal and the Loing river, 200m from a small lake)

Opening times : from beginning April to end Oct.

3 ha (160 pitches)

Tariff : 🧍 2,95 € 🚗 🔲 2,45 € – (½) (10A) 4,65 €

Located between a canal and the river, but in an industrial area.

Surroundings : 🏕 ♨
Leisure activities : 🏠 🛶 🏓
Facilities : 🚿 ⛽ ☑ 🏢 🍴 launderette
Nearby : 🎣

G P S Longitude : 2.70376
Latitude : 48.24069

BOULANCOURT

77760 – Michelin map **312** D6 – pop. 357 – alt. 79

▶ Paris 79 – Étampes 33 – Fontainebleau 28 – Melun 44

⛺ Île de Boulancourt

📞 01 64 24 13 38, www.camping-iledeboulancourt.com – limited spaces for one-night stay

Address : 6 allée des Marronniers (to the south, follow the signs for Augerville-la-Rivière)

Opening times : Permanent

5,5 ha (110 pitches) flat, grassy

Tariff : 17,50 € 🧍🧍 🚗 🔲 (½) (3A) – Extra per person 4,80 €

Rental rates : Permanent 🏕 – 3 🚐 – 1 🏠 – 1 canvas bungalow 3 chalets (without sanitary facilities). Per night 54 € – Per week 358 €

🚐 borne 5 € – 2 🔲 15 €

A pleasant wooded setting in a bend of the Essonne river.

Surroundings : 🏞 ♨
Leisure activities : 🏠
Facilities : ⛽ 🏢 🍴 📷

G P S Longitude : 2.435
Latitude : 48.25583

CHAMPIGNY-SUR-MARNE

94500 – Michelin map **312** E3 – pop. 75 090 – alt. 40

▶ Paris 13 – Créteil 10 – Amiens 150 – Bobigny 13

🏕 Homair Vacances Paris Est

📞 01 43 97 43 97, www.campingchampigny.fr – reserved for residents outside the Île de France

Address : boulevard des Alliés

Opening times : Permanent

(383 pitches) flat, grassy

Tariff : 35,40 € 🧍🧍 🚗 🔲 (½) (10A) – Extra per person 7 € – Reservation fee 10 €

Rental rates : Permanent – 6 caravans – 148 🚐 – 40 🏠. Per night from 29 to 129 € – Per week from 203 to 903 € – Reservation fee 10 €

🚐 borne 9 € – 32 🔲 31 €

Beside the Marne river with a view of the Pavillon Baltard (19th-century concert hall).

Leisure activities : 🍴 🍽 jacuzzi 🚴
Facilities : 🚿 ⛽ 🏢 🔥 🍴 launderette 🗑 🛁
Nearby : 🎣

G P S Longitude : 2.47701
Latitude : 48.82958

CREVECOEUR-EN-BRIE

77610 – Michelin map **312** G3 – pop. 299 – alt. 116

▶ Paris 51 – Melun 36 – Boulogne-Billancourt 59 – Argenteuil 66

🏕 Caravaning des 4 Vents

📞 01 64 07 41 11, www.caravaning-4vents.fr – limited spaces for one-night stay

Address : 22 rue de Beauregard (located 1km west following signs for la Houssaye and take turning to the left)

Opening times : from mid March to end Oct.

9 ha (199 pitches) flat, grassy

Tariff : 30 € 🧍🧍 🚗 🔲 (½) (6A) – Extra per person 6 €

Rental rates : (from mid March to end Oct.) 🏕 – 5 🏠. Per night from 83 € Per week from 560 €

🚐 borne 30 € – 30 🔲 30 €

In a pleasant leafy setting with large, well marked out pitches.

Surroundings : 🏞 ♨
Leisure activities : 🏠 🛶 🏊
Facilities : 🚿 ⛽ ☑ 🏢 🔥 🍴 launderette
Nearby : 🏓 🐎

G P S Longitude : 2.89722
Latitude : 48.75065

Michelin classification:

⛺⛺⛺⛺	*Extremely comfortable, equipped to a very high standard*
⛺⛺⛺	*Very comfortable, equipped to a high standard*
⛺⛺	*Comfortable and well equipped*
⛺	*Reasonably comfortable*
⛺	*Satisfactory*

ÉTAMPES

91150 – Michelin map **312** B5 – pop. 22 182 – alt. 80

▶ Paris 51 – Chartres 59 – Évry 35 – Fontainebleau 45

🏕 Le Vauvert

📞 01 64 94 21 39, caravaning.levauvert@orange.fr – limited spaces for one-night stay

Address : route de Saclas (2.3km south along the D 49)

8 ha (230 pitches) flat, grassy

Only 25 to 30 places for tents and caravans alongside 200 pitches for owner-occupiers.

Surroundings : 🏕 ♨
Leisure activities : 🍴 🏠 🛶 🏓
Facilities : 🚿 ⛽ 🛁 🗑
At the leisure/activities centre : 🏊 🚣 ⛷ 🐎 climbing

G P S Longitude : 2.14532
Latitude : 48.41215

JABLINES

77450 – Michelin map **312** F2 – pop. 629 – alt. 46
▶ Paris 44 – Meaux 14 – Melun 57

⚑ L' International

📞 0160260937, www.camping-jablines.com

Address : at the base de loisirs (leisure centre) (situated 2km southwest along the D 45, follow the signs for Annet-sur-Marne, 9km from the Disneyland-Paris park)

Opening times : from mid April to beginning Nov.

300 ha/4 for camping (154 pitches) flat, grassy

Tariff : 29€ �!♦ ⇔ 🔲 💧 (10A) – Extra per person 8€ – Reservation fee 12€

Rental rates : (from mid April to beginning Nov.) ✂ – 9 🚐. Per night from 68 to 97€ – Per week from 476 to 680€ Reservation fee 12€

🔄 borne 2,50€ – 150 🔲 29€

An attractive location in a bend of the Marne river, next to a large leisure and activity park.

Surroundings : 🌿 🗬 ⬡⬡
Leisure activities : ⛹
Facilities : ♿ ⊶ 🔲 ⊞ ↻ launderette 🗲
At the leisure/activities centre : 🍴 ✕ 🛶
🚴 🎿 ⛾ ◨ (fresh water) 🚣 🐎 cable wake-boarding

G P S Longitude : 2.73437
Latitude : 48.91367

LOUAN VILLEGRUIS FONTAINE

77560 – Michelin map **312** J4 – pop. 512 – alt. 168
▶ Paris 101 – Melun 77 – Provins 21 – Troyes 68

⚑ Yelloh! Paris Ile de France

(rental of mobile homes, tents and cabins in the trees only)

📞 0164000014, www.yellohvillage-paris-iledefrance.com

Address : at Louan, at La Cerclière (D 131)

Opening times : from mid April to mid Nov.

11 ha (200 pitches)
Rental rates : (2013 Price) – 160 🚐 – 2 cabins in the trees 10 tent lodges. Per night from 35 to 199€ – Per week from 210 to 1 194€

In the heart of the forest, surrounded by green space, 1 hour from Paris and the Disneyland-Paris park.

Surroundings : 🌿 ⬡⬡
Leisure activities : 🍴 ✕ 🛖 🛝 ⛹ 🚴
🚣 ◨ 🎿 cinema, zip wire, forest trail, paintballing, multi-sports ground
Facilities : ♿ ⊶ 🔲 ↻ launderette 🗲 🛒

G P S Longitude : 3.49077
Latitude : 48.6306

MAISONS-LAFFITTE

78600 – Michelin map **311** I2 – pop. 22 717 – alt. 38
▶ Paris 23 – Versailles 24 – Pontoise 20 – Nanterre 13

⚑ Sandaya International

📞 0139122191, www.sandaya.fr

Address : 1 rue Johnson (on the Île de la Commune)

Opening times : from beginning April to beginning Nov.

6,5 ha (336 pitches) flat, grassy

Tariff : 35,50€ ♦♦ ⇔ 🔲 💧 (6A) – Extra per person 7,10€ Reservation fee 15€

Rental rates : (from beginning April to beginning Nov.) ♿ (1 mobile home) – 87 🚐 – 3 cabins in the trees. Per night from 69 to 150€ – Reservation fee 30€
🔄 borne
Situated on an island in the Seine.

Surroundings : 🗬 🚣
Leisure activities : 🍴 ✕ 🛖 ⛹ 🛝
Facilities : ♿ ⊶ 🔲 ⊞ ↻ launderette 🗲
Nearby : ✕

G P S Longitude : 2.1458
Latitude : 48.94156

MELUN

77000 – Michelin map **312** E4 – pop. 39 400 – alt. 43
▶ Paris 47 – Chartres 105 – Fontainebleau 18 – Meaux 55

⚑ Kawan Village La Belle Étoile

📞 0164394812, www.campinglabelleetoile.com

Address : 64bis quai Maréchal Joffre (to the southeast along the N 6, follow the signs for Fontainebleau (left bank)

Opening times : from beginning April to mid Oct.

3,5 ha (180 pitches) flat, grassy

Tariff : ♦ 7€ ⇔ 🔲 8€ – 💧 (6A) 4€ – Reservation fee 8€
Rental rates : (from beginning April to mid Oct.) ✂ – 11 🚐 4 🏠 – 3 canvas bungalows. Per night from 32 to 120€ – Per week from 192 to 800€ – Reservation fee 8€
🔄 borne 3€
In a very lush setting, right next to the Seine river.

Surroundings : ⬡⬡
Leisure activities : 🛖 ⛹ ⛝ (pool)
Facilities : ⊶ 🔲 ⊞ ↻ launderette
Nearby : ≋ hammam ✕ ◨ ◨ ⛝
G P S Longitude : 2.66765
Latitude : 48.50929

Routes nationales are main roads and their identifying numbers begin with N or RN. Routes départementales are generally quieter roads and begin with D or DN.

MONTJAY-LA-TOUR

77410 – Michelin map **312** E2
▶ Paris 38 – Melun 50 – Boulogne-Billancourt 45 – Argenteuil 41

⚑ Le Parc de Paris

📞 0160262079, www.campingleparc.fr – limited spaces for one-night stay

Address : rue Adèle Claret (take the eastern exit along the D 105 towards the D 104 for Annet)

Opening times : Permanent

10 ha (363 pitches)

Tariff : (2013 Price) 33€ ♦♦ ⇔ 🔲 💧 (6A) – Extra per person 8€ Reservation fee 25€

Rental rates : Permanent – 30 🚐 . Per night from 42 to 158€ Per week from 252 to 948€ – Reservation fee 25€
🔄 borne
Well situated for Paris and the Disneyland-Paris park.

Surroundings : 🗬 ⬡⬡
Leisure activities : 🍴 ✕ 🛖 ⛹ multi-sports ground
Facilities : ♿ ⊶ 🔲 ⊞ ↻ launderette 🗲
Nearby : ✕
G P S Longitude : 2.66724
Latitude : 48.91118

PARIS

75000 – pop. 2 234 105 – alt. 30
Au Bois de Boulogne – 75016

▲▲▲ Indigo Paris Bois de Boulogne

✆ 01 45 24 30 00, www.camping-indigo.com – reserved for residents outside the Île de France

Address : 2 allée du Bord de l'Eau (between the bridges at Suresnes and Puteaux; beside the Seine)

Opening times : Permanent

7 ha (510 pitches)

Tariff : 41,20€ ♦♦ ⊿ 回 ⑭ (10A) Extra per person 7,80€ – Reservation fee 22€

Rental rates : Permanent ♿ (1 mobile home) – 17 caravans – 58 ⊡. Per night from 83 to 152€ – Per week from 523 to 955€ – Reservation fee 22€

⊡ borne 9€

Choose the pitches along the Seine river, which are little more peaceful; bus for La Porte Maillot, Paris (RER-metro).

Surroundings : ⊏ ♀♀
Leisure activities : ♀ ✕ ⊡
Facilities : ♿ ⚷ ⊞ ⊿ ⊌ ¶ launderette ⊿ ⊰

GPS Longitude : 2.23464
Latitude : 48.86849

POMMEUSE

77515 – Michelin map **312** H3 – pop. 2 756 – alt. 67
▶ Paris 58 – Château-Thierry 49 – Créteil 54 – Meaux 23

▲▲▲ Iris Parc Le Chêne Gris ♦♦

✆ 01 64 04 21 80, www.lechenegris.com

Address : 24 place de la Gare (situated 2km southwest, behind Faremoutiers-Pommeuse station)

Opening times : from beginning April to end Oct.

6 ha (350 pitches)

Tariff : 44€ ♦♦ ⊿ 回 ⑭ (6A) – Extra per person 3,50€ – Reservation fee 3,50€

Rental rates : (from beginning April to end Oct.) – 212 ⊡. Per night from 54 to 125€ – Per week from 378 to 875€ Reservation fee 20€

A well-equipped indoor children's play area.

Surroundings : ⊏ ♀♀
Leisure activities : ✕ ⊡ ⊚ ⊰ ⊰ ⊡ ⊿
Facilities : ♿ ⚷ cc ⊞ ⊿ ⊌ ¶ launderette ⊿ ⊰

GPS Longitude : 2.99368
Latitude : 48.80814

Key to rentals symbols :

12 ⊡	Number of mobile homes	
20 ⊡	Number of chalets	
6 ⊨	Number of rooms to rent	
Per night 30–50€	Minimum/maximum rate per night	
Per week 300–1,000€	Minimum/maximum rate per week	

RAMBOUILLET

78120 – Michelin map **311** G4 – pop. 26 065 – alt. 160
▶ Paris 53 – Chartres 42 – Étampes 44 – Mantes-la-Jolie 50

▲▲▲ Huttopia Rambouillet ♦♦

✆ 01 30 41 07 34, www.huttopia.com

Address : route du Château d'Eau (head 4km south along the N 10, follow the signs for Chartres)

Opening times : from end March to beginning Nov.

8 ha (93 pitches)

Tariff : (2013 Price) 34,40€ ♦♦ ⊿ 回 ⑭ (10A) – Extra per person 7,70€ – Reservation fee 22€

Rental rates : (2013 Price) (from end March to beginning Nov.) ⓟ 10 caravans – 10 ⊡ – 14 tent lodges. Per night from 82 to 145€ – Per week from 516 to 1015€ – Reservation fee 22€

⊡ borne 7€

Beside a lake, in the heart of the forest.

Surroundings : ⊰ ⊏ ♀♀
Leisure activities : ♀ ✕ ⊡ ⊰ ⊰ ⊿ ⊿
Facilities : ♿ ⚷ ⊞ ⊿ ⊌ ¶ launderette ⊿
Nearby : ⊡ ⊿ wildlife park

GPS Longitude : 1.84374
Latitude : 48.62634

These symbols are used for a campsite that is exceptional in its category:

▲▲▲....▲ *Particularly pleasant setting, quality and range of services available*

⊰ ⊰ *Tranquil, isolated site – quiet site, particularly at night*

⊰ ⊰ *Exceptional view – interesting or panoramic view*

TOUQUIN

77131 – Michelin map **312** H3 – pop. 1 095 – alt. 112
▶ Paris 57 – Coulommiers 12 – Melun 36 – Montereau-Fault-Yonne 48

▲▲▲ Les Étangs Fleuris

✆ 01 64 04 16 36, www.etangsfleuris.com

Address : route de La Couture (3km east)

Opening times : from beginning April to mid Sept.

5,5 ha (195 pitches)

Tariff : 22€ ♦♦ ⊿ 回 ⑭ (10A) – Extra per person 11€

Rental rates : (from beginning April to end Sept.) – 16 ⊡. Per week from 395 to 650€

In a green setting, shady, close to the Étangs Fleuris (lakes).

Surroundings : ⊰ ⊏ ♀♀
Leisure activities : ♀ ⊡ ⊰ ⊰ ⊿ ⊿ multi-sports ground
Facilities : ⚷ ⊞ ⊿ ⊌ ¶ launderette
Nearby : ✂ ⊰

GPS Longitude : 3.04728
Latitude : 48.73279

TOURNAN EN BRIE

77220 – Michelin map **312** F3 – pop. 8 116 – alt. 102
▶ Paris 44 – Melun 29 – Amiens 176 – Créteil 38

🏕 FranceLoc Fredland - Parc de Combreux

🞄 01 64 07 96 44, www.campings-franceloc.fr

Address : 1.5 km at the south by the D 10, route de Liverdy-en-Brie

Opening times : Permanent

26 ha/7 for camping (189 pitches) flat, grassy

Tariff : (2013 Price) 25€ ♛♛ ⇌ 🔲 💧 (6A) – Extra per person 7€
Rental rates : Permanent – 106 🚐 – 6 🏠. Per night from 39 to 129€ – Per week from 252 to 805€
800m from the RER train station (25min to Paris).

Surroundings : ♋♋	
Leisure activities : 🍷 ⚓⚡ 🏊 (small swimming pool) 🏌🪁🎣	**G P S** Longitude : 2.76915 Latitude : 48.73517
Facilities : 🚿 ⌖ 🏧 🚰 launderette 🚙	

For more information on visiting particular towns or regions, consult the relevant regional MICHELIN Green Guide. We also recommend you use the appropriate Michelin regional map to locate your selected campsite, to calculate distances and to work out the best route.

VENEUX-LES-SABLONS

77250 – Michelin map **312** F5 – pop. 4 788 – alt. 76
▶ Paris 72 – Fontainebleau 9 – Melun 26 – Montereau-Fault-Yonne 14

🏕 Les Courtilles du Lido

🞄 01 60 70 46 05, http://www.les-courtilles-du-lido.fr

Address : chemin du Passeur (located 1.5km to the northeast)

Opening times : from end March to end Sept.

5 ha (160 pitches) flat, grassy

Tariff : 19,50€ ♛♛ ⇌ 🔲 💧 (10A) – Extra per person 4€
Rental rates : (from end March to end Sept.) – 15 🚐 2 canvas bungalows. Per night from 85 to 140€ – Per week from 250 to 688€
🚐 borne – 🔌💧16€

Surroundings : 🌳 ♋♋	
Leisure activities : 🍷 ⚓⚡ 👟 🎣	**G P S** Longitude : 2.80194 Latitude : 48.38333
Facilities : ⌖ 🚿 🚰 launderette	

VERSAILLES

78000 – Michelin map **311** I3 – pop. 86 477 – alt. 130
▶ Paris 29 – Chartres 80 – Fontainebleau 73 – Rambouillet 35

🏕 Huttopia Versailles

HUTTOPIA

🞄 01 39 51 23 61, www.huttopia.com

Address : 31 rue Berthelot

Opening times : from end March to beginning Nov.

4,6 ha (180 pitches)

Tariff : (2013 Price) 43,50€ ♛♛ ⇌ 🔲 💧 (10A) – Extra per person 9,70€ Reservation fee 22€

Rental rates : (from end March to beginning Nov.) 🦽 (1 chalet) 15 caravans – 20 🏠 – 14 tent lodges. Per night from 61 to 179€ – Per week from 384 to 1 253€ – Reservation fee 22€

🚐 borne 9€
A wooded setting close to the town.

Surroundings : 🌳 ♋♋♋	
Leisure activities : ✕ ⚓⚡ 🏊	**G P S** Longitude : 2.15912 Latitude : 48.79441
Facilities : 🚿 ⌖ 🏧 ⛵ launderette	

VILLIERS-SUR-ORGE

91700 – Michelin map **312** C4 – pop. 3 896 – alt. 75
▶ Paris 25 – Chartres 71 – Dreux 89 – Évry 15

🏕 Le Beau Village de Paris

🞄 01 60 16 17 86, www.campingaparis.com – limited spaces for one-night stay

Address : 1 voie des Prés (600m southeast via the le town centre, 800m from St-Geneviève-des-Bois station - from A 6, take exit 6)

Opening times : Permanent

2,5 ha (124 pitches) flat, grassy

Tariff : 22,50€ ♛♛ ⇌ 🔲 💧 (10A) – Extra per person 6,50€
Rental rates : Permanent ⚡ – 15 🚐. Per night from 70 to 120€ Per week from 270 to 580€
🚐 borne 2€ – 25 🔲 20€
In a green setting, slightly shady beside the Orge river, with proper pitches for campervans.

Surroundings : 🌳 🌳 ♟	
Leisure activities : 🍷 🚣 ⚓⚡	**G P S** Longitude : 2.30421 Latitude : 48.65511
Facilities : 🚿 ⌖ 🏧 ⛵ 🚰 launderette	
Nearby : 🍴 🏊	

R. Mattes / hemis.fr

Languedoc-Roussillon is a kaleidoscope of landscapes, cultures and sensations. You will be seduced by the feverish rhythm of its festivals, the dizzying beauty of the Tarn gorges and the Pyrenees, the magical spell of its caves and stone statues, the seclusion of its cliff-top 'Citadels of Vertigo' with their panoramic views and the heady perfumes of its sun-drenched *garrigue*, the local scrubland fragrant with wild herbs. Admire the nonchalant flamingoes that thrive on its long stretches of salt flats, enjoy discovering the splendour of Carcassonne's medieval ramparts or explore the quiet waters of the Midi Canal and the harsh majesty of the Cévennes. Taking in so many different sights may exhaust some visitors, but remedies are close at hand: a plate of *aligot*, made from mashed potato, butter, cream, garlic and cheese, and a simmering *cassoulet*, the famously rich combination of duck, sausage, beans and herbs, followed by a slice of Roquefort cheese and a glass of ruby-red wine.

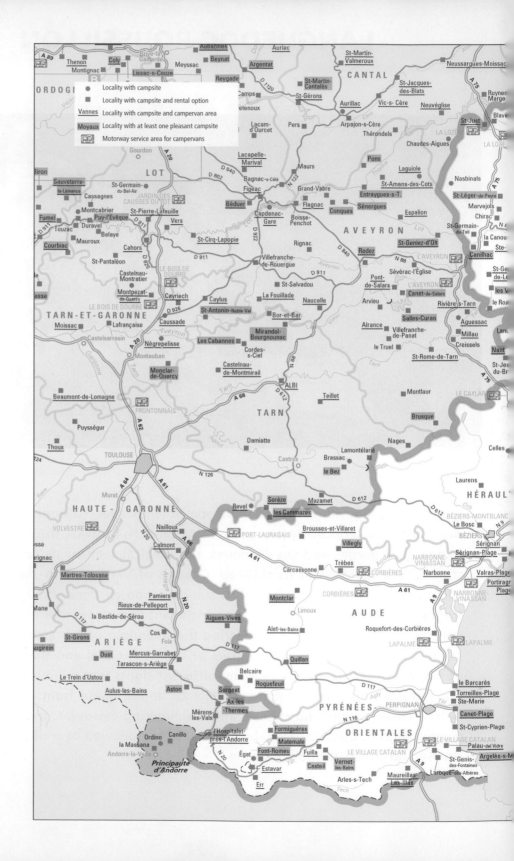

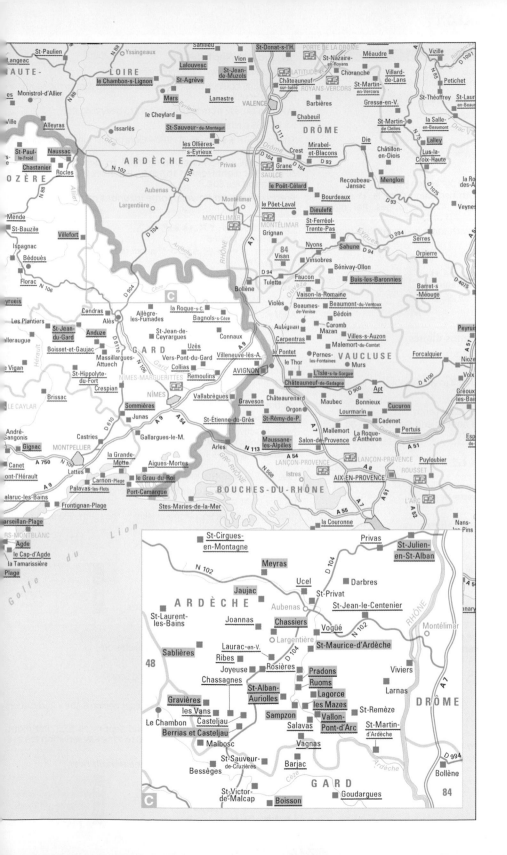

AGDE

34300 – Michelin map **339** F9 – pop. 24 031 – alt. 5
▶ Paris 754 – Béziers 24 – Lodève 60 – Millau 118

Yelloh! Village Mer et Soleil ▲▲

📞 0467942114, www.camping-mer-soleil.com

Address : chemin de Notre Dame at Saint Martin, route de Rochelongue (3km to the south)

Opening times : from mid April to beginning Oct.

8 ha (477 pitches)

Tariff : 46 € ♦♦ ⌂ 🔲 (6A) – Extra per person 8 €
Rental rates : (from mid April to beginning Oct.) ⅗ (1 mobile home) ⅗ – 231 ⌂ – 9 ⌂ – 42 tent lodges. Per night from 29 to 245 € – Per week from 203 to 1715 €

An impressive indoor spa area with some luxury mobile homes in a pedestrian zone.

Surroundings : ⌂ 00
Leisure activities : ♦ ✕ ⌂ ⊙ nighttime ⚶
↟ ⇌ jacuzzi ⚶ 🚲 ⚶ ⚶ ⚶ spa centre
Facilities : ⚶ ⊶ ⌂ ⚶ 🏠 launderette ⚶ ⚶
Nearby : ⚶
GPS Longitude : 3.47812
Latitude : 43.28621

Kawan Village Les Champs Blancs

📞 0467942342, www.champs-blancs.fr

Address : route de Rochelongue

Opening times : from beginning April to end Sept.

15 ha/4 for camping (336 pitches)

Tariff : 57,50 € ♦♦ ⌂ 🔲 (10A) – Extra per person 5 €
Rental rates : (from beginning April to end Sept.) ⅗ – 80 ⌂ 20 ⌂. Per week from 336 to 999 €

Surroundings : ⌂ 00
Leisure activities : ♦ ✕ ⌂ ⊙ ⚶ ⚶ ⚶
⚶ ⚶ multi-sports ground
Facilities : ⚶ ⊶ ⌂ – 120 individual sanitary facilities (⚶ ⚶ ⚶ wc) 🏠 launderette ⚶ ⚶
GPS Longitude : 3.47666
Latitude : 43.29644

Village Vacances Les Pescalunes

(rental of chalets only)

📞 0467013706, www.grandbleu.fr

Address : route de Luxembourg (follow the signs for Le Cap-d'Agde)

Opening times : from beginning April to end Oct.

3 ha

Rental rates : ⚶ (2 chalets) Ⓟ – 78 ⌂. Per night from 80 to 110 € Per week from 273 to 1050 €

A peaceful chalet village on the side of a hill, with a view of the surrounding area and the Cévennes mountains.

Surroundings : ⚶ ≤ 00
Leisure activities : ⌂ ⚶ ⚶ ⚶
Facilities : ⊶ ⚶ 🏠 launderette
GPS Longitude : 3.50223
Latitude : 43.30109

Some information or pricing may have changed since the guide went to press. We recommend you check the price list online in advance or at the entrance to the campsite and enquire about possible restrictions.

Flower Neptune ▲▲

📞 0467942394, www.campingleneptune.com

Address : 46 boulevard du Saint-Christ (situated 2km to the south, near the Hérault)

Opening times : from beginning April to beginning Oct.

2,1 ha (165 pitches) flat, grassy

Tariff : 36,50 € ♦♦ ⌂ 🔲 (10A) – Extra per person 8 € – Reservation fee 30 €
Rental rates : (from beginning April to beginning Oct.) ⅗ 30 ⌂. Per night from 31 to 148 € – Per week from 217 to 1036 € Reservation fee 30 €

Pretty shrubs and flowers; some luxurious mobile homes.

Surroundings : ⌂ 0
Leisure activities : ♦ ✕ ⚶ ⚶ 🚲 ⚶
multi-sports ground
Facilities : ⚶ ⊶ ⚶ ⚶ ⚶ ⚶ ⚶ 🏠 launderette
Nearby : ⚶

GPS Longitude : 3.4581
Latitude : 43.29805

Les Romarins

📞 0467941859, www.romarins.com

Address : 6 route du Grau (3km to the south, near the Hérault)

Opening times : from beginning April to end Sept.

2 ha (120 pitches) flat, grassy, sandy

Tariff : 32 € ♦♦ ⌂ 🔲 (8A) – Extra per person 7,55 € – Reservation fee 22 €
Rental rates : (from beginning April to end Sept.) ⅗ – 40 ⌂ 2 studios – 2 canvas bungalows. Per night from 34 to 148 € Per week from 170 to 1036 € – Reservation fee 22 € ⌂ borne 2,50 € – ⚶ 11 €

Surroundings : ⌂ 00
Leisure activities : ♦ ✕ ⌂ ⚶ ⚶
multi-sports ground
Facilities : ⚶ ⊶ ⚶ 🏠 🔳
GPS Longitude : 3.4468
Latitude : 43.29131

Le Rochelongue ▲▲

📞 0467212551, www.camping-le-rochelongue.fr – limited spaces for one-night stay

Address : route de Rochelongue (4km to the south, 500m from the beach)

2 ha (107 pitches)

Rentals : ⅗ – 27 ⌂.

Surroundings : ⌂ 00
Leisure activities : ♦ ✕ ⚶ ⚶ ⚶
Facilities : ⚶ ⊶ ⚶ 🏠 launderette ⚶
Nearby : ⚶ ⚶ ⚶ ⚶ watersports centre

GPS Longitude : 3.48139
Latitude : 43.27917

La Pépinière

📞 0467941094, www.campinglapepiniere.com

Address : 3 route du Grau

Opening times : from mid April to end Sept.

3 ha (100 pitches) flat, grassy

Tariff : 29 € ♦♦ ⌂ 🔲 (10A) – Extra per person 6,30 € – Reservation fee 25 €
Rental rates : (from mid April to end Sept.) – 28 ⌂. Per night from 40 to 104 € – Per week from 280 to 728 € – Reservation fee 25 € ⌂ borne

Family-orientated site very near the Hérault river.

Surroundings : ⚶ ⌂
Leisure activities : ♦ ✕ ⚶ ⇌ ⚶ ⚶
Facilities : ⚶ ⊶ 🏠 🔳 ⚶
Nearby : ⚶ ⚓

GPS Longitude : 3.45368
Latitude : 43.29488

AIGUES-MORTES

30220 – Michelin map **339** K7 – pop. 8 116 – alt. 3
▶ Paris 745 – Arles 49 – Montpellier 38 – Nîmes 42

⚠ Yelloh! Village La Petite Camargue ▲▲

📞 04 66 53 98 98, www.yellohvillage-petite.camargue.com

Address : 3.5km west along the D 62, follow the signs for Montpellier

Opening times : from end April to mid Sept.

42 ha/10 for camping (553 pitches)

Tariff : 52€ ★★ ⇔ 回 (16A) – Extra per person 9€

Rental rates : (from end April to mid Sept.) ⚡ – 300 🏠.
Per night from 39 to 249€ – Per week from 273 to 1743€
🚐 borne
Activities and services suitable for teenagers. Free shuttle service to the beaches.

Surroundings : 🚗 ♀♀
Leisure activities : ▼ ✕ 🖼 ⊕ 🏃 🚵 🚴 ✂
🏊 🐎 disco, multi-sports ground
Facilities : ♿ ⚬ 🚿 ▝ launderette 🚰 🚿

Longitude : 4.15963
Latitude : 43.56376

To visit a town or region, use the MICHELIN Green Guides.

ALET-LES-BAINS

11580 – Michelin map **344** E5 – pop. 436 – alt. 186
▶ Paris 786 – Montpellier 187 – Carcassonne 35 – Castelnaudary 49

⚠ Val d'Aleth

📞 04 68 69 90 40, www.valdaleth.com

Address : in the town (D 2118 and take the right turning beside the Aude river)

Opening times : Permanent

0,5 ha (37 pitches)

Tariff : 21,50€ ★★ ⇔ 回 (10A) – Extra per person 4,20€

Rental rates : Permanent ⚡ – 4 🛏. Per night from 46 to 58€
Per week from 290 to 365€
🚐 10 回 17,50€
Well-shaded pitches near the river and a ruined château.

Surroundings : 🚗 ♀♀
Leisure activities : 🚵 🐎
Facilities : ♿ ⚬ ▝ launderette

Longitude : 2.25564
Latitude : 42.99486

ALLÈGRE-LES-FUMADES

30500 – Michelin map **339** K3 – pop. 695 – alt. 135
▶ Paris 696 – Alès 16 – Barjac 102 – La Grand-Combe 28

⚠ FranceLoc Le Domaine des Fumades ▲▲

📞 04 66 24 80 78, www.domaine-des-fumades.com

Address : Les Fumade – Les Bains (access via the D 241)

15 ha/6 for camping (253 pitches) relatively flat, flat, grassy, stony

Rentals : 171 🏠 – 27 🏠 – 5 apartments – 8 tent lodges.
Beside the Alauzène river and close to the spa centre.

Surroundings : 🚢 🚗 ♀♀
Leisure activities : ▼ ✕ 🖼 ⊕ 🏃 🚵 ✂
🎯 🏊 🚣 cinema, multi-sports ground, entertainment room
Facilities : ♿ ⚬ 🚿 ▝ launderette 🚰 🚿
Nearby : 🐎

Longitude : 4.22904
Latitude : 44.18484

ANDUZE

30140 – Michelin map **339** I4 – pop. 3 303 – alt. 135
▶ Paris 718 – Alès 15 – Florac 68 – Lodève 84

⚠ L'Arche ▲▲

📞 04 66 61 74 08, www.camping-arche.fr

Address : 1105 chemin de Recoulin (situated 2km to the northwest; beside the Gardon)

Opening times : from beginning April to end Sept.

5 ha (302 pitches) terraced, relatively flat, flat, grassy, sandy

Tariff : 42€ ★★ ⇔ 回 (10A) – Extra per person 8,90€ – Reservation fee 15€

Rental rates : (from beginning April to end Sept.) ⚡ – 25 🏠
11 🏠. Per night from 56 to 169€ – Per week from 390 to 1180€
Reservation fee 15€
🚐 borne 2€
A pleasant swimming pool and indoor wellness area.

Surroundings : 🚢 ♀ ⛰
Leisure activities : ▼ ✕ 🖼 ⊕ 🏃 ⛵
hammam 🚵 🎯 🏊 🚣 multi-sports ground, spa centre
Facilities : ♿ ⚬ 🛋 🚿 🚰 ▝ launderette 🚰 🚿

Longitude : 3.97284
Latitude : 44.06873

⚠ Cévennes-Provence ▲▲

📞 04 66 61 73 10, www.camping-cevennes-provence.fr

Address : at Corbès-Thoiras (By Le Mas du Pont; beside the Gardon de Mialet and near the Gardon de St-Jean (rivers)

Opening times : from mid March to end Sept.

30 ha/15 for camping (242 pitches) very uneven, terraced, flat and relatively flat, grassy, stony

Tariff : 30,50€ ★★ ⇔ 回 (10A) – Extra per person 8,20€
Reservation fee 16€

Rental rates : (from mid March to end Sept.) – 16 🏠. Per week from 340 to 730€ – Reservation fee 16€
🚐 borne
Choose pitches near the river for swimming or higher up for the view over the valley.

Surroundings : 🚢 ⛵ 🚗 ♀♀ ⛰
Leisure activities : ▼ ✕ 🖼 🏃 🚵 ✂ ⚓
🚣
Facilities : ♿ ⚬ 🛋 🚿 ▝ launderette 🚰 🚿
Nearby : adventure park

Longitude : 3.96643
Latitude : 44.07711

⚠ Les Fauvettes ▲▲

📞 04 66 61 72 23, www.lesfauvettes.fr

Address : route de St-Jean-du-Gard (1.7km to the northwest)

Opening times : from beginning May to end Sept.

7 ha/3 for camping (144 pitches)

Tariff : (2013 Price) 26€ ★★ ⇔ 回 (10A) – Extra per person 5,70€

Rental rates : (from beginning April to end Nov.) – 22 🏠
20 🏠. Per night from 50 to 70€ – Per week from 199 to 750€
Reservation fee 17€
Choose the pitches away from the road in preference.

Surroundings : 🚗 ♀
Leisure activities : ▼ ✕ 🖼 🏃 🚵 🚣 ⚓
entertainment room
Facilities : ♿ ⚬ 🚿 ▝ 🖼 🚿
Nearby : 🚴

Longitude : 3.9738
Latitude : 44.06027

Le Bel Eté d'Anduze

0466617604, www.camping-bel-ete.com

Address : 1870 route de Nîmes (2.5km southeast)

2,26 ha (97 pitches) flat, grassy

Rentals : 22 – 3 mobile homes (without sanitary facilities).

Choose the pitches near the Gardon river and away from the road in preference.

Surroundings :
Leisure activities : multi-sports ground
Facilities : refrigerators
Nearby :

Longitude : 3.99468
Latitude : 44.03827

ARGELÈS-SUR-MER

66700 – Michelin map **344** J7 – pop. 10 033 – alt. 19

Paris 872 – Céret 28 – Perpignan 22 – Port-Vendres 9

Centre

Le Front de Mer

0468810870, www.camping-front-mer.com

Address : avenue du Grau (250m from the beach)

Opening times : from beginning April to end Sept.

10 ha (588 pitches) flat, grassy

Tariff : 40,70€ (6A) – Extra per person 7,20€
Reservation fee 25€

Rental rates : (from beginning April to end Sept.) – 150 . Per night from 50 to 75€ – Per week from 265 to 1130€
Reservation fee 25€

A pretty water park and indoor spa area.

Surroundings :
Leisure activities : hammam, jacuzzi multi-sports ground, spa centre
Facilities : launderette

Longitude : 3.04687
Latitude : 42.54684

Pujol

0468810025, www.campingdepujol.com

Address : avenue de la Rétirada 1939

Opening times : from beginning April to end Sept.

6,2 ha (312 pitches)

Tariff : 35,80€ (6A) – Extra per person 7,20€
Reservation fee 15€

Rental rates : (from beginning April to end Sept.) – 50 . Per night from 26 to 119€ – Per week from 182 to 833€
Reservation fee 15€

Numerous pitches for tents or caravans, many with plenty of shade.

Surroundings :
Leisure activities : nighttime
Facilities : launderette
Nearby :

Longitude : 3.02768
Latitude : 42.55532

FranceLoc Paris-Roussillon

0468811971, www.parisroussillon.com

Address : avenue de la Retirada

3,5 ha (208 pitches) flat, grassy

Rentals : 106 – 2 studios – 2 apartments.

Shaded surroundings, plenty of mobile homes, but pitches for tents and caravans always available.

Surroundings :
Leisure activities : launderette
Facilities :
Nearby :

Longitude : 3.03117
Latitude : 42.55782

La Chapelle - Les Ombrages

0468812983, www.les-ombrages.com

Address : avenue du Général de Gaulle (400m from the beach)

Opening times : from mid April to end Sept.

4,1 ha (270 pitches)

Tariff : (2013 Price) 31€ (10A) – Extra per person 6,20€
Reservation fee 20€

Rental rates : (from mid March to end Sept.) – 13
2 . Per night from 35 to 98€ – Per week from 250 to 690€
Reservation fee 20€ – borne

Some attractively shaded areas beneath plane trees.

Surroundings :
Leisure activities :
Facilities : launderette
Nearby :

Longitude : 3.04214
Latitude : 42.55074

Europe

0468810810, www.camping-europe.net

Address : avenue du Général de Gaulle (500m from the beach)

Opening times : from beginning April to end Sept.

1,2 ha (91 pitches) flat, grassy

Tariff : 30,10€ (10A) – Extra per person 7€ – Reservation fee 20€

Rental rates : (from beginning April to end Sept.) – 13 . Per night from 50 to 90€ – Per week from 220 to 700€
Reservation fee 20€

borne

Attractively shaded in places by plane trees, and good sanitary facilities.

Surroundings :
Leisure activities :
Facilities : launderette
Nearby :

Longitude : 3.04185
Latitude : 42.54987

Le Stade

0468810440, www.campingdustade.com

Address : 87 avenue du 8 Mai 1945 (known as: route de la Plage)

Opening times : from beginning April to end Sept.

2,4 ha (185 pitches) flat, grassy

Tariff : (2013 Price) 26,50€ (10A)
Extra per person 5,90€

Rental rates : (2013 Price) (from beginning April to end Sept.)
10 . Per night from 35 to 92€ – Per week from 210 to 610€
Reservation fee 10€

borne

Choose pitches away from the road; the sanitary facilities are rather old.

Surroundings :
Leisure activities :
Facilities : launderette
Nearby :

Longitude : 3.03544
Latitude : 42.54774

⚠ La Massane

📞 04 68 81 06 85, www.camping-massane.com

Address : avenue Molière (opposite the "Espace Jean Carrère")

Opening times : from beginning April to end Sept.

2,7 ha (184 pitches) flat, grassy

Tariff : 27,50€ ✦✦ 🚐 🔲 🔌 (6A) – Extra per person 6,60€
Reservation fee 12€

Rental rates : (from beginning April to mid Sept.) ✂ – 23 🏚. Per week from 250 to 660€ – Reservation fee 12€

Rather old but well maintained sanitary facilities.

Surroundings : 🏕 ⚑⚑
Leisure activities : 🏊 ⛹ 🎯 🏊
Facilities : ♿ ⚿ 🛁 🍴 launderette
Nearby : ⚔

G P S Longitude : 3.03115
Latitude : 42.55137

⚠ Comangès

📞 04 68 81 15 62, www.campingcomanges.com

Address : avenue Général de Gaulle (300m from the beach)

1,2 ha (90 pitches) flat, grassy

Rentals : 19 🏚.

Surroundings : ⚑⚑
Leisure activities : ⛹
Facilities : ♿ ⚿ 🍴 📺
Nearby : 🚲 ⚔ 🎯 ⚓

G P S Longitude : 3.04423
Latitude : 42.55145

Nord

⛰ La Sirène et l'Hippocampe ♟

(rental of mobile homes and chalets only)

📞 04 68 81 04 61, www.camping-lasirene.fr

Address : route de Taxo

Opening times : from mid April to end Sept.

21 ha (903 pitches)

Rental rates : ♿ (1 mobile home) – 500 🏚 – 20 🏠. Per night from 41 to 270€ – Per week from 287 to 1890€ – Reservation fee 20€

Divided into 2 separate sections with 2 water parks; the 'Hippocampe' side is more peaceful and family-orientated.

Surroundings : 🏕 ⚑⚑
Leisure activities : 🍴 ✗ 🎬 🎯 ⛹ 🚲 🎯 🎣 ⛱ 🏊 ⛵ disco, pub, scuba diving, multi-sports ground
Facilities : ♿ ⚿ 🛁 🍴 launderette 🛒

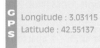

G P S Longitude : 3.0326
Latitude : 42.57058

⛰ Le Soleil ♟

📞 04 68 81 14 48, www.campmed.com

Address : route du Littoral

Opening times : from beginning May to end Sept.

17 ha (844 pitches)

Tariff : 46,30€ ✦✦ 🚐 🔲 🔌 (6A) – Extra per person 11,90€
Reservation fee 25€

Rental rates : (from beginning May to end Sept.) – 130 🏚. Per night from 33 to 190€ – Per week from 231 to 1330€ – Reservation fee 25€

A lush, green setting with lots of shade, close to the beach.

Surroundings : 🏕 ⚑⚑ ⚠
Leisure activities : 🍴 ✗ 🎬 🎯 ⛹ 🎣 disco
Facilities : ♿ ⚿ 🍴 launderette 🛒

G P S Longitude : 3.04618
Latitude : 42.5744

⛰ Les Marsouins ♟

📞 04 68 81 14 81, http://campmed.com/argeles/camping-les-marsouins

Address : avenue de la Retirada

Opening times : from mid April to end Sept.

10 ha (587 pitches) flat, grassy

Tariff : 44€ ✦✦ 🚐 🔲 🔌 (6A) – Extra per person 8€ – Reservation fee 20€

Rental rates : (from mid April to end Sept.) ♿ (1 mobile home) 180 🏚. Per night from 28 to 190€ – Per week from 196 to 1330€ Reservation fee 20€

🚐 borne 4€ – 10 🔲 16€

Attractive pitches for tents and caravans in green and floral surroundings.

Surroundings : 🏕 ⚑⚑
Leisure activities : 🍴 ✗ 🎬 🎯 ⛹ 🏊 scuba diving, multi-sports ground
Facilities : ♿ ⚿ 🛁 ⛱ ✂ 🍴 launderette 🛒
Nearby : ⚔

G P S Longitude : 3.03471
Latitude : 42.56376

⛰ La Marende ♟

📞 04 68 81 12 09, www.marende.com

Address : avenue du Littoral (400m from the beach)

3 ha (208 pitches)

Rentals : 67 🏚.

Good shade from pine and eucalyptus trees, but choose pitches away from the road.

Surroundings : 🏕 ⚑⚑
Leisure activities : 🍴 ✗ 🎬 nighttime 🎯 jacuzzi ⛹ 🚲 🏊 multi-sports ground
Facilities : ♿ ⚿ ▥ 🛁 🍴 launderette 🛒 🛒
Nearby : ⚔ 🎯 ⚔

G P S Longitude : 3.0422
Latitude : 42.57395

⛰ Club Airotel Les Galets ♟

📞 04 68 81 08 12, http://www.campinglesgalets.fr/ – limited spaces for one-night stay

Address : route de Taxo at la mer

Opening times : from mid April to end Sept.

5 ha (232 pitches) flat, grassy

Tariff : 44€ ✦✦ 🚐 🔲 🔌 (10A) – Extra per person 9,40€ – Reservation fee 45€

Rental rates : (from mid April to end Sept.) ♿ (2 mobile homes) 170 🏚. Per night from 29 to 179€ – Per week from 203 to 1253€ Reservation fee 45€

🚐 borne 4€ – 2 🔲 10€ – 🚿 🔌 17€

A family site with plenty of owner-occupier mobile homes, but few places for tents and caravans.

Surroundings : 🏕 ⚑⚑
Leisure activities : 🍴 ✗ 🎬 nighttime 🎯 ⛹ 🏊 multi-sports ground
Facilities : ♿ ⚿ 🛁 🍴 launderette 🛒
Nearby : ⚔

G P S Longitude : 3.0144
Latitude : 42.57249

The Michelin classification (⛰⛰⛰ ... ⚠) is totally independent of the official star classification system awarded by the local prefecture or other official organisation.

⛰ Le Roussillonnais ♣♣

📞 04 68 81 10 42, www.leroussillonnais.com

Address : boulevard de la mer

10 ha (690 pitches)

Rentals : 🏠 – 105 🚐.

🚐 borne

Close to a beach, attractive and shady with plenty of pitches for tents, caravans; groups welcome.

Surroundings : 🏖🏛
Leisure activities : 🍴✕🎬🎣🏊⛵ 🎾
multi-sports ground
Facilities : ♿ ⚡ 🏪 🚿 launderette 🛒🚸
Nearby : 🚣🏇

GPS
Longitude : 3.04367
Latitude : 42.56842

Sud

⛰ Les Castels Les Criques de Porteils ♣♣

📞 04 68 81 12 73, www.lescriques.com

Address : corniche de Collioure, road RD 114

Opening times : from end March to end Oct.

4,5 ha (250 pitches) very uneven, terraced, relatively flat, flat, grassy, stony

Tariff : 52,50€ ♣♣ 🚗 📺 ⚡ (10A) – Extra per person 12,50€
Reservation fee 26€

Rental rates : (from end March to end Oct.) – 35 🚐 – 10 canvas bungalows. Per week from 230 to 1 490€ – Reservation fee 26€

🚐 borne 6€ – 5 📺 38€

Direct access to the beach via steep steps. A panoramic view of Argelès-sur-Mer bay and the Roussillon wine estates.

Surroundings : 🏖 ⬦Baie d'Argelès-sur-Mer
🏖🏛
Leisure activities : 🍴✕🏊🎣⛵ 🎾🏊🏖
scuba diving, multi-sports ground
Facilities : ♿ ⚡ 🏪 🚿 launderette 🛒🚸
refrigerated food storage facilities

GPS
Longitude : 3.06778
Latitude : 42.53389

⛰ La Coste Rouge

📞 04 68 81 08 94, www.lacosterouge.com – limited spaces for one-night stay

Address : route de Collioure (3km southeast)

Opening times : from beginning April to end Sept.

3,7 ha (145 pitches) terrace, flat and relatively flat, grassy

Tariff : 34,60€ ♣♣ 🚗 📺 ⚡ (6A) – Extra per person 5,90€
Reservation fee 20€

Rental rates : (from beginning April to end Sept.) 🏠 – 52 🚐
2 🏠 – 6 studios. Per night 125€ – Per week 850€ – Reservation fee 20€

Away from the hustle and bustle of Argelès-sur-Mer, but access to the beaches via a free shuttle service.

Surroundings : 🏖🏛
Leisure activities : 🍴✕🏊🛶🎣🏊🏖
Facilities : ♿ ⚡ 🚿 launderette 🛒🚸
Nearby : 🚴🚣🏇 water skiing

GPS
Longitude : 3.05285
Latitude : 42.53301

The prices listed were supplied by the campsite owners in 2013 (if prices were not available, those from the previous year are given). The fees should be regarded as basic charges and may fluctuate with inflation.

66150 – Michelin map **344** G8 – pop. 2 757 – alt. 280
▶ Paris 886 – Amélie-les-Bains-Palalda 4 – Perpignan 45 – Prats-de-Mollo-la-Preste 19

⛰ Le Vallespir

📞 04 68 39 90 00, http://www.campingvallespir.com/fr/index.html

Address : situated 2km to the northeast, follow the signs for Amélie-les-Bains-Palalda; beside the Tech river

Opening times : from end March to mid Nov.

2,5 ha (141 pitches)

Tariff : (2013 Price) 24,60€ ♣♣ 🚗 📺 ⚡ (10A)
Extra per person 6,20€

Rental rates : (2013 Price) (from end March to mid Nov.) 51 🚐 – 1 apartment. Per night from 32 to 93€ – Per week from 196 to 667€

An attractive and sheltered site that always has plenty of pitches for tents and caravans.

Surroundings : 🏞🏖🏛
Leisure activities : 🍴✕🏊🎣🎾🏊🏖
Facilities : ♿ ⚡ 🚿 launderette

GPS
Longitude : 2.65306
Latitude : 42.46671

30200 – Michelin map **339** M4 – pop. 18 105 – alt. 51
▶ Paris 653 – Alès 54 – Avignon 34 – Nîmes 56

⛰ Les Genêts d'Or

📞 04 66 89 58 67, www.camping-genets-dor.com 🏠

Address : chemin de Carmignan (take the northern exit along the N 86 then continue 2km along the D 360 to the right; beside the Cèze river)

8 ha/3,5 for camping (95 pitches) flat, grassy

Rentals : 🏠 – 8 🚐.

🚐 borne

There are well-shaded pitches beside the river.

Surroundings : 🏖🏛
Leisure activities : 🍴✕🎣🏊🏖
Facilities : ♿ ⚡ 🏪 🚿 launderette 🛒🚸
refrigerators

GPS
Longitude : 4.63694
Latitude : 44.17358

34540 – Michelin map **339** H8 – pop. 6 622 – alt. 3 – ♨
▶ Paris 781 – Agde 32 – Béziers 52 – Frontignan 8

⛰ Sites et Paysages Le Mas du Padre ♣♣

DURAND

📞 04 67 48 53 41, www.mas-du-padre.com

Address : 4 chemin du Mas du Padre (situated 2km northeast along the D 2e and take road to the right)

Opening times : from end March to end Oct.

1,8 ha (116 pitches) relatively flat, flat, grassy, fine gravel

Tariff : 33,20€ ♣♣ 🚗 📺 ⚡ (10A)
Extra per person 5,50€ – Reservation fee 13€

Rental rates : (from end March to end Oct.) ♿ (1 chalet) – 14 🚐
1 🏠. Per night 160€ – Per week 959€ – Reservation fee 21€

Pretty shrubs and flowers decorate the site.

Surroundings : 🏖🏞🏛
Leisure activities : 🎬🏊🎣🏊
Facilities : ♿ ⚡ 🚿 🖼 refrigerators

GPS
Longitude : 3.6924
Latitude : 43.4522

ᴍ Les Vignes

℘ 04 67 48 04 93, www.camping-lesvignes.com – limited spaces for one-night stay

Address : 1 chemin des Vignes (1.7km northeast along the D 129, D 2e follow the signs for Sète and take road to the left)

Opening times : from beginning April to beginning Nov.

2 ha (169 pitches)

Tariff : 25,50€ ♦♦ ⇌ 🔲 🗲 (10A) – Extra per person 6€

Rental rates : (from end March to beginning Nov.) ♿ (1 mobile home) – 22 🚐 – 8 🏠. Per night from 30 to 85€ – Per week from 210 to 595€

🚰 borne 4€ – 2 🔲 17,50€

Clearly marked-out pitches on a gravel base, usually for clients visiting the nearby spa town (3 weeks).

Surroundings : ⌂ ♌♌		
Leisure activities : ✗ 🎣 🏄 🛶	**G**	Longitude : 3.68806
Facilities : ♿ ⚬🔫 🚿 🏕 🍴 🎯	**P** **S**	Latitude : 43.45351

The guide covers all 22 regions of France – see the map and list of regions on pages 4–5.

LE BARCARÈS

66420 – Michelin map **344** J6 – pop. 4 018 – alt. 3
▶ Paris 839 – Narbonne 56 – Perpignan 23 – Quillan 84

ᴍ L'Oasis ♦♦

℘ 04 68 86 12 43, www.camping-oasis.com

Address : route de St-Laurent-de-la-Salanque (1.3km southwest along the D 90)

Opening times : from mid June to end Sept.

10 ha (492 pitches)

Tariff : 39,50€ ♦♦ ⇌ 🔲 🗲 (10A) – Extra per person 8€ – Reservation fee 28€

Rental rates : (from end June to mid Sept.) – 207 🚐. Per night from 34 to 152€ – Reservation fee 28€

A good choice of mobile homes, but pitches for tents and caravans are always available.

Surroundings : ⌂ ♌		
Leisure activities : 🍴 ✗ 🎯 🏄 🏄 🛶 ⛳ 🛶 🏊	**G**	Longitude : 3.02462
Facilities : ♿ ⚬🔫 🔲 🚿 🍴 launderette 🚻 🚿	**P** **S**	Latitude : 42.77619

ᴍ Sunêlia Le California ♦♦

℘ 04 68 86 16 08, www.camping-california.fr

Address : route de St-Laurent (located 1.5km southwest along the D 90 – on D 83, take exit 9: Canet-en-Roussillon)

Opening times : from beginning May to end Sept.

5 ha (265 pitches)

Tariff : 44,50€ ♦♦ ⇌ 🔲 🗲 (10A) – Extra per person 8€ – Reservation fee 35€

Rental rates : (from beginning May to end Sept.) ♿ (2 mobile homes) – 140 🚐 – 20 🏠 – 7 tent lodges. Per night from 40 to 189€ – Per week from 280 to 1323€ – Reservation fee 35€

🚰 borne 10€

A large sports area.

Surroundings : ⌂ ♌♌		
Leisure activities : 🍴 ✗ 🎣 🎯 🏄 🏄 🛶 ⛳ 🛶 🏊	**G**	Longitude : 3.02346
Facilities : ♿ ⚬🔫 🚿 🍴 launderette 🚻 🚿	**P** **S**	Latitude : 42.77606

ᴍ Yelloh! Village Le Pré Catalan ♦♦

℘ 04 68 86 12 60, www.precatalan.com

Address : route de St-Laurent-de-la-Salanque (located 1.5km southwest along the D 90 then continue 600m along the road to the right)

Opening times : from end April to mid Sept.

4 ha (250 pitches)

Tariff : 44€ ♦♦ ⇌ 🔲 🗲 (10A) – Extra per person 8€ – Reservation fee 28€

Rental rates : (from end April to mid Sept.) – 90 🚐. Per night from 35 to 210€ – Per week from 245 to 1470€ – Reservation fee 28€

A pleasant site with activities and services suitable for families with young children.

Surroundings : 🌳 ⌂ ♌♌		
Leisure activities : 🍴 ✗ 🎣 🎯 🏄 🏄 🛶 🏊 multi-sports ground	**G**	Longitude : 3.02272
Facilities : ♿ ⚬🔫 🚿 🍴 launderette 🚿	**P** **S**	Latitude : 42.78086

ᴍ L'Europe

℘ 04 68 86 15 36, www.europe-camping.com – limited spaces for one-night stay

Address : route de St-Laurent-de-la-Salanque (situated 2km southwest along the D 90, 200m from the Agly river)

6 ha (360 pitches) flat, grassy

Rentals : 50 🚐 – 25 bungalows.

Choose the pitches away from the road. Good-quality rental options in mobile homes as well as some rather old bungalows.

Surroundings : ⌂ ♌		
Leisure activities : 🍴 ✗ 🎣 🎯 🏄 🏄 🛶 ⛳ 🛶 🏊	**G**	Longitude : 3.02064
Facilities : ♿ ⚬🔫 – 339 individual sanitary facilities (🚿 🚽 wc) 🚿 🍴 🎯 🚻 🚿	**P** **S**	Latitude : 42.775

ᴍ La Croix du Sud ♦♦

℘ 04 68 86 16 61, www.lacroixdusud.fr – limited spaces for one-night stay

Address : route de Saint-Laurent-de-la-Salanque (1.4km southwest along the D 90; from D 83, take exit 10)

Opening times : from mid April to end Sept.

3,5 ha (200 pitches) flat, grassy

Tariff : (2013 Price) 43€ ♦♦ ⇌ 🔲 🗲 (10A) – Extra per person 9€ Reservation fee 34€

Rental rates : (2013 Price) (from mid April to end Sept.) ♿ (2 mobile homes) – 122 🚐 – 22 🏠. Per night from 36 to 178€ Per week from 252 to 1252€ – Reservation fee 34€

Numerous rental options, but pitches for tents and caravans are always available.

Surroundings : ⌂ ♌♌		
Leisure activities : 🍴 ✗ 🎯 🏄 🏄 🛶 🏊 multi-sports ground	**G**	Longitude : 3.02757
Facilities : ♿ ⚬🔫 🚿 🍴 launderette 🚿 refrigerators	**P** **S**	Latitude : 42.77669

This guide is not intended as a list of all the camping sites in France; its aim is to provide a selection of the best sites in each category.

🏔 Flower Le Soleil Bleu 👥

(rental of mobile homes and chalets only)

📞 04 68 86 15 50, www.lesoleilbleu.com

Address : at Mas de la Tourre (1.4km southwest along the D 90 follow the signs for St-Laurent-de-la-Salanque; 100m from the Agly river)

Opening times : from beginning April to beginning Oct.

3 ha (175 pitches) flat, grassy

Rental rates : 🚐 (1 mobile home) – 18 🚐 – 158 🏠. Per night from 45 to 193€ – Per week from 225 to 1 351€ – Reservation fee 30€

Choose the sites away from the road in preference.

Surroundings : 🏕 🌳🌳
Leisure activities : 🍽🍴 🛶 🎣🚶‍♂️🏊🏸🚴🎣 🛶
multi-sports ground
Facilities : 🚿 🛁🚽 launderette 🛒🧺
G P S Longitude : 3.02842
Latitude : 42.77663

🏔 FranceLoc Las Bousigues 👥

📞 04 68 86 16 19, www.campings-franceloc.fr – limited spaces for one-night stay

Address : avenue des Corbières (900m west)

3 ha (306 pitches)

Rentals : 🚐 (2 mobile homes) – 143 🚐 – 4 tipis – 95 bungalows.
A very large children's playground and a range of rental options, but the bungalows are very old.

Surroundings : 🏕 🌳🌳
Leisure activities : 🍽🍴 🛶 🚶‍♂️🎣🏞🏊🛶
multi-sports ground
Facilities : 🚿 🛁 – 31 individual sanitary facilities (🚿♨wc) launderette 🧺
G P S Longitude : 3.0254
Latitude : 42.7869

🏔 Cybele Vacances La Presqu'Île 👥

📞 04 68 86 12 80, www.lapresquile.com – limited spaces for one-night stay

Address : rue de la Presquile (to the north, on the D 83 exit 12)

Opening times : from mid April to end Sept.

3,5 ha (163 pitches)

Tariff : 41€ 🚻🚻 🚗 📧 ⚡ (10A) – Extra per person 6,50€ – Reservation fee 30€

Rental rates : (from mid April to end Sept.) – 83 🚐 – 29 🏠 – 8 studios. Per night from 27 to 139€ – Per week from 190 to 1 020€ Reservation fee 30€

This site is surrounded by the sea on a peninsula. Some pitches are rather noisy; there is a swimming pool with a snack bar across the road.

Surroundings : 🏕 🌳🌳
Leisure activities : 🍽🍴 🛶 🚶‍♂️jacuzzi 🎣
🚴🎾🏊🏞🪂 multi-sports ground
Facilities : 🚿 🛁 launderette 🛒🧺
Nearby : ⚓
G P S Longitude : 3.02672
Latitude : 42.80528

Key to rentals symbols:

12 🚐 *Number of mobile homes*
20 🏠 *Number of chalets*
6 🛏 *Number of rooms to rent*
Per night *Minimum/maximum rate per night*
30–50€
Per week *Minimum/maximum rate per week*
300–1,000€

30430 – Michelin map **339** L3 – pop. 1 546 – alt. 171
▶ Paris 666 – Alès 34 – Aubenas 45 – Pont-St-Esprit 33

🏔 La Combe

📞 04 66 24 51 21, www.campinglacombe.com

Address : at Mas de Reboul (3km west along the D 901, follow the signs for Les Vans and turn right onto the D 384)

Opening times : from beginning April to end Sept.

2,5 ha (100 pitches)

Tariff : (2013 Price) 25,30€ 🚻🚻 🚗 📧 ⚡ (6A) – Extra per person 8,60€ Reservation fee 15€

Rental rates : (2013 Price) (from beginning April to end Sept.) 10 🚐 – 4 🏠 – 4 canvas bungalows. Per night from 30 to 60€ Per week from 260 to 595€ – Reservation fee 15€

🚰 borne 4€

A peaceful, family-orientated site with plenty of shade.

Surroundings : 🏞 🌳🌳
Leisure activities : 🍽 🛶 🚶‍♂️🏊
Facilities : 🚿 🛁 📧
G P S Longitude : 4.34784
Latitude : 44.30917

48400 – Michelin map **330** J8 – pop. 291 – alt. 565
▶ Paris 624 – Alès 69 – Florac 5 – Mende 39

🏔 Chon du Tarn

📞 04 66 45 09 14, http://www.camping-chondutarn.com

Address : chemin du Chon du Tarn (take the northeastern exit, follow the signs for Cocurès)

Opening times : from beginning May to beginning Oct.

2 ha (100 pitches)

Tariff : 16,60€ 🚻🚻 🚗 📧 ⚡ (6A) – Extra per person 4,50€

🚰 borne

In a pleasant setting with lots of green space beside the Tarn river.

Surroundings : 🏞 🌳
Leisure activities : 🚶‍♂️🏊 🚣
Facilities : 🚿🛁 🚿🚿 launderette
Nearby : 🍽🍴 climbing
G P S Longitude : 3.60531
Latitude : 44.3446

11340 – Michelin map **344** C6 – pop. 440 – alt. 1 002
▶ Paris 810 – Ax-les-Thermes 26 – Axat 32 – Foix 54

⛺ Municipal la Mousquière

📞 04 68 20 39 47, www.camping-pyrenees-cathare.fr

Address : 4 chemin du Lac (take the western exit onto the D 613, follow the signs for Ax-les-Thermes, 150m from a small lake)

Opening times : Permanent

0,6 ha (37 pitches)

Tariff : 14€ 🚻🚻 🚗 📧 ⚡ (16A) – Extra per person 3€

Rental rates : Permanent – 1 🚐 – 2 🏠 – 2 canvas bungalows Per night from 40 to 80€ – Per week from 180 to 420€

An attractively shaded site with a pretty lake nearby.

Surroundings : 🌳🌳🌳
Leisure activities : 🛶
Facilities : 🚿 🚿🚿 📧
Nearby : 🚶‍♂️🎾🏊🎣 pedalos
G P S 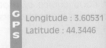 Longitude : 1.95022
Latitude : 42.81637

BESSÈGES

30160 – Michelin map **339** J3 – pop. 3 169 – alt. 170
▶ Paris 651 – Alès 32 – La Grand-Combe 20 – Les Vans 18

⛰ Les Drouilhèdes

✆ 04 66 25 04 80, www.campingcevennes.com

Address : situated 2km west along the D 17, follow the signs for Génolhac then continue 1km along the D 386 to the right; beside the Cèze river

Opening times : from beginning May to end Sept.

2 ha (90 pitches)

Tariff : 31,70€ ✶✶ ⬅ 🅴 (6A) – Extra per person 5,70€
Reservation fee 15,50€

Rental rates : (from beginning May to end Sept.) – 6 🏠. Per week from 365 to 675€ – Reservation fee 15,50€

Surroundings : ⌂ ⟨ ⌂ 🛁🛁
Leisure activities : 🍸 ⬅ ⛳ 🛶
Facilities : ⛸ ⊶ 🛁🛁 🚿 🚾 🍴 🅰 🛁

| G P S | Longitude : 4.0678 |
| | Latitude : 44.29143 |

In order for the guide to remain wholly objective, the selection of campsites is made on an entirely independent basis.

BLAVIGNAC

48200 – Michelin map **330** H5 – pop. 236 – alt. 800
▶ Paris 542 – Montpellier 218 – Mende 58 – Clermont-Ferrand 126

⛰ Les Chalets de la Margeride (rental of chalets only)

✆ 04 66 42 56 00, www.chalets-margeride.com

Address : at Chassagnes (4.5km northwest along the D 989, follow the signs for St-Chély-d'Apcher and take the D 4, following signs for La Garde – from A 75: take exit 32)

Opening times : Permanent

50 ha/2 for camping terraced

Rental rates : ⛸ – 21 🏠 – 21 gîtes. Per night from 122 to 135€ Per week from 285 to 695€ – Reservation fee 9€

In an attractive panoramic location among the Margeride mountains.

Surroundings : ⌂ ⟨ Plateau de la Margeride
Leisure activities : 🛋 ⬅ 🚲 🛝 (open-air in season)
Facilities : 🚿 🛁🛁 🍴 launderette

| G P S | Longitude : 3.30631 |
| | Latitude : 44.87017 |

BOISSET-ET-GAUJAC

30140 – Michelin map **339** J4 – pop. 2 302 – alt. 140
▶ Paris 722 – Montpellier 103 – Nîmes 53 – Alès 14

⛰ Domaine de Gaujac ♣♦

✆ 04 66 61 67 57, www.domaine-de-gaujac.com

Address : 2406 chemin de la Madelaine

Opening times : from beginning April to mid Sept.

10 ha/6,5 for camping (293 pitches) terraced, relatively flat, grassy

Tariff : 30,70€ ✶✶ ⬅ 🅴 (6A) – Extra per person 7,20€
Reservation fee 20€

Rental rates : Permanent – 50 🛖 – 12 🏠. Per night from 53 to 123€ – Per week from 265 to 860€ – Reservation fee 20€

🚐 borne 5€ – 8 🅴 10€

The lower pitches enjoy lots of shade, those on the terraces get plenty of sun.

Surroundings : 🛁🛁
Leisure activities : 🍸 🍴 🛋 ⛳ ⟲ jacuzzi ⬅ 🛶 🎣 🛝 launderette
Facilities : ⛸ ⊶ 🆑🛁🛁 🚿 🍴 launderette 🏊 🍴
Nearby : ⟿ ⟲

| G P S | Longitude : 4.02771 |
| | Latitude : 44.03471 |

BOISSON

30500 – Michelin map **339** K3
▶ Paris 682 – Alès 19 – Barjac 17 – La Grand-Combe 28

⛰ Les Castels Le Château de Boisson ♣♦

✆ 04 66 24 85 61, www.chateaudeboisson.com ✀ (July–Aug.)

Address : Hameau de Boisson (Boisson hamlet)

Opening times : from mid April to end Sept.

7,5 ha (165 pitches) very uneven, terraced, flat, grassy

Tariff : 43,90€ ✶✶ ⬅ 🅴 (6A) – Extra per person 9,90€
Reservation fee 26€

Rental rates : (from mid April to end Sept.) ✀ (July–Aug.) 57 🛖 – 11 🏠 – 15 gîtes. Per night from 45 to 263€ – Per week from 210 to 1 631€ – Reservation fee 26€

🚐 borne 10€ – 🔌 🅴15€

Attractive pitches set near a restored Cévennes château, with a view over the Cévennes from some chalets.

Surroundings : ⌂ ⌂ 🛁🛁
Leisure activities : 🍸 🍴 🛋 ⟲ ⟲ ⬅ ⛳ 🛝 🏊 🛝
Facilities : ⛸ ⊶ 🛁🛁 🚿 – 7 individual sanitary facilities (🛁 🚿 🚽 wc) 🍴 launderette 🏊 🍴 refrigerators

| G P S | Longitude : 4.25673 |
| | Latitude : 44.20966 |

Michelin classification:

⛰	Extremely comfortable, equipped to a very high standard
⛰	Very comfortable, equipped to a high standard
⛰	Comfortable and well equipped
⛰	Reasonably comfortable
⛰	Satisfactory

LE BOSC

34490 – Michelin map **339** F6 – pop. 1 046 – alt. 90
▶ Paris 706 – Montpellier 51 – Béziers 58 – Sète 68

⛰ Relais du Salagou (mobile home and chalet rental only)

✆ 04 67 44 76 44, www.relais-du-salagou.com

Address : at Salelles, 8 rue des Terrasses (4.5km southeast along the D 140 – A 75, take exit 56)

Opening times : from mid March to mid Nov.

12 ha/3 for camping flat

Rental rates : ⛸ 🅿 – 28 🏠. Per night from 83 to 99 € – Per week from 379 to 672 € – Reservation fee 9€

Surroundings : 🛁🛁
Leisure activities : 🍸 🛋 ⟿ hammam, jacuzzi ⬅ ⛳ 🛝 🛝 fitness trail, spa centre
Facilities : ⊶ 🆑🛁🛁 🍴 launderette

| G P S | Longitude : 3.41539 |
| | Latitude : 43.68268 |

BRISSAC

34190 – Michelin map **339** H5 – pop. 615 – alt. 145
▶ Paris 732 – Ganges 7 – Montpellier 41 – St-Hippolyte-du-Fort 19

🏕 Le Val d'Hérault

🖉 04 67 73 72 29, www.camping-levaldherault.com

Address : avenue d'Issensac (4km south along the D 4, follow the signs for Causse-de-la-Selle, 250m from the Hérault river (direct access)

Opening times : from mid March to end Oct.

4 ha (135 pitches) terraced, flat and relatively flat, grassy, stony

Tariff : 28,50€ ♣♣ ⬅ 🔲 ⚡ (6A) – Extra per person 6,30€
Reservation fee 10€

Rental rates : (from mid March to mid Oct.) – 20 🚐 – 4 🏠
10 canvas bungalows. Per night from 32 to 120€ – Per week from 230 to 970€ – Reservation fee 10€

🚐 borne
Well-shaded pitches, some on small individual terraces.

Surroundings : 🐟 ⌂ ⛰⛰
Leisure activities : 🍴 ✕ 🎳 🌙 nighttime
🏇 🎿 👁
Facilities : 🔥 ⚬━ 🛁 🔧 🚽 🏺 🎱 🍴
Nearby : ⌂ (beach) climbing

Longitude : 3.70433
Latitude : 43.84677

🏕 Le Domaine d'Anglas ♣♣

🖉 04 67 73 70 18, www.camping-anglas.com

Address : 2km east along the D 108

Opening times : from beginning April to end Sept.

115 ha/5 for camping (101 pitches) terraced, flat, grassy, stony

Tariff : (2013 Price) 21€ ♣♣ ⬅ 🔲 ⚡ (10A) – Extra per person 6,50€
Reservation fee 17€

Rental rates : (2013 Price) Permanent – 18 🏠 – 1 gîte. Per night from 77 to 137€ – Per week from 434 to 825€ – Reservation fee 17€

Beside the Hérault river and in the heart of the winegrowing region; varied rental options and average sanitary facilities.

Surroundings : ⌂ ⛰⛰
Leisure activities : 🏃 🏇 🚲 ⌂ 🎣
zip wire 🦅
Facilities : 🔥 ⚬━ 🛁 🔧 🚽 🏺 launderette
🎱 🍴

Longitude : 3.71615
Latitude : 43.87602

Some campsites benefit from proximity to a municipal leisure centre.

BROUSSES-ET-VILLARET

11390 – Michelin map **344** E2 – pop. 313 – alt. 412
▶ Paris 768 – Carcassonne 21 – Castelnaudary 36 – Foix 88

🏕 Le Martinet-Rouge Birdie

🖉 04 68 26 51 98, www.camping-lemartinetrouge.com

Address : 500m south along the D 203 and take the road to the right, 200m from the Dure

Opening times : from mid May to end Aug.

2,5 ha (63 pitches) undulating, flat, grassy, stony, rocks

Tariff : 31€ ♣♣ ⬅ 🔲 ⚡ (10A) – Extra per person 7,50€ – Reservation fee 6€

Rental rates : Permanent – 7 🚐 – 3 🏠 . Per night from 36 to 96€
Per week from 210 to 730€ – Reservation fee 6€

🚐 5 🔲 16€

A very pleasant site with pitches between the rocks and plenty of shade from small Holm oaks.

Surroundings : 🐟 ⌂ ⛰⛰
Leisure activities : 🍴 ✕ 🎳 🏇 🎿 👁
multi-sports ground
Facilities : 🔥 ⚬━ 🛁 🍴 launderette

Longitude : 2.0381
Latitude : 43.33088

CANET

34800 – Michelin map **339** F7 – pop. 3 269 – alt. 42
▶ Paris 717 – Béziers 47 – Clermont-l'Hérault 6 – Gignac 10

🏕 Les Rivières

🖉 04 67 96 75 53, www.camping-lesrivieres.com

Address : at La Sablière (1.8km north along the D 131e)

Opening times : from mid April to mid Sept.

9 ha/5 for camping (110 pitches)

Tariff : 32€ ♣♣ ⬅ 🔲 ⚡ (10A) – Extra per person 6€ – Reservation fee 12€

Rental rates : (from mid March to end Oct.) 🦅 – 25 🚐 – 8 🏠
3 canvas bungalows – 2 gîtes. Per night 69€ – Per week 730€ – Reservation fee 12€

🚐 borne 10€ – 7 🔲 10€ – 🛒 ⚡8€
Plenty of space beside the Hérault river, where swimming is always an option.

Surroundings : 🐟 ⌂ ⛰⛰
Leisure activities : 🍴 ✕ 🎳 jacuzzi 🏇 🚲 🎿
⌂ 🎿 climbing wall, multi-sports ground
Facilities : 🔥 ⚬━ 🛁 🍴 🎱 🍴
Nearby : 🐎

Longitude : 3.49229
Latitude : 43.61792

CANET-PLAGE

66140 – Michelin map **344** J6
▶ Paris 849 – Argelès-sur-Mer 20 – Le Boulou 35 – Canet-en-Roussillon 3

🏕 Yelloh! Village Le Brasilia ♣♣

🖉 04 68 80 23 82, www.brasilia.fr

Address : avenue des Anneaux du Roussillon (beside the Têt river; direct access to the beach)

Opening times : from mid April to beginning Oct.

15 ha (735 pitches)

Tariff : 58,50€ ♣♣ ⬅ 🔲 ⚡ (10A)
Extra per person 9€

Rental rates : (from mid April to beginning Oct.) 🔥 (2 mobile homes) – 132 🚐 – 47 🏠 – 3 gîtes
Per night from 39 to 245€ – Per week from 273 to 1715€

🚐 borne
Lush green pitches and plenty of shade, small landscaped mobile homes villages and a variety of activities make this a real village club.

MARLUC

Surroundings : 🐟 ⌂ ⛰⛰ ⌂
Leisure activities : 🍴 ✕ 🎳 🌙 🏃 🎣 jacuzzi
🏇 🚲 🎿 ⌂ disco, multi-sports ground
Facilities : 🔥 ⚬━ 🚽 🛁 🔧 🚽 🍴 launderette
🎱 🚲
Nearby : 🏇 🐎

Longitude : 3.03392
Latitude : 42.69429

⛰ Mar Estang 👥

📞 04 68 80 35 53, www.marestang.com

Address : route de Saint-Cyprien (1.5km south along the D 18a, near the lake and the beach)

Opening times : from end April to mid Sept.

11 ha (600 pitches) flat, grassy

Tariff : 50,20€ 👫 🚗 📧 ⚡ (6A) – Extra per person 15€ – Reservation fee 26€

Rental rates : Permanent ♿ (1 mobile homes) 🅿 – 226 🏠 32 🏕 – 32 canvas bungalows. Per night 138€ – Per week from 166 to 1 255€ – Reservation fee 26€

🚐 borne 4€ – 10 📧 36€

Direct access to the beach along an underground passage; the pitches have some shade; activities aimed at young people and teenagers.

Surroundings : 🏞 ♡♡
Leisure activities : 🍴 ✕ 🚣 🎭 (amphitheatre) 🤸 🎣 🏊 🚴 ⛷ 🏊 ⛷ disco, multi-sports ground
Facilities : ♿ ⚬⊸ ⛺ 🚿 launderette 🛒🚰

G P S	Longitude : 3.03256 Latitude : 42.67262

⛰ Les Peupliers

📞 04 68 80 35 87, www.camping-les-peupliers.fr

Address : avenue des Anneaux-du-Rousssillon (500m from the sea)

4 ha (237 pitches)

Rentals : 91 🏠 – 9 🏕.

Plenty of shade on attractively laid out pitches.

Surroundings : 🏞 ♡♡
Leisure activities : 🍴 ✕ 🚣 🎣 🏊 ⛷
Facilities : ♿ ⚬⊸ ⛺ 🚿 launderette 🚰
Nearby : ✕ 🎣 🏇 💧 🐎

G P S	Longitude : 3.03111 Latitude : 42.70741

⚠ Les Fontaines

ROQUES

📞 04 68 80 22 57, www.camping-les-fontaines.com

Address : 23 avenue de St-Nazaire

Opening times : from beginning May to mid Sept.

5,3 ha (160 pitches)

Tariff : (2013 Price) 34,50€ 👫 🚗 📧 ⚡ (10A) – Extra per person 6,50€ – Reservation fee 15€

Rental rates : (2013 Price) (from beginning May to mid Sept.) 43 🏠. Per night from 35 to 119€ – Per week from 245 to 833€ Reservation fee 15€

🚐 borne 6€

A natural site with slight or no shade; choose the pitches near the lake and away from the road in preference.

Surroundings : 🏞
Leisure activities : 🍴 🚣 🎣 🏊 wildlife park
Facilities : ♿ ⚬⊸ (July–Aug.) ⛺ 🚿 🚰 🚿 launderette

G P S	Longitude : 2.99892 Latitude : 42.68909

Routes nationales are main roads and their identifying numbers begin with N or RN. Routes départementales are generally quieter roads and begin with D or DN.

48500 – Michelin map **330** G8 – pop. 138 – alt. 700
▶ Paris 593 – La Canourgue 8 – Marvejols 26 – Mende 52

⛰ Municipal la Vallée

📞 04 66 32 91 14, http://www.camping--vallee-du-lot.com

Address : at Miège Rivière (12km north along the N 9, follow the signs for Marvejols, turn left onto the D 988, follow the signs for St-Geniez-d'Olt and take the road to the left - from the A 75, take exit 40 towards St-Laurent-d'Olt then continue 5km along the D 988)

Opening times : from mid June to mid Sept.

1 ha (50 pitches) flat, grassy

Tariff : (2013 Price) 🧍 6€ 🚗 📧 – ⚡ (12A) 3€

Rental rates : (2013 Price) (from mid June to mid Sept.) – 3 🏠. Per night from 35 to 50€ – Per week from 250 to 350€

🚐 borne

In a small but lush green valley by the Lot river.

Surroundings : 🚣 ⋦ 🏞 ♡♡
Leisure activities : 🚣 🎣 🏊 ⛵ 🎣
Facilities : ♿ ⚬⊸ ⛺ 🚿 📱
Nearby : ✕

G P S	Longitude : 3.14892 Latitude : 44.4365

These symbols are used for a campsite that is exceptional in its category:

⛰⛰...⛰ *Particularly pleasant setting, quality and range of services available*

🚣🚣 *Tranquil, isolated site – quiet site, particularly at night*

⋦⋦ *Exceptional view – interesting or panoramic view*

48500 – Michelin map **330** H8 – pop. 2 112 – alt. 563
▶ Paris 588 – Marvejols 21 – Mende 40 – Millau 53

⛰ Chalets et camping du golf

📞 04 66 44 23 60, www.lozereleisure.com

Address : route des Gorges du Tarn (3.6km southeast along the D 988, follow the signs for Chanac, after the golf course; beside the Urugne river)

Opening times : from end April to end Sept.

8 ha (72 pitches) grassy

Tariff : (2013 Price) 18,50€ 👫 🚗 📧 ⚡ (6A) – Extra per person 4€

Rental rates : (2013 Price) (from mid April to end Oct.) – 22 🏕 8 gîtes. Per night 57€ – Per week 599€

In a green setting, with chalets ranging from basic to more luxurious; very old sanitary facilities for tent and caravan pitches.

Surroundings : 🚣 🏞 ♡♡
Leisure activities : 🎣 🏊
Facilities : ⚬⊸ 🚿 🚰 launderette
Nearby : 🍴 ✕ golf

G P S	Longitude : 3.24072 Latitude : 44.40842

LE CAP-D'AGDE

34300 – Michelin map **339** G9
▶ Paris 767 – Montpellier 57 – Béziers 29 – Narbonne 59

🏕 La Clape

🖉 04 67 26 41 32, www.camping-laclape.com

Address : 2 rue du Gouverneur (near the beach – direct access)

Opening times : from beginning April to end Sept.

7 ha (450 pitches)

Tariff : 40 € ★★ ⬅ 🔲 🚿 (10A) – Extra per person 7,30 € – Reservation fee 27 €

Rental rates : (from beginning April to end Sept.) ♿ (1 chalet) ✈ 89 🏕 – 31 🏠 – 9 canvas bungalows. Per night from 36 to 127 € Per week from 252 to 889 € – Reservation fee 27 €

🚐 borne 2 € – 22 🔲 10 €

Services and parking for campervans available off the site.

Surroundings : 🏕 🎣🎣
Leisure activities : 🍴 ✕ 🎮 🏄 🏊 multi-sports ground
Facilities : ♿ ⚡ 🏢 🚿 🍴 launderette 🌊 🌡 refrigerators

GPS Longitude : 3.5193
Latitude : 43.28534

CARCASSONNE

11000 – Michelin map **344** F3 – pop. 47 854 – alt. 110
▶ Paris 768 – Albi 110 – Béziers 90 – Narbonne 61

🏕 La Cité 👥

🖉 04 68 10 01 00, www.campingcitecarcassonne.com

Address : route de Saint-Hilaire (take the eastern exit along the N 113, follow the signs for Narbonne then continue 1.8km along the D 104, near a branch of the Aude river)

Opening times : from end March to end Sept.

7 ha (200 pitches) flat, grassy

Tariff : 31,30 € ★★ ⬅ 🔲 🚿 (10A) – Extra per person 7,70 €

Rental rates : (from end March to end Sept.) ♿ (2 mobile homes) 24 🏕 – 11 canvas bungalows. Per night from 60 to 130 € Per week from 490 to 794 €

Very close to the old town of Carcassonne.

Surroundings : 🏕 🎣🎣
Leisure activities : 🍴 ✕ 🎮 🎮 🏄 🏄 🏊 multi-sports ground
Facilities : ♿ ⚡ 🚿 🍴 launderette 🌡

GPS Longitude : 2.33716
Latitude : 43.19874

CARNON-PLAGE

34280 – Michelin map **339** I7
▶ Paris 758 – Aigues-Mortes 20 – Montpellier 20 – Nîmes 56

🏕 Les Saladelles

🖉 04 67 68 23 71, www.paysdelor.fr

Address : rue de l'Aigoual (head for Carnon-est, D 59, 100m from the beach)

Opening times : from mid April to end Sept.

7,6 ha (340 pitches)

Tariff : 21 € ★★ ⬅ 🔲 🚿 (16A) – Extra per person 4 € – Reservation fee 10 €

Rental rates : (from mid April to end Sept.) – 40 🏕. Per week from 185 to 360 € – Reservation fee 10 €

🚐 18 🔲 13 €

Choose the pitches away from the road in preference; parking for campervans nearby but off the site.

Surroundings : 🎣🎣
Leisure activities : 🏃 multi-sports ground
Facilities : ♿ ⚡ 🌊 🚿 🍴 🖼

GPS Longitude : 3.99464
Latitude : 43.55079

CASTEIL

66820 – Michelin map **344** F7 – pop. 120 – alt. 780
▶ Paris 878 – Montpellier 215 – Perpignan 59 – Carcassonne 126

🏕 Domaine St-Martin

🖉 04 68 05 52 09, www.domainesaintmartin.com – help moving caravans onto and off pitches avilable on request

Address : 6 boulevard de la Cascade (take the northern exit along the D 116 and take the road to the right)

Opening times : from end March to end Oct.

4,5 ha (60 pitches) very uneven, terraced, flat, stony, rocks

Tariff : 27,30 € ★★ ⬅ 🔲 🚿 (10A) – Extra per person 5,25 € Reservation fee 16,50 €

Rental rates : (from beginning April to end Oct.) – 7 🏕 – 6 tent lodges. Per night from 46 to 77 € – Per week 645 € – Reservation fee 16,50 €

A natural, wild setting at the foot of the Massif du Canigou, near a waterfall.

Surroundings : 🏞 🏕 🎣🎣🎣
Leisure activities : 🍴 ✕ 🎮 🏊
Facilities : ♿ ⚡ 🏢 🍴 launderette
Nearby : 🍴

GPS Longitude : 2.39464
Latitude : 42.53296

CASTRIES

34160 – Michelin map **339** I6 – pop. 5 671 – alt. 70
▶ Paris 746 – Lunel 15 – Montpellier 19 – Nîmes 44

🏕 Le Fondespierre

🖉 04 67 91 20 03, www.campingfondespierre.com

Address : 277 chemin Pioch Viala (2.5km northeast along the N 110, follow the signs for Sommières and take turning to the left)

3 ha (103 pitches)

Rentals : ✈ – 20 🏕 – 2 🏠 – 7 canvas bungalows.

Surroundings : 🏞 🏕 🎣🎣
Leisure activities : 🏄 🚲 🏊
Facilities : ♿ ⚡ 🚿 🍴 launderette
Nearby : 🍴

GPS Longitude : 3.99903
Latitude : 43.69125

CELLES

34700 – Michelin map **339** F7 – pop. 22 – alt. 140
▶ Paris 707 – Montpellier 55 – Nîmes 111 – Albi 190

🏕 Municipal les Vailhès

🖉 04 67 44 25 98, www.campinglesvailhes.fr

Address : situated 2km northeast along the D 148 E4 follow the signs for Lodève – A75 take exit 54

Opening times : from beginning April to end Sept.

4 ha (246 pitches) terraced, flat, grassy

Tariff : (2013 Price) ★ 4,10 € ⬅ 🔲 7 € – 🚿 (10A) 4 €

In an attractive location beside the Lac du Salagou.

Surroundings : 🦢 ⊰ ⊏⊐ ♤♤ ⚠
Leisure activities : 🏇🏼 🎣 🏊 🚣
Facilities : 🚿 ⚷ 🚰 📷
Nearby : 🎣

G P S   Longitude : 3.36012
Latitude : 43.66865

CENDRAS

30480 – Michelin map **339** J4 – pop. 1 930 – alt. 155
▶ Paris 694 – Montpellier 76 – Nîmes 50 – Avignon 76

⏞ La Croix Clémentine

✆ 04 66 86 52 69, www.clementine.fr

Address : route de Mende, at La Fare (situated 2km northwest along the D 916 and turn left onto the D 32)

Opening times : from beginning April to mid Sept.

10 ha (250 pitches)

Tariff : 31,90€ 🚶🚶 🚐 📋 🔌 (10A) – Extra per person 8,65€
Reservation fee 10€
Rental rates : (from mid March to end Sept.) – 2 🚍 – 30 🏠
15 canvas bungalows. Per night from 34 to 130€ – Per week from 180 to 800€ – Reservation fee 10€
🚐 borne 16€
In a pleasant wooded setting.

Surroundings : 🦢 ⊏⊐ ♤♤
Leisure activities : 🍽 🎯 🎬 🔆 nighttime
🏇🏼 🚴 🛝 ⛸ 🏊 multi-sports ground
Facilities : 🚿 ⚷ 🚰 ⛺ 🚮 🚰 launderette
🧺 🛒 refrigerators
Nearby : 🎣 🏇

G P S   Longitude : 4.04333
Latitude : 44.15167

LE CHAMBON

30450 – Michelin map **339** J3 – pop. 273 – alt. 260
▶ Paris 640 – Alès 31 – Florac 59 – Génolhac 10

⛺ Municipal le Luech

✆ 04 66 61 51 32, mairie-du-chambon@wanadoo.fr

Address : at Palanquis (600m northwest along the D 29, follow the signs for Chamborigaud)

0,5 ha (43 pitches) terraced, relatively flat, grassy, stony

On 2 separate sites on either side of the road, beside the Luech river.

Surroundings : ♤♤
Leisure activities : 🎣
Facilities : 🚿 ⚷
Nearby : 🍴🍽

G P S   Longitude : 4.00317
Latitude : 44.30494

CHASTANIER

48300 – Michelin map **330** K6 – pop. 92 – alt. 1 090
▶ Paris 570 – Châteauneuf-de-Randon 17 – Langogne 10 – Marvejols 71

⛺ Pont de Braye

✆ 04 66 69 53 04, www.camping-lozere-naussac.fr

Address : Les Berges du Chapeauroux (located 1km west, near the junction of D 988 and D 34, by the bridge)

Opening times : from beginning May to mid Sept.

1,5 ha (35 pitches)

Tariff : 16€ 🚶🚶 🚐 📋 🔌 (6A) – Extra per person 4€ – Reservation fee 7€

Rental rates : (from beginning May to mid Sept.) – 3 yurts – 2 tipis 2 tent lodges – 1 gîte. Per night from 40 to 60€ – Per week from 209 to 479 € – Reservation fee 7€
🚐 borne 2,50€ – 🚐 8€
Beside the river; a variety of original rental options, simply equipped facilities.

Surroundings : 🦢 ♤♤
Leisure activities : 🍴 🛖 🎯 🚴 🎣
Facilities : 🚿 ⚷ 🚰 ⛺ 🚰 🚰 launderette 🛒
Nearby : 🍴

G P S   Longitude : 3.74755
Latitude : 44.72656

CHIRAC

48100 – Michelin map **330** H7 – pop. 1 161 – alt. 625
▶ Paris 587 – Montpellier 173 – Mende 37 – Marvejols 6

⏞ Village Vacances (chalet rental only)

✆ 04 66 48 48 48, www.lozere-resa.com

Address : route du Val de Colagne (take the northern exit of the town – take exit 39 from the A75 then the D 809 following the signs for Marvejols)

1,5 ha flat

Rentals : 🚿 🅿 – 15 🏠.
A small village of wooden chalets.

Surroundings : 🦢 ⊰
Leisure activities : 🏇🏼 🎯 🏊 multi-sports ground
Facilities : 🚰 🚰 📷
Nearby : 🎣

G P S   Longitude : 3.26908
Latitude : 44.52684

*The classification (1 to 5 tents, **black** or **red**) that we award to selected sites in this guide is our own system. It should not be confused with the classification (1 to 5 stars) of official organisations.*

CLERMONT-L'HÉRAULT

34800 – Michelin map **339** F7 – pop. 7 627 – alt. 92
▶ Paris 718 – Béziers 46 – Lodève 24 – Montpellier 42

⏞ Municipal Campotel Lac du Salagou

✆ 04 67 96 13 13, www.le-salagou.fr

Address : at the lake du Salagou (5km northwest along the D 156 - E 4, 300m from the lake)

Opening times : Permanent

7,5 ha (388 pitches)

Tariff : (2013 Price) 17€ 🚶🚶 🚐 📋 🔌 (10A) – Extra per person 3€
Reservation fee 15€
Rental rates : (2013 Price) Permanent 🚿 (1 mobile home) 14 🚍 – 13 gîtes. Per night from 60 to 80€ – Per week from 400 to 560€ – Reservation fee 15€
🚐 borne 2€ – 5 📋 7€
A pleasant location close to the lake and the sailing centre.

Surroundings : 🦢 ⊰ ⊏⊐ ♤♤
Leisure activities : 🛖 🏇🏼
Facilities : 🚿 ⚷ 🚰 ⛺ 🚰 🚰 📷 refrigerated food storage facilities
Nearby : 🍴 🍽 🛒 🚴 🏊 🎣 🚣

G P S   Longitude : 3.38957
Latitude : 43.6455

COLLIAS

30210 – Michelin map **339** L5 – pop. 1 002 – alt. 45
▶ Paris 694 – Alès 45 – Avignon 32 – Bagnols-sur-Cèze 35

🏔 Le Barralet

📞 04 66 22 84 52, www.camping-barralet.com

Address : 6 chemin du Grès (located 1km northeast along the D 3, follow the signs for Uzès and take the road to the right)

Opening times : from beginning April to end Sept.

2 ha (132 pitches)

Tariff : 26,70€ ✦✦ 🚗 🔌 (6A) – Extra per person 6€ – Reservation fee 10€

Rental rates : (from beginning April to end Sept.) – 18 🚐 9 🏠. Per night from 39 to 122€ – Per week from 273 to 854€ Reservation fee 10€

🚰 borne

A superb view of the village and surrounding area from the swimming pool or the terrace of the bar.

Surroundings : 🐾 ≤ 🎣
Leisure activities : 🍴 ✕ 🛶 🛝 multi-sports ground
Facilities : 👤 🔌 📶 🗑 🚿

G P S Longitude : 4.48718
Latitude : 43.95769

CONNAUX

30330 – Michelin map **339** M4 – pop. 1 583 – alt. 86
▶ Paris 661 – Avignon 32 – Alès 52 – Nîmes 48

🏔 Le Vieux Verger

📞 04 66 82 91 62, www.campinglevieuxverger.com

Address : 526 avenue des Platanes (south of the town, 200m from the N 86)

Opening times : Permanent

3 ha (60 pitches)

Tariff : (2013 Price) 23,90€ ✦✦ 🚗 🔌 (10A) Extra per person 4,80€ – Reservation fee 10€

Rental rates : Permanent 🚫 – 10 🚐 – 5 🏠. Per night from 99 to 209€ – Per week from 369 to 740€ – Reservation fee 25€

There are more pitches for tents and caravans at the top of the site, plus plenty of shade.

Surroundings : 🗺 🎣
Leisure activities : ✕ 🛝
Facilities : 👤 🔌 📶 🗑
Nearby : ✕

G P S Longitude : 4.59108
Latitude : 44.08478

CRESPIAN

30260 – Michelin map **339** J5 – pop. 325 – alt. 80
▶ Paris 731 – Alès 32 – Anduze 27 – Nîmes 24

🏔 Kawan Village Le Mas de Reilhe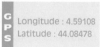

📞 04 66 77 82 12, www.camping-mas-de-reilhe.fr

Address : chemin du Mas de Reilhe (take the southern exit along the N 110)

Opening times : from end April to mid Sept.

2 ha (95 pitches)

Tariff : (2013 Price) 29,80€ ✦✦ 🚗 🔌 (10A) Extra per person 6,50€ – Reservation fee 20€

Rental rates : (2013 Price) (from end April to mid Sept.) – 14 🚐 7 🏠 – 4 canvas bungalows. Per night from 25 to 110€ – Per week from 175 to 770€ – Reservation fee 20€

🚰 borne

Surroundings : 🗺 🎣
Leisure activities : 🍴 ✕ 🛶 🛝 🛷 🚲 🛝 multi-sports ground
Facilities : 👤 🔌 🗑 🚿 🗑 🍴 launderette 🚿
Nearby : ✕

G P S Longitude : 4.09676
Latitude : 43.88015

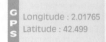

EGAT

66120 – Michelin map **344** D7 – pop. 453 – alt. 1 650
▶ Paris 856 – Andorra-la-Vella 70 – Ax-les-Thermes 53 – Bourg-Madame 15

🏔 Las Clotes

📞 04 68 30 26 90, pro.pagesjaunes.fr/camping-las-clotes

Address : 400m north of the town; beside a little stream

Opening times : from mid Nov. to mid Oct.

2 ha (80 pitches)

Tariff : (2013 Price) 17€ ✦✦ 🚗 🔌 (6A) – Extra per person 4€

An attractive elevated location, on the side of a rocky hill.

Surroundings : 🐾 ≤ Sierra del Cadi and Puigmal (peak) 🎣
Leisure activities : 🎣
Facilities : 👤 🔌 📶 🗑 🚿 🍴 🗑

G P S Longitude : 2.01765
Latitude : 42.499

ERR

66800 – Michelin map **344** D8 – pop. 640 – alt. 1 350 – Winter sports : 1 850/2 520m
▶ Paris 854 – Andorra-la-Vella 77 – Ax-les-Thermes 52 – Bourg-Madame 10

🏔 Le Puigmal

📞 04 68 04 71 83, www.camping-le-puigmal.com

Address : 30 route du Puigmal (along the D 33b; beside a stream)

Opening times : from end April to end Sept., school holidays and weekends in winter

3,2 ha (125 pitches)

Tariff : 20,20€ ✦✦ 🚗 🔌 (6A) – Extra per person 4,65€

Rental rates : 10 🚐. Per night from 59 to 80€ – Per week from 312 to 460€

A pleasant setting, lots of green spaces, shaded in places. Well-equipped sanitary facilities in the centre.

Surroundings : 🐾 🎣
Leisure activities : 🎣 🛶
Facilities : 👤 🔌 📶 🍴 launderette
Nearby : 🛝 🎿

G P S Longitude : 2.03539
Latitude : 42.43751

🏔 Las Closas

📞 04 68 04 71 42, www.camping-las-closas.com

Address : 1 place Saint-Génis (along the D 33b)

Opening times : Permanent

2 ha (114 pitches)

Tariff : (2013 Price) 21,40€ ✦✦ 🚗 🔌 (10A) Extra per person 4,25€

Rental rates : Permanent – 12 🛏 – 1 apartment. Per night from 65 to 80€ – Per week from 400 to 455€

🚿 6 🅔 13,20€

In the centre of the village close to the church; a pleasant site with good sanitary facilities.

Surroundings : 👯
Leisure activities : 🎱 🏇
Facilities : 🚻 ⚓ 🏢 🔥 ♨ 🍴 launderette
Nearby : 🎿 ⛷ ⛸

GPS Longitude : 2.03138
Latitude : 42.44014

ESTAVAR

66800 – Michelin map **344** D8 – pop. 429 – alt. 1 200
▶ Paris 852 – Montpellier 247 – Perpignan 97

🏕 L'Enclave 🏕

🕽 0468047227, www.camping.lenclave.com

Address : 2 rue Vinyals (take the eastern exit along the D 33; beside the Angoust river)

Opening times : from beginning Dec. to end Sept.

3,5 ha (175 pitches) terraced, flat and relatively flat, stony, grassy

Tariff : 30,60€ ⛺⛺ 🚐 🅔 ⚡ (10A) – Extra per person 5,60€ Reservation fee 10€

Rental rates : (from beginning Dec. to end Sept.) – 28 🛏. Per night from 28 to 117€ – Per week from 195 to 820€ Reservation fee 10€

🚿 borne 6€

An attractive shady area along a stream with a lovely play-ground at the bottom of the site.

Surroundings : 🌳 👯
Leisure activities : 🎱 🏇 🛶 jacuzzi 🏇
🎿 ⛷ 🏄 guided walks, entertainment room
Facilities : 🚻 ⚓ 🏢 🔥 🍴 launderette
Nearby : 🚲 🍷 🍴 🛶 🏇

GPS Longitude : 1.99813
Latitude : 42.4688

🏕 Yelloh! Village l'Escapade (chalet rental only)

🕽 0466739739, www.lescapade.com

Address : cami del Segre (800m to the south)

Opening times : Permanent

5 ha flat, grassy

Rental rates : 🚻 (5 chalets) – 44 🏠. Per night from 39 to 115€ Per week from 273 to 805€

A village of genuine wooden chalets, very luxurious.

Surroundings : 🌳 👯
Leisure activities : 🍷 🍴 🎱 🏇 multi-sports ground, entertainment room
Facilities : 🚻 ⚓ 🏢 🔥 🍴 launderette 🚿

GPS Longitude : 1.99921
Latitude : 42.46182

For more information on visiting particular towns or regions, consult the relevant regional MICHELIN Green Guide. We also recommend you use the appropriate Michelin regional map to locate your selected campsite, to calculate distances and to work out the best route.

FLORAC

48400 – Michelin map **330** J9 – pop. 1 921 – alt. 542
▶ Paris 622 – Alès 65 – Mende 38 – Millau 84

🏕 Municipal le Pont du Tarn 🏕

PITAT

🕽 0466451826, www.camping-florac.com

Address : route du Pont-de-Montvert (situated 2km north along the N 106, follow the signs for Mende and take D 998 to the right, direct access to the Tarn river)

Opening times : from end March to beginning Nov.

3 ha (181 pitches)

Tariff : 24,20€ ⛺⛺ 🚐 🅔 ⚡ (10A) – Extra per person 4,50€ – Reservation fee 12€

Rental rates : (from end March to beginning Nov.) – 22 🛏 6 canvas bungalows. Per week from 185 to 830€ – Reservation fee 12€

🚿 borne 4,50€

Some pitches beside the Tarn river, but choose those furthest from the road.

Surroundings : 🌊 👯
Leisure activities : 🍷 🏇 🛶 🎱 🏄
Facilities : 🚻 ⚓ 🏢 🔥 🌡 🍴 launderette 🚿
Nearby : 🎿

GPS Longitude : 3.59013
Latitude : 44.33625

Do not confuse:
△ *to* 🏕 *: MICHELIN classification with*
★ *to* ★★★★★ *: official classification*

FONT-ROMEU

66120 – Michelin map **344** D7 – pop. 2 003 – alt. 1 800 – Winter sports : 🎿 🏂 🛷
▶ Paris 860 – Montpellier 245 – Perpignan 90 – Canillo 62

🏕 Huttopia Font Romeu 🏕

HUTTOPIA

🕽 0468300932, www.huttopia.com – alt. 1 800

Address : route de Mont-Louis (RN 618)

Opening times : from mid June to mid Sept.

7 ha (175 pitches)

Tariff : 32,90€ ⛺⛺ 🚐 🅔 ⚡ (10A) Extra per person 7,20€ – Reservation fee 22€

Rental rates : (from mid June to mid Sept.) 🅟 – 34 🏠 – 20 tent lodges. Per night from 63 to 162€ Per week from 330 to 1134€ Reservation fee 22€

🚿 borne 7€

300m from the cable car station. High quality rental options.

Surroundings : 🌳 ≤ Pyrénées 👯
Leisure activities : 🍷 🍴 🎱 🛶 🏇 🏇 🎿
Facilities : ⚓ 🅟 🏢 🚿 launderette 🚿

GPS Longitude : 2.04666
Latitude : 42.50628

FORMIGUERES

66210 – Michelin map **344** D7 – pop. 435 – alt. 1 500
▶ Paris 883 – Montpellier 248 – Perpignan 96

⚠ La Devèze

✆ 06 37 59 73 89, http://www.campingladeveze.com – alt. 1 600

Address : route de la Devèze

Opening times : from beginning Dec. to beginning Oct.

4 ha (117 pitches) terraced, flat, grassy, stony

Tariff : (2013 Price) 18,60€ ✝✝ ⇔ 🗉 (½) (10A) – Extra per person 4€

Rental rates : (2013 Price) (from beginning Dec. to beginning Oct.)
1 caravan – 13 🚐 – 13 – 1 tipi – 4 tent lodges. Per night
from 50 to 60€ – Per week from 335 to 490€

🚰 borne 3€ – 10 🗉 10,30€

*A natural, shaded setting among pretty mountain pines. Horses
and their riders welcome.*

Surroundings : 🌲 🗠 ♀♀ Leisure activities : ✗ 🏛 ⛵ Facilities : ♿ ⚷ 🏠 ⛺ 🚿 ⚑ launderette 🚿	**GPS** Longitude : 2.0922 Latitude : 42.61035

FRONTIGNAN PLAGE

34110 – Michelin map **339** H8 – pop. 23 068 – alt. 2
▶ Paris 775 – Lodève 59 – Montpellier 26 – Sète 10

⚠ Les Tamaris ♣♣

✆ 04 67 43 44 77, www.les-tamaris.fr

Address : 140 avenue d'Ingril (to the northeast along the D 60)

Opening times : from beginning April to beginning Oct.

4 ha (250 pitches)

Tariff : 54€ ✝✝ ⇔ 🗉 (½) (10A) – Extra per person 10€ – Reservation
fee 25€

Rental rates : (from beginning April to beginning Oct.) – 70 🚐
30 🏠. Per night from 44 to 88€ – Per week from 250 to 1 310€
Reservation fee 25€

🚰 borne 5€

A pleasant setting close to the beach.

Surroundings : 🌲 🗠 ♀ ⚓ Leisure activities : ♀ ✗ 🏛 ⛵ ✝ ⛵ 🏊 Facilities : ♿ ⚷ 🏠 ⛺ 🚿 ⚑ launderette 🚿 🚿 refrigerated food storage facilities	**GPS** Longitude : 3.80572 Latitude : 43.44993

FUILLA

66820 – Michelin map **344** F7 – pop. 372 – alt. 547
▶ Paris 902 – Font-Romeu-Odeillo-Via 42 – Perpignan 55 – Prades 9

⚠ Le Rotja

✆ 04 68 96 52 75, www.camping-lerotja.com

Address : 34 avenue de la Rotja (in the village of Fuilla)

Opening times : from beginning April to mid Oct.

1,6 ha (100 pitches) fruit trees

Tariff : 29,75€ ✝✝ ⇔ 🗉 (½) (10A) – Extra per person 5€ – Reservation
fee 12,50€

Rental rates : (from beginning April to mid Oct.) – 10 🚐.
Per night from 25 to 100€ – Per week from 190 to 600€
Reservation fee 12,50€

🚰 borne 15,50€

Pitches laid out on terraces, some with plenty of shade.

Surroundings : 🌲 ≤ 🗠 ♀♀ Leisure activities : ✗ 🏊 (small swimming pool) Facilities : ♿ ⚷ 🏠 🚿 📶 Nearby : 🏊 ♀	**GPS** Longitude : 2.35883 Latitude : 42.56181

GALLARGUES-LE-MONTUEUX

30660 – Michelin map **339** K6 – pop. 3 257 – alt. 55
▶ Paris 727 – Aigues-Mortes 21 – Montpellier 39 – Nîmes 25

⚠ Les Amandiers ♣♣

✆ 04 66 35 28 02, www.camping-lesamandiers.fr

Address : 20 rue des stades (southwestern exit, follow the signs for
Lunel)

Opening times : from beginning April to end Sept.

3 ha (150 pitches)

Tariff : 27€ ✝✝ ⇔ 🗉 (½) (16A) – Extra per person 6€ – Reservation
fee 20€

Rental rates : (from beginning April to end Sept.) 🚲 – 45 🚐
9 tent lodges. Per night from 24 to 140€ – Per week
from 168 to 980€ – Reservation fee 20€

*A swimming pool area given over to spa and wellness: large
jacuzzi, counterflow swimming, bath with water jets.*

Surroundings : 🗠 ♀♀ Leisure activities : ♀ ✗ 🏛 🎣 ⛵ 💆 🏋 hammam, jacuzzi ⛵ 🏋 🏊 spa centre Facilities : ♿ ⚷ 🏠 ⚑ launderette 🚿 Nearby : 🏊	**GPS** Longitude : 4.16609 Latitude : 43.71612

*There are several different types of sani-station
('borne' in French) – sanitation points providing
fresh water and disposal points for grey water.
See page 12 for further details.*

GIGNAC

34150 – Michelin map **339** G7 – pop. 5 271 – alt. 53
▶ Paris 719 – Béziers 58 – Clermont-l'Hérault 12 – Lodève 25

⚠ Municipal la Meuse

✆ 04 67 57 92 97, www.campinglameuse.fr

Address : chemin de la Meuse (1.2km northeast along the D 32,
follow the signs for Aniane then take the road to the left, 200m from
the Hérault and a water sports centre)

Opening times :

3,4 ha (100 pitches) flat, grassy

Tariff : 13,80€ ✝✝ ⇔ 🗉 (½) (16A)

Rental rates : (from mid April to end Sept.) 🚲 – 9 🚐. Per week
from 402 to 510€

🚰 borne

Pleasant, spacious, marked-out pitches with plenty of shade.

Surroundings : 🗠 ♀♀ Leisure activities : ✗ 🏋 Facilities : ♿ ⚷ ⚑ 📶 Nearby : 🏊 🚣 fitness trail	**GPS** Longitude : 3.55927 Latitude : 43.662

GOUDARGUES

30630 – Michelin map **339** L3 – pop. 1 032 – alt. 77
▶ Paris 667 – Alès 51 – Bagnols-sur-Cèze 17 – Barjac 20

🏔 St-Michelet ♨♨

✆ 04 66 82 24 99, www.lesaintmichelet.com

Address : route de Frigoulet (located 1km northwest along the D 371; beside the Cèze river)

Opening times : from end April to mid Sept.

4 ha (160 pitches) terrace, flat and relatively flat, grassy, stony

Tariff : 26,90€ ♟♟ ⬠ ▣ 🔌 (10A) – Extra per person 6,70€

Rental rates : (from end April to mid Sept.) 🛪 – 52 🚐.
Per night from 45 to 73€ – Per week from 305 to 680€

The lower part of the site beside the Cèze river is for tents and caravans and the upper part, where the swimming pool is located, has mobile homes.

Surroundings : 🌿 🏕 ♨♨		
Leisure activities : 🍷✕ 🏠 🏃 🐎 🎿 🏊 🛶	**G**	Longitude : 4.46271
Facilities : 🚿 ⚡ 🛠🚽 🖼	**P** **S**	Latitude : 44.22123

🏔 Les Amarines 2

✆ 04 66 82 24 92, www.campinglesamarines.com

Address : at La Vérune Cornillon (located 1km northeast along the D 23; beside the Cèze river)

Opening times : from beginning April to beginning Oct.

3,7 ha (120 pitches) flat, grassy

Tariff : 26,50€ ♟♟ ⬠ ▣ 🔌 (10A) – Extra per person 5,90€
Reservation fee 8€

Rental rates : (from beginning April to end Sept.) 🛪 – 22 🚐.
Per week from 528 to 740€ – Reservation fee 8€

Beside the Cèze river, a linear site shaded by poplars and surrounded by vineyards.

Surroundings : 🏕 ♨♨		
Leisure activities : 🏠 🐎 🎿 🏊 🛶	**G**	Longitude : 4.47924
Facilities : 🚿 ⚡ 🛠 🚽 🔥 🖼 launderette, refrigerators	**P** **S**	Latitude : 44.22047

🏔 Sites et Paysages La Grenouille

✆ 04 66 82 21 36, www.camping-la-grenouille.com

Address : avenue du Lavoir (near the Cèze river - direct access)

Opening times : from beginning April to end Sept.

0,8 ha (50 pitches)

Tariff : 24,90€ ♟♟ ⬠ ▣ 🔌 (6A) – Extra per person 5,30€

Rental rates : (from beginning April to end Sept.) – 3 canvas bungalows. Per night from 37 to 58€ – Per week from 259 to 406€
🚐 borne – 🔌11€

Small but very pleasant site with a stream running through it, located in the centre of the village.

Surroundings : 🌿 🏕 ♨♨		
Leisure activities : 🐎 🎿 (small swimming pool) 🛶	**G**	Longitude : 4.46847
Facilities : 🚿 ⚡ 🛠🚽 🖼 refrigerators	**P** **S**	Latitude : 44.21468
Nearby : ✕		

The information in the guide may have changed since going to press.

LA GRANDE-MOTTE

34280 – Michelin map **339** J7 – pop. 8 391 – alt. 1
▶ Paris 747 – Aigues-Mortes 12 – Lunel 16 – Montpellier 28

🏔 Le Garden ♨♨

✆ 04 67 56 50 09, www.legarden.fr – ♨

Address : avenue de la Petite Motte (take the western exit along the D 59, 300m from the beach)

Opening times : from beginning April to beginning Oct.

3 ha (209 pitches)

Tariff : 44€ ♟♟ ⬠ ▣ 🔌 (10A)

Rental rates : (from beginning April to beginning Oct.) – 121 🚐.
Per night from 62 to 150€ – Per week from 336 to 960€
Reservation fee 20€

Good sanitary facilities and upmarket rental options.

Surroundings : 🏕 ♨♨		
Leisure activities : 🍷✕ 🏠 🏃 🐎 🎿	**G**	Longitude : 4.07235
Facilities : 🚿 ⚡ ✉ 🛠 🔥 🚽 launderette 🛒🔥	**P** **S**	Latitude : 43.56229
Nearby : 🐴 🐎		

🏔 Les Cigales

✆ 04 67 56 50 85, www.paysdelor.fr

Address : allée des Pins (take the western exit along the D 59)

Opening times : from mid April to end Sept.

2,5 ha (180 pitches)

Tariff : (2013 Price) 22,50€ ♟♟ ⬠ ▣ 🔌 (10A)

Extra per person 6,30€ – Reservation fee 10€

Rental rates : (2013 Price) (from mid April to mid Sept.) – 20 🚐.
Per week from 190 to 690€ – Reservation fee 10€
🚐 borne 16€ – 30 ▣ 16€ – 🔌11€

There is a large parking area for campervans adjoining the campsite.

Surroundings : ♨♨		
Leisure activities : 🐎	**G**	Longitude : 4.07612
Facilities : 🚿 ⚡ 🔥 🚽 🛠 launderette	**P** **S**	Latitude : 43.56722
Nearby : 🐎		

A 'quartier' is a district or area of a town or village.

LE GRAU-DU-ROI

30240 – Michelin map **339** J7 – pop. 7 995 – alt. 2
▶ Paris 751 – Aigues-Mortes 7 – Arles 55 – Lunel 22

🏔 FranceLoc Le Boucanet ♨♨

✆ 04 66 51 41 48, http://campingboucanet.franceloc.fr/ – 🛪

Address : route de Carnon (situated 2km northwest of Le Grau-du-Roi (right bank) following signs for la Grande-Motte; beside beach)

7,5 ha (462 pitches)

Rentals : 🛪 – 2 caravans – 312 🚐.
🚐 borne

In an exclusive location beside a beautiful beach

Surroundings : 🏕 🍷 ⚓ 🏖		
Leisure activities : 🍷✕ 🏠 🎣 🏃 🐎 🚴 ✕ 🎣 🎿 🏊	**G**	Longitude : 4.10753
Facilities : 🚿 ⚡ 🛠 🚽 launderette 🛒🔥 refrigerated food storage facilities	**P** **S**	Latitude : 43.55428
Nearby : 🐎		

ISPAGNAC

48320 – Michelin map **330** J8 – pop. 851 – alt. 518
▶ Paris 612 – Florac 11 – Mende 28 – Meyrueis 46

▲▲ Municipal du Pré Morjal

✆ 04 66 45 43 57, www.campingdupremorjal.com

Address : chemin du Beldiou (take the western exit along the D 907bis, follow the signs for Millau and take road to the left; near the Tarn)

Opening times : from beginning April to beginning Nov.

2 ha (123 pitches) flat, grassy

Tariff : 22,90€ ✻✻ ⇌ 🔲 🌃 (10A) – Extra per person 4€

Rental rates : (from beginning April to beginning Nov.) – 8 🏠 8 canvas bungalows. Per night from 40 to 100€ – Per week from 175 to 580€

🚐 borne

In a pleasant wooded setting at the entrance to the Tarn river gorges.

Surroundings : 🏞 ❮ ⌂ ♨♨
Leisure activities : 🎱 🏊 🚲 ⚓
Facilities : 🚿 🅾 🧺 launderette
Nearby : ✖ 🐎

G P S Longitude : 3.53038
Latitude : 44.37223

JUNAS

30250 – Michelin map **339** J6 – pop. 1 085 – alt. 75
▶ Paris 730 – Aigues-Mortes 30 – Aimargues 15 – Montpellier 42

▲▲ Les Chênes

✆ 04 66 80 99 07, www.camping-les-chenes.com

Address : 95 chemin des Tuileries Basses (1.3km south along the D 140, follow the signs for Sommières and take road to the left)

Opening times : from mid April to mid Oct.

1,7 ha (90 pitches)

Tariff : 21€ ✻✻ ⇌ 🔲 🌃 (10A) – Extra per person 4,60€ – Reservation fee 11€

Rental rates : (from mid April to mid Oct.) ✗ – 4 caravans 9 🛖. Per week from 190 to 590€ – Reservation fee 11€

Attractively shaded by Holm oaks, with pitches laid out on terraces, some of which are marked out with low stone walls.

Surroundings : 🏞 ♨♨
Leisure activities : 🏊 ⚓
Facilities : 🚿 🅾 🧺 🖥

G P S Longitude : 4.123
Latitude : 43.76921

▲ L'Olivier

✆ 04 66 80 39 52, www.campinglolivier.fr

Address : 112 route de Congenies (take the eastern exit along the D 140 and take the road to the right)

1 ha (45 pitches)

Rentals : 7 🛖 – 6 🏠 – 3 canvas bungalows.

A family-friendly establishment in the shade of Holm oaks near the village.

Surroundings : 🏞 ♨♨
Leisure activities : 🏊 🚲 ⛳ ⚓
Facilities : 🚿 🅾 🧺 🖥

G P S Longitude : 4.12489
Latitude : 43.77081

We value your opinion and welcome your feedback. Do email us at campingfrance@tp.michelin.com

LANUÉJOLS

30750 – Michelin map **339** F4 – pop. 334 – alt. 905
▶ Paris 656 – Alès 109 – Mende 68 – Millau 35

▲ Domaine de Pradines

✆ 04 67 82 73 85, www.domaine-de-pradines.com – alt. 800

Address : route de Millau, D28 (3.5km west along the D 28, follow the signs for Roujarie and take road to the left)

Opening times : from mid June to mid Sept.

150 ha/30 for camping (75 pitches)

Tariff : ✻ 8€ ⇌ 🔲 – 🌃 (16A) 3€

Rental rates : (from beginning April to end Oct.) – 5 🛖 – 4 🏠 4 yurts – 4 apartments – 4 tipis. Per night from 52 to 90€ Per week from 364 to 690€

Right in the heart of the countryside, various rental options, extensive pitches, but only average and rather old sanitary facilities.

Surroundings : 🏞 ❮ ♨
Leisure activities : ✖ 🎱 🏊 ✂ ⚓
Facilities : 🚿 🅾 🧺 launderette 🍽 🚐

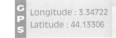

G P S Longitude : 3.34722
Latitude : 44.13306

The information in the guide may have changed since going to press.

LAROQUE-DES-ALBÈRES

66740 – Michelin map **344** I7 – pop. 2 028 – alt. 100
▶ Paris 881 – Argelès-sur-Mer 11 – Le Boulou 14 – Collioure 18

▲▲▲ Cybele Vacances Les Albères

✆ 04 68 89 23 64, www.camping-des-alberes.com

Address : route du Moulin de Cassagnes (take the northeastern exit along the D 2, follow the signs for Argelès-sur-Mer then continue 0.4km along the road to the right)

Opening times : from mid April to end Sept.

5 ha (211 pitches) very uneven, terraced, relatively flat, flat, grassy, stony

Tariff : 29€ ✻✻ ⇌ 🔲 🌃 (10A) – Reservation fee 25€

Rental rates : (from mid April to end Sept.) – 59 🛖 – 9 🏠 3 tent lodges. Per night from 26 to 120€ – Per week from 185 to 849€ – Reservation fee 25€

The pitches laid out on terraces have a good amount of shade.

Surroundings : 🏞 ⌂ ♨♨
Leisure activities : 🍸 ✖ 🎱 🏸 🏊 ✂ ⚓ multi-sports ground
Facilities : 🚿 🅾 🧺 🖥 🍽 🚐

G P S Longitude : 2.94418
Latitude : 42.52404

LATTES

34970 – Michelin map **339** I7 – pop. 15 804 – alt. 3
▶ Paris 766 – Montpellier 7 – Nîmes 54 – Béziers 68

▲▲ Le Parc

✆ 04 67 65 85 67, www.leparccamping.com

Address : route de Mauguio (situated 2km northeast along the D 172)

Opening times : Permanent

1,6 ha (100 pitches)

Tariff : 28,50€ ✻✻ ⇌ 🔲 🌃 (10A) – Extra per person 6€ – Reservation fee 15€

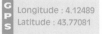

Rental rates : Permanent – 31 🛏. Per night from 60 to 80€ Per week from 280 to 755€ – Reservation fee 15€

Close to the tramway (line 3) for Montpellier and Pérols or Lattes.

Surroundings : 🏕 ΩΩ
Leisure activities : 🎣 🛝 🛶
Facilities : 🚿 🕳 🚮 🍴 launderette
Nearby : 🍴

G P S   Longitude : 3.92578
       Latitude : 43.57622

LAURENS

34480 – Michelin map **339** E7 – pop. 1 349 – alt. 140
▸ Paris 736 – Bédarieux 14 – Béziers 22 – Clermont-l'Hérault 40

⛰ Sites et Paysages L'Oliveraie

✆ 04 67 90 24 36, www.oliveraie.com

Address : 1600 chemin de Bédarieux (situated 2km north and take the road to the right)

Opening times : from end March to end Oct.

7 ha (110 pitches)

Tariff : 31€ ☂☂ 🚗 🔌 🔋 (10A) – Extra per person 5€ – Reservation fee 20€

Rental rates : (from end March to end Oct.) 🛖 – 10 🛏 – 2 🏠. Per night from 84 to 98€ – Per week from 340 to 710€ Reservation fee 20€

A shady site laid out across terraces, with a swimming pool surrounded by olive trees.

Surroundings : 🏕 ΩΩ
Leisure activities : 🍴 🍴 🌙 nighttime 🛝 🚡 🛶 🎣 🍴 🎯 🐴
Facilities : 🚿 🕳 🚮 🚽 🍴 🛁 🛒 🚿

G P S   Longitude : 3.18571
       Latitude : 43.53631

LE MALZIEU-VILLE

48140 – Michelin map **330** I5 – pop. 868 – alt. 860
▸ Paris 541 – Mende 51 – Le Puy-en-Velay 74 – Saint-Flour 150

⛰ La Piscine

✆ 04 66 31 47 63

Address : chemin de la Chazette (located 1.5km north along the D 989, follow the signs for St-Chély-d'Apcher and take road to the left after the bridge; near the swimming pool and a small lake)

1 ha (64 pitches)
Rentals : 🚿 – 13 🏠.

Surroundings : 🏞 🏕 Ω
Facilities : 🚿 🕳 🚮 🚽 🔲
Nearby : 🍴 🍴 🛶 🍴 🛝 🛁 ⛵ pedalos

G P S   Longitude : 3.33775
       Latitude : 44.85152

MARSEILLAN-PLAGE

34340 – Michelin map **339** G8
▸ Paris 765 – Montpellier 51 – Nîmes 100 – Carcassonne 114

⛰ Les Méditerranées - Beach Club Nouvelle Floride

✆ 04 67 21 94 49, www.lesmediterranees.com

Address : 262 avenue des Campings

Opening times : from mid April to end Sept.

7 ha (475 pitches) grassy

Tariff : 55€ ☂☂ 🚗 🔌 🔋 (10A) – Extra per person 10€ – Reservation fee 30€

Rental rates : (from mid April to end Sept.) 🛖 – 160 🛏. Per night from 35 to 255€ – Per week from 245 to 1785€ Reservation fee 30€

🅿 borne
In a pleasant location close to a beach.

Surroundings : 🏕 ΩΩ ⛱
Leisure activities : 🍴 🍴 🍴 🎣 🛝 🚡 🛶 🍴 🏊 multi-sports ground, entertainment room
Facilities : 🚿 🕳 🚮 🛁 🍴 🍴 launderette 🛒 🚿
Nearby : disco

G P S   Longitude : 3.54244
       Latitude : 43.30923

⛰ Les Méditerranées - Beach Garden

✆ 04 67 21 92 83, www.lesmediterranees.com

Address : avenue des Campings

Opening times : from mid April to end Sept.

14 ha (600 pitches)

Tariff : 63€ ☂☂ 🚗 🔌 🔋 (6A) – Extra per person 10€ – Reservation fee 30€
Rental rates : (from mid April to end Sept.) 🛖 – 80 🛏. Per night from 50 to 310€ – Per week from 350 to 2170€ – Reservation fee 30€

Close to a beach with a panoramic restaurant.

Surroundings : 🏊 🏕 ΩΩ ⛱
Leisure activities : 🍴 🍴 🎣 🍴 🛝 🚡 🛶 🚲 🛶 🍴
Facilities : 🚿 🕳 🛁 🍴 🍴 launderette 🛒 🚿

G P S   Longitude : 3.538
       Latitude : 43.3058

⛰ Les Méditerranées - Beach Club Charlemagne

✆ 04 67 21 92 49, www.lesmediterranees.com

Address : avenue des Campings (250m from the beach)

Opening times : from mid April to end Sept.

6,7 ha (480 pitches)

Tariff : 55€ ☂☂ 🚗 🔌 🔋 (6A) – Extra per person 10€ – Reservation fee 30€
Rental rates : (from mid April to end Sept.) 🛖 – 172 🛏. Per night from 35 to 255€ – Per week from 245 to 1785€ Reservation fee 30€

Free use of the services and leisure facilities at the Les Méditerranées Beach Club Nouvelle Floride situated opposite, beside the beach.

Surroundings : 🏕 ΩΩ
Leisure activities : 🍴 🍴 🎣 🍴 🛝 🛶 🏊 disco
Facilities : 🚿 🕳 🛁 🍴 🍴 launderette 🛒 🚿
Nearby : 🛝 🎣

G P S   Longitude : 3.54337
       Latitude : 43.31052

⛰ Le Galet

✆ 04 67 21 95 61, www.camping-galet.com

Address : avenue des Campings (250m from the beach)

Opening times : from beginning April to end Sept.

3 ha (275 pitches)

Tariff : 43€ ☂☂ 🚗 🔌 🔋 (10A) – Extra per person 7€ – Reservation fee 25€

Rental rates : (from beginning April to end Sept.) – 65 🛏. Per night from 31 to 138€ – Per week from 210 to 965€ Reservation fee 25€

A linear site leading to a pretty water park.

Surroundings : 🏕 Ω
Leisure activities : 🍴 🛶 🛝 🏊
Facilities : 🚿 🕳 🛁 🍴 launderette
Nearby : 🍴 🚿

G P S   Longitude : 3.5421
       Latitude : 43.31108

⚠ La Créole

📞 04 67 21 92 69, www.campinglacreole.com

Address : 74 avenue des Campings

Opening times : from beginning April to mid Oct.

1,5 ha (110 pitches)

Tariff : 36 € ♦♦ ⟷ ▣ ⟨≉⟩ (6A) – Extra per person 6,50 € – Reservation fee 17 €

Rental rates : (from beginning April to mid Oct.) ⌇ – 18 ⟦⟧. Per week from 200 to 750 € – Reservation fee 17 €

⟦⟧ 8 ▣ 12 €

Situated beside a beautiful beach of fine sand.

Surroundings : ⌁ 🌑🌑 ⚠		
Leisure activities : ✗ ⟋⟍		Longitude : 3.54375
Facilities : 🏃 ⟞ 🍴 🛅		Latitude : 43.31047
Nearby : 🛶 🍷 ⟋ 🏇		

MARVEJOLS

48100 – Michelin map **330** H7 – pop. 5 053 – alt. 650

▶ Paris 573 – Espalion 64 – Florac 50 – Mende 28

⛰ Village VAL V.V.F. et Camping de l'Europe

📞 04 66 32 03 69, www.vvf-villages.fr

Address : at Le Colagnet (1.3km east along the D 999, D 1, follow the signs for Montrodat and take the road to the right; beside the Colagnet – from A 75, take exit 38)

Opening times : from mid May to mid Sept.

3 ha (100 pitches) flat, grassy

Tariff : 12,30 € ♦♦ ⟷ ▣ ⟨≉⟩ (5A) – Extra per person 3,30 € – 30 €

Rental rates : (from end April to mid Sept.) – 9 ⟦⟧ – 41 gîtes. Per night from 35 to 120 € – Per week from 245 to 840 € Reservation fee 32 €

Well-shaded pitches beside the river; basic gîtes available and chalets equipped to a higher standard.

Surroundings : 🌊 ⌁ 🌑🌑		
Leisure activities : ⟐ ⟋⟍ ✗ ⟍ multi-sports ground		Longitude : 3.30432
Facilities : 🏃 ⟞ 🅿 ⟍ ⟍ 🍴 launderette		Latitude : 44.55075

MASSILLARGUES-ATTUECH

30140 – Michelin map **339** J4 – pop. 675 – alt. 156

▶ Paris 726 – Montpellier 56 – Nîmes 43 – Avignon 78

⛰ Le Fief d'Anduze ♠♣

📞 04 66 61 81 71, https://www.campinglefiefdanduze.com

Address : at Attuech, 195 chemin du Plan d'Eau (located 1.5km to the north along the D 982, near a lake)

Opening times : from beginning April to end Sept.

5,5 ha (80 pitches) flat, grassy

Tariff : 25,70 € ♦♦ ⟷ ▣ ⟨≉⟩ (6A) – Extra per person 5,30 € Reservation fee 10 €

Rental rates : (from beginning April to end Sept.) – 20 ⟦⟧. Per night from 93 to 106 € – Per week from 598 to 688 € Reservation fee 10 €

Well-shaded pitches but poor sanitary facilities.

Surroundings : 🌊 🌑🌑🌑		
Leisure activities : 🍷 ✗ ⟐ ⟋⟍ ⟍ hammam, jacuzzi ⟋⟍ ⟍ multi-sports ground		Longitude : 4.02576
Facilities : 🏃 ⟞ 🍴 🛅 ⟍		Latitude : 44.02946
Nearby : ⟍		

MATEMALE

66210 – Michelin map **344** D7 – pop. 294 – alt. 1 514

▶ Paris 855 – Font-Romeu-Odeillo-Via 20 – Perpignan 92 – Prades 46

⛰ Le Lac

📞 04 68 30 94 49, www.camping-lac-matemale.com – alt. 1 540

limited spaces for one-night stay

Address : 1.7km southwest along the D 52, follow the signs for Les Angles and take the turning to the left, 150m from the lake

Opening times : Permanent

3,5 ha (110 pitches)

Tariff : ♦ 5,50 € ⟷ ▣ 5 € – ⟨≉⟩ (6A) 4,20 €

Rental rates : Permanent – 5 ⟦⟧. Per night from 65 to 90 € Per week from 250 to 570 €

⟦⟧ borne 2,50 €

A pleasant mountain location in the shade of a pretty pine forest, direct access to the village along a pedestrian path.

Surroundings : 🌊 🌑🌑		
Leisure activities : ⟐ ⟍ jacuzzi ⟋⟍		Longitude : 2.10673
Facilities : 🏃 ⟞ 🏛 🛅 🍴 launderette		Latitude : 42.58164
Nearby : 🍷 ✗ 🎣 🐎 ⟍ ⟍ ⟍ ⟍ sports/ activities centre at 800m		

MAUREILLAS-LAS-ILLAS

66480 – Michelin map **344** H8 – pop. 2 649 – alt. 130

▶ Paris 873 – Gerona 71 – Perpignan 31 – Port-Vendres 31

⚠ Les Bruyères

📞 04 68 83 26 64, www.camping-lesbruyeres.fr

Address : route de Céret (1.2km west along the D 618)

Opening times : from mid March to mid Nov.

4 ha (106 pitches) very uneven, terraced, flat, grassy, stony

Tariff : 26 € ♦♦ ⟷ ▣ ⟨≉⟩ (10A) – Extra per person 5,60 € – Reservation fee 8 €

Rental rates : (from mid March to mid Nov.) – 17 ⟦⟧ – 4 ⟦⟧. Per night from 55 to 126 € – Per week from 288 to 665 € Reservation fee 15 €

⟦⟧ borne 3 €

In a pleasant wooded setting among cork oaks, but choose the pitches away from the road in preference.

Surroundings : ⌁ 🌑🌑		
Leisure activities : ⟐ ⟍ ⟍	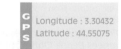	Longitude : 2.79509
Facilities : 🏃 ⟞ 🛅 ⟍ 🍴 🛅		Latitude : 42.49249
Nearby : ⟍		

MENDE

48000 – Michelin map **330** J7 – pop. 12 285 – alt. 731

▶ Paris 584 – Clermont-Ferrand 174 – Florac 38 – Langogne 46

⛰ Tivoli

📞 04 66 65 31 10, www.campingtivoli.com

Address : chemin de Tivoli (situated 2km southwest along the N 88, follow the signs for Rodez and take the road to the right, opposite the shopping centre; beside the Lot river)

Opening times : Permanent

1,8 ha (100 pitches) flat, grassy

Tariff : 24 € ♦♦ ⟷ ▣ ⟨≉⟩ (6A) – Extra per person 7 € – Reservation fee 25 €

Rental rates : (from beginning May to mid Sept.) ⚡ – 18 🚐. Per night from 60€ – Per week from 180 to 625€ – Reservation fee 25€
🚰 borne
Below the road to Rodez and opposite a sports complex accessible by footbridge over the Lot river.

Surroundings : ♨♨
Leisure activities : ⛺ 🏊 🎣
Facilities : 👤 ⛽ 🚻 🚿 📷 🛒
Nearby : 🍴

G P S Longitude : 3.45693
Latitude : 44.51268

MEYRUEIS

48150 – Michelin map **330** I9 – pop. 853 – alt. 698
▶ Paris 643 – Florac 36 – Mende 57 – Millau 43

ᴍᴍ Kawan Villages le Capelan

🕿 0466456050, www.campingcapelan.com
Address : route de Millau (located 1km northwest along the D 996; beside the Jonte)
Opening times : from beginning May to mid Sept.
2,8 ha (100 pitches) flat, grassy
Tariff : 30,50€ ⚹⚹ 🚐 🔌 💡 (10A) – Extra per person 6,10€
Reservation fee 16€
Rental rates : (from beginning May to mid Sept.) ⚡ – 44 🚐. Per night from 41 to 114€ – Per week from 185 to 798€
Reservation fee 19€
🚰 borne – 🔵 💡18,40€
In a pleasant location in the steep valley of the Jonte river, with a path to the village and a swimming pool across the road.

Surroundings : ♨ 🏠 ♨♨
Leisure activities : 🍸 ⛺ 🏊 🎣 🏊 🏊 climbing
Facilities : 👤 ⛽ 🖂 ❸ –3 individual sanitary facilities (🚿 🚻 wc) 🔌 🛒 🚿 launderette 🚿

G P S Longitude : 3.4199
Latitude : 44.1859

ᴍᴍ Le Champ d'Ayres

🕿 0466456051, www.campinglechampdayres.com
Address : route de la Brèze (500m east along the D 57, follow the signs for Campis, near the Brèze)
Opening times : from end April to end Sept.
1,5 ha (91 pitches)
Tariff : 28,50€ ⚹⚹ 🚐 🔌 💡 (10A) – Extra per person 5,20€
Reservation fee 16€
Rental rates : (from end April to end Sept.) ⚡ – 19 🚐. 3 🚐. Per night from 40 to 102€ – Per week from 180 to 710€
Reservation fee 19€
🚰 borne 4,50€
A green and flowery setting.

Surroundings : ♨ ♨ 🏠 ♨
Leisure activities : 🍸 ⛺ 🏊 🏊
Facilities : 👤 ⛽ 🚿 launderette
Nearby : 🍴 🐴

G P S Longitude : 3.43536
Latitude : 44.18079

⛺ La Via Natura La Cascade

🕿 0466454545, www.camping-la-cascade.com
Address : at Salvinsac (3.8km northeast along the D 996, follow the signs for Florac and take the road to the right, near the Jonte river and a waterfall)
Opening times : from end April to mid Sept.
1 ha (54 pitches)
Tariff : 22,50€ ⚹⚹ 🚐 🔌 💡 (16A) – Extra per person 4,50€
Rental rates : (from end April to mid Sept.) – 13 🏠. Per week from 280 to 665€
🚰 borne 3,50€
In the Vallée de la Jonte, a site with a passion for nature and ecology.

Surroundings : 🏊 ♨ ♨
Leisure activities : 🏠 🏊 🏊
Facilities : 👤 ⛽ ❸ 🚿 📷

G P S Longitude : 3.45567
Latitude : 44.19645

⛺ Le Pré de Charlet

🕿 0466456365, www.camping-cevennes-meyrueis.com
Address : route de Florac (located 1km northeast along the D 996; beside the Jonte)
Opening times : from mid April to mid Oct.
2 ha (70 pitches) terraced, relatively flat, flat, grassy
Tariff : 18€ ⚹⚹ 🚐 🔌 💡 (16A) – Extra per person 3,50€
Rental rates : (from mid April to mid Oct.) – 6 🚐 – 3 canvas bungalows. Per night from 30 to 60€ – Per week from 160 to 480€
🚰 borne 3,50€
Below the road, pitches partly alongside the river, with refurbished sanitary facilities.

Surroundings : 🏊 ♨♨
Leisure activities : 🏠 🏊 🏊
Facilities : 👤 ⛽ ❸ 🚿 launderette
Nearby : 🏊

G P S Longitude : 3.43831
Latitude : 44.18587

The pitches of many campsites are marked out with low hedges of attractive bushes and shrubs.

MONTCLAR

11250 – Michelin map **344** E4 – pop. 186 – alt. 210
▶ Paris 766 – Carcassonne 19 – Castelnaudary 41 – Limoux 15

ᴍᴍᴍ Yelloh! Village Domaine d'Arnauteille 👥

🕿 0468268453, www.camping-arnauteille.com
Address : 2.2km southeast along the D 43
Opening times : from mid April to mid Sept.
115 ha/12 for camping (198 pitches) very uneven, terraced, relatively flat, flat, grassy
Tariff : 39€ ⚹⚹ 🚐 🔌 💡 (10A) – Extra per person 8€
Rental rates : Permanent – 78 🚐 – 10 🏠. Per night from 39 to 115€ – Per week from 273 to 805€
🚰 borne
On a sloping, spacious and pleasant site set on a hill, with shaded and sunny pitches.

Surroundings : 🏊 ♨ ♨
Leisure activities : 🍴 🏠 🏊 🏃 jacuzzi 🏊 🏊 🏊 🐴 multi-sports ground, spa centre
Facilities : 👤 ⛽ 🚻 ❸ 🚿 launderette 🔌 🚿

G P S Longitude : 2.26107
Latitude : 43.12431

NARBONNE

11100 – Michelin map **344** J3 – pop. 51 227 – alt. 13
▶ Paris 787 – Béziers 28 – Carcassonne 61 – Montpellier 96

▲▲▲ Yelloh! Village Les Mimosas ▲▲

☏ 0468490372, www.lesmimosas.com

Address : chaussée de Mandirac (10km to the south, after the suburb La Nautique)

Opening times : from mid April to end Oct.

9 ha (266 pitches)

Tariff : 46€ ★★ ⇔ 🖻 🔌 (10A) – Extra per person 8€
Rental rates : (from mid April to end Oct.) – 81 🚐 – 28 🏠
4 studios. Per night from 36 to 195€– Per week from 252 to 1365€
🚽 borne
Pitches nestling among Languedoc vineyards and a welcoming wine bar for tastings.

Surroundings : 🌳 ⛲ ♨
Leisure activities : 🍷 ✗ 🎱 ⛳ 🏹 🎿 🛶
🏇 🎣 🎮 🏊 🛥 multi-sports ground
Facilities : ♿ ⚡ 🏕 🚿 🚰 🍴 launderette 🧺
Nearby : 🐎

| **G P S** | Longitude : 3.02592 |
| --- | Latitude : 43.13658 |

▲▲▲ La Nautique

☏ 0468904819, www.campinglanautique.com

Address : chemin de La Nautique (4km to the south; at Port La Nautique)

Opening times : from beginning March to end Oct.

16 ha (390 pitches)

Tariff : 46€ ★★ ⇔ 🖻 🔌 (10A) – Extra per person 8,50€
Rental rates : (from beginning March to end Oct.) ♿ (1 chalet, 4 mobile homes) – 75 🚐 – 1 🏠. Per night from 37 to 137€
Per week from 259 to 987€
🚽 borne
Beside the Etang de Bages and Etang de Sigean (coastal lagoons).

Surroundings : ⛲ ⛲ ♨
Leisure activities : 🍷 ✗ 🎱 ⛳ 🏹 🚣 🚴 🎮
🏊 🛶 pedalos 🎣
Facilities : ♿ ⚡ 390 individual sanitary facilities (🚿 🚽 wc) 🚰 🍴 launderette 🧺
🧺
Nearby : ♨

| **G P S** | Longitude : 3.00424 |
| --- | Latitude : 43.14703 |

NASBINALS

48260 – Michelin map **330** G7 – pop. 498 – alt. 1 180
▶ Paris 573 – Aumont-Aubrac 24 – Chaudes-Aigues 27 – Espalion 34

▲ Municipal

☏ 0466325187, mairie.nasbinals@laposte.net – alt. 1 100 – 🐎

Address : route de Saint-Urcize (located 1km northwest along the D 12)

Opening times : from mid May to end Sept.

2 ha (75 pitches)

Tariff : (2013 Price) 11€ ★★ ⇔ 🖻 🔌 (15A) Extra per person 3€

Surroundings : 🌳 ⛰
Leisure activities : 🎱
Facilities : ♿ ⚡ (July–Aug.)
Nearby : 🐎

| **G P S** | Longitude : 3.04016 |
| --- | Latitude : 44.67022 |

NAUSSAC

48300 – Michelin map **330** L6 – pop. 206 – alt. 920
▶ Paris 575 – Grandrieu 26 – Langogne 3 – Mende 46

▲▲▲ Les Terrasses du Lac

☏ 0466692962, www.naussac.com

Address : at the lake Naussac (north of the town along the D 26, follow the signs for Saugues and take the turning to the left; 200m from the lake (direct access)

Opening times : from mid April to end Sept.

6 ha (180 pitches) terraced, relatively flat, flat, grassy

Tariff : 21,50€ ★★ ⇔ 🖻 🔌 (10A) – Extra per person 4,90€
Reservation fee 10€
Rental rates : (from mid April to mid Oct.) – 3 🚐 – 6 🏠
17 🛏 – hotel, 9 huts (without sanitary facilities). Per night from 68 to 73€ – Per week from 325 to 675€ – Reservation fee 10€
🚽 borne 9€ – 🚐9€
All the pitches and rentals benefit from a panoramic view over the large lake.

Surroundings : 🌳 ≼Lac de Naussac
Leisure activities : 🍷 ✗ 🎱 🏹 🎮 🏊
Facilities : ♿ ⚡ 🏕 🍴 launderette 🧺
Nearby : 🏇 🏖 (beach) 🎣 ♨

| **G P S** | Longitude : 3.83505 |
| --- | Latitude : 44.73478 |

PALAU-DEL-VIDRE

66690 – Michelin map **344** I7 – pop. 2 736 – alt. 26
▶ Paris 867 – Argelès-sur-Mer 8 – Le Boulou 16 – Collioure 15

▲▲ Kawan Village Le Haras

☏ 0468221450, www.camping-le-haras.com

Address : 1 ter avenue Juliot Curie, au Domaine Saint-Galdric (take the northeastern exit along the D 11)

Opening times : from beginning April to end Sept.

2,3 ha (131 pitches) flat, grassy

Tariff : 37,50€ ★★ ⇔ 🖻 🔌 (10A) – Extra per person 6,70€
Reservation fee 20€
Rental rates : (from beginning April to end Sept.) – 18 🚐 – 1 tent lodge. Per night from 39 to 121€ – Per week from 273 to 847€
Reservation fee 20€
🚽 borne
Attractively shaded with floral decoration.

Surroundings : ⛲ ♨♨
Leisure activities : 🍷 ✗ 🎱 🏹 🏊
Facilities : ♿ ⚡ 🖾 🚰 🍴 launderette 🧺

| **G P S** | Longitude : 2.96474 |
| --- | Latitude : 42.57575 |

PALAVAS-LES-FLOTS

34250 – Michelin map **339** I7 – pop. 5 996 – alt. 1
▶ Paris 765 – Montpellier 13 – Sète 41 – Lunel 33

▲▲▲ Les Roquilles

☏ 0467680347, www.camping-les-roquilles.fr 🏊

Address : 267 bis avenue Saint-Maurice (follow the signs for Carnon-Plage, 100m from the beach)

Opening times : from mid April to mid Sept.

15 ha (792 pitches)

Tariff : 42,10€ ★★ ⇔ 🖻 🔌 (6A) – Extra per person 5,90€
Reservation fee 29€

Rental rates : (from mid April to mid Sept.) &. (1 mobile home) 🚲 – 80 🏠 – 35 🏡. Per night from 56 to 92€ – Per week from 265 to 1240€ – Reservation fee 29€

🚐 borne

Some pitches are beside the lake, which is occasionally frequented by feeding flamingoes.

Surroundings : 🏊 ♀
Leisure activities : 🍴 ✕ 🏠 🎱 🏇 🎿 🎯 🎿 🏊 multi-sports ground
Facilities : 🚹 🔌 🚿 🧺 🚽 🚮

Longitude : 3.96037
Latitude : 43.53851

ᴧᴧᴧ Vacances-Directes Palavas 👥

🌀 0467680128, www.palavas-camping.fr – limited spaces for one-night stay 🚲

Address : route de Maguelone (right bank)

8 ha (438 pitches)

Rentals : 386 🏠.

🚐 borne

A mobile home village with some pitches for tents and caravans beside the sea.

Surroundings : 🏊 🌊
Leisure activities : 🍴 ✕ 🏠 🎱 🏇 🎿 🚲 🎿 kite-surfing, multi-sports ground
Facilities : 🚹 🔌 🚿 🚽 launderette 🚮 🚮

Longitude : 3.9095
Latitude : 43.51963

LES PLANTIERS

30122 – Michelin map **339** H4 – pop. 252 – alt. 400
▶ Paris 667 – Alès 48 – Florac 46 – Montpellier 85

ᴧᴧᴧ Caylou

🌀 0466839285, www.camping-caylou.fr

Address : at Le Caylou (located 1km northeast along the D 20, follow the signs for Saumane; beside the Gardon au Borgne)

Opening times :

4 ha (75 pitches) terraced, relatively flat, flat, grassy, stony

Tariff : (2013 Price) 14,30€ 👥👥 🚐 🔲 ⚡ (6A) – Extra per person 2€

Rental rates : (from mid April to mid Oct.) – 2 🏠 – 2 gîtes. Per week from 280 to 590€

Comfortable gîtes and a lovely bar terrace looking out over the valley.

Surroundings : 🏊 ≤ 🌊 ♀♀
Leisure activities : 🍴 ✕ 🏠 🎿 🎿 🐎 🌊 entertainment room
Facilities : 🚹 🔌 🚿 🚮

Longitude : 3.73101
Latitude : 44.12209

PORT-CAMARGUE

30240 – Michelin map **339** J7
▶ Paris 762 – Montpellier 36 – Nîmes 47 – Avignon 93

ᴧᴧᴧ Yelloh! Village Secrets de Camargue

🌀 0466800800, www.secretsdecamargue.com – limited spaces for one-night stay

Address : route de l'Espiguette

Opening times : from mid April to mid Nov.

3,5 ha (177 pitches)

Tariff : 52€ 👥👥 🚐 🔲 ⚡ (10A) – Extra per person 9€

Rental rates : (from mid April to mid Nov.) 🅿 – 155 🏠. Per night from 39 to 206€ – Per week from 273 to 1442€

A campsite reserved for over 18s with some pitches for tents and caravans. Free shuttle service to the beaches.

Surroundings : 🏊 🌊 ♀
Leisure activities : 🍴 ✕ 🎱 daytime 🚲 🏊
Facilities : 🚹 🔌 🅿 🚿 🚽 launderette 🚮
Nearby : 🏊 🏇

Longitude : 4.14105
Latitude : 43.5052

ᴧᴧᴧ Yelloh! Village Les Petits Camarguais 👥

(rental of mobile homes only)

🌀 0466511616, www.yellohvillage-petits-camarguais.com

Address : route de l'Espiguette

Opening times : Permanent

3,5 ha

Rental rates : 🚲 – 331 🏠. Per night from 39 to 285€ – Per week from 273 to 1995€

Activities and services suitable for young children. Free shuttle service to the beaches.

Surroundings : 🌊 ♀♀
Leisure activities : 🍴 ✕ 🎱 🏇 Jacuzzi 🎿 🚲 🌊 🏊 multi-sports ground, entertainment room
Facilities : 🚹 🔌 🚿 🚽 launderette 🚮 🚮
Nearby : 🏇

Longitude : 4.14456
Latitude : 43.50472

ᴧᴧᴧ Vacances Directes La Marine 👥

(rental of mobile homes only)

🌀 0825133400, www.campinglamarine.com

Address : 2196 route de l'Espiguette

Opening times : from mid April to mid Sept.

5 ha

Rental rates : 🚹 🚲 – 270 🏠 – 15 tent lodges. Per night from 32 to 163€ – Per week from 224 to 1141€ – Reservation fee 30€

Choose the pitches away from the road in preference; free shuttle service to the beaches.

Surroundings : ♀♀
Leisure activities : 🍴 ✕ 🏠 🎱 🏇 🎿 🚲 🏊 🏊
Facilities : 🚹 🔌 🚿 🚽 launderette 🚮 🚮
Nearby : 🏇 casino

Longitude : 4.1457
Latitude : 43.5074

ᴧᴧᴧ Abri de Camargue

🌀 0466515483, www.abridecamargue.fr – limited spaces for one-night stay

Address : 320 route de l'Espiguette (near the Casino (gaming) and opposite the fairground)

Opening times : from beginning April to end Sept.

4 ha (277 pitches)

Tariff : 51€ 👥👥 🚐 🔲 ⚡ (6A) – Extra per person 9€ – Reservation fee 21€

Rental rates : (from beginning April to end Sept.) – 108 🏠. Per night from 61 to 142€ – Per week from 427 to 994€ Reservation fee 21€

🚐 borne 7€ – 🚐 ⚡25,65€

A free shuttle service to the beaches.

Surroundings : 🌊 ♀♀
Leisure activities : 🍴 ✕ 🎱 🏇 🎿 🌊 🏊 cinema, multi-sports ground
Facilities : 🔌 🚿 🚽 launderette 🚮 🚮
Nearby : 🏇 casino

Longitude : 4.1488
Latitude : 43.52272

PORTIRAGNES-PLAGE

34420 – Michelin map **339** F9
▶ Paris 768 – Montpellier 72 – Carcassonne 99 – Nîmes 121

▲▲▲ Les Sablons ▲▲

℘ 04 67 90 90 55, www.les-sablons.com

Address : Plage Est (take the northern exit)

Opening times : from mid April to end Sept.

15 ha (800 pitches) flat, grassy, sandy, pond

Tariff : 55€ ♣♣ ⛟ ▤ ⓔ (10A)
Extra per person 11€ – Reservation fee 25€

Rental rates : Permanent – 242 🚐 85 🏠. Per night from 35 to 286€ Per week from 210 to 2002€ Reservation fee 25€

🚰 borne – 🔋ⓔ14€

Close to the beach and a lake.

Surroundings : 🛏 ♨♨ ⛰
Leisure activities : 🍷✕ 🎦 ⑨ 🏊 🛶 🏄
🚣 🎿 🎿 disco
Facilities : 🚿 ⊶ 🔥 🍴 launderette 🦮🛒 refrigerated food storage facilities
Nearby : 🎣 ⚓

```
G  Longitude : 3.36469
P  Latitude : 43.2788
S
```

▲▲▲ Les Mimosas ▲▲

℘ 04 67 90 92 92, www.mimosas.com limited spaces for one-night stay

Address : at Port Cassafières

Opening times : from end May to beginning Sept.

7 ha (400 pitches) flat, grassy

Tariff : 46€ ♣♣ ⛟ ▤ ⓔ (6A) –
Extra per person 10€ – Reservation fee 36€

Rental rates : (from end May to beginning Sept.) 🚿 (1 mobile home) – 217 🚐 – 4 🏠 – 12 canvas bungalows. Per night from 35 to 260€ Per week from 245 to 1820€ Reservation fee 36€

🚰 borne 2€

A large water and play park.

Surroundings : 🛏 ♨♨
Leisure activities : 🍷✕ 🎦 ⑨ 🏊 🛶 ⛵
🚣 🚲 🎿 🎿 multi-sports ground
Facilities : 🚿 ⊶ 🔥 – 17 individual sanitary facilities (🚿 🚻 wc) 🍴 launderette 🦮🛒 refrigerated food storage facilities
Nearby : 🎣 ⚓

```
G  Longitude : 3.37305
P  Latitude : 43.2915
S
```

Using the traditional Michelin classification method, the guide provides you with an easy, speedy reference for assessing the category of each site: 1 to 5 tents (see page 10).

▲▲▲ L'Émeraude

℘ 04 67 90 93 76, www.campinglemeraude.com

Address : located 1km north, follow the signs for Portiragnes

Opening times : from end May to beginning Sept.

4,2 ha (280 pitches)

Tariff : 30€ ♣♣ ⛟ ▤ ⓔ (5A) – Extra per person 6,50€ – Reservation fee 25€

Rental rates : (from end May to beginning Sept.) 🚿 – 160 🚐 11 🏠. Per night from 35 to 100€ – Per week from 245 to 700€ Reservation fee 20€

A pleasant water park.

Surroundings : ♨♨
Leisure activities : 🍷✕ 🎦 ⑨ 🏊 🛶 🎿
Facilities : 🚿 ⊶ 🔥 🍴 ▤ 🔥 🚣 refrigerated food storage facilities
Nearby : 🎠

```
G  Longitude : 3.36199
P  Latitude : 43.28766
S
```

Key to rentals symbols:

12 🚐	*Number of mobile homes*	
20 🏠	*Number of chalets*	
6 🛏	*Number of rooms to rent*	
Per night 30–50€	*Minimum/maximum rate per night*	
Per week 300–1,000€	*Minimum/maximum rate per week*	

QUILLAN

11500 – Michelin map **344** E5 – pop. 3 352 – alt. 291
▶ Paris 797 – Andorra-la-Vella 113 – Ax-les-Thermes 55 – Carcassonne 52

▲▲▲ Village Vacances Domaine de l'Espinet

(rental of studios and maisonnettes only)
℘ 04 68 20 88 88, www.lespinet.com

Address : located 1km north along the D 118

Opening times : Permanent

25 ha

Rental rates : (2013 Price) 🚿 🅿 – 24 studios. Per night from 40 to 298€ – Per week from 280 to 2086€

An upmarket, well-appointed holiday village.

Surroundings : 🏞 ≤ ⑨
Leisure activities : 🍷✕ 🎦 🚣 🎿 🎣 hammam, jacuzzi 🚣 ✿ ▤ 🎿 spa centre
Facilities : ⊶ 🍴 launderette

```
G  Longitude : 2.19776
P  Latitude : 42.89268
S
```

▲▲▲ Municipal la Sapinette

℘ 04 68 20 13 52, www.villedequillan.fr

Address : 21 avenue René Delpech (0.8km west along the D 79, follow the signs for Ginoles)

Opening times : from beginning April to end Oct.

1,8 ha (90 pitches) terraced, relatively flat, flat, grassy

Tariff : (2013 Price) 20,60€ ♣♣ ⛟ ▤ ⓔ (16A) Extra per person 4,40€

Rental rates : (2013 Price) (from beginning April to end Oct.) 🚿 26 🚐 – 26 gîtes. Per week from 305 to 729€

🚰 borne 10,50€ – 4 ▤ 10,50€ – 🔋ⓔ13,80€

Pitches arranged on terraces with a modicum of shade.

Surroundings : 🏞 ≤ ⑨
Leisure activities : 🎦 🚣 🎿
Facilities : 🚿 ⊶ 🔥 🍴 ▤

```
G  Longitude : 2.18445
P  Latitude : 42.87495
S
```

REMOULINS

30210 – Michelin map **339** M5 – pop. 2 405 – alt. 27
▶ Paris 685 – Alès 50 – Arles 37 – Avignon 23

La Sousta 👥

✆ 04 66 37 12 80, www.lasousta.com

Address : avenue du Pont du Gard (situated 2km to the northwest, follow the signs for Le Pont du Gard, right bank)

Opening times : from beginning March to end Oct.

14 ha (300 pitches) undulating, relatively flat, flat, grassy, sandy

Tariff : 29,90€ ★★ ⚌ ▤ ฿ (6A) – Extra per person 9€ – Reservation fee 15€

Rental rates : Permanent – 60 ⌂ – 4 ⌂. Per night from 65 to 70€ – Per week from 252 to 872€ – Reservation fee 15€

In a pleasant wooded setting beside the Gardon river, on the right bank near the Pont du Gard.

Surroundings : 🌳
Leisure activities :
Facilities : 🚿 launderette
GPS Longitude : 4.54
Latitude : 43.94

FranceLoc Domaine de La Soubeyranne 👥

✆ 04 66 37 03 21, www.soubeyranne.com

Address : 1110 route de Beaucaire (2.5km south along the N 86 and D 986, right bank)

4 ha (200 pitches)

Rentals : 142 ⌂.

🚰 borne

Numerous, well laid-out mobile homes and a very well-equipped children's playground.

Surroundings : 🌳
Leisure activities :
multi-sports ground
Facilities : 🚿 launderette
GPS Longitude : 4.56236
Latitude : 43.93031

ROCLES

48300 – Michelin map **330** K6 – pop. 209 – alt. 1 085
▶ Paris 581 – Grandrieu 20 – Langogne 8 – Mende 44

Rondin des Bois

✆ 04 66 69 50 46, www.camping-rondin.com – alt. 1 000

Address : at Palhere (3km north following signs for Bessettes and take road for Vaysset to the right.)

Opening times : from beginning May to end Sept.

2 ha (78 pitches)

Tariff : 20,30€ ★★ ⚌ ▤ ฿ (10A) – Extra per person 4,70€ Reservation fee 10€

Rental rates : (from mid April to end Oct.) – 6 ⌂ – 8 ⌂. Per night from 45 to 78€ – Per week 520€ – Reservation fee 10€
🚰 borne 20€ – 5 ▤ 6€

On an unspoilt site, close to the Lac de Naussac.

Surroundings : 🌳
Leisure activities : forest trail
Facilities : 🚿 launderette
Nearby :
GPS Longitude : 3.78105
Latitude : 44.73814

ROQUEFEUIL

11340 – Michelin map **344** C6 – pop. 276 – alt. 900
▶ Paris 813 – Montpellier 226 – Carcassonne 78

La Mare aux Fées

✆ 04 68 31 11 37, www.pyrenees-camping.com

Address : rue de l'Église (in the village)

Opening times : from mid Jan. to end Nov.

0,5 ha (23 pitches)

Tariff : 18,50€ ★★ ⚌ ▤ ฿ (16A) – Extra per person 5€ – Reservation fee 9€

Rental rates : Permanent ♿ (1 chalet) – 3 ⌂ – 6 ⌂. Per night from 75€ – Per week from 370 to 550€ – Reservation fee 9€
🚰 borne 3€ – 🚿 17€

A well-maintained site in the shadow of the church bell tower.

Surroundings :
Leisure activities : (small swimming pool)
Facilities :
Nearby :
GPS Longitude : 1.9952
Latitude : 42.8193

ROQUEFORT-DES-CORBIÈRES

11540 – Michelin map **344** I5 – pop. 947 – alt. 50
▶ Paris 813 – Montpellier 118 – Carcassonne 78 – Perpignan 45

Gîtes La Capelle (rental of gîtes only)

✆ 06 19 50 95 26, http://giteslacapelle.chez-alice.fr

Address : 4 rue la Capelle (in the town)

Opening times : from mid March to mid Oct.

0,3 ha flat

Rental rates : ℗ – 13 gîtes. Per week from 270 to 1 320€

A small group of 'semi-detached' gîtes around a swimming pool.

Surroundings :
Leisure activities :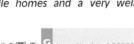
Facilities :
GPS Longitude : 2.95345
Latitude : 42.9897

LA ROQUE-SUR-CÈZE

30200 – Michelin map **339** M3 – pop. 173 – alt. 90
▶ Paris 663 – Alès 53 – Bagnols-sur-Cèze 13 – Bourg-St-Andéol 35

Les Cascades

✆ 04 66 82 72 97, www.campinglescascades.com

Address : route de Donnat (600m south along the D 166, direct access to the Cèze river)

Opening times : from mid April to mid Oct.

5 ha (118 pitches)

Tariff : 24€ ★★ ⚌ ▤ ฿ (10A) – Extra per person 4,50€ – Reservation fee 15€

Rental rates : (from mid April to mid Oct.) – 53 ⌂. Per night from 30 to 135€ – Per week from 210 to 945€ – Reservation fee 15€
🚰 borne

Pitches arranged on terraces with lots of shade, descending to a rocky river with a beach and a bathing place.

Surroundings :
Leisure activities : (beach) multi-sports ground
Facilities :
GPS Longitude : 4.52
Latitude : 44.19

LE ROZIER

48150 – Michelin map **330** H9 – pop. 145 – alt. 400
▶ Paris 632 – Florac 57 – Mende 63 – Millau 23

⛰ Les Prades ♣

℘ 05 65 62 62 09, www.
campinglesprades.com
✉ 12720 Peyreleau

Address : on the D 187 (head along the
Peyreleau (left bank), 4km west along
the D 187; beside the Tarn)

Opening times : from beginning May
to mid Sept.

3,5 ha (150 pitches)

Tariff : 31,50€ ♦♦ ⇔ 🔲 [♫] (6A)
Extra per person 6,50€ – Reservation
fee 15€

Rental rates : (from beginning May
to mid Sept.) ⚡ – 30 🏠 – 3 🛏.
Per night from 56 to 92€ – Per week
from 245 to 650€ – Reservation
fee 15€

*Below the road, some pitches
beside the Tarn river with good
sanitary facilities and an attractive small water park.*

Surroundings : 🌳🌿
Leisure activities : 🍽✕ 🎯 🛶 ⚡ 🏊 🚴
🎠 🎣 🛝
Facilities : 🚻 🔌 ░ 🚿 🚰 🍴 🔲 🏊 🧺

GPS Longitude : 3.17332
Latitude : 44.1996

⛰ Le St Pal et son Parc Longue Lègue

℘ 05 65 62 64 46, www.campingsaintpal.com ✉ 12720 Mostuéjouls

Address : at La Muse-St Pal, route des Gorges du Tarn (located
1km northwest along the D 907, follow the signs for Millau; beside
the Tarn)

Opening times : from end May to end Aug.

2 ha (105 pitches) flat, grassy

Tariff : 31€ ♦♦ ⇔ 🔲 [♫] (10A) – Extra per person 5,50€ – Reservation
fee 18€

Rental rates : (from end May to end Aug.) – 17 🏠. Per night
from 51 to 98€ – Per week from 214 to 686€ – Reservation fee 18€

*Below the road, pitches partly alongside the Tarn river with a
good standard of sanitary facilities.*

Surroundings : 🌳🌿⛰
Leisure activities : 🍽✕ 🛶 🏊 🚣 🎣
Facilities : 🚻 🔌 🚿🍴 launderette 🧺

GPS Longitude : 3.19822
Latitude : 44.19639

ST-ALBAN-SUR-LIMAGNOLE

48120 – Michelin map **330** I6 – pop. 1 519 – alt. 950
▶ Paris 558 – Montpellier 214 – Mende 39 – Le Puy-en-Velay 76

⛰ Le Galier

℘ 04 66 31 58 80, www.campinglegalier.fr
Address : route de St-Chély-d'Apcher
Opening times : from beginning March to end Sept.
12 ha/3,5 for camping (77 pitches) terraced, flat, grassy, wood
Tariff : 19,40€ ♦♦ ⇔ 🔲 [♫] (6A) – Extra per person 4,60€

Rental rates : (from beginning May to end Sept.) ⚡ – 11 🏠.
Per night from 35 to 70€ – Per week from 180 to 590€
*Some pitches are surrounded by trees and shrubs through
which the Limagnole river runs.*

Surroundings : 🛶 🌿
Facilities : 🚻 🔌 ░ 🍴

GPS Longitude : 3.37167
Latitude : 44.7752

ST-ANDRÉ-DE-SANGONIS

34725 – Michelin map **339** G7 – pop. 5 175 – alt. 65
▶ Paris 715 – Béziers 54 – Clermont-l'Hérault 8 – Gignac 5

⛰ Le Septimanien

℘ 04 67 57 84 23, www.camping-leseptimanien.com

Address : route de Cambous (located 1km southwest along the D 4,
follow the signs for Brignac; beside a stream)

Opening times : from beginning May to end Sept.

2,6 ha (86 pitches)

Tariff : (2013 Price) 25€ ♦♦ ⇔ 🔲 [♫] (10A) – Extra per person 4,50€
Reservation fee 10€

Rental rates : (2013 Price) (from beginning May to end Sept.)
10 🏠 – 9 🏠. Per week from 250 to 560€ – Reservation fee 10€

A peaceful, family-orientated site.

Surroundings : 🛶 🏚 🌳🌿
Leisure activities : 🍽 🛶 🏊
Facilities : 🚻 🔌 🍴 🔲

GPS Longitude : 3.49508
Latitude : 43.64066

*For more information on visiting particular towns or
regions, consult the relevant regional MICHELIN Green
Guide. We also recommend you use the appropriate
Michelin regional map to locate your selected campsite,
to calculate distances and to work out the best route.*

ST-BAUZILE

48000 – Michelin map **330** J8 – pop. 579 – alt. 750
▶ Paris 598 – Chanac 19 – Florac 29 – Marvejols 30

⛰ Municipal les Berges de Bramont

℘ 04 66 47 05 97, www.saint-bauzile.fr

Address : at Rouffiac (located 1.5km southwest along the D 41,
N 106, follow the signs for Mende, near the Bramont and the sports
centre)

Opening times : from beginning July to end Sept.

1,5 ha (50 pitches)

Tariff : 14,50€ ♦♦ ⇔ 🔲 [♫] (16A) – Extra per person 2,50€

Rental rates : (from beginning July to end Aug.) – 4 🏠. Per week
from 350€

🚐 borne 2,50€

*A green setting with wooden chalets equipped to a good
standard.*

Surroundings : ≤ 🌿
Leisure activities : 🎬 🛶
Facilities : 🚻 🔌 🚿 🚰 🍴
Nearby : 🍽✕ 🚲 🎯

GPS Longitude : 3.49428
Latitude : 44.47666

ST-CYPRIEN-PLAGE

66750 – Michelin map **344** J7
▶ Paris 870 – Montpellier 173 – Perpignan 21 – Carcassonne 135

⛰ Cala Gogo ♣♣

🖉 04 68 21 07 12, www.campmed.com

Address : avenue Armand Lanoux – Les Capellans (4km to the south; beside the beach)

Opening times : from beginning May to end Sept.

11 ha (649 pitches)

Tariff : 47,10€ ✚✚ ⇔ 🔲 🔌 (10A) – Extra per person 11,70€
Reservation fee 25€

Rental rates : (from beginning May to end Sept.) ♿ (1 mobile home) – 92 🚐. Per night from 33 to 190€ – Per week from 231 to 1330€ – Reservation fee 25€

New, well-appointed rental options, landscaped water park and direct access to the beach.

Surroundings : ⌐ ⚲ ⚱
Leisure activities : ♀ ✕ 🏛 🛝 🏋 ⛷ ✕ 🛝 disco
Facilities : ♿ ⚷ 🏢 ♨ 🚿 ⚶ 🚰 launderette 🗑 🛒

Longitude : 3.03789
Latitude : 42.59998

ST-GENIS-DES-FONTAINES

66740 – Michelin map **344** I7 – pop. 2 792 – alt. 63
▶ Paris 878 – Argelès-sur-Mer 10 – Le Boulou 10 – Collioure 17

⛺ La Pinède

🖉 04 68 89 75 29, www.campinglapinede66.fr

Address : avenue des Albères (south of the town along the D 2)

Opening times : from beginning June to end Aug.

1 ha (71 pitches) flat, grassy

Tariff : 29€ ✚✚ ⇔ 🔲 🔌 (10A) – Extra per person 6€ – Reservation fee 19€

Rental rates : (from beginning June to end Aug.) ✂ – 9 🚐.
Per week from 400 to 510€ – Reservation fee 19€

Attractively shaded in places by pine trees; some rental mobile homes are a little old.

Surroundings : ⚲⚲
Leisure activities : 🛝
Facilities : ♿ ⚷ 🏢 ♨ 🗑
Nearby : ✕

Longitude : 2.9245
Latitude : 42.54093

ST-GEORGES-DE-LÉVÉJAC

48500 – Michelin map **330** H9 – pop. 259 – alt. 900
▶ Paris 603 – Florac 53 – Mende 45 – Millau 49

⛺ Cassaduc

🖉 04 66 48 85 80, www.camping-cassaduc.com

Address : route du Point Sublime (1.4km southeast)

Opening times : from beginning July to end Aug.

2,2 ha (75 pitches)

Tariff : 20€ ✚✚ ⇔ 🔲 🔌 (15A) – Extra per person 6€

Rental rates : (from beginning July to end Aug.) ✂ – 2 🚐.
Per week from 430 to 480 €

🚰 borne 16€ – 6 🔲 16€

500m from the Point Sublime headland, pitches on terraces in the shade of a pretty pine wood.

Surroundings : 🐾 ⚲⚲
Leisure activities : 🏛
Facilities : ♿ ⚷ 🏢 ♨ 🚿 🚰 🗑
Nearby : ♀ ✕

Longitude : 3.24282
Latitude : 44.31532

ST-GERMAIN-DU-TEIL

48340 – Michelin map **330** H8 – pop. 810 – alt. 760
▶ Paris 601 – Montpellier 166 – Mende 46 – Millau 58

⛰ Les Chalets du Plan d'Eau de Booz

(rental of chalets only)

🖉 04 66 48 48 48, www.lozere-resa.com

Address : Booz's pond (8km southeast along the D 52, turn onto D 809, after the motorway)

5 ha flat, grassy, lake

Rentals : ♿ (1 chalet) – 43 🚐.

A wooden chalet village in a green setting, some have a good view over a bend in the Lot river. Half board available.

Surroundings : ⚲
Leisure activities : ♀ ✕ 🏛 🏋 jacuzzi ⛷ 🛝 ✿ pedalos 🏸
Facilities : ⚷ 🏢 🚰 launderette
Nearby : 🚲 forest trail

Longitude : 3.19764
Latitude : 44.45787

Michelin classification:

⛰ *Extremely comfortable, equipped to a very high standard*

⛰ *Very comfortable, equipped to a high standard*

⛰ *Comfortable and well equipped*

⛰ *Reasonably comfortable*

⛺ *Satisfactory*

ST-HIPPOLYTE-DU-FORT

30170 – Michelin map **339** I5 – pop. 3 803 – alt. 165
▶ Paris 703 – Alès 35 – Anduze 22 – Nîmes 48

⛰ Graniers

🖉 04 66 85 21 44, camping-graniers.com

Address : head 4km northeast following signs for Uzès then take D 133, follow the signs for Monoblet and take the road to the right; beside a stream

Opening times : Permanent

2 ha (50 pitches)

Tariff : (2013 Price) 24,10€ ✚✚ ⇔ 🔲 🔌 (6A) – Extra per person 4,10€

Rental rates : (2013 Price) Permanent – 2 🚐 – 3 🏠 – 2 yurts
3 canvas bungalows. Per night from 31 to 116€ – Per week from 205 to 680€

🚰 borne 5€ – 5 🔲 12€

A shady site with a range of old and new rental options.

Surroundings : 🐾 ⚲⚲
Leisure activities : ♀ ✕ 🏋 🚲 🛝
Facilities : ♿ ⚷ ♨ 🚰 🗑 🛒

Longitude : 3.88722
Latitude : 43.98084

ST-JEAN-DE-CEYRARGUES

30360 – Michelin map **339** K4 – pop. 158 – alt. 180
▶ Paris 700 – Alès 18 – Nîmes 33 – Uzès 21

⚠ Les Vistes

✆ 04 66 83 28 09, www.lesvistes.com

Address : 1 route des Vistes (500m south along the D 7)

Opening times : from beginning April to end Sept. and All Saints' Day holiday (1 Nov./half-term)

6 ha/3 for camping (52 pitches) open site, relatively flat, flat, grassy, stony

Tariff : 27,50€ ✶✶ ⇔ 🔲 ⚡ (6A) – Extra per person 6,70€

Rental rates : (from beginning April to end Sept. All Saints' Day (1 Nov./half-term) and Christmas holidays) ♿ (1 chalet) – 12 🏠 5 canvas bungalows. Per week from 240 to 710€

An attractive, panoramic location.

Surroundings : ≼ Mt Aigoual ♒
Leisure activities : 🎮 🏄 ♨
Facilities : ♿ ⛽ 🅿 🚿 🛁 🍴 📦 refrigerators
GPS Longitude : 4.23016
Latitude : 44.04734

ST-JEAN-DU-GARD

30270 – Michelin map **339** I4 – pop. 2 687 – alt. 183
▶ Paris 675 – Alès 28 – Florac 54 – Lodève 91

⚠ Mas de la Cam 👥

✆ 04 66 85 12 02, www.masdelacam.fr

Address : route de Saint-André-de-Valborgne (3km northwest along the D 907; beside the Gardon de St-Jean)

Opening times : from end April to end Sept.

6 ha (200 pitches)

Tariff : (2013 Price) 38,50€ ✶✶ ⇔ 🔲 ⚡ (6A) – Extra per person 8,50€ Reservation fee 17€

Rental rates : (2013 Price) (from end April to end Sept.) ♨ 6 gîtes. Per night from 55 to 91€ – Per week from 385 to 635€ Reservation fee 17€

An attractive children's playground area.

Surroundings : 🌲 ≼ 🏞 ♒
Leisure activities : 🍴 🍽 🎮 ♿ 🏄 🏸 ♨ 🌊 🎣 multi-sports ground
Facilities : ♿ ⛽ 🛁 🍴 📦 🚿 🛒
GPS Longitude : 3.85319
Latitude : 44.1123

⚠ Les Sources

✆ 04 66 85 38 03, www.camping-des-sources.fr

Address : route de Mialet (located 1km northeast along the D 983 and D 50)

Opening times : from beginning April to end Sept.

3 ha (92 pitches)

Tariff : 16,50€ ✶✶ ⇔ 🔲 ⚡ (10A)

Extra per person 3,50€ – Reservation fee 10€

Rental rates : (from beginning April to end Sept.) – 3 🏕 – 15 🏠 3 canvas bungalows. Per night 92 € – Per week from 45 to 644€ Reservation fee 12€

🚐 borne 2€ – 🚰 ⚡16,50€

A family atmosphere and well shaded pitches.

Surroundings : 🌲 ≼ 🏞 ♒
Leisure activities : 🍴 🍽 🎮 🏄 ♨
Facilities : ♿ ⛽ 🛒 🛁 🚿 🍴 launderette 🛒
GPS Longitude : 3.89258
Latitude : 44.11393

⚠ La Forêt

✆ 04 66 85 37 00, www.campingalaforet.com

Address : route de Falguières (situated 2km north along the D 983, follow the signs for St-Étienne-Vallée-Française then continue 2km along the D 333)

Opening times : from mid May to beginning Sept.

3 ha (65 pitches) terraced, flat, grassy, stony

Tariff : (2013 Price) 33€ ✶✶ ⇔ 🔲 ⚡ (10A) – Extra per person 7,50€ Reservation fee 5€

Rental rates : (2013 Price) (from mid May to beginning Sept.) ♨ 3 🏠. Per week from 273 to 583€

At the edge of a spacious pine grove.

Surroundings : 🌲 ≼ 🏞 ♒
Leisure activities : 🏄 ♨
Facilities : ♿ ⛽ 🛁 🍴 📦 🛒 refrigerators
GPS Longitude : 3.89072
Latitude : 44.12948

ST-LÉGER-DE-PEYRE

48100 – Michelin map **330** H7 – pop. 174 – alt. 780
▶ Paris 581 – Montpellier 188 – Mende 34 – Marvejols 6

⚠ Village Vacances Hameau Ste-Lucie

(rental of gîtes only)

✆ 04 66 48 48 48, www.lozere-resa.com – alt. 1 100

Address : at Sainte-Lucie

30 ha/2 for camping

Rentals : 12 gîtes.

A 180° view of the Lozère river, with absolute peace, very close to the wolf park.

Surroundings : 🌲 ≼ Mont Lozère, Mont Aigoual
Leisure activities : 🍴 🍽
Facilities : ⛽ 🅿 🍴 📦
Nearby : Parc aux loups du Gévaudan (wolf park)
GPS Longitude : 3.28517
Latitude : 44.60649

Some campsites benefit from proximity to a municipal leisure centre.

ST-PAUL-LE-FROID

48600 – Michelin map **330** J6 – pop. 147 – alt. 1 302 – Winter sports : ⛷
▶ Paris 582 – Montpellier 237 – Mende 54 – Le Puy-en-Velay 61

⚠ Village Vacances les Baraques des Bouviers

(rental of chalets and 'nordiques' chalets only)

✆ 04 66 48 48 48, www.lesbouviers.com – alt. 1 418

Address : la Baraque des Bouviers (8.5km southeast along the D 58 and D 5, follow the signs for St-Alban-sur-Limagnole)

Opening times : Permanent

20 ha/2 for camping open site, terraced

Rental rates : (2013 Price) ♿ – 14 🏠. Per week from 206 to 766€

Chalets spaced out across the Plateau de La Margeride, at the foot of cross-country ski pistes and snowshoe hiking trails.

Surroundings : 🌲 ≼ ♒
Leisure activities : 🎮
Facilities : ⛽ 🛁 🍴 📦
Nearby : 🍴 🍽 🚴 climbing
GPS Longitude : 3.50574
Latitude : 44.76617

ST-VICTOR-DE-MALCAP

30500 – Michelin map **339** K3 – pop. 683 – alt. 140
▶ Paris 680 – Alès 23 – Barjac 15 – La Grand-Combe 25

🏕 Domaine de Labeiller 🏃

☎ 04 66 24 15 27, www.labeiller.fr

Address : 1701 route de Barjac (located 1km southeast, access via the D 51, follow the signs for St-Jean-de-Maruéjols and take road to the left)

Opening times : from mid May to end Aug.

3 ha (132 pitches)

Tariff : 37€ 🏃 🏃 🚐 🔲 🔌 (6A) – Extra per person 7€ – Reservation fee 15€

Rental rates : (from mid May to end Aug.) – 20 🚐 – 3 gîtes. Per week from 250 to 910€ – Reservation fee 15€

In a pleasant oak wood set around an attractive swimming area.

Surroundings : 🏞 🏕 🎣
Leisure activities : 🍷 ✗ 🎯 🏃 🎿
🏊
Facilities : 🚿 🔧 🚮 ⛺ 🚰 launderette
Nearby : 🍴

GPS Longitude : 4.22727
Latitude : 44.24154

STE-ÉNIMIE

48210 – Michelin map **330** I8 – pop. 525 – alt. 470
▶ Paris 612 – Florac 27 – Mende 28 – Meyrueis 30

🏕 Le Couderc

☎ 04 66 48 50 53, www.campingcouderc.fr

Address : route de Millau (situated 2km southwest along the D 907bis; beside the Tarn river)

Opening times : from beginning April to end Sept.

2,5 ha (130 pitches)

Tariff : 28€ 🏃 🏃 🚐 🔲 🔌 (16A) – Extra per person 5€ – Reservation fee 15€

Rental rates : (from beginning April to end Sept.) – 7 🚐. Per week from 250 to 650€– Reservation fee 15€

🚐 borne 4€

Below the road, with very well-shaded pitches beside the Tarn river.

Surroundings : 🎣 🏕 ⛺
Leisure activities : 🍷 🏊 🎣 🛶
Facilities : 🚿 🔧 🚮 ⛺ 🚰 launderette

GPS Longitude : 3.39917
Latitude : 44.35194

⛺ Les Fayards

☎ 04 66 48 57 36, www.camping-les-fayards.com

Address : route de Millau (3km southwest along the D 907bis; beside the Tarn river)

Opening times : from beginning May to mid Sept.

2 ha (77 pitches)

Tariff : (2013 Price) 30€ 🏃 🏃 🚐 🔲 🔌 (16A) – Extra per person 4€

Rental rates : (2013 Price) (from beginning May to mid Sept.) 2 caravans – 14 🚐 – 4 🏠. Per night from 53 to 70€ – Per week from 280 to 695€

Below the road, pitches on terraces beside the Tarn river.

Surroundings : 🏞 🏕 ⛺
Leisure activities : 🍷 🎣 🛶 🛶
Facilities : 🚿 🔧 ⛺ 🚰 launderette

GPS Longitude : 3.39504
Latitude : 44.34583

⛺ Le Site

☎ 04 66 48 58 08, www.gorges-du-tarn.fr

Address : place known : Castelbouc (7km southeast along the D 907b, follow the signs for Ispagnac then continue 500m to the right following signs for Castelbouc; beside the Tarn river)

Opening times : from mid April to end Sept.

1 ha (60 pitches) open site, relatively flat, flat, grassy

Tariff : 18€ 🏃 🏃 🚐 🔲 🔌 (5A) – Extra per person 4€

Rental rates : (from mid May to mid Sept.) – 10 🚐. Per week from 450 to 560€

Bordered by the river and opposite a small waterfall.

Surroundings : 🏊 🏕 ⛺ ⛺
Leisure activities : 🛶 🛶
Facilities : 🚿 🔧 🚰 📷

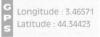

GPS Longitude : 3.46571
Latitude : 44.34423

STE-MARIE

66470 – Michelin map **344** J6 – pop. 4 641 – alt. 4
▶ Paris 845 – Argelès-sur-Mer 24 – Le Boulou 37 – Perpignan 14

🏕 Le Palais de la Mer 🏃

☎ 04 68 73 07 94, www.palaisdelamer.com

Address : avenue de Las Illes (600m north of the resort, 150m from the beach (direct access)

Opening times : from mid May to end Sept.

8 ha/3 for camping (181 pitches)

Tariff : 45€ 🏃 🏃 🚐 🔲 🔌 (10A) – Extra per person 7,50€ – Reservation fee 35€

In a shaded setting with rows of laurel trees marking out the paths.

Surroundings : 🏕 ⛺
Leisure activities : 🍷 ✗ 🎯 nighttime 🏃 🎿 hammam, jacuzzi 🛶 🏸 🏊 wildlife park
Facilities : 🚿 🔧 ⛺ 🚐 🚰 launderette 🏊 🛒

GPS Longitude : 3.03307
Latitude : 42.74045

⛺ Camp'Atlantique La Pergola

☎ 04 68 73 03 07, www.campinglapergola.com

Address : 21 avenue Frédéric Mistral (500m from the beach)

3,5 ha (181 pitches)

Rentals : 🏠 – 20 🚐 – 9 mobile homes (without sanitary facilities).

Surroundings : ⛺
Leisure activities : ✗ 🎯 🛶 🏊
Facilities : 🚿 🔧 🏊 🚐 🚰 launderette 🧊 refrigerators
Nearby : 🍴

GPS Longitude : 3.03315
Latitude : 42.72672

These symbols are used for a campsite that is exceptional in its category:

🏕🏕🏕 ... ⛺ *Particularly pleasant setting, quality and range of services available*

🏊🏊 *Tranquil, isolated site – quiet site, particularly at night*

≤≤ *Exceptional view – interesting or panoramic view*

SÉRIGNAN

34410 – Michelin map **339** E9 – pop. 6 631 – alt. 7
▶ Paris 765 – Agde 22 – Béziers 11 – Narbonne 34

▲▲▲ FranceLoc Le Domaine Les Vignes d'Or ▲▲

(rental of mobile homes and chalets only)

✆ 04 67 32 37 18, www.vignesdor.com

Address : chemin de l'Hermitage (3.5km to the south, take the side road located behind the Citroën garage)

Opening times : from beginning April to end Sept.

4 ha (240 pitches)

Rental rates : ♿ (2 mobile homes) – 165 🏠 – 15 🏠. Per night from 28 to 108€ – Per week from 196 to 756€ – Reservation fee 27€

Surroundings : ⛱ ⛺ 🌳🌳
Leisure activities : ▼ ✕ 🎯🏊‍♂️ 🚣 🎣 ⛵ 🏖 multi-sports ground
Facilities : ♿ ⛽ 🚿 💈 🛒 🚰
Nearby : ✕ 🐎

GPS Longitude : 3.2757
     Latitude : 43.2593

▲▲ Le Paradis

✆ 04 67 32 24 03, www.camping-leparadis.com ⚡

Address : route de Valras-Plage (located 1.5km to the south)

Opening times : from beginning April to end Sept.

2,2 ha (129 pitches) flat, grassy

Tariff : 33,50€ ✦✦ 🚗 🔲 💡 (10A) – Extra per person 6€ – Reservation fee 17€

Rental rates : (from beginning April to end Sept.) ⚡ – 19 🏠 5 mobile homes (without sanitary facilities). Per night from 43 to 92€ – Per week from 190 to 640€ – Reservation fee 17€
🚰 borne

A pleasant setting with flowers and large pitches.

Surroundings : ⛺ 🌳🌳
Leisure activities : ✕ 🏖 🚣 🏊
Facilities : ♿ ⛽ 🚽 💈 🏊 🚰 💈 launderette 🚰

GPS Longitude : 3.28628
     Latitude : 43.26829

▲▲ Le Mas des Lavandes (rental of mobile homes only)

✆ 04 67 39 75 88, www.lemasdeslavandes.fr

Address : chemin de la mer (D 19 follow the signs for Valras-Plage – from the A9 take exit Béziers-est)

Opening times : Permanent

3,8 ha flat

Rental rates : ♿ (1 mobile home) – 134 🏠. Per night from 32 to 142€ – Per week from 220 to 990€ – Reservation fee 21€

Luxury mobile homes, but choose those further away from the road in preference.

Surroundings : ⛺ 🌳🌳
Leisure activities : ▼ ✕ 🏖 🎯🏊‍♂️ 🚣 ⚡ 🏊 🏖
Facilities : ♿ ⛽ 💈 🛒 🚰

GPS Longitude : 3.2831
     Latitude : 43.25732

Routes nationales are main roads and their identifying numbers begin with N or RN. Routes départementales are generally quieter roads and begin with D or DN.

SÉRIGNAN-PLAGE

34410 – Michelin map **339** E9
▶ Paris 769 – Montpellier 73 – Carcassonne 100

▲▲▲▲ Yelloh! Village Le Sérignan Plage ▲▲

✆ 04 67 32 35 33, www.leserignanplage.com

Address : at L'Orpellière (On the edge of the beach, direct access)

Opening times : from end April to end Sept.

20 ha (1200 pitches)

Tariff : 57€ ✦✦ 🚗 🔲 💡 (10A) – Extra per person 10€

Rental rates : Permanent ⚡ – 432 🏠 – 18 🏠. Per night from 39 to 312€ – Per week from 273 to 2184€
🚰 borne

Natural, sunny pitches, close to the marsh; luxury rental options with plenty of shade close to the beach.

Surroundings : ⛱ ⛺ 🌳🌳 ⚓
Leisure activities : ▼ ✕ 🏖 🎯🏊‍♂️ 🎣 🚣 🚴 ⚡ 🏊 🏖 spa centre (naturist in mornings), disco, multi-sports ground
Facilities : ♿ ⛽ 💈 🛒 launderette 🚰 🚰
Nearby : 🐎 🐎

GPS Longitude : 3.3213
     Latitude : 43.26401

▲▲▲ Yelloh! Village Aloha ▲▲

✆ 04 67 39 71 30, www.alohacamping.com

Address : chemin des Dunes

Opening times : from end April to mid Sept.

9,5 ha (470 pitches)

Tariff : 57€ ✦✦ 🚗 🔲 💡 (10A) – Extra per person 9€

Rental rates : (from end April to mid Sept.) 🅿 – 184 🏠 – 15 🏠. Per night from 49 to 369€ – Per week from 343 to 2583€
🚰 borne – 3 🔲 57€

On both sides of the path leading to the beach, with rental options in a landscaped setting.

Surroundings : ⛱ ⛺ 🌳🌳 ⚓
Leisure activities : ▼ ✕ 🏖 🎯🏊‍♂️ 🎣 jacuzzi 🚣 🚴 ⚡ 🏊 multi-sports ground
Facilities : ♿ ⛽ 💈 🛒 launderette 🚰 🚰
Nearby : 🎣 🐎 🐎

GPS Longitude : 3.33941
     Latitude : 43.26745

▲▲▲ Domaine de Beauséjour ▲▲

✆ 04 67 39 50 93, www.camping-beausejour.com

Address : beside the beach

Opening times : from beginning April to end Sept.

10 ha/6 for camping (380 pitches)

Tariff : 45€ ✦✦ 🚗 🔲 💡 (10A) – Extra per person 7,80€ – Reservation fee 15€

Rental rates : (from beginning April to end Sept.) – 84 🏠 6 🏠. Per night from 33 to 156 € – Per week from 231 to 1092€ Reservation fee 15€

A very pleasant spa centre, open year round.

Surroundings : ⛱ ⛺ 🌳🌳 ⚓
Leisure activities : ▼ ✕ 🌙 nighttime 🎯🏊‍♂️ 🎣 hammam, jacuzzi 🚣 🚴 🏊 disco, watersports centre, spa centre
Facilities : ♿ ⛽ 💈 🛒 launderette 🚰 🚰

GPS Longitude : 3.33692
     Latitude : 43.26711

🏔 Le Clos Virgile 👥

📞 04 67 32 20 64, www.leclosvirgile.com

Address : 500m from the beach

Opening times : from beginning May to mid Sept.

5 ha (300 pitches)

Tariff : (2013 Price) 41€ 🚶🚶 🚗 🔲 🔌 (10A) – Extra per person 7,50€
Reservation fee 25€

Rental rates : (2013 Price) Permanent 🛏 – 100 🚐 – 18 🏠.
Per night from 28 to 128€ – Per week from 195 to 890€
Reservation fee 25€

🚉 borne – 49 🔲

Shady pitches with rather old sanitary facilities.

Surroundings : 🛏 🌿🌿
Leisure activities : 🍽🍴 🛶 🎣🏃 jacuzzi 🏄🛷🛝🏊 multi-sports ground
Facilities : ♿🔓 🚿🍴🔲🛁🚰
Nearby : 🏊🐎

GPS Longitude : 3.33152
Latitude : 43.27204

This guide is updated regularly, so buy your new copy every year!

SOMMIÈRES

30250 – Michelin map **339** J6 – pop. 4 496 – alt. 34
▶ Paris 734 – Alès 44 – Montpellier 35 – Nîmes 29

🏔 Les Castels Le Domaine de Massereau

📞 04 66 53 11 20, www.massereau.com

Address : 1990 route d'Aubais (Les Hauteurs de Sommières (heights)

Opening times : from mid April to mid Oct.

90 ha/7,7 for camping (120 pitches)

Tariff : 46,40€ 🚶🚶 🚗 🔲 🔌 (16A)
Extra per person 11€ – Reservation fee 24€

Rental rates : (from mid April to mid Oct.) ♿ – 35 🚐 – 24 🏠.
Per night from 50 to 195€ – Per week from 300 to 1370€ – Reservation fee 24€

🚉 borne 2€ – 4 🔲 25,80€

Luxury rental options, in the middle of a vineyard complex with a cycling trail running across it (Sommières–Nîmes).

Surroundings : 🏊 🛏 🌿🌿
Leisure activities : 🍽🍴 ♨ hammam, jacuzzi 🏄🚴🏓🎣🏊🏛 fitness trail, multi-sports ground
Facilities : ♿🔓 🛁🚰🍴 launderette 🛁🚰
Nearby : 🎣

GPS Longitude : 4.09735
Latitude : 43.76574

🏕 Municipal de Garanel

📞 04 66 80 33 49, campingmunicipal.sommieres@wanadoo.fr

Address : chemin Princesse (In the town, near the Vidourle river)

Opening times : from beginning April to end Sept.

7 ha (60 pitches)

Tariff : (2013 Price) 16,45€ 🚶🚶 🚗 🔲 🔌 (10A)
Extra per person 3,80€ – Reservation fee 16€

🚉 borne 3,30€

Very close to a sports arena and the town centre.

Surroundings : 🛏 🌿🌿
Facilities : ♿🔓 🗄🛁🍴🔲
Nearby : 🏊🍽🍴🛁🏊

GPS Longitude : 4.08703
Latitude : 43.78738

LA TAMARISSIÈRE

34300 – Michelin map **339** F9
▶ Paris 761 – Montpellier 62 – Béziers 24 – Narbonne 54

🏔 La Tama

📞 04 67 94 79 46, www.camping-latama.com

Address : 4 rue du Commandant Malet

Opening times : from mid April to mid Sept.

10 ha (700 pitches) undulating, flat and relatively flat, grassy, sandy

Tariff : 33€ 🚶🚶 🚗 🔲 🔌 (10A) – Extra per person 6,50€ – Reservation fee 27€

Rental rates : (from mid April to mid Sept.) ♿ (2 chalets) 60 🏠 – 30 tent lodges. Per night from 30 to 65€ – Per week from 210 to 819€ – Reservation fee 27€

A pleasant location beside the sea, sheltered by pine trees.

Surroundings : 🌿🌿🏖
Leisure activities : 🏄 multi-sports ground
Facilities : ♿🔓🏛 🛁🍴 launderette, refrigerated food storage facilities
Nearby : 🏊🍽🍴🛁🎣

GPS Longitude : 3.44249
Latitude : 43.28821

*The classification (1 to 5 tents, **black** or red) that we award to selected sites in this guide is our own system. It should not be confused with the classification (1 to 5 stars) of official organisations.*

TORREILLES-PLAGE

66440 – Michelin map **344** I6
▶ Paris 853 – Montpellier 157 – Perpignan 20 – Carcassonne 119

🏔 Sunêlia Les Tropiques 👥

CARRERAS

📞 04 68 28 05 09, www.campinglestropiques.com

Address : boulevard de la Plage (500m from the beach)

Opening times : from mid April to end Sept.

8 ha (450 pitches)

Tariff : 57,10€ 🚶🚶 🚗 🔲 🔌 (10A)
Extra per person 11,55€ – Reservation fee 35€

Rental rates : (from mid April to end Sept.) ♿ (2 mobile homes) 240 🚐 – 26 🏠 – 2 tent lodges. Per night from 42 to 213€ Per week from 250 to 1 491€ – Reservation fee 35€

🚉 borne – 🚰🔌 18,20€

Shady pitches and a pleasant spa centre.

Surroundings : 🛏 🌿🌿
Leisure activities : 🍽🍴 🛶🎣🏃🎿♨ hammam, jacuzzi 🏄🏓🏊 disco, multi-sports ground, spa centre
Facilities : ♿🔓 🛁🍴 launderette 🛁🚰
Nearby : 🐎🏃

GPS Longitude : 3.02972
Latitude : 42.7675

▲ Mar I Sol ▲▲

℘ 0468280407, www.camping-marisol.com – limited spaces for one-night stay

Address : boulevard de la Plage (150m from the beach – direct access)

Opening times : from mid April to mid Sept.

7 ha (377 pitches)

Tariff : 61€ ♠♠ ⌂ 🔲 🛢 (10A) – Extra per person 11€ – Reservation fee 49,50€

Rental rates : (from mid April to mid Sept.) ⛲ (from mid April to mid Sept) – 100 🚐 – 6 🏠. Per night from 29 to 188€ – Per week from 203 to 1316€ – Reservation fee 49,50€

A real village club with lots of activities and a large water park.

Surroundings : 🏕 ♀	
Leisure activities : ♟ ✕ 🏛 ⊙ 🏃 🎣 ⛵ hammam, jacuzzi 🚲 🏊 ⛸ disco, multi-sports ground	**G** Longitude : 3.03327 **P** Latitude : 42.76746 **S**
Facilities : 🚿 🔌 🛢 🍴 launderette 🗑	
Nearby : 🏇	

▲ Le Calypso ▲▲

℘ 0468280947, www.camping-calypso.com – limited spaces for one-night stay

Address : boulevard de la Plage

Opening times : from mid April to end Sept.

6 ha (308 pitches)

Tariff : 50€ ♠♠ ⌂ 🔲 🛢 (10A) – Extra per person 10,50€ – Reservation fee 30€

Rental rates : (from mid April to end Sept.) ⛲ – 80 🚐 – 28 🏠. Per night from 20 to 200€ – Per week from 140 to 1400€ Reservation fee 30€

A pretty play and paddling pool area and individual sanitary facilities for some pitches.

Surroundings : 🏕 ♀♀	
Leisure activities : ♟ ✕ 🏛 ⊙ 🏃 🎣 jacuzzi 🚲 🚲 🏊 ⛸ multi-sports ground	**G** Longitude : 3.03043 **P** Latitude : 42.77128 **S**
Facilities : 🚿 🔌 🛢 – 9 individual sanitary facilities (🚿 🚽 wc) 🍴 launderette 🗑 🗑 refrigerators	
Nearby : 🏇 🐎	

▲ Homair Vacances La Palmeraie ▲▲

℘ 0468282064, www.homair.com

Address : boulevard de la Plage

Opening times : from mid April to mid Sept.

4,5 ha (229 pitches)

Tariff : 41€ ♠♠ ⌂ 🔲 🛢 (6A) – Extra per person 8,50€ – Reservation fee 20€

Rental rates : 180 🚐. Per night from 17 to 185€ – Per week from 119 to 1295€ – Reservation fee 20€

Good covering of shade for the mobile homes, but very few pitches for tents and caravans.

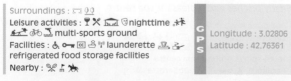

Surroundings : 🏕 ♀♀	
Leisure activities : ♟ ✕ 🏛 ⊙ nighttime 🏃 🚲 🚲 🏊 multi-sports ground	**G** Longitude : 3.02806 **P** Latitude : 42.76361 **S**
Facilities : 🚿 🔌 🅿 🛢 🍴 launderette 🗑 🗑 refrigerated food storage facilities	
Nearby : 🎣 🏇 🐎	

11800 – Michelin map **344** F3 – pop. 5 416 – alt. 84

▶ Paris 776 – Carcassonne 8 – Conques-sur-Orbiel 9 – Lézignan-Corbières 28

▲ A l'Ombre des Micocouliers

℘ 0468786175, www.campingmicocouliers.com

Address : chemin de la Lande

Opening times : from beginning April to end Sept.

1,5 ha (70 pitches)

Tariff : 22€ ♠♠ ⌂ 🔲 🛢 (16A) – Extra per person 5,50€

Rental rates : (from beginning April to end Sept.) – 5 canvas bungalows. Per night from 26 to 44€ – Per week from 130 to 480€ 🚐 borne 5€

Situated beside the Aude river in the shade of hackberry trees, but with rather old sanitary facilities.

Surroundings : 🏕 ♀♀	
Leisure activities : ✕ 🏛 🚲 🎣 🛶	**G** Longitude : 2.44237 **P** Latitude : 43.20682 **S**
Facilities : 🚿 🔌 🛢 🍴 🅿 🗑	
Nearby : 🎣 🏊	

30700 – Michelin map **339** L4 – pop. 8 339 – alt. 138

▶ Paris 682 – Alès 34 – Arles 52 – Avignon 38

▲ Le Moulin Neuf ▲▲

℘ 0466221721, www.le-moulin-neuf.fr

Address : at Saint-Quentin-La-Poterie (4.5km northeast along the D 982, follow the signs for Bagnols-sur-Cèze and take the D 5 to the left)

Opening times : from beginning April to end Sept.

5 ha (140 pitches)

Tariff : (2013 Price) 24€ ♠♠ ⌂ 🔲 🛢 (5A) – Extra per person 6,40€ Reservation fee 10€

Rental rates : (2013 Price) Permanent – 35 🏠. Per night from 50 to 100 € – Per week from 245 to 650 € – Reservation fee 10€ 🚐 borne

A rectangular site, shaded by poplars, featuring rather old gîtes of modest comfort levels.

Surroundings : 🌲 🏕 ♀♀	
Leisure activities : ♟ ✕ 🏛 🏃 🚲 🎣 🏊 🛶 multi-sports ground	**G** Longitude : 4.45569 **P** Latitude : 44.0321 **S**
Facilities : 🚿 🔌 🛢 🍴 🅿 🗑 🗑	
Nearby : 🐎	

▲ Le Mas de Rey

℘ 0466221827, www.campingmasderey.com

Address : route d'Anduze (3km southwest along the D 982)

Opening times : from beginning April to mid Oct.

5 ha/2,5 for camping (66 pitches) flat, grassy

Tariff : 26,50€ ♠♠ ⌂ 🔲 🛢 (10A) – Extra per person 8€ – Reservation fee 10€

Rental rates : (from beginning April to mid Oct.) 🚿 (1 chalet) 6 🚐 – 2 🏠 – 2 tent lodges. Per night from 60 to 100€ Per week from 375 to 880€ – Reservation fee 10€

Very peaceful pitches and luxurious wooden chalets in pleasant shade.

Surroundings : 🌲 🏕 ♀♀	
Leisure activities : 🏛 🚲 🏊	**G** Longitude : 4.38471 **P** Latitude : 43.99806 **S**
Facilities : 🚿 🔌 🛢 🍴 🅿 🗑	

VALLABRÈGUES

60300 – Michelin map **339** M5 – pop. 1 318 – alt. 8

◨ Paris 698 – Arles 26 – Avignon 22 – Beaucaire 9

⛺ Lou Vincen

℘ 04 66 59 21 29, www.campinglouvincen.com

Address : to the west of the town, 100m from the Rhône and a small lake

Opening times : from beginning April to end Oct.

1,4 ha (75 pitches) flat, grassy

Tariff : 26,50 € ♛♛ ⇔ 🔲 🔌 (6A) – Extra per person 7,80 €

Reservation fee 17 €

Rental rates : (from mid April to mid Oct.) ⌘ – 10 🚐. Per week from 297 to 615 € – Reservation fee 17 €

🚰 borne

At the entrance to the town, on the left bank of the Rhône.

		G P S	
Surroundings : ⌁ ⌂ 🌿🌿			
Leisure activities : ⤢		Longitude : 4.62546	
Facilities : ⌖ ⌕ ⤳ ⤳ 🏳 🔳		Latitude : 43.85493	
Nearby : ✕			

VALLERAUGUE

30570 – Michelin map **339** G4 – pop. 1 070 – alt. 346

◨ Paris 684 – Mende 100 – Millau 75 – Nîmes 86

⛺ Le Mourétou

℘ 04.67.82.22.30, www.camping-mouretou.com

Address : route de l'Aigoual and on the right way (3km west on the D 986)

1 ha (33 pitches)

Rentals : 4 🚐 – 2 gîtes.

Well-shaded pitches beside the Hérault river and a small lake.

		G P S	
Surroundings : ⌂ 🌿🌿			
Leisure activities : ✕ ⤢ ⤢ (small swimming pool)		Longitude : 3.60785	
Facilities : 🔳 🚿		Latitude : 44.0871	
Nearby : ⥿ (fresh water)			

VALRAS-PLAGE

34350 – Michelin map **339** E9 – pop. 4 649 – alt. 1

◨ Paris 767 – Agde 25 – Béziers 16 – Montpellier 76

🏔 Domaine de La Yole ♟♟

℘ 04 67 37 33 87, www.campinglayole.com

Address : situated 2km southwest, 500m from the beach

Opening times : from mid April to mid Sept.

23 ha (1273 pitches)

Tariff : 53 € ♛♛ ⇔ 🔲 🔌 (5A) – Extra per person 9,20 € – Reservation fee 30 €

Rental rates : (from mid April to mid Sept.) ℗ – 225 🚐

49 🏠. Per night from 58 to 212 € – Per week from 407 to 1 484 € Reservation fee 30 €

There's a vineyard nearby, plus a farmhouse restaurant.

		G P S	
Surroundings : ⌂ 🌿🌿			
Leisure activities : ♟ ✕ 📷 ⌾ ⤢ ⤢ ⤢ 🚲 ⌫ ⤢ ⤢ forest trail, multi-sports ground		Longitude : 3.27181	
Facilities : ⌖ ⌕ ⤳ ⤳ ⤳ 🏳 launderette 🛒 🚿		Latitude : 43.23639	
Nearby : 🐴			

🏔 La Plage et du Bord de Mer ♟♟

℘ 04 67 37 34 38, www.camping-plage-mediterranee.com ⌘

Address : route de Vendres (located 1.5km southwest; beside the sea)

Opening times : from beginning May to end Sept.

13 ha (655 pitches)

Tariff : 48 € ♛♛ ⇔ 🔲 🔌 (6A) – Extra per person 6 € – Reservation fee 30 €

Rental rates : (from beginning May to end Sept.) ⌘ – 44 🚐 6 tent lodges. Per night from 40 to 220 € – Per week from 280 to 1 540 € – Reservation fee 30 €

A good choice of pitches for tents and caravans, with sanitary facilities that are well maintained but rather old-fashioned.

		G P S	
Surroundings : ⌂ 🌿 ⥿			
Leisure activities : ♟ ✕ 📷 ⤢ ⤢ ⤢ 🚲 ⌫ ⌂ ⤢ ⤢ multi-sports ground		Longitude : 3.26889	
Facilities : ⌖ ⌕ ⤳ ⤳ 🏳 launderette 🛒 🚿		Latitude : 43.23559	
Nearby : 🐴 🐴			

🏔 Lou Village ♟♟

℘ 04 67 37 33 79, www.louvillage.com – limited spaces for one-night stay

Address : chemin des Montilles (2km southwest, 100m from the beach)

Opening times : from beginning May to mid Sept.

8 ha (470 pitches)

Tariff : 53,50 € ♛♛ ⇔ 🔲 🔌 (10A) – Extra per person 9 € – Reservation fee 30 €

Rental rates : (from beginning May to mid Sept.) ⌘ – 105 🚐 20 🏠. Per night from 51 to 180 € – Per week from 460 to 1 270 € Reservation fee 30 €

🚰 borne

A water park and direct access to the beach are the site's plus points.

		G P S	
Surroundings : ⌂ 🌿🌿 ⥿			
Leisure activities : ♟ ✕ 📷 ⌾ nighttime 🏃 ⤢ ⌫ ⤢ ⤢		Longitude : 3.26046	
Facilities : ⌖ ⌕ ⤳ 🏳 🔳 ⤳ 🛒 🚿 🚿		Latitude : 43.23386	
Nearby : 🐴 🐴 jet skis			

🏔 Le Méditerranée

℘ 04 67 37 34 29, www.camping-le-mediterranee.com

Address : route de Vendres (located 1.5km southwest, 200m from the beach)

4,5 ha (367 pitches)

Rentals : 65 🚐 – 10 🏠 – 5 mobile homes (without sanitary facilities).

A shady site with numerous pitches for tents and caravans.

		G P S	
Surroundings : 🌿🌿			
Leisure activities : ♟ ✕ 📷 ⤢ ⤢ ⤢ ⤢ multi-sports ground		Longitude : 3.26848	
Facilities : ⌖ ⌕ 🏳 launderette 🚿 🚿 refrigerators		Latitude : 43.23592	
Nearby : 🚲 🐴 🐴			

The guide covers all 22 regions of France – see the map and list of regions on pages 4–5.

🏔 Les Foulègues ♣♣

📞 04 67 37 33 65, www.campinglesfoulegues.com

Address : at Grau-de-Vendres, avenue du Port (5km southwest, 400m from the beach)

Opening times : from mid April to end Sept.

5,3 ha (339 pitches)

Tariff : (2013 Price) 48,50€ ♣♣ 🚗 🔲 🔌 (6A) – Extra per person 8,50€ Reservation fee 30€

Rental rates : (2013 Price) (from end April to mid Sept.) – 39 🚐 4 🏠. Per week from 305 to 965€ – Reservation fee 30€

A pleasant site with lots of shade and rather old chalet rental options.

Surroundings : 🗺 ♀♀
Leisure activities : 🍽 ✕ 🏛 🌙 nighttime 🏃
🏊 🏇 m 🛝 🏊
Facilities : 🛁 ⚡ 👶 🧺 🚰 🍽 🏪 🧺 🛒
Nearby : 🏇

Longitude : 3.24222
Latitude : 43.22575

VERNET-LES-BAINS

66820 – Michelin map **344** F7 – pop. 1 432 – alt. 650 – ♨
▶ Paris 904 – Mont-Louis 36 – Perpignan 57 – Prades 11

🏔 L'Eau Vive

📞 04 68 05 54 14, www.leauvive-camping.com

Address : chemin St Saturnin (take exit towards Sahorre then continue after the bridge 1.3km along the av. St-Saturnin to the right, near the Cady river)

Opening times : from beginning April to end Oct.

2 ha (90 pitches)

Tariff : 26,50€ ♣♣ 🚗 🔲 🔌 (10A) – Extra per person 5€ – Reservation fee 15€

Rental rates : (from beginning April to end Oct.) 🛁 (1 chalet) 7 🚐 – 9 🏠. Per night from 46€ – Per week from 314 to 735€ Reservation fee 15€

In a pleasant location.

Surroundings : 🏞 ⋚ ♀
Leisure activities : 🍽 ✕ jacuzzi 🏊 🛝
Facilities : 🛁 ⚡ 👶 🧺 🚰 🍽 🏪
Longitude : 2.38342
Latitude : 42.5527

VERS-PONT-DU-GARD

30210 – Michelin map **339** M5 – pop. 1 696 – alt. 40
▶ Paris 698 – Montpellier 81 – Nîmes 26 – Avignon 27

🏔 FranceLoc Gorges du Gardon ♣♣

📞 04 66 22 81 81, www.franceloc.fr

Address : 762 chemin Barque-Vieille (to the south, D 981 and D 5; beside the Gardon river)

4 ha (197 pitches)

Rentals : 🛁 (1 mobile home) – 104 🚐 – 4 🏠.

Numerous mobile homes and pitches descending to the banks of the river.

Surroundings : 🏞 🗺 ♀♀
Leisure activities : 🍽 ✕ 🏃 🏊 🛝 🛶 🏊
🏊
Facilities : 🛁 ⚡ 🏛 👶 🍽 launderette 🛒 refrigerators
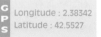
Longitude : 4.51766
Latitude : 43.95599

VIAS-PLAGE

34450 – Michelin map **339** F9 – pop. 5 386 – alt. 10
▶ Paris 752 – Agde 5 – Béziers 19 – Narbonne 46

🏔 Yelloh! Village Club Farret ♣♣

📞 04 67 21 64 45, www.camping-farret.com

Address : chemin des Rosses (Beside the beach)

Opening times : from mid April to end Sept.

7 ha (437 pitches)

Tariff : 57€ ♣♣ 🚗 🔲 🔌 (6A) – Extra per person 9€

Rental rates : (from mid April to end Sept.) 🛁 – 270 🚐 88 🏠 – 19 studios. Per night from 30 to 305€ – Per week from 210 to 2135€

🚐 borne

A pretty landscaped mobile home village with different themes: pirates, Pacific ... and very good sanitary facilities.

Surroundings : 🏊 🗺 ♀♀ ⛰
Leisure activities : 🍽 ✕ 🏛 🌙 🏃 🎮 🏊 🏇
🏊 🛝 🎵 entertainment room
Facilities : 🛁 ⚡ 🏛 👶 🧺 🚰 🍽 launderette
🛒 🛝
Nearby : 🏃 🏇

Longitude : 3.419
Latitude : 43.2911

🏔 Sunêlia Domaine de la Dragonnière

GROEBLI

📞 04 67 01 03 10, www.dragonniere.com – limited spaces for one-night stay

Address : road RD 612 (5km west, follow the signs for Béziers)

Opening times : from beginning April to beginning Nov.

30 ha (980 pitches)

Tariff : 65€ ♣♣ 🚗 🔲 🔌 (10A) Extra per person 11€ Reservation fee 30€

Rental rates : (from beginning April to beginning Nov.) – 322 🚐 364 🏠 – 2 tent lodges. Per night from 38 to 309€ – Per week from 266 to 2163€ – Reservation fee 30€

A wide range of accommodation options at different levels of comfort with an upmarket spa centre and an Olympic-size swimming pool (50m).

Surroundings : 🗺 ♀
Leisure activities : 🍽 ✕ 🏛 🌙 🏃 ⛵ hammam jacuzzi 🏊 🚲 🎮 🛝 🛶 🏊 multi-sports ground, spa centre
Facilities : 🛁 ⚡ 👶 🚰 🍽 launderette 🛒 🛝 🛒
Longitude : 3.36335
Latitude : 43.3126

🏔 Le Napoléon ♣♣

📞 04 67 01 07 80, www.camping-napoleon.fr

Address : 1171 avenue de la Méditerranée (250m from the beach)

Opening times : from beginning April to end Sept.

3 ha (239 pitches)

Tariff : 21€ ♣♣ 🚗 🔲 🔌 (10A) – Extra per person 6€ – Reservation fee 28€

Rental rates : (from end April to end Sept.) ⅋ – 73 ▦ – 39 ▥ 2 ⊨ – 11 apartments – 5 canvas bungalows. Per night from 34 to 156€ – Per week from 238 to 1092€ – Reservation fee 8€

⬚ borne 21€ – ⬚ ⧉18,90€

Surroundings : ⬚ ♨

Leisure activities : ♟✗ ⬚ ⊙ ⊹ ⼼ ⛱ hammam ⚓ ⚲ ⬚ multi-sports ground Facilities : ⅋ ⚬ ⬚ ⬚ ⬚ ⧉ launderette ⬚ ⬚ refrigerated food storage facilities Nearby : disco, sports trail

GPS Longitude : 3.41661
Latitude : 43.29179

⩕ Méditerranée-Plage

⌕ 04 67 90 99 07, www.mediterranee-plage.com

Address : Côte Ouest (6km southwest along the D 137e2)

Opening times : from beginning April to end Sept.

9,6 ha (490 pitches)

Tariff : 44,50€ ⊹⊹ ⬚ ▣ ⧉ (6A) – Extra per person 8,40€ Reservation fee 25€

Rental rates : (from beginning April to end Sept.) ⅋ (1 mobile home) ⚲ – 250 ▦. Per night from 40 to 195€ – Per week from 280 to 1 350€ – Reservation fee 25€

⬚ borne

A pleasant setting beside the sea with high-quality facilities.

Surroundings : ⬚ ⬚ ♨ ⬚

Leisure activities : ♟✗ ⬚ ⊙ ⊹ ⼼ ⚲ ⚲ ⬚ ⬚ multi-sports ground Facilities : ⅋ ⚬ ⬚ ⧉ launderette ⬚ ⬚

GPS Longitude : 3.37106
Latitude : 43.28202

⩕ Les Flots Bleus ⚎

⌕ 04 67 21 64 80, www.camping-flotsbleus.com

Address : Côte Ouest (to the southwest; beside beach)

Opening times : from mid April to end Sept.

5 ha (298 pitches)

Tariff : (2013 Price) 34€ ⊹⊹ ⬚ ▣ ⧉ (8A) – Extra per person 6,50€ Reservation fee 22€

Rental rates : (2013 Price) (from mid April to end Sept.) – 120 ▦ 22 ▥. Per week from 190 to 860€ – Reservation fee 22€

⬚ borne 3€

Jointly run with the France Floride campsite next door.

Surroundings : ⬚ ♨ ⬚

Leisure activities : ♟✗ ⬚ ⊙ nighttime ⊹ ⚓ ⬚ ⬚ multi-sports ground Facilities : ⅋ ⚬ ⬚ ⧉ launderette ⬚ ⬚

GPS Longitude : 3.4055
Latitude : 43.29

⩕ Cap Soleil ⚎

⌕ 04 67 21 64 77, www.capsoleil.fr – limited spaces for one-night stay

Address : chemin de la Grande Cosse (Côte Ouest, 600m from the beach)

Opening times : from mid April to end Sept.

4,5 ha (288 pitches) flat, grassy

Tariff : 53€ ⊹⊹ ⬚ ▣ ⧉ (10A) – Extra per person 13€ – Reservation fee 25€

Rental rates : (from mid April to end Sept.) ⅋ (1 mobile home) 95 ▦. Per night from 69 to 79€ – Per week from 229 to 1099€ Reservation fee 25€

⬚ 12 ▣ 27,50€

The covered swimming pool (uncovered in summer) is reserved for naturists in July and August.

Surroundings : ⬚ ♨

Leisure activities : ♟✗ ⬚ ⊙ ⊹ ⚓ ⚲ ⚲ ⬚ (open-air in season) ⬚ ⬚ multi-sports ground Facilities : ⅋ ⚬ ⬚ – 8 individual sanitary facilities (⬚ ⬚ wc) ⬚ ⬚ ⧉ launderette ⬚, ⬚ refrigerators Nearby : ⬚

GPS Longitude : 3.39953
Latitude : 43.29262

⩕ Californie Plage ⚎

⌕ 04 67 21 64 69, www.californie-plage.fr

Address : chemin du Trou de Ragout (Côte Ouest, to the southwest along the D 137e and take road to the left; beside the sea)

Opening times : from beginning April to end Sept.

5,8 ha (371 pitches)

Tariff : (2013 Price) 42€ ⊹⊹ ⬚ ▣ ⧉ (10A) – Extra per person 8,50€ Reservation fee 25€

Rental rates : (2013 Price) (from beginning April to end Sept.) ⚲ – 122 ▦. Per week from 210 to 1 162€ – Reservation fee 25€

Free admission to the water park at the Cap-Soleil campsite (opposite, 100m away).

Surroundings : ⬚ ♨ ⬚

Leisure activities : ♟✗ ⬚ ⊙ ⊹ ⚓ ⚲ ⬚ multi-sports ground Facilities : ⅋ ⚬ ⬚ ⬚ ⬚ ⧉ launderette ⬚, ⬚ refrigerators Nearby : ⚲ ⬚ ⬚

GPS Longitude : 3.39843
Latitude : 43.29051

⩕ L'Air Marin ⚎

⌕ 04 67 21 64 90, www.camping-air-marin.fr

Address : Côte Est, behind the football pitch

Opening times : from mid April to end Sept.

5,5 ha (305 pitches)

Tariff : (2013 Price) 40€ ⊹⊹ ⬚ ▣ ⧉ (6A) – Extra per person 8€ Reservation fee 25€

Rental rates : (2013 Price) (from mid April to end Sept.) – 150 ▦ 10 ▥. Per night from 40 to 170€ – Per week from 280 to 1 190€ Reservation fee 25€

A linear site in the shade of poplars with an attractive swimming area, very close to the Canal du Midi.

Surroundings : ⬚ ♨

Leisure activities : ♟✗ ⬚ ⊙ nighttime ⊹ ⼼ ⚓ ⚲ ⬚ ⬚ boats to hire ⚲ multi-sports ground Facilities : ⅋ ⚬ ⬚ ⬚ ⧉ launderette ⬚, ⬚ Nearby : ⬚ amusement park

GPS Longitude : 3.42129
Latitude : 43.30076

Key to rentals symbols:

12 ▦	*Number of mobile homes*
20 ▥	*Number of chalets*
6 ⊨	*Number of rooms to rent*
Per night 30–50€	*Minimum/maximum rate per night*
Per week 300–1,000€	*Minimum/maximum rate per week*

▲▲▲ Vacances Directes Le Petit Mousse ▲▲

(rental of mobile homes only)

📞 04 67 90 99 04, www.vacances-directes.com

Address : route de la Grande Cosse

Opening times :

5,2 ha (365 pitches)

Rental rates : 320 🚐 – 6 🏠 – 28 tent lodges. Per night from 35 to 77€ – Per week from 245 to 1 057€ – Reservation fee 25€

Virtually 'on top of the water' with some rental options facing the sea.

Surroundings : 🏊 ⛳⛳ ⛰
Leisure activities : 🍸 ✕ 🎭 🎣 🕴 🚣 🚴 🏊 🎿
Facilities : 🔓 🛁🍴 launderette 🧺 🚿

GPS Longitude : 3.40147
Latitude : 43.28994

▲▲ Hélios

📞 04 67 21 63 66, www.camping-helios.com

Address : avenue des Pêcheurs (near the Libron, 250m from the beach)

Opening times : from end April to end Sept.

2,5 ha (215 pitches)

Tariff : (2013 Price) 33€ ♦♦ 🚗 🔲 🔌 (6A) – Extra per person 4€ – Reservation fee 10€

Rental rates : (2013 Price) (from end April to end Sept.) – 24 🚐 6 🏠 – 4 canvas bungalows. Per night from 32 to 92€ –Per week from 140 to 630€ – Reservation fee 20€

Beside the Libron river, plenty of shade, with an attractive indoor spa area.

Surroundings : 🏊 ⛳⛳
Leisure activities : 🍸 ✕ 🎭 ♨ hammam, jacuzzi 🚴 spa centre
Facilities : 🔓 🛁🍴 🔲 🧺 🚿

GPS Longitude : 3.40764
Latitude : 43.29115

To visit a town or region, use the MICHELIN Green Guides.

LE VIGAN

30120 – Michelin map **339** G5 – pop. 3 959 – alt. 221
▶ Paris 707 – Alès 66 – Lodève 50 – Mende 108

▲▲ Le Val de l'Arre

📞 04 67 81 02 77, www.valdelarre.com

Address : at Roudoulouse, route du Pont de la Croix (2.5km east along the D 999, follow the rte de Ganges and take road to the right; beside the Arre)

Opening times : from beginning April to end Sept.

4 ha (173 pitches)

Tariff : 24,50€ ♦♦ 🚗 🔲 🔌 (10A) – Extra per person 6,50€ – Reservation fee 15€

Rental rates : (from beginning April to mid Sept.) 🚫 – 35 🚐 1 gîte. Per night from 29 to 56€ – Per week from 203 to 714€ Reservation fee 15€

🚐 borne 3€ – 🔋 11€

Divided into 2 separate sections on either side of the road; pitches for tents and caravans with lots of shade, near the river.

Surroundings : ⛳⛳
Leisure activities : 🎭 🚴 🎿 🏊 🚣
Facilities : 🔓 🛁🍴 launderette 🧺 🚿

GPS Longitude : 3.63751
Latitude : 43.99128

LES VIGNES

48210 – Michelin map **330** H9 – pop. 103 – alt. 410
▶ Paris 615 – Mende 52 – Meyrueis 33 – Le Rozier 12

▲▲▲ Beldoire

📞 04 66 48 82 79, www.camping-beldoire.com

Opening times : from mid May to mid Sept.

5 ha (142 pitches) terraced, flat, grassy, stony

Tariff : (2013 Price) 22€ ♦♦ 🚗 🔲 🔌 (6A) – Extra per person 5€ Reservation fee 13€

Rental rates : (2013 Price) (from mid April to mid Sept.) – 1 caravan 8 🚐 – 15 canvas bungalows. Per night from 38 to 45€ – Per week from 229 to 649€ – Reservation fee 13€

Surroundings : ⛳⛳ ⛰
Facilities : 🔓 🛁🍴 🍴

GPS Longitude : 3.23445
Latitude : 44.28717

▲▲ Village Vacances Castel de la Peyre

(exclusive rental small houses)

📞 04 66 48 48 48, www.lozere-resa.com

Address : located 1km south along the D 16

1 ha

Rental rates : 10 🏠.

A pretty village of small houses, with a view over the Tarn Valley.

Surroundings : 🏊 ≈
Leisure activities : 🎭 🎿
Facilities : 🔓 🔲 🍴 📺

GPS Longitude : 3.2283
Latitude : 44.27292

▲ La Blaquière

📞 04 66 48 54 93, www.campinggorgesdutarn.fr

Address : 6km northeast along the D 907bis; beside the Tarn river

Opening times : from mid April to end Sept.

1 ha (79 pitches)

Tariff : 22€ ♦♦ 🚗 🔲 🔌 (10A) – Extra per person 5,50€ – Reservation fee 13€

Rental rates : (from mid April to end Sept.) 🚫 – 10 🚐 3 canvas bungalows. Per night from 35 to 110€ – Per week from 210 to 650€ – Reservation fee 13€

Below the road, beside the Tarn river, well-shaded pitches.

Surroundings : 🚗 ⛳⛳ ⛰
Leisure activities : 🎭 🚴 🛶
Facilities : 🔓 🛁🍴 📺 🧺 🚿

GPS Longitude : 3.2685
Latitude : 44.3042

VILLEFORT

48800 – Michelin map **330** L8 – pop. 618 – alt. 600
▶ Paris 616 – Alès 52 – Aubenas 61 – Florac 63

▲▲ Morangiés - Le Lac

📞 04 66 46 81 27, www.camping-lac-cevennes.com – limited spaces for one-night stay

Address : at Morangiés (3.4km north along the D 901, follow the signs for Mende, take D 906, follow the signs for Prévenchère and take turning to the left down the road for Pourcharesses)

Opening times : from beginning May to end Sept.

4 ha (75 pitches)

Tariff : (2013 Price) 17,20€ ♦♦ 🚗 🔲 🔌 (10A) Extra per person 4,50€

Rental rates : (2013 Price) Permanent – 32 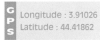 – 19 🏠. Per night from 50 to 70€ – Per week from 235 to 730€

An attractive location beside the lake; some of the infrastructure and rental options are a little old. 'Semi-detached' gîtes.

Surroundings : 🐟 ≤ 🏕 ♨♨
Leisure activities : 🎮 ⚓ 🏊
Facilities : ♿ ⚡ 🏕 🍽 🚿 🚾 🏠 📶
Nearby : 🏊 🎣 🛶 ⚓

G P S	Longitude : 3.92812 Latitude : 44.46183

⛰ La Palhère

📞 0466468063, www.campinglapalhere.com – alt. 750

Address : route du Mas de la Barque (4km southwest along the D 66; beside rapids)

Opening times : Permanent

1,8 ha (45 pitches)

Tariff : 15€ ⚡⚡ 🚗 🅿 [6] (4A) – Extra per person 5€

Rental rates : Permanent 🦅 (from beginning April to end June) 2 caravans – 5 – 1 🏠 – 1 yurt – 2 tipis. Per night from 50€ Per week from 220 to 595€

🚐 12 🅿 16€

Beside a pretty mountain stream with varied rental options.

Surroundings : 🐟 ≤ ♨♨
Leisure activities : 🏊 🏓 🏕 🎣
Facilities : ⚡ 🏕 🚿 🚾 🍽 🏠 📶

G P S	Longitude : 3.91026 Latitude : 44.41862

VILLEGLY

11600 – Michelin map **344** F3 – pop. 1 020 – alt. 130
▶ Paris 778 – Lézignan-Corbières 36 – Mazamet 46 – Carcassonne 14

⛰ Sites et Paysages Moulin de Ste-Anne

📞 0468722080, www.moulindesainteanne.com

Address : 2 chemin de Sainte-Anne (take the eastern exit along the D 435, follow the signs for Villarzel)

Opening times : from beginning April to end Oct.

1,6 ha (60 pitches)

Tariff : 29€ ⚡⚡ 🚗 🅿 [6] (10A) – Extra per person 5,50€ – Reservation fee 17€

Rental rates : (from beginning April to end Oct.) – 15 🏠 – 2 tent lodges. Per week from 304 to 760€ – Reservation fee 17€

🚐 borne 6€ – 🎣 [6]16€

Pretty pitches and upmarket rental options on shady terraces.

Surroundings : 🏕 ♨♨
Leisure activities : 🍷 🍴 🎮 ⚓ 🏊
multi-sports ground
Facilities : ♿ ⚡ 🏛 🏕 🚿 🚾 🍽 🏠 📶
Nearby : 🎾

G P S	Longitude : 2.44347 Latitude : 43.28374

VILLENEUVE-LÈS-AVIGNON

30400 – Michelin map **339** N5 – pop. 12 463 – alt. 23
▶ Paris 678 – Avignon 8 – Nîmes 46 – Orange 28

⛰ Campéole L'Ile des Papes 👥

📞 0490151590, www.avignon-camping.com

Address : Barrage de Villeneuve (4.5km northeast along the D 980, follow the signs for Roquemaure and take D 780 to the right, between the Rhône and the canal)

20 ha (210 pitches)

Rental rates : 46  – 61 canvas bungalows.
🚐 borne

A spacious site, partially shaded, with a pretty play and paddling pool area.

Surroundings : 🐟 ≤ 🏕 ♨♨
Leisure activities : 🍷 🍴 🎮 🌙nighttime 🏃
⚓ 🚴 🏊 🎣 multi-sports ground
Facilities : ♿ ⚡ 🏛 🏕 🍽 launderette 🏠 🚿

G P S	Longitude : 4.81826 Latitude : 43.99383

⛰ Municipal de la Laune

📞 0490257606, www.camping-villeneuvelezavignon.com

Address : chemin Saint Honore (to the northeast, access via the D 980, near the stadium and swimming pools)

Opening times : from beginning April to mid Oct.

2,3 ha (126 pitches)

Tariff : (2013 Price) 23,60€ ⚡⚡ 🚗 🅿 [6] (6A) – Extra per person 5,60€
🚐 borne 5€

Set among the town's sporting facilities, a well-shaded site with modest sanitary facilities.

Surroundings : 🏕 ♨♨
Leisure activities : 🎮 ⚓
Facilities : ♿ ⚡ 📶
Nearby : 🎾 🏊 🏊

G P S	Longitude : 4.79711 Latitude : 43.96331

Michelin classification:

⛰⛰⛰⛰	*Extremely comfortable, equipped to a very high standard*
⛰⛰⛰	*Very comfortable, equipped to a high standard*
⛰⛰	*Comfortable and well equipped*
⛰	*Reasonably comfortable*
⛰	*Satisfactory*

LIMOUSIN

N. Thibaut / Photononstop

Life in Limousin is led at its own easy pace: weary Parisians wanting to reconnect with nature come to enjoy the joys of country life, inhale the bracing air of its high plateaus and wander through its woodlands in search of wild mushrooms and chestnuts. The region boasts hills and gorges and lush green meadows. The sight of cattle grazing happily or lambs frolicking in a spring meadow will rejuvenate the spirits of any jaded city dweller. Limousin is home to ancient village churches as well as imposing abbey churches and fortresses. In autumn, the forests are swathed in rich colours, forming a perfect backdrop to the granite and sandstone of the peaceful towns and villages, where ancestral crafts, such as Limoges enamels and porcelain and Aubusson tapestries, still blend the traditional with the best of the new. The food is wholesome – savoury bacon soup, Limousin stew and, as any proud local will tell you, the most tender, succulent beef in the world.

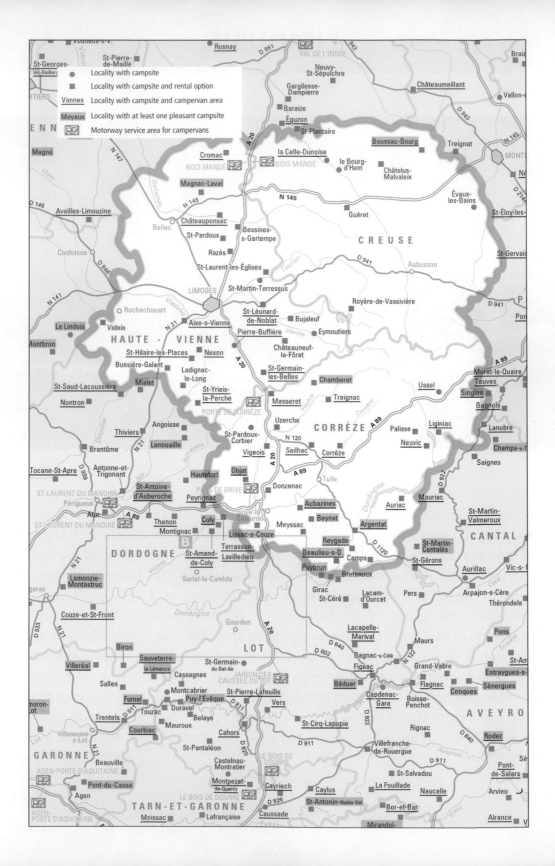

Legend:
- Locality with campsite
- Locality with campsite and rental option
- Vannes — Locality with campsite and campervan area
- Moyaux — Locality with at least one pleasant campsite
- Motorway service area for campervans

Vouneuil-s-V.
St-Georges-lès-Baillarg.
St-Pierre-de-Maillé
Rosnay
D 951
VAL DE L'INDRE
N 145
Braiz
Neuvy-St-Sépulchre
Châteaumeillant
Vallon-e
Gargilesse-Dampierre
Baraize
Éguzon
St-Plantaire
Treignat
Né
Magné
Cromac
la Celle-Dunoise
Boussac-Bourg
MONT
BOIS MANDÉ
BOIS MANDÉ
le Bourg-d'Hem
Châtelus-Malvaleix
Évaux-les-Bains
St-Éloy-les-
D 214
Magnac-Laval
A 20
N 145
Guéret
CREUSE
Availles-Limouzine
D 148
N 147
N 145
Bellac
Châteauponsac
St-Pardoux
Bessines-s-Gartempe
D 941
Aubusson
St-Gervais
Confolens
D 948
Razès
St-Laurent-les-Églises
N 141
LIMOGES
St-Martin-Terressus
Taurion
Royère-de-Vassivière
D 941
P
Pon
Rochechouart
Vienne
St-Léonard-de-Noblat
Bujaleuf
Le Lindois
Videix
Aixe-s-Vienne
Pierre-Buffière
Vienne
Eymoutiers
HAUTE - VIENNE
Châteauneuf-la-Fôret
Montbron
St-Hilaire-les-Places
Nexon
Murat-le-Quaire
A 89
Bussière-Galant
Ladignac-le-Long
A 20
St-Germain-les-Belles
Chambéret
Ussel
Tauves
Singles
St-Saud-Lacoussière
Mialet
St-Yrieix-la-Perche
Masseret
Treignac
Corrèze
A 89
Bagnols
Nontron
PORTE DE CORRÈZE
Palisse
Liginiac
Lanobre
Thiviers
Angoisse
Uzerche
CORRÈZE
Neuvic
Champs-s-T
Brantôme
Lanouaille
Aubazère
N 120
Palisse
Saignes
Tocane-St-Apre
Antonne-et-Trigonant
Isle
Vigeois
A 20
Seilhac
Corrèze
D 922
St-LAURENT DU MANOIRE
Hautefort
Objat
A 89
Tulle
Mauriac
St-Martin-Valmeroux
Périgueux
St-Antoine-d'Auberoche
PAYS DE BRIVE
Donzenac
Dordogne
CANTAL
Atur
A 89
Peyrignac
Brive-la-Gaillarde
St-LAURENT DU MANOIRE
Thenon
Coly
Aubazines
Auriac
St-Martin-Cantalès
Montignac
Lissac-s-Couze
Beynat
Argentat
St-Gérons
Meyssac
Reygade
D 1120
DORDOGNE
St-Amand-de-Coly
Terrasson-Lavilledieu
Beaulieu-s-D.
Camps
Aurillac
Vic-s-C
Lamonzie-Montastruc
Sarlat-la-Canéda
Puybrun
Bretenoux
Arpajon-s-Cère
Thérondels
Couze-et-St-Front
Dordogne
Girac
St-Céré
Lacam-d'Ourcet
Pers
Cère
D 933
N 21
Gourdon
A 20
LOT
Lacapelle-Marival
Maurs
Pons
Biron
D 840
Maurs
N 122
St-Am
geonac
D 933
Villeréal
Sauveterre-la-Lémance
St-Germain-du-Bel-Air
D 802
Bagnac-s-Célé
Grand-Vabre
Entraygues-s-
Cassagnes
JARDIN DES CAUSSES DU LOT
Figeac
Flagnac
Sénergues
Salles
Montcabrier
St-Pierre-Lafeuille
Béduer
Conques
AVEYRO
moron-Lot
Fumel
Puy-l'Évêque
Vers
Capdenac-Gare
Boisse-Penchot
Trentels
Touzac
Duravel
Belaye
St-Cirq-Lapopie
Rignac
Rodez
Courbiac
Mauroux
Cahors
Villefranche-de-Rouergue
D 840
Villeneuve-s-Lot
St-Pantaléon
D 820
D 911
GARONNE
Beauville
Castelnau-Montratier
LE BOIS DE DOURRE
St-Salvadou
Pont-de-Salars
AGEN-PORTE D'AQUITAINE
Pont-du-Casse
Montpezat-de-Quercy
Cayriech
Caylus
La Fouillade
Naucelle
Arviu
Sé
Agen
LE BOIS DE DOURRE
D 926
St-Antonin-Noble-Val
Bor-et-Bar
Pont-de-Salars
AGEN-PORTE D'AQUITAINE
TARN-ET-GARONNE
Moissac
Lafrançaise
Caussade
Mirandol-
Alrance
V
B

AIXE-SUR-VIENNE

87700 – Michelin map **325** D6 – pop. 5 464 – alt. 204
▶ Paris 400 – Châlus 21 – Confolens 60 – Limoges 14

⚠ Municipal les Grèves

🕽 05 55 70 12 98, www.mairie-aixesurvienne.fr

Address : rue Jean-Claude Papon (beside the Vienne river)

Opening times : from beginning June to end Sept.

3 ha (80 pitches) flat, grassy

Tariff : 15,20€ ✿✿ ⏦ 🔲 🌢 (10A) – Extra per person 4€

Rental rates : (from beginning April to end Oct.) – 3 🖼.
Per night 50€ – Per week from 200 to 420€

🚐 borne
A pleasant site with some pitches beside the Vienne river.

Surroundings : 🌢🌢	
Leisure activities : 🍴🏠 🛶 🛶 🌢	**G P S**
Facilities : 🚿🚰 🍴 🏠	Longitude : 1.11477
Nearby : 🏊	Latitude : 45.8065

*The information in the guide may have changed since
going to press.*

ARGENTAT

19400 – Michelin map **329** M5 – pop. 3 052 – alt. 183
▶ Paris 503 – Aurillac 54 – Brive-la-Gaillarde 45 – Mauriac 49

🏔 Le Gibanel

🕽 05 55 28 10 11, www.camping-gibanel.com

Address : 4.5km northeast along the D 18, follow the signs for
Égletons then take the road to the right

Opening times : from beginning June to end Aug.

60 ha/8,5 for camping (250 pitches)

Tariff : 27,70€ ✿✿ ⏦ 🔲 🌢 (10A) – Extra per person 5,30€
Reservation fee 10€

Rental rates : (from beginning June to end Aug.) – 11 🖼.
2 apartments. Per night 109 € – Per week 760 € – Reservation
fee 10€

In the grounds of a 16th-century château, beside a lake.

Surroundings : 🌢🌢🌢🏔	
Leisure activities : 🍴🏠🏠🌢🛶🛶🌢	**G P S**
multi-sports ground	Longitude : 1.95852
Facilities : 🚿🚰 🏠🌢🍴 launderette 🌢🌢	Latitude : 45.1107

🏔 Sunêlia Au Soleil d'Oc 🅰🅱

🕽 05 55 28 84 84, www.dordogne-soleil.com

Address : at Monceaux-sur-Dordogne (4.5km southwest along the
D 12, follow the signs for Beaulieu then take the D 12e following signs
for Vergnolles and take road to the left after the bridge; beside the
Dordogne river)

Opening times : from mid April to mid Nov.

4 ha (120 pitches)

Tariff : (2013 Price) 29€ ✿✿ ⏦ 🔲 🌢 (10A) – Extra per person 6€

Rental rates : (2013 Price) (from mid April to mid Nov.) – 28 🖼.
12 🏠 – 5 canvas bungalows. Per night from 40 to 128€
Per week from 280 to 896€

Surroundings : 🌢🌢🌢🏔	
Leisure activities : 🍴🏠🏠🌢🛶🛶🏍🏠	**G P S**
🏠🌢🌢	Longitude : 1.91836
Facilities : 🚰🔲🍴 launderette 🌢	Latitude : 45.07618

🏔 Le Vaurette 🅰🅱

🕽 05 55 28 09 67, www.vaurette.com

Address : place known : Vaurette (9km southwest along the D 12,
follow the signs for Beaulieu; beside the Dordogne river)

Opening times : from beginning May to mid Sept.

4 ha (120 pitches)

Tariff : 31,80€ ✿✿ ⏦ 🔲 🌢 (6A) – Extra per person 6,40€
Reservation fee 15€

Rental rates : (from mid May to mid Sept.) 🌢 – 2 🖼. Per week
from 340 to 750€ – Reservation fee 15€

🚐 borne 28€

Surroundings : 🌢🌢🌢	
Leisure activities : 🍴🏠🏠🌢 daytime 🏃	**G P S**
🏃🌢🌢🌢 entertainment room	Longitude : 1.8825
Facilities : 🚿🚰 🏠🍴 launderette 🌢	Latitude : 45.04568

AUBAZINE

19190 – Michelin map **329** L4 – pop. 852 – alt. 345
▶ Paris 480 – Aurillac 86 – Brive-la-Gaillarde 14 – St-Céré 50

🏔 Campéole Le Coiroux 🅰🅱

🕽 05 55 27 21 96, www.camping-coiroux.com

Address : Coiroux Tourist Park (5km east along the D 48, follow the
signs for Le Chastang, not far from a small lake and a leisure park)

Opening times : from beginning April to end Sept.

165 ha/6 for camping (174 pitches) relatively flat, flat, grassy, wood

Tariff : 25,90€ ✿✿ ⏦ 🔲 🌢 (10A) – Extra per person 6,50€
Reservation fee 25€

Rental rates : (from beginning April to beginning Nov.) 🚿
(2 mobile homes) – 40 🖼 – 10 🏠 – 25 canvas bungalows.
Per night from 26 to 141€ – Per week from 217 to 987€
Reservation fee 25€

🚐 borne 3€

Surroundings : 🌢🌢🌢🌢	
Leisure activities : 🍴🏠🏠🌢🏃🛶🌢🏠	**G P S**
🌢 climbing wall	Longitude : 1.70739
Facilities : 🚿🚰 🏠🍴 launderette 🌢🌢	Latitude : 45.18611
Nearby : 🏖 (beach) 🌢 forest trail	

AURIAC

19220 – Michelin map **329** N4 – pop. 226 – alt. 608
▶ Paris 517 – Argentat 27 – Égletons 33 – Mauriac 23

⚠ Municipal

🕽 05 55 28 23 02, www.auriac.fr

Address : in the village (take the southeastern exit along the D 65,
follow the signs for St-Privat, near a lake and a wooded park)

Opening times : from mid April to end Oct.

1,7 ha (70 pitches)

Tariff : (2013 Price) ✿ 3,80€ ⏦ 1,95€ 🔲 1,95€ – 🌢 (16A) 3,80€

Rental rates : Permanent – 8 🖼. Per night from 53 to 63€
Per week from 220 to 390€

🚐 borne
There's a view of the lake from some pitches.

Surroundings : 🌢🌢🌢🌢🏔	
Leisure activities : 🏠🛶	**G P S**
Facilities : 🚰 (mid July to mid Aug.) 🌢🍴🔲	Longitude : 2.14772
Nearby : 🌢🏠🏖 (beach) 🌢 pedalos	Latitude : 45.20206

BEAULIEU-SUR-DORDOGNE

19120 – Michelin map **329** M6 – pop. 1 283 – alt. 142
▶ Paris 513 – Aurillac 65 – Brive-la-Gaillarde 44 – Figeac 56

⚠ Flower Les Îles

✆ 05 55 91 02 65, www.campingdesiles.com

Address : boulevard Rodolphe de Turenne (east of the town centre)

Opening times : from end April to end Sept.

4 ha (120 pitches) flat, grassy

Tariff : 28,90€ ✶✶ ⇌ 🄴 (10A) – Extra per person 6,90€
Reservation fee 17€

Rental rates : (from end April to end Sept.) – 24 🛏 – 2 🛖.
Per night from 39 to 125€ – Per week from 196 to 775€.
Reservation fee 17€

🚐 borne – 5 🄴 – 🔋12€

A picturesque site and setting on an island in the Dordogne river.

Surroundings : 🏖 ♨ ⚠	G
Leisure activities : 🍸 🏛 ⚽ 🎿 🏹	P	Longitude : 1.84049
Facilities : ♿ ⚊ 🎱 🏃 launderette 🚿	S	Latitude : 44.97968
Nearby : 🏃 ✗	

To visit a town or region, use the MICHELIN Green Guides.

BESSINES-SUR-GARTEMPE

87250 – Michelin map **325** F4 – pop. 2 847 – alt. 335
▶ Paris 355 – Argenton-sur-Creuse 58 – Bellac 29 – Guéret 55

⚠ Le Sagnat

✆ 05 55 76 17 69

Address : located 1.5km southwest along the D 220, follow the signs for Limoges, take the D 27 following signs for St-Pardoux to the right and take turning to the left; beside the lake

0,8 ha (50 pitches)
Rentals : 3 🛖.

Surroundings : ♨ 🏖	G
Leisure activities : ✗ 🏛 🏊 (beach) 🏹	P	Longitude : 1.35269
Facilities : ♿ ⚊ 🎱	S	Latitude : 46.10001
Nearby : 🍸	

BEYNAT

19190 – Michelin map **329** L5 – pop. 1 253 – alt. 420
▶ Paris 496 – Argentat 47 – Beaulieu-sur-Dordogne 23 – Brive-la-Gaillarde 21

⚠ Village Vacances Chalets en France Les Hameaux de Miel

(rental of chalets only)

✆ 05 55 84 34 48, www.chalets-en-france.com

Address : at Miel

Opening times : Permanent

12 ha

Rental rates : ♿ (3 chalets) – 98 🛖 . Per night 65€ – Per week from 260 to 859€ – Reservation fee 13€

Surroundings : 🏖 ♨	G
Leisure activities : 🍸 🏛 🎯 🏃 ⚽ 🎿 🏹 🎿	
multi-sports ground	P	Longitude : 1.76141
Facilities : ⚊ 🎱 🏃 launderette	S	Latitude : 45.12932
Nearby : ✗ 🏃 🏊 ⚾ 🏹 pedalos	

⚠ Club Airotel Le Lac de Miel

✆ 05 55 85 50 66, www.camping-miel.com

Address : 4km east along the N 121, follow the signs for Argentat; beside a small lake

50 ha/9 for camping (140 pitches)

Rentals : 2 caravans – 50 🛏 – 5 🛖 – 3 canvas bungalows – 8 gîtes.

Surroundings : 🏖 ◁ ♨ 📷	G
Leisure activities : 🍸 ✗ 🏛 ⚽ 🎿 🏹 🔲	
(open air in season) 🏹	P	Longitude : 1.77103
Facilities : ♿ ⚊ 🏃 🎱 🏃 🄴	S	Latitude : 45.13332
Nearby : 🏊 (beach) pedalos	

LE BOURG-D'HEM

23220 – Michelin map **325** H3 – pop. 225 – alt. 320
▶ Paris 333 – Aigurande 20 – Le Grand-Bourg 28 – Guéret 21

⚠ Municipal

✆ 05 55 62 84 36, www.paysdunois.fr

Address : to the west along the D 48, follow the signs for Bussière-Dunoise and take the road to the right

Opening times : from beginning May to end Sept.

0,33 ha (36 pitches)

Tariff : ✶ 2,70€ ⇌ 1,65€ 🄴 1,65€ – 🔋 (10A) 2,70€

A pleasant site and setting beside the Creuse river.

Surroundings : 🏖 🗒 ♨ ⚠	G
Leisure activities : 🏹	P	Longitude : 1.82316
Facilities : ♿ (July-Aug.) 🚽 🚿 🏃	S	Latitude : 46.29756
Nearby : 🍸 ⚽ boats to hire	

Routes nationales are main roads and their identifying numbers begin with N or RN. Routes départementales are generally quieter roads and begin with D or DN.

BOUSSAC-BOURG

23600 – Michelin map **325** K2 – pop. 787 – alt. 423
▶ Paris 334 – Aubusson 52 – La Châtre 37 – Guéret 43

⚠ Les Castels Le Château de Poinsouze

✆ 05 55 65 02 21, www.camping-de-poinsouze.com 🐾 (from mid July to mid Aug.)

Address : route de La Châtre (2.8km north along the D 917)

Opening times : from mid May to mid Sept.

150 ha/22 for camping (144 pitches)

Tariff : 36€ ✶✶ ⇌ 🄴 🔋 (20A) – Extra per person 6€ – Reservation fee 15€

Rental rates : (from mid May to mid Sept.) 🐾 – 2 caravans 25 🛏 – 2 🛖 – 2 gîtes. Per week from 240 to 700€ – Reservation fee 15€

🚐 borne – 10 🄴 12€

A spacious site laid out around a 16th-century château and its outbuildings.

Surroundings : 🏖 ◁ 🗒 ♨	G
Leisure activities : 🍸 ✗ 🏛 🎯 🏃 ⚽ 🚴 🎿	
🏊 🏹 pedalos 🚣	P	Longitude : 2.20472
Facilities : ♿ ⚊ 🎱 🏃 🚿 🏃 launderette 🏃	S	Latitude : 46.3725
🚿	

BUJALEUF

87460 – Michelin map **325** G6 – pop. 881 – alt. 380
▸ Paris 423 – Bourganeuf 28 – Eymoutiers 14 – Limoges 35

⚠ Municipal du Lac

✆ 05 55 69 54 54, www.bujaleuf.fr

Address : located 1km north along the D 16 and take the turning to the left, near the lake

Opening times : from mid May to end Sept.

2 ha (110 pitches) very uneven, terraced, flat, grassy

Tariff : (2013 Price) 12 € ♦♦ ⇔ 🔲 ⚡ (10A) – Extra per person 3 €
Rental rates : (2013 Price) (from mid May to end Sept.) – 10 gîtes. Per night from 76 to 110 € – Per week from 170 to 330 €

Surroundings : 🌿 🌼🌼 Leisure activities : 🚲 Facilities : ♿ (July–Aug.) 🧺 launderette Nearby : 🍽 ✕ 🏖 (beach) 🎣	**GPS** Longitude : 1.6297 Latitude : 45.80166

BUSSIÈRE-GALANT

87230 – Michelin map **325** D7 – pop. 1 394 – alt. 410
▸ Paris 422 – Aixe-sur-Vienne 25 – Châlus 6 – Limoges 36

⚠ Municipal Espace Hermeline

✆ 05 55 78 86 12, www.espace-hermeline.com

Address : avenue du Plan-d'eau (1.7km southwest along the D 20, follow the signs for La Coquille and take the road to the right, near the stadium and 100m from a small lake)

1 ha (25 pitches) terraced, relatively flat, grassy

Rentals : 2 yurts.

Surroundings : ≼ 🏕 🌼🌼 Facilities : ♿ 🚿 🏛 🛁 Nearby : ✕ 🏊 🏖 (beach) 🎣 forest trail	**GPS** Longitude : 1.03086 Latitude : 45.61364

CAMPS

19430 – Michelin map **329** M6 – pop. 246 – alt. 520
▸ Paris 520 – Argentat 17 – Aurillac 45 – Bretenoux 18

⚠ Municipal la Châtaigneraie

✆ 05 55 28 53 15, www.correze-camping.fr

Address : in the village (to the west along the D 13 and take the road to the right)

Opening times : from beginning May to end Sept.

1 ha (23 pitches)

Tariff : ♦ 2,50 € ⇔ 🔲 3 € – ⚡ (2A) 2,50 €
Rental rates : Permanent – 9 🏠. Per night 80 € – Per week 476 €

Surroundings : 🌿 ≼🌼🌼 Leisure activities : 🎠 Facilities : ♿ 🚿 🧺 🏛 🔳 Nearby : 🚲 ✕ 🏖 (beach) 🎣	**GPS** Longitude : 1.98756 Latitude : 44.98368

LA CELLE-DUNOISE

23800 – Michelin map **325** H3 – pop. 607 – alt. 230
▸ Paris 329 – Aigurande 16 – Aubusson 63 – Dun-le-Palestel 11

⚠ Municipal de la Baignade

✆ 05 55 89 10 77, www.lacelledunoise.fr

Address : east, along the D 48a, follow the signs for Le Bourg d'Hem, near the Creuse river (direct access)

1,4 ha (30 pitches)

🚐 borne Surroundings : 🌼🌼 Leisure activities : 🏠 ✕ Facilities : ♿ 🛁 launderette Nearby : 🏖 (beach) 🎣 🏇	**GPS** Longitude : 1.76928 Latitude : 46.31015

CHAMBERET

19370 – Michelin map **329** L2 – pop. 1 318 – alt. 450
▸ Paris 453 – Guéret 84 – Limoges 66 – Tulle 45

🏔 Village Vacances Les Roulottes des Monédières

(rental of 'gypsy' caravans only)

✆ 05 55 98 03 03, www.roulottes-monedieres.com

Address : at L'Arboretum

3 ha

Rentals : ♿ 🚫 Ⓟ – 20 caravans.
Self-catering or accommodation on a hotel-style basis is available.

Surroundings : 🌿 ≼ 🌼 Leisure activities : ✕ 🏠 🎳 🎣 🎯 🚲 🎱 billiards Facilities : 🚰 🏛 🍴 launderette 🐴	**GPS** Longitude : 1.71971 Latitude : 45.5926

🏔 Village Vacances Les Chalets du Bois Combet

(rental of chalets only)

✆ 05 55 98 96 83, www.chamberet.net – traditional camp. spaces also available

Address : 1.3km southwest along the D 132, follow the signs for Meilhards and take the road to the right, 100m from a small lake and a lake

Opening times : from end March to beginning Nov.

1 ha flat, grassy

Rental rates : ♿ Ⓟ – 2 🚐 – 10 🏠. Per night from 42 to 78 €
Per week from 191 to 530 €

Surroundings : 🌿 Leisure activities : 🎯 Facilities : 🚰 🍴 launderette Nearby : 🔳 🏊 🛶 🎣	**GPS** Longitude : 1.70994 Latitude : 45.57541

In order for the guide to remain wholly objective, the selection of campsites is made on an entirely independent basis.

CHÂTEAUNEUF-LA-FORÊT

87130 – Michelin map **325** G6 – pop. 1 641 – alt. 376
▸ Paris 424 – Eymoutiers 14 – Limoges 36 – St-Léonard-de-Noblat 19

⚠ Le Cheyenne

✆ 05 55 69 39 29, www.camping-le-cheyenne.com

Address : avenue Michel Sinibaldi (800m west of the town centre, follow rte du Stade, 100m from a small lake)

1 ha (45 pitches) flat, grassy

Rentals : 9 🚐.

Surroundings : 🏕 🌼🌼 Leisure activities : 🍽 ✕ Facilities : ♿ 🚿 🍴 launderette Nearby : 🎯 ✕ 🏖 (beach) 🎣	**GPS** Longitude : 1.60127 Latitude : 45.71633

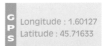

CHÂTEAUPONSAC

87290 – Michelin map **325** E4 – pop. 2 158 – alt. 290
▶ Paris 361 – Bélâbre 55 – Limoges 48 – Bellac 21

⛰ Centre Touristique - La Gartempe

🖋 05 55 76 55 33, www.camping-chateauponsac.com

Address : avenue de Ventenat (take the southwestern exit along the D 711, follow the signs for Nantiat; 200m from the river)

1,5 ha (43 pitches)

Rentals : 2 🚐 – 3 🏠 – 11 gîtes.

Surroundings : 🌳🌳
Leisure activities : 🍽✕🏠🏃🚣
Facilities : 🔧🔑🏢🚰 launderette
Nearby : 🎿🏊🚣

GPS Longitude : 1.27046
Latitude : 46.1318

CHÂTELUS-MALVALEIX

23270 – Michelin map **325** J3 – pop. 563 – alt. 410
▶ Paris 333 – Aigurande 25 – Aubusson 46 – Boussac 19

⛰ Municipal La Roussille

🖋 05 55 80 70 31, chatelusmalvaleix.fr – 🚏

Address : 10 place de la Fontaine (to the west of the village)

Opening times : from beginning June to end Sept.

0,5 ha (33 pitches)

Tariff : 🧍 3 € 🚗 1,50 € 🔌 2 € – ⚡ (16A) 4 €

Rental rates : Permanent 🔧 – 8 🏠. Per night from 50 to 55 €
Per week from 380 to 450 €

Surroundings : 🌲🌳🌳⛰
Leisure activities : 🎿🚴(mountain biking) 🚣
Facilities : 🚐🚮🚰
Nearby : 🍽🏃🍴

GPS Longitude : 2.01818
Latitude : 46.3031

CORRÈZE

19800 – Michelin map **329** M3 – pop. 1 168 – alt. 455
▶ Paris 480 – Argentat 47 – Brive-la-Gaillarde 45 – Égletons 22

⛰ Municipal la Chapelle

🖋 05 55 21 25 21, http://www.mairie-correze.fr/

Address : at La Chapelle (take the eastern exit along the D 143, follow the signs for Egletons and take a right turn, follow the signs for Bouysse – divided into two separate parts)

Opening times : from mid April to mid Oct.

3 ha (54 pitches)

Tariff : (2013 Price) 🧍 2,65 € 🚗 1,40 € 🔌 2,50 € – ⚡ (15A) 2,30 €

Rental rates : (from mid April to mid Oct.) – 3 🚐 – 1 gîte.
Per week from 200 to 300 €

🚰 borne – 10 🔌 8 € – 🔧⚡8 €

The camping part of the site has a small road running through it; located beside the Corrèze river and near a small chapel.

Surroundings : 🌲🌳🌳
Leisure activities : 🎿🏃🚣
Facilities : 🔧🚐🚰
Nearby : 🚣

GPS Longitude : 1.8798
Latitude : 45.37191

CROMAC

87160 – Michelin map **325** E2 – pop. 266 – alt. 224
▶ Paris 339 – Argenton-sur-Creuse 41 – Limoges 68 – Magnac-Laval 22

⛰ Lac de Mondon

🖋 05 55 76 93 34, www.campingdemondon.com

Address : at Les Forges de Mondon (situated 2km south along the D 105, follow the signs for St-Sulpice-les-Feuilles and take the D 60 - recommended route via the D 912)

Opening times : from beginning April to end Sept.

2,8 ha (100 pitches)

Tariff : 13 € 🧍🧍 🚗 🔌 ⚡ (10A)
Extra per person 4 €

🚰 borne 2 €

Surroundings : 🌲🏞🌳🌳
Leisure activities : 🍽✕🏠🏃🚴🎿🚣 🛶🚣 pedalos
Facilities : 🔧🚰📷🔧
Nearby : 🎿

GPS Longitude : 1.31153
Latitude : 46.3322

A 'quartier' is a district or area of a town or village.

DONZENAC

19270 – Michelin map **329** K4 – pop. 2 492 – alt. 204
▶ Paris 469 – Brive-la-Gaillarde 11 – Limoges 81 – Tulle 27

⛰ La Rivière

🖋 05 55 85 63 95, www.campingdonzenac.com

Address : route d'Ussac (1.6km south of the town, following the signs for Brive; beside the Maumont river)

1,2 ha (60 pitches) flat, grassy

Rentals : 🚐 – 14 🏠.

Surroundings : 🏞🌳🌳
Leisure activities : 🚣
Facilities : 🔧 launderette
Nearby : 🍴🎿🏊

GPS Longitude : 1.52149
Latitude : 45.21761

ÉVAUX-LES-BAINS

23110 – Michelin map **325** L3 – pop. 1 486 – alt. 469 – ♨
▶ Paris 353 – Aubusson 44 – Guéret 52 – Marcillat-en-Combraille 16

⛰ Municipal

🖋 05 55 65 55 82, www.evaux-les-bains.net

Address : at Ouche du Budelle (north of the town, behind the château)

1 ha (49 pitches)

Surroundings : 🏞🏞🌳🌳
Leisure activities : 🎿🏃
Facilities : 🔧
Nearby : 🍴🎿🛶

GPS Longitude : 2:48994
Latitude : 46.17851

We value your opinion and welcome your feedback.
Do email us at campingfrance@tp.michelin.com

EYMOUTIERS

87120 – Michelin map **325** H6 – pop. 2 033 – alt. 417
▶ Paris 432 – Aubusson 55 – Guéret 62 – Limoges 44

⚠ Municipal

✆ 05 55 69 10 21, mairie-eymoutiers@wanadoo.fr

Address : at St-Pierre (situated 2km southeast along the D 940, follow the signs for Tulle and take road to the left)

1 ha (33 pitches)

Surroundings : ⌂ 🏕 ⚐⚐
Facilities : ⚹

G
P
S
Longitude : 1.75296
Latitude : 45.73161

GUÉRET

23000 – Michelin map **325** I3 – pop. 13 844 – alt. 457
▶ Paris 351 – Bourges 122 – Châteauroux 90 – Clermont-Ferrand 132

⚠ Municipal du Plan d'Eau de Courtille

✆ 05 55 81 92 24, www.camping-courtille.com

Address : route de Courtille (2.5km southwest along the D 914, follow the signs for Benevent and take road to the left)

Opening times : from beginning April to end Oct.

2,4 ha (70 pitches)

Tariff : ☝ 2,90€ ⛟ 1,90€ 🔲 8€ – [⚡] (10A) 2,60€
Rental rates : (from beginning April to end Oct.) – 4 🚐 – 1 🏠. Per night from 47 to 60€ – Per week from 231 to 539€

A pleasant location near a small lake (direct access).

Surroundings : ⌂ 🏕 ⚐⚐
Leisure activities : 🛶
Facilities : ⚹ ⚲ 🍴 🏠
Nearby : ≊ (beach) 🎣 🛶

G
P
S
Longitude : 1.85824
Latitude : 46.16094

LADIGNAC-LE-LONG

87500 – Michelin map **325** D7 – pop. 1 124 – alt. 334
▶ Paris 426 – Brive-la-Gaillarde 74 – Limoges 35 – Nontron 44

🏘 Municipal le Bel Air

✆ 05 55 09 39 82, www.atouvert.com

Address : rue Bel'Air (located 1.5km north along the D 11, follow the signs for Nexon and take road to the left)

2,5 ha (100 pitches)

Rentals : 5 🚐.

Wooded setting and pleasant location on the edge of a small lake.

Surroundings : ⌂ 🏕 ⚐⚐
Leisure activities : 🛶
Facilities : ⚹ ⚲ 🍴 launderette
Nearby : 🛶 pedalos

G
P
S
Longitude : 1.11185
Latitude : 45.59089

For more information on visiting particular towns or regions, consult the relevant regional MICHELIN Green Guide. We also recommend you use the appropriate Michelin regional map to locate your selected campsite, to calculate distances and to work out the best route.

LIGINIAC

19160 – Michelin map **329** P3 – pop. 641 – alt. 665
▶ Paris 464 – Aurillac 83 – Bort-les-Orgues 24 – Clermont-Ferrand 107

⚠ Municipal le Maury

✆ 05 55 95 92 28, www.camping-du-maury.com

Address : 4.6km southwest following signs for the beach; beside the Lac de Triouzoune - recommended route via the D 20, follow the signs for Neuvic

Opening times : from mid June to mid Sept.

2 ha (50 pitches) terraced, relatively flat, flat, grassy

Tariff : ☝ 3€ ⛟ 🔲 3,50€ – [⚡] (16A) 3,50€
Rental rates : (from mid April to mid Nov.) – 12 🏠. Per night from 35 to 90€ – Per week from 196 to 504€
🚐 borne

Surroundings : ⌂ 🏕 ⚐
Leisure activities : 🛶 🚣 🍴
Facilities : ⚲ launderette
Nearby : 🍴 ✗ ⚲ ≊ (beach) 🎣

G
P
S
Longitude : 2.30498
Latitude : 45.39143

The prices listed were supplied by the campsite owners in 2013 (if prices were not available, those from the previous year are given). The fees should be regarded as basic charges and may fluctuate with inflation.

LISSAC-SUR-COUZE

19600 – Michelin map **329** J5 – pop. 710 – alt. 170
▶ Paris 486 – Brive-la-Gaillarde 11 – Périgueux 68 – Sarlat-la-Canéda 42

🏘 Village Vacances Les Hameaux du Perrier

(rental of chalets only)

✆ 05 55 84 34 48, www.chalets-en-france.com

Address : at Le Perrier

17 ha/10 for camping, terraced
Rentals : 94 🏠.

Surroundings : ⌂ ≤ ⚐⚐
Leisure activities : 🍴 ✗ 🚣 🎿 🏊
Facilities : ⚲ 🏠 🍴 launderette 🛒
Nearby : 🚲 ✗ ≊ 🎣 🛶 water skiing

G
P
S
Longitude : 1.43848
Latitude : 45.10029

🏘 Village Vacances La Prairie (rental of chalets only)

✆ 05 55 85 37 97, www.caussecorrezien.fr – traditional camp. spaces also available

Address : 1.4km southwest along the D 59 and take road to the left, near the Lac du Causse

Opening times : Permanent

5 ha terraced

Rental rates : (2013 Price) – 20 🏠 – 25 gîtes. Per week from 204 to 545€

Surroundings : ⌂ ≤ 🌊
Leisure activities : 🍴 ✗ 🚣
Facilities : ⚹ ⚲ 🚐 🏠 🍴 launderette
At the leisure/activities centre : 🚲 ≊ (beach) 🛶 🎣 🐎 pedalos

G
P
S
Longitude : 1.45465
Latitude : 45.10125

MAGNAC-LAVAL

87190 – Michelin map **325** D3 – pop. 1 850 – alt. 231
▶ Paris 366 – Limoges 64 – Poitiers 86 – Guéret 62

⛰ Village Vacances Le Hameau de Gîtes des Pouyades

(rental of gîtes only)

✆ 05 55 60 73 45, www.lelimousinsejoursvacances.com/

Address : at Les Pouyades

Opening times : from beginning Feb. to beginning Jan.

1,5 ha flat

Rentals : 12 gîtes. Reservation fee 16€

Surroundings : 🏊 ≤ On the lake ♀ Leisure activities : 🏠 🎿 🛶 Facilities : 🚿 📶 🍴 launderette	**GPS** Longitude : 1.19236 Latitude : 46.20331

MASSERET

19510 – Michelin map **329** K2 – pop. 675 – alt. 380
▶ Paris 432 – Guéret 132 – Limoges 45 – Tulle 48

⛺ Intercommunal Masseret-Lamongerie

✆ 05 55 73 44 57, www.domaine-des-forgescampingmasseret

Address : 3km east along the D 20, follow the signs for Les Meilhards, near the exit from Masseret-Gare

Opening times : from beginning April to end Sept.

100 ha/2 for camping (80 pitches) relatively flat, flat, grassy, fine gravel

Tariff : (2013 Price) 🚶 2,80€ 🚐 2€ 📧 3,80€ – ⚡ (6A) 2,50€

Rental rates : (from beginning April to end Sept.) – 4 🚙. Per night from 50 to 55€ – Per week from 231 to 440€

🚗 borne

A pleasant wooded setting near a small lake.

Surroundings : 🏊 ≤ ♀♀ Leisure activities : 🏠 Facilities : 🚿 ☛ 🚮 📶 Nearby : 🍴 🍽 🛶 🚵 ✂ 🏓 🎿 🏖 (beach) 🛶 sports trail	**GPS** Longitude : 1.54908 Latitude : 45.54154

MEYSSAC

19500 – Michelin map **329** L5 – pop. 1 245 – alt. 220
▶ Paris 507 – Argentat 62 – Beaulieu-sur-Dordogne 21 – Brive-la-Gaillarde 23

⛰ Intercommunal Moulin de Valane

✆ 05 55 25 41 59, www.meyssac.fr

Address : located 1km to the northwest, follow the signs for Collonge-la-Rouge; beside a stream

Opening times : from beginning May to end Sept.

4 ha (115 pitches) terraced, relatively flat, flat, grassy

Tariff : (2013 Price) 17€ 🚶🚶 🚐 📧 ⚡ (10A) – Extra per person 4€

Rental rates : (from mid April to mid Oct.) – 21 🚙. Per night from 50 to 60€ – Per week from 180 to 520€

Surroundings : 🗐 ♀♀ Leisure activities : ✗ 🏠 🛶 🚲 🏓 🎿 🛶 Facilities : 🚿 ☛ (July–Aug.) 🍴 launderette ⛴	**GPS** Longitude : 1.66381 Latitude : 45.06102

NEUVIC

19160 – Michelin map **329** O3 – pop. 1 868 – alt. 620
▶ Paris 465 – Aurillac 78 – Mauriac 25 – Tulle 56

⛰ Municipal du Lac

✆ 05 55 95 85 48, www.campingdulac-neuvic-correze.com

Address : route de la Plage (2.3km east along the D 20, follow the signs for Bort-les-Orgues and turn left onto the beach road; beside the Lac de la Triouzoune)

Opening times : from beginning March to end Nov.

5 ha (100 pitches)

Tariff : (2013 Price) 🚶 3,20€ 🚐 1,70€ 📧 3,50€ – ⚡ (8A) 3€
Reservation fee 8€

Rental rates : (from beginning March to end Nov.) – 28 🏠. Per night from 42 to 49€ – Per week from 200 to 530€ Reservation fee 8€

🚗 borne 3,15€ – 40 📧 12,60€ – ⚡ ⚡7,60€

Surroundings : 🏊 🗐 ♀♀ Leisure activities : 🏠 🛥 🛶 🛶 Facilities : ☛ 🍴 📧 Nearby : 🍴 ✗ ✂ 🚮 🏖 (beach) 🛶 ⚓ pedalos	**GPS** Longitude : 2.2909 Latitude : 45.38677

NEXON

87800 – Michelin map **325** E6 – pop. 2 457 – alt. 359
▶ Paris 412 – Châlus 20 – Limoges 22 – Nontron 53

⛺ Municipal de l'Étang de la Lande

✆ 05 55 58 35 44, www.camping-nexon.fr

Address : located 1km south following signs for St-Hilaire, access near the pl. de l'Hôtel-de-Ville

Opening times : from beginning June to end Sept.

2 ha (53 pitches)

Tariff : 10€ 🚶🚶 🚐 📧 ⚡ (10A) – Extra per person 3,20€

Rental rates : (from beginning April to beginning Nov.) – 6 🏠. Per night from 42 to 57€ – Per week from 191 to 470€

🚗 borne – 4 📧 10€

Situated near a small lake.

Surroundings : 🗐 ♀♀ Leisure activities : 🏠 🚲 Facilities : 🚿 ☛ 🚮 🍴 📧 Nearby : 🏖 (beach) pedalos	**GPS** Longitude : 1.17997 Latitude : 45.67078

OBJAT

19130 – Michelin map **329** J4 – pop. 3 605 – alt. 131
▶ Paris 495 – Limoges 106 – Tulle 46 – Brive-la-Gaillarde 20

⛰ Village Vacances Les Grands Prés

(rental of chalets only)

✆ 05 55 25 96 73, www.tourismeobjat.com

Address : at l'espace loisirs : Les Grands Prés

Opening times : Permanent

18 ha/4 for camping flat

Rental rates : 20 🏠. Per week from 245 to 505€ – Reservation fee 8€

🚗 borne 2€ – 26 📧 7€

Pleasant pitches for campervans close to the chalet village.

Surroundings : 🏊 ≤ Leisure activities : ⛹ Facilities : 🚿 🚮 📶 launderette Nearby : 🛶 🚲 🎿 🛶 🛶	**GPS** Longitude : 1.41069 Latitude : 45.26687

PALISSE

19160 – Michelin map **329** O3 – pop. 233 – alt. 650
▶ Paris 460 – Aurillac 87 – Clermont-Ferrand 102 – Mauriac 33

⛺ Le Vianon ♣♦

☎ 05 55 95 87 22, www.levianon.com

Address : at Les Plaines (1.1km north along the D 47, follow the signs for Combressol and take turning to the right; beside a lake)

4 ha (59 pitches) terraced, flat and relatively flat, grassy, fine gravel, wood, pond
Rentals : 16 ⌂.

Surroundings : ♨ 〰 Leisure activities : ⛴ ✗ 🏠 🏃 🏊 🚴 ✂ 🏊 〰 Facilities : ♿ ⚷ 🧺 launderette 🚿	**GPS** Longitude : 2.2061 Latitude : 45.42662

PIERRE-BUFFIÈRE

87260 – Michelin map **325** F6 – pop. 1 143 – alt. 330
▶ Paris 408 – Limoges 20 – St-Yriex-la-Perche 29 – Uzerche 38

⛺ Intercommunal de Chabanas

☎ 05 55 00 96 43, www.pierre-buffiere.com

Address : 1.8km south along the D 420, follow the signs for Château-Chervix, towards A 20 and take road to the left, near the stadium - from A 20: take exit 40

Opening times : from mid May to end Sept.

1,5 ha (60 pitches)

Tariff : (2013 Price) 12€ ♣♣ 🚐 📧 🔌 (6A)
🚐 borne 4€
Pretty shrubs and flowers decorate the site.

Surroundings : 〰 〰 🍃 Leisure activities : 🏠 🏊 Facilities : ♿ 🏠 🧺 🚿 🎣 Nearby : ✗	**GPS** Longitude : 1.37108 Latitude : 45.68936

RAZÈS

87640 – Michelin map **325** F4 – pop. 1 107 – alt. 440
▶ Paris 366 – Argenton-sur-Creuse 68 – Bellac 32 – Guéret 65

⛺ Aquadis Loisirs Santrop ♣♦

☎ 05 55 71 08 08, www.lac-saint-pardoux.com

Address : lake St-Pardoux (4km west along the D 44; beside the lake)

5,5 ha (152 pitches)
Rentals : 6 ⌂.

Surroundings : ♨ 〰 〰 Leisure activities : ⛴ ✗ 🏠 🏃 🏊 Facilities : ♿ ⚷ 🧺 📧 🚿 Nearby : ✂ 🏖 (beach) 🎿 water skiing	**GPS** Longitude : 1.29579 Latitude : 46.03254

*The classification (1 to 5 tents, **black** or **red**) that we award to selected sites in this guide is our own system. It should not be confused with the classification (1 to 5 stars) of official organisations.*

REYGADES

19430 – Michelin map **329** M5 – pop. 193 – alt. 460
▶ Paris 516 – Aurillac 56 – Brive-la-Gaillarde 56 – St-Céré 26

⛺ La Belle Etoile

☎ 05 55 28 50 08, www.campingbelle-etoile.fr

Address : at Lestrade (located 1km north off the D 41, follow the signs for Beaulieu-sur-Dordogne)

Opening times : from beginning June to end Sept.

5 ha/3 for camping (25 pitches)

Tariff : ♣ 4€ 🚐 📧 5,15€ – 🔌 (6A) 3€
Rental rates : Permanent – 6 🚐 – 6 ⌂ – 4 canvas bungalows. Per week from 185 to 620€
🚐 3 📧

Surroundings : 〰 ♨ 〰 Leisure activities : 🏊 🏊 (small swimming pool), quad biking Facilities : ♿ ⚷ 🏠 🧺 launderette 🚐	**GPS** Longitude : 1.90538 Latitude : 45.02405

Key to rentals symbols :

12 🚐	*Number of mobile homes*
20 ⌂	*Number of chalets*
6 🛏	*Number of rooms to rent*
Per night 30–50€	*Minimum/maximum rate per night*
Per week 300–1,000€	*Minimum/maximum rate per week*

ROYÈRE-DE-VASSIVIÈRE

23460 – Michelin map **325** I5 – pop. 563 – alt. 735
▶ Paris 412 – Bourganeuf 22 – Eymoutiers 25 – Felletin 29

⛺ Les Terrasses du Lac

☎ 05 55 64 76 77, campings.lelacdevassiviere.com

Address : at Vauveix (10km southwest along the D 3 and D 35, follow the signs for Eymoutiers; by the port (direct access))

4 ha (142 pitches) terraced, relatively flat, flat, grassy, gravelled

Surroundings : ♨ Lac de Vassivière 〰 〰 Leisure activities : 🏠 🏖 (beach) 🍃 Facilities : ⚷ 🚾 🧺 launderette Nearby : 🚐 ⛴ ✗ 🏃 🏊 🎣 🎣 water skiing	**GPS** Longitude : 1.89526 Latitude : 45.78979

⛺ La Presqu'île

☎ 05 55 64 78 98, www.campings.lelacdevassiviere.com

Address : at Broussas (8.5km south along the D 8, D 34, D 3 and take turning to the right, near the Lac de Vassivière)

Opening times : Permanent

7 ha (150 pitches) undulating, relatively flat, flat, grassy

Tariff : (2013 Price) 17,50€ ♣♣ 🚐 📧 🔌 (10A) –
Extra per person 3,50€ – Reservation fee 5€
Rental rates : Permanent – 20 ⌂ – 3 tent lodges. Per night from 36 to 78€ – Per week from 168 to 397€ – Reservation fee 5€
In a natural setting beside the lake.

Surroundings : ♨ 〰 〰 Leisure activities : 🏠 🏊 🏖 Facilities : ⚷ (July–Aug.) 🧺 📧 Nearby : electric boats	**GPS** Longitude : 1.9223 Latitude : 45.79151

ST-GERMAIN-LES-BELLES

87380 – Michelin map **325** F7 – pop. 1 151 – alt. 432
▶ Paris 422 – Eymoutiers 33 – Limoges 34 – St-Léonard-de-Noblat 31

⚠ Le Montréal

📞 05 55 71 86 20, www.campingdemontreal.com

Address : rue du Petit Moulin (take the southeastern exit, follow the signs for La Porcherie; beside a small lake)

Opening times : Permanent

1 ha (60 pitches) Tariff : 19,70€ ♣♣ ⇔ 🔳 🔌 (10A) Extra per person 3,80€

Rental rates : (from beginning April to end Oct.) – 1 🚐 5 🏠. Per night from 44 to 97€ – Per week from 172 to 679€ Reservation fee 15€

🚐 borne 4€ – 3 🔳 17€

Surroundings : 🏞 ≤ 🗔 ⚲
Facilities : 🚻 ⚬ॼ 🚾📶 🍴 launderette
Nearby : ✕ 🏊 ✗ 🏖 (beach) 🎣

G P S Longitude : 1.5011
Latitude : 45.61143

ST-HILAIRE-LES-PLACES

87800 – Michelin map **325** D7 – pop. 870 – alt. 426
▶ Paris 417 – Châlus 18 – Limoges 27 – Nontron 52

⚠ Municipal du Lac

📞 05 55 58 12 14, www.campingdulacplaisance.com

Address : at the lake Plaisance (1.2km south of the town along the D 15a and take road to the left; 100m from the lake)

Opening times : from beginning May to end Sept.

2,5 ha (92 pitches)

Tariff : 14,30€ ♣♣ ⇔ 🔳 🔌 (10A) – Extra per person 5,60€

Rental rates : (from beginning May to end Sept.) 🏕 – 11 🚐 15 gîtes. Per night from 43 to 67€ – Per week from 413 to 518€

🚐 borne 9€ – 🚐 11€

Surroundings : 🗔 ⚲⚲
Leisure activities : 🏊 🏓 🏊 🎿
Facilities : 🚻 ⚬ॼ (July–Aug.) 🍴 🖨
Nearby : ✗ 🏊 🏖 (beach) 🛶 🎣 🐎 pedalos

G P S Longitude : 1.16038
Latitude : 45.63511

ST-LAURENT-LES-ÉGLISES

87240 – Michelin map **325** F5 – pop. 830 – alt. 388
▶ Paris 385 – Bellac 55 – Bourganeuf 31 – Guéret 50

⚠⚠ Municipal Pont du Dognon

📞 05 55 56 57 25, campingpontdudognon@orange.fr

Address : 1.8km southeast along the D 5, follow the signs for St-Léonard-de-Noblat; beside the Taurion river

Opening times : Permanent

3 ha (90 pitches)

Tariff : (2013 Price) 15€ ♣♣ ⇔ 🔳 🔌 (6A) – Extra per person 4€ Reservation fee 16€

Rental rates : Permanent – 2 🚐 – 5 🏠. Per night 52€ Per week 464€ – Reservation fee 16€

Surroundings : 🏞 ≤ 🗔 ⚲
Leisure activities : 🗔 🏓 🏊 🎿 🛶 fitness trail
Facilities : 🚻 ⚬ॼ 🚾 🍴 launderette
Nearby : ✕ 🏊 ⚓ pedalos

G P S Longitude : 1.5145
Latitude : 45.94293

ST-LÉONARD-DE-NOBLAT

87400 – Michelin map **325** F5 – pop. 4 665 – alt. 347
▶ Paris 407 – Aubusson 68 – Brive-la-Gaillarde 99 – Guéret 62

⚠⚠ Municipal de Beaufort

📞 05 55 56 02 79, www.campingdebeaufort.fr

Address : at Beaufort (1.7km along the N 141, following signs for Limoges then continue 1.5km to the left following signs for Masleon; beside the Vienne river)

Opening times : from mid April to end Sept.

2 ha (98 pitches)

Tariff : (2013 Price) ♣ 2,50€ ⇔ 2,50€ 🔳 7€ – 🔌 (15A) 3,50€

Rental rates : (2013 Price) (from mid April to mid Nov.) – 10 🚐 2 🏠. Per night from 30 to 65€ – Per week from 175 to 400€

🚐 borne 3€

Surroundings : 🗔 ⚲⚲
Leisure activities : 🍴 🗔 🏊 🎣
Facilities : 🚻 ⚬ॼ 🎿 🍴 launderette

G P S Longitude : 1.49211
Latitude : 45.82276

We have selected the best campsites in France with our usual care, listing those with the best facilities in the most pleasant surroundings.

ST-MARTIN-TERRESSUS

87400 – Michelin map **325** F5 – pop. 545 – alt. 280
▶ Paris 383 – Ambazac 7 – Bourganeuf 31 – Limoges 20

⚠ Municipal Soleil Levant

📞 05 55 39 83 78, www.st-martin-terressus.fr – 🇫🇷

Address : in the village (continue west along the D 29 and take the road to the right; beside a small lake)

Opening times : Permanent

0,5 ha (36 pitches)

Tariff : ♣ 5€ ⇔ – 🔌 (18A) 2€

Surroundings : 🏞 ≤ 🗔 ⚲ ▲
Leisure activities : 🍴 🗔
Facilities : 🚻 🎿🖨

G P S Longitude : 1.43995
Latitude : 45.91854

ST-PARDOUX

87250 – Michelin map **325** E4 – pop. 536 – alt. 370
▶ Paris 366 – Bellac 25 – Limoges 33 – St-Junien 39

⚠⚠ Aquadis Loisirs Le Freaudour

📞 05 55 76 57 22, www.aquadis-loisirs.com

Address : at the base de loisirs (leisure centre) (1.2km to the south; beside the Lac de St-Pardoux)

Opening times : from end March to beginning Nov.

4,5 ha (200 pitches)

Tariff : 18,80€ ♣♣ ⇔ 🔳 🔌 (10A) – Extra per person 5,10€ Reservation fee 9,90€

Rental rates : (from end March to beginning Nov.) – 20 🚐 10 🏠. Per night from 68 to 89€ – Per week from 168 to 590€ Reservation fee 19,80€

Surroundings : 🏞 ≤ 🗔 ⚲
Leisure activities : 🍴 🗔 🏓 🎿 🎿
Facilities : 🚻 ⚬ॼ (July–Aug.) 🚾 🛒 🎿 🖇 🍴 🖨
Nearby : 🏖 (beach)

G P S Longitude : 1.2788
Latitude : 46.04931

ST-PARDOUX-CORBIER

19210 – Michelin map **329** J3 – pop. 360 – alt. 404
▶ Paris 448 – Arnac-Pompadour 8 – Brive-la-Gaillarde 44 – St-Yrieix-la-Perche 27

⚠ Le Domaine Bleu

✆ 0555735989, www.ledomainebleu.eu

Address : take the eastern exit along the D 50, follow the signs for Vigeois and take the road to the right, near a lake

Opening times : from beginning July to end Aug.

1 ha (40 pitches)

Tariff : 16€ �★☆ ⌗ ▣ ⚡ (16A) – Extra per person 4€

Surroundings : ☁ ⌂ ♤♤
Leisure activities : ⚓
Facilities : ⚬ ⚯ ⌗⚷▥ ⚘ ⚸
Nearby : ※

G P S	Longitude : 1.45449 Latitude : 45.42973

ST-YRIEIX-LA-PERCHE

87500 – Michelin map **325** E7 – pop. 6 932 – alt. 360
▶ Paris 430 – Brive-la-Gaillarde 63 – Limoges 40 – Périgueux 63

⚠ Municipal d'Arfeuille

✆ 0555750875, camping@saint-yrieix.fr

Address : route du Viaduc (2.5km north following signs for Limoges and take the road to the left; beside a small lake)

Opening times : from mid April to mid Sept.

2 ha (100 pitches)

Tariff : 12,60€ ☆★☆ ⌗ ▣ ⚡ (10A) – Extra per person 3,80€
Rental rates : (from beginning March to end Dec.) ⚬ – 11 ⌂.
Per week from 280 to 460€
⛽ borne

Surroundings : ☁ ⌂ ♤♤
Leisure activities : ⚓⚶ ⚷⚿ ⚹ ⚬ (beach)
pedalos ⚹
Facilities : ⚯ ▥
Nearby : ⚑※⚓

G P S	Longitude : 1.20009 Latitude : 45.52791

SEILHAC

19700 – Michelin map **329** L3 – pop. 1 721 – alt. 500
▶ Paris 461 – Aubusson 97 – Brive-la-Gaillarde 33 – Limoges 73

⚠ Le Lac de Bournazel

✆ 0555270565, www.camping-lac-bournazel.com

Address : located 1.5km northwest along the N 120, follow the signs for Uzerche then turn right after 1km

Opening times : from beginning April to end Oct.

6,5 ha (155 pitches)

Tariff : 17,40€ ☆★☆ ⌗ ▣ ⚡ (12A) – Extra per person 4,40€
Reservation fee 9€
Rental rates : (from beginning April to end Oct.) – 2 caravans 10 ⌂ – 2 tipis. Per night from 24 to 88€ – Per week from 168 to 616€ – Reservation fee 9€
⛽ borne 4€ – ⚯ ⚡11,40€

Surroundings : ☁ ⌂ ♤♤
Leisure activities : ⚑ ⚓⚶ ⚷
Facilities : ⚬ ⚯▥⚹ ⚸
Nearby : ※⚓⚓⚶ disco, sports trail

G P S	Longitude : 1.7022 Latitude : 45.37838

TREIGNAC

19260 – Michelin map **329** L2 – pop. 1 383 – alt. 500
▶ Paris 463 – Égletons 32 – Eymoutiers 33 – Limoges 75

⚠ Flower La Plage

✆ 0555980854, www.camping-correze.com

Address : at the lake des Barriousses (4.5km north along the D 940, follow the signs for Eymoutiers)

3,5 ha (130 pitches) terraced, flat and relatively flat, grassy, stony, adjacent wood

Rentals : 26 – 6 tent lodges – 2 huts on stilts.
⛽ borne

Surroundings : ⚖ ⌂ ♤♤
Leisure activities : ⚑
Facilities : ⚬ ⚯ ▥ ⚹ launderette
Nearby : ※ ⚓⚶ ⚷⚿ ⚬ (beach) ⚸
pedalos

G P S	Longitude : 1.81373 Latitude : 45.55992

This guide is not intended as a list of all the camping sites in France; its aim is to provide a selection of the best sites in each category.

USSEL

19200 – Michelin map **329** O2 – pop. 10 226 – alt. 631
▶ Paris 448 – Limoges 142 – Clermont-Ferrand 82 – Brive-la-Gaillarde 89

⚠ Municipal de Ponty

✆ 0555723005, www.ussel19.fr

Address : rue du Lac (2.7km west following signs for Tulle and take D 157 to the right; near a small lake)

Opening times : from end May to end Sept.

2 ha (50 pitches)

Tariff : 9€ ☆★☆ ⌗ ▣ ⚡ (8A) – Extra per person 2,70€
⛽ borne 2€ – 10 ▣ 9€

Surroundings : ☁ ⚖ on the lake ⌂ ♤
Leisure activities : ⚑ ⚓⚶
Facilities : ⚬ ⚯ ⌗⚹ ▥
Nearby : ⚑※⚷ ※⚹ ⚶ ⚬ (beach) ⚑⚸
mountain biking

G P S	Longitude : 2.28603 Latitude : 45.54593

UZERCHE

19140 – Michelin map **329** K3 – pop. 3 226 – alt. 380
▶ Paris 444 – Aubusson 95 – Bourganeuf 76 – Brive-la-Gaillarde 38

⚠ Municipal la Minoterie

✆ 0555731275, http://camping.uzerche.fr

Address : at the base de loisirs (leisure centre) of la Minoterie (located to the southwest of the town centre, access via quai Julian-Grimau, between the N 20 and the bridge at Turgot (D 3))

1,5 ha (65 pitches) terrace, flat, grassy, stony
Rentals : gîte d'étape (lodge, 49 beds).
A picturesque setting beside the Vézère river (left bank).

Surroundings : ☁ ⚖ ♤♤
Leisure activities : ⚑ ⚓⚶ ⚷⚿ ⚬ ⚹ ⚸
Facilities : ⚬ ⚯ ▥ ⚸ launderette
Nearby : climbing wall

G P S	Longitude : 1.56882 Latitude : 45.41927

VIDEIX

87600 – Michelin map **325** B6 – pop. 234 – alt. 260
▶ Paris 443 – Angoulême 53 – Limoges 53 – Nontron 36

⛰ Village Vacances Le Hameau de gîtes

(rental of chalets only)

🖉 0555488339, www.rochechouart.com

Address : Plage de La Chassagne (head 1.7km north along the D 87, follow the signs for Pressignac; the area is known as La Chassagne)

Opening times : Permanent

3 ha flat, grassy

Rental rates : (2013 Price) Ⓟ – 16 🏠. Per night from 70 to 90€
Per week from 240 to 480€

Surroundings : 🐟 ⩽ lake ⚠
Leisure activities : 🏛 ⚒
Facilities : ♿ 🚿🏕🏛 🚰 launderette
Nearby : 🍴✕ 🚤 🐟 🦆 pedalos

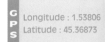
Longitude : 0.71585
Latitude : 45.80106

VIGEOIS

19410 – Michelin map **329** K3 – pop. 1 194 – alt. 390
▶ Paris 457 – Limoges 68 – Tulle 32 – Brive-la-Gaillarde 41

⚠ Municipal du Lac de Pontcharal

🖉 0555989086, www.vigeois.com

Address : at Pontcharal (situated 2km southeast along the D 7, follow the signs for Brive, near the lake at Pontcharal)

Opening times : from beginning June to mid Sept.

32 ha/1,7 (85 pitches)

Tariff : 🚶 3,60€ 🚗 🏕 4,50€ – (≠) (15A) 4€

Rental rates : (from beginning April to end Oct.) – 7 🛖.
Per night from 70€ – Per week from 270 to 400€
🚰 borne 3€

Surroundings : 🐟 ♨ ⚠
Leisure activities : 🍴✕ 🏖 (beach) 🎣
Facilities : ♿ ☎ (July–Aug.) 🚿🚰 🏛 🚤
Nearby : pedalos

Longitude : 1.53806
Latitude : 45.36873

LORRAINE

Christian Legay / Mairie de Metz

If you want to do justice to the collage of stunning sights of Lorraine, a region that shares borders with Luxembourg, Germany and Belgium, don't forget to pack your walking boots. But before you head for the hills, make sure you leave enough time to discover the artistic heritage of Nancy and admire the lights and contemporary art gallery of historic Metz. Then embark upon the trail of tiny spa resorts and the famous centres of craftsmanship that produce the legendary Baccarat crystal, Longwy enamels and Lunéville porcelain. From there head to historic Domrémy and Colombey. The water, forests and wildlife of the Vosges regional park, nestling in the 'Valley of Lakes', will keep you entranced as you make your way down hillsides dotted with orchards bursting with plums. Stop for a little light refreshment in a *marcairerie* (traditional farmhouse inn) and sample the famous *quiche Lorraine* tarts, a slab of Munster cheese and a delicious kirsch-flavoured dessert.

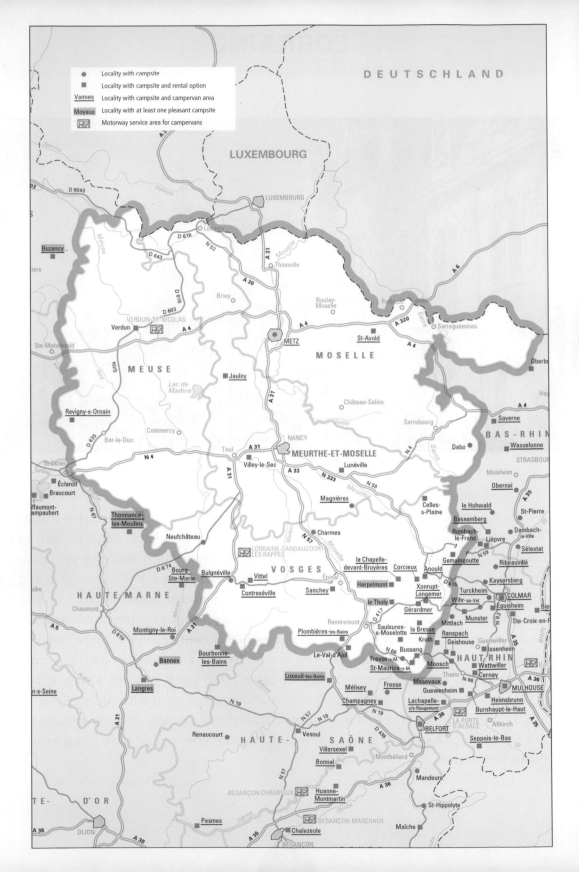

ANOULD

88650 – Michelin map **314** J3 – pop. 3 336 – alt. 457
▶ Paris 430 – Colmar 43 – Épinal 45 – Gérardmer 15

⚠ Les Acacias

✆ 03 29 57 11 06, www.acaciascamp.com

Address : 191 rue Léonard de Vinci (take the western exit along the N 415, follow the signs for Colmar and take the road to the right)

Opening times : from beginning Dec. to end Sept.

2,5 ha (84 pitches) terraced, flat, grassy

Tariff : (2013 Price) 15,20€ ✿✿ ⇌ 🔲 🔌 (6A) – Extra per person 3,90€

Rental rates : (from beginning Dec. to end Sept.) – 2 caravans 8 🛏 – 8 🏠 – 6 bungalows (without sanitary facilities). Per night from 38 to 80€ – Per week from 205 to 550€

🚐 borne 10€ – 5 🔲 10€ – 🚐 10€

Surroundings : 🏞 ♨
Leisure activities : 🍴 🏛 ⚽ 🏊 (small swimming pool)
Facilities : ♿ ⚲ (June–Sept.) 🚻 🛁 🍴 launderette
Nearby : walking trails

G P S Longitude : 6.95786
Latitude : 48.18437

LA BRESSE

88250 – Michelin map **314** J4 – pop. 4 732 – alt. 636 – Winter sports : 650/1 350m
▶ Paris 437 – Colmar 52 – Épinal 52 – Gérardmer 13

⚠ Municipal le Haut des Bluches

✆ 03 29 25 64 80, www.hautdesbluches.com – alt. 708

Address : 5 route des Planches (head 3.2km east along the D 34, follow the signs for Le Col de la Schlucht; beside the Moselotte river)

Opening times : from mid Dec. to mid Nov.

4 ha (140 pitches) terraced, relatively flat, flat, grassy, rocks

Tariff : 24,80€ ✿✿ ⇌ 🔲 🔌 (13A) – Extra per person 3,40€

Rental rates : (from mid Dec. to mid Nov.) ♿ (2 chalets) – 7 🏠 13 🛏. Per night from 39 to 54€ – Per week from 266 to 642€

🚐 borne 3,30€ – 17 🔲 6,10€ – 🚐 🔌 11,70€

A picturesque setting crossed by a stream.

Surroundings : ⚘ ≼
Leisure activities : 🍴 ✗ 🏛 ⚽ 🎣 adventure park, multi-sports ground
Facilities : ♿ ⚲ 🚻 🛁 🍴 launderette 🚿
Nearby : sports trail

G P S Longitude : 6.91831
Latitude : 47.99878

⚠ Belle Hutte

✆ 03 29 25 49 75, www.camping-belle-hutte.com – alt. 900

Address : 1bis Vouille de Belle Hutte (head 9km northeast along the D 34, follow the signs for Le Col de la Schlucht; beside the Moselotte river)

Opening times : from mid Dec. to mid Nov.

5 ha (125 pitches)

Tariff : 29,80€ ✿✿ ⇌ 🔲 🔌 (10A) – Extra per person 8,30€
Reservation fee 10€

Rental rates : (from mid Dec. to mid Nov.) ♿ (2 chalets) – 15 🏠. Per night from 36 to 125€ – Per week from 252 to 875€
Reservation fee 10€

🚐 borne 5€

On a pleasant, wooded site.

Surroundings : ⚘ ≼ 🏞
Leisure activities : 🍴 ✗ 🏛 ⚽ 🏊 🎣
Facilities : ♿ ⚲ 🚻 🛁 🍴 launderette 🚿
Nearby : ✗

G P S Longitude : 6.96254
Latitude : 48.0349

BULGNÉVILLE

88140 – Michelin map **314** D3 – pop. 1 400 – alt. 350
▶ Paris 331 – Contrexéville 6 – Épinal 53 – Neufchâteau 22

⚠ Porte des Vosges

✆ 03 29 09 12 00, www.Camping-Portedesvosges.com – 🔣

Address : at La Grande Tranchée (head 1.3km southeast along the D 164, follow the signs for Contrexéville and take D 14, follow the signs for Suriauville to the right)

Opening times : from beginning April to end Oct.

3,2 ha (100 pitches)

Tariff : 20,50€ ✿✿ ⇌ 🔲 🔌 (6A) – Extra per person 4,60€

Rental rates : (from beginning April to end Oct.) – 2 tent lodges . Per night from 25 to 42€ – Per week from 175 to 294€

🚐 50 🔲 7,20€

Situated in a rural setting.

Surroundings : ♨
Facilities : ♿ ⚲ ✉ 🛁 🍴

G P S Longitude : 5.84514
Latitude : 48.19529

BUSSANG

88540 – Michelin map **314** J5 – pop. 1 604 – alt. 605
▶ Paris 444 – Belfort 44 – Épinal 59 – Gérardmer 38

⚠ Sunêlia Domaine de Champé

✆ 03 29 61 61 51, www.domaine-de-champe.com

Address : 14 rue des Champs-Navets (located to the northeast, access via the turning to the left of the church)

Opening times : Permanent

3,5 ha (100 pitches) flat, grassy

Tariff : (2013 Price) 31€ ✿✿ ⇌ 🔲 🔌 (6A) – Extra per person 7€

Rental rates : (2013 Price) Permanent – 22 🛏 – 8 🏠. Per night from 70 to 170€ – Per week from 490 to 1190€

Situated beside the Moselle river and a stream.

Surroundings : ≼
Leisure activities : 🍴 ✗ 🏛 🕐 daytime 🎣 📿 ♨ hammam ⚽ 🏊 🎿 multi-sports ground
Facilities : ♿ ⚲ ✉ 🚻 🍴 launderette 🚿
Nearby : 🏊

G P S Longitude : 6.85748
Latitude : 47.8889

CELLES-SUR-PLAINE

88110 – Michelin map **314** J2 – pop. 857 – alt. 318
▶ Paris 391 – Baccarat 23 – Blâmont 23 – Lunéville 49

⚠ Les Lacs 🔣

✆ 03 29 41 28 00, www.camping-paysdeslacs.com

Address : place de la gare (to the southwest of town)

15 ha/4 for camping (135 pitches)

Rentals : 20 🏠 – 6 canvas bungalows – 10 chalets (without sanitary facilities).

Beside the river and close to the lake.

Surroundings : ≼ 🏞
Leisure activities : 🍴 🏛 🎣 ⚽ 🎿 🏊 🎣
Facilities : ♿ ⚲ 🚻 🛁 🚿 🍴 launderette 🚿
At the lake : 🚲 🚣 🛶

G P S Longitude : 6.94756
Latitude : 48.4557

LA CHAPELLE-DEVANT-BRUYÈRES

88600 – Michelin map **314** I3 – pop. 621 – alt. 457
▶ Paris 416 – Épinal 31 – Gérardmer 22 – Rambervillers 26

⚑ Les Pinasses

✆ 03 29 58 51 10, www.camping-les-pinasses.fr

Address : 215 route de Bruyères (located 1.2km to the northwest on the D 60)

Opening times : from beginning April to end Sept.

3 ha (139 pitches) small lake

Tariff : 24,40€ ✶✶ ⇌ 🔲 ⚡ (6A) – Extra per person 5,30€

Rental rates : (from beginning April to end Sept.) – 4 ⛺
8 🛖 – 2 apartments. Per night from 36 to 82€ – Per week from 230 to 580€

🚐 borne 4€ – 🚐 ⚡23€

Surroundings : 🗺 ♤♤
Leisure activities : ✗ 🏠 🛶 ※ 🎣 🏊 🎿
Facilities : ⚘ 🛁 🚿 🚾 ♜ launderette

GPS Longitude : 6.77411
Latitude : 48.18974

CHARMES

88130 – Michelin map **314** F2 – pop. 4 613 – alt. 282
▶ Paris 381 – Mirecourt 17 – Nancy 43 – Neufchâteau 58

⚑ Les Îles

✆ 03 29 38 87 71, www.campinglesiles.blogspot.fr

Address : 20 rue de l'Écluse (located 1km to the southwest along the D 157 and take the road to the right; near the stadium)

Opening times : from beginning April to end Sept.

3,5 ha (67 pitches) flat, grassy

Tariff : (2013 Price) 14€ ✶✶ ⇌ 🔲 ⚡ (10A) – Extra per person 3,25€

In a pleasant setting between the Canal de l'Est and the Moselle river.

Leisure activities : 🛶 ☄ 🎣
Facilities : ⚷ ⚘ 🚿 ♜
Nearby : ※ 🎣

GPS Longitude : 6.28668
Latitude : 48.37583

CONTREXÉVILLE

88140 – Michelin map **314** D3 – pop. 3 440 – alt. 342 – ⚱
▶ Paris 337 – Épinal 47 – Langres 75 – Luxeuil 73

⚑ Le Tir aux Pigeons

✆ 03 29 08 15 06, www.camping-letirauxpigeons.fr

Address : rue du 11 Septembre (located 1km southwest along the D 13, follow the signs for Suriauville)

Opening times : from mid March to end Oct.

1,8 ha (80 pitches)

Tariff : (2013 Price) 19,50€ ✶✶ ⇌ 🔲 ⚡ (6A) – Extra per person 5€

Rental rates : (2013 Price) (from mid March to end Oct.) – 6 ⛺
4 🛖 – 4 canvas bungalows. Per night from 45 to 70€ – Per week from 220 to 480€

🚐 borne – 20 🔲

Situated at the edge of a wood.

Surroundings : 🌲 ♤♤
Leisure activities : 🍴 🏠
Facilities : ⚷ ⚘ 🏕 🛁 🚿 🚾 ♜ 🔲

GPS Longitude : 5.88517
Latitude : 48.18022

CORCIEUX

88430 – Michelin map **314** J3 – pop. 1 668 – alt. 534
▶ Paris 424 – Épinal 39 – Gérardmer 15 – Remiremont 43

⚑⚑⚑⚑ Yelloh! Village en Voges Domaine des Bans

✆ 03 29 51 64 67, www.domaine-des-bans.fr

Address : 6 rue James Wiese (near the pl. Notre-Dame)

Opening times : Permanent

15,7 ha (634 pitches)

Tariff : 44€ ✶✶ ⇌ 🔲 ⚡ (6A) – Extra per person 8€

Rental rates : Permanent – 250 ⛺ – 65 🛖 – 10 studios – 30 gîtes.
Per night from 35 to 235€ – Per week from 245 to 1645€
🚐 8 🔲 17€

A pleasant setting, in two separate campsites (the des Bans site has 600 pitches, the la Tour site has 34 pitches); beside a small lake.

Surroundings : ⟨ 🗺 ♤
Leisure activities : 🍴 ✗ 🏠 🎡 🎳 🛶 ☄ ※
🎿 🎿 ♨ 🎣 disco
Facilities : ⚷ ⚘ 🏛 🛁 🚾 ♜ launderette 🔲
🍴
Nearby : 🏇

GPS Longitude : 6.87985
Latitude : 48.16867

⚑ Sites et paysages Au Clos de la Chaume

✆ 03 29 50 76 76, www.camping-closdelachaume.com

Address : 21 rue d'Alsace

Opening times : from end April to mid Sept.

4 ha (90 pitches) flat, grassy

Tariff : 24,60€ ✶✶ ⇌ 🔲 ⚡ (10A)
Extra per person 6,10€ – Reservation fee 10€

Rental rates : (from beginning April to end Sept.) – 15 ⛺
5 🛖 – 2 tent lodges . Per night from 42 to 110€ – Per week from 299 to 775€ – Reservation fee 15€

🚐 borne 5,80€ – 5 🔲 11€ – 🚐 ⚡11€

Surroundings : ♤
Leisure activities : 🏠 🛶 ♨ 🏇 🏊
Facilities : ⚷ ⚘ 🛁 ♜ launderette

GPS Longitude : 6.88383
Latitude : 48.17026

A 'quartier' is a district or area of a town or village.

DABO

57850 – Michelin map **307** O7 – pop. 2 636 – alt. 500
▶ Paris 453 – Baccarat 63 – Metz 127 – Phalsbourg 18

⚑ Le Rocher

✆ 03 87 07 47 51, www.ot-dabo.fr

Address : route du Rocher (located 1.5km southeast along the D 45, at the junction with the road for Le Rocher)

Opening times : from end March to beginning Oct.

0,5 ha (42 pitches)

Tariff : (2013 Price) ✶ 3,40€ ⇌ 1,30€ 🔲 1,80€ – ⚡ (10A) 3,90€

Located in a wood of fir trees.

Surroundings : ♤
Leisure activities : 🛶
Facilities : 🏕 🏛

GPS Longitude : 7.25267
Latitude : 48.64844

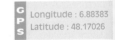

FRESSE-SUR-MOSELLE

88160 – Michelin map **314** I5 – pop. 1 868 – alt. 515
▶ Paris 447 – Metz 178 – Épinal 54 – Mulhouse 56

⛺ Municipal Bon Accueil

☎ 03 29 25 08 98, camping.bonaccueil@orange.fr

Address : 36ter rue de Lorraine (take northwestern exit along the N 66, follow the signs for LeThillot; 80m from the Moselle river)

Opening times : from beginning April to mid Nov.

0,6 ha (50 pitches) flat, grassy

Tariff : ♣ 2,53€ ⟵ 🅿 1,43€ – [⚡] (16A) 2,63€
🚐 borne 3,16€

Surroundings : ≺
Leisure activities :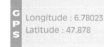
Facilities : 🚿
Nearby : ✗

G P S Longitude : 6.78023
Latitude : 47.878

GEMAINGOUTTE

88520 – Michelin map **314** K3 – pop. 119 – alt. 446
▶ Paris 411 – Colmar 59 – Ribeauvillé 31 – St-Dié 14

⛺ Municipal le Violu

☎ 03 29 57 70 70, www.gemaingoutte.fr

Address : take the western exit along the RD 59, follow the signs for St-Dié; beside a stream

Opening times : from beginning May to end Oct.

1 ha (48 pitches) flat, grassy

Tariff : ♣ 2,50€ ⟵ 1,70€ 🅿 1,80€ – [⚡] (6A) 2,20€
Rental rates : Permanent – 2 🏠. Per night from 55 € – Per week from 220 to 425€
🚐 borne 2€ – 10 🅿 6,50€

Leisure activities :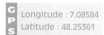
Facilities : ⛴ 🚿 🔲

G P S Longitude : 7.08584
Latitude : 48.25361

GÉRARDMER

88400 – Michelin map **314** J4 – pop. 8 757 – alt. 669 – Winter sports : 660/1 350m
▶ Paris 425 – Belfort 78 – Colmar 52 – Épinal 40

⛺ Les Sapins

☎ 03 29 63 15 01, www.camping-gerardmer.com

Address : 18 chemin de Sapois (located 1.5km southwest, 200m from the lake)

Opening times : from beginning April to mid Oct.

1,3 ha (70 pitches)

Tariff : 20,64€ ♣♣ ⟵ 🅿 [⚡] (10A) – Extra per person 4,50€ – Reservation fee 8€
Rental rates : (from beginning March to mid Nov.) – 3 🛖 1 apartment. Per week 550€ – Reservation fee 10€
🚐 borne 3€ – 🛢9€

Surroundings : ⌒ Ω
Leisure activities : 🍸
Facilities : ⛴ 🚿 🔲
Nearby : 🏊 🐎

G P S Longitude : 6.85614
Latitude : 48.0635

To visit a town or region, use the MICHELIN Green Guides.

⛺ Les Granges-Bas

☎ 03 29 63 12 03, www.lesgrangesbas.fr

Address : 116 chemin des Granges Bas (4km west along the D 417 then turn left at Costet-Beillard, follow road for 1km)

Opening times : from mid Dec. to mid Oct.

2 ha (100 pitches)

Tariff : 16,55€ ♣♣ ⟵ 🅿 [⚡] (6A) – Extra per person 3,85€
Rental rates : (from mid Dec. to mid Oct.) – 11 🛖 – 2 apartments 1 tent lodge. Per week from 238 to 623€ – Reservation fee 10€
🚐 2 🅿 12,70€

Surroundings : ≺ ⌒
Leisure activities : 🏠 🏊 ✗
Facilities : 🚿 launderette

G P S Longitude : 6.80653
Latitude : 48.06927

HERPELMONT

88600 – Michelin map **314** I3 – pop. 247 – alt. 480
▶ Paris 413 – Épinal 28 – Gérardmer 20 – Remiremont 33

⛺ Domaine des Messires

☎ 03 29 58 56 29, www.domainedesmessires.com

Address : rue des Messires (located 1.5km to the north)

Opening times : from end April to end Sept.

11 ha/2 for camping (100 pitches) flat, grassy

Tariff : (2013 Price) ♣ 6,50€ ⟵ 🅿 13,50€ [⚡] (6A) – Reservation fee 12€
Rental rates : (from end April to end Sept.) – 22 🛖. Per night from 39 to 97€ – Per week from 234 to 679€ – Reservation fee 12€

A pleasant site and setting beside a lake.

Surroundings : ≺ lake and mountain ⌒ ♨ ⛰
Leisure activities : 🍸 ✗ 🏠 🏊 kayaking ⛵
Facilities : ⛴ 🚿 launderette

G P S Longitude : 6.74278
Latitude : 48.17854

Some campsites benefit from proximity to a municipal leisure centre.

JAULNY

54470 – Michelin map **307** G5 – pop. 262 – alt. 230
▶ Paris 310 – Commercy 41 – Metz 33 – Nancy 51

⛺ La Pelouse

☎ 03 83 81 91 67, www.campingdelapelouse.com – limited spaces for one-night stay

Address : chemin de Fey (500m south of the town, access located near the bridge)

Opening times : from end March to beginning Oct.

2,9 ha (100 pitches)

Tariff : 19,65€ ♣♣ ⟵ 🅿 [⚡] (6A) – Extra per person 4,10€
Rental rates : Permanent ⛴ (2 chalets) – 5 🛖 – 5 🏠. Per week from 340 to 452€
🚐 borne 15€ – 🛢11€
On a small wooded hill overlooking the river.

Surroundings : ⌒ ♨
Leisure activities : ✗ 🏠 🏊
Facilities : ⛴ 🚿 🔲
Nearby : 🚣

G P S Longitude : 5.88658
Latitude : 48.9705

LUNÉVILLE

54300 – Michelin map **307** J7 – pop. 19 937 – alt. 224
▶ Paris 347 – Épinal 69 – Metz 95 – Nancy 36

⚠ Les Bosquets

🕿 0674724973, www.cc-lunevillois.fr

Address : chemin de la Ménagerie (head north towards Château-Salins and take a right turn; after the bridge over the Vézouze)

1 ha (36 pitches)
Rentals : 4 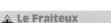.

Close to the château grounds and gardens.

Surroundings : ♀
Leisure activities : 🎴
Facilities : ♿ ⌁ 🚿 launderette
Nearby : 🚣 🍴 🖼 🎿

G P S Longitude : 6.49886
Latitude : 48.59647

MAGNIÈRES

54129 – Michelin map **307** K8 – pop. 341 – alt. 250
▶ Paris 365 – Baccarat 16 – Épinal 40 – Lunéville 22

⚠ Le Pré Fleury

🕿 0383738221, www.campingduprefleury.com

Address : 18 rue de la Barre (500m west along the D 22, follow the signs for Bayon, 200m from the Mortagne river)

Opening times : from beginning April to end Sept.

1 ha (34 pitches)

Tariff : 14,50€ ♦♦ 🚐 🔲 ⚡ (10A) – Extra per person 3€
🚐 6 🔲 11€ – ♨ 11€

By the old railway station and beside a lake.

Surroundings : 🌳 🖾
Leisure activities : 🎴 🚣 🚲 🏊 draisines (handcars/rail cycling)
Facilities : ♿ 🚿 🖾
Nearby : 🍴

G P S Longitude : 6.55735
Latitude : 48.44653

METZ

57000 – Michelin map **307** I4 – pop. 121 841 – alt. 173
▶ Paris 330 – Longuyon 80 – Pont-à-Mousson 31 – St-Avold 44

⚠ Municipal Metz-Plage

🕿 0387682648, tourisme.mairie-metz.fr

Address : allée de Metz-Plage (to the north, between the Les Morts bridge and the bridge at Thionville; beside the Moselle - from A 31: take the exit for Metz-Nord Pontiffroy)

2,5 ha (150 pitches)
🚐 borne

Surroundings : ♀♀
Leisure activities : 🍴 🚣 🚲 🏊
Facilities : ♿ ⌁ 🖾 🚿 🖾 🍴 launderette 🖾
Nearby : 🎿

G P S Longitude : 6.17058
Latitude : 49.12569

The Michelin classification (🏕🏕🏕... 🏕) is totally independent of the official star classification system awarded by the local prefecture or other official organisation.

NEUFCHÂTEAU

88300 – Michelin map **314** C2 – pop. / 040 – alt. 300
▶ Paris 321 – Chaumont 57 – Contrexéville 28 – Épinal 75

⚠ Intercommunal

🕿 0329941903, n.merlin@paysdeneufchateau.com

Address : rue Georges Joecker (take the western exit, follow the signs for Chaumont and take a right turn, near the sports centre)

0,8 ha (50 pitches) flat, grassy

Surroundings : ♀♀
Facilities : ♿ ⌁ 🚿 🚿
Nearby : 🍴 🖼 🎿 skateboarding

G P S Longitude : 5.68605
Latitude : 48.35725

PLOMBIÈRES-LES-BAINS

88370 – Michelin map **314** G5 – pop. 1 869 – alt. 429 – ♨
▶ Paris 378 – Belfort 79 – Épinal 38 – Gérardmer 43

🏕 L'Hermitage

🕿 0329300187, www.hermitage-camping.com

Address : 54 rue du Boulot (located 1.5km northwest along the D 63, follow the signs for Xertigny then take the D 20, follow the signs for Ruaux)

Opening times : from mid April to mid Oct.

1,4 ha (55 pitches) terraced, relatively flat, flat, grassy, gravelled

Tariff : 19€ ♦♦ 🚐 🔲 ⚡ (10A) – Extra per person 4,70€ – Reservation fee 10€

Rental rates : Permanent – 3  – 4 🏠. Per week from 260 to 435€ – Reservation fee 10€
🚐 borne 4€ – ♨ ⚡17,10€

Surroundings : 🌳 ♀
Leisure activities : 🎴 🚣 🏊
Facilities : ♿ ⌁ 🍴 🖾 🚿

G P S Longitude : 6.4431
Latitude : 47.96859

⚠ Le Fraiteux

🕿 0329660071, www.campingdufraiteux.fr

Address : 81 rue du Camping (4km west along the D 20 and D 20e)

Opening times : from mid March to end Oct.

0,8 ha (35 pitches)

Tariff : ♦ 3,70€ 🚐 🔲 4,40€ – ⚡ (10A) 4,10€

Rental rates : Permanent – 2 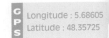 – 3 🏠. Per night from 50 to 60€ Per week from 290 to 440€
🚐 borne 2,50€ – 7 🔲 10,80€ – ♨ ⚡12€

Surroundings : 🌳 🖾
Leisure activities : 🚣
Facilities : ⌁ 🖾 launderette

G P S Longitude : 6.41647
Latitude : 47.96573

REVIGNY-SUR-ORNAIN

55800 – Michelin map **307** A6 – pop. 3 145 – alt. 144
▶ Paris 239 – Bar-le-Duc 18 – St-Dizier 30 – Vitry-le-François 36

⚠ Municipal du Moulin des Gravières

🕿 0329787334, www.ot-revigny-ornain.fr

Address : 1 rue du Stade (in the town towards southern exit, follow the signs for Vitry-le-François and turn right; 100m from the Ornain)

Opening times : from mid April to end Sept.

1 ha (27 pitches) flat, grassy

Tariff : (2013 Price) ♦ 2,50€ 🚐 🔲 7,10€ – ⚡ (6A) 3,20€

Rental rates : Permanent 🐾 – 3 🚐. Per night from 42 to 65€
Per week from 376 to 587€

🚰 borne

In a pleasant setting beside a stream.

Surroundings : 🏕 🌳
Leisure activities : 🏛
Facilities : & ⚡ 🚿 🍴 🔥
Nearby : ✂ 🎣 🧗

GPS Longitude : 4.98373
Latitude : 48.82669

ST-AVOLD

57500 – Michelin map **307** L4 – pop. 16 298 – alt. 260
▶ Paris 372 – Haguenau 117 – Lunéville 77 – Metz 46

🔺 Le Felsberg

📞 03 87 92 75 05, www.mairie-saint-avold.fr

Address : rue en Verrerie (to the north; near D 603, opposite the Record service station - from A 4: take the exit for St-Avold Carling)

Opening times : Permanent

1,2 ha (33 pitches) terraced, relatively flat, flat, grassy, stony

Tariff : 19€ ⚤ 🚗 🔌 💧 (10A) – Extra per person 4€
Rental rates : Permanent 🐾 – 3 🏠 – 11 🛏. Per night from 55 to 65€ – Per week from 280 to 350€

🚰 borne 3€

On the pleasantly wooded slopes of the town.

Surroundings : 🌿 🏕 🌳
Leisure activities : 🍴 ✕ 🏛 🏊 🚴
Facilities : & ⚡ 🔥 🍴

GPS Longitude : 6.71579
Latitude : 49.11102

These symbols are used for a campsite that is exceptional in its category:

🔺🔺...🔺 *Particularly pleasant setting, quality and range of services available*

🌿🌿 *Tranquil, isolated site – quiet site, particularly at night*

≤≤ *Exceptional view – interesting or panoramic view*

ST-MAURICE-SUR-MOSELLE

88560 – Michelin map **314** I5 – pop. 1 486 – alt. 560 – Winter sports : 550/1 250m
▶ Paris 441 – Belfort 41 – Bussang 4 – Épinal 56

🔺 Les Deux Ballons

📞 03 29 25 17 14, www.camping-deux-ballons.fr

Address : 17 Rye du Stade (take the southwestern exit along the N 66, follow the signs for Le Thillot; beside a stream)

Opening times : from mid April to end Sept.

4 ha (160 pitches)

Tariff : 29,50€ ⚤ 🚗 🔌 💧 (16A) – Extra per person 7€ – Reservation fee 15€
Rental rates : (from mid April to end Sept.) 🐾 – 7 🏠. Per week from 450 to 750€

🚰 borne 7,50€

Surroundings : ≤ 🌳
Leisure activities : 🍴 ✕ 🏛 🏊 🚴 ✂

Facilities : & ⚡ 🚿 🔥 🍴 launderette 🚮
Nearby : 🥾 walking trails

GPS Longitude : 6.81124
Latitude : 47.8554

SANCHEY

88390 – Michelin map **314** G3 – pop. 789 – alt. 368
▶ Paris 390 – Metz 129 – Épinal 8 – Nancy 69

🔺🔺 Kawan Village Club Lac de Bouzey

📞 03 29 82 49 41, www.lacdebouzey.com

Address : 19 rue du Lac (to the south along the D 41)

Opening times : Permanent

3 ha (160 pitches) terraced, relatively flat, flat, grassy

Tariff : (2013 Price) 27€ ⚤ 🚗 🔌 💧 (10A) – Extra per person 10€
Reservation fee 25€

Rental rates : (2013 Price) Permanent – 32 🚐. Per night from 110 to 160€ – Per week from 770 to 1 120€ – Reservation fee 25€

🚰 borne – 25 💧 27€

Opposite the lake; a pleasant reception area and leisure facilities.

Surroundings : 🌿 🏕 🌳🌳
Leisure activities : 🍴 ✕ 🏊 🏇 🚴 🏊 disco 🐾
multi-sports ground, entertainment room
Facilities : & ⚡ 🖥 🔥 🛁 🚿 🍴 launderette 🚮

GPS Longitude : 6.3602
Latitude : 48.1667

SAULXURES-SUR-MOSELOTTE

88290 – Michelin map **314** I5 – pop. 2 782 – alt. 464
▶ Paris 431 – Épinal 46 – Gérardmer 24 – Luxeuil-les-Bains 53

🔺 Lac de la Moselotte

📞 03 29 24 56 56, www.lac-moselotte.fr

Address : 336 route des Amias (located 1.5km west on the old D 43)

Opening times : Permanent

23 ha/3 for camping (75 pitches)

Tariff : 21,80€ ⚤ 🚗 🔌 💧 (10A) – Extra per person 5€
Rental rates : Permanent – 7 🚐 – 20 🏠. Per night from 49 to 88€ – Per week from 273 to 702€– Reservation fee 18€

On a wooded site beside a lake and near a leisure and activity park.

Surroundings : ≤ 🏕 🔺
Leisure activities : 🍴 🏛 🏇 🏊 🚴
entertainment room
Facilities : & ⚡ 🖥 🔥 🍴 🔥
At the leisure/activities centre : 🏊 🐾
climbing

GPS Longitude : 6.75236
Latitude : 47.95264

LE THOLY

88530 – Michelin map **314** I4 – pop. 1 589 – alt. 628
▶ Paris 414 – Bruyères 21 – Épinal 30 – Gérardmer 11

🔺 Noirrupt

📞 03 29 61 81 27, www.jpvacances.com

Address : 15 chemin de l'Étang de Noirrupt (1.3km northwest along the D 11, follow the signs for Épinal and take road to the left)

Opening times : from beginning May to end Sept.

2,9 ha (70 pitches)

Tariff : ⚤ 5,90€ 🚗 🔌 💧 9,50€ – 💧 (6A) 5€ – Reservation fee 13€
Rental rates : Permanent – 12 🏠. Per night from 50 to 70€ Per week from 275 to 690€ – Reservation fee 13€

Surroundings : ≤ 🌳
Leisure activities : 🍴 🏛 🏊 🏊 ✂ 🏊
Facilities : & ⚡ 🛁 🚿 🍴 launderette
Nearby : 🐾

GPS Longitude : 6.72893
Latitude : 48.08881

LE VAL-D'AJOL

88340 – Michelin map **314** G5 – pop. 4 069 – alt. 380
▶ Paris 382 – Épinal 41 – Luxeuil-les-Bains 18 – Plombières-les-Bains 10

⚠ Municipal

✆ 03 29 66 55 17, mairie@valdajol.fr

Address : rue des Oeuvres (take the northwestern exit along the D 20, follow the signs for Plombières-les-Bains)

1 ha (46 pitches) flat, grassy
Rentals : ♿ (1 chalet) – 2 🛖 .

Surroundings : ≼ 🛏
Leisure activities : 🏠
Facilities : ♿ ⊶ 🧺 ♨ ♈ ♈ 🚿
Nearby : ✂ 🏞 ⛵ ⤳

G P S Longitude : 6.47586
Latitude : 47.92488

VERDUN

55100 – Michelin map **307** D4 – pop. 18 557 – alt. 198
▶ Paris 263 – Bar-le-Duc 56 – Châlons-en-Champagne 89 – Metz 78

⛰ Les Breuils

✆ 03 29 86 15 31, www.camping-lesbreuils.com

Address : 7 allée des Breuils (take the southwestern exit along the bypass (rocade) D S1 towards Paris and take road to the left)

Opening times : from beginning April to end Sept.

5,5 ha (162 pitches) terraced, relatively flat, flat, grassy, gravelled, wood

Tariff : (2013 Price) 🚶 5,90 € ⤳ 🅴 5,20 € – (½) (6A) 4,40 €

Rental rates : (2013 Price) (from beginning April to end Sept.) 13 🛖. Per week from 270 to 650 €

In a rural setting beside a lake.

Surroundings : 🛏 Ⴍ
Leisure activities : 🍴 🏠 🎣 multi-sports ground
Facilities : ♿ ⊶ 🧺 ♨ ♈ launderette ⤳

G P S Longitude : 5.36598
Latitude : 49.15428

VILLEY-LE-SEC

54840 – Michelin map **307** G7 – pop. 415 – alt. 324
▶ Paris 302 – Lunéville 49 – Nancy 20 – Pont-à-Mousson 51

⛰ Camping de Villey-le-Sec

✆ 03 83 63 64 28, www.campingvilleylesec.com

Address : 34 rue de la Gare (situated 2km south along the D 909, follow the signs for Maron and take turning to the right)

2,5 ha (100 pitches) flat, grassy
Rentals : ✂ – 4 🛖.

In a pleasant setting beside the Moselle river.

Surroundings : ⤳
Leisure activities : 🍴 volleyball
Facilities : ♿ ⊶ 🧺 ♨ ♈ launderette ⤳ ⤳

G P S Longitude : 5.98559
Latitude : 48.6526

VITTEL

88800 – Michelin map **314** D3 – pop. 5 434 – alt. 347
▶ Paris 342 – Belfort 129 – Épinal 43 – Chaumont 84

⚠ Aquadis Loisirs de Vittel

✆ 03 29 08 02 71, www.aquadis-loisirs.com

Address : 270 rue Claude Bassot (take the northeastern exit along the D 68, follow the signs for They-sous-Montfort)

Opening times : from beginning April to mid Oct.

3,5 ha (120 pitches)

Tariff : 16,95 € 🚶🚶 ⤳ 🅴 (½) (10A) – Extra per person 4,85 € Reservation fee 9,90 €

Rental rates : (from beginning April to mid Oct.) – 12 🛖. Per night from 73 to 83 € – Per week from 196 to 500 € Reservation fee 19,80 €

🚐 borne 8,50 € – 🛢 11 €

Surroundings : 🛏 Ⴍ
Leisure activities : 🏠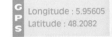
Facilities : ♿ ⊶ cc 🧺 ♈ launderette

G P S Longitude : 5.95605
Latitude : 48.2082

XONRUPT-LONGEMER

88400 – Michelin map **314** J4 – pop. 1 580 – alt. 714 – Winter sports : 750/1 300m
▶ Paris 429 – Épinal 44 – Gérardmer 4 – Remiremont 32

⚠ La Vologne

✆ 03 29 60 87 23, www.lavologne.com

Address : 3030 route de Retournemer (4.5km southeast along the D 67a)

2,5 ha (100 pitches) flat, grassy
Rental rates : 3 🛖 – 1 yurt – 1 apartment – 2 canvas bungalows.

On a wooded site beside the river.

Surroundings : ≼
Leisure activities : 🏠
Facilities : ♿ ⊶ ♨ ♈ 🚿
Nearby : ⌖

G P S Longitude : 6.96919
Latitude : 48.06245

⚠ Les Jonquilles

✆ 03 29 63 34 01, www.camping-jonquilles.com

Address : 2586 route du Lac (2.5km southeast)

Opening times : from end April to beginning Oct.

4 ha (247 pitches)

Tariff : 17,74 € 🚶🚶 ⤳ 🅴 (½) (10A) – Extra per person 3,60 € Reservation fee 7 €

🚐 borne 5 € – 5 🅴 14 €

In a pleasant location beside the lake.

Surroundings : ≼ Lac de Longemer and wooded mountains ⛰
Leisure activities : 🍴 🏠 🎣
Facilities : ♿ ⊶ ♨ ♈ launderette ⤳ ⤳

G P S Longitude : 6.94871
Latitude : 48.0677

G. Bertolissio / hemis.fr

Lourdes may be famous for its many miracles and is visited by millions of pilgrims every year, but some would say that the whole of the Midi-Pyrénées has been uniquely blessed. France's leading agricultural region – larger in size than Belgium or Switzerland – offers sanctuary to a host of exceptional fauna and flora, including the wild bears that still roam the high peaks of the Pyrenees. At sunset, the towers of medieval cities and fortresses are bathed in the evening light. Forbidding Cathar castles are stained with a blood red glow, Albi is veiled in crimson and Toulouse is tinged a romantic pink. This list of the marvels of the region would not be complete without a mention of the Garonne Valley's thriving and fertile 'Garden of France', famous for its vegetables, fruit and wine. This land of milk and honey is rich in culinary traditions, and it would be a crime not to experience the delights of *foie gras* or a *confit de canard* (duck confit) before leaving.

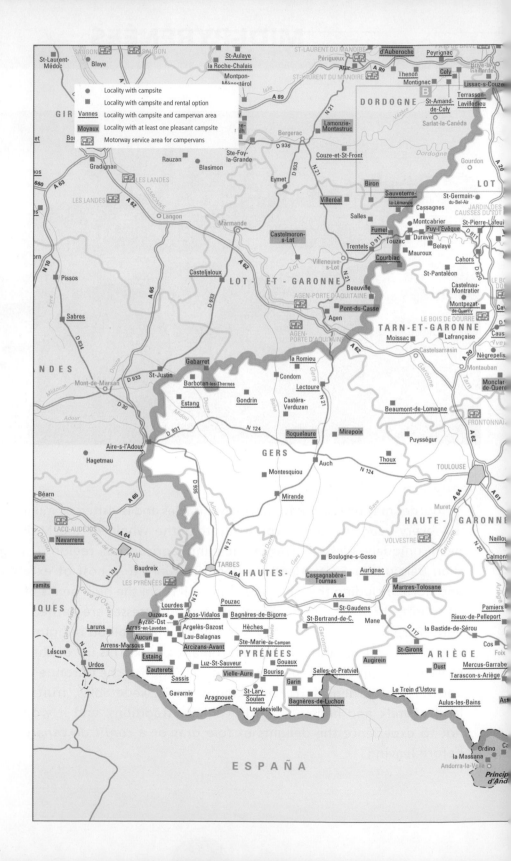

Locality with campsite
Locality with campsite and rental option
Vannes Locality with campsite and campervan area
Moyaux Locality with at least one pleasant campsite
Motorway service area for campervans

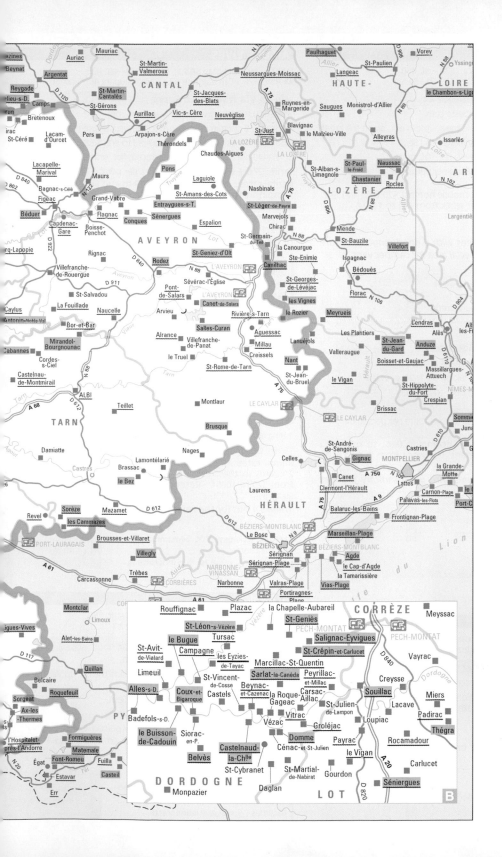

AGOS-VIDALOS

65400 – Michelin map **342** L4 – pop. 380 – alt. 450
▶ Paris 859 – Toulouse 185 – Tarbes 32 – Pau 51

🏔 Flower Le Soleil du Pibeste 👥

🖉 05 62 97 53 23, www.campingpibeste.com

Address : 16 avenue Lavedan (take the southern exit, along the N 21)

Opening times : from beginning May to end Sept.

1,5 ha (80 pitches) terraced, relatively flat, flat, grassy

Tariff : 28€ ♦♦ ⇌ 🖵 ⚡ (10A) – Extra per person 8€ – Reservation fee 24€

Rental rates : Permanent ♿ (2 mobile homes) – 29 🚐 – 11 🏠. Per night from 63 to 171€ – Per week from 441 to 1197€
Reservation fee 24€

🚐 borne 5€ – 12 🖵 9,60€

Situated opposite the Pyrenees with a good range of leisure facilities and services and a special area for camper vans.

Surroundings : ≼ ♀	
Leisure activities : 🍸 ✗ 🎞 🎨daytime 🏃 jacuzzi 🏊 🛝 multi-sports ground Facilities : ♿ ⚬⇥ 🏛 ♨ ♒ ⚶ 🍴 launderette 🛁	**G P S** Longitude : -0.07081 Latitude : 43.03562

🏔 Club Airotel La Châtaigneraie

🖉 05 62 97 07 40, www.camping-chataigneraie.com

Address : 46, avenue du Lavedan (along the N 21; at Vidalos)

Opening times : from beginning Dec.. to mid Oct.

1,5 ha (80 pitches)

Tariff : (2013 Price) 29€ ♦♦ ⇌ 🖵 ⚡ (6A) – Extra per person 6€
Reservation fee 17€

Rental rates : (2013 Price) (from beginning Dec.. to mid Oct.) 17 🚐 – 3 studios – 1 apartment. Per week from 215 to 650€
Reservation fee 17€

Situated opposite the Pyrenees with good sanitary facilities and a variety of rental options.

Surroundings : ≼ ♀♀	
Leisure activities : 🎞 🏊 🛝 🛶 Facilities : ♿ ⚬⇥ 🏛 ♨ 🍴 launderette	**G P S** Longitude : -0.07534 Latitude : 43.03201

To make the best possible use of this guide, please read pages 2–15 carefully.

AGUESSAC

12520 – Michelin map **338** K6 – pop. 860 – alt. 375
▶ Paris 635 – Toulouse 198 – Rodez 62 – Montpellier 129

🏔 La Via Natura Les Cerisiers

🖉 05 65 59 87 96, www.campinglescerisiers.com

Address : at Pailhas (3km north along the D 907, follow the signs for Gorges du Tarn – from the A 75 take exit 44-1)

2,5 ha (80 pitches) flat, grassy

🚐 borne

LPO (French bird protection organization) sanctuary on the banks of the Tarn river.

Surroundings : 🌄 ≼ ♀	
Leisure activities : 🎞 🏖 🛶 Facilities : ♿ ⚬⇥ 🖼 Nearby : 🚲	**G P S** Longitude : 3.12053 Latitude : 44.16745

AIGUES VIVES

09600 – Michelin map **343** J7 – pop. 559 – alt. 425
▶ Paris 776 – Carcassonne 63 – Castelnaudary 46 – Foix 36

🏔 La Via Natura La Serre

🖉 05 61 03 06 16, www.camping-la-serre.com

Address : 5 chemin de La Serre (to the west of the town)

Opening times : from beginning April to end Sept.

6,5 ha (40 pitches) undulating, terraced, flat, grassy, fine gravel

Tariff : 27€ ♦♦ ⇌ 🖵 ⚡ (5A) – Extra per person 7€

Rental rates : (from beginning April to end Sept.) – 6 🚐 – 8 🏠 1 cabin in the trees. Per night from 100 to 190€ – Per week from 330 to 830€

🚐 borne 4€ – 6 🖵 23€

A spacious site with valleys and trees, some pitches have a view of the Pyrenees.

Surroundings : 🌄 ⛰ ♀♀	
Leisure activities : 🎞 🏊 🚵(mountain biking) 🛝 Facilities : ♿ ⚬⇥ ♨ ♒ 🍴 🖼	**G P S** Longitude : 1.87199 Latitude : 42.99741

ALBI

81000 – Michelin map **338** E7 – pop. 48 858 – alt. 174
▶ Paris 699 – Toulouse 77 – Montpellier 261 – Rodez 71

🏔 Albirondack Park

🖉 05 63 60 37 06, www.albirondack.fr

Address : 1 allée de la Piscine

Opening times : from beginning April to end Oct.

1,8 ha (84 pitches) terraced, flat, grassy, stony

Tariff : (2013 Price) 33,70€ ♦♦ ⇌ 🖵 ⚡ (10A) – Extra per person 7€

Rental rates : Permanent ♿ (1 chalet) ⚘ – 10 🚐 – 27 🏠 2 cabins in the trees. Per night from 50 to 155 € – Per week from 320 to 1000€ – Reservation fee 25€

🚐 borne

There's a bus for the town centre.

Surroundings : ⛰ ♀♀	
Leisure activities : 🍸 ✗ ≋s hammam, jacuzzi 🛝 spa centre Facilities : ♿ ⚬⇥ ♒ ⚶ 🍴 launderette 🛁	**G P S** Longitude : 2.16397 Latitude : 43.93445

ALRANCE

12430 – Michelin map **338** I6 – pop. 404 – alt. 750
▶ Paris 664 – Albi 63 – Millau 52 – Rodez 37

🏔 Les Cantarelles

🖉 05 65 46 40 35, www.lescantarelles.com

Address : 3km south along the D 25; beside the Lac du Villefranche-de-Panat

Opening times : from mid April to end Sept.

3,5 ha (165 pitches) relatively flat, flat, grassy

Tariff : 22€ ♦♦ ⇌ 🖵 ⚡ (6A) – Extra per person 4,80€

Rental rates : (from beginning April to end Sept.) – 10 🚐. Per night 85€ – Per week 595€

🚐 borne 6€

Surroundings : ≼ ♀ ⛰	
Leisure activities : 🍸 ✗ 🎞 🏊 🚲 🛝 🏖 🐬 pedalos 🪁 Facilities : ♿ ⚬⇥ ♒ 🍴 launderette	**G P S** Longitude : 2.68933 Latitude : 44.10669

ARAGNOUET

65170 – Michelin map **342** N8 – pop. 244 – alt. 1 100
▶ Paris 842 – Arreau 24 – Bagnères-de-Luchon 56 – Lannemezan 51

⛺ Fouga Pic de Bern

✆ 05 62 39 63 37, fouga.marc@orange.fr

Address : at Fabian (2.8km northeast along the D 118, follow the signs for St-Lary-Soulan, near the Neste-d'Avre)

Opening times : from beginning June to end Sept.

3 ha (80 pitches) open site, terraced, flat, grassy

Tariff : (2013 Price) ♦ 3,60€ 🚗 📧 340€ – (½) (13A) 6,90€
🚐 borne
Choose the meadow area, with both sun and shade, furthest away from the road.

Surroundings : 🌿 ≤ ♀
Leisure activities : 🍴 ✕ 🏖
Facilities : ᵭ ⌨ ⛟ 🏠

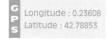 Longitude : 0.23608
Latitude : 42.78853

ARCIZANS-AVANT

65400 – Michelin map **342** L5 – pop. 360 – alt. 640
▶ Paris 868 – Toulouse 194 – Tarbes 41 – Pau 61

⛰ Le Lac

✆ 05 62 97 01 88, www.camping-du-lac-pyrenees.com

Address : 29 chemin d'Azun (take the western exit, not far from the lake)

Opening times : from end May to mid Sept.

2 ha (97 pitches) relatively flat

Tariff : (2013 Price) 32€ ♦♦ 🚗 📧 (½) (10A) – Extra per person 8€
Reservation fee 25€
Rental rates : (2013 Price) Permanent – 14 🛏. Per night from 44 to 111€ – Per week from 305 to 780€ – Reservation fee 25€
🚐 borne 26,90€ – 🔌 (½)18€
Many pitches have an uninterrupted view of the Pyrenees, the village and church.

Surroundings : 🌿 ≤ ♀♀
Leisure activities : 🏖 🚴 🏊
Facilities : ᵭ ⌨ 🏠⛟ launderette 🌿
Nearby : 🎣

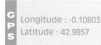 Longitude : -0.10803
Latitude : 42.9857

⛰ Les Chataigniers

✆ 05 62 97 94 77, www.camping-les-chataigniers.com

Address : 6 rue Cap Deth Vilatge

3 ha (51 pitches) terraced, relatively flat, flat, grassy, wood

Rentals : 2 🏠 – 4 mobile homes (without sanitary facilities).
Shaded pitches with a view of the valley and the village.

Surroundings : 🌿 ≤ ♀♀
Leisure activities : 🏖 🏊
Facilities : ᵭ ⌨ launderette
Nearby : 🎣

 Longitude : -0.10488
Latitude : 42.98505

The Michelin classification (⛰⛰⛰ ... ⛺) is totally independent of the official star classification system awarded by the local prefecture or other official organisation.

ARGELÈS-GAZOST

65400 – Michelin map **342** L6 – pop. 3 297 – alt. 462 – ⚓
▶ Paris 863 – Lourdes 13 – Pau 58 – Tarbes 32

⛰⛰⛰⛰ Sunêlia Les Trois Vallées ♣♣

✆ 05 62 90 35 47, www.L3v.fr

Address : avenue des Pyrénées (take the northern exit)

Opening times : from mid April to mid Oct.

11 ha (438 pitches) flat, grassy

Tariff : 47€ ♦♦ 🚗 📧 (½) (10A) – Extra per person 13,50€
Reservation fee 30€
Rental rates : (from mid April to mid Oct.) ᵭ (2 mobile homes) 🌾 – 250 🛏. Per night from 52 to 102€ – Per week from 511 to 1575€ – Reservation fee 30€
Swimming area, playground and shops all boast floral displays and the sanitary facilities are extremely well-appointed.

Surroundings : 🔲 ♀♀
Leisure activities : 🍴 ✕ 🏖 🎣 ⛹ jacuzzi
🏋 🏊 ⛷ disco, multi-sports ground, entertainment room
Facilities : ᵭ ⌨ 🏛 🏠⛟ launderette 🌿
Nearby : ✕ 🏇

Longitude : -0.09718
Latitude : 43.0121

ARRAS-EN-LAVEDAN

65400 – Michelin map **342** L5 – pop. 527 – alt. 700
▶ Paris 868 – Toulouse 193 – Tarbes 40 – Pau 60

⛰ L'Idéal

✆ 05 62 97 03 13, www.camping-ideal-pyrenees.com – alt. 600

Address : route du Val d'Azun (300m northwest along the D 918, follow the signs for Argelès-Gazost)

Opening times : from beginning June to mid Sept.

2 ha (60 pitches) terraced, flat, grassy

Tariff : (2013 Price) ♦ 4,40€ 🚗 📧 4,40€ – (½) (10A) 9,50€
Rental rates : (2013 Price) Permanent 🌾 – 2 🏠. Per night from 60 to 80€ – Per week from 260 to 550€
🚐 borne 3€
A pleasant site, but choose the pitches the furthest away from the road.

Surroundings : ≤ ♀♀
Leisure activities : 🏖 🏋 🏊
Facilities : ᵭ ⌨ 🛒 🏠⛟ launderette

Longitude : -0.11954
Latitude : 42.99483

ARRENS-MARSOUS

65400 – Michelin map **342** K7 – pop. 741 – alt. 885
▶ Paris 875 – Argelès-Gazost 13 – Cauterets 29 – Laruns 37

⛺ La Hèche

✆ 05 62 97 02 64, www.campinglaheche.com – ₽

Address : 54 route d'Azun (800m east along the D 918, follow the signs for Argelès-Gazost and take the road to the right; beside the Gave d'Arrens (river)

Opening times : from mid June to end Sept.

5 ha (166 pitches) flat, grassy

Tariff : (2013 Price) 12,10€ ♦♦ 🚗 📧 (½) (4A) – Extra per person 3,40€
Rental rates : (2013 Price) (from beginning Feb. to end Oct.) 🌾
4 🛏. Per week from 220 to 490€

Surroundings : 🌿 ≤ ♀
Leisure activities : 🏖 🏋
Facilities : ᵭ ⌨ 🏛 🏊 launderette
Nearby : 🏊 ✕ 🏇 🏊 ⛷

 Longitude : -0.20534
Latitude : 42.95847

⚠ Le Moulian

📞 05 62 97 41 18, www.le-moulian.com

Address : 42 rue du Bourg (500m southeast of the village of Marsous)

Opening times : Permanent

12 ha/4 for camping (75 pitches) flat, grassy

Tariff : 21,50€ 👥 🚐 📧 (⚡) (10A) – Extra per person 4,50€

Rental rates : Permanent – 10 🚍 – 1 🏠. Per night from 50 to 85€ – Per week from 350 to 600€
🚽 borne 5€ – 🚐8€

The site is near a large equestrian centre with donkeys, ponies and horses.

Surroundings : 🌳 ≤ ♨
Leisure activities :
Facilities : 🚻 ⚡ 🚿 🔥 ⬆ launderette 🚿
Nearby : 🎿 🎾 🎣 ⛷ ⛵

G P S Longitude : -0.19638
Latitude : 42.96232

ARVIEU

12120 – Michelin map **338** H5 – pop. 861 – alt. 730
▶ Paris 663 – Albi 66 – Millau 59 – Rodez 31

⚠ Le Doumergal

📞 05 65 74 24 92, www.camping-doumergal-aveyron.fr

Address : rue de la Rivière (to the west of the town; beside a stream)

1,5 ha (27 pitches) relatively flat, flat, grassy

Surroundings : 🌳 🚐 ♀
Leisure activities :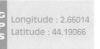
Facilities : 🚻 ⚡ 🚿 ⬇
Nearby : ⛷

G P S Longitude : 2.66014
Latitude : 44.19066

ASTON

09310 – Michelin map **343** I8 – pop. 219 – alt. 563
▶ Paris 788 – Andorra-la-Vella 78 – Ax-les-Thermes 20 – Foix 59

⚠ Le Pas de l'Ours

📞 05 61 64 90 33, www.lepasdelours.fr

Address : at Les Gesquis (south of the town, near the rapids)

Opening times : from beginning June to beginning Sept.

3,5 ha (50 pitches)

Tariff : 👤 6,50€ 🚐 📧 9€ – (⚡) (6A) 4€ – Reservation fee 7€

Rental rates : (from mid Oct. to mid Sept.) – 27 🏠 – 4 gîtes. Per night from 50 to 85€ – Per week from 230 to 642€ Reservation fee 7€

A pleasant site with rental options of a high standard.

Surroundings : 🌳 ≤ 🚐 ♨
Leisure activities : 🏠 🏃 🚲 🎾 ⛵ entertainment room
Facilities : 🚻 ⚡ (July-Aug.) ⬆ launderette
Nearby : 🎣 ⛷

G P S Longitude : 1.67181
Latitude : 42.77245

For more information on visiting particular towns or regions, consult the relevant regional MICHELIN Green Guide. We also recommend you use the appropriate Michelin regional map to locate your selected campsite, to calculate distances and to work out the best route.

AUCH

32000 – Michelin map **336** F8 – pop. 21 792 – alt. 169
▶ Paris 713 – Agen 74 – Bordeaux 205 – Tarbes 74

⚠ Le Castagné

📞 06 07 97 40 37, www.domainelecastagne.com

Address : chemin de Naréoux (4km east along the N 21, follow the signs for Toulouse and take a right turn)

Opening times : from beginning June to end Sept.

70 ha/2 for camping (24 pitches)

Tariff : 👤 5€ 🚐 📧 5€ – (⚡) (12A) 4€ – Reservation fee 20€

Rental rates : Permanent – 4 🚍 – 9 🏠 – 4 🛏 – 1 apartment. Per night from 80 to 100€ – Per week from 420 to 700€ Reservation fee 20€

The accommodation includes 4 B&B rooms.

Surroundings : 🌳 ≤ ♨
Leisure activities : 🏠 🏃 🚲 🎾 ⛵ pedalos
Facilities : 🚻 ⚡ 🚿 ⬆ 📺

G P S Longitude : 0.6337
Latitude : 43.6483

AUCUN

65400 – Michelin map **342** K7 – pop. 261 – alt. 853
▶ Paris 872 – Argelès-Gazost 10 – Cauterets 26 – Lourdes 22

⚠ Azun Nature

📞 05 62 97 45 05, www.camping-azun-nature.com

Address : 1 route des Poueyes (700m east along the D 918, follow the signs for Argeles-Gazost and take turning to the right, 300m from the Gave d'Azun (river)

Opening times : from beginning May to mid Oct.

1 ha (43 pitches) flat, grassy

Tariff : 18,50€ 👥 🚐 📧 (⚡) (10A) – Extra per person 5€

Rental rates : Permanent – 10 🚍 – 1 gîte. Per week from 200 to 505€

A well-kept site with good quality rental options, open summer and winter.

Surroundings : 🌳 ≤ 🚐 ♀
Leisure activities : 🏠 🏃
Facilities : 🚻 ⚡ 🔥 ⬆ launderette
Nearby : 🚲 ⛵ walking trails

G P S Longitude : -0.18796
Latitude : 42.97399

⚠ Lascrouts

📞 05 62 97 42 62, www.camping-lascrouts.com – limited spaces for one-night stay

Address : 2 route de Las Poueyes (700m east along the D 918, follow the signs for Argelès-Gazost and take turning to the right, 300m from the Gave d'Azun (river)

Opening times : Permanent

4 ha (72 pitches) terrace, relatively flat, flat, grassy

Tariff : 13,30€ 👥 🚐 📧 (⚡) (6A) – Extra per person 3,40€

Rental rates : Permanent – 4 🚍 – 15 🏠. Per week from 240 to 505€

A good choice of mobile homes and owner-occupied chalets, but very few pitches for tents or caravans.

Surroundings : 🌳 ≤
Leisure activities : 🏠 🏃
Facilities : 🚻 ⚡ 🚿 📺 ⬆ 📺
Nearby : paragliding

G P S Longitude : -0.18612
Latitude : 42.97361

AUGIREIN

09800 – Michelin map **343** D7 – pop. 63 – alt. 629
▶ Paris 788 – Aspet 22 – Castillon-en-Couserans 12 – St-Béat 30

⚠ La Vie en Vert

✆ 05 61 96 82 66, www.lavieenvert.com

Address : east of the town; beside the Bouigane river

Opening times : from beginning June to beginning Sept.

0,3 ha (15 pitches) flat, grassy

Tariff : 20€ ♦♦ ⇌ 🔲 🔋 (6A) – Extra per person 5€

Rental rates : (from beginning June to beginning Sept.) 🐾 – 1 ⇌
2 tipis. Per night from 35 to 55€ – Per week from 240 to 350€

*Based around an old farmhouse made of local stone that has
been painstakingly restored.*

Surroundings : 🐾 ⇌ 🔲🔲
Leisure activities : 🏛 🔧
Facilities : ♿ ⊶ 🚿 🍴 🔲
Nearby : 🍽 ✕

G P S   Longitude : 0.91978
   Latitude : 42.93161

AULUS-LES-BAINS

09140 – Michelin map **343** G8 – pop. 221 – alt. 750 – ⚓
▶ Paris 807 – Foix 76 – Oust 17 – St-Girons 34

⚠ Le Coulédous

✆ 05 61 66 43 56, www.camping-aulus-couledous.com

Address : route de Saint-Girons (take northwestern exit along the
D 32, near the Garbet)

Opening times : Permanent

1,6 ha (70 pitches)

Tariff : 21€ ♦♦ ⇌ 🔲 🔋 (10A) – Extra per person 4,50€

Rental rates : Permanent – 18 🏠. Per night from 50 to 70€
Per week from 210 to 490€

🚐 borne

*In the middle of a park boasting some ancient trees, but the
chalets and sanitary facilities are also rather old.*

Surroundings : ⇐ 🔲🔲
Leisure activities : 🏛 ⤢
Facilities : ♿ ⊶ 🔲 🍴 launderette
Nearby : ✕ 🎣 🔧 forest trail

G P S   Longitude : 1.33215
   Latitude : 42.79394

AURIGNAC

31420 – Michelin map **343** D5 – pop. 1 187 – alt. 430
▶ Paris 750 – Auch 71 – Bagnères-de-Luchon 69 – Pamiers 92

⚠ Les Petites Pyrénées

✆ 05 61 87 06 91, camping.aurignac@live.fr*

Address : route de Boussens (take the southeastern exit along the
D 635, to the right, near the stadium – A64 take exit 21)

0,9 ha (38 pitches) flat, grassy

Rentals : 2 🚐.

🚐 borne

*A small, simple site, rather old sanitary facilities, free use of the
municipal pool. Groups welcome.*

Surroundings : ⇌ 🔲🔲
Leisure activities : 🏛
Facilities : ⊶ 🍴 launderette
Nearby : ✕ 🔧 🐎

G P S   Longitude : 0.89132
   Latitude : 43.21389

AX-LES-THERMES

09110 – Michelin map **343** J8 – pop. 1 384 – alt. 720 – ⚓
▶ Paris 805 – Toulouse 129 – Foix 43 – Pamiers 62

🏔 Sunêlia Le Malazeou 👥

✆ 05 61 64 69 14, www.campingmalazeou.com

Address : road RN 20, route de l'Espagne (situated at Savignac-les-
Ormeaux, 1km to the northwest, follow the signs for Foix)

Opening times : closed mid Nov. to beginning Dec.

6,5 ha (244 pitches) terraced, flat, grassy, stony

Tariff : 29,50€ ♦♦ ⇌ 🔲 🔋 (10A) – Extra per person 7,50€ –
Reservation fee 30€

Rental rates : (closed from mid Nov.to beginning Dec.) – 56 🚐
21 🏠. Per night from 48 to 128€ – Per week from 336 to 896€
Reservation fee 30€

*In the shade, beside the Ariège river, but choose the pitches
away from the road in preference.*

Surroundings : 🔲🔲
Leisure activities : 🍴 ✕ 🏛 🌙 nighttime ⤾
 🎿 🐎 🎿 🐬
Facilities : ♿ ⊶ 🔲 🛁 🍴 launderette ♿

G P S   Longitude : 1.82538
   Latitude : 42.72852

🏔 Village Vacances Résidence et Chalets Isatis

(rental of chalets and apartments only)

✆ 05 34 09 20 05, www.grandbleu.fr – alt. 1 000

Address : at Ignaux (head 6km north along the D 613 and take D 52)

Opening times : from beginning June to beginning Oct.

2 ha terraced

Rental rates : ♿ (2 apartments) 🅿 – 20 🏠 – 20 apartments.
Per night from 60 to 90€ – Per week from 203 to 728€

A panoramic view over the Bonascre Ax 3 Domaines ski resort.

Surroundings : 🐾 ⇐ Dent d'Orlu (peak)
Leisure activities : 🎿
Facilities : 🔲 🍴 launderette

G P S   Longitude : 1.8449
   Latitude : 42.73015

*Some campsites benefit from proximity to a municipal
leisure centre.*

AYZAC-OST

65400 – Michelin map **342** L4 – pop. 399 – alt. 430
▶ Paris 862 – Toulouse 188 – Tarbes 35 – Pau 54

🏔 La Bergerie

✆ 05 62 97 59 99, www.camping-labergerie.com

Address : 8 chemin de la Bergerie (take the southern exit along the
N 21 and take road to the left)

Opening times :

2 ha (105 pitches) flat, grassy

Tariff : 29,60€ ♦♦ ⇌ 🔲 🔋 (6A) – Extra per person 7,20€
Reservation fee 15€

Rental rates : Permanent 🐾 – 9 🚐. Per night from 45 to 122€
Per week from 290 to 735€

*A pleasant, small, landscaped water park surrounded by a num-
ber of owner-occupied mobile homes.*

Surroundings : ⇐ 🔲🔲
Leisure activities : 🍴 🏛 ⤢ 🎿 🛶
Facilities : ♿ ⊶ 🛁 🍴 🔲
Nearby : ✕ ♿

G P S   Longitude : -0.0961
   Latitude : 43.01824

BAGNAC-SUR-CÉLÉ

46270 – Michelin map **337** I3 – pop. 1 562 – alt. 234
▶ Paris 593 – Cahors 83 – Dec.azeville 16 – Figeac 15

⛺ Les Berges du Célé

✆ 06 64 99 82 33, www.camping-sudouest.com

Address : at La Plaine (to the southeast of the town, behind the station; beside the Célé river)

1 ha (44 pitches) flat, grassy

Rentals : 5 🛖 – 2 canvas bungalows.

Surroundings : 🌳🌳		
Leisure activities : 🏊🛶🎣	**G**	Longitude : 2.16009
Facilities : ⚡🚰🚿	**P**	Latitude : 44.66461
Nearby : 🍴	**S**	

This guide is updated regularly, so buy your new copy every year!

BAGNÈRES-DE-BIGORRE

65200 – Michelin map **342** M6 – pop. 8 040 – alt. 551 – ♨
▶ Paris 829 – Lourdes 24 – Pau 66 – St-Gaudens 65

⛰ Le Monlôo

ABADIE

✆ 05 62 95 19 65, www.lemonloo.com

Address : 5 chemin de Monlôo (take the northeastern exit, along the D 938, follow the signs for Toulouse then take left turn 1.4km along the D 8, follow the signs for Tarbes and take the road to the right)

Opening times : Permanent

4 ha (199 pitches)

Tariff : (2013 Price) 22,20€ ✶✶ 🚗 ▣
🔌 (10A) – Extra per person 5,50€

Rental rates : (2013 Price) Permanent – 20 🛖 – 10 🏠. Per night from 55 to 90€ – Per week from 270 to 740€
🚐 borne 15€ – 4 ▣ 15€
A range of good quality rental options with a small eco lake (no chemicals) and a pretty beach.

Surroundings : 🏖 ≤ 🌳🌳		
Leisure activities : 🏓 🏊 🎣 ≋ (lake) 🏕	**G**	Longitude : 0.15107
Facilities : 🚿🚰 🚿🍴 launderette	**P**	Latitude : 43.0817
	S	

⛺ Les Fruitiers

✆ 05 62 95 25 97, www.camping-les-fruitiers.com

Address : 8 rue Pierre Latécoère (rte de Toulouse)

Opening times : from mid April to end Oct.

1,5 ha (88 pitches) flat, grassy

Tariff : (2013 Price) ✶ 4,40€ 🚗 ▣ 4,40€ – 🔌 (6A) 3€

Rental rates : (2013 Price) (from beginning April to beginning Nov.) 🐾 – 2 🛖 – 3 apartments. Per night from 50€ Per week from 250 to 400€
🚐 borne 5,50€
Lovely shaded grass areas, but choose the pitches away from the road.

Surroundings : ≤ Pic du Midi (peak) 🌳🌳		
Leisure activities : 🏓 🏊	**G**	Longitude : 0.15746
Facilities : 🚰 🍴 launderette	**P**	Latitude : 43.07108
Nearby : 🖼	**S**	

BAGNÈRES-DE-LUCHON

31110 – Michelin map **343** B8 – pop. 2 600 – alt. 630 – ♨ – Winter sports : at Superbagnères : 1 440/2 260m
▶ Paris 814 – Bagnères-de-Bigorre 96 – St-Gaudens 48 – Tarbes 98

⛰ Pradelongue

OUILÀ‰

✆ 05 61 79 86 44, www.camping-pradelongue.com

Address : at Moustajon (2km north along the D 125, near the Intermarché supermarket)

Opening times : from beginning April to end Sept.

4 ha (142 pitches) flat, grassy

Tariff : ✶ 6,95€ 🚗 ▣ 7,15€
🔌 (10A) 4,50€ – Reservation fee 13€

Rental rates : (from beginning April to end Sept.) 🐾 – 18 🛖.
Per week from 270 to 660€ – Reservation fee 13€
🚐 borne – 7 ▣ 18,50€
Plenty of green spaces, perfect for team sports or just relaxing.

Surroundings : ≤ 🏞 🌳🌳		
Leisure activities : 🏛 🏊 🎣	**G**	Longitude : 0.5981
Facilities : 🚿🚰 🏢 🚿🍴 launderette	**P**	Latitude : 42.81667
Nearby : 🐎	**S**	

⛰ Les Myrtilles 🛖👥

✆ 05 61 79 89 89, www.camping-myrtilles.com

Address : at Moustajon (2.5km north along the D 125, beside a stream.)

2 ha (100 pitches) flat, grassy

Rentals : 19 🛖 – 5 canvas bungalows – 1 gîte.
🚐 borne
A free shuttle to the thermal baths.

Surroundings : ≤ 🏞 🌿		
Leisure activities : 🍴🍽 🏛 🏃 🏊 🎣	**G**	Longitude : 0.59975
Facilities : 🚿🚰🏢 🚿🍴 launderette	**P**	Latitude : 42.81663
🚿	**S**	
Nearby : 🐎		

⛰ Domaine Arôme Vanille 🛖👥

✆ 05 61 79 00 38, camping-aromevanille.com

Address : at Montauban-de-Luchon, route de Subcarrère, (located 1.5km east along the D 27)

Opening times : Permanent

5 ha (194 pitches) flat and relatively flat, grassy

Tariff : 20,50€ ✶✶ 🚗 ▣ 🔌 (10A) – Extra per person 4,50€

Rental rates : Permanent – 8 🛖 – 21 🏠. Per night from 60 to 75€ – Per week from 319 to 639€ – Reservation fee 10€
🚐 borne
Pitches in both the shade and the sun.

Surroundings : 🏖 🏞 🌿		
Leisure activities : 🍴🍽 🏃 🏊 🚴	**G**	Longitude : 0.60814
Facilities : 🚿🚰 🚿🍴 🖼 🚿	**P**	Latitude : 42.79496
	S	

⛺ Au Fil de l'Oô

✆ 05 61 79 30 74, campingaufildeloo@gmail.com

Address : 37 avenue de Vénasque (1.5km south along the D 618)

2,5 ha (104 pitches) flat, grassy

Rentals : 8 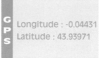.
🚐 borne

A good amount of shade, beside a stream, but choose those pitches furthest away from the road.

Surroundings : 🏕 ᵠᵠ
Leisure activities : 🏠
Facilities : 🕭 ⚲ launderette 🍴

G P S Longitude : 0.6003
Latitude : 42.77777

BARBOTAN-LES-THERMES

32150 – Michelin map **336** B6 – ⚘
▶ Paris 703 – Aire-sur-l'Adour 37 – Auch 75 – Condom 37

🏕 Club Airotel Le Lac de l'Uby 👥

🕿 0562095391, www.camping-uby.com

Address : avenue du Lac (located 1.5km southwest, follow the signs for Cazaubon and take the turning to the left, at the leisure and activity park (beside the lake)

Opening times : from beginning April to end Oct.

6 ha (274 pitches)

Tariff : 26€ ✶✶ 🚐 🗉 ⚡ (10A) – Extra per person 7€ – Reservation fee 8€
Rental rates : (from beginning April to end Oct.) – 50 🚐 7 🏠. Per night from 33 to 106€ – Per week from 230 to 740€ Reservation fee 8€
🚐 15 🗉 19€

A pleasant parking spot for campervans 300m away.

Surroundings : 🌲 ᐸᵠᵠ⛰
Leisure activities : ✗ 🏠 ⚷ 🚴 ⛵ 🏊 🎣 ᐳ
multi-sports ground, skate park
Facilities : 🕭 ⚲ 🍴 🍴 launderette
refrigerators
Nearby : 🍴 🏊 🏖 (beach) pedalos

G P S Longitude : -0.04431
Latitude : 43.93971

*The classification (1 to 5 tents, **black** or **red**) that we award to selected sites in this guide is our own system. It should not be confused with the classification (1 to 5 stars) of official organisations.*

LA BASTIDE DE SÉROU

09240 – Michelin map **343** G6 – pop. 959 – alt. 410
▶ Paris 779 – Foix 18 – Le Mas-d'Azil 17 – Pamiers 38

🏕 Club Airotel L'Arize

🕿 0561658151, www.camping-arize.com

Address : take the eastern exit along the D 117, follow the signs for Foix then continue 1.5km along the D 15, follow signs to Nescus to the right; beside the river

7,5 ha/1,5 (90 pitches) flat, grassy
Rentals : 16 🚐 – 4 🏠.

A small stream runs through the site, separating the shady side from the sunny side.

Surroundings : 🌲🏕 ᵠᵠ
Leisure activities : 🏠 ⚷ 🚴 🏊 ᐳ
Facilities : 🕭 ⚲ ᕕ 🍴 🍴 launderette
Nearby : ✗ 🐎

G P S Longitude : 1.44509
Latitude : 43.00168

⚠ Village Vacances Les Lambrilles (rental of chalets only)

🕿 0561645353, www.seronais.com

Address : in the town; beside the Arize river

1 ha flat, grassy
Rentals : 24 🏠.

Semi-detached chalets in pairs near a stream and a small fishing lake.

Surroundings : 🌲
Leisure activities : 🏠 ⚷ 🏊 ᐳ
Facilities : ⚲ 🍴 🍴 🖾
Nearby : 🍴 ♨

G P S Longitude : 1.42958
Latitude : 43.00974

BEAUMONT-DE-LOMAGNE

82500 – Michelin map **337** B8 – pop. 3 809 – alt. 400
▶ Paris 662 – Agen 60 – Auch 51 – Castelsarrasin 27

🏕 Municipal Le Lomagnol 👥

🕿 0563261200, www.villagelelomagnol.fr

Address : avenue du Lac (800m east, access via the diversion and a road; beside a small lake)

Opening times : from beginning April to end Oct.

6 ha/1,5 (100 pitches) flat, grassy

Tariff : 17€ ✶✶ 🚐 🗉 ⚡ (10A) – Extra per person 3,80€ – Reservation fee 7€
Rental rates : Permanent 🕭 (1 mobile home) 🅿 – 4 🚐 24 gîtes. Per night from 60€ – Per week from 260 to 499€ – Reservation fee 15€
🚐 borne 17€

The site is spread out beside the lake; there's the opportunity to take part in different water sports, but bathing is not permitted.

Surroundings : 🏕 ᵠᵠ
Leisure activities : 🏠 🌙 nighttime ⚷ 🏃
jacuzzi ⚷ 🚴 🍴 🎣 🏊 ᐳ pedalos 🛶
Facilities : 🕭 ⚲ ᕕ 🍴 🖾 🍴
Nearby : ✗ fitness trail

G P S Longitude : 0.99864
Latitude : 43.88295

BÉDUER

46100 – Michelin map **337** H4 – pop. 730 – alt. 260
▶ Paris 572 – Cahors 63 – Figeac 9 – Villefranche-de-Rouergue 36

🏕 Pech Ibert

🕿 0565400585, www.camping-pech-ibert.com

Address : at Pech Ibert (located 1km northwest along the D 19, follow the signs for Cajarc and take turning to the right)

Opening times : from mid March to end Oct.

1 ha (18 pitches) flat, grassy, stony, fine gravel

Tariff : ✶ 3,30€ 🚐 1,20€ 🗉 3,40€ – ⚡ (6A) 3,50€
Rental rates : (from mid March to end Oct.) – 1 caravan – 3 🚐 4 🏠 – 1 canvas bungalow. Per week from 280 to 645€ Reservation fee 10€
🚐 borne 6€ – 2 🗉 8,50€ – 🚐 8,50€

Surroundings : 🌲 🏕 ♀
Leisure activities : 🍴 🏠 ⚷ 🏊
Facilities : 🕭 ⚲ 🍴 🍴 🖾 refrigerators
Nearby : 🍴

G P S Longitude : 1.9375
Latitude : 44.57833

BELAYE

46140 – Michelin map **337** D5 – pop. 216 – alt. 209
▶ Paris 594 – Cahors 30 – Fumel 21 – Gourdon 46

⛰ La Tuque

𝒫 05 65 21 34 34, www.campinglatuque.fr – access difficult for 6km

Address : take the southern exit, 3.5km along the D 50, follow the signs for La Boulvée and take the road to the right

9 ha/4 for camping (90 pitches)

Rentals : 🛖 – 9 🚐 – 4 canvas bungalows – 2 tent lodges 2 gîtes.

In a pleasant setting on a pretty, wooded site.

Surroundings : 🏞 ♨
Leisure activities : 🍸 ✕ 🎦 🌙nighttime 🏃
🛶 🎿 🏛 ⛵ 🏊
Facilities : 🚿 ⛷ 🏕 🍴 launderette 🚰

G P S Longitude : 1.17244
Latitude : 44.44407

LE BEZ

81260 – Michelin map **338** G9 – pop. 803 – alt. 644
▶ Paris 745 – Albi 63 – Anglès 12 – Brassac 5

⛰ Le Plô

𝒫 05 63 74 00 82, www.leplo.com

Address : in the village (900m west along the D 30, follow the signs for Castres and take road to the left)

Opening times : from end April to end Sept.

2,5 ha (60 pitches) terraced, relatively flat, grassy, wood

Tariff : 24,87 € ✶✶ 🚐 🔌 ⚡ (6A) – Extra per person 4 € – Reservation fee 12,50 €

Rental rates : Permanent 🛖 – 9 tent lodges. Per night from 40 to 78 € – Per week from 250 to 595 € – Reservation fee 12,50 €

Surroundings : 🏞 ♨
Leisure activities : 🎦 🛶 🚲 🏊
Facilities : 🚿 ⛷ 🏕 🍴 launderette

G P S Longitude : 2.47064
Latitude : 43.60815

BOISSE-PENCHOT

12300 – Michelin map **338** F3 – pop. 539 – alt. 169
▶ Paris 594 – Toulouse 193 – Rodez 46 – Aurillac 65

⛰ Le Roquelongue

𝒫 05 65 63 39 67, www.camping-roquelongue.com

Address : 4.5km northwest along the D 963, D 21 and take the D 42, follow the signs for Boisse-Penchot, near the Lot (direct access)

Opening times : Permanent

3,5 ha (66 pitches) flat, grassy

Tariff : ✶ 4,60 € 🚐 🔌 8,80 € – ⚡ (10A) 4,75 €

Rental rates : Permanent – 9 🚐 – 7 🏠. Per night from 56 to 101 € – Per week from 300 to 645 €

Surroundings : ≤ 🏕 ♨
Leisure activities : 🍸 ✕ 🛶 🏊 🐟 pedalos 🏊
Facilities : 🚿 ⛷ 🏕 🍴 🖼

G P S Longitude : 2.22179
Latitude : 44.58224

In order for the guide to remain wholly objective, the selection of campsites is made on an entirely independent basis.

BOR-ET-BAR

12270 – Michelin map **338** E5 – pop. 194 – alt. 250
▶ Paris 631 – Toulouse 109 – Rodez 61 – Albi 47

⛰ Le Gourpassou

𝒫 05 65 65 76 98, www.camping-legourpassou.com

Address : ferme de Cessetière

Opening times :

2,5 ha (39 pitches) flat, grassy

Tariff : (2013 Price) ✶ 3 € 🚐 🔌 2,40 € – ⚡ 3,20 €

Rental rates : (2013 Price) (from beginning April to end Sept.) 7 🚐 – 2 🏠. Per night from 30 to 35 € – Per week from 155 to 390 €

🚐 borne

A campsite on a farm.

Surroundings : ≤ 🌳
Leisure activities : 🎦 🐟
Facilities : ⛷ 🏕 🍴

G P S Longitude : 5.01096
Latitude : 47.32128

BOULOGNE-SUR-GESSE

31350 – Michelin map **343** B5 – pop. 1 612 – alt. 320
▶ Paris 735 – Auch 47 – Aurignac 24 – Castelnau-Magnoac 13

⛰ Village Vacances Le Lac (rental of chalets only)

𝒫 05 61 88 20 54, www.ville-boulogne-sur-gesse.fr

Address : route du Lac (1.3km southeast along the D 633, follow the signs for Montréjeau and take turning to the left, 300m from the lake)

Opening times : Permanent

2 ha terraced

Rental rates : (2013 Price) 🅿 – 24 🏠. Per week from 265 to 560 €

Surroundings : 🏞 ≤ on the lake ♨
Leisure activities : 🎦 🐟
Facilities : 🚿 ⛷ 🏛 🖼
Nearby : 🍸 ✕ 🏃 🛶 🎿 🏛 🏊 ⛵ pedalos

G P S Longitude : 0.65712
Latitude : 43.28328

BOURISP

65170 – Michelin map **342** O6 – pop. 147 – alt. 790
▶ Paris 828 – Toulouse 155 – Tarbes 70 – Lourdes 66

⛰ Le Rioumajou 👥

𝒫 05 62 39 48 32, www.camping-le-rioumajou.com

Address : 1.3km northwest along the D 929, follow the signs for Arreau and take road to the left; beside the Neste d'Aure river

Opening times : Permanent

5 ha (192 pitches) flat, grassy, fine gravel

Tariff : (2013 Price) ✶ 6,50 € 🚐 🔌 6,50 € – ⚡ (10A) 6 € – Reservation fee 14 €

Rental rates : Permanent 🛖 – 5 🚐 – 11 canvas bungalows. Per night from 36 to 78 € – Per week from 250 to 540 € Reservation fee 14 €

🚐 borne 4 € – 🚐 ⚡ 14 €

Plenty of green space in which to unwind, beside a stream.

Surroundings : ❄ 🏞 ≤ ♨
Leisure activities : 🍸 ✕ 🎦 🌙 🏃 ⛷ jacuzzi 🛶 🎿 🐟
Facilities : 🚿 ⛷ 🏛 ⛷ launderette 🚰

G P S Longitude : 0.33943
Latitude : 42.83786

BRASSAC

81260 – Michelin map **338** G9 – pop. 1 396 – alt. 487
▶ Paris 747 – Albi 65 – Anglès 14 – Castres 26

⚠ Municipal de la Lande

✆ 05 63 74 09 11, www.camping.brassac.fr

Address : at the stade (take the southwestern exit towards Castres and take a right turn after the bridge; near the Agout river and crossed by a stream)

Opening times : from mid June to end Sept.

1 ha (50 pitches) flat, grassy

Tariff : ♥ 2€ ⇌ 1,30€ 回 1,70€ – (½) (5A) 1,70€

Surroundings : ⑤ ♀♀
Leisure activities : 🏠
Facilities : 🚿 ⚿ 🔥
Nearby : 🚴 ✗ 🏊 🤿

GPS Longitude : 2.4952
Latitude : 43.63067

These symbols are used for a campsite that is exceptional in its category:

ᐃᐃᐃ ... ᐃ *Particularly pleasant setting, quality and range of services available*

🦢 🦢 *Tranquil, isolated site – quiet site, particularly at night*

≤ ≤ *Exceptional view – interesting or panoramic view*

BRETENOUX

46130 – Michelin map **337** H2 – pop. 1 342 – alt. 136
▶ Paris 521 – Brive-la-Gaillarde 44 – Cahors 83 – Figeac 48

⚠ La Bourgnatelle

✆ 05 65 10 89 04, www.dordogne-vacances.fr

Address : take the northwestern exit, turn left after the bridge

2,3 ha (135 pitches) flat, grassy

Rentals : 74 🛖 – 5 canvas bungalows.

Surroundings : ⑤ ♀♀ ⚠
Leisure activities : 🏠 🤸 🏊 🤿
Facilities : 🚿 ⚿ launderette 🧺
Nearby : ✗

GPS Longitude : 1.83772
Latitude : 44.91679

BRUSQUE

12360 – Michelin map **338** J8 – pop. 309 – alt. 465
▶ Paris 698 – Albi 91 – Béziers 75 – Lacaune 30

ᐃᐃᐃ Village Vacances Val-VVF Le Domaine de Céras

✆ 05 65 49 50 66, www.vvfvillages.fr

Address : 1.6km south along the D 92, follow the signs for Arnac; beside the Dourdou river and a small lake

14 ha (160 pitches) undulating, flat, grassy

Rentals : ♿ (3 apartments) – 67 apartments – 20 canvas bungalows.

Situated in a peaceful and secluded small green valley.

Surroundings : 🦢 ≤ ♀♀ ⚠
Leisure activities : 🍴 ✗ 🏠 🎮 🤸 🚣 ✗ 🏊 (fresh water) 🏃 fitness trail, multi-sports ground
Facilities : ⚿ 🏌 launderette 🧺

GPS Longitude : 2.95742
Latitude : 43.75666

LES CABANNES

81170 – Michelin map **338** D6 – pop. 353 – alt. 200
▶ Paris 653 – Albi 27 – Montauban 57 – Rodez 80

ᐃᐃ Le Garissou

✆ 05 63 56 27 14, legarissou@wanadoo.fr

Address : 500m to the west along the D 600, follow the signs for Vindrac and take road to the left

7 ha/4 for camping (72 pitches) terraced, flat, grassy, stony

Rentals : 🅿 – 30 🛖.
🛢 ⚡ (½)11€

Situated in an attractive elevated location.

Surroundings : 🦢 ≤ Cordes-sur-Ciel and valley ⌂ ♀
Leisure activities : 🏠 🤸 🏃 🏊 🤿 multi-sports ground
Facilities : ♿ ⚿ 🚐 🏌 launderette

GPS Longitude : 1.94247
Latitude : 44.06767

CAHORS

46000 – Michelin map **337** E5 – pop. 19 940 – alt. 135
▶ Paris 575 – Agen 85 – Albi 110 – Bergerac 108

ᐃᐃᐃ Rivière de Cabessut

✆ 05 65 30 06 30, www.cabessut.com

Address : rue de la Rivière (3km south along the D 911 towards Rodez then take the road to the left, take quai Ludo-Rolles; beside the Lot river)

Opening times : from beginning April to end Sept.

2 ha (113 pitches) flat, grassy

Tariff : ♥ 5€ ⇌ 回 8€ – (½) (10A) 2€

Rental rates : (from beginning April to end Sept.) 🚫 – 8 🛖.
Per night from 60 to 90€ – Per week from 310 to 590€
🛢 borne 4€ – 10 回 18€ – ⚡11€

Surroundings : ⌂ ♀♀
Leisure activities : 🏠 🤸 🏃 🏊 🤿
Facilities : ♿ ⚿ 🚿 🏛 🏌 🔥
Nearby : ⚠

GPS Longitude : 1.44192
Latitude : 44.46364

CALMONT

31560 – Michelin map **343** H5 – pop. 2 177 – alt. 220
▶ Paris 724 – Toulouse 48 – Ordino 144 – Canillo 127

⚠ Le Mercier

✆ 05 34 48 81 31, www.camping-mercier.com

Address : 2.4km south along the D 11, follow the signs for Pamiers

Opening times : Permanent

0,6 ha (22 pitches) flat, grassy

Tariff : (2013 Price) 20€ ♥♥ ⇌ 回 (½) (5A) – Extra per person 5€

Rental rates : (2013 Price) Permanent – 4 🛖 – 1 gîte. Per night from 35 to 85€ – Per week from 170 to 480€ – Reservation fee 15€

🛢 borne 4€ – 3 回

A friendly welcome in a well-kept setting with a variety of rental options.

Surroundings : 🦢 ⌂ ♀
Leisure activities : 🏊
Facilities : ♿ 🚐 🏌 🔥

GPS Longitude : 1.6334
Latitude : 43.2819

LES CAMMAZES

81540 – Michelin map **338** E10 – pop. 309 – alt. 610
▶ Paris 736 – Aurillac 241 – Castres 35 – Figeac 183

⚑ La Rigole

✆ 05 63 73 28 99, www.campingdelarigole.com

Address : route du Barrage (take the southern exit from the D 629 and road to the left)

Opening times : from end April to end Sept.

3 ha (66 pitches)Tariff : 27€ ♦♦ ⟺ 回 (52) (13A) –
Extra per person 5,90€

Rental rates : (from end April to end Sept.) – 11 🚐 – 9 🏠.
Per night from 42 to 102€ – Per week from 252 to 714€

🚐 borne 3 回 12€ – 🚐 12€

Surroundings : ⬡ 🏕 💭💭 Leisure activities : ⛳ ✗ 🚣 🚲 ⛷ Facilities : ♿ ☕ 🏕 🚿 launderette 🗑	**GPS** Longitude : 2.08625 Latitude : 43.40787

CANET-DE-SALARS

12290 – Michelin map **338** I5 – pop. 416 – alt. 850
▶ Paris 654 – Pont-de-Salars 9 – Rodez 33 – St-Beauzély 28

⚑ Les Castels Le Caussanel ♦♦

SINGLA

✆ 05 65 46 85 19, www.lecaussanel.com

Address : at the lake Pareloup (2.7km southeast along the D 538 and take a right turn)

Opening times : from mid May to beginning Sept.

10 ha (228 pitches) terraced, flat, grassy

Tariff : (2013 Price) 34,80€ ♦♦ ⟺ 回 (52) (6A) – Extra per person 7,50€
Reservation fee 30€

Rental rates : (from mid May to beginning Sept.) – 80 🚐 – 40 🏠.
Per week from 357 to 833€
Reservation fee 30€

Surroundings : ⬡ ⬡on the lake ♀⛰ Leisure activities : ⛳ ✗ 🏛 🎣 ⛵ 🚣 🚲 ⛷ ⛷ ⛰ 🌲treetop adventure trail, pedalos ✈ multi-sports ground, entertainment room Facilities : ♿ ☕ 回 🏕 🚿 🚿 launderette 🗑🚐	**GPS** Longitude : 2.76651 Latitude : 44.21426

⚑ Soleil Levant

✆ 05 65 46 03 65, www.camping-soleil-levant.com

Address : at the lake Pareloup (3.7km southeast along the D 538 and D 993, follow the signs for Salles-Curan, to the left, before the bridge)

Opening times : from beginning May to end Sept.

11 ha (206 pitches) terraced, flat, grassy

Tariff : 27,50€ ♦♦ ⟺ 回 (52) (6A) – Extra per person 7,50€
Reservation fee 17,50€

Rental rates : (from beginning May to end Sept.) – 16 🚐. Per night from 100€ – Per week from 195 to 695€ – Reservation fee 17,50€

In a pleasant location beside the Lac de Pareloup.

Surroundings : ⬡ ⬡♀♀⛰ Leisure activities : ⛳ 🏛 🚣 ✈ Facilities : ♿ ☕ 🏕 🚿 launderette Nearby : 🚲⚓	**GPS** Longitude : 2.77795 Latitude : 44.21551

CAPDENAC-GARE

12700 – Michelin map **338** F3 – pop. 4 492 – alt. 175
▶ Paris 587 – Dec.azeville 20 – Figeac 9 – Maurs 24

⚑ Municipal les Rives d'Olt

✆ 05 65 80 88 87, www.campingcapdenac.fr – 🍴

Address : 8 boulevard Paul Ramadier (take the western exit along the D 994, follow the signs for Figeac and take the turning to the left before the bridge, near the Lot river)

Opening times : from end April to mid Sept.

1,3 ha (60 pitches) flat, grassy

Tariff : ♦ 4,50€ ⟺ 回 5€ – (52) (10A) 3,10€

🚐 borne 2€

In a pleasant setting, green and leafy with good shade.

Surroundings : 🏕 💭💭 Leisure activities : ⬡ Facilities : ♿ ☕ 🏕 🚿 📷 Nearby : ⛳ ✗ ✂ 🎣 🖥 sports trail	**GPS** Longitude : 2.07294 Latitude : 44.57209

CARLUCET

46500 – Michelin map **337** F3 – pop. 228 – alt. 322
▶ Paris 542 – Cahors 47 – Gourdon 26 – Labastide-Murat 11

⚑ Château de Lacomté

✆ 05 65 38 75 46, www.chateaulacomte.com

Address : at Lacomté (located 1.8km northwest of the town, by the castle)

Opening times : from beginning May to mid Sept.

12 ha/4 for camping (100 pitches)

Tariff : 36€ ♦♦ ⟺ 回 (52) (16A) – Extra per person 10€ – Reservation fee 15€

Rental rates : (from beginning May to mid Sept.) ✈
4 🚐 – 5 🏠 – 1 gîte. Per night from 30 to 80€ – Per week from 200 to 300€ – Reservation fee 15€

A very peaceful and tranquil campsite reserved for adults (18 years and over).

Surroundings : ⬡ 🏕 ♀♀ Leisure activities : ⛳ ✗ 🏛 🎣 🚲 ✂ ⛷ Facilities : ♿ ☕ 🏕 🚿 🚿 launderette 🗑	**GPS** Longitude : 1.59692 Latitude : 44.72881

CASSAGNABÈRE-TOURNAS

31420 – Michelin map **343** C5 – pop. 415 – alt. 380
▶ Paris 758 – Auch 78 – Bagnères-de-Luchon 65 – Pamiers 101

⚑ Pré Fixe

✆ 05 61 98 71 00, www.camping-pre-fixe.com

Address : route de St-Gaudens (situated southwest of the town)

Opening times : from beginning April to end Oct.

1,2 ha (40 pitches)

Tariff : 24€ ♦♦ ⟺ 回 (52) (6A) – Extra per person 6€
Rental rates : Permanent ✈ – 6 🏠 – 2 tent lodges. Per night from 45 to 125€ – Per week from 245 to 760€

A pleasant site laid out in terraces with a variety of upmarket rental options and a small wine bar run by the owner.

Surroundings : ⬡ 🏕 ♀♀ Leisure activities : ⛳ 🏛 🏓 ⛷ Facilities : ♿ ☕ 🚿 📷 🗑 Nearby : ✂	**GPS** Longitude : 0.79 Latitude : 43.22889

CASSAGNES

46700 – Michelin map **337** C4 – pop. 209 – alt. 185
▶ Paris 577 – Cahors 34 – Cazals 15 – Fumel 19

⚠ Le Carbet

✆ 05 65 36 61 79, www.camping-le-carbet.fr

Address : at La Barte (located 1.5km northwest along the D 673, follow the signs for Fumel; near a lake)

Opening times : from beginning April to mid Sept.

3 ha (29 pitches) open site, terraced, flat, grassy, stony

Tariff : 17,50€ ★★ ⚊ 🔲 ⚡ (6A) – Extra per person 6,20€ Reservation fee 10€

Rental rates : (from beginning April to mid Sept.) – 10 🏠. Per night from 40€ – Per week from 205 to 535€ – Reservation fee 10€

Surroundings : ⌂ ♨
Leisure activities : ♈ ✕ ⛵ ⚓
Facilities : ⚬ ♨ 🔲 ⚓

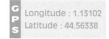

Longitude : 1.13102
Latitude : 44.56338

CASTELNAU-DE-MONTMIRAL

81140 – Michelin map **338** C7 – pop. 950 – alt. 287
▶ Paris 645 – Albi 31 – Bruniquel 22 – Cordes-sur-Ciel 22

⚠ Le Chêne Vert

✆ 05 63 33 16 10, www.camping-du-chene-vert.com

Address : at Travers du Rieutort (head 3.5km northwest along the D 964, follow the signs for Caussade, take D 1 and D 87, follow the signs for Penne; on the left)

10 ha/2 for camping (130 pitches)

Rentals : 37 🏠 – 5 canvas bungalows.

🚰 borne

Surroundings : ♨ ◁ ⌂ ♨
Leisure activities : ♈ ✕ ⛵ ⚓
Facilities : ⚬ ♨ 🔲 ⚓
At the leisure/activities centre (800m) : ✕ ♨ ⚊ (beach) ⚓

Longitude : 1.78947
Latitude : 43.97702

CASTELNAU-MONTRATIER

46170 – Michelin map **337** E6 – pop. 1 837 – alt. 240
▶ Paris 600 – Cahors 30 – Caussade 24 – Lauzerte 23

⚠ Municipal des 3 Moulins

✆ 0565219421, www.castelnau-montratier.fr – ℞

Address : route de Lauzette (take the northwestern exit along the D 19)

Opening times : from mid June to mid Sept.

1 ha (50 pitches)

Tariff : (2013 Price) ★ 2,50€ ⚊ 🔲 2,60€ – ⚡ (10A) 1,50€

Surroundings : ♨
Facilities : ⚊
Nearby : ✕ ⚓ ⚓

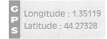

Longitude : 1.35119
Latitude : 44.27328

The Michelin classification (⚠⚠⚠ ... ⚠) is totally independent of the official star classification system awarded by the local prefecture or other official organisation.

CASTÉRA-VERDUZAN

32410 – Michelin map **336** E7 – pop. 937 – alt. 114
▶ Paris 720 – Agen 61 – Auch 40 – Condom 20

⚠ La Plage de Verduzan

✆ 05 62 68 12 23, www.camping-verduzan.com

Address : 30 rue du Lac (north of the town; beside the Aulone river)

2 ha (100 pitches) flat, grassy

Rentals : 18 🏠.

Beside a small lake; well-kept pitches.

Surroundings : ⌂ ♨
Leisure activities : ⚊ ♈
Facilities : ⚓ ⚬ ⚊ 🔲 ♨ 🔲
Nearby : ✕ ⚊ (beach) ⚓ pedalos

Longitude : 0.43116
Latitude : 43.80817

We value your opinion and welcome your feedback. Do email us at campingfrance@tp.michelin.com

CAUSSADE

82300 – Michelin map **337** F7 – pop. 6 586 – alt. 109
▶ Paris 606 – Albi 70 – Cahors 38 – Montauban 28

⚠ Municipal la Piboulette

✆ 05 63 93 09 07, mairie-caussade.fr

Address : located 1km northeast along the D 17, follow the signs for Puylaroque and take the turning to the left, by the stadium, 200m from a lake

Opening times : from beginning May to end Sept.

1,5 ha (100 pitches) flat, grassy

Tariff : ★ 2,75€ ⚊ 🔲 1,95€ – ⚡ (6A) 1,85€

🚰 borne 4,10€ – 5 🔲 4,10€

Surroundings : ♨ ♨
Facilities : ⚓ ⚬ ⚊ 🔲 ♨ launderette
Nearby : ⚓ ✕ 🔲 🏹 fitness trail

Longitude : 1.54624
Latitude : 44.16877

CAUTERETS

65110 – Michelin map **342** L7 – pop. 1 118 – alt. 932 – ⚡ – Winter sports : 1 000/2 350m
▶ Paris 880 – Argelès-Gazost 17 – Lourdes 30 – Pau 75

⚠ Les Glères

✆ 05 62 92 55 34, www.gleres.com

Address : 19 route de Pierrefitte (take the northern exit along the D 920; beside the Gave de Cauterets (river)

Opening times : from beginning Dec.. to end Oct.

1,2 ha (80 pitches)

Tariff : 19,70€ ★★ ⚊ 🔲 ⚡ (6A) – Extra per person 4,70€ – Reservation fee 10€

Rental rates : (from beginning Dec.. to mid Oct.) ✕ – 16 🏠 5 🏠. Per night 90€ – Per week 620€

🚰 40 🔲 19€ – 🔲 19€

Good sanitary facilities, but slightly antiquated rental options for a location so close to the town centre.

Surroundings : ❄ ◁ ♨
Leisure activities : ⚊ ⚓ 🏹
Facilities : ⚓ ⚬ 🔲 ⚊ ⚓ ⚬ launderette
Nearby : ✕ skating rink

Longitude : -0.11275
Latitude : 42.89625

⚠ Le Cabaliros

✆ 05 62 92 55 36, www.camping-cabaliros.com

Address : 93 avenue du Mamelon Vert (1.6 km north following signs for Lourdes, left across the bridge)

Opening times : from end May to end Sept.

2 ha (100 pitches) relatively flat to hilly, grassy

Tariff : 19 € ♦♦ ⇦ 🗐 🔌 (6A) – Extra per person 5,30 €

Rental rates : Permanent – 6 🚐. Per night from 65 to 90 € Per week from 270 to 570 €

🚰 borne 3 €

Pitches in the shade or the sun, on a gentle slope leading down to the Gave de Pau river.

Surroundings : 🏞 ≤ ♤♤ Leisure activities : 🏊 🏌 🎣 Facilities : 🚿 ⊶ 🎿 🛒 ♈ launderette	**GPS** Longitude : -0.10735 Latitude : 42.90406

⚠ GR 10

✆ 06 20 30 25 85, www.gr10camping.com

Address : at Concé (2.8 km north along the D 920, follow the signs for Lourdes, near the Gave de Pau (river)

Opening times : from end June to mid Sept.

1,5 ha (69 pitches) relatively flat, flat, grassy, rocks

Tariff : ♦ 6,50 € ⇦ 🗐 5 € – 🔌 (8A) 4 €

Rental rates : Permanent – 1 🚐 – 2 🏠 – 5 🛏 – 2 gîtes. Per night from 50 to 150 € – Per week from 490 to 690 €

🚰 borne 4 € – 4 🗐 18 €

A good departure point for many mountain activities.

Surroundings : 🏞 ≤ ♤ ♁ Leisure activities : 🏊 🏌 🎿 forest trail, rafting and canyoning, climbing Facilities : 🚿 ⊶ 🎿 ♈ launderette	**GPS** Longitude : -0.09892 Latitude : 42.91107

⚠ Le Péguère

✆ 05 62 92 52 91, www.campingpeguere.com

Address : 31 route de Pierrefitte (located 1.5km north following signs for Lourdes; beside the Gave de Pau (river)

Opening times : from beginning April to end Sept.

3,5 ha (160 pitches)

Tariff : 14,85 € ♦♦ ⇦ 🗐 🔌 (6A) – Extra per person 4,35 €

Rental rates : (from beginning April to mid Sept.) 🎿 (from beginning April to mid Sept.) – 3 🚐 – 2 🏠. Per night from 37 to 47 € – Per week from 176 to 443 €

🚰 borne 2 €

A site that lies between the road heading north from the town and the Gave de Cauterets river.

Surroundings : ≤ ♁ Leisure activities : 🏊 🎣 Facilities : 🚿 ⊶ 🎿 🛒 ♈ launderette	**GPS** Longitude : -0.10683 Latitude : 42.9024

The prices listed were supplied by the campsite owners in 2013 (if prices were not available, those from the previous year are given). The fees should be regarded as basic charges and may fluctuate with inflation.

CAYLUS

82160 – Michelin map **337** G6 – pop. 1 536 – alt. 228

▶ Paris 628 – Albi 60 – Cahors 59 – Montauban 50

⚠ La Bonnette

✆ 05 63 65 70 20, www.campingbonnette.com

Address : at Les Condamines (take the northeastern exit along the D 926, follow the signs for Villefranche-de-Rouergue and turn right onto the D 97, follow the signs for St-Antonin-Noble-Val)

Opening times : from end March to beginning Oct.

1,5 ha (51 pitches) flat, grassy

Tariff : 19 € ♦♦ ⇦ 🗐 🔌 (10A) – Extra per person 6 €

Rental rates : (from end March to beginning Oct.) – 6 🚐 Per night from 45 to 90 € – Per week from 300 to 595 €

🚰 borne 10 €

Beside the Bonnette river and near a lake.

Surroundings : 🌳 ♤♤ Leisure activities : 🍴 ✗ 🏌 🎿 Facilities : 🚿 ⊶ 🎿 🏊 🛒 ♈ launderette Nearby : 🎣	**GPS** Longitude : 1.77629 Latitude : 44.23375

The pitches of many campsites are marked out with low hedges of attractive bushes and shrubs.

CAYRIECH

82240 – Michelin map **337** F6 – pop. 264 – alt. 140

▶ Paris 608 – Cahors 39 – Caussade 11 – Caylus 17

⚠ Le Clos de la Lère

✆ 05 63 31 20 41, www.camping-leclosdelalere.com

Address : at Clergue (take the southeastern exit along the D 9, follow the signs for Sept.fonds)

Opening times : from beginning March to mid Nov.

1 ha (55 pitches) flat, grassy

Tariff : 21,50 € ♦♦ ⇦ 🗐 🔌 (10A) – Extra per person 5,20 €

Rental rates : (from beginning March to mid Nov.) – 7 🚐 6 🏠. Per night from 29 to 53 € – Per week from 172 to 683 € Reservation fee 8 €

🚰 borne 3 € – 4 🗐 8 € – 🚗 🔌 10 €

Attractive shrubs and flowers decorate the site.

Surroundings : 🏞 🌳 ♤♤ Leisure activities : 🏌 🎿 Facilities : 🚿 ⊶ 🏊 ♈ launderette 🚗 Nearby : 🍴	**GPS** Longitude : 1.61291 Latitude : 44.21735

CONDOM

32100 – Michelin map **336** E6 – pop. 7 099 – alt. 81

▶ Paris 729 – Agen 41 – Auch 46 – Mont-de-Marsan 80

⚠ Municipal

✆ 05 62 28 17 32, www.condom.org/index.php/camping-municipal

Address : chemin de l'Argenté (2 km, southern exit from the D 931, follow the signs for Eauze; near the Baïse river)

Opening times : from beginning April to end Sept.

2 ha (75 pitches) flat, grassy

Tariff : ♦ 3,50 € ⇦ 🗐 5 € – 🔌 (10A) 3,70 €

Rental rates : (from beginning April to mid Oct.) ♿ ⚿ – 10 🏠.
Per week from 289 to 461€

Surroundings : ⌂ ♤♤
Leisure activities : 🎣
Facilities : ♿ ⚿ 🛖 🏕 🔥 ⚙ 📶 📺
Nearby : ♈ ✗ jacuzzi ✂ 🎿 ⛷ 🛶

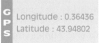
Longitude : 0.36436
Latitude : 43.94802

CONQUES

12320 – Michelin map **338** G3 – pop. 280 – alt. 350
▶ Paris 601 – Aurillac 53 – Dec.azeville 26 – Espalion 42

⛺ Beau Rivage

✆ 0565698223, www.campingconques.com
Address : at Molinols (to the west of the town, along the D 901; beside the Dourdou river)
1 ha (60 pitches) flat, grassy
Rentals : 12 🚐.

Situated on the river bank, just below the medieval village.

Surroundings : ⌂ ♤♤
Leisure activities : ✗ 🎣 🎿
Facilities : ♿ ⚿ 📶 launderette ♨

Longitude : 2.39285
Latitude : 44.59891

CORDES-SUR-CIEL

81170 – Michelin map **338** D6 – pop. 1 006 – alt. 279
▶ Paris 655 – Albi 25 – Montauban 59 – Rodez 78

⛰ Moulin de Julien

✆ 0563561110, www.campingmoulindejulien.com
Address : 1.5 km southeast along the D 922, follow the signs for Gaillac; beside a stream
Opening times : from beginning May to mid Sept.
9 ha (130 pitches)
Tariff : (2013 Price) 23,80€ 👤👤 🚗 🔌 [⚡] (5A) – Extra per person 6€
Reservation fee 10€
Rental rates : (from beginning May to mid Sept.) ⚿ – 3 🚐
5 🏠. Per week from 285 to 590€ – Reservation fee 10€

Surroundings : ♤♤
Leisure activities : ♈ 🎣 🎿 🎯 🎿 🛶 ⛷
Facilities : ♿ ⚿ 🏕 📶 📺
Nearby : ✂

Longitude : 1.97628
Latitude : 44.05036

⛺ Camp Redon

✆ 0563561464, www.campredon.com
Address : at Livers Cazelles (5km southeast along the D 600, follow the signs for Albi then continue 800m along the D 107, follow the signs for Virac to the left)
Opening times : from beginning April to mid Oct.
2 ha (40 pitches)
Tariff : 28,35€ 👤👤 🚗 🔌 [⚡] (10A) – Extra per person 7,80€
Rental rates : (from beginning April to mid Oct.) ⚿ – 2 🚐
3 canvas bungalows – 4 tent lodges. Per night from 50 to 135€
Per week from 310 to 925€

Surroundings : 🏞 ≤ ⌂ ♧
Leisure activities : 🎣 🎿 🎿
Facilities : ⚿ 📶 📺

Longitude : 2.01767
Latitude : 44.04318

COS

09000 – Michelin map **343** H7 – pop. 369 – alt. 486
▶ Paris 766 – La Bastide-de-Sérou 14 – Foix 5 – Pamiers 25

⛺ Municipal

✆ 0671181038, www.camping-municipal-cos09.fr
Address : Le Rieutort (700m southwest on the D 61; beside a stream)
Opening times : Permanent
0,7 ha (32 pitches) open site
Tariff : (2013 Price) 11,80€ 👤👤 🚗 🔌 [⚡] (6A) – Extra per person 1,50€
Rental rates : Permanent – 2 🏠. Per week from 200 to 300€
A small, shady site with basic and rather old sanitary facilities.

Surroundings : 🏞 ♤♤
Leisure activities : 🎣 ✂
Facilities : ♿ ⚿ 🛖 🏕 🎿 📶 📺
Nearby : 🎣 🎿

Longitude : 1.57332
Latitude : 42.97102

This guide is not intended as a list of all the camping sites in France; its aim is to provide a selection of the best sites in each category.

CREISSELS

12100 – Michelin map **338** K6 – pop. 1 487 – alt. 330
▶ Paris 646 – Toulouse 184 – Rodez 69 – Montpellier 115

⛺ St-Martin

✆ 0565603183, www.campingsaintmartin.fr
Opening times : from beginning April to end Sept.
3 ha (90 pitches) flat, grassy
Rentals : 9 🚐.

Surroundings : 🏞 ≤ ⌂ ♧
Leisure activities : 🎣 🎣 🎿
Facilities : ♿ ⚿ launderette
Nearby : ✂

Longitude : 3.04907
Latitude : 44.07461

CREYSSE

46600 – Michelin map **337** F2 – pop. 296 – alt. 110
▶ Paris 517 – Brive-la-Gaillarde 40 – Cahors 79 – Gourdon 40

⛰ Le Port

✆ 0565322082, www.campingduport.com
Address : south of the town, near the château; beside the Dordogne river
Opening times : from mid April to end Sept.
3,5 ha (100 pitches)
Tariff : 18,20€ 👤👤 🚗 🔌 [⚡] (10A) – Extra per person 5€ – Reservation fee 10€
Rental rates : (from mid April to end Sept.) – 9 🚐. Per night from 35 to 47€ – Per week from 185 to 565€ – Reservation fee 10€
Close to a pleasant beach beside the Dordogne river.

Surroundings : 🏞 ♤♤ ⛰
Leisure activities : ♈ 🎣 🚲 🎿 🛶 climbing ✂
Facilities : ⚿ 🏕 📶 launderette

Longitude : 0.56537
Latitude : 44.85455

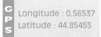

DAMIATTE

81220 – Michelin map **338** D9 – pop. 931 – alt. 148
▶ Paris 698 – Castres 26 – Graulhet 16 – Lautrec 18

⚠ Sites et Paysages Le Plan d'Eau St-Charles ♣♣

✆ 05 63 70 66 07, www.campingplandeau.com

Address : la Cahuziere (take the exit following signs for Graulhet then continue 1.2km along the turning to the left before the level crossing)

Opening times : from mid May to mid Sept.

7,5 ha/2 for camping (82 pitches)

Tariff : 23,50€ ♣♣ ⇔ ▤ ⚡ (6A) – Extra per person 6,30€ Reservation fee 17€

Rental rates : (from beginning April to end Oct.) – 22 ⏚ 16 🏠. Per night from 60 to 75€ – Per week from 630 to 800€ Reservation fee 17€

Attractive location arranged around a small but pretty lake.

Surroundings : ⌁ ⇐ ⊏ 🏞 ▲
Leisure activities : ✕ 🏛 ⚞ ⚟ ⚐ ⟋
Facilities : ♿ ⛵ ☃ 🚿 🕴 🖼 ⚒
Nearby : 🏇
GPS Longitude : 1.97011
Latitude : 43.66289

DURAVEL

46700 – Michelin map **337** C4 – pop. 957 – alt. 110
▶ Paris 610 – Toulouse 153 – Cahors 39 – Villeneuve-sur-Lot 37

⚠ FranceLoc Le Domaine Duravel ♣♣

✆ 05 65 24 65 06, www.franceloc.fr

Address : route du Port-de-Vire (2.3km south along the D 58; beside the Lot)

Opening times : from beginning May to mid Sept.

9 ha (260 pitches) flat, grassy

Tariff : (2013 Price) 14€ ♣♣ ⇔ ▤ ⚡ (10A) – Reservation fee 27€

Rental rates : (2013 Price) (from beginning May to mid Sept.) 115 ⏚ – 32 🏠. Per night from 39 to 158€ – Per week from 140 to 1190€ – Reservation fee 27€

Surroundings : ⌁ ⊏ 🏞
Leisure activities : 🍴 ✕ 🏛 ⚞ ⚟ 🚴 ⚿
⚐ ⟋ ⚐ ⚐
Facilities : ♿ ⛵ ☃ 🕴 launderette ⚒
Nearby : ⚐ climbing
GPS Longitude : 1.08201
Latitude : 44.49633

ENTRAYGUES-SUR-TRUYÈRE

12140 – Michelin map **338** H3 – pop. 1 224 – alt. 236
▶ Paris 600 – Aurillac 45 – Figeac 58 – Mende 128

⚠ Le Val de Saures

✆ 05 65 44 56 92, www.camping-valdesaures.com

Address : chemin de Saures (1.6km south along the D 904, follow the signs for Espeyrac, on the banks of the Lot river (direct access)

Opening times : from beginning May to end Sept.

4 ha (126 pitches) terraced, flat, grassy

Tariff : 22,50€ ♣♣ ⇔ ▤ ⚡ (16A) – Extra per person 4€ – Reservation fee 20€

Rental rates : (from mid April to end Sept.) – 11 🏠 – 5 tent lodges. Per night from 29 to 99€ – Per week from 189 to 693€ Reservation fee 30€

Surroundings : ⌁ ⇐ ⊏ 🏞
Leisure activities : 🏛 ⚞ ⟋
Facilities : ♿ ⛵ ☃ 🕴 launderette
Nearby : ⚐
GPS Longitude : 2.56352
Latitude : 44.64248

⚠ Le Lauradiol

✆ 05 65 44 53 95, www.camping-lelauradiol.com

Address : at Campouriez (5km northeast along the D 34, follow the signs for St-Amans-des-Cots; beside the Selves river)

Opening times : from end June to end Aug.

1 ha (31 pitches) flat, grassy

Tariff : 17,50€ ♣♣ ⇔ ▤ ⚡ (10A) – Extra per person 4€ – Reservation fee 20€

Rental rates : (from end June to end Aug.) – 2 ⏚. Per night from 30 to 84€ – Per week from 210 to 588€ – Reservation fee 30€

A pleasant location at the bottom of a small valley, on the banks of the river.

Surroundings : ⌁ ⊏ 🏞
Leisure activities : 🏛 ⚞ ✕ ⚐ ⟋
Facilities : ♿ ⛵ (July–Aug.) ☃ 🕴 🖼
GPS Longitude : 2.58289
Latitude : 44.67768

ESPALION

12500 – Michelin map **338** I3 – pop. 4 409 – alt. 342
▶ Paris 592 – Aurillac 72 – Figeac 93 – Mende 101

⚠ Le Roc de l'Arche

SINGLA

✆ 05 65 44 06 79, www.rocdelarche.com

Address : Le Foirail (to the east, Rue du Foirail via Ave. de la Gare, turn off to the left, after the sports grounds, beside the Lot river)

Opening times : from mid May to beginning Sept.

2,5 ha (95 pitches) flat, grassy

Tariff : (2013 Price) 23,60€ ♣♣ ⇔ ▤ ⚡ (10A) – Extra per person 5,40€

Reservation fee 15€

Rental rates : (from mid May to beginning Sept.) – 20 ⏚. Per night from 44 to 74€ – Per week from 262 to 518€ Reservation fee 15€

🚰 borne 3€

Surroundings : ⊏ 🏞
Leisure activities : 🏛 ⚞ 🚴 ⟋
Facilities : ♿ ⛵ ☃ ⚿ 🕴 🖼
Nearby : ✕ ⚐
GPS Longitude : 2.76959
Latitude : 44.52244

Some campsites benefit from proximity to a municipal leisure centre.

ESTAING

65400 – Michelin map **342** K7 – pop. 77 – alt. 970
▶ Paris 874 – Argelès-Gazost 12 – Arrens 7 – Laruns 43

⚠ La Via Natura Pyrénées Natura

✆ 05 62 97 45 44, www.camping-pyrenees-natura.com – alt. 1 000

Address : route du Lac (north of the town)

Opening times : from mid April to mid Oct.

3 ha (65 pitches)

Tariff : 31,80€ ♣♣ ⇔ ▤ ⚡ (10A) – Extra per person 6€ – Reservation fee 25€

Rental rates : (from mid April to mid Oct.) – 19 🏠. Per night
from 41€ – Per week from 285 to 640€ – Reservation fee 25€
🛒 borne – 4 ▣ 22,60€ – 🚌 🚿10€

*A beautiful 19th-century barn building, good quality rental
options and good sanitary facilities.*

Surroundings : 🐟 ⬅ 🛏 🌳
Leisure activities : 🍴 ✕ 🖼 🌊 jacuzzi
🏄 🚤
Facilities : 🚿 🔌 ♨ 🏊 🚮 🍴 launderette 🛁

G P S Longitude : -0.17725
Latitude : 42.94145

ESTANG

32240 – Michelin map **336** B6 – pop. 643 – alt. 120
▶ Paris 712 – Aire-sur-l'Adour 25 – Eauze 17 – Mont-de-Marsan 35

🏔 Les Lacs de Courtès 🏕

✆ 05 62 09 61 98, www.lacsDec.ourtes.com
Address : south of the town along the D 152, behind the church and
beside a lake
Opening times : Permanent
7 ha (136 pitches) terraced, relatively flat, flat, grassy
Tariff : (2013 Price) 🚶 5,25€ – 🚗 2,75€ ▣ 14€ – 🚿 (10A) 3€ –
Reservation fee 20€
Rental rates : (2013 Price) Permanent – 20 🏠 – 2 canvas
bungalows – 22 gîtes. Per night from 40 to 135€ – Per week
from 280 to 945€ – Reservation fee 20€
🛒 borne 5€ – 6 ▣ 15€ – 🚌 13€

Surroundings : 🐟 🌳
Leisure activities : 🍴 ✕ 🖼 🏃 jacuzzi 🏄
🏊 🚤 🐟 🍴
Facilities : 🚿 🔌 🅲🅲 🏊 🍴 launderette 🛁

G P S Longitude : -0.10254
Latitude : 43.8891

FIGEAC

46100 – Michelin map **337** I4 – pop. 9 847 – alt. 214
▶ Paris 578 – Aurillac 64 – Rodez 66 – Villefranche-de-Rouergue 36

🏔 Le Domaine du Surgié

✆ 05 61 64 88 54, www.domainedusurgie.com
Address : at the Domaine du Surgié (1.2km to the east along the
N 140, follow the signs for Rodez, beside the river and a small lake)
Opening times : from beginning April to end Sept.
2 ha (163 pitches)
Tariff : 26€ 🚶 🚶 🚗 ▣ 🚿 (10A) – Extra per person 7,50€ – Reservation
fee 10€
Rental rates : (from beginning April to end Sept.) 🚿 – 20 🏠
30 🏠 – 6 canvas bungalows. Per night from 60 to 70€
Per week from 200 to 795€ – Reservation fee 21€
🛒 borne 19€ – 🚌 🚿26€

Surroundings : 🌳
Leisure activities : 🖼 🏃 🐟
Facilities : 🚿 🔌 🅲🅲launderette
Nearby : 🍴 ✕ 🛁 🏄 🚴 🏊 🛶

G P S Longitude : 2.04942
Latitude : 44.61189

*Routes nationales are main roads and their identifying
numbers begin with N or RN. Routes départementales are
generally quieter roads and begin with D or DN.*

FLAGNAC

12300 – Michelin map **338** F3 – pop. 972 – alt. 220
▶ Paris 603 – Conques 19 – Dec.azeville 5 – Figeac 25

🏔 Flower Le Port de Lacombe

✆ 05 65 64 10 08, www.campingleportdelacombe.fr
Address : located 1km north along the D 963 and take road to the
left; near a small lake and the Lot river (direct access)
Opening times : from beginning April to end Sept.
4 ha (97 pitches) flat, grassy
Tariff : 29,50€ 🚶 🚶 🚗 ▣ 🚿 (10A) – Extra per person 5,50€ –
Reservation fee 20€
Rental rates : (from beginning April to end Sept.) – 36 🏠
10 canvas bungalows. Per night from 45 to 110€ – Per week
from 170 to 770€ – Reservation fee 20€
🛒 borne 5€ – 🚌 🚿10€

Surroundings : 🐟 🛏 🌳
Leisure activities : 🍴 ✕ 🖼 🏄 🚴 🏊 🐟
Facilities : 🚿 🔌 🍴 launderette
Nearby : 🐎 🏊 pedalos

G P S Longitude : 2.23533
Latitude : 44.60819

LA FOUILLADE

12270 – pop. 1 110 – alt. 420
▶ Paris 624 – Toulouse 109 – Rodez 61 – Albi 52

🏔 Le Bosquet

✆ 06 63 95 30 65, www.campinglafouillade.fr
Address : rue Genêts
Opening times : from mid April to mid Oct.
5 ha (76 pitches) terraced, flat, grassy
Tariff : (2013 Price) 20€ 🚶 🚶 🚗 ▣
Rental rates : (2013 Price) (from mid April to mid Oct.) – 12 🏠
4 🏠. Per week from 240 to 650€
🛒 borne

Surroundings : 🐟 ⬅ 🌳
Leisure activities : 🏄 🚴 🏊 🐟
Facilities : 🚿 🔌 🚮 🏊 launderette
Nearby : 🛁 🍴

G P S Longitude : 2.03717
Latitude : 44.22635

GARIN

31110 – Michelin map **343** B8 – pop. 133 – alt. 1 100
▶ Paris 827 – Toulouse 153 – Tarbes 85 – Lourdes 84

🏔 Les Frênes (rental of chalets only)

✆ 05 61 79 88 44, www.chalets-luchon-peyragudes.com – traditional
camp. spaces also available
Address : east of the town along the D 618, follow the signs for
Bagnères-de-Luchon and take the turning to the left, D 76e towards
Billière
Opening times : Permanent
0,8 ha terraced
Rental rates : 🅿 – 9 🏠. Per night from 70 to 147€ – Per week
from 202 to 729€
Rentals available on a nightly basis outside school holidays.

Surroundings : 🐟 ⬅ 🌳
Leisure activities : 🖼
Facilities : 🔌 🚮 🏢 🍴 launderette
Nearby : 🛁 ✕

G P S Longitude : 0.51976
Latitude : 42.80933

GAVARNIE

65120 – Michelin map **342** L8 – pop. 140 – alt. 1 350 – Winter sports : 1 350/2 400m
▶ Paris 901 – Lourdes 52 – Luz-St-Sauveur 20 – Pau 96

⚠ Le Pain de Sucre

✆ 05 62 92 47 55, www.camping-gavarnie.com – alt. 1 273

Address : Couret quartier (3km north along the D 921, follow the signs for Luz-St-Sauveur; beside the Gave de Gavarnie river)

Opening times : from mid Dec.. to end Sept.

1,5 ha (54 pitches) open site, flat, grassy

Tariff : ☀ 4,60€ ⬡ 🅴 4,80€ – [⚡] (10A) 6,50€ – Reservation fee 5€
Rental rates : (from mid Dec.. to end Sept.) ⚞ – 4 🚍 – 5 🏠.
Per night from 32 to 40€ – Per week from 205 to 520€
A mountain setting beside a stream with good-quality sanitary facilities.

Surroundings : ❄ ≤ 🟢🟢
Leisure activities : 🍷 ✕ 🚣 🎣
Facilities : 🔧 ⊶ 🕯 🍴 launderette

G P S Longitude : 0.00137 Latitude : 42.75983

GIRAC

46130 – Michelin map **337** G2 – pop. 379 – alt. 123
▶ Paris 522 – Beaulieu-sur-Dordogne 11 – Brive-la-Gaillarde 42 – Gramat 27

⚠ Les Chalets sur la Dordogne

✆ 05 65 10 93 33, www.camping-chalet-sur-dordogne.com

Address : at the Port (located 1km northwest along the D 703, follow the signs for Vayrac and take road to the left; beside the Dordogne river)

Opening times : from beginning May to end Sept.

2 ha (39 pitches)

Tariff : 20,20€ ☀☀ ⬡ 🅴 [⚡] (10A) – Extra per person 5,40€
Reservation fee 8€
Rental rates : (from beginning March to end Sept.) – 7 🚍
3 🏠 – 1 gîte. Per night 65€ – Per week from 150 to 599€
Reservation fee 12€

Surroundings : 🏕 🟢🟢 ⛰
Leisure activities : 🍷 ✕ 🚣 🛶 🏊 🚤
Facilities : 🔧 ⊶ (Jun–Aug.) 🍴 launderette 🧺
Nearby : ⛳

G P S Longitude : 1.80501 Latitude : 44.91809

GONDRIN

32330 – Michelin map **336** D6 – pop. 1 180 – alt. 174
▶ Paris 745 – Agen 58 – Auch 42 – Condom 17

⚠ Le Pardaillan 🧍🧍

✆ 05 62 29 16 69, www.camping-le-pardaillan.com

Address : 27 rue Pardaillan (situated east of the town)

Opening times : from mid April to end Sept.

2,5 ha (115 pitches)

Tariff : 24€ ☀☀ ⬡ 🅴 [⚡] (6A) – Extra per person 6,20€ – Reservation fee 15€
Rental rates : (from beginning April to end Sept.) – 23 🚍
27 🏠 – 5 canvas bungalows. Per week from 245 to 790€
Reservation fee 15€
🚐 borne 3,50€ – 2 🅴 11,50€ – 🛒 [⚡]11,50€

Surroundings : 🏞 🏕 🟢🟢
Leisure activities : 🍷 ✕ 🎱 🏇 🚣 🚲 🎣
Facilities : 🔧 ⊶ 🖥 🛁 🚿 🍴 launderette 🧺
Nearby : ✂ 🏊

G P S Longitude : 0.23873 Latitude : 43.88165

GOUAUX

65240 – Michelin map **342** O5 – pop. 73 – alt. 923
▶ Paris 824 – Toulouse 151 – Tarbes 65 – Foix 149

⚠ Le Ruisseau

✆ 05 62 39 95 49, www.camping-aure-pyrenees.com

Address : in the village

Opening times : from beginning April to mid Oct.

2 ha (115 pitches) terraced, flat, grassy

Tariff : (2013 Price) ☀ 4,40€ ⬡ 🅴 5€ – [⚡] (6A) 4,70€ – Reservation fee 5€

Rental rates : (from beginning April to mid Oct.) – 20 🚍
Per night from 30 to 83€ – Per week from 199 to 582€
Reservation fee 15€
🚐 borne – 10 🅴 5€
Half of the pitches are occupied by rental or owner-occupied mobile homes.

Surroundings : ≤
Leisure activities : ✕
Facilities : 🔧 ⊶ 🛒 🖥 🛁 🍴 launderette 🧺

G P S Longitude : 0.36085 Latitude : 42.86423

We have selected the best campsites in France with our usual care, listing those with the best facilities in the most pleasant surroundings.

GOURDON

46300 – Michelin map **337** E3 – pop. 4 622 – alt. 250
▶ Paris 543 – Bergerac 91 – Brive-la-Gaillarde 66 – Cahors 44

⚠ Aire Naturelle le Paradis

✆ 05 65 41 65 01, www.campingleparadis.com

Address : at La Peyrugue (situated 2km southwest along the D 673, follow the signs for Fumel and take road to the left, near the Intermarché car park)

1 ha (25 pitches)
Rentals : 6 🚍 – 1 🏠.

Surroundings : 🌳 🟢🟢
Leisure activities : 🏊
Facilities : 🔧 ⊶ 🍴 🖥

G P S Longitude : 1.37397 Latitude : 44.72323

GRAND-VABRE

12320 – Michelin map **338** G3 – pop. 406 – alt. 213
▶ Paris 615 – Aurillac 47 – Dec.azeville 18 – Espalion 50

⚠ Village Vacances Grand-Vabre Aventures et Nature

(rental of chalets only)

✆ 05 65 72 85 67, www.grand-vabre.com

Address : at Les Passes (located 1km southeast along the D 901, follow the signs for Conques; besides the Dourdou river)

Opening times : from beginning April to end Oct.

1,5 ha flat, grassy
Rental rates : 🔧 – 20 🏠. Per night from 60 to 80€ – Per week from 260 to 675€

Surroundings : 🟢🟢
Leisure activities : 🎱 🏇 🚣 🚲 🎣
Facilities : ⊶ 🖥 🍴 launderette

G P S Longitude : 2.36297 Latitude : 44.62473

HÈCHES

65250 – Michelin map **342** O6 – pop. 631 – alt. 690
▶ Paris 805 – Arreau 14 – Bagnères-de-Bigorre 35 – Bagnères-de-Luchon 47

⚠ La Bourie

✆ 05 62 98 73 19, www.camping-labourie.com

Address : at Rebouc (2km south along the D 929, follow the signs for Arreau and turn left onto the D 26, beside the Neste d'Aure river)

Opening times : Permanent

2 ha (122 pitches) flat, grassy

Tariff : 16€ ♦♦ ⚐ ▣ 🔌 (10A) – Extra per person 4,20€ – Reservation fee 15€

Rental rates : Permanent ⚡ – 15 ⛺. Per week from 270 to 470€ Reservation fee 15€

⛽ borne 5€ – 3 ▣ 12,50€ – 🚐 12,50€

On the site of an former factory, with many owner-occupiers.

Surroundings : ≤ 🏠 🞡🞡
Leisure activities : ✗ 🏠 ⚓ 🏊
Facilities : ⚐ ⚬🔑 🌲⛲ 🛉 🚻 🔲

GPS	Longitude : 0.37887
	Latitude : 43.03815

L'HOSPITALET-PRÈS-L'ANDORRE

09390 – Michelin map **343** I9 – pop. 91 – alt. 1 446
▶ Paris 822 – Andorra-la-Vella 40 – Ax-les-Thermes 19 – Bourg-Madame 26

⚠ Municipal La Porte des Cimes

✆ 05 61 05 21 10, www.camping.hospitalet.com – alt. 1 500

Address : 600m north along the N 20, follow the signs for Ax-les-Thermes and take turning to the right.

Opening times : from beginning June to end Oct.

1,5 ha (62 pitches)

Tariff : (2013 Price) ♦ 3,50€ ⚐ 1€ ▣ 4€ – 🔌 (5A) 4€

⛽ borne

Choose the pitches further away from the road in preference.

Surroundings : ≤ 🞡
Leisure activities : 🞥🞥
Facilities : ⚐ ⚬🔑 (July–Aug.) 🌲⛲ 🛉 ⚓ 🞡🞡 🚻 launderette
Nearby : ⚓ 🏊

GPS	Longitude : 1.80343
	Latitude : 42.59135

LACAM-D'OURCET

46190 – Michelin map **337** I2 – pop. 129 – alt. 520
▶ Paris 544 – Aurillac 51 – Cahors 92 – Figeac 38

⚠ Les Teuillères

✆ 05 65 11 90 55, www.lesteuilleres.com

Address : 4.8km southeast along the D 25, follow the signs for Sousceyrac and then Sénaillac-Latronquière, towards the Lac du Tolerme

Opening times : from beginning June to mid Sept.

3 ha (30 pitches)

Tariff : ♦ 5,50€ ⚐ ▣ 5,50€ – 🔌 (6A) 2,95€

Rentals : (from beginning May to mid Sept.) – 2 gîtes.

Surroundings : 🞥 ≤ 🏠 🞡
Leisure activities : ⚓
Facilities : ⚐ ⚬🔑 🌲⛲🞡 🛉 🔲

GPS	Longitude : 2.04086
	Latitude : 44.8342

LACAPELLE-MARIVAL

46120 – Michelin map **337** H3 – pop. 1 326 – alt. 375
▶ Paris 555 – Aurillac 66 – Cahors 64 – Figeac 21

⚠ Municipal Bois de Sophie

✆ 05 65 40 82 59, http://lacapelle-marival.fr

Address : route d'Aynac (located 1km northwest along the D 940, follow the signs for St-Céré)

Opening times : from beginning May to end Sept.

1 ha (66 pitches)

Tariff : (2013 Price) ♦ 2,85€ ⚐ ▣ 3,60€ – 🔌 (10A) 10€

Rental rates : (from beginning May to end Sept.) – 3 ⛺ – 6 tent lodges. Per night from 12€ – Per week from 210 to 434€

⛽ borne 10,75€

Surroundings : 🞡🞡
Leisure activities : 🏠
Facilities : ⚐ ⚬🔑 🌲⛲ 🛉 🚻
Nearby : 🞥 🏊

GPS	Longitude : 1.91796
	Latitude : 44.73314

A chambre d'hôte is a guesthouse or B & B-style accommodation.

LACAVE

46200 – Michelin map **337** F2 – pop. 284 – alt. 130
▶ Paris 528 – Brive-la-Gaillarde 51 – Cahors 58 – Gourdon 26

⚠ La Rivière

✆ 05 65 37 02 04, www.campinglariviere.com

Address : at Le Bougayrou (2.5km northeast along the D 23, follow the signs for Martel and take road to the left; beside the Dordogne river)

Opening times : from end April to mid Sept.

2,5 ha (110 pitches)

Tariff : (2013 Price) 23,60€ ♦♦ ⚐ ▣ 🔌 (10A) Extra per person 5,80€ Reservation fee 9,50€

Rental rates : (from end April to mid Sept.) – 17 ⛺. Per night from 85 to 110€ – Per week from 630 to 750€ – Reservation fee 9,50€

Surroundings : 🞥 🞡🞡 ⛰
Leisure activities : 🍷 ✗ ⚓ 🏇 🏊 🞥 🏊
Facilities : ⚐ ⚬🔑 ⛲🛉 launderette 🞥

GPS	Longitude : 1.559
	Latitude : 44.8613

LAFRANÇAISE

82130 – Michelin map **337** D7 – pop. 2 828 – alt. 183
▶ Paris 621 – Castelsarrasin 17 – Caussade 41 – Lauzerte 23

⚠ Le Lac

✆ 05 63 65 89 69, www.campings82.fr

Address : rue Jean Moulin (take the southeastern exit along the D 40, follow the signs for Montastruc and take the turning to the left, 250m from a small lake (direct access)

0,9 ha (34 pitches) relatively flat

Rentals : 19 ⛺ – 11 gîtes.

Surroundings : 🞥 🞠 🞡🞡
Leisure activities : 🚲
Facilities : ⚬🔑 🛉 🔲
Nearby : ⚓ ✗ 🏊 🞥 🏊 pedalos

GPS	Longitude : 1.24675
	Latitude : 44.1246

LAGUIOLE

12210 – Michelin map **338** J2 – pop. 1 267 – alt. 1 004 – Winter sports : 1 100/1 400m
▶ Paris 571 – Aurillac 79 – Espalion 22 – Mende 83

⚠ Municipal les Monts d'Aubrac

✆ 05 65 44 39 72, tourisme@aubrac-laguiole.com – alt. 1 050

Address : take the southern exit along the D 921, follow the signs for Rodez then continue 600m along the turning to the left; by the stadium

Opening times : from mid May to mid Sept.

1,2 ha (57 pitches) relatively flat

Tariff : (2013 Price) 10€ ♦♦ ⛺ 🅿 🔌 (10A) – Extra per person 3€
🚰 borne 2€ – 💧 🚰10€

Surroundings : 🌳 ≤ ⚲
Facilities : 🚿 🖦 📋 🏠 🚽
Nearby : 🛹 skateboarding

GPS Longitude : 2.85501
Latitude : 44.6815

LAMONTÉLARIÉ

81260 – Michelin map **338** H9 – pop. 62 – alt. 847
▶ Paris 736 – Toulouse 116 – Albi 83 – Castres 44

⛰ Rouquié

✆ 05 63 70 98 06, www.campingrouquie.fr

Address : at the Lac de la Raviège

Opening times : from beginning May to end Oct.

3 ha (97 pitches)

Tariff : 24,54€ ♦♦ ⛺ 🅿 🔌 (6A) – Extra per person 4,30€
Reservation fee 15€

Rental rates : (from beginning April to end Oct.) – 10 🚐
6 🏠. Per night from 55 to 70€ – Per week from 380 to 770€
Reservation fee 15€

Surroundings : 🌳 ≤ ⚲⚲ ⛰
Leisure activities : 🍽 ✗ 🏊 🎣 pedalos 🚣
Facilities : 🚿 🖦 🚽 🍴 launderette 🚮
Nearby : ⚓

GPS Longitude : 2.60663
Latitude : 43.60038

LAU-BALAGNAS

65400 – Michelin map **342** L5 – pop. 499 – alt. 430
▶ Paris 864 – Toulouse 188 – Tarbes 36 – Pau 70

⛰ Kawan Village Le Lavedan

✆ 05 62 97 18 84, www.lavedan.com

Address : 44 route des Vallées (located 1km southeast)

Opening times : Permanent

2 ha (108 pitches) flat, grassy

Tariff : 39,70€ ♦♦ ⛺ 🅿 🔌 (10A) – Extra per person 10€
Reservation fee 25€

Rental rates : Permanent – 33 🚐 – 2 🏠 – 2 canvas bungalows.
Per night from 42 to 149€ – Per week from 257 to 907€
Reservation fee 25€

Rental and owner-occupied mobile homes and pitches for tents and caravans, best chosen away from the road.

Surroundings : ⚲⚲
Leisure activities : 🍽 ✗ 🏊 🎣 🏊 📺 (open air in season), entertainment room
Facilities : 🚿 🖦 🔧 🍴 🚽 🍴 launderette 🚮
🚰

GPS Longitude : -0.08896
Latitude : 42.98818

LECTOURE

32700 – Michelin map **336** F6 – pop. 3 766 – alt. 155
▶ Paris 708 – Agen 39 – Auch 35 – Condom 26

⛰⛰⛰ Yelloh! Village Le Lac des 3 Vallées 👥

✆ 05 62 68 82 33, www.lacdes3vallees.fr

Address : 2.4km southeast along the N 21, follow the signs for Auch, then continue 2.3km along the turning to the left beside the lake

Opening times : from beginning June to mid Sept.

40 ha (600 pitches)

Tariff : 47€ ♦♦ ⛺ 🅿 🔌 (10A) – Extra per person 9€

Rental rates : (from beginning June to mid Sept.) – 300 🚐
23 canvas bungalows – 20 tent lodges. Per night from 35 to 149€
Per week from 245 to 1043€
🚰 borne 18€

Surroundings : 🌳 ≤ 🚣 ⚲⚲
Leisure activities : 🍽 ✗ 🏊 🎣 🎯 🏃 ⛷ ⛵
jacuzzi 🏊 🏓 🛴 🏊 🏖 (beach) 🏄 🎭 disco,
pedalos 🚣 multi-sports ground, skate park
Facilities : 🚿 🖦 🚽 🍴 🚱 🍴 launderette 🛒
🚰 refrigerators

GPS Longitude : 0.64533
Latitude : 43.91252

LOUDENVIELLE

65510 – Michelin map **342** O8 – pop. 308 – alt. 987
▶ Paris 833 – Arreau 15 – Bagnères-de-Luchon 27 – La Mongie 54

⛰ Flower Pène Blanche

Flower PÈNE BLANCHE

✆ 05 62 99 68 85, www.peneblanche.com

Address : take the northwestern exit along the D 25, follow the signs for Génos; near the Neste de Louron (stream) and not far from a small lake

Opening times : from mid Dec.. to beginning Nov.

4 ha (120 pitches) terraced, relatively flat, flat, grassy

Tariff : 25,90€ ♦♦ ⛺ 🅿 🔌 (10A) – Extra per person 5,50€
Reservation fee 30€

Rental rates : (from mid Dec.. to beginning Nov.) – 19 🚐
2 canvas bungalows. Per night from 41 to 100€ – Per week from 196 to 700€ – Reservation fee 49€

A good choice of entertainment and water parks nearby.

Surroundings : 🌳 ≤ ⚲
Facilities : 🖦 (July–Aug.) 🍴 🍴 launderette
Nearby : 🍽 ✗ 🏊 🏓 🛴 🎣 🏊 fitness centre,
paragliding

GPS Longitude : 0.40722
Latitude : 42.79611

LOUPIAC

46350 – Michelin map **337** E3 – pop. 274 – alt. 230
▶ Paris 527 – Brive-la-Gaillarde 51 – Cahors 51 – Gourdon 16

⛰ Sites et Paysages Les Hirondelles 👥

✆ 05 65 37 66 25, www.camping-leshirondelles.com

Address : at Al Pech (3km north following signs for Souillac and take road to the right; 200m from the N 20)

Opening times : from mid April to mid Sept.

2,5 ha (70 pitches)

Tariff : 17,20€ ♦♦ ⛺ 🅿 🔌 (6A) – Extra per person 4,40€

Rental rates : (from mid April to mid Sept.) & ✈ – 21 ⊡
4 ⌂ – 5 tent lodges. Per week from 172 to 598€ – Reservation
fee 15€

Surroundings : ♨♨
Leisure activities : ♈ ✗ ⌂ ⚐ ⚐ ⚐
Facilities : & ⚬ ▥ ♨♈ launderette ⚐ ⚐
Nearby : ⚐

G P S Longitude : 1.46455
Latitude : 44.82934

LOURDES

65100 – Michelin map **342** L6 – pop. 15 127 – alt. 420
▶ Paris 850 – Bayonne 147 – Pau 45 – St-Gaudens 86

Plein Soleil

📞 05 62 94 40 93, www.camping-pleinsoleil.com

Address : 11 avenue du Monge (located 1km to the north)

Opening times : from mid April to mid Oct.

0,5 ha (35 pitches) terraced, flat, grassy, fine gravel

Tariff : 23€ ⚥⚥ ⚐ ▣ ⚐ (13A) – Extra per person 5€

Rental rates : (from beginning April to mid Oct.) – 7 ⌂. Per night
from 53 to 56€ – Per week from 320 to 610€

⚐ borne 5€ – 15 ▣ 18€

Pitches laid out in terraces with good sanitary facilities.

Surroundings : ♨♨
Leisure activities : ⌂ ⚐ ▣ (open air
in season)
Facilities : ⚬ ▥ ⚐ ⚐ ⚐ ♨♈ launderette

G P S Longitude : -0.03646
Latitude : 43.11438

Sarsan

📞 05 62 94 43 09, www.lourdes-camping.com

Address : 4 avenue Jean Moulin (located 1.5km east via a diversion)

Opening times : from beginning April to mid Oct.

1,8 ha (67 pitches)

Tariff : 19€ ⚥⚥ ⚐ ▣ ⚐ (10A) – Extra per person 4,80€

Rental rates : (from beginning April to mid Oct.) – 8 ⊡.
Per night from 50 to 80€ – Per week from 250 to 550€

⚐ borne 3€

*A shady meadow around a swimming pool; choose the pitches
furthest away from the road.*

Surroundings : ♨♨
Leisure activities : ⌂ ⚐ ▣ (open air
in season)
Facilities : & ⚬ ⚐ ♨♈ ▣

G P S Longitude : -0.02744
Latitude : 43.10226

Le Moulin du Monge

📞 05 62 94 28 15, www.camping-lourdes.com

Address : 28 avenue Jean Moulin (1.3km to the north)

Opening times : from beginning April to beginning Oct.

1 ha (67 pitches) terrace, relatively flat, flat, grassy

Tariff : 22,40€ ⚥⚥ ⚐ ▣ ⚐ (6A) – Extra per person 5,90€

Rental rates : (from beginning April to beginning Oct.) – 12 ⊡ .
Per night from 57 to 103€ – Per week from 399 to 721€

⚐ borne 4€ – 9 ▣ 17,70€

*Lovely shady grass areas but bear in mind the proximity of the
road and the railway line.*

Surroundings : ♨♨
Leisure activities : ⌂ ⚐ ⚐ ⚐
Facilities : & ⚬ ▥ ♨♈ launderette ⚐

G P S Longitude : -0.03148
Latitude : 43.11575

Le Ruisseau Blanc

📞 05 62 42 94 83, www.camping-lourdes-ruisseau-blanc.com

Address : at Anclades, route de Bagnères-de-Bigorre (1.5km
east along the D 97, follow the signs for Jarret. Caravans are
recommended to take the D 937 towards Bagnère-de-Bigorre)

1,8 ha (102 pitches) flat, grassy

Rentals : ✈ – 3 ⊡.

⚐ borne – 14 ▣ – ⚐ ⚐ 12€

Pleasant shady meadows, but very old sanitary facilities.

Surroundings : ⚐ ⚐ ♨♨
Leisure activities : ⌂ ⚐
Facilities : & ⚬ launderette

G P S Longitude : -0.01816
Latitude : 43.09531

To visit a town or region, use the MICHELIN Green Guides.

LUZ-ST-SAUVEUR

65120 – Michelin map **342** L7 – pop. 1 014 – alt. 710 – ⚐ – Winter
sports : 1 800/2 450m
▶ Paris 882 – Argelès-Gazost 19 – Cauterets 24 – Lourdes 32

Club Airotel Pyrénées ⚐⚐

📞 05 62 92 89 18, www.airotel-pyrenees.com

Address : at Esquièze-Sère, 46 avenue du Barège (located 1km
northwest along the D 921, follow the signs for Lourdes)

Opening times : from beginning Dec.. to end Sept.

2,5 ha (146 pitches) terraced, relatively flat, flat, grassy

Tariff : 34,50€ ⚥⚥ ⚐ ▣ ⚐ (10A) – Extra per person 8€ – Reservation
fee 25€

Rental rates : (from beginning Dec.. to end Sept.) ✈ – 48 ⊡
12 ⌂. Per night from 100 to 240€ – Per week from 205 to 1130€
Reservation fee 25€

⚐ borne 9€

*A small, pretty, well-equipped chalet village, several swimming
pools, but choose pitches away from the road.*

Surroundings : ⚐ ⚐ ♨♨
Leisure activities : ⌂ ⚐ ♨ ⚐ hammam,
jacuzzi ⚐ ▣ ⚐ ⚐ climbing wall,
multi-sports ground, spa centre
Facilities : & ⚬ ▥ ♨♈ launderette ⚐ ⚐

G P S Longitude : -0.01152
Latitude : 42.88014

International

📞 05 62 92 82 02, www.international-camping.fr

Address : at Esquièze-Sère, 50 avenue du Barège (1.3km northwest
along the D 921, follow the signs for Lourdes)

Opening times : from mid May to end Sept.

4 ha (180 pitches) very uneven, terraced, flat, grassy

Tariff : 32€ ⚥⚥ ⚐ ▣ ⚐ (6A) – Extra per person 6,50€ – Reservation
fee 20€

Rental rates : (from mid May to end Sept.) ✈ (from mid May
to end Sept.) – 21 ⊡. Per week from 220 to 800€ – Reservation
fee 20€

⚐ borne

*Varied rental options and of a good standard; good quality
sanitary facilities for tents and caravans, but choose pitches
away from the road.*

Surroundings : ⚐ ⚐ ♨♨
Leisure activities : ♈ ⌂ jacuzzi ⚐ ⚐ ▣
(open air in season) ⚐ multi-sports ground
Facilities : & ⚬ ▥ ♨♈ launderette ⚐

G P S Longitude : -0.01388
Latitude : 42.88322

▲▲▲ Sites et Paysages Pyrénévasion

📞 05 62 92 91 54, www.campingpyrenevasion.com – alt. 834

Address : at Sazos, route de Luz-Ardiden (3.4km northwest along the D 921, follow the signs for Gavarnie and the D 12)

Opening times : from beginning Dec.. to mid Oct.

3,5 ha (99 pitches) terraced, flat, grassy, rocks

Tariff : 15,60€ ♟♟ ⇔ 🔲 ⚡ (10A) – Extra per person 6€ – Reservation fee 10€

Rental rates : (from mid Nov. to mid Oct.) – 15 🚐 – 8 🏠. Per night from 45 to 120€ – Per week from 295 to 950€ Reservation fee 12€

🚐 borne 6€

A pleasant indoor pool with a panoramic view over the Vallée de Luz for some pitches.

Surroundings : 🏔 ≤ ▱ 〰〰
Leisure activities : 🍽 ✕ 🎬 🆎 jacuzzi 🏊 🎳 ☒ multi-sports ground
Facilities : 🚻 ⊶ 🏢 ♨ 🔥 ☂ 👕 launderette 🚿
Longitude : -0.02417
Latitude : 42.8831

▲▲ Les Cascades

📞 05 62 92 85 85, www.camping-luz.com

Address : rue Ste-Barbe (south of the town; beside rapids, recommended route via Gavarnie road)

Opening times : from beginning Dec.. to end Sept.

1,5 ha (77 pitches) terraced, relatively flat, flat, grassy, rocks

Tariff : 28€ ♟♟ ⇔ 🔲 ⚡ (10A) – Extra per person 6,50€

Rental rates : (from beginning Dec.. to end Sept.) – 18 🚐. Per night from 60 to 75€ – Per week from 300 to 650€

A very good standard of sanitary facilites for tents and caravans.

Surroundings : 🏔 ≤ 〰〰
Leisure activities : 🍽 ✕ 🎬 🆎 jacuzzi 🏊 ☒
Facilities : 🚻 ⊶ 🏢 👕 launderette 🚿
Longitude : -0.00292
Latitude : 42.86973

▲ Le Bergons

📞 05 62 92 90 77, www.camping-bergons.com

Address : route de Barèges (500m east along the D 918)

Opening times : Permanent

1 ha (74 pitches) terraced, flat, grassy

Tariff : 15,20€ ♟♟ ⇔ 🔲 ⚡ (6A) – Extra per person 3,50€ Reservation fee 10€

Rental rates : (from beginning Dec.. to end Oct.) – 4 🚐 – 1 🏠 1 studio – 1 apartment. Per night from 35 to 85€ – Per week from 240 to 510€

Choose the pitches the furthest away from the road.

Surroundings : ❄ ≤ 〰〰
Leisure activities : 🎬 🏊
Facilities : 🚻 ⊶ (July–Aug.) 🏢 👕 launderette
Longitude : 0.00281
Latitude : 42.87334

▲ Toy

📞 05 62 92 86 85, www.camping-toy.com

Address : 17 place du 8-Mai (town centre; beside the Bastan river)

Opening times : from mid May to end Sept.

1,2 ha (83 pitches) terraced, flat, grassy, stony

Tariff : 18,10€ ♟♟ ⇔ 🔲 ⚡ (6A) – Extra per person 4,30€

🚐 borne 12,90€

Beside a mountain stream, but in the centre of Luz, with shops close by.

Surroundings : 🏔 ≤ 〰〰
Leisure activities : 🏊
Facilities : ⊶ 🏢 ☒ 🏢 👕 launderette
Nearby : 🍽 ✕ 🏊
Longitude : -0.00312
Latitude : 42.87328

MANE

31260 – Michelin map **343** D6 – pop. 998 – alt. 297
▶ Paris 753 – Aspet 19 – St-Gaudens 22 – St-Girons 22

▲ Village Vacances de la Justale

📞 05 61 90 68 18, www.village-vacances-mane.fr

Address : 2 allée de la Justale (500m southwest of the village, along the road near the town hall)

3 ha (43 pitches) flat, grassy

Rentals : 19 gîtes.

A pleasant, leafy setting beside the Arbas river, with some basic somewhat old rental options.

Surroundings : 🏔 ▱ 〰〰
Leisure activities : 🎬 🏊 👟 🛶
Facilities : 🚻 ⊶ 👕 launderette
Nearby : ✂ 🐎
Longitude : 0.94716
Latitude : 43.07621

*The classification (1 to 5 tents, **black** or **red**) that we award to selected sites in this guide is our own system. It should not be confused with the classification (1 to 5 stars) of official organisations.*

MARTRES-TOLOSANE

31220 – Michelin map **343** E5 – pop. 2 236 – alt. 268
▶ Paris 735 – Auch 80 – Auterive 48 – Bagnères-de-Luchon 81

▲▲▲ Sites et Paysages Le Moulin 👥

SLADDEN

📞 05 61 98 86 40, www. DomaineLeMoulin.com

Address : at Le Moulin (head 1.5km southeast along the rte du Stade, take av. de St-Vidian and then the road to the left after the bridge; beside a stream and a canal, near the Garonne river (direct access)

Opening times : from beginning April to beginning Oct.

6 ha/3 for camping (99 pitches)

Tariff : 29,90€ ♟♟ ⇔ 🔲 ⚡ (10A) – Extra per person 7€ – Reservation fee 9€

Rental rates : (from beginning Jan. to end Nov.) ♿ (1 chalet) 2 caravans – 4 🚐 – 17 🏠 – 2 canvas bungalows – 2 tent lodges. Per night from 29 to 119€ – Per week from 196 to 924€ Reservation fee 18€

🚐 borne 16,90€ – 💧 14€

In a spacious green setting near the Garonne river and an old mill with a range of good quality rental options.

Surroundings : 🏔 ▱ 〰〰
Leisure activities : 🍽 ✕ 🎬 ☒ 🆎 🏊 ✂ ☒ ⬚ entertainment room
Facilities : 🚻 ⊶ ♨ ☂ 👕 launderette 🚿
Longitude : 1.0181
Latitude : 43.1905

MAUROUX

46700 – Michelin map **337** C5 – pop. 528 – alt. 213
▶ Paris 622 – Toulouse 152 – Cahors 49 – Agen 50

▲▲▲ Village Vacances du Soleil (rental of chalets only)

✆ 05 65 30 82 59, www.villagedusoleil.fr

Address : at Le Reynou et Clos del Capre

7,5 ha

Rentals : ⅌ – 58 🏠 .

Surroundings :
Leisure activities :
Facilities : launderette

GPS	Longitude : 1.06093 Latitude : 44.45062

MAZAMET

81200 – Michelin map **338** G10 – pop. 9 975 – alt. 241
▶ Paris 739 – Albi 64 – Béziers 90 – Carcassonne 50

▲ Municipal la Lauze

✆ 05 63 61 24 69, www.camping mazamet.com

Address : chemin de la Lauze (take the eastern exit along the N 112, follow the signs for Béziers and take a right turn)

Opening times : from beginning May to end Sept.

1,7 ha (53 pitches)

Tariff : 18,38€ ⅌⅌ ⇔ 🔲 🔌 (16A) – Extra per person 3€

Rental rates : Permanent – 5 🛖. Per night from 55 to 77€
Per week from 300 to 500€

🚐 borne – 20 🔲 11€

Mazamet-Bédarieux Voie Verte (Green Trail, 80km).

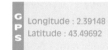

Surroundings :
Leisure activities :
Facilities :
Nearby : sports trail

GPS	Longitude : 2.39148 Latitude : 43.49692

MERCUS-GARRABET

09400 – Michelin map **343** H7 – pop. 1 153 – alt. 480
▶ Paris 772 – Ax-les-Thermes 32 – Foix 12 – Lavelanet 25

▲ Le Lac

✆ 05 61 05 90 61, www.campingdulacmercus.com

Address : 1 promenade du Camping (800m south along the D 618, follow the signs for Tarascon and take a right turn at the level crossing)

Opening times : from end April to end Sept.

1,2 ha (50 pitches)

Tariff : (2013 Price) 30€ ⅌⅌ ⇔ 🔲 🔌 (10A) – Extra per person 7€
Reservation fee 15€

Rental rates : (from mid April to mid Oct.) – 7 🛖 – 16 🏠 .
Per week from 290 to 705€ – Reservation fee 15€

🚐 borne 9€

Pitches and rental options with plenty of shade spread out along the Ariège river.

Surroundings :
Leisure activities : (small swimming pool)
Facilities :

GPS	Longitude : 1.62252 Latitude : 42.87154

MÉRENS-LES-VALS

09110 – Michelin map **343** J9 – pop. 185 – alt. 1 055
▶ Paris 812 – Ax-les-Thermes 10 – Axat 61 – Belcaire 36

▲ Municipal de Ville de Bau

✆ 05 61 02 85 40, http://camping.merenslesvals.fr – alt. 1 100

Address : at Ville de Bau (located 1.5km southwest along the N 20, follow the signs for Andorra and take the road to the right; beside the Ariège)

Opening times : Permanent

2 ha (70 pitches)

Tariff : ⅌ 3,20€ ⇔ 🔲 3,20€ – 🔌 (10A) 5,50€

Rental rates : Permanent 🏠 – 3 🏠. Per night from 70 to 90€
Per week from 360 to 455€

Beside the Ariège river. Choose the pitches further away from the road in preference.

Surroundings :
Leisure activities :
Facilities : launderette

GPS	Longitude : 1.83104 Latitude : 42.64622

MIERS

46500 – Michelin map **337** G2 – pop. 435 – alt. 302
▶ Paris 526 – Brive-la-Gaillarde 49 – Cahors 69 – Rocamadour 12

▲ Le Pigeonnier

✆ 05 65 33 71 95, www.campinglepigeonnier.com

Address : 700m east along the D 91, follow the signs for Padirac and take the road to the right behind the cemetery

Opening times : from beginning April to beginning Oct.

1 ha (45 pitches) terraced, relatively flat, flat, grassy

Tariff : ⅌ 5,60€ ⇔ 🔲 5,80€ – 🔌 (16A) 3,70€ – Reservation fee 13€

Rental rates : (from beginning April to beginning Oct.)
12 🛖. Per night from 35 to 70€ – Per week from 230 to 689€
Reservation fee 13€

🚐 borne 6€

Surroundings :
Leisure activities :
Facilities :

GPS	Longitude : 1.71028 Latitude : 44.85289

MILLAU

12100 – Michelin map **338** K6 – pop. 22 013 – alt. 372
▶ Paris 636 – Albi 106 – Alès 138 – Béziers 122

▲▲▲ Club Airotel Les Rivages 👥

✆ 05 65 61 01 07, www.campinglesrivages.com

Address : 860 avenue de l'Aigoual (1.7km east along the D 991, follow the signs for Nant; beside the Dourbie river)

Opening times : from mid April to end Sept.

7 ha (314 pitches) flat, grassy

Tariff : 37€ ⅌⅌ ⇔ 🔲 🔌 (10A) – Extra per person 8€ – Reservation fee 17€

Rental rates : (from mid April to end Sept.) – 32 🛖 – 1 studio
12 canvas bungalows. Per night from 37 to 135€ – Per week from 222 to 945€ – Reservation fee 17€

🚐 borne – 8€

A pretty view over the wooded massif (mountains).

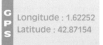

Surroundings :
Leisure activities : jacuzzi
Facilities : launderette
Nearby : hang-gliding

GPS	Longitude : 3.09616 Latitude : 44.10161

⛰ Viaduc ♨

✆ 05 65 60 15 75, www.camping-du-viaduc.com

Address : 121 avenue de Millau-Plage (800m northeast along the D 991, follow the signs for Nant and turn left onto the D 187 following signs for Paulhe)

Opening times : from end April to mid Sept.

5 ha (237 pitches) flat, grassy

Tariff : 36€ ♦♦ ⬅ 📧 ⚡ (6A) – Extra per person 8€ – Reservation fee 17€

Rental rates : (from end April to mid Sept.) – 39 🚐 6 canvas bungalows. Per night from 35 to 122€ – Per week from 220 to 854€

Reservation fee 17€

Beside the Tarn river

> Surroundings : ▭ 🌳 ⛰
> Leisure activities : 🍴✕ 🏠 ⛹ 🚣 🏊 ⛷ 🐴
> Facilities : & ⚲ ▥ 🚿 ⛺ ⚿ 💧 launderette 🚗
> Nearby : 🚲 ✕ 🐎 paragliding
>
> **GPS** Longitude : 3.08853 Latitude : 44.10578

⛰ Les Érables

✆ 05 65 59 15 13, www.campingleserables.fr

Address : avenue de Millau-Plage (900m northeast along the D 991, following signs for Nant and turn left onto D 187, follow the signs for Paulhe; beside the Tarn river)

Opening times : from beginning April to end Sept.

1,4 ha (78 pitches) flat, grassy

Tariff : 18€ ♦♦ ⬅ 📧 ⚡ (4A) – Extra per person 4€ – Reservation fee 16€

Rental rates : (from beginning April to end Sept.) – 6 🚐. Per night from 42 to 49€ – Per week from 294 to 567€ Reservation fee 16€

> Surroundings : ← ▭ 🌳
> Leisure activities : 🏠
> Facilities : & ⚲ 💧 launderette
> Nearby : ✕ 🏊 🚣
>
> **GPS** Longitude : 3.08704 Latitude : 44.11022

MIRANDE

32300 – Michelin map **336** E8 – pop. 3 705 – alt. 173
▶ Paris 737 – Auch 25 – Mont-de-Marsan 98 – Tarbes 49

⛰ L'Île du Pont

✆ 05 62 66 64 11, www.groupevla.fr

Address : at Le Batardeau (east of the town, on an island in the Grande Baïse river)

Opening times : from beginning May to end Sept.

10 ha/5 for camping (164 pitches)

Tariff : 19,80€ ♦♦ ⬅ 📧 ⚡ (16A) – Extra per person 6,10€ Reservation fee 12€

Rental rates : (from beginning April to end Sept.) & (3 mobile homes) – 35 🚐 – 12 🏠. Per night from 40 to 144€ – Per week from 239 to 1011€ – Reservation fee 20€

🚐 borne 3€

A pleasant location on an island.

> Surroundings : 🐟 🌳
> Leisure activities : 🍴✕ 🏠 ⛹ 🚣 🐎
> Facilities : & ⚲ 💧 launderette 🚗
> Nearby : 🚣 ⛷ fitness trail
>
> **GPS** Longitude : 0.40932 Latitude : 43.51376

MIRANDOL-BOURGNOUNAC

81190 – Michelin map **338** E6 – pop. 1 077 – alt. 393
▶ Paris 653 – Albi 29 – Rodez 51 – St-Affrique 79

⛰ Les Clots

✆ 05 63 76 92 78, www.domainelesclots.com

Address : at Les Clots (5.5km north along the D 905, follow the signs for Rieupeyroux and take road on the left; 500m from the Viaur river (direct access)

Opening times : from beginning June to mid Sept.

7 ha/4 for camping (62 pitches) very uneven, terraced, flat, grassy, stony

Tariff : 33€ ♦♦ ⬅ 📧 ⚡ (6A) – Extra per person 6,20€

Rental rates : (from beginning June to mid Sept.) – 6 🏠 – 3 canvas bungalows – 1 gîte. Per night 58€ – Per week from 304 to 895€

> Surroundings : 🐟 🌳
> Leisure activities : 🏠 🚣 🐎 🚣
> Facilities : ⚲ 🚿 💧 🛒
> Nearby : 🚣
>
> **GPS** Longitude : 2.17881 Latitude : 44.17713

A 'quartier' is a district or area of a town or village.

MIREPOIX

32390 – Michelin map **336** G7 – pop. 204 – alt. 150
▶ Paris 696 – Auch 17 – Fleurance 13 – Gimont 25

⛰ Village Vacances Les Chalets des Mousquetaires

(rental of chalets only)

✆ 05 62 64 33 66, www.chalets-mousquetaires.com

Address : at En Luquet (situated 2km southeast of the town)

Opening times : Permanent

1 ha

Rental rates : & – 1 caravan – 11 🏠. Per night from 49 to 75€ Per week from 299 to 785€ – Reservation fee 20€

Near a farm, the site looks out over the undulating coutryside of the Gers.

> Surroundings : 🐟 ← ▭ 🌳
> Leisure activities : 🏠 ⛹ 🚣 🐎 🚣
> Facilities : & ⚲ ▥ 💧 🛒
> Nearby : 🚣
>
> **GPS** Longitude : 0.69271 Latitude : 43.73682

MOISSAC

82200 – Michelin map **337** C7 – pop. 12 244 – alt. 76
▶ Paris 632 – Agen 57 – Auch 120 – Cahors 63

⛰ L'Île de Bidounet ♨

✆ 05 63 32 52 52, www.camping-moissac.com

Address : at St-Benoît (located 1km south along the N 113, follow the signs for Castelsarrasin and turn left onto D 72)

Opening times : from beginning April to end Sept.

4,5 ha/2,5 for camping (109 pitches) flat, grassy

Tariff : (2013 Price) 21,20€ ♦♦ ⬅ 📧 ⚡ (6A) – Extra per person 5,20€ Reservation fee 7€

Rental rates : (from mid June to mid Sept.) 🐟 – 12 canvas bungalows. Per night from 35 to 50€ – Per week from 200 to 350€ Reservation fee 7€

🚐 borne

n an attractive location on an island in the Tarn river.

Surroundings : 🏞 🚐 ♧♧
Leisure activities : 🍸 🏠 🏃 🚣 🎣 🏊
Facilities : ♿ �o— 🏕 ⛟ launderette
Nearby : watersports centre

GPS Longitude : 1.09005
Latitude : 44.09671

MONCLAR-DE-QUERCY

82230 – Michelin map **337** F8 – pop. 1 692 – alt. 178
▶ Paris 644 – Toulouse 73 – Montauban 22 – Albi 58

⛰ Village Vacances Les Hameaux des Lacs
(rental of chalets only)

𝒫 05 55 84 34 48, www.chalets-en-france.com

Address : at the base de loisirs (leisure centre)

Opening times : Permanent

5 ha very uneven

Rental rates : 113 🏠. Per night from 65€ – Per week from 260 to 859€ – Reservation fee 13€

In a setting surrounded by lakes and woods.

Surroundings : 🏞 ♤ ♧♧
Leisure activities : 🍸 🏠 🏊 🚣 ⛳ ⛖ 🖼 (open air in season), multi-sports ground
Facilities : o— ⛟ 🖼
Nearby : 🚤 ⛷ ◐

GPS Longitude : 1.59544
Latitude : 43.96957

MONTCABRIER

46700 – Michelin map **337** C4 – pop. 367 – alt. 191
▶ Paris 584 – Cahors 39 – Fumel 12 – Tournon-d'Agenais 24

⛰ Moulin de Laborde

𝒫 05 65 24 62 06, www.moulindelaborde.com 🏊

Address : situated 2km northeast along the D 673, follow the signs for Gourdon; beside the Thèze river

Opening times : from beginning May to beginning Sept.

4 ha (90 pitches) flat, grassy, small lake

Tariff : ☀ 7,20€ 🚘 🖳 10,50€ – ⚡ (10A) 4,30€

Set around the buildings of an old mill; attractive, shaded pitches.

Surroundings : ♧♧
Leisure activities : 🍸 ✕ 🏠 🚣 🚲 🎣
Facilities : ♿ o— 🚮🖂 ⛟ launderette 🔧

GPS Longitude : 1.08247
Latitude : 44.54819

MONTESQUIOU

32320 – Michelin map **336** D8 – pop. 603 – alt. 214
▶ Paris 741 – Auch 32 – Mirande 12 – Mont-de-Marsan 87

⛰ Le Haget

𝒫 05 62 70 95 80, www.lehaget.com

Address : route de Miélan (600m west along the D 943, follow the signs for Marciac then take left turn, 1.5km along the D 34 following signs for Miélan)

Opening times : from beginning May to end Sept.

10 ha (70 pitches)

Tariff : 26,75€ ☀☀ 🚘 🖳 ⚡ (3A) – Extra per person 6,50€ – Reservation fee 14€

Rental rates : (from beginning April to end Sept.) – 5 🚐 – 18 🏠 10 ⊨. Per night from 30 to 125€ – Per week from 195 to 875€ Reservation fee 14€

In the grounds of the château.

Surroundings : 🏞 ♧♧
Leisure activities : 🍸 ✕ 🏠 🚣
Facilities : ♿ o— ⛟ 🖼

GPS Longitude : 0.32002
Latitude : 43.56579

MONTLAUR

12400 – Michelin map **338** I7 – pop. 664 – alt. 320
▶ Paris 686 – Toulouse 145 – Rodez 88 – Montpellier 138

⛰ Le Hameau des Genêts (rental of gîtes only)

𝒫 05 65 99 86 06, www.hameaudesgenets.com

Address : in the village

2 ha flat

Rentals : ♿ (1 gîte) – 31 🏠.

Some farm animals.

Surroundings : ♤ ♀
Leisure activities : 🏠 🚴 🎣 🏊
Facilities : o— ⛟ launderette
Nearby : 🚤 🚣 ✕

GPS Longitude : 2.83404
Latitude : 43.87653

Key to rentals symbols:

12 🚐	*Number of mobile homes*	
20 🏠	*Number of chalets*	
6 ⊨	*Number of rooms to rent*	
Per night 30–50€	*Minimum/maximum rate per night*	
Per week 300–1,000€	*Minimum/maximum rate per week*	

MONTPEZAT-DE-QUERCY

82270 – Michelin map **337** E6 – pop. 1 461 – alt. 275
▶ Paris 598 – Cahors 28 – Caussade 12 – Castelnau-Montratier 13

⛰ Révéa Le Faillal

𝒫 05 63 02 07 08, http://www.revea-camping.fr/fr/accueil-camping-le-faillal.html

Address : at the Parc de Loisirs Le Faillal (take the northern exit along the D 20, follow the signs for Cahors and take the turning to the left)

Opening times : from mid April to end Sept.

0,9 ha (69 pitches)

Tariff : 16,60€ ☀☀ 🚘 🖳 ⚡ (6A) – Extra per person 4€ – Reservation fee 10€

Rental rates : (from beginning Jan. to beginning Nov.) Ⓟ 24 🏠. Per night from 85 to 115€ – Per week from 200 to 665€ Reservation fee 25€

🚐 9 🖳 16,60€

Attractive pitches for tents and caravans; some gîtes that are a little old.

Surroundings : 🏞 🚐 ♧♧
Leisure activities : 🏠 🚣 🚴 ⛳
Facilities : o— 🆑📶 ⛺ 🚮 ⛟ 🖼
Nearby : ✕ 🚣

GPS Longitude : 1.47725
Latitude : 44.24318

NAGES

81320 – Michelin map **338** I8 – pop. 340 – alt. 800
▶ Paris 717 – Brassac 36 – Lacaune 14 – Lamalou-les-Bains 45

⛰ Village Center Rieu-Montagné 👥

Interaview Production

🕿 05 63 37 24 71, www.village-center.fr

Address : at the base de loisirs du Lac de Laouzas (leisure centre) (4.5km south along the D 62 and take turning to the left; 50m from the lake)

Opening times : from end April to end Sept.

8,5 ha (179 pitches)

Tariff : 26€ 👫 🚗 📺 🔌 (10A) Extra per person 5€

Rental rates : (from end April to end Sept.) – 30 🛏 – 13 🏠. Per night from 32 to 119€ – Per week from 224 to 833€ Reservation fee 30€

Attractive elevated location.

Surroundings : 🏞 ← Lac du Laouzas and wooded mountains 💤 🦆🦆
Leisure activities : 🍽 ✗ 🎣 ☀daytime 🏃 🏊 🏄
Facilities : 🔌 cc 🛁 🚿 ⛽ 🍴 launderette 🧺 🛒
Nearby : 🚲 ✗ 🏓 ⛵ (beach) 🛶 🐴 pedalos

G P S Longitude : 2.77806 Latitude : 43.64861

NAILLOUX

31560 – Michelin map **343** H4 – pop. 2 717 – alt. 285
▶ Paris 711 – Auterive 15 – Castelnaudary 42 – Foix 50

⛰ Le Lac de la Thésauque

🕿 05 61 81 34 67, www.camping-thesauque.com

Address : 3.4km east along the D 622, follow the signs for Villefranche-de-Lauragais, turn left onto D 25 and take road; 100m from the lake

Opening times : Permanent

6 ha (57 pitches) terraced, flat, grassy, stony

Tariff : 21,20€ 👫 🚗 📺 🔌 (6A) – Extra per person 5,70€ Reservation fee 13€

Rental rates : Permanent ♿ (1 mobile home) – 5 🛏 – 14 🏠. Per night from 46 to 105€ – Per week from 229 to 595€ Reservation fee 13€

🚐 borne – 15 📺 6€
Near a lake with water activities.

Surroundings : 🏞 🦆🦆
Leisure activities : 🍽 ✗ 🎣 🏄 ✂ 🏓 🍴 🏊 pedalos 🌊
Facilities : ♿ 🔌 🍴 📺 🛒

G P S Longitude : 1.64834 Latitude : 43.3554

Michelin classification:

⛰⛰⛰⛰ *Extremely comfortable, equipped to a very high standard*
⛰⛰⛰ *Very comfortable, equipped to a high standard*
⛰⛰ *Comfortable and well equipped*
⛰ *Reasonably comfortable*
△ *Satisfactory*

NANT

12230 – Michelin map **338** L6 – pop. 919 – alt. 490
▶ Paris 669 – Le Caylar 21 – Millau 33 – Montpellier 92

⛰ RCN Le Val de Cantobre 👥

🕿 05 65 58 43 00, www.rcn.fr

Address : Domaine de Vellas (4.5km north along the D 991, follow the signs for Millau and take the road to the right; beside the Dourbie river)

Opening times : from beginning April to end Sept.

6 ha (216 pitches) very uneven, rocky

Tariff : 50,50€ 👫 🚗 📺 🔌 (6A) – Extra per person 5,50€ Reservation fee 19,75€

Rental rates : (from beginning April to end Sept.) – 22 🛏 15 🏠. Per night from 35 to 185€ – Per week from 245 to 1 295€ Reservation fee 19,75€

🚐 borne
Based around an old 15th-century Caussenarde farmhouse.

Surroundings : 🏞 ← 💤 🦆🦆
Leisure activities : 🍽 ✗ 🎣 📺 🏃 🏄 🏓 🍴 🛷 🏊 multi-sports ground
Facilities : ♿ 🔌 🛁 🚿 ⛽ 🍴 launderette 🧺 🛒 refrigerated food storage facilities

G P S Longitude : 3.30177 Latitude : 44.04554

△ Sites et Paysages Les 2 Vallées

VALDEYRON

🕿 05 65 62 26 89, www.lesdeuxvallees.com

Address : route de l'Estrade Basse

Opening times : from mid April to beginning Oct.

2 ha (80 pitches) flat, grassy

Tariff : 21€ 👫 🚗 📺 🔌 (6A) Extra per person 4€

Rental rates : (from mid April to beginning Oct.) – 14 🛏. Per night from 30 to 62€ – Per week from 210 to 637€

🚐 borne 5€

Surroundings : 🏞 💤 🦆🦆
Leisure activities : ✗ 🎣 🏄 🚲 🏓 🍴 🏊
Facilities : ♿ 🔌 🛁 🚿 ⛽ 🍴 launderette
Nearby : 🐴

G P S Longitude : 3.35457 Latitude : 44.0241

Do not confuse:
△ *to* ⛰⛰⛰⛰ *: MICHELIN classification with*
★ *to* ★★★★★ *: official classification*

NAUCELLE

12800 – Michelin map **338** G5 – pop. 2 049 – alt. 490
▶ Paris 652 – Albi 46 – Millau 90 – Rodez 32

⛰ Flower Le Lac de Bonnefon

🕿 05 65 69 33 20, www.camping-du-lac-de-bonnefon.com

Address : take the southeastern exit along the D 997, follow the signs for Naucelle-Gare then continue 1.5km following signs for Crespin and turn left towards St-Just; 100m from the lake (direct access)

Opening times : from beginning April to mid Oct.

4,5 ha (112 pitches) terraced

Tariff : 27,90€ 👫 🚗 📺 🔌 (10A) – Extra per person 6€ – Reservation fee 10€

Rental rates : (from beginning April to mid Oct.) &. (1) – 8 🚐
18 🏠 – 15 canvas bungalows – 2 tent lodges. Per night
from 28 to 134€ – Per week from 196 to 938€ – Reservation fee
45€

🚰 borne 16,50€ – 4 🔲 12,50€

Surroundings : 🏞 🗔 ♨♨
Leisure activities : ♍ ✕ 🚣 ⚓ 🎣 ⛵ 🚴
Facilities : &. ⚓ 🛁 🚽 🔲
Nearby : ✕ 🐎

GPS Longitude : 2.34867
Latitude : 44.18902

NÈGREPELISSE

82800 – Michelin map **337** F7 – pop. 5 056 – alt. 87
▶ Paris 614 – Bruniquel 13 – Caussade 11 – Gaillac 46

⚑ Municipal le Colombier

📞 0563642034, www.ville-negrepelisse.fr

Address : to the southwest, near the D 115

Opening times : from mid June to mid Sept.

1 ha (53 pitches) terraced

Tariff : 12€ ✝✝ 🚐 🔲 🔌 (10A) – Extra per person 2€
🚰 borne – 🚿 🔌10,80€

Surroundings : ♨♨
Facilities : ⚓ 🛁 🚽 🔲
Nearby : 🚣 🎣 🔲

GPS Longitude : 1.51843
Latitude : 44.07286

OUST

09140 – Michelin map **343** F7 – pop. 545 – alt. 500
▶ Paris 792 – Aulus-les-Bains 17 – Castillon-en-Couserans 31
– Foix 61

⚑ Les Quatre Saisons

📞 0561965555, www.camping4saisons.com

Address : route d'Aulus-les-Bains (take southeastern exit along the
D 32, near the Garbet)

3 ha (108 pitches) flat, grassy

Rentals : 21 🚐 – 3 🏠 – 6 ⛺ – 3 gîtes.

*Behind the hotel restaurant, a very pleasant campsite, with
lots of shade, well-kept.*

Surroundings : 🗔 ♨♨
Leisure activities : ♍ ✕ 🚣 ⚓ 🎣
Facilities : &. ⚓ ▓ 🚽 launderette 🛁
Nearby : ✕ 🐎

GPS Longitude : 1.22103
Latitude : 42.87215

OUZOUS

65400 – Michelin map **342** L4 – pop. 202 – alt. 550
▶ Paris 862 – Toulouse 188 – Tarbes 35 – Pau 55

⚑ La Ferme du Plantier

📞 0562975801, b.capdevielle@laposte.net

Address : rue de l'Oulet (in the village, D 102)

Opening times : from beginning May to end Oct.

0,6 ha (15 pitches) terraced

Tariff : ✝ 3€ 🚐 2,50€ 🔲 2,50€ – 🔌 (6A) 3,50€

Surroundings : 🏞 ◁ mountains ♀
Leisure activities : 🚣
Facilities : &. ⚓ 🛁 🚽 🔲

GPS Longitude : -0.1042
Latitude : 43.02958

PADIRAC

46500 – Michelin map **337** G2 – pop. 194 – alt. 360
▶ Paris 531 – Brive-la-Gaillarde 50 – Cahors 68 – Figeac 41

⚑ FranceLoc Les Chênes de Padirac 👥

📞 0565336554, www.camping.franceloc.fr

Address : route du Gouffre (located 1.5km northeast along the D 90)

5 ha (194 pitches)

Rentals : &. 🚿 – 196 🚐 – 17 canvas bungalows.
🚰 borne

The site is in 2 sections, one of which is next to the leisure park.

Surroundings : 🏞 🗔 ♨♨
Leisure activities : ♍ ✕ 🏛 🔲 🏃 ⚓ 🎣 ⛵
cinema, entertainment room
Facilities : &. ⚓ 🛁 🚽 launderette 🔲 🛁
At 500m, leisure/activities park : pedalos

GPS Longitude : 1.74567
Latitude : 44.85125

PAMIERS

09100 – Michelin map **343** H6 – pop. 15 383 – alt. 280
▶ Paris 746 – Toulouse 70 – Carcassonne 77 – Castres 105

⚑ Kawan Village L' Apamée

📞 0561600689, http://camping-apamee-ariege-pyrenees.fr

Address : route de St-Girons (0.8km northwest along the D119)

Opening times :

2 ha (80 pitches) flat, grassy

Tariff : 29€ ✝✝ 🚐 🔲 🔌 (10A) – Extra per person 9€ – Reservation
fee 25€

Rental rates : (closed from mid Dec..to beginning Jan) – 20 🚐
10 🏠 – 8 canvas bungalows. Per night from 51 to 107€
Per week from 357 to 749€ – Reservation fee 25€
🚰 borne 3€

*A shaded grass area with a range of rental options, but choose
the pitches away from the road in preference.*

Surroundings : ♨♨
Leisure activities : ♍ ✕ 🏃 🚴 ⛵ 🎣
Facilities : &. ⚓ 🔲 🛁 🚽 launderette

GPS Longitude : 1.60205
Latitude : 43.1249

PAYRAC

46350 – Michelin map **337** E3 – pop. 670 – alt. 320
▶ Paris 530 – Bergerac 103 – Brive-la-Gaillarde 53 – Cahors 48

⚑ Flower Les Pins 👥

📞 0565379632, www.les-pins-camping.com

Address : D 820 (take the southern exit)

Opening times : from mid April to beginning Sept.

4 ha (137 pitches) terraced, relatively flat, flat, grassy

Tariff : 33,50€ ✝✝ 🚐 🔲 🔌 (10A) – Extra per person 6,90€
Reservation fee 20€

Rental rates : (from mid April to beginning Sept.) – 50 🚐 – 3 🏠
5 canvas bungalows – 2 tent lodges. Per night from 37 to 133€
Per week from 185 to 931€ – Reservation fee 20€
🚰 borne 6€ – 🚿 🔌16€

Surroundings : ♨♨
Leisure activities : ♍ ✕ 🏛 🏃 🏊 jacuzzi
🚣 ✕ ⛵ 🏄 multi-sports ground
Facilities : &. ⚓ ▓ 🛁 🚿 🚽 launderette
🛁

GPS Longitude : 1.47214
Latitude : 44.78952

PONS

12140 – Michelin map **338** H2
▶ Paris 588 – Aurillac 34 – Entraygues-sur-Truyère 11 – Montsalvy 12

⚠ Municipal de la Rivière

🖉 05 65 66 18 16, www.sainthippolyte.fr

Address : located 1km southeast of the town, along the D 526, follow the signs for Entraygues-sur-Truyère; beside the Goul river

Opening times : from mid June to mid Sept.

0,9 ha (46 pitches) flat, grassy

Tariff : 17,50€ ✦✦ 🚗 🗐 🖭 (10A) – Extra per person 4€ – Reservation fee 20€

Rental rates : (from mid April to end Sept.) – 11 🏠. Per night from 29 to 69€ – Per week from 203 to 483€ – Reservation fee 30€

Surroundings : 🌊 🗭 ♨♨
Leisure activities : 🏛 🚣 🎯 🎣 🛶
Facilities : 🕭 ⚲ 🎐 🚿 🚻 🖥

GPS Longitude : 2.56363
Latitude : 44.71119

PONT-DE-SALARS

12290 – Michelin map **338** I5 – pop. 1 606 – alt. 700
▶ Paris 651 – Albi 86 – Millau 47 – Rodez 25

🏔 Flower Les Terrasses du Lac 🛂

🖉 05 65 46 88 18, www.campinglesterrasses.com

Address : route du Vibal (4km north along the D 523)

Opening times : from beginning April to mid Sept.

6 ha (180 pitches) very uneven

Tariff : 29,90€ ✦✦ 🚗 🗐 🖭 (6A) – Extra per person 6€ – Reservation fee 20€

Rental rates : (from beginning April to mid Sept.) – 45 🚐. 9 canvas bungalows. Per night from 46 to 80€ – Per week from 196 to 889€ – Reservation fee 20€

🚐 borne 29,90€ – 3 🗐 29,90€

An attractive location overlooking the lake.

Surroundings : 🌊 ⇐ 🗭 ♨
Leisure activities : 🏋 🗙 🏛 🎯 🚣 🎣 🛶 water park
Facilities : 🕭 ⚲ (July–Aug.) 🎐 🚿 🚻 launderette 🔧
Nearby : 🎯 🎣 🚲 🐎

GPS Longitude : 2.73478
Latitude : 44.30473

POUZAC

65200 – Michelin map **342** M4 – pop. 1 101 – alt. 505
▶ Paris 823 – Toulouse 149 – Tarbes 19 – Pau 60

⚠ Bigourdan

🖉 05 62 95 13 57, www.camping-bigourdan.com

Address : 79 avenue de la Mongie (on the D 935, between the Renault garage and the Intermarché supermarket)

Opening times : from beginning April to mid Oct.

1 ha (48 pitches) flat, grassy

Tariff : ✦ 4,45€ 🚗 🗐 4,45€ – 🖭 (10A) 6€

Rental rates : (from beginning April to mid Oct.) – 8 🚐. Per night from 48 to 80€ – Per week from 273 to 555€

🚐 2 🗐

Choose the pitches away from the road.

Surroundings : ♨♨
Leisure activities : 🏛 🚣 🛶
Facilities : 🕭 ⚲ 🚿 🏛 🚻 launderette

GPS Longitude : 0.13977
Latitude : 43.08036

PUYBRUN

46130 – Michelin map **337** G2 – pop. 906 – alt. 146
▶ Paris 520 – Beaulieu-sur-Dordogne 12 – Brive-la-Gaillarde 39 – Cahors 86

🏔 La Sole

🖉 05 65 38 52 37, www.la-sole.com

Address : take the eastern exit, follow the signs for Bretenoux and take the road to the right after the service station

2,3 ha (72 pitches) flat, grassy

Rentals : 9 🚐 – 5 🏠 – 17 canvas bungalows.

Surroundings : 🌊 🗭 ♨♨
Leisure activities : 🗙 🏛 🚣 🛶 multi-sports ground
Facilities : 🕭 ⚲ 🎐 🚿 🚻 🖥

GPS Longitude : 1.71431
Latitude : 44.95364

PUY-L'ÉVÊQUE

46700 – Michelin map **337** C4 – pop. 2 159 – alt. 130
▶ Paris 601 – Cahors 31 – Gourdon 41 – Sarlat-la-Canéda 52

🏔 Sites et Paysages L'Évasion

🖉 05 65 30 80 09, www.lotevasion.com

Address : at Martignac (3km northwest along the D 28, follow the signs for Villefranche-du-Périgord and take the road to the right)

Opening times : from beginning April to end Sept.

4 ha/2 for camping (50 pitches)

Tariff : 26,30€ ✦✦ 🚗 🗐 🖭 (10A) – Extra per person 11,55€ Reservation fee 10€

Rental rates : (from mid March to mid Oct.) 🕭 – 8 🚐 30 🏠 – 3 tent lodges. Per night from 55 to 130€ – Per week from 480 to 935€ – Reservation fee 10€

A pretty water park and chalets set among trees, shrubs and bushes.

Surroundings : 🌊 ♨♨
Leisure activities : 🏋 🗙 🏛 🚣 🏌 🎣 🚣 🎯 🛶 multi-sports ground
Facilities : 🕭 ⚲ 🚻 🖥 🔧

GPS Longitude : 1.12704
Latitude : 44.52546

PUYSSÉGUR

31480 – Michelin map **343** E2 – pop. 119 – alt. 265
▶ Paris 669 – Agen 83 – Auch 51 – Castelsarrasin 48

🏔 Namasté

🖉 05 61 85 77 84, http://www.camping-namaste.com

Address : take the northern exit along the D 1, follow the signs for Cox and take the road to the right

Opening times : from beginning May to mid Oct.

10 ha/2 for camping (60 pitches) terraced, relatively flat, flat, grassy, pond, adjacent wood

Tariff : 28,50€ ✦✦ 🚗 🗐 🖭 (10A) – Extra per person 7€

Rental rates : (from mid April to mid Oct.) – 6 🚐 – 15 🏠. Per night from 90 to 120€ – Per week from 300 to 700€ Reservation fee 15€

The site also holds photographic exhibitions, sometimes outside, around the pitches.

Surroundings : 🌊 🗭 ♨♨
Leisure activities : 🏛 🎣 🚣 🛶 🎯 fitness trail
Facilities : 🕭 ⚲ 🚿 🏛 🎐 🚿 🚻 launderette 🔧

GPS Longitude : 1.06134
Latitude : 43.75082

REVEL

31250 – Michelin map **343** K4 – pop. 9 253 – alt. 210
▶ Paris 727 – Carcassonne 46 – Castelnaudary 21 – Castres 28

⚠ Municipal du Moulin du Roy

🕿 05 61 83 32 47, www.mairie-revel.fr

Address : chemin de la Pergue (take southeastern exit along the D 1, follow the signs for Dourgne and take a right turn)

Opening times : from beginning June to end Aug.

1,2 ha (50 pitches) flat, grassy

Tariff : ♦ 3,10€ ⟵ 2,20€ 🔲 2,60€ – (ℓ) (10A) 3,40€
🚐 10 🔲 11,30€

In a green setting, but choose pitches furthest away from the road.

Surroundings : 🚏 ♤♤
Facilities : ♿ ⟶ 🗑 ♨ ⚲ ⊤ ⊥ 🔲
Nearby : ✂ 🔲 ♨

GPS Longitude : 2.01519
Latitude : 43.45464

RIEUX-DE-PELLEPORT

09120 – Michelin map **343** H6 – pop. 1 209 – alt. 333
▶ Paris 752 – Foix 13 – Pamiers 8 – St-Girons 47

⚠ Les Mijeannes

🕿 05 61 60 82 23, www.campinglesmijeannes.com

Address : route de Ferries (1.4km to the northeast, access via the D 311; beside a canal and near the Ariège river)

Opening times : Permanent

10 ha/5 for camping (152 pitches)

Tariff : 25,90€ ♦♦ ⟵ 🔲 (ℓ) (10A) – Extra per person 5,60€

Rental rates : Permanent – 12 🛏 – 2 🏠. Per night from 42 to 105€ – Per week from 279 to 737€ – Reservation fee 15€

🚐 borne 4€ – 🚽 11€

Spacious, pleasant site with good shade, near the river.

Surroundings : ♨ ♤ 🚏 ♤♤
Leisure activities : ⊤ 🔲 ♨♨ ⚲ ♨ ♨
Facilities : ♿ ⟶ 🔲 ⊤ launderette

GPS Longitude : 1.62134
Latitude : 43.06293

RIGNAC

12390 – Michelin map **338** F4 – pop. 1 918 – alt. 500
▶ Paris 618 – Aurillac 86 – Figeac 40 – Rodez 27

⚠ La Peyrade

🕿 09 51 53 21 13, www.campinglapeyrade.fr

Address : south of the town, near a little lake

Opening times : from beginning June to end Sept.

0,7 ha (36 pitches) terraced

Tariff : 25€ ♦♦ ⟵ 🔲 (ℓ) (10A) – Extra per person 6€ – Reservation fee 20€

Rental rates : (from beginning June to end Sept.) – 5 🛏. Per night from 45 to 78€ – Per week from 225 to 546€ Reservation fee 20€

Surroundings : ♨ 🚏 ♤♤
Facilities : ♿ ⟶ 🔲 ♨ ⊤ ⊥ launderette
Nearby : 🔲 ♨ ✂ ♨

GPS Longitude : 2.28956
Latitude : 44.4058

RIVIÈRE-SUR-TARN

12640 – Michelin map **338** K5 – pop. 1 042 – alt. 380
▶ Paris 627 – Mende 70 – Millau 14 – Rodez 65

⚠⚠⚠ Flower Le Peyrelade ♣♣

🕿 05 65 62 62 54, www.campingpeyrelade.com

Address : route des Gorgers du Tarn (situated 2km east along the D 907, follow the signs for Florac; beside the Tarn river)

Opening times : from mid May to mid Sept.

4 ha (190 pitches) terraced

Tariff : 38€ ♦♦ ⟵ 🔲 (ℓ) (10A) – Extra per person 8€ – Reservation fee 18€

Rental rates : (from mid May to mid Sept.)  – 45 🛏 8 canvas bungalows. Per night from 40 to 141€ – Per week from 196 to 987€ – Reservation fee 18€

🚐 borne

A pleasant site and setting at the entrance to the Tarn river gorges.

Surroundings : ≤ ♀
Leisure activities : ⊤ ✗ 🔲 ♨ ♨♨ ♨♨
♨♨
Facilities : ♿ ⟶ ♨ ♨ ⊤ ⊥ 🔲 ♨ ♨
Nearby : ♨♨ ✂ forest trail

GPS Longitude : 3.15807
Latitude : 44.18929

⚠⚠ Kawan Village Les Peupliers

🕿 05 65 59 85 17, www.campinglespeupliers.fr

Address : 11 rue de la Combe (take the southwestern exit follow the signs for Millau and take road to the left; beside the Tarn river)

Opening times : from beginning April to end Sept.

1,5 ha (115 pitches) flat, grassy

Tariff : 32€ ♦♦ ⟵ 🔲 (ℓ) (10A) – Extra per person 7,50€ – Reservation fee 25€

Rental rates : (from beginning April to end Sept.) – 15 🛏 – 5 🛏 2 apartments – 1 gîte. Per night from 60 to 120€ – Per week from 280 to 840€ – Reservation fee 25€

🚐 borne 5€

Surroundings : ≤ 🚏 ♀
Leisure activities : ⊤ ✗ ♨ ♨♨ ♨♨ ♨ ♨ ♨
Facilities : ♿ ⟶ 🔲 ♨ ♨ ⊤ launderette

GPS Longitude : 3.12985
Latitude : 44.18747

ROCAMADOUR

46500 – Michelin map **337** F3 – pop. 689 – alt. 279
▶ Paris 531 – Brive-la-Gaillarde 54 – Cahors 60 – Figeac 47

⚠⚠ Les Cigales

🕿 05 65 33 64 44, www.camping-cigales.com

Address : route de Gramat (take the eastern exit along the D 36)

Opening times : from beginning April to end Sept.

3 ha (100 pitches)

Tariff : (2013 Price) 24€ ♦♦ ⟵ 🔲 (ℓ) (10A) – Extra per person 8€ Reservation fee 15€

Rental rates : (2013 Price) (from beginning April to end Sept.) – 2 caravans – 42 🛏 – 13 🏠. Per week from 199 to 775€ Reservation fee 15€

🚐 borne

Surroundings : ♨ ♀♀
Leisure activities : ⊤ ✗ 🔲 ♨♨ ♨ ♨
Facilities : ♿ ⟶ ♨ ⊤ ⊥ launderette
♨ refrigerators
Nearby : ♨

GPS Longitude : 1.63221
Latitude : 44.80549

⚠ Le Roc

📞 0565336850, www.camping-leroc.com

Address : at Pech-Alis (3km northeast along the D 673, follow the signs for Alvignac, 200m from the station)

Opening times : from beginning April to beginning Nov.

2 ha/0,5 (49 pitches)

Tariff : 🛉 6€ ⇌ 🖃 6€ – 🔌 (10A) 3,50€ – Reservation fee 10€

Rental rates : (from beginning April to mid Nov.) – 4 🚐 – 8 🏠. Per week from 195 to 695€ – Reservation fee 14€

🚽 borne 6€ – 4 🖃

Surroundings : 🗀 ♤♤
Leisure activities : ✗ 🏊 🛶
Facilities : ♿ ⌒ 🗂 🚾 📺 🖥

⚠ Le Relais du Campeur

📞 0565336328, www.lerelaisducampeur.com

Address : l'Hospitalet (in the town)

1,7 ha (100 pitches)

Surroundings : ♤♤
Leisure activities : 🛶
Facilities : ⌒ 🚾 launderette
Nearby : 🏊 ⛾ ✗

The information in the guide may have changed since going to press.

12000 – Michelin map **338** H4 – pop. 24 358 – alt. 635
▶ Paris 623 – Albi 76 – Alès 187 – Aurillac 87

🏔 Village Vacances Campéole Domaine de Combelles 👥

(rental of mobile homes, chalets and canvas bungalows only)

📞 0565782953, www.camping-rodez.info

Address : at Le Monastère, at the domaine de Combelles (situated 2km southeast along the D 12, follow the signs for Ste-Radegonde, D 62, turn right towards Flavin and take road to the left)

Opening times : from beginning May to end Sept.

120 ha/20 for camping undulating

Rental rates : ♿ (2 chalets) – 30 🚐 – 35 🏠 – 28 canvas bungalows. Per night from 57 to 120€ – Per week from 400 to 820€ – Reservation fee 25€

Plenty of activities for young and old based around a large horse riding centre.

Surroundings : 🌲 ≼ 🗀 ♤♤
Leisure activities : ⛾ 🎠 🎮 🏃 🏇 🚲 ⚾ 🛶
🐎 entertainment room
Facilities : ⌒ 🅿 🗂🚾 launderette 🚿

⚠ Municipal de Layoule

📞 0565670952, www.ville-rodez.com

Address : rue de la Chapelle (to the northeast of the town)

Opening times : from beginning May to end Sept.

2 ha (79 pitches) terraced, flat, grassy

Tariff : 10€ 🛉🛉 ⇌ 🖃 🔌 (6A) – Extra per person 4€

🚽 10 🖃 12€

In a pleasant, leafy setting with plenty of shade near the Aveyron river.

Surroundings : ≼ 🗀 ♤♤
Leisure activities : 🎮 🏊
Facilities : ♿ ⌒ 🗂 🚾 🖥
Nearby : 🚶 walking trails

GPS Longitude : 2.58532
Latitude : 44.35367

32480 – Michelin map **336** E6 – pop. 551 – alt. 188
▶ Paris 694 – Agen 32 – Auch 48 – Condom 12

🏔 Le Camp de Florence 👥

📞 0562281558, www.lecampdeflorence.com

Address : route Astaffort (take the eastern exit from the town along the D 41)

Opening times : from beginning April to beginning Oct.

10 ha/4 for camping (183 pitches) terraced, flat, grassy

Tariff : 36€ 🛉🛉 ⇌ 🖃 🔌 (10A) – Extra per person 8€

Rental rates : (from beginning April to beginning Oct.) ♿ (3 chalets) – 28 🚐 – 1 🏠 – 6 canvas bungalows. Per night from 48 to 160€ – Per week from 336 to 1120€

🚽 borne 4€ – 20 🖃 18€

Surroundings : 🌲 ≼ 🗀 ♤♤
Leisure activities : ⛾ ✗ 🎮 🎠 🏃 🏋 🏇 🚲
⚾ 🏊 wildlife park
Facilities : ♿ ⌒ 🗂 🚾 launderette 🚿

GPS Longitude : 0.50155
Latitude : 43.98303

Routes nationales are main roads and their identifying numbers begin with N or RN. Routes départementales are generally quieter roads and begin with D or DN.

32810 – Michelin map **336** F7 – pop. 558 – alt. 206
▶ Paris 711 – Agen 67 – Auch 10 – Condom 39

🏔 Yelloh! Village Le Talouch 👥

📞 0562655243, www.camping-talouch.com

Address : at Cassou (3.5km north along the D 272, follow the signs for Mérens then take left turn D 148, follow the signs for Auch)

Opening times : from mid April to end Sept.

9 ha/5 for camping (147 pitches)

Tariff : 40€ 🛉🛉 ⇌ 🖃 🔌 (6A) Extra per person 8€

Rental rates : Permanent – 17 🚐 35 🏠. Per night from 39 to 173€ Per week from 273 to 1211€

🚽 borne 15€ – 3 🖃 19€

Surroundings : 🌲 🗀 ♤♤
Leisure activities : ✗ 🎮 🎠 🏃 🛝 hammam, jacuzzi 🏊 🚲 ⚾ 🏊 🛶
Facilities : ♿ ⌒ 🗂🚾 launderette 🚿

GPS Longitude : 0.56437
Latitude : 43.71284

ST-AMANS-DES-COTS

2460 – Michelin map **338** H2 – pop. 775 – alt. 735

▣ Paris 585 – Aurillac 54 – Entraygues-sur-Truyère 16 – Espalion 31

⛰ **Village Center Les Tours** ♠♠

(rental of mobile homes and tents only)

☏ 0825002030, www.village-center.fr – alt. 600

Address : at Les Tours (6km southeast along the D 97 and turn left onto D 599; beside the Lac de la Selves)

Opening times : from beginning April to beginning Oct.

15 ha (290 pitches) very uneven

Rental rates : 8 🚐. Per night from 26 to 102€ – Reservation fee 30€

🚮 borne 5€

In a pleasant site overlooking the lake.

Surroundings : 🏊 ≼ 🗪 🎠 ⛰
Leisure activities : 🍴🍽 🏛 ☝🤸 🎣🚴 ✂
🛶 🎿 watersports centre
Facilities : 🚿 ☎ ♿ 🚽 🔥 🍴 launderette 🧺 🛒

G P S Longitude : 2.68056
Latitude : 44.66803

⛰ **La Romiguière**

☏ 0565444464, www.laromiguiere.com – alt. 600

Address : at the lake la Selve (8.5km southeast along the D 97 and turn left onto D 599; beside the Lac de la Selves)

Opening times : from beginning April to beginning Nov.

2 ha (62 pitches) terrace

Tariff : (2013 Price) 26,40€ ☝☝ 🚐 🔲 🔌 (10A) – Extra per person 6€ – Reservation fee 16€

Rental rates : (from beginning April to beginning Nov.) – 19 🚐. Per week from 245 to 651€ – Reservation fee 16€

🚮 borne 3€ – 🛥11€

In a peaceful location beside a lake.

Surroundings : 🏊 ≼ 🗪 🎠 ⛰
Leisure activities : 🍴🍽 🎿 🛶 pedalos, scuba diving 🤿
Facilities : 🚿 ☎ 🍴 🧺 🍴 launderette 🛒
Nearby : ⚓ water skiing

G P S Longitude : 2.70639
Latitude : 44.65528

The guide covers all 22 regions of France – see the map and list of regions on pages 4–5.

ST-ANTONIN-NOBLE-VAL

82140 – Michelin map **337** G7 – pop. 1 829 – alt. 125

▣ Paris 624 – Cahors 55 – Caussade 18 – Caylus 11

⛰ **Sites et Paysages Les Trois Cantons** ♠♠

☏ 0563319857, www.3cantons.fr

Address : 7.7km northwest along the D 19, follow the signs for Caylus and take road to the left, after the little bridge over the Bonnette, between an area known as Tarau and the D 926, between Sept.fonds (6km) and Caylus (9km)

Opening times : from mid April to mid Sept.

5 ha/4 for camping (99 pitches)

Tariff : (2013 Price) ☝ 6,50€ 🚐 🔲 9,60€ – 🔌 (10A) 6€

Rental rates : (2013 Price) (from mid April to mid Sept.) – 21 🚐. Per night from 40 to 79€ – Per week from 252 to 700€

In a natural setting among trees, shrubs and bushes.

Surroundings : 🏊 🗪 🎏
Leisure activities : 🍴🍽 🏛 ☝🤸 🎣🚴 ✂
🎿 climbing wall
Facilities : 🚿 ☎ 🍴 🔥 🔲 🛒 refrigerators

G P S Longitude : 1.69612
Latitude : 44.1933

⛰ **Flower Les Gorges de l'Aveyron** ♠♠

☏ 0563306976, www.camping-gorges-aveyron.com

Address : at Marsac bas

Opening times : from beginning April to end Sept.

3,8 ha (80 pitches) flat, grassy

Tariff : 18€ ☝☝ 🚐 🔲 🔌 (10A) – Extra per person 3€ – Reservation fee 5€

Rental rates : (from beginning April to end Sept.) – 23 🚐
4 canvas bungalows – 4 tent lodges. Per night from 34 to 119€ Per week from 170 to 833€ – Reservation fee 15€

Pretty, well-shaded pitches, some beside the Aveyron river, with a variety of rental options.

Surroundings : 🏊 🎏
Leisure activities : 🍴 🏛 ☝🤸 🎣 🎿 🛶
Facilities : 🚿 ☎ ♿ 🍴 launderette 🧺 🛒

G P S Longitude : 1.77256
Latitude : 44.15211

These symbols are used for a campsite that is exceptional in its category:

⛰⛰…⛰ *Particularly pleasant setting, quality and range of services available*

🏊 🏊 *Tranquil, isolated site – quiet site, particularly at night*

≼ ≼ *Exceptional view – interesting or panoramic view*

ST-BERTRAND-DE-COMMINGES

31510 – Michelin map **343** B6 – pop. 259 – alt. 581

▣ Paris 783 – Bagnères-de-Luchon 33 – Lannemezan 23 – St-Gaudens 17

⛰ **Es Pibous**

☏ 0561883142, www.es-pibous.fr

Address : chemin de St-Just (800m southeast along the D 26a, follow the signs for St-Béat and take road to the left)

2 ha (80 pitches) flat, grassy

Rentals : 4 🚐 – 1 🏠 .

🚮 borne

Some pitches have a view over the Sainte-Marie cathedral. The rentals are not of the highest quality, sometimes rather old.

Surroundings : 🏊 ≼ Cathédrale de St-Bertrand-de-Comminges 🗪 🎏
Leisure activities : 🏛 🎣 🎏
Facilities : 🚿 ☎ 🔥 🍴 🔲
Nearby : 🎣

G P S Longitude : 0.57799
Latitude : 43.02868

There are several different types of sani-station ('borne' in French) – sanitation points providing fresh water and disposal points for grey water. See page 12 for further details.

ST-CÉRÉ

46400 – Michelin map **337** H2 – pop. 3 563 – alt. 152
▶ Paris 531 – Aurillac 62 – Brive-la-Gaillarde 51 – Cahors 80

🏔 Le Soulhol

📞 05 65 38 12 37, www.campinglesoulhol.com

Address : quai Salesses (take southeastern exit along the D 48; beside the Bave river)

Opening times : from beginning April to end Sept.

3,5 ha (120 pitches) flat, grassy

Tariff : 14,20€ ✻✻ 🚐 🔲 ⚡ (10A) – Extra per person 5€ – Reservation fee 20€

Rental rates : (from beginning April to end Sept.) ⚘ – 5 🚐
10 gîtes. Per night from 50 to 58€ – Per week from 198 to 490€
Reservation fee 10€

Surroundings : 🌲 ♨
Leisure activities : 🛶 ⛵ 🚣
Facilities : ♿ ⛽ 🛁 ♨ launderette
Nearby : 🍷 ✗ 🍴

Longitude : 1.89617
Latitude : 44.85876

ST-CIRQ-LAPOPIE

46330 – Michelin map **337** G5 – pop. 217 – alt. 320
▶ Paris 574 – Cahors 26 – Figeac 44 – Villefranche-de-Rouergue 37

🏔 La Truffière ⚐⚐

📞 05 65 30 20 22, www.camping-truffiere.com

Address : at Pradines (3km south along the D 42, follow the signs for Concots)

Opening times : from mid April to end Sept.

4 ha (96 pitches) natural setting among trees and bushes

Tariff : (2013 Price) 22,90€ ✻✻ 🚐 🔲 ⚡ (6A) – Extra per person 6€ Reservation fee 12€

Rental rates : (from mid April to end Sept.) – 13 🏠. Per night from 65 to 90€ – Per week from 280 to 790€ – Reservation fee 12€

🚐 borne – 6 🔲 18€
A small and pretty chalet village.

Surroundings : 🌲 ≤ ♨
Leisure activities : ✗ 🛶 🏃 🚣 🚣
Facilities : ♿ ⛽ 🍴♨ 🛁♨ launderette 🐕

Longitude : 1.6746
Latitude : 44.44842

🏔 La Plage ⚐⚐

📞 05 65 30 29 51, www.campingplage.com

Address : at Poroute Roques (1.4km northeast along the D 8, follow the signs for Tour-de-Faure, turn left before the bridge)

Opening times : from mid April to end Sept.

3 ha (120 pitches)

Tariff : 21€ ✻✻ 🚐 🔲 ⚡ (10A) – Extra per person 6€ – Reservation fee 10€

Rental rates : (from mid April to end Sept.) – 22 🚐. Per night from 40 to 70€ – Per week from 280 to 690€ – Reservation fee 10€

🚐 borne 7€ – 20 🔲 7€

On the banks of the Lot river, opposite one of the prettiest villages in France.

Surroundings : 🚤 ♨♨
Leisure activities : 🍷 ✗ 🕐 daytime 🏃 🏃
🚴 🏖 (beach) 🚣 🚣
Facilities : ♿ ⛽ 🛁 🚿 🚽 ♨ launderette 🐕
Nearby : adventure park

Longitude : 1.6812
Latitude : 44.46914

ST-GAUDENS

31800 – Michelin map **343** C6 – pop. 11 225 – alt. 405
▶ Paris 766 – Bagnères-de-Luchon 48 – Tarbes 68 – Toulouse 94

🏔 Municipal Belvédère des Pyrénées

📞 05 62 00 16 03, www.st-gaudens.com

Address : rue des Chanteurs du Comminges (located 1km west along the N 117, towards Tarbes)

Opening times : from beginning June to end Sept.

1 ha (83 pitches) flat, grassy, fine gravel

Tariff : ✻ 3,50€ 🚐 🔲 8€ – ⚡ (13A) 6,50€

Rental rates : (from end June to end Sept.) – 2 🚐. Per night from 40€ – Per week from 200€

🚐 borne

A panoramic view over the Pyrenees, but some pitches also look down on the road.

Surroundings : ≤ Pyrénées 🚤 ♨♨
Facilities : ♿ ⛽ 🚿 🚽 🛒 ♨ launderette
Nearby : 🍷 ✗

Longitude : 0.70814
Latitude : 43.11

The prices listed were supplied by the campsite owners in 2013 (if prices were not available, those from the previous year are given). The fees should be regarded as basic charges and may fluctuate with inflation.

ST-GENIEZ-D'OLT

12130 – Michelin map **338** J4 – pop. 2 068 – alt. 410
▶ Paris 612 – Espalion 28 – Florac 80 – Mende 68

🏔 Campéole La Boissière ⚐⚐

📞 05 65 70 40 43, www.camping-aveyron.info

Address : route de la Cascade (1.2km northeast along the D 988, follow the signs for St-Laurent-d'Olt and turn left following signs for Pomayrols; beside the Lot river)

Opening times : from beginning April to end Sept.

5 ha (250 pitches) terraced, flat, grassy

Tariff : (2013 Price) 25,90€ ✻✻ 🚐 🔲 ⚡ (10A)
Extra per person 6,50€ – Reservation fee 15€

Rental rates : (from beginning April to end Sept.) – 23 🚐 –
19 🏠 – 19 canvas bungalows. Per night from 26 to 52€
Per week from 294 to 819€ – Reservation fee 25€

🚐 borne 1€ – 🛢 ⚡ 22€

Pleasant wooded setting beside the Lot river.

Surroundings : 🌲 🚤 ♨♨
Leisure activities : 🍷 🛶 🕐 🏃 🚣 🚣 ♨ 🚣 🚣
Facilities : ♿ ⛽ 🛁 ♨ launderette, refrigerators
Nearby : 🚴 🏃

Longitude : 2.98366
Latitude : 44.47011

⛰ Residence Les Clédelles Revea du Colombier

(rental of gîtes only)

☎ 05 65 71 52 88, www.lescledelles.com

Address : rue Rivié (located 1km northeast via D 988, follow the signs for St-Laurent-d'Olt and turn left following signs for Pomayrols; near the Lot)

5 ha flat

Rentals : 42 gîtes.

Surroundings : 🌳
Leisure activities : 🚴 🛶
Facilities : ⚡ 🏪 🚰 🖥
Nearby : 🎣

Longitude : 2.97809
Latitude : 44.46893
GPS

⛰ Kawan Village Marmotel ♟

☎ 05 65 70 46 51, www.marmotel.com

Opening times : from end April to end Sept.

4 ha (173 pitches) flat, grassy

Tariff : 31,60€ ♟♟ 🚐 🔲 [⚡] (10A) – Extra per person 6,50€
Reservation fee 25€

Rental rates : (from end April to end Sept.) – 48 🚐 – 30 🏠.
Per night from 35 to 50€ – Per week from 259 to 924€
Reservation fee 25€

Surroundings : 🌳 🌲 ♨♨
Leisure activities : 🍽❌🎣🚴🛶⛵
multi-sports ground, entertainment room
Facilities : ⚕ ⚡ 🚿 – 42 individual sanitary
facilities (🛁 🚽 🚾 wc) 🚰 🧺 🏪 launderette
🚰

Longitude : 2.9644
Latitude : 44.462
GPS

46310 – Michelin map **337** E4 – pop. 518 – alt. 215
▶ Paris 551 – Cahors 28 – Cazals 20 – Fumel 52

⛺ Municipal le Moulin Vieux ♟

☎ 05 65 31 00 71, www-camping-moulin-vieux-lot.com

Address : to the northwest of the town; beside the Céou river

2 ha (90 pitches) flat, grassy

Surroundings : 🌳 ♨♨
Leisure activities : 🏤 🚴🎣 🎯 🛶
Facilities : ⚡ 🚰 🖥
Nearby : 🛶 🏊

Longitude : 1.43476
Latitude : 44.64986
GPS

09200 – Michelin map **343** E7 – pop. 6 608 – alt. 398
▶ Paris 774 – Auch 123 – Foix 45 – St-Gaudens 43

⛰ Audinac ♟

☎ 05 61 66 44 50, www.audinac.com

Address : at Audinac-les-Bains, au plan d'eau (head 4.5km northeast along the D 117, follow the signs for Foix and take D 627, follow the signs for Ste-Croix-Volvestre)

Opening times : from beginning April to end Sept.

15 ha/6 for camping (115 pitches) small lake

Tariff : 24,50€ ♟♟ 🚐 🔲 [⚡] (16A) – Extra per person 7€ – Reservation fee 10€

Rental rates : (from beginning April to mid Oct.) ⚕ (1 mobile home) – 30 🚐 – 15 🏠 – 22 canvas bungalows. Per night from 30 to 75€– Per week from 160 to 750€ – Reservation fee 10€
🚌 borne

A spacious site with 3 small springs, a lake and a swimming pool in front of an old 19th-century spa building.

Surroundings : 🌳 ♨♨
Leisure activities : 🍽❌🏤 🌙nighttime 🎯
🚣🚲❌🛶 multi-sports ground
Facilities : ⚕ ⚡ 🏪 🚰🏪 launderette 🚰
refrigerators

Longitude : 1.18407
Latitude : 43.00705
GPS

12230 – Michelin map **338** M6 – pop. 695 – alt. 520
▶ Paris 687 – Toulouse 295 – Rodez 128 – Millau 41

⛰ La Dourbie

☎ 05 65 46 06 40, www.camping-la-dourbie.com

Address : route de Nant

2,5 ha (78 pitches) flat, grassy

Rentals : 8 🚐 – 2 🏠.

A magnificent view over wooded hills.

Surroundings : 🌳 ♀
Leisure activities : 🍽❌🚣🛶🛶
Facilities : ⚕ ⚡ 🏪 🚰🚾🏪🖥🚰

Longitude : 3.3466
Latitude : 44.02004
GPS

65170 – Michelin map **342** N8 – pop. 946 – alt. 820 – Winter sports : 1 680/2 450m
▶ Paris 830 – Arreau 12 – Auch 103 – Bagnères-de-Luchon 44

⛺ Municipal

☎ 05 62 39 41 58, www.saintlary-vacances.com

Address : rue Lalanne (in the village)

Opening times : from beginning Dec.. to mid Oct.

1 ha (77 pitches) relatively flat, flat, grassy, stony

Tariff : (2013 Price) ♟ 5,60€ 🚐 🔲 5,60€ – [⚡] 6€
🚌 borne 6€

A pleasant oasis of greenery in the centre of the village.

Surroundings : ❄ ≤ ♨♨
Leisure activities : 🏤 🚣
Facilities : ⚕ ⚡ 🚪🏪 🚰🚾 launderette
Nearby : ❌ 🛶

Longitude : 0.32282
Latitude : 42.81548
GPS

46800 – Michelin map **337** D5 – pop. 239 – alt. 269
▶ Paris 597 – Cahors 22 – Castelnau-Montratier 18 – Montaigu-de-Quercy 28

⛰ Les Arcades

☎ 05 65 22 92 27, www.des-arcades.com

Address : at Le Moulin de St. Martial (4.5km east on the D 653, follow the signs for Cahors; beside the Barguelonnette river)

Opening times : from end April to end Sept.

12 ha/2,6 for camping (80 pitches) small lake

Tariff : ♟ 6,20€🚐 🔲 11€ – [⚡] (6A) 4,10€ – Reservation fee 17€
Rental rates : (from end April to end Sept.) ⚕ – 11 🚐
3 canvas bungalows – 3 tent lodges. Per night from 40 to 130€
Per week from 260 to 895 € – Reservation fee 17€

There's a clubroom and small pub in a restored mill.

Surroundings : 🌳 ♨♨
Leisure activities : 🍽❌🏤 🚴🚣🛶🏊
Facilities : ⚕ ⚡ 🚰🏪🖥🚰

Longitude : 1.30667
Latitude : 44.36918
GPS

ST-PIERRE-LAFEUILLE

46090 – Michelin map **337** E4 – pop. 352 – alt. 350
▶ Paris 566 – Cahors 10 – Catus 14 – Labastide-Murat 23

⚠ Quercy-Vacances

⚲ 05 65 36 87 15, www.quercy-vacances.com

Address : at Mas de la Combe (located 1.5km northeast along the N 20, follow the signs for Brive and take road to the left)

Opening times : from beginning April to end Sept.

3 ha (80 pitches)

Tariff : (2013 Price) ♦ 5€ ⇔ 🔲 8€ – 🔌 (10A) 4,50€

Rental rates : (from beginning April to end Sept.) – 14 ⌂⌂ – 6 ⌂ 3 canvas bungalows. Per night from 55 to 110€ – Per week from 210 to 595€

🚐 3 🔲 18,80€

Surroundings : 🏞 ♨
Leisure activities : 🍽 ✕ 🏛 🛶 multi-sports ground
Facilities : 🚿 ⚲ 🔧 📷 🛁

G P S	Longitude : 1.45925 Latitude : 44.53165

This guide is updated regularly, so buy your new copy every year!

ST-ROME-DE-TARN

12490 – Michelin map **338** J6 – pop. 853 – alt. 360
▶ Paris 655 – Millau 18 – Pont-de-Salars 42 – Rodez 66

🏔 La Cascade

⚲ 05 65 62 56 59, www.camping-cascade-aveyron.com – pitches accessed via steep slope, help moving caravans onto and off pitches avilable on request

Address : route du Pont (300m north along the D 993, follow the signs for Rodez; beside the Tarn river)

Opening times : Permanent

4 ha (99 pitches) terraced

Tariff : 29,90€ ♦♦ ⇔ 🔲 🔌 (6A) – Extra per person 7€ – Reservation fee 16€

Rental rates : Permanent – 28 ⌂⌂ – 14 ⌂ – 9 canvas bungalows. Per night from 60 to 135€ – Per week from 190 to 510€ Reservation fee 16€

🚐 borne 6€ – 10 🔲 19,50€
A terraced site on the side of a hill overlooking the Tarn river.

Surroundings : 🏞 ♨
Leisure activities : ✕ 🏛 🛶 🚲 🏓 🎣
Facilities : 🚿 ⚲ 🛁 🛒 🔧 launderette 🛁 🛁
Nearby : pedalos

G P S	Longitude : 2.89947 Latitude : 44.05336

ST-SALVADOU

12200 – Michelin map **338** E5 – pop. 410 – alt. 450
▶ Paris 619 – Toulouse 120 – Rodez 54 – Albi 63

⚠ Le Muret

⚲ 05 65 81 80 69, www.lemuret.com

Opening times : from end April to beginning Sept.

3 ha (44 pitches) flat, grassy

Tariff : 23€ ♦♦ ⇔ 🔲 🔌 (16A) – Extra per person 4€

Rental rates : (from end April to beginning Sept.) – 4 ⌂⌂ – 4 tent lodges. Per night from 38 to 84€ – Per week from 221 to 610€
Situated on the Le Muret estate with its 18th-century farm buildings.

Surroundings : 🏞 ♨♨
Leisure activities : 🏛 🛶 🚲 🎣 🎣
multi-sports ground
Facilities : 🚿 ⚲ 🛁 📷 🛁
Nearby : 🛶 ✕ 🐴 🎣

G P S	Longitude : 2.11563 Latitude : 44.26712

STE-MARIE-DE-CAMPAN

65710 – Michelin map **342** N5
▶ Paris 841 – Arreau 26 – Bagnères-de-Bigorre 13 – Luz-St-Sauveur 37

🏔 L'Orée des Monts

⚲ 05 62 91 83 98, www.camping-oree-des-monts.com – alt. 950

Address : at La Séoube (3km southeast along the D 918, follow the signs for Le Col d'Aspin; beside the Adour de Payolle river)

Opening times : Permanent

1,8 ha (99 pitches)

Tariff : 25,90€ ♦♦ ⇔ 🔲 🔌 (10A) – Extra per person 4,80€ Reservation fee 10€

Rental rates : Permanent – 9 ⌂⌂. Per week from 170 to 610€ Reservation fee 10€

🚐 borne 15,90€ – 5 🔲 15,90€
A mountain site beside a stream.

Surroundings : ❮ ♨
Leisure activities : 🍽 ✕ 🏛 🛶 🛶 🎣
Facilities : ⚲ 🛒 🛁 🔧 📷 🛁

G P S	Longitude : 0.24522 Latitude : 42.96664

This guide is not intended as a list of all the camping sites in France; its aim is to provide a selection of the best sites in each category.

SALLES-CURAN

12410 – Michelin map **338** I5 – pop. 1 067 – alt. 887
▶ Paris 650 – Albi 77 – Millau 39 – Rodez 40

🏔 Kawan Village Les Genêts ♣♣

⚲ 05 65 46 35 34, www.camping-les-genets.fr – alt. 1 000

Address : at the lake Pareloup (5km northwest along the D 993 then take left turning along the D 577, follow the signs for Arvieu and continue 2km along the road to the right)

Opening times : from mid May to mid Sept.

3 ha (163 pitches) terraced

Tariff : 36€ ♦♦ ⇔ 🔲 🔌 (6A) – Extra per person 8,30€ – Reservation fee 30€

Rental rates : (from mid May to mid Sept.) – 45 ⌂⌂ – 11 ⌂ 7 canvas bungalows. Per night from 37 to 116€ – Per week from 200 to 910€ – Reservation fee 30€

Beside the Lac de Pareloup.

Surroundings : 🏞 ❮ 🛶 ♨ ⛰
Leisure activities : 🍽 ✕ 🏛 👫 🛶 🚲 🎣 🛶
🎣 entertainment room
Facilities : 🚿 ⚲ (from mid June to beg. Sept.) 🔲 🛁 🛒 🔧 launderette 🛁

G P S	Longitude : 2.76776 Latitude : 44.18963

⚴ Sites et Paysages Beau Rivage

𝒫 05 65 46 33 32, www.beau-rivage.fr – alt. 800

Address : route des Vernhes - lake Pareloup (3.5km north along the D 993, follow the signs for Pont-de-Salars and turn left onto D 243)

Opening times : from beginning May to end Sept.

2 ha (80 pitches) terraced, flat, grassy

Tariff : (2013 Price) 34,90€ ✦✦ ⇐⊡ ▣
⒟ (10A) – Extra per person 6,90€ – Reservation fee 20€

Rental rates : (from beginning April to end Sept.) – 16 ▭
6 ☖. Per night from 46 to 138€ – Per week from 196 to 966€
Reservation fee 30€

🛒 borne 8€ – 🜂 ⒟14€

In a pleasant location beside the Lac de Pareloup.

Surroundings : ⇐ ▱ ♀ ⚐
Leisure activities : 🍴✗ ⌂ ⚓ ⛵ ⚲
Facilities : & ⊶ ☖⍦ launderette ⚏
Nearby : ♪ forest trail

| | Longitude : 2.77585 |
| GPS | Latitude : 44.20081 |

⚴ Parc du Charrouzech

𝒫 06 83 95 04 42, www.parcducharrouzech.fr

Address : 5km northwest along the D 993 then take left turning along the D 577, follow the signs for Arvieu and continue 3.4km along the road to the right; near the Lac du Pareloup (direct access)

Opening times : from beginning July to end Aug.

3 ha (104 pitches) terraced, relatively flat, flat, grassy

Tariff : 28€ ✦✦ ⇐⊡ ▣ ⒟ (5A) – Extra per person 4€

Rental rates : (from beginning July to end Aug.) – 20 ▭
34 canvas bungalows – 8 (without sanitary facilities). Per week from 180 to 800€– Reservation fee 30€

Situated with a view looking out over the lake.

Surroundings : ⚏ ⇐ ▱ ♀
Leisure activities : ⌂ ⚓ ⚓ ☐ ≋ ⚲ ⚲
Facilities : & ⊶ ⚏ ⍦ launderette

| | Longitude : 2.75659 |
| GPS | Latitude : 44.1968 |

Some campsites benefit from proximity to a municipal leisure centre.

SALLES-ET-PRATVIEL

31110 – Michelin map **343** B8 – pop. 136 – alt. 625
▶ Paris 814 – Toulouse 141 – Tarbes 86 – Lourdes 105

⚴ Le Pyrénéen

𝒫 05 61 79 59 19, www.campingdepyreneen-luchon.com

Address : at Les Sept Molles (600m south along the D 27 and a road; beside the Pique river)

Opening times : Permanent

1,1 ha (75 pitches) flat, grassy

Tariff : 20,90€ ✦✦ ⇐⊡ ▣ ⒟ (10A) – Extra per person 4,80€
Reservation fee 15€

Rental rates : Permanent – 25 ▭. Per night from 40 to 75€
Per week from 280 to 650€ – Reservation fee 15€

🛒 borne 5€

A free shuttle to the Bagnères-de-Luchon thermal baths.

Surroundings : ❄ ⚏ ⇐ ♀♀
Leisure activities : 🍴✗ ⌂ ⚓ ⚲
Facilities : & ⊶ ⍦ ☖⍦ launderette
Nearby : 🐎

| | Longitude : 0.60637 |
| GPS | Latitude : 42.8224 |

SASSIS

65120 – Michelin map **342** L5 – pop. 92 – alt. 700
▶ Paris 879 – Toulouse 206 – Tarbes 53 – Pau 72

⚴ Le Hounta

𝒫 05 62 92 95 90, www.campinglehounta.com

Address : 600m south along the D 12

Opening times : Permanent

2 ha (125 pitches) relatively flat, flat, grassy

Tariff : 20,60€ ✦✦ ⇐⊡ ▣ ⒟ (10A) – Extra per person 4,30€
Reservation fee 4,10€

Rental rates : Permanent – 11 ▭ – 1 ☖. Per night from 39 to 87€
Per week from 195 to 561€ – Reservation fee 7,40€

🛒 borne 5€ – 10 ▣ 11,10€

Choose pitches near the small canal, further away from the road.

Surroundings : ❄ ⚏ ⇐ ♀
Leisure activities : ⚓
Facilities : & ⊶ ⍦ ☖⍦ launderette
Nearby : ⚲

| | Longitude : -0.01491 |
| GPS | Latitude : 42.87252 |

SÉNERGUES

12320 – Michelin map **338** G3 – pop. 481 – alt. 525
▶ Paris 630 – Toulouse 197 – Rodez 50 – Aurillac 62

⚴ L'Étang du Camp

𝒫 05 65 46 01 95, www.etangducamp.fr

Address : at Le Camp (6km southwest along the D 242, follow the signs for St-Cyprien-sur-Dourdou; beside a lake)

Opening times : from beginning April to end Sept.

5 ha (60 pitches) flat and relatively flat

Tariff : 19,50€ ✦✦ ⇐⊡ ▣ ⒟ (6A) – Extra per person 3,50€

Rental rates : (from mid May to end Sept.) ⚌ (Sept.) – 1 ▭
4 tipis. Per night 44€ – Per week from 182 to 490€

Ornamental flowers and shrubs Dec.orate the site.

Surroundings : ⚏ ▱ ♀♀
Leisure activities : 🍴✗ ⌂ ⚲ ⚲
Facilities : & ⊶ ☖⍦ ▣

| | Longitude : 2.46391 |
| GPS | Latitude : 44.55837 |

Michelin classification:

⚴⚴⚴⚴	*Extremely comfortable, equipped to a very high standard*
⚴⚴⚴	*Very comfortable, equipped to a high standard*
⚴⚴	*Comfortable and well equipped*
⚴	*Reasonably comfortable*
⚴	*Satisfactory*

SÉNIERGUES

46240 – Michelin map **337** F3 – pop. 136 – alt. 390
▶ Paris 540 – Cahors 45 – Figeac 46 – Fumel 69

Domaine de la Faurie

HOCHART

✆ 05 65 21 14 36, www.camping-lafaurie.com

Address : at La Faurie (6km south along the D 10, follow the signs for Montfaucon then take the D 2, follow the signs for St-Germain-du-Bel-Air and take the road to the right; from the A 20, take exit 56)

Opening times : from beginning April to end Sept.

27 ha/5 for camping (63 pitches)

Tariff : (2013 Price) ♣ 7€ ⬚ 🅿 11,30€ – (6A) 5€

Rental rates : (from beginning April to end Sept.) 🅿 – 8 🚐 17 🏠. Per night from 41 to 117€ – Per week from 287 to 819€
🚰 borne 11,30€ – 7 🅿 11,30€

Surroundings : 🐟 ≤ ♨
Leisure activities : 🍹 ✕ 🏛 ♣ 🚴 ⛷
Facilities : & ⊶ 🆔 🏖 🏊 🚿 ¶ launderette
🍴

Longitude : 1.53444
Latitude : 44.69175

SÉVÉRAC-L'ÉGLISE

12310 – Michelin map **338** J4 – pop. 412 – alt. 630
▶ Paris 625 – Espalion 26 – Mende 84 – Millau 58

Flower La Grange de Monteillac 👥

✆ 05 65 70 21 00, www.aveyron-location.com

Address : chemin de Monteillac (take the northeastern exit along the D 28, follow the signs for Laissac, opposite the cemetery)

Opening times : from beginning May to mid Sept.

4,5 ha (59 pitches) terraced, flat, grassy

Tariff : 35,90€ ♣♣ ⬚ 🅿 (20A) – Extra per person 6,80€
Reservation fee 15€

Rental rates : (from beginning April to end Sept.) 🅿 – 10 🚐 22 🏠 – 9 canvas bungalows – 4 tent lodges. Per night from 38 to 144€ – Per week from 266 to 1 008€ – Reservation fee 15€

Pretty decorative flowers and shrubs.

Surroundings : ⬚ ♀
Leisure activities : 🍹 ✕ 🏛 ⛳ 🏃 ♣ 🚴 ✕ 🏊 ⛷
Facilities : & ⊶ (July-Aug.) 🏖 🏊 ¶ launderette 🍴

Longitude : 2.85101
Latitude : 44.36434

SORÈZE

81540 – Michelin map **338** E10 – pop. 2 564 – alt. 272
▶ Paris 732 – Castelnaudary 26 – Castres 27 – Puylaurens 19

St-Martin

✆ 05 63 50 20 19, www.campingsaintmartin.com

Address : rue du 19 Mars 1962 at Les Vigariés (north of the town, access via the r. de la Mairie; by the stadium)

Opening times : from beginning April to end Sept.

1 ha (54 pitches)

Tariff : 21,60€ ♣♣ ⬚ 🅿 (6A) – Extra per person 5€

Rental rates : Permanent – 3 🚐 – 6 🏠. Per night from 44 to 65€ Per week from 264 to 679€
🚰 borne – 4 🅿 11€

Surroundings : 🐟 ⬚ ♨
Leisure activities : ♣ ⛷
Facilities : & ⊶ ¶ 🏖
Nearby : ✕

Longitude : 2.06594
Latitude : 43.45337

SORGEAT

09110 – Michelin map **343** J8 – pop. 95 – alt. 1 050
▶ Paris 808 – Ax-les-Thermes 6 – Axat 50 – Belcaire 23

Municipal La Prade

✆ 05 61 64 36 34, www.sorgeat.com – alt. 1 000 – limited spaces for one-night stay

Address : above the village (800m to the north)

Opening times : Permanent

2 ha (40 pitches)

Tariff : 17€ ♣♣ ⬚ 🅿 (10A) – Extra per person 3,40€

Rental rates : Permanent – 2 🚐. Per night from 45 to 52€ Per week from 280 to 360€

A pleasant location, not far from the Bonascre Ax 3 Domaines ski resort.

Surroundings : 🐟 ≤ Vallée d'Ax-les-Thermes ⬚ ♨
Leisure activities : 🏛
Facilities : & ⊶ (July-Aug.) 🎯 🏊 🚿 ¶ 🏖

Longitude : 1.85378
Latitude : 42.73322

*The classification (1 to 5 tents, **black** or red) that we award to selected sites in this guide is our own system. It should not be confused with the classification (1 to 5 stars) of official organisations.*

SOUILLAC

46200 – Michelin map **337** E2 – pop. 3 864 – alt. 104
▶ Paris 516 – Brive-la-Gaillarde 39 – Cahors 68 – Figeac 74

Les Castels Le Domaine de la Paille Basse 👥

✆ 05 65 37 85 48, www.lapaillebasse.com

Address : 6.5 km northwest along the D 15, follow the signs for Salignac-Eyvignes then continue 2km along the road to the right

Opening times : from mid May to mid Sept.

80 ha/12 for camping (262 pitches) undulating, terraced, flat, grassy, stony

Tariff : 35,90€ ♣♣ ⬚ 🅿 (16A) – Extra per person 9,50€ – Reservation fee 20€

Rental rates : (from beginning May to mid Sept.) – 82 🚐 – 2 tent lodges. Per week from 250 to 1120€ – Reservation fee 20€
🚰 borne

A spacious, undulating site with trees and bushes, set around an old renovated hamlet.

Surroundings : 🐟 ⬚ ♨♨
Leisure activities : 🍹 ✕ 🏛 ⛳ 🏃 ♣ 🚴 ✕ 🏊 disco, entertainment room
Facilities : & ⊶ 🆔 🏖 🏊 🚿 ¶ launderette 🏊 🍴

Longitude : 1.44175
Latitude : 44.94482

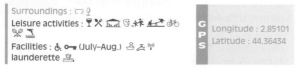

🏔 Flower les Ondines

📞 05 65 37 86 44, www.camping-lesondines.com

Address : at Les Ondines (located 1km southwest following signs for Sarlat and take road to the left; near the Dordogne river)

4 ha (242 pitches) flat, grassy

Rentals : 22 🏠 – 10 tent lodges.

Surroundings : 🏞
Leisure activities : 🛶 🎣
Facilities : 👤 ⚡ ♨ 🖥
Nearby : 🚲 🎯 🏠 🎿 ⛷ 🏇 🐎 forest trail

G P S Longitude : 1.47604
Latitude : 44.89001

Routes nationales are main roads and their identifying numbers begin with N or RN. Routes départementales are generally quieter roads and begin with D or DN.

TARASCON-SUR-ARIÈGE

09400 – Michelin map **343** H7 – pop. 3 515 – alt. 474
▶ Paris 777 – Ax-les-Thermes 27 – Foix 18 – Lavelanet 30

🏔 Yelloh! Village Le Pré Lombard ⚑⚑

📞 05 61 05 61 94, www.prelombard.com

Address : located 1.5km southeast along the D 23; beside the Ariège

Opening times : from mid April to end Sept.

4 ha (210 pitches) flat, grassy

Tariff : 38€ ⚑⚑ 🚗 🔌 💡 (10A) – Extra per person 8€

Rental rates : (from mid April to end Sept.) – 42 🏠 – 19 🏠 14 canvas bungalows. Per night from 31 to 169€ – Per week from 217 to 1 183€

🚐 borne 3€ – 🚐 💧18€

Situated alongside the Ariège river, plenty of shade, with a range of quality rental options.

Surroundings : 🏞 🌳
Leisure activities : 🍽 🍴 🏛 🎳 🏃 🛶 🚲 🎣 ⚓ multi-sports ground
Facilities : 👤 ⚡ ♨ launderette 🚿

G P S Longitude : 1.61227
Latitude : 42.83984

TEILLET

81120 – Michelin map **338** G7 – pop. 462 – alt. 475
▶ Paris 717 – Albi 23 – Castres 43 – Lacaune 49

🏔 L'Entre Deux Lacs

📞 05 63 55 74 45, www.campingdutarn.com

Address : 29 rue du Baron de Solignac (take the southern exit along the D 81, follow the signs for Lacaune)

Opening times : from beginning April to end Sept.

4 ha (65 pitches)

Tariff : (2013 Price) 22,90€ ⚑⚑ 🚗 🔌 💡 (10A) Extra per person 4,50€ – Reservation fee 10€

Rental rates : (from beginning April to end Nov.) 🅿 – 17 🏠 2 canvas bungalows. Per week from 260 to 635€ – Reservation fee 10€

🚐 borne 5€ – 🚐 8€

Surroundings : 🏞 🌊 🌳
Leisure activities : 🍽 🍴 🛶 🎣
Facilities : 👤 ⚡ ♨ 🖥 🚿

G P S Longitude : 2.34
Latitude : 43.83

THÉGRA

46500 – Michelin map **337** G3 – pop. 492 – alt. 330
▶ Paris 535 – Brive-la-Gaillarde 58 – Cahors 64 – Rocamadour 15

🏔 Chalets Dordogne Vacances – (exclusive rental chalets)

📞 05 65 10 89 04, www.dordogne-vacances.fr

Address : 500m to the north, behind the new school

Opening times : Permanent

2,5 ha sloping

Rental rates : (2013 Price) – 14 🏠. Per night 80€ – Per week from 350 to 880€

Surroundings : 🌊 🌳
Leisure activities : 🏛 🛶 🎣
Facilities : 👤 ⚡ 🅿 🖥 🖥

G P S Longitude : 1.75607
Latitude : 44.82631

⛺ Sites et Paysages Le Ventoulou ⚑⚑

📞 05 65 33 67 01, www.camping-leventoulou.com

Address : 2.8km northeast along the D 14, follow the signs for Loubressac and take D 60, follow the signs for Mayrinhac-Lentour to the right

Opening times : from beginning April to beginning Nov.

2 ha (66 pitches)

Tariff : 30€ ⚑⚑ 🚗 💡 💡 (10A) – Extra per person 7€ – Reservation fee 18€

Rental rates : (from beginning April to beginning Nov.) – 17 🏠 6 🏠 – 6 canvas bungalows. Per night from 36 to 127€ – Per week from 180 to 889€ – Reservation fee 18€

Surroundings : 🌊 🌳
Leisure activities : 🍽 🏛 🏃 🛶 🎣
Facilities : 👤 ⚡ 🍴 🚿 ♨ 🖥 🚿

G P S Longitude : 1.77778
Latitude : 44.82603

These symbols are used for a campsite that is exceptional in its category:

🏔🏔 ...⛺ *Particularly pleasant setting, quality and range of services available*

🌊🌊 *Tranquil, isolated site – quiet site, particularly at night*

≤≤ *Exceptional view – interesting or panoramic view*

THÉRONDELS

12600 – Michelin map **338** I1 – pop. 486 – alt. 965
▶ Paris 565 – Toulouse 234 – Rodez 87 – Aurillac 45

🏔 Flower La Source

📞 05 65 66 27 10, www.camping-la-source.com

Address : Presqu'Île de Laussac

Opening times : from beginning June to beginning Sept.

4,5 ha (62 pitches) terraced, flat, grassy

Tariff : (2013 Price) 32€ ⚑⚑ 🚗 💡 💡 (10A) – Extra per person 5,80€ Reservation fee 20€

Rental rates : (2013 Price) – 20 🏠 – 11 🏠 – 8 canvas bungalows. Per night from 46 to 122€ – Per week from 215 to 854€ Reservation fee 20€

A pleasant site beside the Lac de Sarrans.

Surroundings : 🌊 ≤ 🌊 🌳
Leisure activities : 🍽 🍴 🏛 🏃 🛶 🎯 🏠 🎿 ⛷ ⚓ pedalos 🏓 multi-sports ground
Facilities : 👤 ⚡ launderette

G P S Longitude : 2.77143
Latitude : 44.85381

THOUX

32430 – Michelin map **336** H7 – pop. 223 – alt. 145
▶ Paris 681 – Auch 40 – Cadours 13 – Gimont 14

▲ Lac de Thoux - Saint Cricq

⌖ 05 62 65 71 29, www.camping-lacdethoux.com

Address : at Lannes (to the northeast along the D 654; beside the lake)

Opening times : from mid April to end Sept.

3,5 ha (130 pitches)

Tariff : 26 € ♣♣ ⟺ ▣ ⚡ (10A) – Extra per person 10 € – Reservation fee 15 €

Rental rates : (from beginning April to mid Oct.) – 42 ⟐ – 12 tent lodges. Per night from 50 to 99 € – Per week from 220 to 916 € Reservation fee 15 €

⟐ borne 5 € – 3 ▣ 16 €

Surroundings : ♋ ▲
Leisure activities : ⚘ ⚲ ⟰
Facilities : ♿ ⟼ ⟛ ⟚ ⟲ ⟟ launderette
Nearby : ⟪ ♟ ✕ ⟲ jacuzzi ⟰ ✂ ⟟ ⟲ (beach) ⟲ ⟟ pedalos

GPS	Longitude : 1.00234 Latitude : 43.68587

TOUZAC

46700 – Michelin map **337** C5 – pop. 352 – alt. 75
▶ Paris 603 – Cahors 39 – Gourdon 51 – Sarlat-la-Canéda 63

▲ Le Ch'Timi

⌖ 05 65 36 52 36, www.campinglechtimi.com

Address : at La Roque (direct access to the Lot river (via steep steps)

Opening times : from beginning April to end Sept.

3,5 ha (79 pitches)

Tariff : ♣ 6,25 € ⟺ ▣ 9,50 € – ⚡ (6A) 3,90 € – Reservation fee 10 €

Rental rates : (from beginning April to end Sept.) – 1 ⟐ 6 ⟰. Per night from 50 to 100 € – Per week from 325 to 675 € Reservation fee 10 €

Surroundings : ♋
Leisure activities : ⟰ ⚲ ✕ ⟰ ⟲
Facilities : ⟼ ⟛ ⟟ ⟲

GPS	Longitude : 1.06533 Latitude : 44.49889

LE TREIN D'USTOU

09140 – Michelin map **334** F8 – pop. 351 – alt. 739
▶ Paris 804 – Aulus-les-Bains 13 – Foix 73 – St-Girons 31

▲ Le Montagnou

⌖ 05 61 66 94 97, www.lemontagnou.com

Address : route de Guzet (take northwestern exit along the D 8, follow the signs for Seix, near the Alet)

Opening times : from beginning Dec.. to end Oct.

1,2 ha (40 pitches) flat, grassy

Tariff : (2013 Price) 21 € ♣♣ ⟺ ▣ ⚡ (6A) – Extra per person 5 €

Rental rates : Permanent – 2 caravans – 3 ⟐ – 2 tent lodges. Per night from 30 to 90 € – Per week from 185 to 620 €

⟐ borne – 8 €

Pleasant pine grove with pitches near the stream.

Surroundings : ⚘
Leisure activities : ⟲ ⟲
Facilities : ♿ ⟼ ⟥ ⟚ ⟲ ⟟ launderette ⟲
Nearby : ✕

GPS	Longitude : 1.25618 Latitude : 42.81178

LE TRUEL

12430 – Michelin map **338** I6 – pop. 348 – alt. 290
▶ Paris 677 – Millau 40 – Pont-de-Salars 37 – Rodez 52

▲ Municipal la Prade

⌖ 05 65 46 41 46

Address : head east of the town along the D 31, turn left after the bridge; beside the Tarn river

0,6 ha (28 pitches) flat, grassy

Rental rates : ⟰ – 3 ⟐ – lodging stage.

The site is situated beneath the poplars beside the Tarn river.

Surroundings : ⟪ ♋ ⚘
Leisure activities : ⟲ ⚲ ⟲
Facilities : ⟼ ⟲
Nearby : ✕ ⟰ ⟲ pedalos

GPS	Longitude : 2.76317 Latitude : 44.04937

VAYRAC

46110 – Michelin map **337** G2 – pop. 1 330 – alt. 139
▶ Paris 512 – Beaulieu-sur-Dordogne 17 – Brive-la-Gaillarde 32 – Cahors 89

▲ Chalets Mirandol Dordogne – (exclusive rental chalets)

⌖ 05 65 32 57 12, www.mirandol-dordogne.com

Address : at Vormes (2.3km south along the D 116, towards the leisure and activity park)

Opening times : from beginning April to end Sept.

2,6 ha

Rental rates : ⟟ – 22 ⟰ . Per night from 35 to 65 € – Per week from 180 to 680 €

Surroundings : ⟲ ⚘
Leisure activities : ⚲ ⟰
Facilities : ⟼ ⟥ ▣ ⟲
Nearby : ♟ ✕ ⟲ ⟲ ⟲

GPS	Longitude : 1.69771 Latitude : 44.93657

▲ Municipal la Palanquière

⌖ 05 65 32 43 67, www.vayrac.fr

Address : at La Palanquière (located 1km south along the D 116, towards the leisure and activity park)

Opening times : from beginning June to end Sept.

1 ha (33 pitches) flat, grassy

Tariff : ♣ 3,60 € ⟺ ▣ 3,40 € – ⚡ (10A) 3,60 €

Surroundings : ⚘
Facilities : ♿ ⟼ ⟥ ⟚ ⟟ ▣

GPS	Longitude : 1.70389 Latitude : 44.94464

VERS

46090 – Michelin map **337** F5 – pop. 415 – alt. 132
▶ Paris 565 – Cahors 15 – Villefranche-de-Rouergue 55

▲ La Chêneraie

⌖ 05 65 31 40 29, www.cheneraie.com – limited spaces for one-night stay

Address : at Le Cuzoul (2.5km southwest along the D 653, follow the signs for Cahors and take the road to the right after the level crossing)

Opening times : from beginning May to mid Oct.

2,6 ha (58 pitches) flat, grassy

Tariff : (2013 Price) 27 € ♣♣ ⟺ ▣ ⚡ (10A) – Extra per person 4 € Reservation fee 9 €

Rental rates : (from beginning May to mid Oct.) – 8 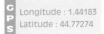 – (with/ without sanitary facilities). Per night from 35 to 120€ – Per week from 195 to 1150€ – Reservation fee 9€

🚐 borne 3€ – 2 ▣ 15€

Surroundings : ⬧ ☐ ♤♤
Leisure activities : ♈ ✕ ⌂ ⚓ ✂ ⛵
Facilities : ⚷ ♒ ℐ ⌂ ⚚

G P S Longitude : 1.54593
Latitude : 44.47154

VIELLE-AURE

65170 – Michelin map **342** N6 – pop. 355 – alt. 800
▶ Paris 828 – Toulouse 155 – Tarbes 70 – Lourdes 66

⛰ Le Lustou

✆ 05 62 39 40 64, www.lustou.com

Address : at Agos (situated 2km northeast along the D 19, near the Neste-d'Aure and a lake)

Opening times : Permanent

2,8 ha (65 pitches) flat, grassy

Tariff : ⚹ 4,70€ ⇔ ▣ 4,90€ – (½) (10A) 7,20€
Rental rates : (from beginning Dec.. to mid Oct.) ⚡ – 6 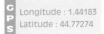 7 ⊨ – 1 gîte. Per night from 48 to 70€ Per week from 340 to 440€

In 2 separate sections on either side of a small road; the site's owner organises hiking trips.

Surroundings : ❅ ◅ ♤♤
Leisure activities : ♈ ⌂ ⚓
Facilities : ⚷ ♒ ⚏ ⌂ ⚚ ⚐ ♈ launderette
Nearby : ⚓ rafting and canyoning

G P S Longitude : 0.33841
Latitude : 42.84492

LE VIGAN

46300 – Michelin map **337** E3 – pop. 1 457 – alt. 224
▶ Paris 537 – Cahors 43 – Gourdon 6 – Labastide-Murat 20

⛰ Le Rêve

✆ 05 65 41 25 20, www.campinglereve.com

Address : at Revers (3.2km north along the D 673, follow the signs for Souillac then continue 2.8km along the road to the left)

Opening times : from mid May to mid Sept.

8 ha/2,5 for camping (60 pitches)

Tariff : (2013 Price) 22,20€ ⚹⚹ ⇔ ▣ (½) (6A) – Extra per person 5,70€ Reservation fee 5€

Rental rates : (from mid May to mid Sept.) – 4 ⌂. Per week from 245 to 560€

🚐 borne

Decorative flowers and shrubs; some pitches surrounded by bushes and shrubs.

Surroundings : ⬧ ☐ ♤♤
Leisure activities : ♈ ⚓ ⚓
Facilities : ⚷ ♒ ⌂ ♈ launderette ⚚

G P S Longitude : 1.44183
Latitude : 44.77274

VILLEFRANCHE-DE-PANAT

12430 – Michelin map **338** I6 – pop. 771 – alt. 710
▶ Paris 676 – Toulouse 177 – Rodez 45 – Millau 46

⛰ Le Hameau des Lacs – (exclusive rental chalets)

✆ 05 65 65 81 81, www.les-hameaux.fr

Address : route de Rodez

1 ha terraced, flat, grassy

Rental rates : ℗ – 22 ⌂.

Set in a large green meadow beside a lake.

Surroundings : ⬧ ◅ ♀
Leisure activities : ⌂ ⚿ ⚓ ⚓
multi-sports ground
Facilities : ⚷ ♒ launderette
Nearby : ⚓ (beach)

G P S Longitude : 2.69457
Latitude : 44.09654

VILLEFRANCHE-DE-ROUERGUE

12200 – Michelin map **338** E4 – pop. 12 213 – alt. 230
▶ Paris 614 – Albi 68 – Cahors 61 – Montauban 80

⛰ Le Rouergue

✆ 05 65 45 16 24, www.campingdurouergue.com

Address : 35bis avenue de Fondies (located 1.5km southwest along the D 47, follow the signs for Monteils)

1,8 ha (93 pitches) flat, grassy

Rental rates : 7 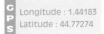 – 6 canvas bungalows.

Surroundings : ☐ ♤♤
Leisure activities : ⌂ ⚓
Facilities : ⚷ ♒ ⚑ ⚐ ♈ ▣
Nearby : ≋ jacuzzi ✂ ▦ ⛷ ⚓

G P S Longitude : 2.02615
Latitude : 44.3423

P. Cheuve / Photononstop

A local saying claims that the hearts of the men of the north are warm enough to thaw the chilly climate. They certainly throw themselves body and soul into the traditional 'dance of the giants' at local fairs and carnivals. Giants are huge in this part of France, as are the street markets: several tonnes of *moules-frites* (mussels and chips) and countless litres of beer sustain around a million visitors to the Braderie, Lille's annual giant street market where people turn out their attics and sell their goods on the streets of the town. The influence of Flanders can be heard in the names of towns and people, seen in the wealth of Gothic architecture and tasted in such delicious regional dishes as beef in amber beer and *potjevleesch*, a terrine made with rabbit, chicken and veal. The sound of bells ringing from tall, slender belfries, neat rows of miners' houses and the distant silhouettes of windmills, all remind visitors that they are on the border with Belgium and within sight of the white cliffs of Dover.

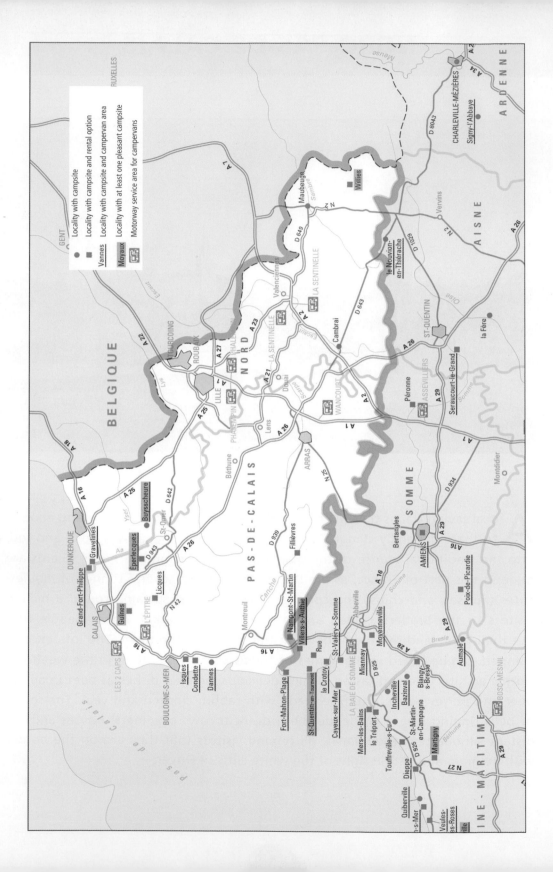

BUYSSCHEURE

59285 – Michelin map **302** B3 – pop. 510 – alt. 25
▶ Paris 269 – Béthune 44 – Calais 47 – Dunkerque 31

▲ La Chaumière

℘ 03 28 43 03 57, www.campinglachaumiere.com

Address : 529 Langhemast Straete (in the village)

Opening times : from beginning April to end Oct.

1 ha (29 pitches) small lake

Tariff : 22€ ♚♚ ⇔ ▣ ⒮ (6A) – Extra per person 8€

⬚ borne 19€ – 6 ▣ 19€

Surroundings : ⌂ ⌐ ⌂⌂
Leisure activities : ♟✗ ⬚⬚ ⌂ ⬚ ⬚ ⬚
Facilities : ⚬⟷ ⬚⬚⬚⬚ ⬚ ⬚ ⬚ ⬚ ▣

GPS Longitude : 2.33942
Latitude : 50.80166

CAMBRAI

59400 – Michelin map **302** H6 – pop. 32 518 – alt. 53
▶ Paris 183 – Lille 67 – Amiens 100 – Namur 139

▲ Municipal Les 3 Clochers

℘ 03 27 70 91 64, emerick.marecheau@orange.fr

Address : 77 rue Jean

1 ha (50 pitches) flat, grassy

Tourist information about Cambrai on the site.

Surroundings : ⌐ ⌂
Facilities : ⚬ ⬚⟷ ⬚ ⬚ ⬚
Nearby : ♟✗

GPS Longitude : 3.21476
Latitude : 50.17533

CONDETTE

62360 – Michelin map **301** C4 – pop. 2 575 – alt. 35
▶ Paris 254 – Boulogne-sur-Mer 10 – Calais 47 – Desvres 19

▲ Caravaning du Château ♟♟

℘ 03 21 87 59 59, www.camping-caravaning-du-chateau.com

Address : 21 rue Nouvelle (take the southern exit along the D 119)

Opening times : from beginning April to end Oct.

1,2 ha (70 pitches)

Tariff : 26,90€ ♚♚ ⇔ ▣ ⒮ (10A) – Extra per person 6,15€

Rental rates : (from beginning April to end Oct.) – 2 ⬚⬚.
Per night from 54 to 69€ – Per week from 445 to 650€

⬚ borne 5€

Surroundings : ⌐ ⌂⌂
Leisure activities : ⬚⬚ ⬚
Facilities : ⚬ ⬚⟷ ⬚ ⬚ ⬚ launderette, refrigerators
Nearby : ⬚

GPS Longitude : 1.62557
Latitude : 50.64649

DANNES

62187 – Michelin map **301** C4 – pop. 1 303 – alt. 30
▶ Paris 242 – Lille 136 – Arras 133 – Amiens 114

▲ Municipal Le Mont-St-Frieux

℘ 03 21 33 24 76, www.mairiededannes.fr

Address : rue de l'Eglise (in the town)

Opening times : Permanent

1,5 ha (52 pitches) flat, grassy

Tariff : ♚ 4,60€ ⇔ 3,10€ ▣ 4,60€ – ⒮ (16A) 5€

⬚ borne 5,10€

Surroundings : ⌐ ⌂
Leisure activities : ⬚⬚ ⬚ ⬚
Facilities : ⚬ ⬚ ⬚ launderette

GPS Longitude : 1.60997
Latitude : 50.58924

ÉPERLECQUES

62910 – Michelin map **301** G3 – pop. 3 162 – alt. 42
▶ Paris 271 – Lille 78 – Arras 86 – St-Omer 14

▲▲▲ Kawan Village Château du Gandspette

℘ 03 21 93 43 93, www.chateau-gandspette.com

Address : 133 rue du Gandspette

Opening times : from beginning April to end Sept.

11 ha/4 for camping (167 pitches)

Tariff : 31€ ♚♚ ⇔ ▣ ⒮ (6A) – Extra per person 7€ – Reservation fee 7€

Rental rates : (from beginning April to end Sept.) ⬚ – 8 ⬚⬚.
Per night from 56 to 87€ – Per week from 350 to 605€
Reservation fee 7€

⬚ borne 21€ – 10 ▣ 21€

In the wooded grounds of the château.

Surroundings : ⌂ ⌂
Leisure activities : ♟✗ ⬚⬚ ⬚ ⬚ ⬚ multi-sports ground
Facilities : ⚬ ⚬⟷ ⬚ ⬚ ⬚ launderette ⬚

GPS Longitude : 2.1789
Latitude : 50.81894

FILLIÈVRES

62770 – Michelin map **301** F6 – pop. 523 – alt. 46
▶ Paris 206 – Arras 52 – Béthune 46 – Hesdin 13

▲▲ Les Trois Tilleuls

℘ 03 21 47 94 15, www.camping3tilleuls.com – limited spaces for one-night stay

Address : 28 rue de Frévent (take the southeastern exit along the D 340)

Opening times : from beginning April to mid Oct.

4,5 ha (120 pitches)

Tariff : ♚ 4,50€ ⇔ 3€ ▣ 3€ – ⒮ (10A) 3,50€

Rental rates : (from beginning April to mid Oct.) ⚬ (1 mobile home) – 1 caravan – 7 ⬚⬚. Per week from 210 to 640€

In the heart of the Vallée de la Canche.

Surroundings : ⌐ ⌂⌂
Leisure activities : ⬚⬚ ⬚ ⬚ ⬚ multi-sports ground, entertainment room
Facilities : ⚬ ⚬⟷ ⬚ ⬚ launderette
Nearby : ⬚

GPS Longitude : 2.15952
Latitude : 50.31417

GRAND-FORT-PHILIPPE

59153 – Michelin map **302** A2 – pop. 5 491 – alt. 5
▶ Paris 289 – Calais 28 – Cassel 40 – Dunkerque 24

▲ La Plage

℘ 03 28 65 31 95, www.camping-de-la-plage.info

Address : 115 rue du Maréchal Foch (to the northwest)

Opening times : from beginning April to end Oct.

1,5 ha (84 pitches) flat, grassy

Tariff : 20,10€ ♚♚ ⇔ ▣ ⒮ (10A) – Extra per person 5,10€

Rental rates : (from beginning April to end Oct.) – 5 ⬚. Per night from 59€ – Per week from 184 to 435€

⬚ borne 2€

Surroundings : ⌂⌂
Leisure activities : ⬚⬚
Facilities : ⚬ ⚬⟷ ⬚ ⬚ launderette

GPS Longitude : 2.09746
Latitude : 51.00264

GRAVELINES

59820 – Michelin map **302** A2 – pop. 11 499
▶ Paris 309 – Lille 94 – Arras 125 – Brugge 100

⚠ Les Dunes

✆ 03 28 23 09 80, www.camping-des-dunes.com

Address : at Petit-Fort-Philippe, rue Victor-Hugo (beside the beach)

Opening times : from beginning April to end Oct.

8 ha (304 pitches)

Tariff : 24,15€ ♣♣ ⇔ 🔲 (⚡) (10A) – Extra per person 6,20€
Rental rates : (from beginning April to end Oct.) – 14 🚐 – 10 🏠
3 canvas bungalows. Per week from 244 to 770€

🚐 borne

| Surroundings : 🏖 ⌂ | | G P S | Longitude : 2.11802 |
| Facilities : ♿ ⊶ ▥ ᵠ launderette | | | Latitude : 51.00754 |

GUÎNES

62340 – Michelin map **301** E2 – pop. 5 501 – alt. 5
▶ Paris 282 – Arras 102 – Boulogne-sur-Mer 29 – Calais 11

⚑ Les Castels La Bien Assise ♣♣

✆ 03 21 35 20 77, www.camping-bien-assise.fr

Address : take the southwestern exit along the D 231, follow the signs for Marquise

20 ha/12 for camping (198 pitches) small lake

Rentals : 6 🚐 – 4 🏠 – 7 🛏.

There's a hotel and haute cuisine restaurant in the out-buildings of the château.

Surroundings : 🏖 ♀♀			
Leisure activities : ♍ ✕ 🎦 ⚡ ⛵ ⛳ 🎱 ⚓		G P S	Longitude : 1.85815
🖼 (open air in season) ⛷			Latitude : 50.86631
Facilities : ♿ ⊶ ▥ ⛲ ᵠ launderette ▨ ⚒			

ISQUES

62360 – Michelin map **301** C3 – pop. 1 173 – alt. 15
▶ Paris 247 – Lille 125 – Arras 122 – Calais 44

⚠ Les Cytises

✆ 03 21 31 11 10, www.lescytises.fr

Address : chemin Geoges Ducrocq (access via the N 1, near the stadium; from the A 16 take exit 28)

Opening times : from beginning April to end Oct.

2,5 ha (100 pitches) terrace, flat, grassy

Tariff : (2013 Price) 18,50€ ♣♣ ⇔ 🔲 (⚡) (10A) – Extra per person 4,50€
Rental rates : (2013 Price) – 2 🚐. Per night 50€ – Per week from 350 to 450€

🚐 borne 3€ – 3 🔲 17,80€

Surroundings : ⌂ ♀♀			
Leisure activities : 🎦 ⚡		G P S	Longitude : 1.64332
Facilities : ♿ ⊶ ᵠ launderette			Latitude : 50.67749
Nearby : ✕			

LICQUES

62850 – Michelin map **301** E3 – pop. 1 563 – alt. 81
▶ Paris 276 – Arras 97 – Boulogne-sur-Mer 31 – Calais 25

⚑ Pommiers des Trois Pays

✆ 03 21 35 02 02, www.pommiers-3pays.com

Address : 273 rue du Breuil

Opening times : from beginning April to end Oct.

2 ha (58 pitches) flat, grassy

Tariff : (2013 Price) ♣ 6€ ⇔ 🔲 8,50€ – (⚡) (16A) 4,80€
Rental rates : (from beginning April to end Oct.) ♿ (1 chalet)
10 🚐 – 5 🏠. Per night from 65 to 95€ – Per week from 300 to 600€

🚐 borne 5€ – 5 🔲 8,50€

Surroundings : 🏖 ⟨ ⌂ ♀			
Leisure activities : ♍ ✕ 🎦 ⚡ ⛷ (covered		G P S	Longitude : 1.94776
off season)			Latitude : 50.77991
Facilities : ♿ ⊙ ⛲ ⚓ ⟿ ᵠ launderette			

MAUBEUGE

59600 – Michelin map **302** L6 – pop. 31 970 – alt. 134
▶ Paris 242 – Charleville-Mézières 95 – Mons 21 – St-Quentin 114

⚠ Municipal du Clair de Lune

✆ 03 27 62 25 48, www.ville-maubeuge.fr

Address : 212 route de Mons (located 1.5km north along the N 2)

Opening times : from beginning April to end Sept.

2 ha (92 pitches) flat, grassy

Tariff : (2013 Price) ♣ 3,60€ ⇔ 🔲 3,50€ – (⚡) (10A) 4,50€

Ornamental flowers and shrubs decorate the site.

Surroundings : ⌂ ♀♀♀			
Leisure activities : ⚡		G P S	Longitude : 3.9766
Facilities : ♿ ⊶ ▥ ᵠ			Latitude : 50.29573

WILLIES

59740 – Michelin map **302** M7 – pop. 165 – alt. 167
▶ Paris 225 – Avesnes-sur-Helpe 16 – Cambrai 69 – Charleroi 48

⚑ Val Joly

✆ 03 27 61 83 76, www.valjoly.com

Address : at Eppé Sauvage, base nautique du Val Joly (located 1.5km east along the D 133, 300m from the lake)

Opening times : from end March to end Sept.

4 ha (180 pitches)

Tariff : (2013 Price) ♣ 4,95€ ⇔ 🔲 7,50€ (⚡) (6A)
Rental rates : (2013 Price) (and school holidays) – 30 🏠. Per night from 69 to 199€ – Per week from 310 to 1 049€

Located 1.5km from the tourist resort and the leisure and activity park.

Surroundings : 🏖 ♀♀			
Leisure activities : 🎦 ⚡ ⛳		G P S	Longitude : 4.11518
Facilities : ⊶ 🚫 ♿ ▥ launderette ▨			Latitude : 50.12245
Nearby : 🎣 ⚓			

B. Rieger / hemis.fr

Normandy has inspired many poets and artists, including Baudelaire, Turner and Monet. Today, it also offers rural relaxation and coastal rejuvenation. Take a walk along the coast to fill your lungs with sea air and admire the elegant resorts. You may need to catch your breath when you first see the medieval Benedictine abbey of Mont Saint-Michel rising up from the sands or glimpse the view over Étretat's white cliffs. No visitor could fail to be moved by the memory of the brave men who gave their lives on the Normandy beaches in World War II. Further inland, you will discover acres of neat, hedge-lined fields. Drink in the scent of apple blossom, admire the pretty half-timbered cottages and follow the River Seine as it meanders past medieval cities, impressive castles and venerable abbeys. No experience would be complete without savouring the region's culinary classics, including a plate of boat-fresh seafood, creamy Camembert, cider and Calvados, the famous apple brandy.

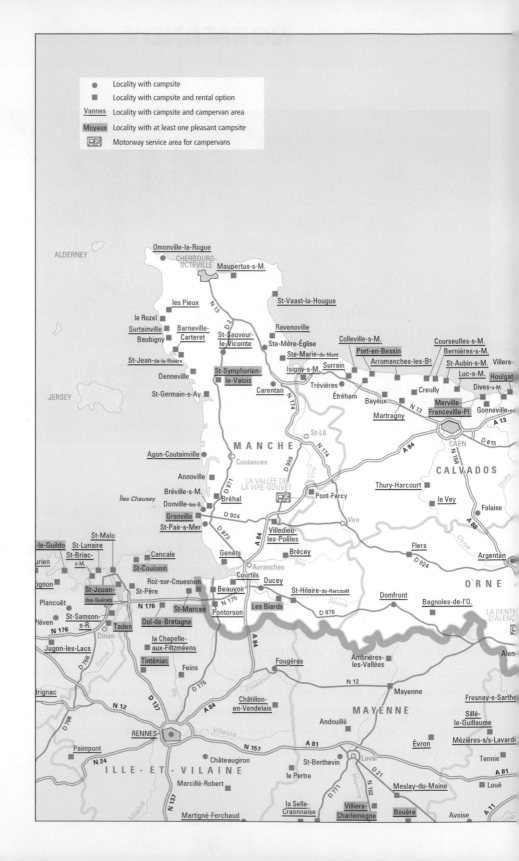

Legend:
- ● Locality with campsite
- ■ Locality with campsite and rental option
- <u>Vannes</u> Locality with campsite and campervan area
- Moyaux Locality with at least one pleasant campsite
- 🚐 Motorway service area for campervans

ALDERNEY

JERSEY

Omonville-la-Rogue
CHERBOURG-OCTEVILLE
Maupertus-s-M.

les Pieux
le Rozel
Surtainville
Baubigny
Barneville-Carteret
St-Sauveur-le-Vicomte
St-Jean-de-la-Rivière
St-Vaast-la-Hougue
Ravenoville
Ste-Mère-Église
Ste-Marie-du-Mont
Colleville-s-M.
Port-en-Bessin
Arromanches-les-Bs
Courseulles-s-M.
Bernières-s-M.
St-Aubin-s-M.
Luc-s-M.
Villers-
Houlgat
Denneville
St-Symphorien-le-Valois
Isigny-s-M.
Surrain
St-Germain-s-Ay
Carentan
Trévières
Étréham
Bayeux
Creully
Dives-s-M.
Merville-Franceville-Pl.
Gonneville-
Martragny
N 13
A 13
D 6 13

MANCHE
St-Lô
CAEN
CALVADOS
N 174
A 84
N 158
Agon-Coutainville
Coutances
Annoville
Thury-Harcourt
le Vey
Falaise
Bréville-s-M.
Donville-les-B.
Bréhal
Pont-Farcy
D 971
D 999
Îles Chausey
LA VALLÉE DE LA VIRE-GOUVET
Granville
St-Pair-s-Mer
D 924
Villedieu-les-Poêles
Flers
Argentan
Vire
D 973
A 84
Brécey
D 924
ORNE
le-Guildo
St-Malo
St-Lunaire
St-Briac-s-M.
urien
Cancale
Genêts
Avranches
Courtils
Ducey
St-Coulomb
Roz-sur-Couesnon
Beauvoir
St-Hilaire-du-Harcouët
Domfront
Bagnoles-de-l'O.
ignon
St-Jouan-des-Guérets
St-Père
N 176
Pontorson
N 175
Les Biards
D 976
LA DENTE D'ALENÇ
Plancoët
St-Marcan
Pléven
St-Samson-s-R.
Taden
Dol-de-Bretagne
Dinan
Alen
Jugon-les-Lacs
la Chapelle-aux-Filtzméens
Fougères
Ambrières-les-Vallées
drignac
Tinténiac
Feins
N 12
Mayenne
Fresnay-s-Sarthe
D 766
N 12
D 137
A 84
D 175
Châtillon-en-Vendelais
MAYENNE
Andouillé
Sillé-le-Guillaume
Mézières-s/s-Lavardi
RENNES
Vilaine
N 157
A 81
Évron
Tennie
Paimpont
N 24
Châteaugiron
St-Berthevin
Laval
Loué
A 81
ILLE-ET-VILAINE
le Pertre
Meslay-du-Maine
Marcillé-Robert
Avoise
A 11
N 137
la Selle-Craonnaise
Villiers-Charlemagne
Bouère
Martigné-Ferchaud

AGON-COUTAINVILLE

50230 – Michelin map **303** C5 – pop. 2 826 – alt. 36
▶ Paris 348 – Barneville-Carteret 48 – Carentan 43 – Cherbourg 80

⚠ Municipal le Marais

🖉 02 33 47 05 20, http://www.agoncoutainville.fr

Address : boulevard Lebel-Jéhenne (take the northeastern exit, near the racecourse)

Opening times : from beginning July to end Aug.

2 ha (104 pitches) flat, grassy

Tariff : 🚶 3,90€ ⟺ 🅴 5,50€ – 🔌 (5A) 3,20€
🚐 borne 6,10€ – 34 🅴 6,10€

Surroundings : 🗭
Leisure activities : 🏇
Facilities : ♿ ⛱ ⓣ
Nearby : 🍴 🚣 🛶

G P S Longitude : -1.59283
Latitude : 49.04975

⚠ Municipal le Martinet

🖉 02 33 47 05 20, www.agoncoutainville.fr

Address : bd Lebel-Jéhenne (take the northeastern exit, near the racecourse (hippodrome))

Opening times : from beginning April to end Oct.

1,5 ha (122 pitches) flat, grassy

Tariff : 🚶 3,90€ ⟺ 🅴 5,50€ – 🔌 (5A) 3,20€
🚐 borne 6,10€ – 34 🅴 6,10€

Surroundings : 🗭 🎣
Leisure activities : 🏇
Facilities : ♿ ⛱ ⓣ launderette
Nearby : 🍴 🚣 🛶 🐎

G P S Longitude : -1.59283
Latitude : 49.04958

ALENÇON

61000 – Michelin map **310** J4 – pop. 27 325 – alt. 135
▶ Paris 190 – Chartres 119 – Évreux 119 – Laval 90

⚠ Municipal de Guéramé

🖉 02 33 26 34 95, camping.guerame@orange.fr

Address : 65 route de Guéramé (to the southwest along the ring road (périphérique))

1,5 ha (54 pitches)

Pleasant setting beside the Sarthe river.

Surroundings : 🗭 🎣
Leisure activities : 🏛 🏇 🎾
Facilities : ♿ ⛱ ▥ 🛁 🛒 launderette
Nearby : 🍴 🚣 🛶 🏌 🐎

G P S Longitude : 0.0728
Latitude : 48.4259

ANNOVILLE

50660 – Michelin map **303** C6 – pop. 619 – alt. 28
▶ Paris 348 – Barneville-Carteret 57 – Carentan 48 – Coutances 14

⚠ Municipal les Peupliers

🖉 02 33 47 67 73, www.camping-annoville.fr

Address : rue des Peupliers (3km southwest along the D 20 and take the road to the right, 500m from the beach)

Opening times : from mid June to beginning Sept.

2 ha (100 pitches)

Tariff : (2013 Price) 🚶 3€ ⟺ 🅴 3,40€ – 🔌 (6A) 3,20€

Rental rates : (from beginning April to end Sept.) 🚫 – 5 🚍.
Per week from 400 to 450€

Surroundings : 🐟
Leisure activities : 🏇 🚲 ⛵
Facilities : ⛱ ⓣ ▣ 🛁

G P S Longitude : -1.55309
Latitude : 48.95767

ARGENTAN

61200 – Michelin map **310** I2 – pop. 14 356 – alt. 160
▶ Paris 191 – Alençon 46 – Caen 59 – Dreux 115

⚠⚠ Municipal de la Noë

🖉 02 33 36 05 69, www.argentan.fr/tourisme

Address : rue de la Noé

Opening times : from beginning April to end Sept.

0,3 ha (23 pitches) flat, grassy

Tariff : 🚶 2,30€ ⟺ 2€ 🅴 2,60€ – 🔌 (6A) 2,60€
🚐 borne 2,20€

Pleasant location near a park and a small lake.

Surroundings : 🗭
Leisure activities : 🏛
Facilities : ♿ ⛱ ⓣ launderette
Nearby : 🏊 🚣 ⛳ fitness trail

G P S Longitude : -0.01687
Latitude : 48.73995

ARROMANCHES-LES-BAINS

14117 – Michelin map **303** I3 – pop. 608 – alt. 15
▶ Paris 266 – Bayeux 11 – Caen 34 – St-Lô 46

⚠ Municipal

🖉 02 31 22 36 78, camping.arromanches@wanadoo.fr

Address : 9 avenue de Verdun

Opening times : from beginning April to beginning Nov.

1,5 ha (126 pitches)

Tariff : 17,40€ 🚶🚶 ⟺ 🅴 🔌 (10A) – Extra per person 4,15€
Rental rates : (from beginning April to beginning Nov.) – 6 🚍.
Per night from 75€ – Per week from 355 to 406€
🚐 borne

Surroundings : 🎣
Leisure activities : 🏇
Facilities : ♿ ⛱ (from mid June to mid Sept.) ⓣ launderette
Nearby : 🍴 🖼 🚣 🛶 🐎

G P S Longitude : -0.62642
Latitude : 49.3381

AUMALE

76390 – Michelin map **304** K3 – pop. 2 405 – alt. 130
▶ Paris 136 – Amiens 48 – Beauvais 49 – Dieppe 69

⚠ Municipal le Grand Mail

🖉 02 35 93 40 50, www.aumale.com – 🏕

Address : 6 Le Grand Mail

Opening times : from beginning April to end Sept.

0,6 ha (40 pitches) flat, grassy

Tariff : 🚶 2,70€ ⟺ 2,70€ 🅴 2,70€ – 🔌 (10A) 2,70€
🚐 borne 2€

Situated on the side of a hill, on the slopes above the town.

Surroundings : 🐟 🎣
Facilities : ♿ 🛁 ▥ ▥

G P S Longitude : 1.74202
Latitude : 49.76566

BAGNOLES-DE-L'ORNE

61140 – Michelin map **310** G3 – pop. 2 454 – alt. 140 – ⚓
▶ Paris 236 – Alençon 48 – Argentan 39 – Domfront 19

⚠ Municipal la Vée

✆ 02 33 37 87 45, www.campingbagnolesdelorne.com
Address : avenue du Président Coty (1.3km southwest, near Tessé-la-Madeleine, 30m from the river)
Opening times : from mid March to mid Nov.
2,8 ha (250 pitches)
Tariff : 16,80 € ★★ 🚗 🅿 🔌 (10A) – Extra per person 4,30 €
Rental rates : (from mid March to mid Nov.) – 14 🏠. Per week from 342 to 420 €
🚐 51 🅿 7,70 €

Surroundings : 🌿 ♡
Leisure activities : 🏛 🏇
Facilities : ♿ ☎ 🚿 🛁 ⚡ 🚰 launderette 🚰
Nearby : 🍴 🎿 🏊 🏇 fitness trail

G P S Longitude : -0.41982
Latitude : 48.54787

BARNEVILLE-CARTERET

50270 – Michelin map **303** B3 – pop. 2 282 – alt. 47
▶ Paris 356 – Caen 123 – Carentan 43 – Cherbourg 39

⚠ Les Bosquets

✆ 02 33 04 73 62, www.camping-lesbosquets.com
Address : rue du Capitaine Quenault (2.5km southwest following signs for Barneville-Plage and take turning to the left, 450m from the beach)
Opening times : from beginning April to mid Sept.
15 ha/6 for camping (331 pitches)
Tariff : ★ 6,30 € 🚗 🅿 6,30 € – 🔌 (10A) 4,30 €
🚐 borne
Set in wild surroundings among pine trees and dunes.

Surroundings : 🌿 ♡ ♨
Leisure activities : 🍴 🏛 🎱 🏇 🎿
Facilities : ☎ 🛁 launderette
Nearby : 🍴 ♨ 🏇 sand yachting

G P S Longitude : -1.76081
Latitude : 49.36587

⚠ La Gerfleur

✆ 02 33 04 38 41, www.lagerfleur.fr
Address : rue Guillaume-le-Conquérant (800m west along the D 903e, follow the signs for Carteret)
2,3 ha (93 pitches)
Rentals : 🏠 – 9 🏠.
Situated beside a small lake.

Surroundings : ♡ ♨
Leisure activities : 🍴 🏛 🏇 🎿 🐟
Facilities : ♿ 🚰 launderette
Nearby : 🍴 🏛 🎿 ♨ 🏇

G P S Longitude : -1.76435
Latitude : 49.38346

There are several different types of sani-station ('borne' in French) – sanitation points providing fresh water and disposal points for grey water. See page 12 for further details.

BAUBIGNY

50270 – Michelin map **303** B3 – pop. 154 – alt. 30
▶ Paris 361 – Barneville-Carteret 9 – Cherbourg 33 – Valognes 28

⚠ Bel Sito

✆ 02 33 04 32 74, www.bel-sito.com – 🍴
Address : north of the village
Opening times : from mid April to mid Sept.
6 ha/4 for camping (85 pitches) dunes
Tariff : ★ 6,60 € 🚗 🅿 9,10 € – 🔌 (6A) 3,80 €
Rental rates : Permanent – 1 🏠 – 7 🏠. Per week from 330 to 830 €
In a rural setting among the dunes.

Surroundings : 🌿 ⬆
Leisure activities : 🏛 🏇
Facilities : ☎ (July–Aug.) 🚿 🛁 🚰 launderette

G P S Longitude : -1.80513
Latitude : 49.42954

The Michelin classification (⚠⚠⚠ ... ⚠) is totally independent of the official star classification system awarded by the local prefecture or other official organisation.

BAYEUX

14400 – Michelin map **303** H4 – pop. 13 348 – alt. 50
▶ Paris 265 – Caen 31 – Cherbourg 95 – Flers 69

⚠ Municipal

✆ 02 31 92 08 43, www.camping-bayeux.fr
Address : boulevard Eindhoven (north of the town)
2,5 ha (140 pitches) flat, grassy
Rentals : 5 🏠.
Ornamental trees and shrubs decorate the site.

Surroundings : ♨♨
Leisure activities : 🏛 🏇
Facilities : ♿ ☎ 🚰 launderette
Nearby : 🍴 🏊 (open air in season)

G P S Longitude : -0.69774
Latitude : 49.28422

BAZINVAL

76340 – Michelin map **304** J2 – pop. 350 – alt. 120
▶ Paris 165 – Abbeville 33 – Amiens 62 – Blangy-sur-Bresle 9

⚠ Municipal de la Forêt

✆ 02 32 97 04 01, bazinval2@wanadoo.fr
Address : 10 rue de Saulx (take the southwestern exit along the D 115 and take turning to the left, near the town hall)
Opening times : from beginning April to end Oct.
0,4 ha (20 pitches)
Tariff : 12 € ★★ 🚗 🅿 🔌 (10A) – Extra per person 2 €
🚐 borne 3,50 € – 2 🅿 3,50 €
Ornamental trees and shrubs surround the pitches.

Surroundings : ♡ ♨
Facilities : 🚰 🚽 🛁

G P S Longitude : 1.55136
Latitude : 49.95487

BEAUVOIR

50170 – Michelin map **303** C8 – pop. 419
▶ Paris 358 – Caen 125 – St-Lô 91 – Rennes 63

⚞ Aux Pommiers

𝒫 0233601136, www.camping-auxpommiers.com

Address : 28 route du Mont Saint Michel

Opening times : from beginning April to mid Nov.

1,79 ha (107 pitches) flat, grassyTariff : 24,80€ ♣♣ ⟵ 🔲 🔌 (10A) – Extra per person 6,50€

Rental rates : (from beginning April to mid Nov.) – 1 caravan 16 🛏 – 5 🏠 – 4 🏡 – 4 canvas bungalows. Per night from 40 to 68€ – Per week from 200 to 625€

🚐 borne – 10 🔲 19,64€ – 🚐🔌17,72€

Surroundings : ♀
Leisure activities : 🍸🏊🚣🎣🏇🧖🛶
Facilities : 🔗 – 2 individual sanitary facilities (🚿💧 wc) 🍴 launderette
Nearby : 🍴🎯🏇

GPS Longitude : -1.51264
Latitude : 48.59618

To make the best possible use of this guide, please read pages 2–15 carefully.

LE BEC-HELLOUIN

27800 – Michelin map **304** E6 – pop. 419 – alt. 101
▶ Paris 153 – Bernay 22 – Évreux 46 – Lisieux 46

⚞ Municipal St-Nicolas

𝒫 0232448355, www.campingstnicolas.fr

Address : 15 rue St-Nicolas (situated 2km east, along the D 39 and D 581, follow the signs for Malleville-sur-le-Bec and take road to the left)

Opening times : from mid March to mid Oct.

3 ha (90 pitches) flat, grassy

Tariff : (2013 Price) 17,60€ ♣♣ ⟵ 🔲 🔌 (10A) – Extra per person 4,10€

Rental rates : (2013 Price) (from mid March to mid Oct.) 4 🛏. Per night from 48 to 102€ – Per week from 180 to 450€ Reservation fee 8€

🚐 borne 3,10€

A well-kept site with flowers.

Surroundings : 🏊♀
Leisure activities : 🚣🍴 library
Facilities : 🔗🔗🚿🍴 launderette
Nearby : 🏇

GPS Longitude : 0.72268
Latitude : 49.23586

BELLÊME

61130 – Michelin map **310** M4 – pop. 1 547 – alt. 241
▶ Paris 168 – Alençon 42 – Chartres 76 – La Ferté-Bernard 23

⚞ Le Val

𝒫 0624705517, beulay-automobiles@wanadoo.fr

Address : take the western exit along the D 955, follow the signs for Mamers and take road to the left, near the swimming pool

Opening times : Permanent

1,5 ha (50 pitches)

Tariff : (2013 Price) 19€ ♣♣ ⟵ 🔲 🔌 (10A) – Extra per person 4,50€

Rental rates : Permanent 🏕 – 1 🛏 – 1 cabin in the trees Per night from 65 to 159€ – Per week from 390 to 890€
🚐 borne 11€ – 4 🔲 11€

Surroundings : 🏊🛒♀
Facilities : 🔗🚮🛁🍴
Nearby : 🍴🧖🛶

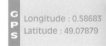

GPS Longitude : 0.555
Latitude : 48.3747

BERNAY

27300 – Michelin map **304** D7 – pop. 10 285 – alt. 105
▶ Paris 155 – Argentan 69 – Évreux 49 – Le Havre 72

⚞ Municipal

𝒫 0232433047, www.bernay-tourisme.fr

Address : rue des Canadiens (situated 2km southwest along the N 138, follow the signs for Alençon and take turning to the left - recommended route via the diversion (déviation) and ZI Malouve)

Opening times : from beginning May to end Sept.

1 ha (50 pitches) flat, grassy

Tariff : (2013 Price) 17,25€ ♣♣ ⟵ 🔲 🔌 (8A) – Extra per person 3,20€

Rental rates : (from beginning May to end Sept.) – 2 🛏 Per night 46€ – Per week from 290 to 367€
🚐 borne 2,50€

A well-kept, lush green campsite.

Surroundings : 🛒♀
Leisure activities : 🎪🚣
Facilities : 🔗🔗🛁🛒🍴 launderette
Nearby : 🍴🛶🧖

GPS Longitude : 0.58683
Latitude : 49.07879

The prices listed were supplied by the campsite owners in 2013 (if prices were not available, those from the previous year are given). The fees should be regarded as basic charges and may fluctuate with inflation.

BERNIÈRES-SUR-MER

14990 – Michelin map **303** J4 – pop. 2 351
▶ Paris 253 – Caen 20 – Le Havre 114 – Hérouville-Saint-Clair 21

⚞ Le Havre de Bernières

𝒫 0231966709, www.camping-normandie.com

Address : chemin de Quintefeuille

Opening times : from beginning April to end Oct.

6,5 ha (240 pitches) flat, grassy

Tariff : 40,30€ ♣♣ ⟵ 🔲 🔌 (20A) – Extra per person 7,10€

Rental rates : (from beginning April to end Oct.) – 32 🛏 Per night from 91 to 188€ – Per week from 510 to 1313€
🚐 borne 3€

Surroundings : ♀♀
Leisure activities : 🍸🏓🎪🎮🚿🚣🛶
Facilities : 🔗🔗📶🛒🧖🍴 launderette 🚿
Nearby : 🍴🧖🏖 (beach) 🎳 bowling

GPS Longitude : -0.42795
Latitude : 49.33245

We value your opinion and welcome your feedback. Do email us at campingfrance@tp.michelin.com

LES BIARDS

50540 – Michelin map **303** E8 – alt. 495
▶ Paris 358 – Alençon 108 – Avranches 22 – Caen 126

⚠ Municipal La Mazure

📞 02 33 89 19 50, www.lamazure.com

Address : at the base de loisirs (leisure centre) (2.3km southwest along the D 85e, on the banks of the lake at Vezins)

3,5 ha/0,4 (28 pitches)

Rentals : 12 🏠 – 4 tipis.

Surroundings : 🌳 🏕
Leisure activities : ♟ 🏛 🎣 🚣 🚲 ✂
Facilities : ♿ ⚬━ 🚿 🚽 ♨ launderette 🧺
At the leisure/activities centre : 🎿 🐎
electric boats

Longitude : -1.2047
Latitude : 48.5734

BLANGY-LE-CHÂTEAU

14130 – Michelin map **303** N4 – pop. 670 – alt. 60
▶ Paris 197 – Caen 56 – Deauville 22 – Lisieux 16

⚠ Les Castels Le Brevedent 🔼

📞 02 31 64 72 88, www.campinglebrevedent.com ✂

Address : route du Pin (3km southeast along the D 51, by the château; beside a lake)

Opening times : from beginning May to mid Sept.

6 ha/3,5 for camping (140 pitches)

Tariff : (2013 Price) ♣ 8€ ⭢ 🄴 12,10€ – ⚡ (10A) 4,50€

Rental rates : (from beginning April to end Sept.) ✂ – 8 🛖.
Per night from 90 to 120€ – Per week from 225 to 680€
🚰 borne
In the grounds of a 14th-century château that also features a lake.

Surroundings : 🌳 ≼ 🌳🌳
Leisure activities : ♟ 🏛 🌙nighttime 🤸
🚣 🚲 🛶 🎣 ✂
Facilities : ♿ ⚬━ 🚿 🚽 ♨ launderette 🧺 🧺
Nearby : ✂ 🐎 🏇

Longitude : 0.3045
Latitude : 49.2253

BLANGY-SUR-BRESLE

76340 – Michelin map **304** J2 – pop. 3 000 – alt. 70
▶ Paris 156 – Abbeville 29 – Amiens 56 – Dieppe 55

⚠ Aux Cygnes d'Opale

📞 02 35 94 55 65, www.auxcygnesdopale.fr

Address : rue du Marais (southeast, between two lakes and 200m from the Bresle river; access via the r. du Maréchal-Leclerc, near the church)

Opening times : from beginning April to end Oct.

0,8 ha (57 pitches) flat, grassy

Tariff : (2013 Price) 19,50€ ♣♣ ⭢ 🄴 ⚡ (10A) –
Extra per person 3,50€

Rental rates : (from beginning April to end Oct.) – 10 🛖.
Per night from 70 to 150€ – Per week from 350 to 550€

Surroundings : ≼
Leisure activities : 📺 🎣
Facilities : ♿ ⚬━ ♨
Nearby : 🚣 ✂ 🏇 🎣

Longitude : 1.63638
Latitude : 49.93096

BOURG-ACHARD

27310 – Michelin map **304** E5 – pop. 2 948 – alt. 124
▶ Paris 141 – Bernay 39 – Évreux 62 – Le Havre 62

⚠ Le Clos Normand

📞 02 32 56 34 84, www.leclosnormand.eu

Address : 235 route de Pont-Audemer (take the western exit)

Opening times : from mid April to end Sept.

1,4 ha (75 pitches)

Tariff : 20,50€ ♣♣ ⭢ 🄴 ⚡ (6A) – Extra per person 5€

Rental rates : (from beginning April to end Sept.) ✂ – 6 🛖.
Per night from 70€ – Per week from 250 to 470€
🚰 borne
In a green setting with flowers.

Surroundings : 🗩 🌿
Leisure activities : ♟ 🏛 🚣 🎿
Facilities : ⚬━ ♨ 🄴 🧺

Longitude : 0.80765
Latitude : 49.35371

The pitches of many campsites are marked out with low hedges of attractive bushes and shrubs.

BRÉCEY

50370 – Michelin map **303** F7 – pop. 2 165 – alt. 75
▶ Paris 328 – Avranches 17 – Granville 42 – St-Hilaire-du-Harcouët 20

⚠ Intercommunal le Pont Roulland

📞 02 33 48 60 60, www.camping-brecey.com

Address : 1.1km east along the D 911, follow the signs for Cuves

Opening times : from end April to beginning Sept.

1 ha (52 pitches)

Tariff : (2013 Price) ♣ 2,70€ ⭢ 🄴 3,60€ – ⚡ (6A) 2,80€

Rental rates : (from end April to beginning Sept.) – 4 🛖.
Per night from 60 to 80€ – Per week from 300 to 400€
🚰 borne 4,65€
In a rural setting near a small lake.

Surroundings : 🌳 🌿
Leisure activities : 🚣 🎣 🎿
Facilities : 🧺 ♨ 🄴
Nearby : ✂

Longitude : -1.15235
Latitude : 48.72184

BRÉHAL

50290 – Michelin map **303** C6 – pop. 3 017 – alt. 69
▶ Paris 345 – Caen 113 – St-Lô 48 – St-Malo 101

⚠ La Vanlée

📞 02 33 61 63 80, www.camping-vanlee.com

Address : rue des Gabions

Opening times : from beginning May to mid Sept.

11 ha (466 pitches)

Tariff : (2013 Price) 24,30€ ♣♣ ⭢ 🄴 ⚡ (6A) – Extra per person 5,80€
Reservation fee 9€
🚰 borne 4,50€ – 🚐 18€
In a pleasant setting on an unspoilt site beside the sea.

Surroundings : 🌳 ⛱
Leisure activities : ♟ 🏛 🚣 🎣 multi-sports ground
Facilities : ♿ ♨ launderette 🚏

Longitude : -1.56474
Latitude : 48.90913

BRÉVILLE-SUR-MER

50290 – Michelin map **303** K4 – pop. 803 – alt. 70
▶ Paris 341 – Caen 108 – St-Lô 50 – St-Malo 95

⛰ Kawan Village La Route Blanche 👥

✆ 02 33 50 23 31, www.camping-breville.com

Address : 6 rue de La Route Blanche (located 1km northwest following signs for the beach, near the golf course)

5,5 ha (273 pitches)
Rentals : ※ – 25 🚐.

Surroundings : 🖵		
Leisure activities : ✗ 🏠 🎣 ⛳ 🚴 🏊 ⛷ multi-sports ground	**G**	Longitude : -1.56376
Facilities : ♿ ⛟ ☕ 🍴 launderette ⚐,	**P**	Latitude : 48.86966
Nearby : 🍴 ♨ 🐎 sports trail	**S**	

CANY-BARVILLE

76450 – Michelin map **304** D3 – pop. 3 080 – alt. 25
▶ Paris 187 – Bolbec 34 – Dieppe 45 – Fécamp 21

⛰ Municipal

✆ 02 35 97 70 37, www.cany-barville.fr

Address : route de Barville (take the southern exit along the D 268, follow the signs for Yvetot, after the stadium)

Opening times : from beginning April to end Sept.

2,9 ha (100 pitches) flat, grassy, concrete surface areas

Tariff : 14,45€ ★★ 🚐 🔳 🔌 (10A) – Extra per person 3,45€
🚰 borne 2,65€ – 62 🔳 5,20€

Surroundings : 🖵		
Leisure activities : 🏠 🚴	**G**	Longitude : 0.64231
Facilities : ♿ ⛟ 🎱 🚿 🚽 🍴 launderette	**P**	Latitude : 49.7834
	S	

CARENTAN

50500 – Michelin map **303** E4 – pop. 6 056 – alt. 18
▶ Paris 308 – Avranches 89 – Caen 74 – Cherbourg 52

⛰ Flower Le Haut Dick

✆ 02 33 42 16 89, www.camping-lehautdick.com

Address : 30 chemin du Grand Bas Pays (beside the canal, near the swimming pool)

Opening times : from end March to end Sept.

2,5 ha (130 pitches)

Tariff : 26,50€ ★★ 🚐 🔳 🔌 (10A) – Extra per person 5€
Rental rates : (from end March to end Sept.) – 4 tent lodges. Per night from 55 to 79€ – Per week from 385 to 553€
🚰 borne – 2 🔳 14,50€ – 🔌 11€
In a pleasant, leafy setting.

Surroundings : 🌳 🖵 ♨		
Leisure activities : 🍴 ✗ 🏠 🚴 ⛷	**G**	Longitude : -1.23917
Facilities : ♿ ⛟ 🍴	**P**	Latitude : 49.3087
Nearby : 🍴 🎮 🏊 🚣	**S**	

Using the traditional Michelin classification method, the guide provides you with an easy, speedy reference for assessing the category of each site: 1 to 5 tents (see page 10).

COLLEVILLE-SUR-MER

14710 – Michelin map **303** G3 – pop. 171 – alt. 42
▶ Paris 281 – Bayeux 18 – Caen 48 – Carentan 36

⛰ Le Robinson

✆ 02 31 22 45 19, www.campinglerobinson.com

Address : at Hameau de Cabourg (800m northeast along the D 514, follow the signs for Port-en-Bessin)

Opening times : from beginning April to end Sept.

1 ha (67 pitches) flat, grassy

Tariff : ★ 6,20€ 🚐 2,75€ 🔳 6€ – 🔌 (6A) 4,75€ – Reservation fee 17€
Rental rates : (from beginning April to mid Sept.) ※ – 13 🚐 2 🏠 – 1 canvas bungalow. Per night from 50 to 70€ – Per week from 298 to 696€ – Reservation fee 17€
🚰 borne

Surroundings : 🖵		
Leisure activities : 🍷 ✗ 🚴 ⛷ ⛷	**G**	Longitude : -0.83497
Facilities : ♿ ⛟ 🍴 launderette	**P**	Latitude : 49.34968
Nearby : 🍴 🐎	**S**	

*The classification (1 to 5 tents, **black** or **red**) that we award to selected sites in this guide is our own system. It should not be confused with the classification (1 to 5 stars) of official organisations.*

COURSEULLES-SUR-MER

14470 – Michelin map **303** J4 – pop. 4 185
▶ Paris 252 – Arromanches-les-Bains 14 – Bayeux 24 – Cabourg 41

⛰ Municipal le Champ de Course

✆ 02 31 37 99 26, www.campingcourseulles.com

Address : avenue de la Libération (to the north)

Opening times : from beginning April to mid Oct.

7,5 ha (381 pitches) flat, grassy

Tariff : 22€ ★★ 🚐 🔳 🔌 (10A) – Extra per person 5€ – Reservation fee 4€
Rental rates : (from beginning April to mid Oct.) – 26 🚐 – 4 🏠 2 tent lodges. Per night from 60 to 120€ – Per week 680€ Reservation fee 4€
🚰 borne 6,20€
Situated near the beach.

Surroundings : 🖵		
Leisure activities : 🏠 🚴	**G**	Longitude : -0.44606
Facilities : ♿ ⛟ 🎱 🚿 🚽 🍴 launderette	**P**	Latitude : 49.33289
Nearby : ✗ 🍴 🎮 🏊 ♨ 🐎	**S**	

COURTILS

50220 – Michelin map **303** D8 – pop. 245 – alt. 35
▶ Paris 349 – Avranches 13 – Fougères 43 – Pontorson 15

⛰ St-Michel

✆ 02 33 70 96 90, www.campingsaintmichel.com

Address : 35 route du Mont Saint Michel (take the western exit along the D 43)

Opening times : from mid March to mid Nov.

2,5 ha (100 pitches)

Tariff : 25€ ★★ 🚐 🔳 🔌 (6A) – Extra per person 7€

Rental rates : (from mid March to mid Nov.) – 42 🚐. Per night from 45 to 110€ – Per week from 252 to 770€
🚐 borne – 5 ▣ 19€ – 🚿14€

Surroundings : 〜 ♀
Leisure activities : ✗ 🏠 🏄 🚴 🛶 wildlife park
Facilities : ♿ ⛽ CC▥ 🚽 launderette 🚿
Nearby : 🍴 🐎

GPS Longitude : -1.41611
Latitude : 48.62829

CREULLY

14480 – Michelin map **303** I4 – pop. 1 610 – alt. 27
▶ Paris 253 – Bayeux 14 – Caen 20 – Deauville 62

⛺ Intercommunal des 3 Rivières

📞 02 31 80 90 17, www.campingdes3rivieres.fr

Address : route de Tierceville (800m to the northeast; beside the Seulles river)

2 ha (82 pitches)

Rentals : 5 🚐.

Pleasant green setting.

Surroundings : 🌳 ← 〜 ♀
Leisure activities : 🏠 🚴 🎣 🛶
Facilities : ⛽ ▥ 🔥
Nearby : 🏃 fitness trail

GPS Longitude : -0.5295
Latitude : 49.28964

DENNEVILLE

50580 – Michelin map **303** C4 – pop. 539 – alt. 5
▶ Paris 347 – Barneville-Carteret 12 – Carentan 34 – St-Lô 53

⛰ L'Espérance

📞 02 33 07 12 71, www.camping-esperance.fr – limited spaces for one-night stay

Address : 36 rue de la Gamburie (3.5km west along the D 137, 500m from the beach)

Opening times : from beginning April to end Sept.

3 ha (134 pitches)

Tariff : (2013 Price) 30€ 👫 🚗 ▣ 🔌 (6A) – Extra per person 6,60€
Rental rates : (from beginning April to end Sept.) – 12 🚐. Per night from 45 to 99€ – Per week from 310 to 690€

Surroundings : 🌳 ♀
Leisure activities : 🍴 ✗ nighttime 🏃 🎣 🛶
Facilities : ⛽ 🚽 launderette 🚿

GPS Longitude : -1.68832
Latitude : 49.30332

DIEPPE

76200 – Michelin map **304** G2 – pop. 32 670 – alt. 6
▶ Paris 197 – Abbeville 68 – Beauvais 107 – Caen 176

⛰ Vitamin'

📞 02 35 82 11 11, www.camping-vitamin.com – limited spaces for one-night stay

Address : 865 chemin des Vertus (3km south along the N 27, follow the signs for Rouen and take a right turn)

Opening times : from beginning April to mid Oct.

5,3 ha (180 pitches) flat, grassy

Tariff : 25,90€ 👫 🚗 ▣ 🔌 (10A) – Extra per person 5,90€
Reservation fee 5€

Rental rates : (from beginning April to mid Oct.) ♿ – 27 🚐 4 🏡. Per night from 49 to 65€ – Per week from 229 to 690€
Reservation fee 5€

Surroundings : 〜
Leisure activities : 🍸 🏠 🎡 ⛵ 🏄 🛶 🎿 multi-sports ground
Facilities : ♿ ⛽ 🚽 launderette
Nearby : ✗ 🏊 🎨 🛶 squash

GPS Longitude : 1.07481
Latitude : 49.90054

⛰ La Source

📞 02 35 84 27 04, www.camping-la-source.fr – limited spaces for one-night stay

Address : 63 rue des Tisserands (3km southwest along the D 925, follow the signs for Le Havre then turn left onto D 153; at Petit-Appeville)

Opening times : from mid March to mid Oct.

2,5 ha (120 pitches) flat, grassy

Tariff : 👤 6,50€ 🚗 2€ ▣ 9,30€ – 🔌 (10A) 4,40€ – Reservation fee 7€
Rental rates : Permanent – 6 🚐. Per night from 100 to 120€
Per week from 303 to 303€ – Reservation fee 13€
🚐 borne 2,50€ – 14 ▣ 28,50€
A picturesque setting beside the Scie river.

Leisure activities : 🍸 🏠 🏃 🚴 🛶 🎣
Facilities : ♿ CC▥ 🚽 launderette

GPS Longitude : 1.05526
Latitude : 49.89619

DIVES-SUR-MER

14160 – Michelin map **303** L4 – pop. 5 935 – alt. 3
▶ Paris 219 – Cabourg 2 – Caen 27 – Deauville 22

⛺ Le Golf

📞 02 31 24 73 09, www.campingdugolf.com – limited spaces for one-night stay

Address : route de Lisieux (take the eastern exit, D 45 for 3.5km)

2,8 ha (155 pitches) flat, grassy

Rentals : 15 🚐 – 3 🏡 – 1 tipi – 1 canvas bungalow.

Surroundings : 〜 ♀
Leisure activities : 🍸 🏃 🛶
Facilities : ♿ ⛽ 🚽 launderette

GPS Longitude : -0.0701
Latitude : 49.2792

This guide is updated regularly, so buy your new copy every year!

DOMFRONT

61700 – Michelin map **310** F3 – pop. 3 866 – alt. 185
▶ Paris 250 – Alençon 62 – Argentan 55 – Avranches 65

⛺ Municipal le Champ Passais

📞 02 33 37 37 66, http://camping-municipal-domfront.jimdo.com

Address : rue du Champ Passais (head south along the station road and take the turning to the left)

1,5 ha (34 pitches)
🚐 borne

Surroundings : 〜
Leisure activities : 🏠 🏃
Facilities : ♿ 🚿 🌱 🔥
Nearby : 🚴 🍴 🛶

GPS Longitude : -0.6505
Latitude : 48.5889

DONVILLE-LES-BAINS

50350 – Michelin map **303** C6 – pop. 3 269 – alt. 40
▶ Paris 341 – Caen 112 – St-Lô 77

⚠ L'Ermitage

📞 02 33 50 09 01, www.camping-ermitage.com

Address : rue de l'Ermitage (located 1km north along the r. du Champ de Courses)

Opening times : from mid April to mid Oct.

5 ha (298 pitches)

Tariff : 👤 5,20€ 🚗 2€ 🔲 4,60€ – ⚡ (10A) 3,70€
Near a beautiful beach of fine sand.

Surroundings : 🔲
Leisure activities : 🏠 🌙 daytime 🛶
Facilities : 🚿 ⚐ 🧺 launderette
Nearby : 🏖 🍴 ✕ 🎯 ✂ 🔲 (open air in season) 🚶 🐎 bowling

G P S	Longitude : -1.58075	Latitude : 48.85212

DUCEY

50220 – Michelin map **303** E8 – pop. 2 465 – alt. 15
▶ Paris 348 – Avranches 11 – Fougères 41 – Rennes 80

⚠ Municipal la Sélune

📞 02 33 48 46 49, www.ducey-tourisme.com

Address : rue de Boishue (take the western exit along the N 176 and take the D 178, follow the signs for St-Aubin-de-Terregatte to the left; by the stadium)

Opening times : from beginning April to end Sept.

0,42 ha (40 pitches) flat, grassy Tariff : (2013 Price) 👤 2,95€ 🚗 1€ 🔲 1,45€ – ⚡ (5A) 1,95€
🚐 2 🔲 8,80€
Pitches well marked out with hedges of thuja.

Surroundings : 🔲
Facilities : 🚿 ⚐ 🍴
Nearby : ✕ 🔲 🏊

G P S	Longitude : -1.29452	Latitude : 48.61686

ÉTRÉHAM

14400 – Michelin map **303** H4 – pop. 271 – alt. 30
▶ Paris 276 – Bayeux 11 – Caen 42 – Carentan 40

⚠⚠ Reine Mathilde

📞 02 31 21 76 55, www.camping-normandie-rm.fr

Address : at Le Marais (located 1km west along the D 123 and take the road to the right)

6,5 ha (115 pitches) flat, grassy

Rentals : 6 🏠 – 6 🏡 – 2 canvas bungalows.

Surroundings : 🏊 🔲 🌳
Leisure activities : 🍴 🏠 🛶 🏊
Facilities : 🚿 ⚐ 🧺 🖼 🚿

G P S	Longitude : -0.8025	Latitude : 49.33131

For more information on visiting particular towns or regions, consult the relevant regional MICHELIN Green Guide. We also recommend you use the appropriate Michelin regional map to locate your selected campsite, to calculate distances and to work out the best route.

ÉTRETAT

76790 – Michelin map **304** B3 – pop. 1 502 – alt. 8
▶ Paris 206 – Bolbec 30 – Fécamp 16 – Le Havre 29

⚠ Municipal

📞 02 35 27 07 67 – 🍴

Address : 69 rue Guy de Maupassant (located 1km southeast along the D 39, follow the signs for Criquetot-l'Esneval)

Opening times : from beginning April to mid Oct.

1,2 ha (73 pitches)

Tariff : (2013 Price) 👤 3,65€ 🚗 3,85€ 🔲 4,70€ – ⚡ (6A) 6€
🚐 borne 8€
An entrance decorated with flowers; the site is very well looked-after in general.

Surroundings : 🌳
Leisure activities : 🏠 🛶
Facilities : ⚐ 🖼 🍴 launderette
Nearby : ✕ 🔲

G P S	Longitude : 0.21557	Latitude : 49.70063

FALAISE

14700 – Michelin map **303** K6 – pop. 8 333 – alt. 132
▶ Paris 264 – Argentan 23 – Caen 36 – Flers 37

⚠⚠ Municipal du Château

📞 02 31 90 16 55, www.falaise-tourisme.com

Address : rue du Val d'Ante (to the west of the town, in the Val d'Ante)

Opening times : from beginning May to end Sept.

2 ha (66 pitches)

Tariff : 18,50€ 👤👤 🚗 🔲 ⚡ (10A) – Extra per person 4,50€
In a green setting in the grounds of the château.

Surroundings : ⪡ Château Val de Meuse 🌳
Leisure activities : 🏠 🛶 ✂ library
Facilities : 🚿 ⚐ 🖼 🍴
Nearby : 🏊 climbing wall

G P S	Longitude : -0.2052	Latitude : 48.89563

The guide covers all 22 regions of France – see the map and list of regions on pages 4–5.

FIQUEFLEUR-ÉQUAINVILLE

27210 – Michelin map **304** B5 – pop. 642 – alt. 17
▶ Paris 189 – Deauville 24 – Honfleur 7 – Lisieux 40

⚠⚠ Domaine Catinière

📞 02 32 57 63 51, www.camping-honfleur.com

Address : route de Honfleur (located 1km south of Fiquefleur along the D 22, between two streams)

Opening times : from mid April to mid Sept.

3,8 ha (130 pitches) flat, grassy

Tariff : (2013 Price) 32€ 👤👤 🚗 🔲 ⚡ (4A) – Extra per person 6€
Rental rates : (2013 Price) (from mid April to mid Sept.) 🖐
19 🏠 – 19 🏡 – 1 🏕 – 1 gîte. Per week from 280 to 818€

Surroundings : 🔲 🌳
Leisure activities : 🍴 ✕ 🏠 🛶 🏊 🎣 🛝
Facilities : 🚿 ⚐ 🖼 🚿 launderette

G P S	Longitude : 0.30382	Latitude : 49.40161

FLERS

51100 – Michelin map **310** F2 – pop. 15 592 – alt. 270
▶ Paris 234 – Alençon 73 – Argentan 42 – Caen 60

⚑ Le Pays de Flers

☎ 02 33 65 35 00, www.flers-agglomeration.fr/130-camping-de-la-fouquerie.htm

Address : at La Fouquerie (1.7km east along the D 924, follow the signs for Argentan and take road to the left)

Opening times : from beginning April to end Oct.

1,5 ha (50 pitches)

Tariff : (2013 Price) 12€ ♟♟ ⇔ 🔲 ⚡ (10A) – Extra per person 3€

Rental rates : Permanent ♿ – 3 🚐. Per night 52€ – Per week from 258 to 361€

🚐 5 🔲 12€ – 🚐⚡11,40€

Surroundings : 🌿 ◻ ♨
Leisure activities : 🎱 🏇 🚲
Facilities : ♿ ⚡ ▦ 🛁 🚿 🚽 🍴
Nearby : 🏊

G P S Longitude : -0.54311
Latitude : 48.75463

GENÊTS

50530 – Michelin map **303** D7 – pop. 427 – alt. 2
▶ Paris 345 – Avranches 11 – Granville 24 – Le Mont-St-Michel 33

⚑ Les Coques d'Or

☎ 02 33 70 82 57, www.campinglescoquesdor.com

Address : 14 Le Bec d'Andaine (700m northwest along the D 35e1, follow the signs for Le Bec d'Andaine)

Opening times : from beginning April to mid Nov.

4,7 ha (225 pitches) flat, grassy

Tariff : 25,50€ ♟♟ ⇔ 🔲 ⚡ (10A)
Extra per person 7,20€

Rental rates : (from beginning April to mid Nov.) – 26 🚐 – 2 🏠. Per night from 60 to 110€ – Per week from 289 to 678€

🚐 20 🔲 10€ – 🚐⚡10,80€

A pleasant indoor pool with a spa area.

Surroundings : 🌿 ◻ ♨
Leisure activities : ♟ ✗ ♨s hammam, jacuzzi 🏇 🚲🌊 🏊 spa centre
Facilities : ♿ ⚡ 🔲 🛁 🍴 launderette 🚿
Nearby : 🏇 walking and horse-riding trail

G P S Longitude : -1.48444
Latitude : 48.68778

GONNEVILLE-EN-AUGE

14810 – Michelin map **303** K4 – pop. 419 – alt. 16
▶ Paris 223 – Caen 20 – Le Havre 84 – Hérouville-St-Clair 16

⚑ Le Clos Tranquille

☎ 02 31 24 21 36, www.campingleclostranquille.fr

Address : 17 route de Troarn (800m south along the D 95a)

Opening times : from beginning April to end Sept.

1,3 ha (78 pitches) flat, grassy

Tariff : ♟ 5€ ⇔ 🔲 6€ – ⚡ (10A) 5€

Rental rates : (from beginning March to end Dec.) – 5 🚐 – 3 🏚 5 gîtes. Per night 100€ – Per week 550€

Surroundings : 🌿 ◻ ♨
Leisure activities : 🎱 🏇
Facilities : ⚡🚿 🛁 🍴 launderette
Nearby : ✗ 🏇 🏇

G P S Longitude : -0.17771
Latitude : 49.23853

GRANVILLE

50400 – Michelin map **303** C6 – pop. 12 847 – alt. 10
▶ Paris 342 – Avranches 27 – Caen 109 – Cherbourg 105

🔺🔺🔺 Les Castels Le Château de Lez-Eaux

☎ 02 33 51 66 09, www.lez-eaux.com

Address : at St-Aubin-des-Préaux (7km southeast along the D 973, follow the signs for Avranches)

Opening times : from beginning April to mid Sept.

12 ha/8 for camping (229 pitches)

Tariff : (2013 Price) 43€ ♟♟ ⇔ 🔲 ⚡ (10A) – Extra per person 8€
Reservation fee 8€

Rental rates : (from beginning April to mid Sept.) ♿ – 9 🚐
45 🏠 – 2 cabins in the trees. Per night from 95 to 222€ Per week 1554€ – Reservation fee 8€

🚐 7 🔲 35€

In the grounds of the château; an attractive swimming area.

Surroundings : 🌿 ♨
Leisure activities : ♟ 🎱 🏇 🏇 🚲 ✗ 🌊 🏊 🏞 🎣
Facilities : ♿ ⚡ ▦ 🛁 🚿 🚽 🍴 launderette 🚿
Nearby : 🏇 🚣 🏇

G P S Longitude : -1.52464
Latitude : 48.79774

🔺🔺 La Vague

☎ 02 33 50 29 97, www.camping-la-vague.com

Address : 126 route de Voudrelin (2.5km southeast along the D 911, follow the signs for St-Pair and take the D 572 to the left; at St Nicolas-Plage)

2 ha (145 pitches)

Rentals : 🚐 – 7 🚐.

In a green setting that is pleasant and well kept.

Surroundings · ◻ ♨
Leisure activities : 🎱 🏇 🏇
Facilities : ♿ ⚡ 🔲
Nearby : 🏊 (open air in season) 🚣 🏇

G P S Longitude : -1.57317
Latitude : 48.82146

The information in the guide may have changed since going to press.

LE GROS-THEIL

27370 – Michelin map **304** F6 – pop. 931 – alt. 145
▶ Paris 136 – Bernay 30 – Elbeuf 16 – Évreux 34

🔺🔺🔺 Salverte

☎ 02 32 35 51 34, www.camping-salverte.com – limited spaces for one-night stay

Address : 3km southwest along the D 26, follow the signs for Brionne and take road to the left

Opening times : Permanent

17 ha/10 for camping (300 pitches) flat, grassy

Tariff : 21€ ♟♟ ⇔ 🔲 ⚡ (10A) – Extra per person 7€

Rental rates : (from beginning May to end Oct.) – 4 🚐. Per night from 65 to 85€ – Per week from 400 to 510€

A pleasant wooded site.

Surroundings : 🌿 ♨♨
Leisure activities : ♟ ✗ 🎱 🏇 🏊 ♨s 🏇 🎣 🏊 library, entertainment room
Facilities : ⚡ ▦ 🚿 🚽 🍴 launderette 🚿

G P S Longitude : 0.84149
Latitude : 49.22619

HONFLEUR

14600 – Michelin map **303** N3 – pop. 8 163 – alt. 5
▶ Paris 195 – Caen 69 – Le Havre 27 – Lisieux 38

▲▲▲ La Briquerie

✆ 02 31 89 28 32, www.campinglabriquerie.com – limited spaces for one-night stay

Address : at Equemauville (follow the signs for Trouville, 3.5km southwest following signs for Pont-l'Évêque and right onto the D 62)

Opening times : from beginning April to end Sept.

11 ha (430 pitches) flat, grassy

Tariff : 34€ ♥♥ ⇔ 🔲 ⚡ (10A) – Extra per person 9€

Rental rates : (from mid March to beginning Nov.) ✂ – 12 🚐
8 🏠 – 1 studio. Per night from 115 to 165€ – Per week from 320 to 795€

🚐 20 🔲 20€ – 🚮 14€

Surroundings : 🔲 ♀
Leisure activities : ♥ ✕ 🏊 ⚂ ♪ ⛵ jacuzzi
⚓ 🏓 🔲 ♨ multi-sports ground
Facilities : ♿ ⚬ 🚐 🔲 ♨ 🚿 ⚑ 🍴
launderette ⚙
Nearby : ✕ 🐎

Longitude : 0.20826
Latitude : 49.39675

HOULGATE

14510 – Michelin map **303** L4 – pop. 1 988 – alt. 11
▶ Paris 214 – Caen 29 – Deauville 14 – Lisieux 33

▲▲▲ Yelloh! Village La Vallée ♣♣

✆ 02 31 24 40 69, www.campinglavallee.com

Address : 88 route de la Vallée (located 1km south along the D 24a, follow the signs for Lisieux and turn right onto the D 24)

Opening times : from beginning April to beginning Nov.

11 ha (350 pitches)

Tariff : 49€ ♥♥ ⇔ 🔲 ⚡ (6A) – Extra per person 8€

Rental rates : (from beginning April to beginning Nov.) ✂
65 🚐. Per night from 59 to 188€ – Per week from 413 to 1316€

🚐 2 🔲 18€

In a pleasant setting surrounding old Norman-style buildings.

Surroundings : ⪕ 🔲 ♀
Leisure activities : ♥ ✕ 🏊 ⚂ 🎿 ⚓ 🚲 ✕
🔲 ♨
Facilities : ♿ ⚬ 🚿 ⚑ 🍴 launderette
♨ ⚙
Nearby : 🔲 ♪

Longitude : -0.06733
Latitude : 49.29422

INCHEVILLE

76117 – Michelin map **304** I1 – pop. 1 357 – alt. 19
▶ Paris 169 – Abbeville 32 – Amiens 65 – Blangy-sur-Bresle 16

▲ Municipal de l'Etang

✆ 02 35 50 30 17, campingdeletang@orange.fr – limited spaces for one-night stay

Address : rue Mozart (take the northeastern exit, follow the signs for Beauchamps and take right turn)

Opening times : from beginning March to end Oct.

2 ha (190 pitches) flat, grassy

Tariff : (2013 Price) ♥ 2,75€ ⇔ 3,55€ 🔲 3,75€ – ⚡ (10A) 3,75€

🚐 2 🔲 12,80€

Near a fishing lake.

Surroundings : ♀
Leisure activities : 🏊 ⚓
Facilities : ♿ ⚬ 🚐 ♨ ⚑
Nearby : ✕ 🐟

Longitude : 1.50788
Latitude : 50.01238

ISIGNY-SUR-MER

14230 – Michelin map **303** F4 – pop. 2 782 – alt. 4
▶ Paris 298 – Bayeux 35 – Caen 64 – Carentan 14

▲▲▲ Le Fanal

✆ 02 31 21 33 20, www.camping-normandie-fanal.fr

Address : rue du Fanal (to the west, access via the town centre, near the sports field)

Opening times : from beginning April to end Sept.

6,5 ha/5,5 for camping (240 pitches) flat, grassy

Tariff : 30,50€ ♥♥ ⇔ 🔲 ⚡ (10A) – Extra per person 6€ – Reservation fee 5€

Rental rates : (from beginning April to end Sept.) – 96 🚐
4 🏠 – 4 tent lodges. Per night from 30 to 129€ – Per week from 210 to 903€ – Reservation fee 11€

🚐 borne 5€

A pleasant, well-kept setting, around a small lake.

Surroundings : ⚓ ♀
Leisure activities : 🏊 ♪ ⚓ ✕ 🔲
Facilities : ♿ ⚬ ♨ ♨ ⚑ 🍴 launderette
Nearby : 🏊 🐟 ♪ sports trail

Longitude : -1.10872
Latitude : 49.31923

These symbols are used for a campsite that is exceptional in its category:

▲▲▲ ....▲   *Particularly pleasant setting, quality and range of services available*

⚓⚓   *Tranquil, isolated site – quiet site, particularly at night*

⪕ ⪕   *Exceptional view – interesting or panoramic view*

JUMIEGES

76480 – Michelin map **304** E5 – pop. 1 719 – alt. 25
▶ Paris 161 – Rouen 29 – Le Havre 82 – Caen 132

▲▲▲ La Forêt

✆ 02 35 37 93 43, www.campinglaforet.com

Address : rue Mainberte

Opening times : from beginning April to end Oct.

2 ha (111 pitches) flat, grassy

Tariff : 29€ ♥♥ ⇔ 🔲 ⚡ (10A) – Extra per person 5,50€ – Reservation fee 4€

Rental rates : (from mid April to mid Oct.) ✂ – 13 🚐 – 5 🏠
Per night from 110 to 155€ – Per week from 255 to 620€
Reservation fee 4€

🚐 borne 6,50€ – 1 🔲 28,50€

In the Brotonne Regional Park.

Surroundings : ⚓ ♀
Leisure activities : 🏊 ⚓ 🔲 ♨
Facilities : ♿ ⚬ ⚂ ♨ 🍴 launderette
Nearby : ✕

Longitude : 0.82883
Latitude : 49.43485

LISIEUX

14100 – Michelin map **303** N5 – pop. 21 826 – alt. 51

▶ Paris 169 – Caen 54 – Le Havre 66 – Hérouville-St-Clair 53

⚠ La Vallée

𝒫 02 31 62 00 40, www.lisieux-tourisme.com

Address : 9 rue de la Vallée (take the northern exit along the D 48, follow the signs for Pont-l'Évêque)

ha (75 pitches)

Rentals : 5 .

Surroundings : 🞕🞕
Facilities : 🚻 ⚊ 🛁 launderette
Nearby : 🞔

GPS Longitude : 0.22068
Latitude : 49.16423

LES LOGES

76790 – Michelin map **304** B3 – pop. 1 155 – alt. 92

▶ Paris 205 – Rouen 83 – Le Havre 34 – Fécamp 10

🏔 Club Airotel L'Aiguille Creuse

𝒫 02 35 29 52 10, www.campingaiguillecreuse.com

Address : 24 residence de l'Aiguille Creuse

Opening times : from beginning April to end Sept.

ha (80 pitches)

Tariff : (2013 Price) 26,50€ 🛉🛉 🚗 🔲 🕮 (10A)
Extra per person 5,60€ – Reservation fee 7€

Rental rates : (from beginning April to end Sept.) 🚲 – 18 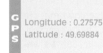.
Per night from 55 to 115€ – Per week from 255 to 700€
Reservation fee 15€

🚰 borne

Surroundings : 🞔
Leisure activities : 🍷 🏋 🖼 (open air in season)
Facilities : 🚻 ⚊ 🆒 🏛 🕮 🎣
Nearby : 🞔

GPS Longitude : 0.27575
Latitude : 49.69884

LOUVIERS

27400 – Michelin map **304** H6 – pop. 17 943 – alt. 15

▶ Paris 104 – Les Andelys 22 – Bernay 52 – Lisieux 75

🏔 Le Bel Air

𝒫 02 32 40 10 77, www.camping-lebelair.fr – limited spaces for one-night stay

Address : route de la-Haye-Malherbe (3km west along the D 81)

Opening times : from mid March to mid Oct.

2,5 ha (92 pitches) flat, grassy

Tariff : (2013 Price) 🛉 5,70€ 🚗 🔲 6,90€ – 🕮 (6A) 4,90€

Rental rates : (from mid March to mid Oct.) 🚲 (from mid March to mid Oct.) – 2  – 3 🏠. Per week from 382 to 582€

🚰 2 🔲 10,60€

Set among trees with plenty of shade.

Surroundings : 🞔 🞕🞕
Leisure activities : 🖼 🏋 🖼
Facilities : ⚊ 🏛 🎣 launderette
Nearby : 🞔 🞕

GPS Longitude : 1.1332
Latitude : 49.2152

A chambre d'hôte is a guesthouse or B & B-style accommodation.

LUC-SUR-MER

14530 – Michelin map **303** J4 – pop. 3 133

▶ Paris 249 – Arromanches-les-Bains 23 – Bayeux 29 – Cabourg 28

🏔 Municipal la Capricieuse

Mairie LUC s/Mer

𝒫 02 31 97 34 43, www.campinglacapricieuse.com

Address : 2 rue Brummel (to the west, allée Brummel; 200m from the beach)

Opening times : from beginning April to end Sept.

4,6 ha (226 pitches)

Tariff : 🛉 5€ 🚗 🔲 5,90€ 🕮 (10A) 6,60€

Rental rates : (from beginning April to end Nov.) 🚻 (1 mobile home) 🚲 – 18 – 10 🏠. Per week from 314 to 720€

🚰 borne 5,20€

Surroundings : 🞔 🞔 🞕
Leisure activities : 🖼 🏋 🞔 🏊 (beach) multi-sports ground
Facilities : 🚻 ⚊ 🆒 🎣 🐾 🕮 launderette
Nearby : 🞔🞔 🏋 🖼 🎣

GPS Longitude : -0.35781
Latitude : 49.3179

Some campsites benefit from proximity to a municipal leisure centre.

LYONS-LA-FORÊT

27480 – Michelin map **304** I5 – pop. 751 – alt. 88

▶ Paris 104 – Les Andelys 21 – Forges-les-Eaux 30 – Gisors 30

⚠ Municipal St-Paul

𝒫 02 32 49 42 02, www.camping-saint-paul.fr – limited spaces for one-night stay

Address : 2 route Saint-Paul (to the northeast along the D 321, by the stadium; beside the Lieure river)

Opening times : from beginning April to end Oct.

3 ha (100 pitches) flat, grassy

Tariff : (2013 Price) 20,50€ 🛉🛉 🚗 🔲 🕮 (6A) – Extra per person 5,20€

Rental rates : (from beginning April to end Oct.) – 7 🏠. Per night from 58 to 82€ – Per week from 200 to 420€

Surroundings : 🞔 🞕
Leisure activities : 🖼 🏋
Facilities : 🚻 ⚊ 🆒 🏛 🎣 🐾 🕮 🎣
Nearby : 🞔 🞔 🏊 🐎

GPS Longitude : 1.47657
Latitude : 49.39869

MARCHAINVILLE

61290 – Michelin map **310** N3 – pop. 207 – alt. 235

▶ Paris 124 – L'Aigle 28 – Alençon 65 – Mortagne-au-Perche 28

⚠ Municipal les Fossés

𝒫 02 33 73 65 80, mairiemarchainville@wanadoo.fr – ⛑

Address : to the north along the D 243

Opening times : from beginning April to end Oct.

1 ha (17 pitches)

Tariff : (2013 Price) 🛉 1,20€ 🚗 🔲 1€ – 🕮 (3A) 2,30€

Surroundings : 🞔 🞔
Leisure activities : 🞔
Facilities : 🚻 🎣 🞔 🎣

GPS Longitude : 0.8135
Latitude : 48.5861

MARTIGNY

76880 – Michelin map **304** G2 – pop. 481 – alt. 24
▶ Paris 196 – Dieppe 10 – Fontaine-le-Dun 29 – Rouen 64

⚠ Les Deux Rivières

𝒫 02 35 85 60 82, www.camping-2-rivieres.com – limited spaces for one-night stay

Address : D 154 (700m to the northwest, off the rte de Dieppe)

Opening times : from end March to mid Oct.

3 ha (110 pitches) flat, grassy

Tariff : (2013 Price) 17,50 € ♦♦ ⟺ 🅴 [⚡] (10A) – Extra per person 4 €
Rental rates : Permanent – 6 🚐. Per night 80 € – Per week from 350 to 580 €
Ina pleasant location beside river and lakes.

Surroundings : ≼ extensive lakeland and the Château d'Arques ⚲
Leisure activities : 🛶 ♞ 🚲 🐟
Facilities : ৬ ⚬⇥ 🍴 launderette 🌊,
Nearby : 🔲 ♨

GPS Longitude : 1.14417
Latitude : 49.87059

MARTRAGNY

14740 – Michelin map **303** I4 – pop. 367 – alt. 70
▶ Paris 257 – Bayeux 11 – Caen 23 – St-Lô 47

🏰 Les Castels Le Château de Martragny

𝒫 02 31 80 21 40, www.chateau-martragny.com

Address : 52 Hameau St Léger (on the old N 13, access via the the town centre)

Opening times : from mid May to mid Sept.

13 ha/4 for camping (160 pitches) flat, grassy

Tariff : ♦ 8,50 € ⟺ 🅴 15,50 € – [⚡] (15A) 5 € – Reservation fee 8 €
Rental rates : (from end May to end Aug.) – 5 ⊨ – 4 tent lodges 2 gîtes. Per week from 400 to 450 € – Reservation fee 8 €
🚐 borne
B&B accommodation in an 18th-century château.

Surroundings : 🌳 ⚲
Leisure activities : ♟ 🛶 ♞ ✻ 🏊 🐟
Facilities : ৬ ⚬⇥ 🅴 🔥 🍴 launderette 🌊, 🚿
Nearby : 🐎

GPS Longitude : -0.60532
Latitude : 49.24406

MAUPERTUS-SUR-MER

50330 – Michelin map **303** D2 – pop. 256 – alt. 119
▶ Paris 359 – Barfleur 21 – Cherbourg 13 – St-Lô 80

🏰 Les Castels l'Anse du Brick 👥

𝒫 02 33 54 33 57, www.anse-du-brick.com

Address : 18 Anse du Brick (to the northwest along the D 116, 200m from the beach, direct access via a walkway)

Opening times : from beginning April to end Sept.

17 ha/7 for camping (180 pitches)
Tariff : 42,60 € ♦♦ ⟺ 🅴 [⚡] (10A)
Extra per person 8,40 € – Reservation fee 8 €
Rental rates : (from beginning April to end Sept.) – 36 🚐 – 6 🏠 3 gîtes. Per night from 130 to 145 € – Per week from 399 to 868 € Reservation fee 8 €
🚐 borne 8 €

An unspoilt site in a pleasantly leafy setting with plenty o shade.

Surroundings : 🌳 ≼ ⟐ ⚲⚲
Leisure activities : ♟ 🛶 🖅 ♣ ♞ 🚲 ✻ 🔲 🏊 △
Facilities : ৬ ⚬⇥ 🔥 🍴 launderette 🌊,
Nearby : ✕ 🔲 watersports centre

GPS Longitude : -1.49
Latitude : 49.66722

MERVILLE-FRANCEVILLE-PLAGE

14810 – Michelin map **303** K4 – pop. 1 991 – alt. 2
▶ Paris 225 – Arromanches-les-Bains 42 – Cabourg 7 – Caen 20

🏰 Les Peupliers

𝒫 02 31 24 05 07, www.camping-peupliers.com

Address : allée des Pins (2.5km east, a right turn off the rte de Cabourg; near the entrance to Hôme)

Opening times : from beginning April to end Oct.

3,6 ha (164 pitches) flat, grassy

Tariff : 33 € ♦♦ ⟺ 🅴 [⚡] (10A) – Extra per person 8,40 €
Rental rates : (from beginning April to end Oct.) – 44 🚐 10 🏠. Per night from 90 to 145 € – Per week from 310 to 990 € 🚐 borne

Leisure activities : ♟ 🛶 🖅 (July–Aug.) ♞ 🏊
Facilities : ৬ ⚬⇥ 🔥 🍴 launderette
Nearby : ✻ ⛳ 🐟 🐎

GPS Longitude : -0.17011
Latitude : 49.2829

🏰 Seasonova Le Point du Jour

𝒫 02 31 24 23 34, www.vacances-seasonova.com

Address : route de Cabourg (take the eastern exit along the D 514)

Opening times : from beginning April to beginning Nov.

2,7 ha (142 pitches)

Tariff : 36 € ♦♦ ⟺ 🅴 [⚡] (10A) – Extra per person 8,60 € – Reservation fee 12 €
Rental rates : (from beginning April to beginning Nov.) ♞ 32 🚐. Per night from 80 to 140 € – Per week from 350 to 975 € Reservation fee 12 €
🚐 7 🅴 23 € – 🚽 [⚡] 20,70 €
In an attractive location close to the beach.

Surroundings : ⟐ △
Leisure activities : ✕ 🛶 ≈ jacuzzi ♞ 🔲 (open air in season)
Facilities : ৬ ⚬⇥ 🔥 🍴 launderette
Nearby : ✻ ⛳ 🐟 🐎

GPS Longitude : -0.19392
Latitude : 49.2833

MOYAUX

14590 – Michelin map **303** O4 – pop. 1 356 – alt. 160
▶ Paris 173 – Caen 64 – Deauville 31 – Lisieux 13

🏰 Le Colombier

𝒫 02 31 63 63 08, www.camping-lecolombier.com

Address : 3km northeast along the D 143, follow the signs for Lieurey

15 ha/6 for camping (180 pitches) flat, grassy

Rentals : 5 gîtes.

There's a swimming pool in the château's formal garden.

Surroundings : 🌳 ⚲
Leisure activities : ♟ ✕ 🛶 🖅 ♞ 🚲 ✻ ⛳ 🔲 library
Facilities : ৬ ⚬⇥ 🔥 △ 🍴 launderette 🌊, 🚿

GPS Longitude : 0.3897
Latitude : 49.2097

OMONVILLE-LA-ROGUE

50440 – Michelin map **303** A1 – pop. 534 – alt. 25
▶ Paris 377 – Caen 144 – St-Lô 99 – Cherbourg 24

⚠ Municipal du Hable

📞 02 33 52 86 15, www.omonvillelarogue.fr – ℝ

Address : 4 route de la Hague

Opening times : from beginning April to beginning Sept.

1 ha (60 pitches)

Tariff : ✱ 3€ ⛟ 2,32€ 🅴 2,32€ – 🔌 (10A) 5,96€
🚐 borne 3,45€

Surroundings : 🦢
Facilities : 🚿 launderette
Nearby : 🏖 🎣 🚣

G P S Longitude : -1.84087 Latitude : 49.70439

ORBEC

14290 – Michelin map **303** O5 – pop. 2 381 – alt. 110
▶ Paris 175 – L'Aigle 30 – Alençon 60 – Argentan 53

⚠ Les Capucins

📞 09 62 57 96 00, camping.sivom@orange.fr

Address : 13 avenue du Bois (located 1.5km northeast along the D 4, follow the signs for Bernay and take road to the left, by the stadium)

Opening times : from mid May to beginning Sept.

0,9 ha (35 pitches) flat, grassy

Tariff : ✱ 2,50€ ⛟ 2€ 🅴 2€ – 🔌 (3A) 3€
🚐 20 🅴 12€

In a green setting; a very well-kept site.

Surroundings : 🌳
Leisure activities :
Facilities : 🚿 🔥 🚿
Nearby : 🎣 🏇 🐎

G P S Longitude : 0.40875 Latitude : 49.02982

LES PIEUX

50340 – Michelin map **303** B2 – pop. 3 588 – alt. 104
▶ Paris 366 – Barneville-Carteret 18 – Cherbourg 22 – St-Lô 48

⚠⚠ Le Grand Large

📞 02 33 52 40 75, www.legrandlarge.com

Address : 11 route du Grand Large (3km southwest along the D 117 and turn right onto the D 517 then continue 1km along the road to the left)

Opening times : from mid April to mid Sept.

3,7 ha (236 pitches)

Tariff : 38,50€ ✱✱ ⛟ 🅴 🔌 (10A) – Extra per person 8,50€
Rental rates : (from mid April to mid Sept.) – 50 🏠. Per night from 80 to 140€ – Per week from 340 to 950€
🚐 borne 8€

An attractive location among the dunes close to the Plage de Sciottot (beach).

Surroundings : 🦢 🌊 🦆 ⛰
Leisure activities : 🍽 📺 jacuzzi 🏊 🎾 🏊 paddling pool
Facilities : 🚿 🔥 cc🆙 🍳 🚿 launderette

G P S Longitude : -1.8425 Latitude : 49.49361

PONT-AUDEMER

27500 – Michelin map **304** D5 – pop. 8 599 – alt. 15
▶ Paris 165 – Rouen 58 – Évreux 91 – Le Havre 44

⚠ Municipal Risle-Seine - Les Étangs

📞 02 32 42 46 65, http://www.camping-risle-seine.com

Address : 19 route des Étangs at Toutainville (2.5km east, turn left under the motorway bridge, near the water sports centre)

Opening times : from beginning April to end Oct.

2 ha (61 pitches) flat, grassy

Tariff : ✱ 3,25€ ⛟ 🅴 6,85€ – 🔌 (10A) 4€
Rental rates : Permanent – 10 🏠. Per night from 45 to 79€
Per week from 299 to 552€

A small but pretty chalet village on stilts!

Surroundings : 🦆 ⛺
Leisure activities : 🎣 🏊 🚲
Facilities : 🚿 🔥 🚿 🍳 🔥
Nearby : 🏊 (pool) 🚣 🎣

G P S Longitude : 0.48739 Latitude : 49.3666

A chambre d'hôte is a guesthouse or B & B-style accommodation.

PONT-AUTHOU

27290 – Michelin map **304** E6 – pop. 711 – alt. 49
▶ Paris 152 – Bernay 22 – Elbeuf 26 – Évreux 45

⚠ Municipal les Marronniers

📞 02 32 42 75 06, campingmunicipaldesmarronniers@orange.fr – limited spaces for one-night stay

Address : 8 rue Louise Givon (south of the town, along the D 130, follow the signs for Brionne; beside a stream)

Opening times : Permanent

2,5 ha (64 pitches) flat, grassy

Tariff : ✱ 2,70€ ⛟ 1,95€ 🅴 2,70€ – 🔌 (10A) 3,40€
Rental rates : Permanent – 5 🚐. Per night 42€ – Per week 220€
🚐 borne 4,35€ – 5 🅴 13,35€

Leisure activities : 🎣
Facilities : 🚿 🔥 🍳
Nearby : 🚲

G P S Longitude : 0.70332 Latitude : 49.24193

PONT-FARCY

14380 – Michelin map **303** F6 – pop. 527 – alt. 72
▶ Paris 296 – Caen 63 – St-Lô 30 – Villedieu-les-Poêles 22

⚠ Municipal

📞 02 31 68 32 06, www.pont.farcy.fr – ℝ

Address : route de Tessy (take the northern exit along the D 21, follow the signs for Tessy-sur-Vire)

Opening times : from beginning May to mid Sept.

1,5 ha (60 pitches) flat, grassy

Tariff : 12,50€ ✱✱ ⛟ 🅴 🔌 (10A) – Extra per person 2,50€
Rental rates : (from beginning May to mid Sept.) – 1 🚐.
Per week from 200€

Beside the Vire river.

Leisure activities : 🎣 🏓 🍳
Facilities : 🚿 🔥 🔥 🚿

G P S Longitude : -1.0349 Latitude : 48.93899

To visit a town or region, use the MICHELIN Green Guides.

PONTORSON

50170 – Michelin map **303** C8 – pop. 4 080 – alt. 15
▶ Paris 359 – Avranches 23 – Dinan 50 – Fougères 39

⚠ Haliotis ♣♣

🖊 02 33 68 11 59, www.camping-haliotis-mont-saint-michel.com

Address : chemin des Soupirs (situated to the northwest along the D 19, follow the signs for Dol-de-Bretagne; near the Couesnon river)

Opening times : from mid March to mid Nov.

8 ha/3,5 for camping (170 pitches) flat, grassy

Tariff : 🛉 6 € 🚐 📧 13,50 € 🔌 (16A)

Rental rates : (from mid March to mid Nov.) – 37 🚐 – 1 🏠.
Per night from 35 to 108 € – Per week from 220 to 750 €
🚱 borne 4,50 €

Surroundings : ⚞ 🗀
Leisure activities : 🍽 🎱 🌣 daytime 🏇 🎣 jacuzzi 🛶 🚲 ⚲ 🏊 fitness trail, multi-sports ground
Facilities : 🖊 🆑 ▦ 🅰 – 12 individual sanitary facilities (🛁 🚿 wc) 🛬 🚰 🍴 launderette
Nearby : 🚣 🖼 🏹 🏇

G P S Longitude : -1.5145 Latitude : 48.55798

PORT-EN-BESSIN

14520 – Michelin map **303** H3 – pop. 2 141 – alt. 10
▶ Paris 277 – Caen 43 – Hérouville-St-Clair 45 – St-Lô 47

⚠ Port'Land ♣♣

🖊 02 31 51 07 06, www.camping-portland.com

Address : chemin du Castel

Opening times : from beginning April to beginning Nov.

8,5 ha (256 pitches) flat, grassy

Tariff : 43 € 🛉🛉 🚐 📧 🔌 (16A) – Extra per person 10 €
Rental rates : (from beginning April to beginning Nov.) – 98 🚐.
Per night from 57 to 190 € – Per week from 399 to 1330 €
🚱 borne 5 € – 5 📧 43 €
Pretty flowers and shrubs and several lakes.

Surroundings : 🏖 🗀
Leisure activities : 🍽 🍴 🎱 🌣 🏇 🛶 📺 🏊 🏊 ⚲ fitness trail, multi-sports ground
Facilities : 🖊 🖊 🅰 🛬 🚰 🍴 launderette 🚣 🛬
Nearby : 🍴 ⚲

G P S Longitude : -0.77044 Latitude : 49.34716

QUIBERVILLE

76860 – Michelin map **304** F2 – pop. 535 – alt. 50
▶ Paris 199 – Dieppe 18 – Fécamp 50 – Rouen 67

⚠ Municipal de la Plage

🖊 02 35 83 01 04, www.campingplagequiberville.fr – limited spaces for one-night stay

Address : 123 rue de la Saane (at Quiberville-Plage, access via the D 127, follow the signs for Ouville-la-Rivière)

Opening times : from beginning April to end Oct.

2,5 ha (202 pitches) flat, grassy

Tariff : (2013 Price) 🛉 5,65 € 🚐 📧 9,85 € – 🔌 (10A) 5,20 €
🚱 borne 3,75 € – 8 📧 6 €
Situated 100m from the sea.

Surroundings : ⚞ 🗀
Leisure activities : 🍴 🛶
Facilities : 🖊 🖊 🅰 🍴 launderette
Nearby : 🍽 ⚲ 🛬 ⚲ ⚲

G P S Longitude : 0.92878 Latitude : 49.90507

RADON

61250 – Michelin map **310** J3 – pop. 1 042 – alt. 175
▶ Paris 200 – Caen 106 – Alençon 11 – Le Mans 67

⚠ Ferme des Noyers

🖊 02 33 28 75 02, www.ecouves.net

Address : at Les Noyers (D 1)

Opening times : Permanent

2 ha (43 pitches) flat, grassy

Tariff : 16,10 € 🛉🛉 🚐 📧 🔌 (16A) – Extra per person 3 €
Rental rates : Permanent – 1 caravan – 3 🏠 – 2 🛏 – 1 gîte
Per night from 58 to 90 € – Per week from 210 to 320 €
🚱 borne 3 € – 8 📧 16,10 € – 🚿 🔌 14,70 €

Surroundings : ⚲
Leisure activities : 🏠 🛶
Facilities : 🖊 🖊 🅰 🍴 🔲
Nearby : 🍽 ≋ (pond)

We have selected the best campsites in France with our usual care, listing those with the best facilities in the most pleasant surroundings.

RAVENOVILLE

50480 – Michelin map **303** E3 – pop. 261 – alt. 6
▶ Paris 328 – Barfleur 27 – Carentan 21 – Cherbourg 40

⚠ Kawan Village Le Cormoran ♣♣

🖊 02 33 41 33 94, www.lecormoran.com – limited spaces for one-night stay

Address : 2 rue du Cormoran (3.5km northeast along the D 421, follow the signs for Utah Beach; near the beach)

Opening times : from beginning April to end Sept.

8 ha (256 pitches)

Tariff : 43 € 🛉🛉 🚐 📧 🔌 (10A) – Extra per person 8,30 € – Reservation fee 10 €
Rental rates : (from beginning April to end Sept.) 🅿 – 40 🚐 46 🏠. Per week from 273 to 959 € – Reservation fee 10 €
🚱 borne 5 € – 8 📧 17 € – 🚿 🔌 17 €
Beautiful flowers and shrubs decorate the site.

Surroundings : 🗀
Leisure activities : 🍽 🏠 🌣 🏇 ≋ jacuzzi 🛶 🚲 ⚲ 📺 🏊 farm or petting farm, radio control boats, multi-sports ground
Facilities : 🖊 🖊 🆑 🅰 🛬 🚰 🍴 launderette 🚣 🛬
Nearby : 🏇

G P S Longitude : -1.23527 Latitude : 49.46658

LE ROZEL

50340 – Michelin map **303** B3 – pop. 281 – alt. 21
▶ Paris 369 – Caen 135 – Cherbourg 26 – Rennes 197

⚠ Le Ranch

🖊 02 33 10 07 10, www.camping-leranch.com

Address : at La Mielle (situated 2km southwest along the D 117 and take the D 62 to the right)

Opening times : from beginning April to end Sept.

4 ha (130 pitches)

Tariff : 🛉 34 € 🚐 📧 – 🔌 (10A) 4,50 €

Rental rates : Permanent – 15 ⌂. Per night from 125 to 140€ – Per week from 385 to 990€
Situated close to the beach.

Surroundings : ⌂ ⌂
Leisure activities : ⟒ ✕ ⌂ ⌂ ⌂ ⌂
⌂ ⌂ ⌂
Facilities : ⌂ ⌂ (July-Aug.) ⌂ ⌂ ⌂ ⌂ ⌂
launderette
Nearby : ⌂ ⌂ sand yachting

G P S	Longitude : -1.84199 Latitude : 49.48013

ST-ARNOULT

14800 – Michelin map **303** M3 – pop. 1 193 – alt. 4
▶ Paris 198 – Caen 43 – Le Havre 41 – Rouen 90

⛰ Yelloh! Village La Vallée de Deauville 🏳

✆ 02 31 88 58 17, www.camping-deauville.com – limited spaces for one-night stay

Address : avenue de la Vallée (located 1km south along the D 27, follow the signs for Varaville and take the D 275 following signs for Beaumont-en-Auge to the left; beside a stream and near a small lake)

Opening times : from mid April to end Oct.

10 ha (411 pitches) flat, grassy

Tariff : 35€ ✶✶ ⇌ ▣ ⚡ (10A) – Extra per person 9€ – Reservation fee 5€

Rental rates : (from beginning April to end Oct.) – 60 ⌂ – 6 tent lodges. Per night from 72 to 120€ – Per week from 220 to 790€ – Reservation fee 5€

⛽ borne 8€

Based around a small, pleasant lake.

Surroundings : ⌂ ⌂
Leisure activities : ⟒ ⌂ ⌂ ⌂ ⌂ hammam, jacuzzi ⌂ ⌂ ⌂ ⌂ multi-sports ground
Facilities : ⌂ ⌂ ⌂ ⌂ launderette ⌂ ⌂
Nearby : ✕ ⌂ ⌂ ⌂

G P S	Longitude : 0.0862 Latitude : 49.3287

ST-AUBIN-SUR-MER

14750 – Michelin map **303** J4 – pop. 2 048
▶ Paris 252 – Arromanches-les-Bains 19 – Bayeux 29 – Cabourg 32

⛰ Yelloh! Village Sandaya Côte de Nacre 🏳

✆ 02 31 97 14 45, www.camping-cote-de-nacre.com – limited spaces for one-night stay

Address : 17 rue du Général Moulton (south of the town along the D 7b)

Opening times : from beginning April to mid Sept.

10 ha (350 pitches) flat, grassy

Tariff : 47€ ✶✶ ⇌ ▣ ⚡ (10A) – Extra per person 9€

Rental rates : (from beginning April to mid Sept.) – 290 ⌂. Per night from 59 to 194€ – Per week from 413 to 1 358€

⛽ borne ,20€

There's a partially covered water park.

Leisure activities : ⟒ ⌂ ⌂ ⌂ ⌂ hammam, jacuzzi ⌂ ⌂ ⌂ ⌂ ⌂ spa facilities, multi-sports ground, spa centre
Facilities : ⌂ ⌂ ⌂ ⌂ launderette ⌂ ⌂
Nearby : ✕ ⌂

G P S	Longitude : -0.3946 Latitude : 49.3324

ST-AUBIN-SUR-MER

76740 – Michelin map **304** F2 – pop. 267 – alt. 15
▶ Paris 191 – Dieppe 21 – Fécamp 46 – Rouen 59

⛺ Municipal le Mesnil

✆ 02 35 83 02 83, www.campinglemesnil.com

Address : route de Sotteville (situated 2km west along the D 68, follow the signs for Veules-les-Roses)

Opening times : from beginning April to end Oct.

2,2 ha (117 pitches)

Tariff : (2013 Price) 24,65€ ✶✶ ⇌ ▣ ⚡ (15A)
Extra per person 5,15€

Rental rates : (from beginning April to end Oct.) ⌂ – 2 ⌂. Per night from 250 to 500€

⛽ 5 ▣ 24,65€

In an old Norman farmhouse.

Surroundings : ⌂ ⌂
Leisure activities : ✕ ⌂ ⌂ ⌂
Facilities : ⌂ ⌂ ⌂ ⌂ ⌂ launderette ⌂

G P S	Longitude : 0.85204 Latitude : 49.88353

This guide is updated regularly, so buy your new copy every year!

ST-EVROULT-NOTRE-DAME-DU-BOIS

61550 – Michelin map **310** L2 – pop. 452 – alt. 355
▶ Paris 153 – L'Aigle 14 – Alençon 56 – Argentan 42

⛺ Municipal des Saints-Pères

✆ 06 78 33 04 94, catherine-motte@orange.fr

Address : to the southeast of the village

Opening times : from mid April to mid Oct.

0,6 ha (27 pitches)

Tariff : ✶ 3€ ⇌ 1,50€ – ⚡ (12A) 2,50€

⛽ borne 2€ – 28 ▣ 6€ – ⌂ 12€

In an attractive location beside a small lake.

Surroundings : ⌂
Leisure activities : ⌂ ⌂ ⌂ pedalos
Facilities : ⌂ ⌂ ⌂ ⌂ ⌂
Nearby : ⌂ ✕ ⌂

G P S	Longitude : 0.4663 Latitude : 48.7888

ST-GEORGES-DU-VIÈVRE

27450 – Michelin map **304** D6 – pop. 720 – alt. 138
▶ Paris 161 – Bernay 21 – Évreux 54 – Lisieux 36

⛺ Municipal du Vièvre

✆ 02 32 42 76 79, www.camping-eure-normandie.fr – ♯

Address : route de Noards (take the southwestern exit along the D 38)

Opening times : from beginning April to end Sept.

1,1 ha (50 pitches) flat, grassy

Tariff : ✶ 2,30€ ⇌ 1,30€ ▣ 2,20€ – ⚡ (5A) 2,20€

Rental rates : (from beginning April to end Sept.) – 2 ⌂. Per week from 200 to 300€

Surroundings : ⌂ ⌂
Leisure activities : ⌂
Facilities : ⌂ ⌂ ⌂ ⌂
Nearby : ✕ ⌂

G P S	Longitude : 0.58064 Latitude : 49.2427

ST-GERMAIN-SUR-AY

50430 – Michelin map **303** C4 – pop. 896 – alt. 5
▶ Paris 345 – Barneville-Carteret 26 – Carentan 35 – Coutances 27

⚞ Aux Grands Espaces

✆ 02 33 07 10 14, www.auxgrandsespaces.com – limited spaces for one-night stay

Address : 6 rue du Camping (4km west along the D 306; at St-Germain-Plage)

Opening times : from beginning April to end Sept.

16 ha (580 pitches)

Tariff : 🚶 5,50€ 🚗 📧 6,90€ – ⚡ (6A) 4,50€
Rental rates : (from beginning April to mid Sept.) ⚡ – 20 🚐
3 canvas bungalows. Per night 80€ – Per week from 280 to 710€

Surroundings : ⚞ ⚲
Leisure activities : 🍴 🏠 🚣 🎿 🎣 🏊
Facilities : ⚭ (July–Aug.) ♨ 🍴 launderette ♨
Nearby : 🐎 sand yachting

G P S	Longitude : -1.64089
	Latitude : 49.23654

ST-HILAIRE-DU-HARCOUËT

50600 – Michelin map **303** F8 – pop. 4 036 – alt. 70
▶ Paris 339 – Alençon 100 – Avranches 27 – Caen 102

⚞ Municipal de la Sélune

✆ 02 33 49 43 74, www.st-hilaire.fr

Address : 700m northwest along the N 176, follow the signs for Avranches and take a right turn, near the river

Opening times : from beginning April to end Sept.

1,9 ha (70 pitches) flat, grassy

Tariff : 🚶 2,35€ 🚗 1€ 📧 – ⚡ (16A) 1,95€
Rental rates : (from beginning April to end Sept.) ⚡ – 2 caravans.
Per night from 50 to 95€ – Per week from 250 to 450€
🚐 borne 3€ – 6 📧 – ⚡10,85€

Leisure activities : 🏠 🚣
Facilities : 🚿 ⚭ 🍴 launderette
Nearby : 🍴 🎿 🎮 🖥 ⚓

G P S	Longitude : -1.09765
	Latitude : 48.58127

ST-JEAN-DE-LA-RIVIÈRE

50270 – Michelin map **303** B3 – pop. 355 – alt. 20
▶ Paris 351 – Caen 119 – St-Lô 63 – Cherbourg 40

⚞ Yelloh! Village Les Vikings

✆ 02 33 53 84 13, www.camping-lesvikings.com

Address : 4 rue des Vikings (along the D 166 and take the road to the right)

Opening times : from beginning April to end Sept.

6 ha (250 pitches)

Tariff : 44€ 🚶🚶 🚗 📧 ⚡ (10A) – Extra per person 8€
Rental rates : (from beginning April to end Sept.) 🚿 – 82 🚐.
Per night from 45 to 175€ – Per week from 315 to 1 225€
🚐 borne
The entrance is decorated with flowers and small palm trees.

Surroundings : ⚞ ⚲
Leisure activities : 🍴 🍴 🏠 🚣 🎿 🖥 🏊 ⚓
multi-sports ground, entertainment room
Facilities : 🚿 ⚭ 🍴 launderette ♨
Nearby : 🎿 ⚓ 🐎 sand yachting

G P S	Longitude : -1.75293
	Latitude : 49.36335

ST-MARTIN-EN-CAMPAGNE

76370 – Michelin map **304** H2 – pop. 1 319 – alt. 118
▶ Paris 209 – Dieppe 13 – Rouen 78 – Le Tréport 18

⚞ Domaine les Goélands

✆ 02 35 83 82 90, www.camping-les-goelands.fr – limited spaces for one-night stay

Address : rue des Grèbes (situated 2km to the northwest, at St-Martin-Plage)

Opening times : from mid March to beginning Nov.

3 ha (140 pitches)

Tariff : 🚶 4,20€ 🚗 📧 13,90€ – ⚡ (16A) 4,10€
Rental rates : (from mid March to beginning Nov.) – 8 🚐
Per week from 410 to 630€

Surroundings : < ⚲
Leisure activities : 🏠 🏊 🚣 🎿 🎣 billiards, multi-sports ground
Facilities : 🚿 ⚭ 🍴 ♨ 🚮 launderette ♨ 🚿
Nearby : 🍴

G P S	Longitude : 1.20425
	Latitude : 49.96632

ST-PAIR-SUR-MER

50380 – Michelin map **303** C7 – pop. 3 788 – alt. 30
▶ Paris 342 – Avranches 24 – Granville 4 – Villedieu-les-Poêles 29

⚞ Angomesnil

✆ 02 33 61 85 87, www.angomesnil.com ⚡ (from mid Junee to mid Sept.)

Address : 891 route du Guigeois (head 4.9km southeast along the D 21, follow the signs for St-Michel-des-Loups and turn left onto D 154, following signs for St-Aubin-des-Préaux)

Opening times : from mid June to mid Sept.

1,2 ha (45 pitches) flat, grassy

Tariff : 🚶 4,80€ 🚗 3,60€ 📧 3,90€ – ⚡ (6A) 3,60€ – Reservation fee 15€
🚐 borne 11,10€

Surroundings : ⚞ ⚲
Leisure activities : 🏠 🚣
Facilities : 🚿 ⚭ 🚮 🎮
Nearby : 🎿 🎣 🖥 (open air in season) ⚓ 🐎
sports trail

G P S	Longitude : -1.5261
	Latitude : 48.79065

ST-SAUVEUR-LE-VICOMTE

50390 – Michelin map **303** C3 – pop. 2 053 – alt. 30
▶ Paris 336 – Barneville-Carteret 20 – Cherbourg 37 – St-Lô 56

⚞ Municipal du Vieux Château

✆ 02 33 41 72 04, www.saintsauveurlevicomte.stationverte.com

Address : avenue Division Leclerc (in the town; beside the Douve)

Opening times : from beginning June to mid Sept.

1 ha (57 pitches) flat, grassy

Tariff : 🚶 2,80€ 🚗 2,80€ 📧 3,80€ – ⚡ (10A) 2,40€
🚐 borne – 5 📧
In the grounds of the medieval château.

Leisure activities : 🏠
Facilities : 🚿 ⚭ 🚮 🖥 launderette
Nearby : 🚣 🎿

G P S	Longitude : -1.52779
	Latitude : 49.38748

ST-SYMPHORIEN-LE-VALOIS

50250 – Michelin map **303** C4 – pop. 822 – alt. 35
▶ Paris 335 – Barneville-Carteret 19 – Carentan 25 – Cherbourg 47

⚠ Club Airotel L'Étang des Haizes ♣♦

☎ 02 33 46 01 16, www.campingetangdeshaizes.com

Address : rue Cauticote (take the northern exit along the D 900, follow the signs for Valognes and turn left onto D 136 towards the town)

Opening times : from beginning April to mid Oct.

4,5 ha (98 pitches)

Tariff : ♦ 8€ ⇔ 🚗 🔲 17€ – ⚡ (10A) 5€

Rental rates : (from mid April to end Sept.) ♿ 🚐 – 24 🚌
4 🏠 – 1 tipi – 2 tent lodges. Per night from 45 to 126€ – Per week from 45 to 882€

🚐 borne 18€ – 5 🔲 16€ – 🚰 ⚡16€

In a charming leafy setting around a pretty lake.

Surroundings : 🏕	
Leisure activities : ♥ 🏛 🎣 🏃 ⛷ 🚲 🛴	**G N S** Longitude : -1.54482
⛰ ⛵	Latitude : 49.29992
Facilities : ♿ ⛲ 🔲 ♨ 🍴 launderette	

ST-VAAST-LA-HOUGUE

50550 – Michelin map **303** E2 – pop. 2 091 – alt. 4
▶ Paris 347 – Carentan 41 – Cherbourg 31 – St-Lô 68

⚠ La Gallouette

☎ 02 33 54 20 57, www.lagallouette.com

Address : 10bis rue de la Gallouette (South of the town, 500m from the beach)

Opening times : from beginning April to end Sept.

2,3 ha (183 pitches) flat, grassy

Tariff : ♦ 6,80€ ⇔ 🚗 🔲 11,45€ – ⚡ (10A) 5€

Rental rates : (from beginning April to end Sept.) – 15 🚌
10 🏠. Per night from 80 to 110€ – Per week from 323 to 859€

🚐 borne 2€ – 15 🔲 13,60€

Surroundings : 🏕	
Leisure activities : ♥ ✕ 🏛 🎣 🏊 🏄	**G P S** Longitude : -1.26873
multi-sports ground	Latitude : 49.5846
Facilities : ♿ ⛲ ♨ 🍴 launderette	
Nearby : ✂ ♦ fitness trail	

ST-VALERY-EN-CAUX

76460 – Michelin map **304** E2 – pop. 4 463 – alt. 5
▶ Paris 190 – Bolbec 46 – Dieppe 35 – Fécamp 33

⚠ Seasonova Etennemare

☎ 02 35 97 15 79, www.seasonova.com – limited spaces for one-night stay

Address : 21 rue du Hameau d'Etennemare (located to the southwest, towards the hamlet of Le Bois d'Entennemare)

Opening times : from end March to beginning Nov.

4 ha (116 pitches)

Tariff : (2013 Price) 22€ ♦♦ ⇔ 🔲 ⚡ (16A) – Extra per person 4€

Rental rates : (2013 Price) (from end March to beginning Nov.)
1 🚌 – 10 🏠. Per night from 55 to 69€ – Per week from 290 to 450€ – Reservation fee 12€

Surroundings : 🏕	
Leisure activities : 🏛	**G P S** Longitude : 0.70378
Facilities : ♿ ⛲ 🎿 ♨ launderette	Latitude : 49.85878

STE-MARIE-DU-MONT

50480 – Michelin map **303** E3 – pop. 761 – alt. 31
▶ Paris 318 – Barfleur 38 – Carentan 11 – Cherbourg 47

⚠ Flower Utah-Beach

☎ 02 33 71 53 69, www.camping-utahbeach.com – limited spaces for one-night stay

Address : 6km northeast along the D 913 and take D 421; 150m from the beach

Opening times : from beginning April to end Sept.

5,5 ha (149 pitches)

Tariff : 29,50€ ♦♦ ⇔ 🔲 ⚡ (6A) – Extra per person 6€ – Reservation fee 10€

Rental rates : (from beginning April to end Sept.) – 13 🚌
12 🏠 – 2 tent lodges. Per night from 44 to 129€ – Per week from 220 to 903€ – Reservation fee 10€

🚐 borne 9,60€ – 🚰 ⚡16€

Surroundings : 🏕 ♦	
Leisure activities : ♥ ✕ 🏛 🎣 jacuzzi 🏄	**G P S** Longitude : -1.18038
🎾 🏃 ♦ multi-sports ground, entertainment room	Latitude : 49.42001
Facilities : ♿ ⛲ ♨ 🍴 launderette 🎿	
Nearby : 🚲 sand yachting	

A 'quartier' is a district or area of a town or village.

STE-MÈRE-ÉGLISE

50480 – Michelin map **303** E3 – pop. 1 643 – alt. 28
▶ Paris 321 – Bayeux 57 – Cherbourg 39 – St-Lô 42

⚠ Municipal

☎ 02 33 41 35 22, mairie-sme@wanadoo.fr

Address : 6 rue Airborne (take the eastern exit along the D 17 and take a right turn; near the sports field)

1,3 ha (70 pitches) flat, grassy

Surroundings : 🏕	
Leisure activities : 🏛 🏄 🚲 ✂ 🎾 multi-sports ground	**G P S** Longitude : -1.31018
Facilities : ⛲ launderette	Latitude : 49.41003

SURRAIN

14710 – Michelin map **303** G4 – pop. 159 – alt. 40
▶ Paris 278 – Cherbourg 83 – Rennes 187 – Rouen 167

⚠ La Roseraie d'Omaha

☎ 02 31 21 17 71, www.camping-calvados-normandie.fr

Address : rue de l'église (take the southern exit along the D 208, follow the signs for Mandeville-en-Bessin)

Opening times : from beginning April to end Sept.

3 ha (66 pitches)

Tariff : 19,10€ ♦♦ ⇔ 🔲 ⚡ (10A) – Extra per person 5,50€

Rental rates : (from beginning April to end Sept.) 🚐
10 🚌 – 15 🏠 – 1 gîte. Per night from 56 to 90€ – Per week from 289 to 740€

🚐 borne – 🚰 14€

Surroundings : 🏕 ♦	
Leisure activities : ✕ 🏛 🏄 🚲 ✂ ♦ 🏊 🎿	**G P S** Longitude : -0.86443
Facilities : ♿ ⛲ 🎿 ♨ 🍴 launderette	Latitude : 49.32574
Nearby : 🐎	

SURTAINVILLE

50270 – Michelin map **303** B3 – pop. 1 255 – alt. 12
▶ Paris 367 – Barneville-Carteret 12 – Cherbourg 29 – St-Lô 42

⌂ Municipal les Mielles

🖉 02 33 04 31 04, camping-surtainville.com

Address : 80 route des Laguettes (head 1.5km west along the D 66 and follow the signs for the sea, 80m from the beach, direct access)

Opening times : Permanent

25 ha (151 pitches)

Tariff : 🛉 3,35€ ⇔ 🗉 3,35€ – (≴) (4A) 3€
Rental rates : Permanent ⛟ – 2 🛏. Per night from 55€
Per week from 236 to 399 €
🚽 borne 4,15€

Surroundings : ⊗ ⊏⊐
Leisure activities : 🏠 ⚞
Facilities : ⛟ ⛽ ⫘ ⛲ ⫱ ⫭ launderette
Nearby : ⚓ sand yachting

GPS Longitude : -1.82881
Latitude : 49.46386

THURY-HARCOURT

14220 – Michelin map **303** J6 – pop. 1 968 – alt. 45
▶ Paris 257 – Caen 28 – Condé-sur-Noireau 20 – Falaise 27

⌂ Le Traspy

🖉 02 31 79 61 80, www.camping-traspy.fr

Address : rue du Pont Benoît (head east of the town along the bd du 30-Juin-1944 and take road to the left)

1,5 ha (78 pitches) terraced, flat, grassy

Rentals : 12 🛏 – 1 🏠.
🚽 borne – 6 🗉 – ⧲ (≴)15€
Beside the Traspy river and near a small lake.

Surroundings : ⊏⊐ �‿
Leisure activities : ✕ 🏠 ⊑⊑ ⚞
Facilities : ⛟ ⛽ ⛲ ⫭ launderette ⛁ ⛳
Nearby : 🚴 ⚓ ⬚ ⛁ ⬚ paragliding

GPS Longitude : -0.46913
Latitude : 48.98896

TOUFFREVILLE-SUR-EU

76910 – Michelin map **304** H2 – pop. 201 – alt. 45
▶ Paris 171 – Abbeville 46 – Amiens 101 – Blangy-sur-Nesle 35

⌂ Municipal Les Acacias

🖉 02 35 50 66 33, www.camping-acacias.fr

Address : at Les Prés du Thil (head 1km to the southeast along the D 226 and take D 454, following the signs for Guilmecourt)

Opening times : Permanent

1 ha (50 pitches) flat, grassy

Tariff : (2013 Price) 🛉 2,20€ ⇔ 1€ 🗉 1,80€ – (≴) (10A) 5€

Surroundings : ⊗ ⊏⊐
Facilities : ⛟ ⫘

GPS Longitude : 1.33537
Latitude : 49.99531

Do not confuse:
⌂ to 🅰 : *MICHELIN classification with*
★ to ★★★★★ : *official classification*

TOUSSAINT

76400 – Michelin map **304** C3 – pop. 743 – alt. 105
▶ Paris 196 – Bolbec 24 – Fécamp 5 – Rouen 69

⌂ Municipal du Canada

🖉 02 35 29 78 34, www.commune-de-toussaint.fr – limited spaces for one-night stay

Address : rue de Rouen (500m northwest along the D 926, follow the signs for Fécamp and take road to the left)

Opening times : from mid March to mid Oct.

2,5 ha (100 pitches)

Tariff : 13,20€ 🛉🛉 ⇔ 🗉 (≴) (6A) – Extra per person 3,60€
Rental rates : (from mid March to mid Oct.) – 2 🛏 – 2 🏠.
Per night from 52 to 61€ – Per week from 335 to 445€
🚽 10 🗉 13,20€

Surroundings : ⊏⊐ �‿
Facilities : ⛟ ⛽ 🗄
Nearby : ⚞ ✕

GPS Longitude : 0.42091
Latitude : 49.73776

*The classification (1 to 5 tents, **black** or **red**) that we award to selected sites in this guide is our own system. It should not be confused with the classification (1 to 5 stars) of official organisations.*

LE TRÉPORT

76470 – Michelin map **304** I1 – pop. 5 416 – alt. 12
▶ Paris 180 – Abbeville 37 – Amiens 92 – Blangy-sur-Bresle 26

🅰 Municipal les Boucaniers

🖉 02 35 86 35 47, www.ville-le-treport.fr/camping

Address : rue Pierre Mendès-France (take the av. des Canadiens; near the stadium)

5,5 ha (166 pitches) flat, grassy

Rentals : 50 🏠.

Surroundings : �‿
Leisure activities : ⧌ 🏠 ⚞
Facilities : ⛟ ⛽ ⫘ ⛺ ⫭ launderette ⛁
Nearby : ✕

GPS Longitude : 1.38882
Latitude : 50.0577

TRÉVIÈRES

14710 – Michelin map **303** G4 – pop. 938 – alt. 14
▶ Paris 283 – Bayeux 19 – Caen 49 – Carentan 31

⌂ Municipal Sous les Pommiers

🖉 02 31 92 89 24, www.ville-trevieres.fr – ⛨

Address : rue du Pont de la Barre (take the northern exit along the D 30, follow the signs for Formigny; near a stream)

Opening times : from beginning April to end Sept.

1,2 ha (75 pitches) flat, grassy

Tariff : 14,30€ 🛉🛉 ⇔ 🗉 (≴) (16A) – Extra per person 3,40€
Pitches in the shade of apple trees.

Surroundings : ⊏⊐ �‿
Leisure activities : ⚞
Facilities : ⛟ ⛁ ⛺ 🗄
Nearby : ⧖ 🐎

GPS Longitude : -0.90637
Latitude : 49.3132

VEULES-LES-ROSES

76980 – Michelin map **304** E2 – pop. 561 – alt. 15
▶ Paris 188 – Dieppe 27 – Fontaine-le-Dun 8 – Rouen 57

⚠ Seasonova Les Mouettes

✆ 02 35 97 61 98, www.camping-lesmouettes-normandie.com

Address : avenue Jean-Moulin (take the eastern exit along the D 68, follow the signs for Sotteville-sur-Mer, 500m from the beach)

Opening times : from beginning April to beginning Nov.

3,6 ha (150 pitches) flat, grassy

Tariff : 27 € ♣ ♣ 🚐 🔲 🔌 (6A) – Extra per person 5,40 € – Reservation fee 15 €
Rental rates : (from beginning April to beginning Nov.) 🏄 26 🚐 – 2 tent lodges. Per week from 75 to 860 € – Reservation fee 15 €
🚰 borne 10 €

Surroundings : 🌊 ⌂ ♀
Leisure activities : 🎮 🎿 ♨ jacuzzi 🚴
🚲 🏊
Facilities : ⚡ ⊶ 🏢 ♨ laundorotto

GPS Longitude : 0.80335
Latitude : 49.87579

LE VEY

14570 – Michelin map **303** J6 – pop. 87 – alt. 50
▶ Paris 269 – Caen 47 – Hérouville-St-Clair 46 – Flers 23

⚠ Les Rochers des Parcs

✆ 02 31 69 70 36, www.camping-normandie-clecy.fr

Address : at La Cour

Opening times :

1,5 ha (90 pitches)

Tariff : ♣ 5,80 € 🚐 🔲 6,50 € – 🔌 (10A) 3,90 € – Reservation fee 5 €
Rental rates : (from beginning April to end Sept.) – 10 🚐 – 2 🏠 5 canvas bungalows. Per night from 66 to 125 € – Per week from 217 to 550 € – Reservation fee 5 €
🚰 borne 2,50 €

Surroundings : ♀ ⛰
Leisure activities : 🎮 🎿 🚴 🎣 🚣
Facilities : ⚡ ⊶ 🏢 launderette
Nearby : 🍴 🐎 adventure park

GPS Longitude : -0.47487
Latitude : 48.91391

VILLEDIEU-LES-POÊLES

50800 – Michelin map **303** E6 – pop. 3 882 – alt. 105
▶ Paris 314 – Alençon 122 – Avranches 26 – Caen 82

⚠ Les Chevaliers

✆ 02 33 61 02 44, www.camping-deschevaliers.com

Address : 2 impasse Pré-de-la-Rose (access via the town centre, take r. des Costils to the left of the post office)

Opening times : from beginning April to end Sept.

1,4 ha (82 pitches)

Tariff : 26,70 € ♣ ♣ 🚐 🔲 🔌 (10A) – Extra per person 4,70 €
Rental rates : (from beginning April to end Sept.) – 21 🚐 . Per night from 41 to 105 € – Per week from 196 to 735 €
🚰 borne – 10 🔲 14 € – 🚰 14 €

Pleasant, well-kept setting, beside the Sienne river.

Surroundings : 🌊 ⌂ ♀
Leisure activities : 🍴 🎮 🎿 🚴 ♨ 🚣 multi-sports ground
Facilities : ⚡ ⊶ ♨ 🏢 launderette 🚰
Nearby : 🎣 🏊

GPS Longitude : -1.21694
Latitude : 48.83639

VILLERS-SUR-MER

14640 – Michelin map **303** L4 – pop. 2 707 – alt. 10
▶ Paris 208 – Caen 35 – Deauville 8 – Le Havre 52

⚠ Bellevue

✆ 02 31 87 05 21, www.camping-bellevue.com – limited spaces for one-night stay

Address : route de Dives (situated 2km southwest along the D 513, follow the signs for Cabourg)

Opening times : from beginning April to end Oct.

5,5 ha (257 pitches)

Tariff : 31 € ♣ ♣ 🚐 🔲 🔌 (6A) – Extra per person 8,50 € – Reservation fee 16 €
Rental rates : (from mid April to mid Oct.) 🏄 – 40 🚐 . Per night from 120 to 315 € – Per week from 280 to 760 € – Reservation fee 16 €
Situated overlooking the bay at Deauville.

Surroundings : < ⌂
Leisure activities : 🍸 🎮 ⏰ nighttime ♨ 🚴 🏊
Facilities : ⚡ ⊶ 🏢 ♨ 🚰 🏢 laundorette
Nearby : 🚴 🍴 🎣 ⛰ ♨ 🐎

GPS Longitude : -0.0195
Latitude : 49.3097

The prices listed were supplied by the campsite owners in 2013 (if prices were not available, those from the previous year are given). The fees should be regarded as basic charges and may fluctuate with inflation.

VIMOUTIERS

61120 – Michelin map **310** K1 – pop. 3 828 – alt. 95
▶ Paris 185 – L'Aigle 46 – Alençon 66 – Argentan 31

⚠ Municipal la Campière

✆ 02 33 39 18 86, www.mairie-vimoutiers.fr

Address : 14 boulevard Dentu (700m north, in the direction of Lisieux, by the stadium; beside La Vie river)

1 ha (40 pitches) flat, grassy
Rental rates : 4 🚐 .

Norman-style buildings in a lush, green setting surrounded by lots of flowers.

Surroundings : ⌂ ♀
Leisure activities : 🎮 🎿 🎣
Facilities : ⚡ ⊶ 🏢

GPS Longitude : 0.1966
Latitude : 48.9326

PAYS-DE-LA-LOIRE

B. Rieger / hemis.fr

The 'Garden of France' is renowned for its tranquil atmosphere, glorious châteaux, magnificent floral gardens and acres of orchards and vineyards. Enjoy a glass of light Loire wine accompanied by a plate of rillettes (pork pâté), *matelote d'anguilles* (eel stew) or a slice of goat's cheese, perfect partners in the gastronomic experience offered by the region. Continue downriver to Nantes, redolent today of the scent of spices first brought back from the New World. This is the home of the famous dry Muscadet wines. Further south, the Vendée region still echoes with the cries of 18th-century Royalists' before revolutionary fervour took hold. Explore the secrets of its salt marshes, relax in balmy seaside resorts or head for the spectacular attractions of the Puy du Fou amusement park. Simple country fare is the order of the day here, so make sure you sample a piping-hot plate of *chaudrée* (fish chowder) or a mouth-watering slice of fresh brioche.

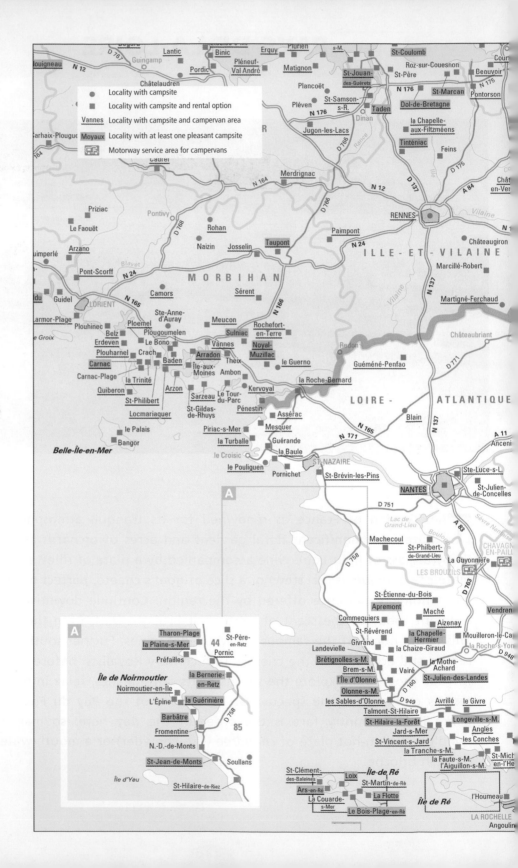

Légende:

- ● Locality with campsite
- ■ Locality with campsite and rental option
- <u>Vannes</u> Locality with campsite and campervan area
- <u>Moyaux</u> Locality with at least one pleasant campsite
- 🚐 Motorway service area for campervans

Mouignau N 12 Boqard D 767 Guingamp Lantic Binic Pordic Erquy Plurien s.-M. St-Coulomb Cour
Pléneuf- Roz-sur-Couesnon Beauvoir
Pléneuf-Val André Matignon St-Jouan- St-Père N 175
Châtelaudren des-Guérets Pontorson
Plancoët St-Marcan
Pléven St-Samson- Taden Dol-de-Bretagne N 176
s.-R. Dinan
Carhaix-Plouguer Jugon-les-Lacs la Chapelle- D 175
aux-Filtzméens
Tinténiac Feins

Merdrignac N 12 D 137 Châ
en-Ver
N 164 A 84

Priziac Pontivy D 768 Rohan Paimpont RENNES Vilaine N 1
Le Faouët Naizin Josselin Taupont N 24 ILLE-ET-VILAINE Châteaugiron
Quimperlé Arzano Marcillé-Robert
Pont-Scorff N 24 MORBIHAN N 137
Blavet Martigné-Ferchaud

Guidel N 165 Camors Sérent N 166 Châteaubriant
LORIENT D 771
Larmor-Plage Ste-Anne- Meucon Rochefort- Redon
d'Auray en-Terre
Plouhinec Ploemel Sulniac le Guerno Guéméné-Penfao
le Groix Belz Plougoumelen Vannes Noyal-
Erdeven Le Bono Muzillac
Plouharnel Crach Arradon Theix la Roche-Bernard
Carnac Baden Île-aux- Ambon LOIRE- ATLANTIQUE
Carnac-Plage Moines
la Trinité Kervoyal
Quiberon Arzon Le Tour- Blain A 11
St-Philibert Sarzeau du-Parc Pénestin Anceni
Locmariaquer St-Gildas- Assérac N 165 N 137
de-Rhuys Mesquer N 171 Ste-Luce-s-L.
le Palais Piriac-s-Mer Guérande St-Julien-
Bangor la Turballe la Baule de-Concelles
Belle-Île-en-Mer le Croisic ST-NAZAIRE NANTES
le Pouliguen Pornichet St-Brévin-les-Pins
Pornichet D 751 Lac de
Grand-Lieu CHAVAGN
EN-PAILL
Machecoul St-Philbert- La Guyonnière
de-Grand-Lieu A 83
LES BROUIL D 763
St-Étienne-du-Bois Vendren
Apremont Maché
Commequiers Aizenay Mouilleron-le-Ca
St-Révérend la Chapelle- la Roche-s-Yon
Givrand Hermier
Landevielle la Chaize-Giraud D 948
Brétignolles-s-M. la Mothe-
Brem-s-M. Vairé Achard
l'Île d'Olonne St-Julien-des-Landes D 160
Olonne-s-M. Avrillé le Givre
les Sables-d'Olonne D 949
Talmont-St-Hilaire Longeville-s-M.
St-Hilaire-la-Forêt Angles
Jard-s-Mer les Conches
St-Vincent-s-Jard la Tranche-s-M. St-Mich
la Faute-s-M. en-l'Île
l'Aiguillon-s-M.
St-Clément- Loix **Île de Ré**
des-Baleines St-Martin-de-Ré l'Houmeau
Ars-en-Ré La Flotte **Île de Ré**
La Couarde- LA ROCHELLE
s-Mer Le Bois-Plage-en-Ré Angouli

A

A
Tharon-Plage St-Père- 44
la Plaine-s-Mer en-Retz Pornic
Préfailles
Île de Noirmoutier la Bernerie-
en-Retz
Noirmoutier-en-Île
L'Épine la Guérinière 85
Barbâtre D 758
Fromentine
N.-D.-de-Monts Soullans
St-Jean-de-Monts
Île d'Yeu
St-Hilaire-de-Riez

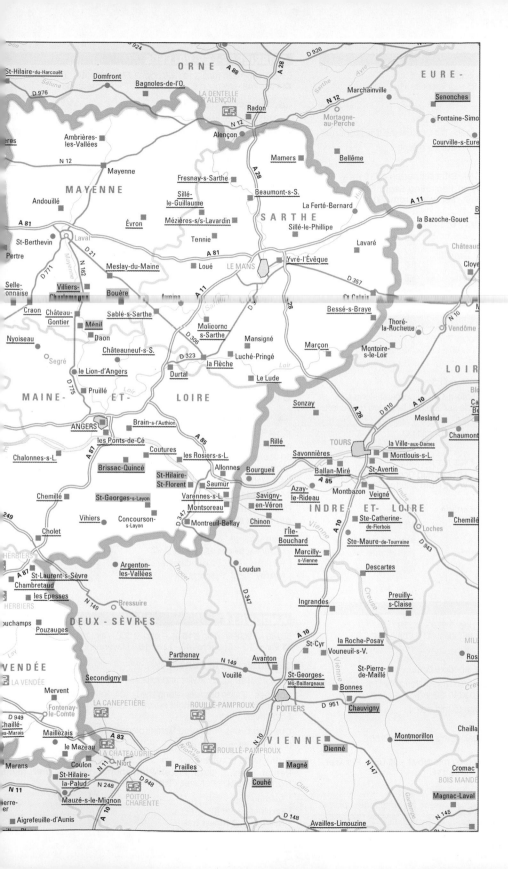

L'AIGUILLON-SUR-MER

85460 – Michelin map **316** I10 – pop. 2 310 – alt. 4
▶ Paris 458 – Luçon 20 – Niort 83 – La Rochelle 51

⚠ La Cléroca

✆ 02 51 27 19 92, www.camping-la-cleroca.com

Address : 2.2km northwest along the D 44, follow the signs for Grues

Opening times : from end May to beginning Sept.

1,5 ha (66 pitches) flat, grassy

Tariff : 27,43 € ✸✸ ⇔ 🗐 [⚡] (10A) – Extra per person 4,75 €
Rental rates : (from end May to beginning Sept.) ⇗ – 1 yurt
1 gîte. Per night from 40 to 60 € – Per week from 300 to 520 €
🚐 borne 12,38 € – 6 🗐 12,38 €
A lush, green setting and plenty of shade.

Surroundings : 🗲🗲
Leisure activities : 🏠 🛶 🏊 🎣 multi-
sports ground
Facilities : ♿ ⚡ 🚮 🔥♨ launderette

Longitude : -1.31513
Latitude : 46.35003

AIZENAY

85190 – Michelin map **316** G7 – pop. 7 930 – alt. 62
▶ Paris 435 – Challans 26 – Nantes 60 – La Roche-sur-Yon 18

⚠ La Forêt

✆ 02 51 34 78 12, www.camping-laforet.com

Address : 1 rue de la Clairière (located 1.5km southeast along the
D 948, follow the signs for la Roche-sur-Yon and take road to the left,
behind the commercial centre)

Opening times : from beginning April to mid Oct.

2,5 ha (96 pitches)

Tariff : 20 € ✸✸ ⇔ 🗐 [⚡] (6A) – Extra per person 3,20 €
Rental rates : (from beginning April to mid Oct.) – 20 🛏 – 1 🏠.
Per night from 45 to 65 € – Per week from 240 to 450 €
🚐 borne 3 € – 🚐 12 €
A pleasant site with plenty of shade.

Surroundings : 🗲🗲
Leisure activities : 🛶 🏊 🎣
Facilities : ♿ ⚡ 🔥♨ launderette
Nearby : 🍷 ✕ 🎣 fitness trail

Longitude : -1.58947
Latitude : 46.73427

ALLONNES

49650 – Michelin map **317** J5 – pop. 2 979 – alt. 28
▶ Paris 292 – Angers 64 – Azay-le-Rideau 43 – Chinon 28

⚠ Club Airotel Le Pô Doré

✆ 02 41 38 78 80, www.camping-lepodore.com

Address : 51 route du Pô (3.2km northwest along the D 10, follow
the signs for Saumur and take road to the left)

Opening times : from mid March to mid Nov.

2 ha (90 pitches) flat, grassy

Tariff : 24,70 € ✸✸ ⇔ 🗐 [⚡] (10A) – Extra per person 5,30 €
Reservation fee 13 €
Rental rates : (from mid March to mid Nov.) – 20 🛏. Per week
from 330 to 731 € – Reservation fee 13 €
🚐 🚐 [⚡] 14 €

Surroundings : 🗲 🗔
Leisure activities : 🍷 ✕ 🏠 🛶 🎣
Facilities : ♿ ⚡ 🚮 🔥 🗣 🔥 🔥

Longitude : -0.01244
Latitude : 47.29923

AMBRIÈRES-LES-VALLÉES

53300 – Michelin map **310** F4 – pop. 2 778 – alt. 144
▶ Paris 248 – Alençon 60 – Domfront 22 – Fougères 46

⚠ Municipal de Vaux

✆ 02 43 04 90 25, www.parcdevaux.com

Address : situated 2km southeast along the D 23, follow the signs for
Mayenne and take the turning to the left; by the swimming pool

1,5 ha (61 pitches)
Rentals : 10 🛏 – 20 🏠 – 5 canvas bungalows.
A pleasant wooded park beside the Varenne (small lake).

Surroundings : 🗲 🗔 🗲🗲
Leisure activities : 🏠 🎣
Facilities : ♿ ⚡ 🚮 🔥 launderette
Nearby : 🛶 🎣 🏊 🎣 🏊 🏇

Longitude : -0.6129
Latitude : 48.39175

*The classification (1 to 5 tents, **black** or **red**) that we
award to selected sites in this guide is our own system.
It should not be confused with the classification
(1 to 5 stars) of official organisations.*

ANCENIS

44150 – Michelin map **316** I3 – pop. 7 543 – alt. 13
▶ Paris 347 – Angers 55 – Châteaubriant 48 – Cholet 49

⚠ L'Île Mouchet

✆ 02 40 83 08 43, www.camping-estivance.com

Address : impasse de l'Île Mouchet (take the western exit along the
bd Joubert and take the turning to the left, behind the municipal
sports centre)

3,5 ha (105 pitches) flat, grassy
Rentals : 11 🛏 – 5 canvas bungalows.
*Beautiful meadow and plenty of shade, near the municipal sta-
dium and the Loire river.*

Surroundings : 🗲🗲
Leisure activities : 🏠 🛶 🎣 🏊
Facilities : ♿ ⚡ 🔥 🔥 launderette
Nearby : ✕ 🏊 🎣 sports trail

Longitude : -1.18707
Latitude : 47.36095

ANDOUILLÉ

53240 – Michelin map **310** E5 – pop. 2 300 – alt. 103
▶ Paris 282 – Fougères 42 – Laval 15 – Mayenne 23

⚠ Municipal le Pont

✆ 02 43 01 18 10, www.ville-andouille.fr

Address : 5 allée des Isles (along the D 104, follow the signs for
St-Germain-le-Fouilloux, right next to municipal gardens; beside the
Ernée river)

Opening times : from end March to end Oct.

0,8 ha (31 pitches) flat, grassy

Tariff : (2013 Price) ✸ 1,52 € ⇔ ,72 € 🗐 ,78 € – [⚡] (6A) 1,42 €
Rental rates : (2013 Price) Permanent – 4 🏠. Per night
from 26 to 52 € – Per week from 183 to 364 €

Surroundings : 🗔 🗲
Facilities : ♿ 🚮 🔥
Nearby : 🛶 fitness trail

Longitude : -0.78697
Latitude : 48.17604

ANGERS

49000 – Michelin map **317** F4 – pop. 147 305 – alt. 41
▶ Paris 294 – Caen 249 – Laval 79 – Le Mans 97

▲▲▲ Lac de Maine ▲:

✆ 02 41 73 05 03, www.lacdemaine.fr

Address : avenue du Lac de Maine (4km southwest along the D 111, follow the signs for Pruniers, near the lake (direct access) and near the leisure and activity park)

Opening times : from mid March to mid Oct.

4 ha (163 pitches)

Tariff : 26,40€ ✹✹ ⇦ 🔳 🗲 (10A) – Extra per person 3,50€
Reservation fee 7€

Rental rates : (from beginning Jan. to mid Oct.) 🦽 (2 mobile homes) – 17 🚐. Per week from 550 to 662€ – Reservation fee 30€

🚐 borne – 80 🔳 22,40€ – 🚐 🗲16€

300 m to public transport links for the centre of Angers,.

Surroundings : 🏕 ⚲⚲
Leisure activities ! ✹ 🎿 🎣 🏊 🛶 spa facilities
Facilities : 🦽 ⚬━ 🍳 🏖 ☂ 🍴 🔲 ⛲
Nearby : 🍽 🚤 🎣 🦆 pedalos

Longitude : -0.59654
Latitude : 47.45551

Some information or pricing may have changed since the guide went to press. We recommend you check the price list online in advance or at the entrance to the campsite and enquire about possible restrictions.

ANGLES

85750 – Michelin map **316** I I9 – pop. 2 329 – alt. 10
▶ Paris 450 – Luçon 23 – La Mothe-Achard 38 – Niort 86

▲▲▲ L'Atlantique ▲:

✆ 02 51 27 03 19, www.camping-atlantique.com

Address : 5bis rue du Chemin de Fer (in the town, take the exit for La Tranche-sur-Mer and take turning to the left)

Opening times : from end March to end Oct.

6,9 ha (363 pitches)

Tariff : 30,50€ ✹✹ ⇦ 🔳 🗲 (10A) – Extra per person 7,50€
Reservation fee 25€

Rental rates : (from end March to end Oct.) – 150 🚐 – 15 🏠. Per night from 30 to 45€ – Per week from 160 to 810€
Reservation fee 25€

A well thought-out site, although sanitary facilities and some rental options are a bit old; free shuttle service to the beaches.

Surroundings : 🏕 ⚲⚲
Leisure activities : ! ✹ 🎿 🎣 🏊 🛶
🚲 🍽 🎿 🛶 entertainment room
Facilities : 🦽 ⚬━ 🏖 ☂ 🍴 launderette ⛲

Longitude : -1.40552
Latitude : 46.40465

▲▲▲ APV Moncalm ▲:

(rental of mobile homes and chalets only)
✆ 02 51 97 55 50, www.camping-apv.com

Address : rue du Chemin de Fer (in the town, take the exit for La Tranche-sur-Mer and take turning to the left)

Opening times : from beginning April to end Sept.

3 ha (200 pitches)

Rental rates : 85 🚐 – 30 🏠. Per night from 61 to 81€
Per week from 238 to 896€ – Reservation fee 27€

A mobile home park and chalets with an open-air play and paddling pool; free shuttle service to the beaches.

Surroundings : 🏕 ⚲⚲
Leisure activities : ! ✹ 🎿 🎣 🏊 🛶 🚴
🚲 🎿 🛶 multi-sports ground
Facilities : 🦽 ⚬━ 🍳 🍴 launderette ⛲ ☂

Longitude : -1.40548
Latitude : 46.40467

▲▲▲ Le Clos Cottet ▲:

✆ 02 51 28 90 72, www.camping-clos-cottet.com

Address : route de La Tranche-sur-Mer (2.2km to the south, near the D 747)

Opening times : from beginning April to end Sept.

4,5 ha (196 pitches) flat, grassy, small lake

Tariff : (2013 Price) 19€ ✹✹ ⇦ 🔳 🗲 (10A) – Extra per person 5€
Reservation fee 25€

Rental rates : (2013 Price) (from beginning April to end Sept.) 90 🚐 – 9 🏠 – 5 canvas bungalows. Per night 140€ – Per week from 99 to 839€ – Reservation fee 25€

🚐 5 🔳 22€

Based around a renovated farmhouse with some animals; free shuttle service to the beaches.

Surroundings : 🏕 ⚲⚲
Leisure activities : ! ✹ 🎿 🎣 🏊 🏋 🛶
hammam ♨ 🏊 🎿 🛶 quad biking
multi-sports ground, entertainment room
Facilities : 🦽 ⚬━ 🍳 🍴 launderette

Longitude : -1.40345
Latitude : 46.39248

APREMONT

85220 – Michelin map **316** F7 – pop. 1 546 – alt. 19
▶ Paris 448 – Challans 17 – Nantes 64 – La Roche-sur-Yon 30

▲▲▲ Les Charmes

✆ 02 51 54 48 08, www.campinglescharmes.com

Address : at Les Lilas (3.6km north along the D 21, follow the signs for Challans and take turning to the right, towards La Roussière)

Opening times : from beginning April to mid Sept.

1 ha (55 pitches) flat, grassy

Tariff : 23,30€ ✹✹ ⇦ 🔳 🗲 (10A) – Extra per person 4,90€
Reservation fee 15€

Rental rates : Permanent 🦽 (1 mobile home) – 12 🚐
5 🏠. Per night from 36 to 70€ – Per week from 230 to 690€
Reservation fee 15€

🚐 🚐13,20€

A pleasant site with upmarket rental options and a small wellness centre.

Surroundings : 🌳 🏕 ⚲⚲
Leisure activities : ! 🎿 🏊 jacuzzi ♨ 🛶
entertainment room
Facilities : 🦽 ⚬━ 🍴 launderette

Longitude : -1.73397
Latitude : 46.77827

For more information on visiting particular towns or regions, consult the relevant regional MICHELIN Green Guide. We also recommend you use the appropriate Michelin regional map to locate your selected campsite, to calculate distances and to work out the best route.

ASSÉRAC

44410 – Michelin map **316** B3 – pop. 1 773 – alt. 12
▶ Paris 454 – Nantes 79 – Rennes 108 – Vannes 48

▲▲▲ Moulin de Leclis

📞 0240017669, www.camping-leclis.com

Address : at Pont Mahé (situated 4km west along the D 82)

Opening times : from beginning April to mid Nov.

3,8 ha (180 pitches)

Tariff : (2013 Price) 14,90€ ✹✹ ⬅ 🔲 ⌀ (10A)
Extra per person 3,60€ – Reservation fee 20€

Rental rates : (from beginning April to mid Nov.) ♿ (1 mobile home) – 31 🚐 – 31 🏠 – 1 tent lodge. Per night 220€ – Per week from 238 to 1162€ – Reservation fee 20€

🚰 borne 4,50€ – 🛒6,90€

In the bay at Pont-Mahé, with a view of La Pointe du Bile (headland).

Surroundings : 🌲 ▭ 🎿⚓
Leisure activities : ♟ ✗ ⛵ 🔲 (open air in season) 🎿
Facilities : ♿ ⚡ ▥ 🚿 ♟ launderette 🧺
Nearby : skate surfing

G P S Longitude : -2.44795
Latitude : 47.44576

AVOISE

72430 – Michelin map **310** H7 – pop. 539 – alt. 112
▶ Paris 242 – La Flèche 28 – Le Mans 41 – Sablé-sur-Sarthe 11

▲ Municipal des Deux Rivières

📞 0243927612, mairie.avoise@wanadoo.fr

Address : place des 2 Fonds (in the town, along the D 57)

Opening times : from beginning April to end Sept.

1,8 ha (50 pitches) flat, grassy

Tariff : (2013 Price) 8,50€ ✹✹ ⬅ 🔲 ⌀ (10A) – Extra per person 2,10€

Beside the Sarthe river.

Surroundings : ▭ 🎿⚓
Leisure activities : ⛵
Facilities : ♿ ⚡ ▥🍴 🚿 🧺 ♟
Nearby : ⚓

G P S Longitude : -0.20554
Latitude : 47.86545

AVRILLÉ

85440 – Michelin map **316** H9 – pop. 1 194 – alt. 45
▶ Paris 445 – Luçon 27 – La Rochelle 70 – La Roche-sur-Yon 27

▲▲▲ FranceLoc Le Domaine Des Forges ♟♟

📞 0251223885, www.campingdomainedesforges.com

Address : rue des Forges (take the northeastern exit along the D 19, follow the signs for Moutiers-les-Mauxfaits and take the turning to the left, 0.7km along the rue des Forges)

12 ha (295 pitches) flat, grassy, pond

Rental rates : ♿ (2 mobile homes) – 2 caravans – 80 🚐 – 2 🏠 11 canvas bungalows.

🚰 borne

The site is laid out around a small but pretty château and a lake.

Surroundings : 🌲 ▭ 🎿
Leisure activities : ♟ ✗ ⛵ 🎣 🏊 🎿 ⛵ 🚴
🎯 🔲 🎿 🚿
Facilities : ♿ ⚡ ▥ 🚿 🧺 🍴 launderette 🧺
🚿🛒

G P S Longitude : -1.49467
Latitude : 46.47587

▲▲ Les Mancellières

📞 0251903597, www.lesmancellieres.com

Address : 1300 route de Longeville (1.7km south along the D 105)

Opening times : from beginning May to mid Sept.

2,6 ha (133 pitches)

Tariff : 26,40€ ✹✹ ⬅ 🔲 ⌀ (6A) – Extra per person 4,40€
Reservation fee 20€

Rental rates : (from mid April to mid Sept.) – 58 🚐 – 4 🏠 Per week from 172 to 755€ – Reservation fee 20€

A pleasant, shady site with lots of green space.

Surroundings : ▭ 🎿🎿
Leisure activities : ✗ 🛁 jacuzzi 🏊 🎿🎿 multi-sports ground
Facilities : ♿ ⚡ ♟ 🍴 launderette

G P S Longitude : -1.48509
Latitude : 46.45608

LA BAULE

44500 – Michelin map **316** B4 – pop. 16 235 – alt. 31
▶ Paris 450 – Nantes 76 – Rennes 120 – St-Nazaire 19

▲▲▲ Club Airotel La Roseraie ♟♟

📞 0240604666, www.laroseraie.com

Address : 20 avenue Jean Sohier (take the northeastern exit for La Baule-Escoublac)

Opening times : from beginning April to end Sept.

5 ha (220 pitches)

Tariff : 40€ ✹✹ ⬅ 🔲 ⌀ (10A) – Extra per person 8€ – Reservation fee 30€

Rental rates : (from beginning April to end Sept.) ♿ (1 mobile home) – 75 🚐 – 3 🏠. Per night from 45 to 110€ – Per week from 301 to 1246€ – Reservation fee 30€

🚰 borne

A pleasant setting, lots of green space but choose the pitches away from the road.

Surroundings : ▭ 🎿
Leisure activities : ♟ ✗ 🛁 🎣 🏊 🎿 jacuzzi 🎿 🚴 🎯 🔲 (open air in season) 🎿 multi-sports ground, entertainment room
Facilities : ♿ ⚡ 🆑 ♟ 🚿 launderette 🧺

G P S Longitude : -2.35776
Latitude : 47.29828

Some campsites benefit from proximity to a municipal leisure centre.

BEAUMONT-SUR-SARTHE

72170 – Michelin map **310** J5 – pop. 2 094 – alt. 76
▶ Paris 223 – Alençon 24 – La Ferté-Bernard 70 – Le Mans 29

▲▲ Municipal du Val de Sarthe

📞 0243970193, www.ville-beaumont-sur-sarthe.fr/

Address : located to the southeast of the town

1 ha (73 pitches) flat, grassy

Rental rates : 🎿 – 2 canvas bungalows.

🚰 borne

A pleasant site and setting beside the Sarthe river.

Surroundings : 🌲 ▭ 🎿
Leisure activities : 🛁 🏊 fitness trail
Facilities : ♿ ⚡ ▥
Nearby : 🎿 🎿

G P S Longitude : 0.13384
Latitude : 48.2261

LA BERNERIE-EN-RETZ

44760 – Michelin map **316** D5 – pop. 2 541 – alt. 24
▶ Paris 426 – Challans 40 – Nantes 46 – St-Nazaire 36

⚠ Les Écureuils ♣♣

☎ 02 40 82 76 95, www.camping-les-ecureuils.com

Address : 24 avenue Gilbert Burlot (take northeastern exit, follow the signs for Nantes and take the turning to the left after the level crossing, 350m from the sea)

Opening times : from beginning April to mid Sept.

5,3 ha (312 pitches)

Tariff : (2013 Price) 44€ ♣♣ ⇌ 🗒 🔌 (10A) – Extra per person 8€
Rental rates : (2013 Price) (from beginning April to end Sept.) 🚲 – 70 🚐 – 19 🏠. Per night from 33 to 200€ – Per week from 231 to 945€

A pretty site with upmarket quality rental options laid out around the swimming and play area.

Surroundings : 🌊 🚲 ♀
Leisure activities : 🍸 🏛 🕙 nighttime 🏃
🚣 ✂ 🏊 ⛱ multi-sports ground
Facilities : ᴦ ⚬ 🏖 🗑 🚿 ⚐ launderette 🛁 refrigerators
Nearby : 🐟

Longitude : - 2.03558
Latitude : 47.08375

BESSÉ-SUR-BRAYE

72310 – Michelin map **310** N7 – pop. 2 363 – alt. 72
▶ Paris 198 – La Ferté-Bernard 43 – Le Mans 57 – Tours 56

⚠ Municipal du Val de Braye

☎ 02 43 35 31 13, www.campingmunicipal-duvaldebraye.jimdo.com/

Address : head southeast along the D 303, follow the signs for Pont de Braye

Opening times : from end March to end Oct.

2 ha (120 pitches) flat, grassy

Tariff : 13,20€ ♣♣ ⇌ 🗒 🔌 (13A) – Extra per person 3,10€
Rental rates : (from end March to end Oct.) ᴦ (1 mobile home) 6 🚐 – 4 tipis – 1 canvas bungalow. Per night from 29 to 52€
Per week from 165 to 309€
🚻 borne 3,10€ – 🚰 🔌 11,30€

Beautiful trees and shrubs, beside the Braye river.

Surroundings : ♀
Leisure activities : 🏛 🚣 🏊
Facilities : ᴦ ⚬ (July–Aug.) ⚐ 🗑
Nearby : ✗ ✂ 🏊 🏖

Longitude : 0.75427
Latitude : 47.83119

BLAIN

44130 – Michelin map **316** F3 – pop. 9 284 – alt. 23
▶ Paris 411 – Nantes 41 – Nort-sur-Erdre 22 – Nozay 16

⚠ Municipal le Château

☎ 02 40 79 11 00, www.ville-blain.fr

Address : rue Henri II de Rohan, at Le Gravier (take the southwestern exit along the N 171, follow the signs for St-Nazaire and take the road to the left, 250m from the Nantes-Brest canal)

Opening times : from mid May to end Sept.

1 ha (44 pitches) flat, grassy

Tariff : 13,50€ ♣♣ ⇌ 🗒 🔌 (10A) – Extra per person 2,60€

🚻 borne – 🚰 9€
A well-kept, green setting, near a 14th-century château.

Surroundings : 🚲 🚲
Leisure activities : 🏛 🚣
Facilities : ᴦ ⚬ (July–Aug.) 🏖 🛁 ⚐
Nearby : 🍸 ✗ 🐴 ⚓

Longitude : -1.76763
Latitude : 47.46772

BOUÈRE

53290 – Michelin map **310** G7 – pop. 1 027 – alt. 81
▶ Paris 273 – Nantes 146 – Laval 39 – Angers 70

⚠ Village Vacances Nature et Jardin

☎ 02 43 06 08 56, www.vacances-nature-jardin.fr

Address : rue Vierge Vacances (to the south, follow r. des Sencies and take the road to the left)

Opening times : Permanent

3 ha

Rental rates : 11 🏠. Per night from 75 to 90€ – Per week from 215 to 430€ – Reservation fee 13€
🚻 borne 2€ – 24 🗒

The Nature et Jardin (Nature and Gardening) workshops are open throughout the year.

Surroundings : 🌊 🚲
Leisure activities : 🏛 🚲 🏊 🚣
Facilities : ⚐ 📷 refrigerators
Nearby : 🚣 🏹

Longitude : -0.47506
Latitude : 47.86306

These symbols are used for a campsite that is exceptional in its category:

⚠⚠ ... ⚠ *Particularly pleasant setting, quality and range of services available*

🌊🌊 *Tranquil, isolated site – quiet site, particularly at night*

≪≪ *Exceptional view – interesting or panoramic view*

BRAIN-SUR-L'AUTHION

49800 – Michelin map **317** G4 – pop. 3 330 – alt. 22
▶ Paris 291 – Angers 16 – BAug.é 28 – Doué-la-Fontaine 38

⚠ Kawan Village du Port Caroline

☎ 02 41 80 42 18, www.campingduportcaroline.fr

Address : rue du Pont Caroline (take the southern exit along the D 113, 100m from L'Authion)

Opening times : from beginning April to end Oct.

3,2 ha (121 pitches) flat, grassy

Tariff : 21€ ♣♣ ⇌ 🗒 🔌 (10A) – Extra per person 4,50€
Rental rates : (from beginning April to end Oct.) – 12 🚐 – 2 🏠 2 canvas bungalows – 4 tent lodges. Per night from 36 to 112€
Per week from 227 to 784€
🚻 borne

Surroundings : 🚲 ♀
Leisure activities : ✗ 🏛 🚣 🏊
Facilities : ᴦ ⚬ ♿ 🚿 ⚐ 🏖
Nearby : 🛹 skateboarding

Longitude : -0.40855
Latitude : 47.44386

BREM-SUR-MER

85470 – Michelin map **316** F8 – pop. 2 565 – alt. 13
▶ Paris 454 – Aizenay 26 – Challans 29 – La Roche-sur-Yon 34

▲▲▲ Le Chaponnet ♨♨

✆ 0251905556, www.le-chaponnet.com

Address : 16 rue du Chaponnet (to the west of the town)

Opening times : from beginning April to end Sept.

6 ha (357 pitches) flat, grassy

Tariff : 35€ ♀♀ ⇌ 圓 ⑭ (6A) – Extra per person 7,10€ – Reservation fee 20€

Rental rates : (from beginning April to end Sept.) ♿ (1 mobile home) – 80 ⌂⌂ – 10 ⌂. Per night from 35 to 149€ – Per week from 182 to 1045€ – Reservation fee 20€

⇌ borne

In a green setting with lots of flowers, plenty of shade in places. A free shuttle service to the beaches.

Surroundings : 🌲 ⛺ ♀
Leisure activities : �YХ ⛺ ⑨ ⛹ 🏄 ⛵
🚣 🚴 ✂ 🎮 ⛸ ⛷ multi-sports ground
Facilities : ♿ ⛽ ⛺ 🚿 🚽 ♥ launderette ⛲

GPS
Longitude : -1.83225
Latitude : 46.6043

▲▲▲ Cybele Vacances L'Océan ♨♨

✆ 0251905916, www.campingdelocean.fr

Address : rue des Gabelous (located 1km west, 600 from the beach)

Opening times : from mid April to end Sept.

13 ha (566 pitches)

Tariff : 28€ ♀♀ ⇌ 圓 ⑭ (16A) – Reservation fee 25€

Rental rates : (from mid April to end Sept.) ♿ (2 mobile homes) 175 ⌂⌂ – 3 tent lodges. Per night from 21 to 140€ – Per week from 150 to 989€ – Reservation fee 25€

Surroundings : 🌲 ⛺
Leisure activities : ♀Х ⛺ ⑨ ⛹ 🏄 🚣 🚴
🎮 ⛷ ⛸ multi-sports ground
Facilities : ♿ ⛽ 🚿 ♥ launderette ⛲ ⛲
Nearby : ✂

GPS
Longitude : -1.83225
Latitude : 46.6043

▲▲ Le Brandais ♨♨

✆ 0251905587, www.campinglebrandais.com – limited spaces for one-night stay

Address : rue du Sablais (take the northwestern exit along the D 38 and take turning to the left)

Opening times : from end March to end Sept.

2,3 ha (165 pitches)

Tariff : (2013 Price) ♀ 16,50€ ⇌ 圓 – ⑭ (10A) 10€ – Reservation fee 18€

Rental rates : (from end March to end Sept.) ♿ (1 mobile home) 65 ⌂⌂. – Reservation fee 18€

In a residential area, with a range of rental options and some pitches for tents and caravans. Free shuttle service to the beaches.

Surroundings : 🌲 ⛺ ♀
Leisure activities : ♀ ⛺ ⛹ 🚣 🚴 🎮 ⛷
Facilities : ♿ ⛽ 🚿 ♥ launderette ⛲
Nearby : ✂

GPS
Longitude : -1.83949
Latitude : 46.60486

BRÉTIGNOLLES-SUR-MER

85470 – Michelin map **316** E8 – pop. 4 127 – alt. 14
▶ Paris 459 – Challans 30 – La Roche-sur-Yon 36 – Les Sables-d'Olonne 18

▲▲▲ Les Vagues ♨♨

✆ 0251901948, www.campinglesvagues.fr – limited spaces for one-night stay

Address : 20 boulevard du Nord (to the north along the D 38 towards St-Gilles-Croix-de-Vie)

Opening times : from beginning April to mid Oct.

4,5 ha (252 pitches) relatively flat, flat, grassy

Tariff : 30€ ♀♀ ⇌ 圓 ⑭ (10A) – Extra per person 7€

Rental rates : (from beginning April to end Sept.) – 40 ⌂⌂ 2 ⌂. Per night from 25 to 40€ – Per week from 250 to 750€ Reservation fee 20€

⇌ ⛺ ⑭25,50€

A pleasant site with shade, always pitches for tents and caravans.

Surroundings : ⛺ ♀♀
Leisure activities : ♀Х ⛺ ⛹ 🚣 🎮 ⛷ ⛸
multi-sports ground
Facilities : ♿ ⛽ 🚿 ♥ 📷

GPS
Longitude : -1.85935
Latitude : 46.63012

Do not confuse:
▲ to ▲▲▲ : *MICHELIN classification with*
★ to ★★★★★ : *official classification*

▲▲ Chadotel La Trevillière

✆ 0251900965, http://chadotel.com/camping-bretignolles-sur-mer/la-trevilliere/

Address : rue de Bellevue (take the northern exit along the rte du Stade and take the turning to the left)

Opening times : from beginning April to end Sept.

3 ha (204 pitches) relatively flat, flat, grassy

Tariff : 30,50€ ♀♀ ⇌ 圓 ⑭ (10A) – Extra per person 6€ – Reservation fee 25€

Rental rates : (from beginning April to end Sept.) ♿ (1 mobile home) – 40 ⌂⌂ – 2 ⌂. Per night from 50 to 97€ – Per week from 170 to 860€ – Reservation fee 25€

In a green setting, with plenty of shade in places.

Surroundings : 🌲 ⛺ ♀
Leisure activities : ♀Х 🚣 ⛹ 🎮 ⛷ ⛸
Facilities : ♿ ⛽ 🚿 ♥ launderette ⛲

GPS
Longitude : -1.85822
Latitude : 46.63627

▲▲ Les Cyprès

✆ 0251553898, www.campinglescypres.com

Address : 41 rue du Pont Jaunay (2.4km southeast along the D 38 then continue 800m along the road to the right, 60m from Le Jaunay river)

4,6 ha (280 pitches)

Rentals : 60 ⌂⌂.

There is direct access to the beach via wooded dunes.

Surroundings : 🌲 ⛺ ♀♀
Leisure activities : ♀Х ⛺ 🚣 🚴 🎮 ⛷
multi-sports ground
Facilities : ♿ ⛽ 🚿 ♥ launderette ⛲ ⛲

GPS
Longitude : -1.90919
Latitude : 46.67077

⚠ Le Marina

🕿 02 51 33 83 17, www.le-marina.com

Address : rue de La Martinière (take the northwestern exit along the D 38, follow the signs for St-Gilles-Croix-de-Vie then take left turn 1km along the r. de la Martignière)

Opening times : from end April to beginning Sept.

2,7 ha (131 pitches) flat, grassy

Tariff : (2013 Price) 23,90€ 🏕🏕 🚐 🗉 🖗 (10A)
Extra per person 4,60€ – Reservation fee 15€

Rental rates : (2013 Price) Permanent – 6 🚐. Per night from 40 to 70€ – Per week from 200 to 550€ – Reservation fee 15€

A green setting in a residential area, but choose the pitches away from the road in preference.

Surroundings : 🗢 ⚲⚲
Leisure activities : 🖼 ⚓
Facilities : ♿ ⚲ 🖼 ♨ ⚒ ⚒ 🖻

G P S Longitude : -1.87185
Latitude : 46.63582

⚠ La Motine

🕿 02 51 90 04 42, www.lamotine.com

Address : 4 rue des Morinières (continue along the av. de la Plage and take a right turn)

Opening times : from beginning April to end Sept.

1,8 ha (103 pitches)

Tariff : (2013 Price) 28€ 🏕🏕 🚐 🗉 🖗 (10A)

Extra per person 5,50€ – Reservation fee 15€

Rental rates : (2013 Price) (from beginning April to mid Sept.) 20 🚐 – 2 🛏 – 1 apartment. Per night from 98 to 160€ Per week from 300 to 670€ – Reservation fee 15€

🚐 borne 11€

Ornamental trees and shrubs surround the pitches; in a residential area.

Surroundings : 🗢 ⚲
Leisure activities : 🖼
Facilities : ♿ ⚲ ♨ ⚒ ⚒ 🎙 launderette
Nearby : ⚐

G P S Longitude : -1.8644
Latitude : 46.62745

⚠ Le Bon Accueil

🕿 02 51 90 15 92, https://sites.google.com/site/campinglebonaccueil/

Address : 24 route de St-Gilles (1.2km northwest along the D 38)

Opening times : from beginning May to mid Sept.

3 ha (146 pitches) relatively flat, flat, grassy

Tariff : 22,40€ 🏕🏕 🚐 🗉 🖗 (6A) – Extra per person 4,60€
Reservation fee 15€

Rental rates : (from beginning May to mid Sept.) – 7 🚐. Per night from 40 to 50€ – Per week from 220 to 500€ – Reservation fee 15€

Few rental options and rather old sanitary facilities but well maintained.

Surroundings : ⚲⚲
Leisure activities : ⚓ ⚓
Facilities : ♿ ⚲ 🖼 🖻

G P S Longitude : -1.86605
Latitude : 46.63625

The prices listed were supplied by the campsite owners in 2013 (if prices were not available, those from the previous year are given). The fees should be regarded as basic charges and may fluctuate with inflation.

49320 – Michelin map **317** G4 – pop. 2 898 – alt. 65
▶ Paris 307 – Angers 18 – Cholet 62 – Doué-la-Fontaine 23

⚠ Sites et Paysages Domaine de l'Étang

🕿 02 41 91 70 61, www.campingetang.com

Address : route de St-Mathurin (situated 2km northeast along the D 55, and take the road to the right; beside the Aubance river and near a lake)

Opening times : from end April to mid Sept.

3,5 ha (150 pitches) flat, grassy, small lake

Tariff : (2013 Price) 34€ 🏕🏕 🚐 🗉 🖗 (10A) – Extra per person 6,60€
Reservation fee 13€

Rental rates : (2013 Price) (from end April to mid Sept.) ⚒ 17 🚐 – 4 canvas bungalows – 4 tent lodges – 3 gîtes. Per night from 34 to 146€ – Per week from 206 to 880€ – Reservation fee 14€

🚐 borne 8€ – 5 🗉 8€ – ♨ 🖗 16€

Spacious and comfortable pitches laid out in the grounds of an old farmhouse.

Surroundings : ⚲ 🗢
Leisure activities : ✕ 🖼 ⚲🖼 (open air in season)
Facilities : ♿ ⚲ 🎐 ♨ 🎙 launderette
Nearby : ⚓ ⚓ leisure park

G P S Longitude : -0.43529
Latitude : 47.36082

Michelin classification:

⚠⚠⚠⚠ *Extremely comfortable, equipped to a very high standard*

⚠⚠⚠⚠ *Very comfortable, equipped to a high standard*

⚠⚠⚠ *Comfortable and well equipped*

⚠⚠ *Reasonably comfortable*

⚠ *Satisfactory*

85450 – Michelin map **316** J9 – pop. 1 902 – alt. 16
▶ Paris 446 – Fontenay-le-Comte 23 – Niort 57 – La Rochelle 34

⚠ L'Île Cariot

🕿 02 51 56 75 27, www.camping-chaille-les-marais.com

Address : rue du 8 Mai (south of the town; beside small streams and near the stadium)

Opening times : from beginning April to end Sept.

1,2 ha (50 pitches) flat, grassy

Tariff : (2013 Price) 17,10€ 🏕🏕 🚐 🗉 🖗 (10A)
Extra per person 4,40€ – Reservation fee 8€

Rental rates : (from beginning April to end Sept.) – 5 🚐 – 5 🏠 2 canvas bungalows. Per night from 35 to 50€ – Per week from 170 to 510€ – Reservation fee 8€

🚐 borne 3€ – ♨ 8€

A very lush and leafy site beside some canals, ideal for canoeing.

Surroundings : 🗢 ⚲⚲
Leisure activities : 🖼 ⚓ ⚲🖼 ⚒ ⚒
Facilities : ♿ ⚲ 🎙 launderette
Nearby : ✕

G P S Longitude : -1.0209
Latitude : 46.3927

LA CHAIZE-GIRAUD

85220 – Michelin map **316** F8 – pop. 878 – alt. 15
▶ Paris 453 – Challans 24 – La Roche-sur-Yon 32 – Les Sables-d'Olonne 21

🏕 Les Alouettes

☎ 0251229621, www.lesalouettes.com – limited spaces for one-night stay

Address : route de Saint-Gilles (located 1km west along the D 12, follow the signs for St-Gilles-Croix-de-Vie)

Opening times : from beginning April to end Oct.

3 ha (130 pitches) terraced, relatively flat, flat, grassy

Tariff : (2013 Price) 29,90€ ✛✛ ⇌ 🖃 (≵) (6A) – Extra per person 6,10€ Reservation fee 25€

Rental rates : (2013 Price) (from beginning April to end Oct.)
66 🚐 – 19 🏠 – 5 canvas bungalows. Per night from 28 to 115€
Per week from 160 to 855€ – Reservation fee 25€

A mobile home park and chalets with some pitches for tents and caravans.

Surroundings : ⌺ ♀
Leisure activities : 🍽 ✕ 🎮 ⛵ jacuzzi 🏊
🎣 ⛷
Facilities : ♿ ⚡ ♨ 🍴 launderette
Longitude : -1.83342
Latitude : 46.64832

CHALONNES-SUR-LOIRE

49290 – Michelin map **317** E4 – pop. 6 421 – alt. 25
▶ Paris 322 – Nantes 82 – Angers 26 – Cholet 40

🏕 Le Candais

☎ 0241780227, www.camping-portesdelaloire.com

Address : route de Rochefort (located 1km east along the D 751, follow the signs for Les Ponts-de-Cé; beside the Loire river and near a small lake)

Opening times : from beginning May to end Sept.

3 ha (210 pitches) flat, grassy

Tariff : (2013 Price) 15,10€ ✛✛ ⇌ 🖃 (≵) (10A)
Extra per person 3,10€ – Reservation fee 25€

Rental rates : (2013 Price) (from beginning May to end Sept.)
2 caravans. Per night from 29 to 59€ – Per week from 203 to 413€
Reservation fee 25€

🚐 30 🖃 5€

Surroundings : ♀
Leisure activities : 🎮 🛶
Facilities : ♿ ⚡ 🚿 🍴 🖃
Nearby : 🚲 ✕ ⛷ ⛷
Longitude : -0.74813
Latitude : 47.35132

CHAMBRETAUD

85500 – Michelin map **316** K6 – pop. 1 460 – alt. 214
▶ Paris 377 – Nantes 83 – La Roche-sur-Yon 56 – Cholet 21

🏕 Au Bois du Cé

☎ 0251915432, www.camping-auboisduce.com 🐾

Address : route du Puy-du-Fou (located 1km to the south, on the D 27)

Opening times : from beginning April to end Sept.

5 ha (110 pitches)

Tariff : 26€ ✛✛ ⇌ 🖃 (≵) (16A) – Extra per person 4,80€ – Reservation fee 10€

Rental rates : (from beginning April to end Sept.) 🐾 – 20 🚐
20 🏠 – 2 studios. Per night from 55 to 181€ – Per week from 310 to 750€ – Reservation fee 10€

🚐 borne

In a green setting laid out around swimming pools, with a range of upmarket rental options.

Surroundings : ≤ ⌺
Leisure activities : 🍽 🎮 ⛵ ⛷
Facilities : ♿ ⚡ 🍴 launderette
Longitude : -0.95
Latitude : 46.915

LA CHAPELLE-HERMIER

85220 – Michelin map **316** F7 – pop. 796 – alt. 58
▶ Paris 447 – Aizenay 13 – Challans 25 – La Roche-sur-Yon 29

🏕 Pin Parasol 👥

☎ 0251346472, http://www.campingpinparasol.fr

Address : at Chateaulong (3.3km southwest along the D 42, follow the signs for L'Aiguillon-sur-Vie then continue 1km along the turning to the left)

Opening times : from mid April to mid Sept.

12 ha (379 pitches) terraced, relatively flat, flat, grassy

Tariff : 41,15€ ✛✛ ⇌ 🖃 (≵) (16A) – Extra per person 7,60€ Reservation fee 20€

Rental rates : (from mid April to mid Sept.) ♿ (1 chalet) 🐾
81 🚐 – 20 🏠 – 6 tent lodges. Per night from 110 to 160€
Per week from 212 to 1 114€ – Reservation fee 20€

A swimming area with colourful play paddling-pool; near the Lac de Jaunay (direct access).

Surroundings : 🏞 ≤ ⌺ ♀
Leisure activities : 🍽 🎮 daytime 🏃 🎣
🆘 hammam 🏊 🚲 ✕ ⛷ ⛷ multi-sports ground
Facilities : ♿ ⚡ 🍴 🚿 🍴 launderette 🖃 ⛷
Nearby : 🛶 pedalos
Longitude : -1.75502
Latitude : 46.66647

🏕 Village Vacances Le Domaine du Pré 👥

(rental of chalets only)

☎ 0251080707, www.domainedupre.com

Address : at Bellevue (5km southwest along the D 42, follow the signs for L'Aiguillon-sur-Vie then continue along the turning to the left)

Opening times : from beginning March to end Nov.

11 ha

Rental rates : ♿ (4 chalets) – 70 🏠 – 12 studios. Per night from 42 to 160€ – Reservation fee 10€

A chalet village laid out around a large spa and wellness centre.

Surroundings : 🏞 ≤
Leisure activities : 🎮 🏃 🆘 hammam, jacuzzi 🏊 🏊 (small swimming pool) ⛷ multi-sports ground, spa centre
Facilities : ♿ ⚡ 🚿 🍴 launderette 🖃 ⛷
Nearby : 🛶 pedalos
Longitude : -1.76769
Latitude : 46.66485

There are several different types of sani-station ('borne' in French) – sanitation points providing fresh water and disposal points for grey water. See page 12 for further details.

CHÂTEAU-GONTIER

53200 – Michelin map **310** E8 – pop. 11 532 – alt. 33
▶ Paris 288 – Angers 50 – Châteaubriant 56 – Laval 30

⚓ Le Parc

📞 02 43 07 35 60, www.campingchateAug.ontier.fr

Address : 15 route de Laval (800m north along the N 162 follow the signs for Laval; near the sports centre)

Opening times : Permanent

2 ha (55 pitches)

Tariff : 15€ ♦♦ 🚙 ▣ ⊠ (10A) – Extra per person 4€

Rental rates : Permanent – 12 🏠. Per week from 192 to 364€

🚐 borne

Shady pitches with a variety of trees on the banks of the Mayenne river.

Leisure activities : 🏊 🎣
Facilities : ⚡ 🍽
Nearby : climbing wall

G P S
Longitude : -0.6995
Latitude : 47.83866

The guide covers all 22 regions of France – see the map and list of regions on pages 4–5.

CHÂTEAUNEUF-SUR-SARTHE

49330 – Michelin map **317** G2 – pop. 2 972 – alt. 20
▶ Paris 278 – Angers 31 – Château-Gontier 25 – La Flèche 33

⚓ Municipal du Port

📞 02 41 69 82 02, chateauneufsursarthe.fr

Address : 14 place R. Le Fort (take the southeastern exit along the D 859, follow the signs for Durtal and take second road to the right after the bridge; beside the Sarthe river (mooring point)

Opening times : from beginning April to end Sept.

1 ha (60 pitches) flat, grassy

Tariff : 8€ ♦♦ 🚙 ▣ ⊠ (16A) – Extra per person 2,47€

🚐 borne 5€ – 8 ▣ 5€

Surroundings : 🗨 🌳
Facilities : ⚡ 🚿 ▣ 🖼

G P S
Longitude : -0.48695
Latitude : 47.67749

CHEMILLÉ

49120 – Michelin map **317** E5 – pop. 6 967 – alt. 84
▶ Paris 331 – Angers 43 – Cholet 22 – Saumur 60

⚓ La Via Natura La Coulvée

📞 02 41 30 39 97, www.camping-coulvee-chemille.com

Address : route de Cholet (take the southern exit along the N 160, follow the signs for Cholet and take the road to the right; near a small lake)

Opening times : from beginning May to mid Sept.

2 ha (42 pitches) flat, grassy

Tariff : 16,70€ ♦♦ 🚙 ▣ ⊠ (15A) – Extra per person 3,50€

Rental rates : Permanent – 12 🏠. Per week from 351 to 455€

🚐 borne 2€ – 🔋 10€

Surroundings : 🗨
Leisure activities : 🚲
Facilities : ⚡ 🚿 ▣ 🛁 🖼
Nearby : 🚣 🛶

G P S
Longitude : -0.7359
Latitude : 47.20308

CHOLET

49300 – Michelin map **317** D6 – pop. 54 121 – alt. 91
▶ Paris 353 – Ancenis 49 – Angers 64 – Nantes 60

⚓⚓ Centre Touristique Lac de Ribou 👥

📞 02 41 49 74 30, www.lacderibou.com

Address : 5km southeast along the D 20, follow the signs for Maulevrier and turn right onto D 600

Opening times : from end April to mid Sept.

5 ha (162 pitches)

Tariff : (2013 Price) 26,50€ ♦♦ 🚙 ▣ ⊠ (10A) – Extra per person 6€

Rental rates : (2013 Price) Permanent – 19 🚐 – 8 🏠 – 19 gîtes.
Per night from 50 to 109€ – Per week from 240 to 740€

🚐 borne 6€ – 🔋 16,50€

100m from the lake (direct access).

Surroundings : 🏞 🗨
Leisure activities : 🍷 ✕ 🏊 🌙 nighttime 🤸
🚣 🎱 🏌 🏄
Facilities : ⚡ ⚡ ▥ 🛁 🧺 launderette 🚿
Nearby : 🚲 🐴 🚴

G P S
Longitude : -0.84017
Latitude : 47.03621

COMMEQUIERS

85220 – Michelin map **316** E7 – pop. 2 910 – alt. 19
▶ Paris 441 – Challans 13 – Nantes 63 – La Roche-sur-Yon 38

⚓ La Vie

📞 02 51 54 90 04, www.campinglavie.com

Address : at Le Motteau (1.3km southeast along the D 82, follow the signs for Coëx and take road to the left)

Opening times : from beginning April to end Sept.

6 ha (110 pitches) flat, grassy, small lake

Tariff : 23€ ♦♦ 🚙 ▣ ⊠ (6A) – Extra per person 5,50€ – Reservation fee 10€

Rental rates : (from mid April to mid Sept.) – 15 🚐. Per night from 20€ – Per week from 590€ – Reservation fee 10€

🚐 20 ▣ 23€

A peaceful, country setting, able to accommodate groups and summer camps.

Surroundings : 🏞 🌳
Leisure activities : 🍷 ✕ 🏊 🎱 🎣
Facilities : ⚡ ⚡ 🛁 🍽 launderette

G P S
Longitude : -1.824
Latitude : 46.75902

⚓ Le Trèfle à 4 feuilles

📞 02 51 54 87 54, www.campingletreflea4feuilles.com

Address : at La Jouère (3.3km southeast along the D 82, follow the signs for Coëx et 1.4km along the road to the left)

Opening times : from mid April to mid Sept.

1,8 ha (50 pitches)

Tariff : 23€ ♦♦ 🚙 ▣ ⊠ (10A) – Extra per person 5€ – Reservation fee 7,50€

Rental rates : (from mid April to end Sept.) – 10 🚐. Per night from 45 to 90€ – Per week from 370 to 580€ – Reservation fee 7,50€

🚐 5 ▣ 22,50€

A farm campsite in the grounds of an arable farm with chickens, sheep, goats, a donkey....

Surroundings : 🏞 🌿
Leisure activities : 🍷 🏊 🚣 🎣
Facilities : ⚡ 🚿 🍽 launderette

G P S
Longitude : -1.78507
Latitude : 46.75935

LES CONCHES

85560 – Michelin map **316** H9
▶ Paris 465 – Nantes 109 – La Roche 37 – La Rochelle 63

⚠ Le Clos des Pins

✆ 02 51 90 31 69, www.campingclosdespins.com

Address : 1336 avenue du Dct Joussemet

1,6 ha (94 pitches)

Rentals : 36 🚐 – 13 🏠.

Some rental options are a little old, but there are also some luxury mobile homes.

Surroundings : 🖼 〰
Leisure activities : 🍹 🏕 🏊 🚲 🎿 ⛵
Facilities : 🔧 🔌 ♨ 🍴 launderette
Nearby : 🎣

G P S Longitude : -1.48842
Latitude : 46.38856

⚠ Le Sous-Bois

✆ 02 51 33 36 90, lesousbois85@gmail.com

Address : at La Haute-Saligotière

Opening times : from beginning June to end Sept.

1,7 ha (140 pitches)

Tariff : 23€ 👫 🚗 🔌 📊 (10A) – Extra per person 4€
Rental rates : (from beginning June to end Sept.) 🍽 – 4 🚐.
Per week from 180 to 490€

🚰 5 📧 19€

A simple, shady site with well-maintained but rather old facilities.

Surroundings : 🏞 🖼 〰
Leisure activities : 🖼 🏊 🎿
Facilities : 🔧 🔌 ⛺ 🍴 🗄

G P S Longitude : -1.48727
Latitude : 46.3956

⚠ Les Ramiers

✆ 02 51 33 32 21, www.campinglesramiers.com

Address : 44 rue des Tulipes, chemin des Pins (to the southeast, follow the signs for La Tranche-sur-Mer)

1,4 ha (80 pitches)

Rentals : 6 🚐.

A simple site, with pitches for tents laid out on terraces or among trees.

Surroundings : 🏞 🖼 〰
Leisure activities : 🍹 🍴
Facilities : 🔧 🔌

G P S Longitude : -1.46735
Latitude : 46.3844

CONCOURSON-SUR-LAYON

49700 – Michelin map **317** G5 – pop. 544 – alt. 55
▶ Paris 332 – Angers 44 – Cholet 45 – Saumur 25

⚠ La Vallée des Vignes

✆ 02 41 59 86 35, www.campingvdv.com

Address : at La Croix Patron (900m west along the D 960, follow the signs for Vihiers and take turning to the right after the bridge; beside the Layon river)

Opening times : from beginning April to end Sept.

3,5 ha (63 pitches) flat, grassy

Tariff : (2013 Price) 29,90€ 👫 🚗 🔌 📊 (10A) – Extra per person 6€
Reservation fee 13€

Rental rates : (2013 Price) (from beginning April to end Sept.)
🍽 – 4 🚐. Per week from 330 to 680€ – Reservation fee 13€
Situated in a rural setting.

Surroundings : 🖼
Leisure activities : 🍹 🏕 🏊 🚲 🎿 ⛵
Facilities : 🔧 🔌 ⛺ 🍴 🗄 🏊

G P S Longitude : -0.34766
Latitude : 47.17394

COUTURES

49320 – Michelin map **317** G4 – pop. 530 – alt. 81
▶ Paris 303 – Angers 25 – BAug.é 35 – Doué-la-Fontaine 23

⚠ Yelloh! Village Parc de Montsabert

✆ 02 41 57 91 63, www.parcdemontsabert.com

Address : route de Montsabert (located 1.5km to the northeast, near the château at Montsabert)

Opening times : from mid April to beginning Sept.

5 ha (150 pitches)

Tariff : 29€ 👫 🚗 🔌 📊 (10A) – Extra per person 7€
Rental rates : (from mid April to beginning Oct.) – 3 caravans
39 🚐 – 14 🏠 – 9 canvas bungalows. Per night from 36 to 143€
Per week from 252 to 1001€

🚰 borne 5€ – 3 📧 29€ – 🚐 16€
A pleasant wooded park.

Surroundings : 🏞 🖼 〰
Leisure activities : ✗ 🖼 🏊 🎿 🎣 🖼 (open air in season)
Facilities : 🔧 🔌 ▦ ⛺ 🍴 launderette

G P S Longitude : -0.34679
Latitude : 47.37448

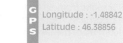

Key to rentals symbols:

12 🚐	*Number of mobile homes*
20 🏠	*Number of chalets*
6 🛏	*Number of rooms to rent*
Per night 30–50€	*Minimum/maximum rate per night*
Per week 300–1,000€	*Minimum/maximum rate per week*

CRAON

53400 – Michelin map **310** D7 – pop. 4 590 – alt. 75
▶ Paris 309 – Fougères 70 – Laval 29 – Mayenne 60

⚠ Municipal du Mûrier

✆ 02 43 06 96 33, www.ville-craon53.fr

Address : rue Alain Gerbault (800m east, follow the signs for Château-Gontier and take road to the left)

Opening times : from beginning June to end Sept.

1 ha (51 pitches) flat, grassy

Tariff : 13,10€ 👫 🚗 🔌 📊 (10A) – Extra per person 3,20€
Rental rates : (from beginning May to end Dec.) – 9 🏠 – 9 huts (without sanitary facilities). Per night from 76 to 142€ – Per week from 213 to 398€ – Reservation fee 32€
🚰 borne 2,95€

In a pleasant setting near a small lake.

Surroundings : 🖼 〰
Leisure activities : 🖼 🏊
Facilities : 🔧 🔌 🍴 🗄
Nearby : 🍹 ✗ 🎿 🖼 🖼 🎿 ⛵ 🐎

G P S Longitude : -0.94398
Latitude : 47.84837

DAON

53200 – Michelin map **310** F8 – pop. 486 – alt. 42
▶ Paris 292 – Angers 46 – Château-Gontier 11 – Châteauneuf-sur-Sarthe 15

🏕 Les Rivières

📞 02 43 06 94 78, www.campingdaon.fr

Address : 1 rue du Port (take the western exit along the D 213, follow the signs for la Ricoullière and take a right turn before the bridge; near the Mayenne river)

Opening times : from beginning April to end Sept.

1,8 ha (98 pitches) flat, grassy

Tariff : 10€ ★ ★ ⇔ 🅴 🅙 (10A) – Extra per person 4€

Rentals : Permanent – 10 🏠. Per week from 166 to 356€

Surroundings : 🏞 ⊏ 🎣
Leisure activities : 🏛
Facilities : ♿ ⌚ 🕪 🛗
Nearby : 🍽 ✗ 🚤 📷 🚣 🏊 ⚓ pedalos

GPS Longitude : -0.64059
Latitude : 47.74996

To visit a town or region, use the MICHELIN Green Guides.

DURTAL

49430 – Michelin map **317** H2 – pop. 3 337 – alt. 39
▶ Paris 261 – Angers 38 – La Flèche 14 – Laval 66

🏕 Les Portes de l'Anjou

📞 02 41 76 31 80, www.lesportesdelanjou.com

Address : 9 rue du Camping (take northeastern exit following signs for la Flèche and take right turn)

Opening times : from beginning April to end Oct.

3,5 ha (127 pitches) flat, grassy

Tariff : 17,80€ ★ ★ ⇔ 🅴 🅙 (10A) – Extra per person 4,60€

Rental rates : (from beginning April to end Oct.) – 9 🛖 11 canvas bungalows – 1 gîte. Per night from 25 to 88€ – Per week from 185 to 679€ – Reservation fee 10€
🚐 borne

A pleasant site and setting along the Loir river.

Surroundings : 🏞 ⊏ 🎣
Leisure activities : 🍽 ✗ 🏛 🏃 🚤 🚣
Facilities : ♿ ⌚ 🕪 🛗
Nearby : 🚣

GPS Longitude : -0.23518
Latitude : 47.67136

LES EPESSES

85590 – Michelin map **316** K6 – pop. 2 575 – alt. 214
▶ Paris 375 – Bressuire 38 – Chantonnay 29 – Cholet 24

🏕 La Bretèche

📞 02 51 57 33 34, www.campinglabreteche.com

Address : at the base de loisirs (leisure centre) (take the northern exit along the D 752, follow the signs for Cholet and take the road to the right)

Opening times : from beginning April to end Sept.

3 ha (164 pitches)

Tariff : 22,10€ ★ ★ ⇔ 🅴 🅙 (10A) – Extra per person 4,50€ Reservation fee 10€

Rental rates : (from beginning April to end Sept.) – 24 🏠 12 canvas bungalows. Per night from 33 to 93€ – Per week from 195 to 705€ – Reservation fee 10€
🚐 borne

Ornamental trees and shrubs; 3km from Le Puy du Fou.

Surroundings : 🏞 ⊏ 🎣
Leisure activities : 🍽 ✗ 🏛 🚤 🚣
Facilities : ♿ ⌚ 🕪 launderette
Nearby : 🎣 amusement park

GPS Longitude : -0.89925
Latitude : 46.88986

ÉVRON

53600 – Michelin map **310** G6 – pop. 7 099 – alt. 114
▶ Paris 250 – Alençon 58 – La Ferté-Bernard 98 – La Flèche 69

🏕 Municipal de la Zone Verte

📞 02 43 01 65 36, www.camping-evron.fr

Address : boulevard du Maréchal Juin (take the western exit)

Opening times : Permanent

3 ha (92 pitches)

Tariff : (2013 Price) ★ 2,20€ ⇔ 🅴 6€ – 🅙 (10A) 3€

Rental rates : (2013 Price) Permanent – 11 🏠. Per week from 155 to 280€
🚐 borne 2€

Surroundings : ⊏ 🎣
Leisure activities : 🏛 🚤 🏃 sports trail
Facilities : ⌚ 🚮 🅿 🛗 🚿 launderette
Nearby : 🍽 📷 🚣 🏊

GPS Longitude : -0.41321
Latitude : 48.15073

LA FAUTE-SUR-MER

85460 – Michelin map **316** I9 – pop. 916 – alt. 4
▶ Paris 465 – Luçon 37 – Niort 106 – La Rochelle 71

🏕 APV Les Flots Bleus

📞 02 51 27 11 11, www.camping-lesflotsbleus.com – limited spaces for one-night stay

Address : av. des Chardons (located 1km southeast following signs for La Pointe d'Arçay (headland))

1,5 ha (104 pitches)

Rentals : 58 🛖 – 2 tent lodges.

In a residential area 200m from the beach.

Surroundings : ⊏ 🎣
Leisure activities : ✗ 🚤 🏊 (open air in season)
Facilities : ♿ ⌚ 🏊 🕪 launderette
Nearby : 🍽

GPS Longitude : -1.31842
Latitude : 46.32508

LA FERTÉ-BERNARD

72400 – Michelin map **310** M5 – pop. 9 278 – alt. 90
▶ Paris 164 – Brou 44 – Châteauroux 65 – Le Mans 54

🏕 Municipal le Valmer

📞 02 43 71 70 03, levalmer@gmail.com

Address : Espace du lac (located 1.5km southwest along the N 23, at the leisure and activity park; beside the Huisne river)

3 ha (90 pitches) flat, grassy

Surroundings : 🏞 ⊏ 🎣
Leisure activities : 🏛 🚤
Facilities : ♿ ⌚ 🚿 🕪 🛗
Nearby : 🍽 📷 🚣 🏊 🏊 (beach) ♨

GPS Longitude : 0.6475
Latitude : 48.17579

LA FLÈCHE

72200 – Michelin map **310** I8 – pop. 15 228 – alt. 33
▶ Paris 244 – Angers 52 – Châteaubriant 106 – Laval 70

⚑ Municipal de la Route d'Or

✆ 02 43 94 55 90, www.camping-laroutedor.com

Address : allée du Camping (take the southern exit towards Saumur and take a right turn; beside the Loir river)

Opening times : from beginning March to end Oct.

4 ha (250 pitches) flat, grassy

Tariff : 16€ ✸✸ ⇌ 🅴 🔋 (10A) – Extra per person 3,15€
Rental rates : (from beginning May to end Sept.) 🚫 **– 10 🚐.** **Per night from 72 to 106€ – Per week from 303 to 517€**
🚰 borne 16€ – 7 🅴 16€

Surroundings : 🏕 ♨
Leisure activities : 🏠 🚴 🎯 🛶
Facilities : 🚿 ⚓ 🏛 🛁 🚾 🖥
Nearby : 🎣

| G |
| P |
| S |

Longitude : -0.07779
Latitude : 47.69509

We value your opinion and welcome your feedback.
Do email us at campingfrance@tp.michelin.com

FRESNAY-SUR-SARTHE

72130 – Michelin map **310** J5 – pop. 2 198 – alt. 95
▶ Paris 235 – Alençon 22 – Laval 73 – Mamers 30

⚑ Municipal Sans Souci 🚹🚺

✆ 02 43 97 32 87, www.camping-fresnaysursarthe.fr

Address : rue du Haut Ary (located 1km west along the D 310, follow the signs for Sillé-le-Guillaume)

Opening times : from beginning April to end Sept.

2 ha (90 pitches)

Tariff : (2013 Price) 13,31€ ✸✸ ⇌ 🅴 🔋 (10A)
Extra per person 2,83€
Rental rates : (2013 Price) Permanent 🚫 **– 5 🏠.** Per week from 171 to 491€
🚰 borne 3,15€
Pretty, clearly marked-out pitches beside the Sarthe river.

Surroundings : 🏕 🏞
Leisure activities : 🏠 🎣 🛶 🎯
Facilities : 🚿 ⚓ 🛁 🚾 🖥 🚾
Nearby : 🏊 🛶 🎣

| G |
| P |
| S |

Longitude : 0.01589
Latitude : 48.28252

FROMENTINE

85550 – Michelin map **316** D6
▶ Paris 455 – Nantes 69 – La Roche 72 – St-Nazaire 70

⚑ Campéole La Grande Côte 🚹🚺

✆ 02 51 68 51 89, www.campeole.com

Address : route de la Grande Côte (situated 2km along the D 38b)

Opening times : from beginning April to mid Sept.

21 ha (810 pitches) terraced, flat, sandy

Tariff : (2013 Price) 28,50€ ✸✸ ⇌ 🅴 🔋 (10A)
Extra per person 7,80€ – Reservation fee 25€
Rental rates : (2013 Price) Permanent 🚫 (1 mobile home) 85 🚐 **– 36 🏠 – 116 canvas bungalows. Per night 133€** Per week 931€ – Reservation fee 25€
🚰 borne

Situated in the Forêt des Pays de Monts, near the Île de Noirmoutier bridge; close to the beach.

Surroundings : ♨♨ ⚠
Leisure activities : 🍷 🏠 🎮 🎣 🛶 🚴 🛶
multi-sports ground
Facilities : 🚿 ⚓ 🛁 🚾 launderette 🖥 🚾
Nearby : 🎿 🎣

| G |
| P |
| S |

Longitude : -2.14732
Latitude : 46.88553

GIVRAND

85800 – Michelin map **316** E7 – pop. 1 946 – alt. 10
▶ Paris 460 – Nantes 79 – La Roche-sur-Yon 39

⚑ FranceLoc Domaine Les Dauphins Bleus 🚹🚺

(rental of mobile homes and chalets only)

✆ 02 51 55 59 34, www.camping-franceloc.fr

Address : 16 rue du Rocher

7 ha flat, grassy

Rentals : 🚿 (2 mobile homes) – 295 🚐 – 12 🏠.
A mobile home village and chalets laid out around a water park.

Surroundings : 🏖 ♨
Leisure activities : 🍷 🍴 🏠 🎮 🎣 🛶 🚴 🎯
🏓 📺 🛶 🏊 cinema, multi-sports ground
Facilities : 🚿 ⚓ 🏛 🛁 🚾 launderette 🖥 🚾

| G |
| P |
| S |

Longitude : -1.89497
Latitude : 46.67292

⚑ Chadotel Le Domaine de Beaulieu

✆ 02 51 55 59 46, http://chadotel.com/camping-saint-gilles-croix-de-vie/le-domaine-d – limited spaces for one-night stay

Address : rue du Parc (at Les Temples)

Opening times : from beginning April to end Sept.

8 ha (340 pitches) flat, grassy

Tariff : 30,50€ ✸✸ ⇌ 🅴 🔋 (10A) – Extra per person 6€ – Reservation fee 25€
Rental rates : (from beginning April to end Sept.) – 46 🚐 6 🏠. Per night from 50 to 82€ – Per week from 170 to 860€ Reservation fee 25€
In a partially shaded setting; ageing sanitary facilities.

Surroundings : 🏞 ♨♨
Leisure activities : 🍷 🍴 🏠 🎮 nighttime
jacuzzi 🛶 🚴 🎯 🏓 🏊 🛶 multi-sports
ground, entertainment room
Facilities : 🚿 ⚓ 🛁 🚾 🚾 🖥 🚾 🚾

| G |
| P |
| S |

Longitude : -1.90389
Latitude : 46.67056

The pitches of many campsites are marked out with low hedges of attractive bushes and shrubs.

LE GIVRE

85540 – Michelin map **316** H9 – pop. 424 – alt. 20
▶ Paris 446 – Luçon 20 – La Mothe-Achard 33 – Niort 88

⚑ La Grisse

✆ 02 51 30 83 03, www.campinglagrisse.com

Address : at Le Givre (continue 2.5km south towards La Jonchère along the D 85)

Opening times : Permanent

1 ha (79 pitches) flat, grassy

Tariff : ✸ 7,60€ ⇌ 🅴 8,60€ – 🔋 (16A) 4,20€

Rental rates : Permanent – 6 🛖 – 1 gîte. Per night from 60 to 90€ Per week from 198 to 598€

🚐 borne 12€ – 3 ▣ 12€

In the grounds of a farm (visits possible); one part of the site has plenty of shade.

Surroundings : 🦢 ♀
Leisure activities : 🏇
Facilities : ♿ ⚬━ 🔥 🍴 launderette

G P S Longitude : -1.39815
Latitude : 46.44484

GUÉMENÉ-PENFAO

44290 – Michelin map **316** F2 – pop. 4 951 – alt. 37
▶ Paris 408 – Bain-de-Bretagne 35 – Châteaubriant 39 – Nantes 59

🏕 Flower L'Hermitage

🖉 0240792348, www.campinglhermitage.com

Address : 46 avenue du Paradis (1.2km east following signs for Châteaubriant and take the road to the right, near the municipal swimming pool)

Opening times : from beginning April to end Oct.

2,5 ha (83 pitches) relatively flat, flat, grassy

Tariff : 21,50€ ✹✹ 🚗 ▣ 🔌 (6A) – Extra per person 5€ – Reservation fee 12€

Rental rates : (from beginning April to end Oct.) – 8 🛖 5 🏠 – 6 🛏 – 1 gîte. Per night from 45 to 91€ – Per week from 315 to 637€ – Reservation fee 12€

🚐 borne 5€ – 4 ▣ 14€

A pleasant wooded site.

Surroundings : 🗔 ♀♀
Leisure activities :  🏛 🏇 ☃🚲 🏊 (small swimming pool) ⛵
Facilities : ♿ ⚬━ 🛒 🔥 🍴 ▣
Nearby : 🏊 ✗ 🎣 🦢 🏇

G P S Longitude : -1.81838
Latitude : 47.62572

GUÉRANDE

44350 – Michelin map **316** B4 – pop. 15 446 – alt. 54
▶ Paris 450 – La Baule 6 – Nantes 77 – St-Nazaire 20

🏕 Trémondec

🖉 0240600007, www.camping-tremondec.com ✄

Address : at Careil, 48 rue du Château

2 ha (107 pitches)

Rentals : 20 🛖 – 23 🏠.

Surroundings : 🗔 ♀
Leisure activities : 🍷 🏛 🏇 ☃🚲 🚙
Facilities : ♿ ⚬━ 🔥 🍴 launderette 🚿

G P S Longitude : -2.40155
Latitude : 47.29792

LA GUYONNIÈRE

85600 – Michelin map **316** I6 – pop. 2 674 – alt. 63
▶ Paris 395 – Nantes 47 – La Roche-sur-Yon 48 – Angers 105

🏕 La Chausselière

🖉 0251419840, www.chausseliere.fr

Address : route des Herbiers (1.2km to the south; beside the Lac de La Chausselière)

Opening times : from mid April to end Sept.

1 ha (51 pitches) flat, grassy

Tariff : 18,70€ ✹✹ 🚗 ▣ 🔌 (16A) – Extra per person 3,50€

Rental rates : Permanent ♿ (1 chalet) ✄ – 10 🛖 – 10 🏠 3 tent lodges. Per night from 35 to 100€ – Per week from 175 to 700€

In a green setting beside the lake.

Surroundings : 🦢 🗔 ♀♀
Leisure activities : 🏇 🏊 multi-sports ground
Facilities : ♿ ⚬━ ☃ ✄ 🍴 ▣
Nearby : 🎣 ♪

G P S Longitude : -1.2457
Latitude : 46.95735

ÎLE DE NOIRMOUTIER

85 – Michelin map **316** – alt. 8

Barbâtre 85630 – Michelin map **316** C6 – pop. 1 802 – alt. 5
▶ Paris 453 – Challans 32 – Nantes 70 – Noirmoutier-en-l'Île 11

🏕 Original Camping Domaine Le Midi 👥

🖉 0251396374, www.domaine-le-midi.com

Address : rue du Camping (continue 1km northwest along the D 948 and take road to the left)

Opening times : from beginning April to end Sept.

13 ha (419 pitches) undulating, flat and relatively flat, grassy, sandy

Tariff : (2013 Price) 34,90€ ✹✹ 🚗 ▣ 🔌 (16A) Extra per person 7,60€ – Reservation fee 20€

Rental rates : (2013 Price) (from beginning April to end Sept.) 42 🛖 – 105 🏠 – 8 tipis – 30 tent lodges. Per week from 199 to 1 349€ – Reservation fee 20€

🚐 borne

Close to the beach; a range of rental options in a well laid-out natural site.

Surroundings : 🦢 ♀ ⛰
Leisure activities : ✗ 🎲 🏓 🎯 🏇 ✄ 🎣
🖥 🏊 ♪ multi-sports ground, entertainment room
Facilities : ♿ ⚬━ 🔥 🍴 launderette 🚿
Nearby : 🏊 🚲

G P S Longitude : -2.18447
Latitude : 46.94531

L'Épine 85740 – Michelin map **316** C6 – pop. 1 727 – alt. 2
▶ Paris 466 – Nantes 79 – La Roche-sur-Yon 81

🏕 Original Camping La Bosse

🖉 0253469747, www.camping-de-la-bosse.com

Address : rue du Port

Opening times : from beginning April to end Sept.

10 ha (350 pitches)

Tariff : 22€ ✹✹ 🚗 ▣ 🔌 (4A) – Extra per person 5,50€ – Reservation fee 20€

Rental rates : (from beginning April to end Sept.) – 8 tent lodges. Per week from 299 to 429€ – Reservation fee 20€

Close to the beach in a natural, undulating setting.

Surroundings : ⛵ Port de Morin marina ♀ ⛰
Leisure activities : 🏇
Facilities : ⚬━ 🚿 launderette

G P S Longitude : -2.2833
Latitude : 46.98523

There are several different types of sani-station ('borne' in French) – sanitation points providing fresh water and disposal points for grey water. See page 12 for further details.

La Guérinière 85680 – Michelin map **316** C6 – pop. 1 488 – alt. 5
▶ Paris 460 – Challans 39 – Nantes 77 – Noirmoutier-en-l'Île 5

⚠ Original Camping Domaine Les Moulins ♨

✆ 02 51 39 51 38, www.domaine-les-moulins.com

Address : rue des Moulins (take the eastern exit along the D 948 and turn right at the roundabout)

Opening times : from beginning April to end Sept.

5,5 ha (175 pitches) dunes

Tariff : 50€ ♦♦ 🚗 🔲 🔌 (10A) – Extra per person 9€ – Reservation fee 30€

Rental rates : (from beginning April to end Sept.) – 75 🏠 – 34 tipis 37 tent lodges. Per week from 235 to 3 499€ Reservation fee 30€
🚰 borne
Close to the beach, with a viariety of original rental options – vehicles not permitted.

Surroundings : 🏊 🛏 ♨ ⚠
Leisure activities : 🍹 ✕ 🏠 🕐 daytime 🏃 🛁 hammam, jacuzzi ⚴ 🏇 🏊 multi-sports ground, entertainment room
Facilities : 🚿 ⛽ 🅿 🎱 🔥 🍳 launderette 🧺
Nearby : 🚣

GPS Longitude : -2.217
Latitude : 46.96675

⚠ Le Caravan'Île ♨

✆ 02 51 39 50 29, www.caravanile.com

Address : 1 rue de la Tresson (take the eastern exit along the D 948 and take a right turn before the roundabout)

Opening times : from mid March to mid Nov.

8,5 ha (385 pitches) relatively flat, flat, grassy, sandy

Tariff : 31,50€ ♦♦ 🚗 🔲 🔌 (8A) – Extra per person 7€ – Reservation fee 20€

Rental rates : (from mid March to mid Nov.) – 95 🏠. Per week from 266 to 945€ – Reservation fee 20€
🚰 borne – 💧 🔌 13€
Close to the beach (direct access via the steps in the dunes).

Surroundings : 🏊 ⚠
Leisure activities : 🍹 ✕ 🏠 🕐 🏃 🛁 jacuzzi ⚴ 🏇 🏊 multi-sports ground
Facilities : 🚿 🔥 🍳 launderette 🚣 🧺

GPS Longitude : -2.21674
Latitude : 46.96569

Noirmoutier-en-l'Île 85330 – Michelin map **316** C5 – pop. 4 661 – alt. 8
▶ Paris 468 – Nantes 80 – St-Nazaire 82 – Vannes 160

⚠ Indigo Noirmoutier

✆ 02 51 39 06 24, www.camping-indigo.com

Address : 23 allée des Sableaux - Bois de la Chaize

Opening times : from mid April to beginning Oct.

12 ha (530 pitches)

Tariff : 28€ ♦♦ 🚗 🔲 🔌 (10A) Extra per person 5,40€ – Reservation fee 22€

Rental rates : (from mid April to beginning Sept.) – 100 tent lodges. Per night from 51 to 110€ – Per week from 250 to 770€ – Reservation fee 22€
🚰 borne 7€

In an attractive location, along the La Plage des Sableaux beach.

Surroundings : 🏊 ⚓ ♀ ⚠
Leisure activities : 🍹 ✕ 🏠 ⚴ 🏇
Facilities : 🚿 ⛽ 🔥 🍳 launderette 🧺
Nearby : 🚣

GPS Longitude : -2.2205
Latitude : 46.9966

⚠ Municipal le Clair Matin

✆ 02 51 39 05 56, www.noirmoutier-campings.fr

Address : at Les Sableaux (at Les Bois de la Chaize)

Opening times : from end March to mid Nov.

6,5 ha (276 pitches)

Tariff : 22,65€ ♦♦ 🚗 🔲 🔌 (10A) – Extra per person 4,30€ Reservation fee 9€
🚰 borne
A site with free access to many natural areas.

Surroundings : 🏊 ♀♀
Leisure activities : ⚴ 🏇
Facilities : 🚿 ⛽ (summer) 🍳 🔥
Nearby : 🍹 ✕ 🚣

GPS Longitude : -2.2205
Latitude : 46.99567

85340 – Michelin map **316** F8 – pop. 2 668 – alt. 5
▶ Paris 455 – Nantes 100 – La Roche-sur-Yon 35 – Challans 37

⚠ Île aux Oiseaux ♨

✆ 02 51 90 89 96, www.ile-aux-oiseaux.fr – limited spaces for one-night stay

Address : rue du Pré Neuf (800m northeast along the D 87)

Opening times : from beginning April to end Oct.

5 ha (215 pitches) flat, grassy

Tariff : 29€ ♦♦ 🚗 🔲 🔌 (10A) – Extra per person 4,75€ – Reservation fee 17€

Rental rates : (from beginning April to end Oct.) – 40 🏠. Per night from 42 to 68€ – Per week from 226 to 535€ Reservation fee 17€
In a pleasant setting, but with very few places for tents or caravans.

Surroundings : 🏊 ⚓ ♀
Leisure activities : 🏠 🏃 ⚴ 🏇 🏊 multi-sports ground
Facilities : 🚿 ⛽ (July–Aug.) 🔥 🧺 🍳 launderette

GPS Longitude : -1.77813
Latitude : 46.56624

85520 – Michelin map **316** G9 – pop. 2 497 – alt. 14
▶ Paris 453 – Challans 62 – Luçon 36 – La Roche-sur-Yon 35

⚠ Chadotel L'Océano d'Or ♨

✆ 02 51 33 65 08, http://chadotel.com/camping-jard-sur-mer/l-oceano-d-or/

Address : 58 rue Georges Clemenceau (to the northeast of Jard sur Mer, along the D 21)

Opening times : from beginning April to end Sept.

8 ha (450 pitches) flat, grassy

Tariff : 31,50€ ♦♦ 🚗 🔲 🔌 (10A) – Extra per person 6€ – Reservation fee 25€

Rental rates : (from beginning April to end Sept.) ♿ (1 chalet)
63 👛 – 8 🏠 – 4 gîtes. Per night from 50 to 97€ – Per week
from 210 to 1150€ – Reservation fee 25€

A pretty site with classic and luxury rental options in mobile homes and gîtes.

Surroundings : ⌂ ♨♨
Leisure activities : ♟ ⌂ ⌲ ⚓ 🏃 ⚄ 🚲 ✂
🏊 ⛵ multi-sports ground, entertainment room

    G P S Longitude : -1.57195
    Latitude : 46.42032

Facilities : ♿ ⚷ 🏛 ♨ 🚿 🐶 launderette
🏊 🚿

△ Club Airotel Le Curty's ♨♨

(rental of mobile homes and chalets only)

☎ 0251330655, www.campinglecurtys.com

Address : rue de la Perpoise (north of Jard sur Mer)

Opening times : from mid April to mid Sept.

8 ha (360 pitches) flat, grassy

Rental rates : 191 👛 – 20 🏠. Per night from 45 to 110€
Per week from 260 to 1090€ – Reservation fee 25€

A mobile home park for rentals and owner-occupiers.

Surroundings : ⌂ ♨
Leisure activities : ♟ ✗ ⌂ ⚓ 🏃 🚲
✂ 🏊 ⛵ multi-sports ground, entertainment room
Facilities : ♿ ⚷ 🚿 🐶 launderette 🚿
Nearby : ⚓

    G P S Longitude : -1.57825
    Latitude : 46.42032

△ Chadotel La Pomme de Pin

☎ 0251334385, www.pommedepin.net – limited spaces for one-night stay

Address : rue Vincent Auriol (southeast, 150m from the beach at Boisvinet)

2 ha (150 pitches)

Rentals : 80 👛 – 11 🏠.

Near the beach, numerous mobile homes laid out around a small (partially covered) water park.

Surroundings : ⌂ ♨
Leisure activities : ♟ ✗ ⌂ 🏃 🚲 🏊 ⛵
Facilities : ♿ ⚷ 🚿 🐶 launderette 🏊 🚿

    G P S Longitude : -1.57264
    Latitude : 46.41084

△ La Mouette Cendrée

☎ 0251335904, www.mouettecendree.com

Address : chemin du Faux Prieur, at Les Malecots (take the northeastern exit along the D 19, follow the signs for St-Hilaire-la-Forêt)

1,8 ha (101 pitches) flat, grassy

Rentals : ♿ (1 mobile home) – 25 👛 – 5 canvas bungalows.

A leafy, green setting with rental mobile homes that are mostly modern.

Surroundings : ⌂ ♨♨
Leisure activities : 🏃 🏊
Facilities : ♿ ⚷ 🐶 📺

    G P S Longitude : -1.56702
    Latitude : 46.42767

The prices listed were supplied by the campsite owners in 2013 (if prices were not available, those from the previous year are given). The fees should be regarded as basic charges and may fluctuate with inflation.

85220 – Michelin map **316** F8 – pop. 1 185 – alt. 37
▶ Paris 452 – Challans 25 – Nantes 83 – La Roche-sur-Yon 32

△ L'Orée de l'Océan ♨♨

☎ 0251229636, www.camping-oreedelocean.com

Address : rue du Capitaine de Mazenod (take the western exit, follow the signs for Brétignolles-sur-Mer)

2,8 ha (240 pitches)

Rentals : ♿ (1 mobile home) – 85 👛 – 23 canvas bungalows.

A pretty, colourful play paddling pool area.

Surroundings : ⛵ ⌂ ♨♨
Leisure activities : ♟ ✗ ⌂ ⚓ 🏃 ⚄ 🚲
⛵ 🏊 ⛵ multi-sports ground, entertainment room
Facilities : ♿ ⚷ 🚿 🐶 launderette
Nearby : ✂

    G P S Longitude : -1.80635
    Latitude : 46.64087

Key to rentals symbols:

12 👛		*Number of mobile homes*
20 🏠		*Number of chalets*
6 🛏		*Number of rooms to rent*
Per night 30–50€		*Minimum/maximum rate per night*
Per week 300–1,000€		*Minimum/maximum rate per week*

72390 – Michelin map **310** M6 – pop. 838 – alt. 122
▶ Paris 173 – Bonnétable 26 – Bouloire 14 – La Ferté-Bernard 19

△ Le Val de Braye

☎ 0243719644, www.basedeloisirs-lavare.fr

Address : route de Vibraye (take the eastern exit along the D 302, at the leisure and activity park)

Opening times : from mid April to end Oct.

0,3 ha (20 pitches) flat, grassy

Tariff : ♟ 2€ ⛺ 1€ ▯ – ⚡ (5A) 2€

In an attractive location near a small lake.

Surroundings : ← ⌂ ♨
Leisure activities : 🏃 ⛵
Facilities : ⚷ 🚿 🏊
Nearby : ✂ ⛵ ⚓ mountain biking

    G P S Longitude : 0.64522
    Latitude : 48.05326

49220 – Michelin map **317** E3 – pop. 3 638 – alt. 45
▶ Paris 295 – Angers 27 – Candé 27 – Château-Gontier 22

△ Municipal les Frênes

☎ 0241953156, www.leliondangers.fr

Address : route de Chateau Gontier (take the northeastern exit along the N 162, beside the Oudon river)

2 ha (94 pitches) flat, grassy

🚐 borne – ♻ 7,45€

Set among majestic ash trees, beside the Oudon river.

Surroundings : ♨
Leisure activities : ⌂ 🏃
Facilities : ♿
Nearby : 🏇 racecourse

    G P S Longitude : -0.71154
    Latitude : 47.63094

LONGEVILLE-SUR-MER

85560 – Michelin map **316** H9 – pop. 2 356 – alt. 10
▶ Paris 448 – Challans 74 – Luçon 29 – La Roche-sur-Yon 31

MS Vacances Les Brunelles ▲▲

⌕ 02 51 33 50 75, www.les-brunelles.com – limited spaces for one-night stay

Address : rue de La Parée (at Le Bouil, 1km to the south)

Opening times : from end April to end Sept.

13 ha (600 pitches) relatively flat, flat, grassy

Tariff : 35€ ★★ ⇌ 🗐 ⚿ (6A) – Extra per person 9€ – Reservation fee 25€

Rental rates : (from end April to end Sept.) ♿ (1 mobile home) 274 🖵 – 10 🏠. Per week from 290 to 1350€ – Reservation fee 25€

Surroundings : 🏊 ⊑ ♀
Leisure activities : 🍸 ✕ 🏛 🎣 ⛷ 🏌 🎣 hammam, jacuzzi 🚲 ✂ 🎲 🏊 △ multi-sports ground
Facilities : ♿ ⛟ 🗑 🚿 ♨ 🚽 ⛽ launderette 🖴 🛒
Nearby : 🎿

G P S Longitude : -1.52191
Latitude : 46.41326

Camp'Atlantique Le Petit Rocher ▲▲

⌕ 02 51 20 41 94, www.camp-atlantique.com

Address : 1250 avenue du Dct Mathevet

Opening times : from beginning April to end Sept.

5 ha (211 pitches) undulating, terraced, relatively flat, flat, grassy

Tariff : 32€ ★★ ⇌ 🗐 ⚿ (10A) – Extra per person 6€ – Reservation fee 25€

Rental rates : (from beginning April to end Sept.) ♿ (1 mobile home) – 5 caravans – 99 🖵 – 9 canvas bungalows – 5 tent lodges. Per week from 139 to 1049€ – Reservation fee 25€

An undulating site with lots of shade, 250m from the beach via a pedestrian path.

Surroundings : ⊑ ♀♀
Leisure activities : ✕ ⚐ 🎣 ⛷ 🏊 △ multi-sports ground
Facilities : ♿ ⛟ 🚿 ♨ launderette
Nearby : 🖴 🍸 🛒

G P S Longitude : -1.50727
Latitude : 46.40344

LOUÉ

72540 – Michelin map **310** I7 – pop. 2 129 – alt. 112
▶ Paris 230 – Laval 59 – Le Mans 30

Village Loisirs

⌕ 02 43 88 65 65, villageloisirs.com

Address : place Hector Vincent (head towards the northeastern exit along the D 21, rte du Mans; by the swimming pool)

Opening times : Permanent

1 ha (16 pitches) flat, grassy

Tariff : ★ 8€ ⇌ 🗐 – ⚿ (10A) 4€

Rental rates : Permanent – 10 🏠. Per night from 60 to 90€ Per week from 280 to 460€

In a pleasant location beside the Vègre river.

Leisure activities : 🍸 ✕ 🏛 🎣 △
Facilities : ♿ ⛟ (June–Sept.) 🗑 🖴
Nearby : 🏊 walking trails

G P S Longitude : -0.14711
Latitude : 47.99734

LUCHÉ-PRINGÉ

72800 – Michelin map **310** J8 – pop. 1 658 – alt. 34
▶ Paris 242 – Château-du-Loir 31 – Écommoy 24 – La Flèche 14

Municipal la Chabotière

⌕ 02 43 45 10 00, www.lachabotiere.com

Address : place des Tilleuls (to the west of the town)

Opening times : from beginning April to end Oct.

3 ha (75 pitches)

Tariff : 15€ ★★ ⇌ 🗐 ⚿ (10A) – Extra per person 4€

Rental rates : Permanent – 10 🏠 – 10 canvas bungalows. Per night from 33 to 90€ – Per week from 185 to 530€

In a leisure and activity park; beside the Loir river.

Surroundings : 🏊 ⊑ ♀
Leisure activities : 🏛 🎣 🚲
Facilities : ♿ ⛟ (July–Aug.) Ⓟ 🚿 ♨ launderette
Nearby : ✂ 🎿 🏊 △ 🐎 boats to hire

G P S Longitude : 0.07364
Latitude : 47.70252

LE LUDE

72800 – Michelin map **310** J9 – pop. 4 049 – alt. 48
▶ Paris 244 – Angers 63 – Chinon 63 – La Flèche 20

Municipal au Bord du Loir

⌕ 02 43 94 67 70, www.campingmunicipallelude.fr

Address : route du Mans (0.8km northwest along the D 307, follow the signs for Le Mans)

Opening times : from mid April to mid Oct.

2,5 ha (111 pitches) flat, grassy

Tariff : (2013 Price) 12€ ★★ ⇌ 🗐 ⚿ (12A) – Extra per person 3,80€

Rental rates : (2013 Price) (from mid April to mid Oct.) ✂ 4 🖵 – 5 🏠 – 4 canvas bungalows. Per night from 25 to 88€ Per week from 130 to 466€

🚐 borne 2€ – 🚐 ⚿ 9€

A rural setting beside the Loir river.

Surroundings : ♀♀
Leisure activities : 🏛 🎣 🚲 🐎
Facilities : ♿ ⛟ 🚿 🚽 ♨ 🖴
Nearby : ✕ ✂ 🎲 🏊 △ pedalos

G P S Longitude : 0.16247
Latitude : 47.65119

MACHÉ

85190 – Michelin map **316** F7 – pop. 1 337 – alt. 42
▶ Paris 443 – Challans 22 – Nantes 59 – La Roche-sur-Yon 26

Le Val de Vie

⌕ 02 51 60 21 02, www.campingvaldevie.fr

Address : 5 rue du Stade (take the exit for Apremont and take the road to the left; 400m from the lake)

Opening times : from mid April to beginning Oct.

2,5 ha (93 pitches)

Tariff : 24,10€ ★★ ⇌ 🗐 ⚿ (10A) – Extra per person 4,20€

Rental rates : Permanent – 2 🖵 – 2 🏠. Per night from 50 to 100€ Per week from 230 to 640€

🚐 borne 2,50€ – 2 🗐 8€

Surroundings : 🏊 ⊑ ♀
Leisure activities : 🎣 🏊 🛶
Facilities : ♿ ⛟ 🚿 ♨ 🖴
Nearby : ✂

G P S Longitude : -1.68595
Latitude : 46.75305

MACHECOUL

44270 – Michelin map **316** F6 – pop. 5 872 – alt. 5

▶ Paris 420 – Beauvoir-sur-Mer 23 – Nantes 39 – La Roche-sur-Yon 56

⚠ La Rabine

🕿 02 40 02 30 48, www.camping-la-rabine.com

Address : allée de la Rabine (take the southern exit along the D 95, follow the signs for Challans; beside the Falleron river)

Opening times : from beginning April to end Sept.

2,8 ha (131 pitches) flat, grassy

Tariff : 13,20€ ★★ ⛺ 🔲 🅿 (13A) – Extra per person 4€

Rental rates : (from beginning April to end Sept.) – 1 caravan 3 🛖 . Per week from 310 to 480€ – Reservation fee 20€

🚐 borne 3€ – 4 🔲 10,80€

Very near the town centre, encircled by a small river.

Surroundings : ♀
Leisure activities : 🏄 🎣
Facilities : 👤 ⛽ 🍴 launderette
Nearby : ✂ 🖼

GPS Longitude : -1.81555
Latitude : 46.9887

A chambre d'hôte is a guesthouse or B & B-style accommodation.

MAILLEZAIS

85420 – Michelin map **316** L9 – pop. 962 – alt. 6

▶ Paris 436 – Fontenay-le-Comte 15 – Niort 27 – La Rochelle 49

⚠ Municipal de l'Autize

🕿 06 43 19 14 90, www.maillezais.fr

Address : rue du Champ de foire (take the southern exit, follow the signs for Courçon)

Opening times : from beginning April to end Sept.

1 ha (40 pitches) flat, grassy

Tariff : 9€ ★★ ⛺ 🔲 🅿 (13A) – Extra per person 2,50€

🚐 borne 2€

In a green setting near the exit from town.

Surroundings : 🏞 ♀♀
Leisure activities : 🏄
Facilities : 👤 ⛽ (July–Aug.) 🏓 🏐 🍴 🖼
Nearby : 🏄 ✂

GPS Longitude : -0.73914
Latitude : 46.37133

MALICORNE-SUR-SARTHE

72270 – Michelin map **310** I8 – pop. 1 962 – alt. 39

▶ Paris 236 – Château-Gontier 52 – La Flèche 16 – Le Mans 32

⚠ Municipal Port Ste Marie

🕿 02 43 94 80 14, www.ville-malicorne.fr

Address : to the west of the town along the D 41

Opening times : from beginning April to end Sept.

1 ha (80 pitches) flat, grassy

Tariff : (2013 Price) 14,75€ ★★ ⛺ 🔲 🅿 (13A) Extra per person 3,25€

Rental rates : (2013 Price) (from beginning April to end Sept.) 4 🛖 – 6 canvas bungalows. Per night from 48 to 146€ – Per week from 145 to 385€

🚐 borne 4€

A pleasant site and setting near the Sarthe river.

Surroundings : ♀
Leisure activities : 🏠 🏄
Facilities : 👤 ⛽ (July–Aug.) 🏐 🍴 launderette
Nearby : 🚲 ✂ 🖼 🏊 🏇 pedalos

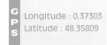

GPS Longitude : -0.0893
Latitude : 47.81763

MAMERS

72600 – Michelin map **310** L4 – pop. 5 545 – alt. 128

▶ Paris 185 – Alençon 25 – Le Mans 51 – Mortagne-au-Perche 25

⚠ Municipal du Saosnois

🕿 02 43 97 68 30, www.mairie-mamers.fr

Address : continue 1km north following signs for Mortagne-au-Perche and take D 113 to the left, following signs for Contilly, near two lakes

Opening times : from beginning March to beginning Nov.

1,5 ha (50 pitches) terraced, relatively flat, flat, grassy

Tariff : (2013 Price) 15€ ★★ ⛺ 🔲 🅿 (6A) – Extra per person 3€

Rental rates : (2013 Price) (from beginning March to beginning Nov.) – 4 🛖 – 5 canvas bungalows. Per night from 25 to 55 € – Per week from 150 to 360€

🚐 borne 7€ – 🚌 11€

Surroundings : 🚐 ♀
Leisure activities : 🍴 🏊 (beach)
Facilities : ⛽ 🏐 🏓 🍴 🖼
Nearby : 🏄 ✂ 🎣 🖼 🏇 fitness trail

GPS Longitude : 0.37303
Latitude : 48.35809

MANSIGNÉ

72510 – Michelin map **310** J8 – pop. 1 579 – alt. 80

▶ Paris 235 – Château-du-Loir 28 – La Flèche 21 – Le Lude 17

⚠ Municipal de la Plage

🕿 02 43 46 14 17, basedeloisirsmansigne.fr

Address : rue du Plessis (take the northern exit along the D 31, follow the signs for La Suze-sur-Sarthe, 100m from a small lake)

Opening times : from mid April to end Oct.

3 ha (175 pitches) flat, grassy

Tariff : 13,58€ ★★ ⛺ 🔲 🅿 (10A) – Extra per person 2,10€ – Reservation fee 19,50€

Rental rates : (from mid April to end Oct.) – 8 🛖 – 21 🛖 7 canvas bungalows. Per night from 40 to 100€ – Per week from 230 to 480€ – Reservation fee 19,50€

🚐 🚌 14,58€

Surroundings : ♀
Leisure activities : 🍴 🏠 🚲 ✂ 🏊 🏊
Facilities : 👤 ⛽ (14 July–16 Aug.) 🍴 launderette
Nearby : 🏄 🖼 🏊 (beach) 🎣 🚣 pedalos

GPS Longitude : 0.13284
Latitude : 47.75078

MARÇON

72340 – Michelin map **310** M8 – pop. 1 028 – alt. 59
▶ Paris 245 – Château-du-Loir 10 – Le Grand-Lucé 51 – Le Mans 52

🔺 Lac des Varennes

📞 02 43 44 13 72, www.lacdesvarennes.com

Address : route de Port Gauthier (located 1km west along the D 61, near the leisure park)

Opening times : from mid April to end Sept.

5,5 ha (250 pitches) flat, grassy

Tariff : 19,40€ ♦♦ ⮐ 🔲 (10A) – Extra per person 5€ – Reservation fee 10€

Rental rates : (from mid April to end Sept.) – 27 🚐 – 1 🏠 10 canvas bungalows. Per night from 35 to 100€ – Per week from 195 to 700€ – Reservation fee 10€

🚱 borne 7€ – 🚰 11€

In a pleasant location laid out around a lake equipped for leisure activities.

Surroundings : 🌳
Leisure activities : 🍸 ✗ 🏛 🏊 🚲 🛶 (beach) 🎣
Facilities : 🔥 🚿 🖂 🛁 🚽 🔲 🛒 🛗
Nearby : 🍴 🎠 🐴 pedalos

G P S
Longitude : 0.4993
Latitude : 47.7125

MAYENNE

53100 – Michelin map **310** F5 – pop. 13 350 – alt. 124
▶ Paris 283 – Alençon 61 – Flers 56 – Fougères 47

🔺 Du Gué St-Léonard

📞 02 43 04 57 14, http://www.paysdemayenne-tourisme.fr

Address : rue du Gué St-Léonard (north of the town, via av. de Loré and turning to the right)

1,8 ha (70 pitches) flat, grassy

Rentals : 5 🚐 .

A pleasant location beside the Mayenne river.

Surroundings : 🌳🌳
Leisure activities : ✗ 🏛 🏊 🎣
Facilities : 🔥 🚿 🛁 🚽 launderette
Nearby : ✗

G P S
Longitude : -0.61387
Latitude : 48.3142

LE MAZEAU

85420 – Michelin map **316** L9 – pop. 427 – alt. 8
▶ Paris 435 – Fontenay-le-Comte 22 – Niort 21 – La Rochelle 53

🔺 Municipal le Relais du Pêcheur

📞 02 51 52 93 23, www.mairielemazeau.fr

Address : route de la Sèvre (700m south of the town, near canals)

Opening times : from beginning April to end Sept.

1 ha (54 pitches) flat, grassy

Tariff : ♦ 3,30€ ⮐ 🔲 4,50€ – (10A) 3,10€

Rental rates : (from beginning May to end Sept.) 🎿 – 3 canvas bungalows. Per night from 31 to 50€ – Per week from 127 to 284€

A pleasant site and setting in the heart of the Venise Verte ('Green Venice').

Surroundings : 🌊 🗺 🌳🌳
Leisure activities : 🏛 🏊
Facilities : 🔥 🚿 (Jul-Aug.) 🚻 🛒
Nearby : 🎣

G P S
Longitude : -0.67535
Latitude : 46.33052

MÉNIL

53200 – Michelin map **310** E8 – pop. 965 – alt. 32
▶ Paris 297 – Angers 45 – Château-Gontier 7 – Châteauneuf-sur-Sarthe 21

🔺 Municipal du Bac

📞 02 43 70 24 54, menil53.fr

Address : rue du Port (east of the village)

Opening times : Permanent

0,5 ha (39 pitches) flat, grassy

Tariff : 11,50€ ♦♦ ⮐ 🔲 (6A) – Extra per person 4€

Rental rates : Permanent – 1 🚐 – 5 🏠 . Per week from 163 to 370€ – Reservation fee 13€

🚱 borne 2€

A pleasant site and setting near the Mayenne river.

Surroundings : 🌊 🗺 🌳
Leisure activities : ✗ 🏊 🚲 🎣
Facilities : 🔥 🚿 🛗

G P S
Longitude : -0.67319
Latitude : 47.77494

This guide is updated regularly, so buy your new copy every year!

MERVENT

85200 – Michelin map **316** L8 – pop. 1 077 – alt. 85
▶ Paris 426 – Bressuire 52 – Fontenay-le-Comte 12 – Parthenay 50

🔺 La Joletière

📞 02 51 00 26 87, www.campinglajoletiere.fr

Address : 700m west along the D 99

Opening times : from beginning April to mid Oct.

1,3 ha (73 pitches)

Tariff : 22,50€ ♦♦ ⮐ 🔲 (16A) – Extra per person 4,50€ Reservation fee 12€

Rental rates : (from beginning April to mid Oct.) – 1 caravan 15 🚐 – 4 🏠 – 3 canvas bungalows. Per night from 45 to 90€ Per week from 240 to 640€ – Reservation fee 12€

Plenty of green spaces on a gentle slope, with a range of rental options.

Surroundings : 🌊 🗺 🌳🌳
Leisure activities : ✗ 🏛 🏊 🚲 🛶 🎿
Facilities : 🔥 🚿 🚐 🚻 🛗 🛒
Nearby : 🍸

G P S
Longitude : -0.7691
Latitude : 46.5214

MESLAY-DU-MAINE

53170 – Michelin map **310** F7 – pop. 2 726 – alt. 90
▶ Paris 268 – Angers 60 – Château-Gontier 21 – Châteauneuf-sur-Sarthe 34

🔺 La Chesnaie

📞 02 43 98 48 08, www.paysmeslaygrez.fr

Address : Waterhole la Chesnaie (2.5km northeast along the D 152, follow the signs for St-Denis-du-Maine)

Opening times : from mid April to end Sept.

7 ha/0,8 (60 pitches) flat, grassy

Tariff : 9,40€ ♦♦ ⮐ 🔲 (8A) – Extra per person 3,50€

Rental rates : Permanent – 8 🚐 – 8 🏠 – 8 gîtes. Per night from 75 to 120€ – Per week from 165 to 430€

🚱 borne

Beside a small but beautiful lake.

Surroundings :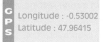
Leisure activities : 🚲
Facilities : & (July–Aug.)
At the leisure/activities centre : ⛺ fitness trail

GPS Longitude : -0.53002
Latitude : 47.96415

Some campsites benefit from proximity to a municipal leisure centre.

MESQUER

44420 – Michelin map **316** B3 – pop. 1 710 – alt. 6
Paris 460 – La Baule 16 – Muzillac 32 – Pontchâteau 35

Soir d'Été

02 40 42 57 26, www.camping-soirdete.com
Address : 401 rue de Bel Air (head 2km northwest along the D 352 and take turning to the left)
Opening times : from beginning April to end Sept.
1,5 ha (92 pitches)
Tariff : 16€ (6A) – Extra per person 6€
Rental rates : (from beginning April to end Sept.) – 18. Per night from 100 to 150 € – Per week from 250 to 760€
borne
In a shaded setting beside a salt marsh.

Surroundings :
Leisure activities : (open air in season), multi-sports ground
Facilities : & launderette
Nearby :

GPS Longitude : -2.47575
Latitude : 47.4064

Le Praderoi

02 40 42 66 72, http://www.camping-le-praderoi.com
Address : at Quimiac, 14 allée des Barges (2.5km to the northwest, 300m from the beach)
Opening times : from beginning April to end Sept.
0,4 ha (32 pitches)
Tariff : 26,50€ (10A) – Extra per person 4,50€
Rental rates : (from beginning April to end Sept.) (from beginning April to end Sept) – 2 caravans – 2 – 3 canvas bungalows. Per week from 230 to 630€
13,50€
A small campsite, very peaceful and family-orientated.

Surroundings :
Leisure activities :
Facilities : & launderette

GPS Longitude : -2.48895
Latitude : 47.40572

MÉZIÈRES-SOUS-LAVARDIN

72240 – Michelin map **310** J6 – pop. 634 – alt. 75
Paris 221 – Alençon 38 – La Ferté-Bernard 69 – Le Mans 25

Parc des Braudières

02 43 20 81 48, www.campinglesbraudieres.com – limited spaces for one-night stay
Address : 4.5km east along the back road to St-Jean
Opening times : Permanent
1,7 ha (52 pitches)
Tariff : 24€ (10A) – Extra per person 5€

Rental rates : Permanent – 3. Per night from 60 to 70€
Per week from 450 to 500€
4 15€
Beside a small fishing lake.

Surroundings :
Leisure activities : jacuzzi
Facilities : &

GPS Longitude : 0.06328
Latitude : 48.15758

MONTREUIL-BELLAY

49260 – Michelin map **317** I6 – pop. 4 041 – alt. 50
Paris 335 – Angers 54 – Châtellerault 70 – Chinon 39

Les Nobis

02 41 52 33 66, www.campinglesnobis.com
Address : rue Georges Girouy (take the northwestern exit, follow the signs for Angers and take the road to the left before the bridge)
Opening times : from end March to beginning Oct.
4 ha (165 pitches) terraced, flat, grassy
Tariff : 26€ (10A) – Extra per person 4€ – Reservation fee 10€
Rental rates : (from end March to beginning Nov.) – 13. Per night from 40 to 90€ – Per week from 226 to 585€ Reservation fee 10€
A pleasant location on the banks of the Thouet river at the foot of a château.

Surroundings :
Leisure activities : daytime
Facilities : & launderette
Nearby : pedalos

GPS Longitude : -0.15897
Latitude : 47.13204

The Michelin classification (⛰⛰⛰ … ⛰) is totally independent of the official star classification system awarded by the local prefecture or other official organisation.

MONTSOREAU

49730 – Michelin map **317** J5 – pop. 485 – alt. 77
Paris 292 – Angers 75 – Châtellerault 65 – Chinon 18

Kawan Village L'Isle Verte

02 41 51 76 60, www.campingisleverte.com
Address : avenue de la Loire (take the northwestern exit along the D 947, follow the signs for Saumur; beside the Loire river)
Opening times : from beginning April to mid Oct.
2,5 ha (105 pitches) flat, grassy
Tariff : 27,50€ (16A) – Extra per person 6€ – Reservation fee 15€
Rental rates : (from beginning April to mid Oct.) – 18 – 7 tent lodges. Per night from 45 to 120 € – Per week from 200 to 840€ Reservation fee 15€
borne
Surroundings :
Leisure activities :
Facilities : &

GPS Longitude : 0.05165
Latitude : 47.21861

LA MOTHE-ACHARD

85150 – Michelin map **316** G8 – pop. 2 524 – alt. 20
▶ Paris 439 – Aizenay 15 – Challans 40 – La Roche-sur-Yon 19

⚠ Le Pavillon

📞 02 51 05 63 46, www.camping-le-pavillon.com

Address : 175 avenue Georges Clemenceau (located 1.5km southwest, follow the signs for Les Sables-d'Olonne)

Opening times : from beginning April to end Sept.

3,6 ha (117 pitches)

Tariff : 28,50€ ✹✹ ⇌ 🔲 [🚿] (10A) – Extra per person 6€ – Reservation fee 8€

Rental rates : (from beginning April to end Sept.) – 16 ⏚ – 6 ⌂ 6 canvas bungalows. Per night from 15 to 20€ – Per week from 190 to 795€ – Reservation fee 16€

In a green location with a range of mostly modern rental options.

Surroundings : 🌳🌳
Leisure activities : 🍴 🏕 🚣 🏊 ⛰ 🥾 multi-sports ground
Facilities : 🚿 ⊙ 🚽 launderette

Longitude : -1.66728
Latitude : 46.60653

MOUCHAMPS

85640 – Michelin map **316** J7 – pop. 2 600 – alt. 81
▶ Paris 394 – Cholet 40 – Fontenay-le-Comte 52 – Nantes 68

⚠ Le Hameau du Petit Lay

📞 02 51 66 25 72, www.lehameaudupetitlay.com

Address : at Chauvin (600m south along the D 113, follow the signs for St-Prouant)

Opening times : from mid June to mid Sept.

0,4 ha (39 pitches) flat, grassy

Tariff : 12,90€ ✹✹ ⇌ 🔲 [🚿] (6A) – Extra per person 3,70€

Rental rates : Permanent – 15 ⌂. Per night from 43 to 53€ Per week from 197 to 497€

Campsite and chalets on both sides of the small wooden bridge crossing the Le Lay stream.

Surroundings : 🚗 🌳🌳
Leisure activities : 🏕 🏊 🚣 🏊 (small swimming pool)
Facilities : 🚿 ⊙ 🚽 🔲
Nearby : 🎣

Longitude : -1.05483
Latitude : 46.77585

MOUILLERON-LE-CAPTIF

85000 – Michelin map **316** h7 – pop. 4 511 – alt. 70
▶ Paris 421 – Challans 40 – La Mothe-Achard 22 – Nantes 63

⚠ L'Ambois

CAMPING L'AMBOIS

📞 02 51 37 29 15, www.campingambois.com – limited spaces for one-night stay

Address : take southeastern exit along the D 2, follow the signs for la Roche-sur-Yon, then continue 2.6km along the road to the right

Opening times : Permanent

1,75 ha (49 pitches) relatively flat, flat, grassy

Tariff : ✹ 4,30€ ⇌ 🔲 3,80€ – [🚿] (10A) 3,80€

Rental rates : Permanent – 41 ⏚ – 3 ⌂ – 3 gîtes. Per night 85€ Per week 515€

In a rural setting with very few places for tents and caravans.

Surroundings : 🏞 🚗 🌳
Leisure activities : 🏕 🚣 🚴 🏊 (open air in season), farm or petting farm
Facilities : 🚿 ⊙ 🚽 ⛺ 🚽 launderette 🧺

Longitude : -1.46092
Latitude : 46.69647

NANTES

44000 – Michelin map **316** G4 – pop. 282 047 – alt. 8
▶ Paris 381 – Angers 88 – Bordeaux 325 – Lyon 660

⚠ Nantes Camping - Le Petit Port

📞 02 40 74 47 94, www.nantes-camping.fr

Address : 21 boulevard du Petit Port (situated beside the Cens river)

Opening times : Permanent

8 ha (151 pitches) relatively flat, flat, grassy, gravelled

Tariff : 36,20€ ✹✹ ⇌ 🔲 [🚿] (16A) – Extra per person 6,20€ Reservation fee 10€

Rental rates : Permanent 🚿 (1 chalet) – 60 ⏚ – 6 ⌂ – 1 tent lodge. Per night from 41 to 161€ – Per week from 246 to 966€ Reservation fee 25€

🚐 borne 2€ – 15 🔲 12€

High-end rentals, free use of the swimming pool and a tram stop for the town centre.

Surroundings : 🏞 🚗 🌳🌳
Leisure activities : 🍴 🍽 🚣 🚴 🎣
Facilities : 🚿 ⊙ 🔳 🚽 🛁 ⛺ 🚽 launderette
Nearby : 🏊 🛼 skating rink

Longitude : -1.5567
Latitude : 47.24346

For more information on visiting particular towns or regions, consult the relevant regional MICHELIN Green Guide. We also recommend you use the appropriate Michelin regional map to locate your selected campsite, to calculate distances and to work out the best route.

NOTRE-DAME-DE-MONTS

85690 – Michelin map **316** D6 – pop. 1 866 – alt. 6
▶ Paris 459 – Nantes 74 – La Roche-sur-Yon 72

⚠ L'Albizia

📞 02 28 11 28 50, www.campinglalbizia.com – limited spaces for one-night stay

Address : 52 rue de la Rive (1.9km to the north)

Opening times : from beginning April to end Sept.

3,6 ha (153 pitches)

Tariff : (2013 Price) 28€ ✹✹ ⇌ 🔲 [🚿] (16A) – Extra per person 5,60€ Reservation fee 12€

Rental rates : (2013 Price) (from mid Feb. to mid Oct.) – 35 ⏚ Per night from 78 to 93€ – Per week from 267 to 824€ Reservation fee 12€

A pleasant campsite, but numerous owner-occupied mobile homes.

Surroundings : 🚗
Leisure activities : 🍴 🍽 🌙 nighttime 🚣 🚴 🎣 🏊 🚤 multi-sports ground
Facilities : 🚿 ⊙ 🚽 launderette

Longitude : -2.12755
Latitude : 46.8503

⛺ Municipal de l'Orgatte

𝄞 0251588431, www.notre-dame-de-monts.fr

Address : avenue Abbé Thibaud (1.2km north along the D 38, turn off to the left, 300m from the beach)

Opening times : from beginning April to end Sept.

,5 ha (315 pitches)

Tariff : (2013 Price) 18,60€ ⛄⛄ 🚗 ▣ ⚡ (10A) – Extra per person 5€
Reservation fee 10€

A pleasant location among hills shaded by a pine grove.

Surroundings : 🏖 ♤♤
Leisure activities : 🚣 multi-sports ground
Facilities : 🚻 ▣

Longitude : -2.13882
Latitude : 46.83972
GPS

⛺ Le Pont d'Yeu

𝄞 0251588376, www.camping-pontdyeu.com

Address : rue du Pont d'Yeu (located 1km south along the D 38, follow the signs for St-Jean-de-Monts, and take turning to the left)

Opening times : from beginning April to end Sept.

,3 ha (90 pitches)

Tariff : 25,30€ ⛄⛄ 🚗 ▣ ⚡ (10A) – Extra per person 4,90€
Reservation fee 10€

Rental rates : (from beginning April to end Sept.) – 28 🚐
? 🏠. Per night from 70 to 95€ – Per week from 215 to 670€
Reservation fee 10€

A peaceful, family atmosphere; half the pitches are for owner-occupied mobile homes.

Surroundings : 🗀 ♤
Leisure activities : 🚣 ▣ (open air in season)
Facilities : 🚻 ☎ 🍽 launderette

Longitude : -2.13585
Latitude : 46.82052
GPS

NYOISEAU

49500 – Michelin map **317** D2 – pop. 1 305 – alt. 40
▶ Paris 316 – Ancenis 50 – Angers 47 – Châteaubriant 39

⛺ La Rivière

𝄞 0241922677, www.campinglariviere.fr

Address : 1.2km southeast along the D 71, follow the signs for Segré and take turning to the left; beside the Oudon river

Opening times : from mid June to end Sept.

▌ ha (25 pitches) flat, grassy

Tariff : (2013 Price) ⛄ 3€ 🚗 ▣ 3€ – ⚡ (10A) 3,50€
🚐 borne 4€

Surroundings : 🏖 ♤♤
Leisure activities : 🏛 🚣
Facilities : 🚻 ☎ (July–15 Sept.) 🍽
Nearby : 🚵 mountain biking

Longitude : -0.90981
Latitude : 47.71216
GPS

Michelin classification:

⛰⛰⛰⛰ *Extremely comfortable, equipped to a very high standard*
⛰⛰⛰ *Very comfortable, equipped to a high standard*
⛰⛰⛰ *Comfortable and well equipped*
⛰⛰ *Reasonably comfortable*
⛺ *Satisfactory*

OLONNE-SUR-MER

85340 – Michelin map **316** F8 – pop. 13 279 – alt. 40
▶ Paris 458 – Nantes 102 – La Roche-sur-Yon 36 – La Rochelle 96

⛰⛰⛰ Sunêlia La Loubine ⛄👤

𝄞 0251331292, www.la-loubine.fr – limited spaces for one-night stay 🚫 (July–Aug..)

Address : 1 route de la Mer (3km to the west)

Opening times : from mid April to mid Sept.

8 ha (401 pitches) flat, grassy Tariff : 40,60€ ⛄⛄ 🚗 ▣ ⚡ (6A)
Extra per person 6,90€ – Reservation fee 22€

Rental rates : Permanent ♿ (1 mobile home) – 148 🚐 – 2 🏠.
Per night from 40 to 155€ – Per week from 280 to 1085€
Reservation fee 22€

Based around a 16th-century Vendée farm, with a charming landscaped water and play park.

Surroundings : 🗀 ♤♤
Leisure activities : 🍷 🍴 🎮 🌙nighttime
🏃 🎠 🏊 jacuzzi 🚣🚴⛳🎯 🏛 🏊 🏖
multi-sports ground
Facilities : ♿ ☎ 🍽 launderette 🏖 🚗
Nearby : 🐎

Longitude : -1.80647
Latitude : 46.54595
GPS

⛰⛰⛰ Le Moulin de la Salle ⛄👤

𝄞 0251959910, www.moulindelasalle.com – limited spaces for one-night stay

Address : rue du Moulin de la Salle (2.7km to the west)

Opening times : from beginning April to end Sept.

2,7 ha (216 pitches) flat, grassy

Tariff : 33€ ⛄⛄ 🚗 ▣ ⚡ (10A) – Extra per person 5€ – Reservation fee 25€

Rental rates : (from beginning April to mid Sept.) – 120 🚐.
Per night from 55 to 80€ – Per week from 220 to 810€
Reservation fee 25€

Numerous mobile homes around a pretty windmill, but with very few pitches for tents and caravans.

Surroundings : 🗀 ♤
Leisure activities : 🍷 🍴 🏛 🏃 🎠 🏊 🚣 🏛 🏊
🏖 multi-sports ground, entertainment room
Facilities : ♿ ☎ 🍽 🚗 🍽 launderette 🚗

Longitude : -1.79217
Latitude : 46.53183
GPS

⛰⛰⛰ Domaine de l'Orée ⛄👤

𝄞 0251331059, www.l-oree.com

Address : 13 route des Amis de la Nature

Opening times : from mid April to mid Sept.

6 ha (320 pitches) flat, grassy

Tariff : (2013 Price) 36,50€ ⛄⛄ 🚗 ▣ ⚡ (10A) – Extra per person 6€
Reservation fee 26€

Rental rates : (2013 Price) (from mid April to mid Sept.) – 145 🚐
6 🏠. Per week from 245 to 403€ – Reservation fee 26€

Divided into 2 separate campsites, some pitches for tents and caravans benefit from private sanitary facilities.

Surroundings : 🗀 ♤
Leisure activities : 🍷 🍴 🎮 🌙nighttime 🏃
🏊 jacuzzi 🚣🚴⛳🎯 🏛 🏖 multi-sports
ground
Facilities : ♿ ☎ 🍽 – 10 individual sanitary
facilities (🚿 🚽 wc) 🚗 🍽 launderette
🏖 🚗
Nearby : 🐎

Longitude : -1.80827
Latitude : 46.5494
GPS

⛰ Le Puits Rochais ♣♦

☎ 02 51 21 09 69, www.puitsrochais.com

Address : 25 rue de Bourdigal (3.5km southeast along the D 559, follow the signs for Bandol)

Opening times : from beginning April to end Sept.

3,9 ha (220 pitches) relatively flat, flat, grassy

Tariff : (2013 Price) 34,95 € ♦♦ ⇔ 📧 🄰 (6A) – Extra per person 6,95 €

Rental rates : (2013 Price) (from beginning April to beginning Oct.) – 60 🚐 – 2 🏠. Per night from 52 to 100 € Per week from 155 to 940 €

A charming site with plenty of owner-occupied and rental mobile homes.

Surroundings : ⌂ 🌳🌳
Leisure activities : 🍽 ✕ 🖼 daytime 🏃
🏇 🚴 🎾 🎣 🏊 🛶
Facilities : ♿ ⚡ 🚿 🔥 🚰 🍴 launderette 🏪
refrigerators

G P S Longitude : -1.73663
Latitude : 46.47978

⛰ Nid d'Été

☎ 02 51 95 34 38, www.leniddete.com

Address : 2 rue de la Vigne Verte (2.5km to the west)

Opening times : from beginning April to end Sept.

2 ha (159 pitches) flat, grassy

Tariff : 26,80 € ♦♦ ⇔ 📧 🄰 (10A) – Extra per person 4,90 € – Reservation fee 15 €

Rental rates : (from beginning April to end Sept.) – 24 🚐. Per night from 34 to 103 € – Per week from 235 to 721 € Reservation fee 15 €

The site is divided into 2 sections, with good sanitary facilities.

Surroundings : 🏞 ⌂ 🌳🌳
Leisure activities : 🍽 ✕ 🖼 jacuzzi 🚣 🏊
(open air in season)
Facilities : ♿ ⚡ 🚿 🍴 launderette 🏪

G P S Longitude : -1.79393
Latitude : 46.53326

⛰ Le Petit Paris ♣♦

☎ 02 51 22 04 44, www.campingpetitparis.com

Address : 41 rue du Petit-Versailles (located 5.5km southeast)

Opening times : from beginning April to end Sept.

3 ha (154 pitches) flat, grassy

Tariff : 28 € ♦♦ ⇔ 📧 🄰 (10A) – Extra per person 4,80 € – Reservation fee 18 €

Rental rates : (from beginning April to end Oct.) – 35 🚐 2 🏠. Per night from 55 to 100 € – Per week from 190 to 820 € Reservation fee 18 €

Green setting with a range of rental options and one area reserved for tents and caravans.

Surroundings : 🏞 ⌂ 🌳🌳
Leisure activities : 🍽 🖼 🏃 🚣 🏊 (open air in season) ⛷ multi-sports ground
Facilities : ♿ ⚡ 🚿 🚰 🍴 launderette 🏪
Nearby : parachuting

G P S Longitude : -1.72041
Latitude : 46.47359

⛰ Les Fosses Rouges

☎ 02 51 95 17 95, www.camping-lesfossesrouges.com

Address : 8 rue des Fosses Rouges, at la Pironnière (3km southeast)

Opening times : from beginning April to end Sept.

3,5 ha (248 pitches) flat, grassy

Tariff : 17,34 € ♦♦ ⇔ 📧 🄰 (10A) – Extra per person 3 € – Reservation fee 12 €

Rental rates : (from beginning April to end Sept.) – 13 🚐 Per night from 45 to 73 € – Per week from 190 to 580 € Reservation fee 12 €

🚐 borne

In a residential area but choose the pitches away from the road.

Surroundings : ⌂ 🌳🌳
Leisure activities : 🍽 🚣 🎾 🎣 🖼 (open air in season)
Facilities : ♿ ⚡ 🚿 🍴 launderette 🏪 🏪

G P S Longitude : -1.74124
Latitude : 46.47956

⛺ Sauveterre

☎ 02 51 33 10 58, www.campingsauveterre.com

Address : 3 route des Amis de la Nature (3km to the west)

Opening times : from beginning April to end Sept.

3,2 ha (234 pitches) flat, grassy

Tariff : (2013 Price) 24,40 € ♦♦ ⇔ 📧 🄰 (10A) Extra per person 5,10 € – Reservation fee 20 €

Rental rates : (2013 Price) (from beginning April to end Sept.) 🛁 23 🚐. Per night from 35 to 85 € – Per week from 140 to 680 € Reservation fee 20 €

*Surroundings : 🌳🌳
Leisure activities : ✕ 🛶 🏊
Facilities : ♿ ⚡ 🚿 🍴 🖼 🏪 🏪
Nearby : 🏇

G P S Longitude : -1.80547
Latitude : 46.54697

PIRIAC-SUR-MER

44420 – Michelin map **316** A3 – pop. 2 245 – alt. 7
▶ Paris 462 – La Baule 17 – Nantes 88 – La Roche-Bernard 33

⛰ Parc du Guibel ♣♦

☎ 02 40 23 52 67, www.parcduguibel.com

Address : route de Kerdrien (3.5km east along the D 52, follow the signs for Mesquer and take turning to the left)

Opening times : from beginning April to end Sept.

14 ha (450 pitches)

Tariff : ♦ 6,40 € ⇔ 4,20 € 📧 6,40 € – 🄰 (10A) 4,60 € – Reservation fee 18 €

Rental rates : (from beginning April to end Sept.) – 91 🚐 34 🏠. Per night from 50 to 119 € – Per week from 266 to 833 € Reservation fee 18 €

🚐 20 📧 13,90 € – 🚐 11 €

The site is divided into 2 distinct sections in a natural, wooded park. There is a partially open-air swimming area.

Surroundings : 🏞 ⌂ 🌳🌳🌳
Leisure activities : 🍽 ✕ 🖼 🏃 🚣 🚴 🖼
🛶 ⛷ multi-sports ground
Facilities : ♿ ⚡ 🚿 🚰 🍴 launderette
🏪 🏪
Nearby : 🏇

G P S Longitude : -2.51024
Latitude : 47.3862

Some information or pricing may have changed since the guide went to press. We recommend you check the price list online in advance or at the entrance to the campsite and enquire about possible restrictions.

Armor Héol ▲▲▲ ♣♣

☎ 02 40 23 57 80, www.camping-armor-heol.com

Address : at Kervin, route de Guérande (located 1km southeast along the D 333)

Opening times : from beginning April to mid Sept.

4,5 ha (270 pitches) flat, grassy, small lake

Tariff : 32 € ♣♣ ⇔ 🄴 ⚡ (6A) – Extra per person 7 € – Reservation fee 20 €

Rental rates : (from beginning April to mid Sept.) – 1 caravan 58 🚐 – 22 🏠. Per night from 55 to 80 € – Per week from 265 to 790 € – Reservation fee 20 €

A partially open-air swimming area and good sanitary facilities.

Surroundings : 🗭 ♨♨
Leisure activities : ♈ ✗ 🏠 🗗 🏊 ⚽ multi-sports ground
Facilities : ♿ ⚓ 🅳 – 20 individual sanitary facilities (🚿 ♨ wc) launderette

Longitude : -2.53563
Latitude : 47.3748

Mon Calme ▲▲

☎ 02 40 23 60 77, www.campingmoncalme.com

Address : rue de Norvoret (located 1km south following signs for La Turballe and take the turning to the left, 450m from the ocean)

1,2 ha (88 pitches) flat, grassy

Rentals : 20 🚐 – 12 apartments.

Upmarket apartment hotel, open 11 months of the year.

Surroundings : ♨
Leisure activities : ✗ 🚴 🚲 🏊
Facilities : ♿ ⚓ 🅳 🔲
Nearby : ❀ 🛶

Longitude : -2.54882
Latitude : 47.37208

LA PLAINE-SUR-MER

44770 – Michelin map **316** C5 – pop. 3 815 – alt. 26
▷ Paris 438 – Nantes 58 – Pornic 9 – St-Michel-Chef-Chef 7

Sites et Paysages La Tabardière ♣♣ ▲▲▲

☎ 02 40 21 58 83, www.camping-la-tabardiere.com

Address : 2 route de la Tabardiere (3.5km east along the D 13, follow the signs for Pornic and take turning to the left)

Opening times : from mid April to mid Sept.

5 ha (270 pitches)

Tariff : 36 € ♣♣ ⇔ 🄴 ⚡ (6A) – Extra per person 7,90 € – Reservation fee 20 €

Rental rates : (from mid April to mid Sept.) ❀ – 10 🚐 20 🏠. Per night from 31 to 118 € – Per week from 205 to 856 €
Reservation fee 20 €

🚐 borne 14 € – 🔋 14 €

Surroundings : ♨♨
Leisure activities : ♈ 🏠 🗗 🏊 🔲 (open air in season) 🛶 multi-sports ground
Facilities : ♿ ⚓ 🅲 🅳 launderette 🔲 🔲

Longitude : -2.15313
Latitude : 47.14087

Le Ranch ▲▲

☎ 02 40 21 52 62, www.camping-le-ranch.com

Address : chemin des Hautes Raillères (3km northeast along the D 96)

Opening times : from beginning April to end Sept.

3 ha (183 pitches) flat, grassy

Tariff : (2013 Price) 31,50 € ♣♣ ⇔ 🄴 ⚡ (10A) – Extra per person 6 €
Reservation fee 15 €

Rental rates : (2013 Price) (from beginning April to end Oct.)
❀ – 12 🚐 – 16 🏠. Per night from 28 to 75 € – Per week from 199 to 756 € – Reservation fee 15 €

🚐 borne

In a green setting with lots of flowers.

Surroundings : 🐾 ♨
Leisure activities : ♈ ✗ 🏠 🗗 🏊 🛶 multi-sports ground, entertainment room
Facilities : ♿ ⚓ 🅳 launderette 🔲

Longitude : -2.16292
Latitude : 47.15412

LES PONTS-DE-CÉ

49130 – Michelin map **317** F4 – pop. 11 575 – alt. 25
▷ Paris 302 – Nantes 92 – Angers 7 – Cholet 57

Île du Château ♣♣ ▲▲▲

☎ 09 83 76 62 05, www.camping-ileduchateau.fr

Address : avenue de la Boire Salée (situated on the Île du Château)

Opening times : from beginning April to end Oct.

2,3 ha (135 pitches) flat, grassy

Tariff : (2013 Price) 20 € ♣♣ ⇔ 🄴 ⚡ (6A) – Extra per person 4 €

Rental rates : (2013 Price) (from beginning April to end Oct.)
1 🚐 – 7 canvas bungalows. Per night from 40 to 110 €
Per week from 280 to 680 €

🚐 borne – 🔋 ⚡ 20 €

Wooded setting near the Loire river and municipal gardens.

Surroundings : 🗭 ♨♨
Leisure activities : ✗ 🏠 🗗 🚴 🚲 🏊
Facilities : ♿ ⚓ 🅳 🏊 🅳 🔲
Nearby : ❀ 🛶 🏊

Longitude : -0.53055
Latitude : 47.4244

*There are several different types of sani-station ('borne' in French) – sanitation points providing fresh water and disposal points for grey water.
See page 12 for further details.*

PORNIC

44210 – Michelin map **316** D5 – pop. 14 052 – alt. 20
▷ Paris 429 – Nantes 49 – La Roche-sur-Yon 89 – Les Sables-d'Olonne 93

Club Airotel La Boutinardière ♣♣ ▲▲▲

☎ 02 40 82 05 68, www.camping-boutinardiere.com

Address : 23 rue de la Plage de la Boutinardiere (5km southeast along the D 13 and take turning to the right, 200m from the beach)

Opening times : from beginning April to end Sept.

7,5 ha (400 pitches) relatively flat, flat, grassy

Tariff : 49 € ♣♣ ⇔ 🄴 ⚡ (10A) – Extra per person 7 € – Reservation fee 25 €

Rental rates : (from beginning April to end Sept.) – 200 🚐 37 🏠 – 15 apartments. Per night from 75 to 115 € – Per week from 240 to 1 300 € – Reservation fee 25 €

🚐 borne 7 € – 2 🄴 15 € – 🔋 10 €

A village club with a range of services, including a spa centre, and apartment rentals equipped to a good standard.

Surroundings : 🐾 🗭 ♨
Leisure activities : ♈ ✗ 🏠 🗗 🚴 🎣
hammam, jacuzzi 🛶 🚲 🔲 🏊 🏊
multi-sports ground, spa centre
Facilities : ♿ ⚓ 🅳 🅳 🅳 launderette
🔲 🔲

Longitude : -2.05222
Latitude : 47.09747

▲▲▲ Yelloh! Village La Chênaie

YELLOH

☎ 02 40 82 07 31, www.campinglachenaie.com

Address : 36 bis rue du Pâtisseau (east along the D 751, follow the signs for Nantes and take turning to the left)

Opening times : from mid April to mid Sept.

8 ha (305 pitches) terraced, relatively flat, flat, grassy

Tariff : 41€ ♥♥ ⇌ 🔲 🔋 (10A)

Extra per person 8€

Rental rates : (from mid April to mid Sept.) – 65 🛏. 3 canvas bungalows. Per night from 36 to 191€ – Per week from 252 to 1 337€

Extensive green spaces for relaxation; there is an enclosure with farm animals for children.

Surroundings : 🌿 ⌁ ♀
Leisure activities : 🍸 ✕ ⑤ 🛶 🚴 🎣 ⛷ ⛸ multi-sports ground, entertainment room
Facilities : 🚿 ⚲ ⛺🍴 launderette 🚰

G P S Longitude : -2.07196
Latitude : 47.1187

PORNICHET

44380 – Michelin map **316** B4 – pop. 10 466 – alt. 12
▶ Paris 449 – Nantes 74 – Vannes 84 – La Roche-sur-Yon 143

▲▲ Les Forges

☎ 02 40 61 18 84, www.campinglesforges.com – limited spaces for one-night stay

Address : 98 route de la Villès-Blais, Les Forges quartier

Opening times : from beginning July to end Aug..

2 ha (130 pitches)

Tariff : (2013 Price) 27,50€ ♥♥ ⇌ 🔲 🔋 (10A) – Extra per person 7€ Reservation fee 30€

Rental rates : (2013 Price) (from beginning July to end Aug.) 23 🛏. Per night from 65 to 10€ – Per week from 413 to 749€ Reservation fee 30€

There's a bus stop for the town centre.

Surroundings : ⌁ ♀
Leisure activities : 🏓 🛶 🔲 (open air in season), multi-sports ground
Facilities : 🚿 ⚲ 🍴 launderette

G P S Longitude : -2.29379
Latitude : 47.26917

LE POULIGUEN

44510 – Michelin map **316** B4 – pop. 4 977 – alt. 4
▶ Paris 453 – Guérande 8 – La Baule 4 – Nantes 80

▲ Municipal les Mouettes

☎ 02 40 42 43 98, www.tourisme-lepouliguen.fr – 🍴

Address : 45 boulevard de l'Atlantique (to the west of the resort along the D 45, right next to the stadium)

Opening times : from end March to end Oct.

4,7 ha (220 pitches) small lake

Tariff : 18,10€ ♥♥ ⇌ 🔲 🔋 (6A) – Extra per person 4,70€
🛏. borne 2€

This guide is not intended as a list of all the camping sites in France; its aim is to provide a selection of the best sites in each category.

Relatively near the town centre and the shops.

Surroundings : ⌁ ♀♀
Leisure activities : 🏠 🛶
Facilities : 🚿 ⚲ (Jul-Aug.) ⛺ 🍴 launderette
Nearby : ♨

G P S Longitude : -2.43942
Latitude : 47.27385

▲ Municipal le Clein

☎ 02 40 42 43 99, leclein@mairie-lepouliguen.fr

Address : 22 avenue de Kerdun

1,5 ha (110 pitches)

🛏. borne – 26 🔲

Near the town centre and the beach with a good parking area for campervans.

Surroundings : ♀♀
Leisure activities : 🛶
Facilities : 🚿 ⚲ ⛺ 🍴 launderette
Nearby : ♨

G P S Longitude : -2.4301
Latitude : 47.27135

POUZAUGES

85700 – Michelin map **316** K7 – pop. 5 428 – alt. 225
▶ Paris 390 – Bressuire 30 – Chantonnay 22 – Cholet 42

▲ Le Lac

☎ 02 51 91 37 55, www.campingpouzAug.es.com

Address : at the lake (located 1.5km west along the D 960 bis, follow the signs for Chantonnay and take the road to the right)

Opening times : Permanent

1 ha (54 pitches) terrace, relatively flat, flat, grassy

Tariff : 19€ ♥♥ ⇌ 🔲 🔋 (10A) – Extra per person 5€ – Reservation fee 20€

🛏. 2 🔲 19€

Shaded by plane trees, 50m from the lake.

Surroundings : 🏔 ⛰
Leisure activities : ✕ 🛶
Facilities : 🚿 ⚲ launderette
Nearby : 🍸 🏊 🎣

G P S Longitude : -0.8532
Latitude : 46.78183

The information in the guide may have changed since going to press.

PRÉFAILLES

44770 – Michelin map **316** C5 – pop. 1 255 – alt. 10
▶ Paris 440 – Challans 56 – Machecoul 38 – Nantes 60

▲▲▲ Éléovic

☎ 02 40 21 61 60, www.camping-eleovic.com

Address : route de la Pointe Saint-Gildas (located 1km west along the D 75)

3 ha (150 pitches) relatively flat, flat, grassy

Rentals : 60 🛏.

A site overlooking the ocean and picturesque creeks.

Surroundings : 🌿 ≤ ocean and Île de Noirmoutier ⌁ ♀
Leisure activities : ✕ 🏠 ⑤ nighttime 🎿 🏂 🛶 🚴 🔲 (open air in season), multi-sports ground
Facilities : 🚿 ⚲ 🍴 launderette 🚰

G P S Longitude : -2.23151
Latitude : 47.13292

PRUILLÉ

49220 – Michelin map **317** F3 – pop. 630 – alt. 30
▣ Paris 308 – Angers 22 – Candé 34 – Château-Gontier 33

▲ Municipal Le Port

𝄞 02 41 32 67 29, www.pruille.mairie49.fr

Address : rue du Bac (north of the town; beside the Mayenne – mooring point-)

Opening times : from beginning April to end Oct.

1,2 ha (41 pitches) flat, grassy

Tariff : (2013 Price) 11€ ♣♣ ⇌ 圓 ⑫ (6A) – Extra per person 2€

Rental rates : (2013 Price) Permanent – 5 🚐. Per night from 42 to 49€ – Per week from 191 to 419€

Surroundings : 🏞 ♀
Leisure activities : ✂
Facilities : ⇄

G P S Longitude : -0.66474
Latitude : 47.57897

A 'quartier' is a district or area of a town or village.

LES ROSIERS-SUR-LOIRE

49350 – Michelin map **317** H4 – pop. 2 348 – alt. 22
▣ Paris 304 – Angers 32 – BAug.é 27 – Bressuire 66

⚏ Flower Le Val de Loire

𝄞 02 41 51 94 33, www.camping-valdeloire.com

Address : 6 rue Sainte-Baudruche (take the northern exit along the D 59, follow the signs for Beaufort-en-Vallée, near the junction with the D 79)

Opening times : from beginning April to end Sept.

5,5 ha (110 pitches) flat, grassy

Tariff : 29€ ♣♣ ⇌ 圓 ⑫ (10A) – Extra per person 5,50€ – Reservation fee 7,50€

Rental rates : (from beginning April to end Sept.) – 35 🚐. Per night from 39 to 115€ – Per week from 196 to 900€
Reservation fee 10€

🚐 borne 12,40€
Pleasant leafy setting.

Surroundings : 🏞 ♀
Leisure activities : ✗ 🏠 🛝🚲🎣⛵
Facilities : ⇄ ⚮ 🏠⚟☵ 🚰 🚿 ▣
Nearby : ✂ 🎣ₘ ⛷

G P S Longitude : -0.22599
Latitude : 47.35821

LES SABLES-D'OLONNE

85100 – Michelin map **316** F8 – pop. 14 572 – alt. 4
▣ Paris 456 – Cholet 107 – Nantes 102 – Niort 115

⚏ Chadotel La Dune des Sables ♣⚌

𝄞 02 51 32 31 21, http://chadotel.com/camping-sables-olonne/la-dune-des-sables/ – limited spaces for one-night stay

Address : at Le Paracou - chemin de la Bernardière (4km to the northwest, follow the signs for l'Aubraie)

Opening times : from beginning April to end Sept.

7,5 ha (290 pitches) undulating, terraced, flat, grassy, sandy

Tariff : 33,50€ ♣♣ ⇌ 圓 ⑫ (10A) – Extra per person 6€ – Reservation fee 25€

Rental rates : (from beginning April to end Sept.) – 62 🚐 – 2 tent lodges. Per night from 50 to 73€ – Per week from 170 to 875€
Reservation fee 25€

🚐 borne

A mobile home park near the beach, overlooking the ocean, with very few pitches for tents or caravans.

Surroundings : 🏞 < 🏘
Leisure activities : ♀ ✗ 🏠 ⚐🛝🏄🎣🚲 ✂ 🎣 🛝⛱
Facilities : ⇄ ⚮ 🏠⚟ 🚰 🚿 launderette 🛗 ⇄

⚏ Chadotel Les Roses

𝄞 02 51 95 10 42, http://chadotel.com/camping-sables-olonne/les-roses/

Address : 61 rue des Roses (400m from the beach)

Opening times : from beginning April to beginning Nov.

3,3 ha (200 pitches) terraced, relatively flat, flat, grassy

Tariff : 33,50€ ♣♣ ⇌ 圓 ⑫ (10A) – Extra per person 6€ – Reservation fee 25€

Rental rates : (from beginning April to beginning Nov.) ⇄ (1 mobile home) – 49 🚐 – 4 🏠. Per night from 50 to 97€ – Per week from 190 to 1 150€ – Reservation fee 25€

🚐 borne

In a residential area, mobile homes for rental, some luxurious; pitches for tents and caravans are always available.

Surroundings : 🏘 ♀♀
Leisure activities : 🏠 🏄🛝🚲⛷
multi-sports ground
Facilities : ⇄ ⚮ 🏠 🚿 launderette
Nearby : ♀ ⇄

G P S Longitude : -1.76482
Latitude : 46.49166

G P S Longitude : -1.81395
Latitude : 46.51207

SABLÉ-SUR-SARTHE

72300 – Michelin map **310** G7 – pop. 12 399 – alt. 29
▣ Paris 252 – Angers 64 – La Flèche 27 – Laval 44

⚏ Municipal de l'Hippodrome ♣⚌

𝄞 02 43 95 42 61, www.tourisme.sablesursarthe.fr

Address : allée du Québec (take the southern exit towards Angers and the turning to the left, next to racecourse (hippodrome)

Opening times : from end March to mid Oct.

2 ha (84 pitches) flat, grassy

Tariff : 13,50€ ♣♣ ⇌ 圓 ⑫ (16A) – Extra per person 3€

Rental rates : (from end March to mid Oct.) ⇄ (1 chalet) ✂ – 3 🚐 – 1 🏠. Per night from 54 to 74€ – Per week from 289 to 376€

🚐 borne 2€

Decorative trees and shrubs; located beside the Sarthe river.

Surroundings : 🏞 🏘 ♀♀
Leisure activities : 🏠 🏄🏄🛝⛷
Facilities : ⇄ ⚮ 🏠 🚿 launderette
Nearby : ✂ 🎮ₘ 🐴 🏇

G P S Longitude : -0.33193
Latitude : 47.83136

Key to rentals symbols:

12 🚐	*Number of mobile homes*
20 🏠	*Number of chalets*
6 🛏	*Number of rooms to rent*
Per night 30–50€	*Minimum/maximum rate per night*
Per week 300–1,000€	*Minimum/maximum rate per week*

PAYS DE LA LOIRE

ST-BERTHEVIN

53940 – Michelin map **310** E6 – pop. 7 097 – alt. 108
▶ Paris 289 – Nantes 128 – Laval 10 – Rennes 66

⚠ Municipal de Coupeau

✆ 02 43 68 30 70, www.laval-tourisme.com

Address : at the base de loisirs (leisure centre) (south of the town, 150m from the Vicoin river)

Opening times : from mid April to end Sept.

0,4 ha (32 pitches)

Tariff : ♦ 3,30€ ⇔ 1,90€ 🔲 2,10€ – (⅙) (16A) 2€

Situated looking out over a green and restful valley.

Surroundings : 🌿🏞
Leisure activities : 🛶
Facilities : ♿ 🚰
Nearby : ✗🎣⛵ fitness trail

> Longitude : -0.83235
> Latitude : 48.06431

The guide covers all 22 regions of France – see the map and list of regions on pages 4–5.

ST-BREVIN-LES-PINS

44250 – Michelin map **316** C4 – pop. 12 133 – alt. 9
▶ Paris 438 – Challans 62 – Nantes 64 – Noirmoutier-en-l'Île 70

⚜ Sunêlia Le Fief 🏕

✆ 02 40 27 23 86, www.lefief.com

Address : 57 chemin du Fief (2.4km south following signs for Saint-Brévin-l'Océan and take the turning to the left)

Opening times : from mid April to end Sept.

7 ha (397 pitches) flat, grassy

Tariff : 48€ ♦♦ ⇔ 🔲 (⅙) (8A) Extra per person 11€ – Reservation fee 35€

Rental rates : (from mid April to end Sept.) ♿ (1 mobile home) 205 🏠. Per night from 54 to 235€ – Per week from 381 to 1645€ Reservation fee 35€

🚐 borne 48€

A superb spa centre and truly upmarket VIP rental village within a green garden area.

Surroundings : 🔲 🌳
Leisure activities : ♀✗🛶🎮🏊‍⛵🎿🏓
hammam, jacuzzi 🚣🚴✗🌊⛷🎿
multi-sports ground, spa centre, entertainment room
Facilities : ♿ 🚰 ⛺🚿♨🚻 launderette 🏊🚿

> Longitude : -2.16768
> Latitude : 47.23465

⚜ La Courance

✆ 02 40 27 22 91, www.campinglacourance.fr – limited spaces for one-night stay

Address : 110 avenue du Maréchal Foch

Opening times : Permanent

2,4 ha (156 pitches) terraced, flat, sandy

Tariff : 21€ ♦♦ ⇔ 🔲 (⅙) (10A) – Extra per person 4,50€ – Reservation fee 25€

Rental rates : Permanent ♿ (1 mobile home) – 1 caravan – 43 🏠 10 🏠 – 12 canvas bungalows. Per night from 59 to 88€ Per week from 205 to 770€ – Reservation fee 25€
🚐 borne 3€ – 5 🔲 17,50€
Beside the beach, with a view of the St-Nazaire bridge Swimming area 500m away.

Surroundings : 🌿🌳
Leisure activities : ♀✗🕹nighttime 🚣
Facilities : ♿ 🚰 ⛺♨🚻 launderette
Nearby : ✗ 🔲

> Longitude : -2.1703
> Latitude : 47.23786

⚜ Le Mindin

✆ 02 40 27 46 41, www.camping-de-mindin.com – limited spaces for one-night stay

Address : 32 avenue du Bois (situated 2km to the north, near the ocean (direct access)

Opening times : Permanent

1,7 ha (87 pitches)

Tariff : 26,50€ ♦♦ ⇔ 🔲 (⅙) (16A) Extra per person 7€ – Reservation fee 25€

Rental rates : Permanent – 34 🏠 – 3 canvas bungalows. Per night from 59 to 88€ – Per week from 245 to 770€ – Reservation fee 25€
🚐 borne 3€ – 🚿11€
A small pine wood close to the beach with view of the port and the bridge at St-Nazaire.

Surroundings : 🌿♀⛰
Leisure activities : ♀✗🛶 🔲
Facilities : ♿ 🚰 ⛺♨🚻 🏊

> Longitude : -2.16915
> Latitude : 47.2648

ST-CALAIS

72120 – Michelin map **310** N7 – pop. 3 482 – alt. 155
▶ Paris 188 – Blois 65 – Chartres 102 – Châteaudun 58

⚠ Le Lac

✆ 02 43 35 04 81, www.saint-calais.fr

Address : rue du Lac (take the northern exit along the D 249, follow the signs for Montaillé)

Opening times : from beginning April to mid Oct.

2 ha (85 pitches) flat, grassy

Tariff : ♦ 3,50€ ⇔ 🔲 3€ – (⅙) (10A) 3,65€

Rental rates : (from beginning April to mid Oct.) – 3 🏠 Per night from 40 to 60€ – Per week from 195 to 250€

The site is near a lake.

Surroundings : 🔲
Leisure activities : 🛶
Facilities : ♿ 🚰 🚻 🏊
Nearby : ✗ 🎿

> Longitude : 0.74426
> Latitude : 47.92688

For more information on visiting particular towns or regions, consult the relevant regional MICHELIN Green Guide. We also recommend you use the appropriate Michelin regional map to locate your selected campsite, to calculate distances and to work out the best route.

BERTHEBAUD

Le site is near a lake.

ST-ÉTIENNE-DU-BOIS

5670 – Michelin map **316** G7 – pop. 1 901 – alt. 38
🚩 Paris 427 – Aizenay 13 – Challans 26 – Nantes 49

⚠ Municipal la Petite Boulogne

📞 02 51 34 54 51, www.stetiennedubois-vendee.fr

Address : rue du Stade (south of the town along the D 81, follow the signs for Poiré-sur-Vie and take the road to the right; near the river and a lake)

Opening times : from beginning May to beginning Oct.

1,5 ha (35 pitches)

Tariff : 12,32 € ✦✦ 🚗 🔲 🚿 (10A) – Extra per person 3,44 €
Rental rates : Permanent – 3 🏠 – 6 🏡. Per night from 60 €
Per week from 197 to 380 €
🚐 20 🔲 15,35 €

A pedestrian path links the campsite to the town and a small chalet village set among trees and undergrowth.

Surroundings : 🐟 🏕 🎣
Leisure activities : 🏊 (small swimming pool)
Facilities : 🚻 🔑 (July–Aug.) 🗒 🚿 🚰 launderette
Nearby : 🏄 🎿 🛶

G P S Longitude : -1.59293
Latitude : 46.82925

This guide is updated regularly, so buy your new copy every year!

ST-GEORGES-SUR-LAYON

9700 – Michelin map **317** G5 – pop. 769 – alt. 65
🚩 Paris 328 – Angers 39 – Cholet 45 – Saumur 27

⚠ Les Grésillons

📞 02 41 50 02 32, www.camping-gresillons.com

Address : chemin des Grésillons (800m south along the D 178, follow the signs for Concourson-sur-Layon and take the road to the right, near the river)

Opening times : from beginning April to end Sept.

1,5 ha (43 pitches) terraced, relatively flat, grassy

Tariff : 17,80 € ✦✦ 🚗 🔲 🚿 (10A) – Extra per person 4,20 €
Rental rates : (from beginning April to end Sept.) – 12 canvas bungalows. Per night from 54 to 154 € – Per week from 152 to 432 € – Reservation fee 32 €

Surroundings : 🐟 🎣
Leisure activities : 🚲 🏊 (small swimming pool) 🎣
Facilities : 🚻 🔑 (July–Aug.) 🚰 📷

G P S Longitude : -0.37032
Latitude : 47.19324

ST-HILAIRE-DE-RIEZ

5270 – Michelin map **316** E7 – pop. 10 504 – alt. 8
🚩 Paris 453 – Challans 18 – Noirmoutier-en-l'Île 48 – La Roche-sur-Yon 48

Le Pissot (4 km au nord)

🏕 Les Biches ♣♦

📞 02 51 54 38 82, www.campingdesbiches.com – limited spaces for one-night stay

Address : chemin de Petite Baisse (situated 2km to the north)

Opening times : from mid April to mid Sept.

3 ha/9 for camping (434 pitches)

Tariff : (2013 Price) 45 € ✦✦ 🚗 🔲 🚿 (10A) – Extra per person 8,50 €
Reservation fee 20 €

Rental rates : (2013 Price) (from mid April to mid Sept.) 🚿
240 🏠 – 57 🏡 – 1 🛏 – 7 studios – 10 mobile homes without sanitary facilities. Per week from 232 to 985 € – Reservation fee 20 €

A pleasant pine wood with a range of rental options, but very few places for tents and caravans.

Surroundings : 🐟 🏕 🎣
Leisure activities : 🍴 🍽 🏊 🎮 🏕 🎿 🚲
🎯 🏓 🔲 🏊 🛶 disco multi-sports ground
Facilities : 🚻 🔑 📷 🚿 🚰 🏠 launderette
🗒 🚰 refrigerators

G P S Longitude : -1.94445
Latitude : 46.74052

Les Demoiselles (10 km au nord-ouest)

🏔 Odalys Vitalys Les Demoiselles

📞 02 51 58 10 71, www.odalys-vacances.com – limited spaces for one-night stay

Address : avenue des Becs (9.5km to the northwest, along the D 123 and 300m from the beach)

Opening times : from beginning April to end Sept.

13,7 ha (180 pitches) undulating, flat and relatively flat, grassy, sandy

Tariff : 22 € ✦✦ 🚗 🔲 🚿 (10A) – Extra per person 5 € – Reservation fee 15 €

Rental rates : (from beginning April to end Sept.) 🚿 (4 mobile homes) – 154 🏠. Per night from 60 to 180 € – Per week from 320 to 1 000 € – Reservation fee 20 €

🚐 15 🔲 22 €

A mobile home park with plenty of shade and some pitches for tents and caravans.

Surroundings : 🐟 🎣
Leisure activities : 🎮 🏕 🎿 🚲 🏊
multi-sports ground
Facilities : 🚻 🔑 🏠 launderette
Nearby : 🍽 🛶

G P S Longitude : -2.04086
Latitude : 46.76815

La Fradinière (7 km au nord-ouest)

🏔 La Puerta del Sol ♣♦

📞 02 51 49 10 10, www.campinglapuertadelsol.com

Address : 7 chemin des Hommeaux (4.5km to the north)

Opening times : from beginning April to end Sept.

4 ha (207 pitches) flat, grassy

Tariff : 35 € ✦✦ 🚗 🔲 🚿 (10A) – Extra per person 6,90 €

Rental rates : (2013 Price) (from beginning April to end Sept.) 🚿
(1 chalet) – 74 🏠 – 40 🏡. Per night from 80 to 130 € – Per week from 180 to 910 €

In a green setting with few pitches for tents and caravans and a rental park with a variety of comfort levels.

Surroundings : 🐟 🏕 🎵
Leisure activities : 🍴 🍽 🏊 🌙 nighttime 🏕
🎿 🛁 jacuzzi 🎯 🚲 🔲 🏊 🛶 multi-sports ground, entertainment room
Facilities : 🚻 🔑 🚿 🚰 🏠 launderette 🗒
🚰 refrigerators

G P S Longitude : -1.95887
Latitude : 46.76452

Do not confuse:
⚠ *to* 🏔 *: MICHELIN classification with*
★ *to* ★★★★★ *: official classification*

La Pège (6 km au nord-ouest)

⛰ Les Écureuils 👥

📞 0251543371, www.camping-aux-ecureuils.com – limited spaces for one-night stay

Address : 98 avenue de la Pège (5.5km to the northwest, 200m from the beach)

Opening times : from beginning April to end Sept.

4 ha (215 pitches)

Tariff : (2013 Price) 38,60€ ♦♦ ⟶ 🔲 (ℎ) (10A)
Extra per person 6,70€ – Reservation fee 25€

Rental rates : (2013 Price) (from end April to beginning Sept.) ⤳ – 19 🏠 – 2 🏡. Per week from 330 to 985€ – Reservation fee 25€

A pleasant setting in 2 separate campsites, with some places for tents and caravans.

Surroundings : 🌿 ⛺ 🌳🌳
Leisure activities : 🍷 ✗ 🎮 🌙nighttime 🏃 🎣 ♨ hammam 🛶 🎿 🎯 🎱 launderette 🛁
Facilities : ♿ ⟶ 🚿 🅿 🔧 🚰 launderette 🛁
Nearby : 🚴

| GPS | Longitude : -2.00897 |
| --- | Latitude : 46.74478 |

⛰ La Ningle

📞 0251540711, www.campinglaningle.com

Address : 66 chemin des Roselières (situated 5.7km to the northwest)

Opening times : from beginning May to mid Sept.

3,2 ha (150 pitches) flat, grassy, small lake

Tariff : (2013 Price) 36,70€ ♦♦ ⟶ 🔲 (ℎ) (10A) –
Extra per person 5,50€ – Reservation fee 16€

Rental rates : (2013 Price) (from mid April to mid Sept.) – 19 🏠. Per night from 50 to 100€ – Per week from 250 to 680€ Reservation fee 16€

A pleasantly leafy setting and a well-kept site.

Surroundings : 🌿 ⛺ 🌳
Leisure activities : 🍷 🎮 🛶 🏄 🎿 🎯 🎱 launderette
Facilities : ♿ ⟶ 🅿 🚿 🔧 🚰 launderette
Nearby : ✗ 🛁 🚴

| GPS | Longitude : -2.00473 |
| --- | Latitude : 46.7446 |

⛰ La Parée Préneau

📞 0251543384, www.campinglapareepreneau.com

Address : 23 avenue de La Parée Préneau (3.5km to the northwest)

Opening times : from beginning April to end Sept.

3,6 ha (217 pitches)

Tariff : 28,90€ ♦♦ ⟶ 🔲 (ℎ) (6A) – Extra per person 5,30€ Reservation fee 18€

Rental rates : Permanent – 44 🏠 – 7 🏡. Per night from 59 to 79€ – Per week from 210 to 250€ – Reservation fee 18€

In a pleasant setting, but choose the pitches away from the road in preference.

Surroundings : ⛺ 🌳🌳
Leisure activities : 🍷 🎮 🌙nighttime 🏄 🚴🎿🎱 multi-sports ground
Facilities : ♿ ⟶ 🚿 🔧 🚰 launderette

| GPS | Longitude : -1.98488 |
| --- | Latitude : 46.74034 |

The pitches of many campsites are marked out with low hedges of attractive bushes and shrubs.

⛰ Le Bosquet

📞 0251543461, www.lebosquet.fr

Address : 62 avenue de la Pège (5km to the northwest)

Opening times : from mid May to mid Sept.

2 ha (115 pitches)

Tariff : (2013 Price) 27,50€ ♦♦ ⟶ 🔲 (ℎ) (10A) – Extra per person 5€ Reservation fee 10€

Rental rates : (2013 Price) (from beginning April to end Sept 40 🏠 – 3 apartments. Per night from 50 to 100€ – Per wee from 210 to 720€

Relatively close to the beach (250 m).

Surroundings : 🌳🌳
Leisure activities : 🍷 ✗ 🎮 🏄 🎿 🏊
Facilities : ♿ ⟶ 🅿 launderette 🛁
Nearby : 🚴

| GPS | Longitude : -2.0032 |
| --- | Latitude : 46.74073 |

⛰ Le Romarin

📞 0251544382, www.leromarin.fr

Address : rue des Martinets (3.8km to the northwest)

Opening times : from beginning April to end Sept.

4 ha/1,5 (97 pitches)

Tariff : (2013 Price) 28€ ♦♦ ⟶ 🔲 (ℎ) (10A) – Extra per person 4,30€ Reservation fee 19€

Rental rates : (2013 Price) (from beginning April to mid Sept.) ⤳ 5 🏠. Per night from 50 to 88€ – Per week from 200 to 625 Reservation fee 19€

Mobile homes and some pitches for tents and caravans se around a small but pretty pine grove.

Surroundings : ⛺ 🌳🌳
Leisure activities : ✗ 🏄 🏊 multi-sports ground
Facilities : ♿ ⟶ (Jul–Aug.) 🚰 launderette 🛁

| GPS | Longitude : -1.9875 |
| --- | Latitude : 46.74243 |

⛰ La Pège

📞 0251543452, www.campinglapege.com

Address : 67 avenue de la Pège (5km to the northwest)

Opening times : from beginning March to mid Oct.

1,8 ha (100 pitches)

Tariff : (2013 Price) 26,50€ ♦♦ ⟶ 🔲 (ℎ) (6A)
Extra per person 5,50€ – Reservation fee 10€

Rental rates : (from beginning April to mid Oct.) – 20 🏠 1 🏡. Per night from 220 to 685€ – Per week from 350 to 850 Reservation fee 18€

🏠 borne 3€

Access to the beach (100 m) along a small road leading directl to the lifeguard station; choose the pitches away from th road in preference.

Surroundings : ⛺ 🌳
Leisure activities : 🏄 🚴 🏊
Facilities : ♿ ⟶ 🚿 🚰 🅿
Nearby : 🍷 ✗ 🛁 🚴

| GPS | Longitude : -2.0054 |
| --- | Latitude : 46.7411 |

Sion-sur-l'Océan (3 km à l'ouest)

⛰ Municipal de la Plage de Riez

📞 0251543659, www.souslespins.com

Address : avenue des Mimosas (3km west, 200m from the beach)

9 ha (560 pitches)

Rentals : 55 🏠 – 1 🏠 – 7 canvas bungalows.

Shaded by a beautiful pine wood with direct access to the beach.

Surroundings : 🏊 🚣 ⛰
Leisure activities : 🍴 🗙 🏠 🎯 🏇 🚴 ⛵ multi-sports ground
Facilities : 🚿 ⚲ 🚽 ♿ 🍴 launderette 🏧 🔌

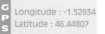

GPS
Longitude : -1.97941
Latitude : 46.72298

⛰ Municipal de la Plage de Sion

☎ 02 51 54 34 23, www.campingsainthilairederiez.com

Address : avenue de la Forêt (take the northern exit)

Opening times : from beginning April to end Oct.

5 ha (164 pitches) undulating, relatively flat, flat, grassy, sandy, gravelled

Tariff : (2013 Price) 28€ 🚻 🚗 🔌 (10A) – Extra per person 6€ – Reservation fee 18€

Rental rates : (2013 Price) (from beginning April to end Oct.) 15 🏠 – 3 canvas bungalows. Per night from 60 to 130€ – Per week from 180 to 800€ – Reservation fee 18€

🚐 borne 4,50€ – 5 ◻ 11€ – ♨ 17€

500m from the beach (direct access), surrounded by forest.

Surroundings : 🏊 🚣 ⛰
Leisure activities : 🏠 🎯 🚴
Facilities : 🚿 ⚲ 🚽 ♿ 🍴 launderette 🔌

GPS
Longitude : -1.97246
Latitude : 46.71695

We value your opinion and welcome your feedback. Do email us at campingfrance@tp.michelin.com

ST-HILAIRE-LA-FORÊT

85440 – Michelin map **316** G9 – pop. 611 – alt. 23
▶ Paris 449 – Challans 66 – Luçon 31 – La Roche-sur-Yon 31

⛰ La Grand' Métairie

☎ 02 51 33 32 38, www.la-grand-metairie.com – limited spaces for one-night stay

Address : 8 rue de La Vineuse en Plaine (north of the town along the D 70)

5,8 ha (172 pitches) flat, grassy

Rentals : 112 🏠 – 18 🏠.

Plenty of mobile homes set in a lush green space with flowers.

Surroundings : 🏊 🚣 ⛰
Leisure activities : 🍴 🗙 🏠 🌙 nighttime 🎿
🏊 🎯 🚴 🎱 🏓 🏊 🚽 🍴 launderette 🔌
Facilities : 🚿 ⚲ 🚽 🚽 🍴 launderette 🔌

GPS
Longitude : -1.52545
Latitude : 46.44776

⛰ Les Batardières

☎ 02 51 33 33 85, www.batardieres.com

Address : 2 rue des Batardières (continue west along the D 70 and take the turning to the left, following signs for Le Poteau)

Opening times : from beginning July to end Aug..

1,6 ha (75 pitches) flat, grassy

Tariff : 25€ 🚻 🚗 🔌 (10A) – Extra per person 4€

Pretty, clearly marked-out pitches with lots of shade.

Surroundings : 🏊 🚣 ⛰
Leisure activities : 🏠 🎯 🏓
Facilities : ⚲ 🚽 🚽 🍴

GPS
Longitude : -1.52934
Latitude : 46.44807

ST-HILAIRE-ST-FLORENT

49400 – Michelin map **317** I5
▶ Paris 324 – Nantes 131 – Angers 45 – Tours 72

⛰ Sites et Paysages Chantepie 👥

TEBOUL

☎ 02 41 67 95 34, www. campingchantepie.com

Address : route de Chantepie (5.5km northwest along the D 751, follow the signs for Gennes and take road to the left; at La Mimerolle)

Opening times : from end April to mid Sept.

10 ha/5 for camping (150 pitches) flat, grassy

Tariff : 40€ 🚻 🚗 🔌 (16A) – Extra per person 6,60€ – Reservation fee 14€

Rental rates : (from end April to mid Sept.) – 21 🏠 – 10 canvas bungalows – 2 tent lodges. Per night from 45 to 156€ – Per week from 270 to 937€ – Reservation fee 14€

Some farm animals can be seen.

Surroundings : 🏊 ⩻ Loire Valley 🚣 ⛰
Leisure activities : 🍴 🗙 🏠 🎯 🏇 🚴 🏊 🏊
Facilities : 🚿 ⚲ 🆓 🚽 🍴 launderette 🏧 🔌

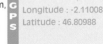

GPS
Longitude : -0.14305
Latitude : 47.2937

ST-JEAN-DE-MONTS

85160 – Michelin map **316** D7 – pop. 8 037 – alt. 16
▶ Paris 451 – Cholet 123 – Nantes 73 – Noirmoutier-en-l'Île 34
Centre

⛰ Aux Coeurs Vendéens 👥

☎ 02 51 58 84 91, www.coeursvendeens.com

Address : 251 route de Notre-Dame-de-Monts (4km northwest on the D 38)

Opening times : from mid April to mid Sept.

2 ha (117 pitches)

Tariff : 32€ 🚻 🚗 🔌 (10A) – Extra per person 5€ – Reservation fee 20€

Rental rates : (from mid April to mid Sept.) 🚫 (from mid April to end June) – 64 🏠 – 1 🏠. Per week from 180 to 885€ Reservation fee 20€

Choose the pitches away from the road in preference.

Surroundings : 🚣 ⛰
Leisure activities : 🍴 🗙 🏠 🎯 ⛵ hammam, jacuzzi 🚴 🎱 🏊 🏊 spa centre
Facilities : 🚿 ⚲ 🚽 🚽 🍴 launderette 🔌
Nearby : 🏧

GPS
Longitude : -2.11008
Latitude : 46.80988

⛰ Les Pins

☎ 02 51 58 17 42, www.camping-despins.fr

Address : 166 avenue Valentine (2.5km southeast on the D 123)

1,2 ha (118 pitches) undulating, terraced, flat, sandy

Rentals : 🚫 – 15 🏠.

A very pleasant, undulating pine wood, but the rental chalets are a little old.

Surroundings : 🚣 ⛰
Leisure activities : 🍴 🏠 🎯 🚴
Facilities : ⚲ 🚽 🍴 🖼
Nearby : 🏧 🔌

GPS
Longitude : -2.03894
Latitude : 46.78081

Nord

▲▲▲ Les Amiaux ♣♣

📞 0251582222, www.amiaux.fr

Address : 223 route de Notre-Dame (3.5km to the northwest, on the D 38)

Opening times : from beginning May to end Sept.

17 ha (543 pitches)

Tariff : 37€ ♣♣ ⊕ 🔲 🔢 (10A)
Extra per person 5€ – Reservation fee 16€

Rental rates : (from beginning May to end Sept.) ⚡ – 27 🚐. Per night from 104€ – Per week from 322 to 789€ – Reservation fee 16€

The site is divided into 2 separate sections connected by a tunnel.

Surroundings : 🏕 ♀
Leisure activities : 🍽 ✗ 🏛 ⊕ ⸚ 🏄 🚴 🎣 🔲 🏊 ⚂ multi-sports ground
Facilities : ♿ ⊶ 🚿 ⛺ 🧺 🍴 launderette 🔲 🚗

Longitude : -2.11517
Latitude : 46.81107
G P S

▲▲▲ Le Bois Joly ♣♣

📞 0251591163, www.camping-lebois-joly.com

Address : 46 route de Notre-Dame-de-Monts (located 1km to the northwest; beside a brook)

Opening times : from mid April to end Sept.

7,5 ha (356 pitches)

Tariff : 35€ ♣♣ ⊕ 🔲 🔢 (10A) – Extra per person 6€ – Reservation fee 22€

Rental rates : (from mid April to end Sept.) ♿ (1 mobile home) ⚡ – 2 caravans – 98 🚐 – 22 🏠. Per night 150€ – Per week from 250 to 960€ – Reservation fee 22€

🚐 borne – 5 🔲 18€

Attractive swimming area.

Surroundings : 🏕 ♀
Leisure activities : 🍽 ✗ 🏛 ⊕ ⸚ 🏄 🎣
jacuzzi ⸚ 🔲 🏊 ⚂ 🎣 multi-sports ground
Facilities : ♿ ⊶ 🚿 ⛺ 🧺 🍴 launderette 🚗
Nearby : 🏇

Longitude : -2.07417
Latitude : 46.79918
G P S

▲▲▲ Club Airotel Les Places Dorées ♣♣

📞 0251590293, www.placesdorees.com – limited spaces for one-night stay

Address : route de Notre-Dame-de-Monts (4km northwest on the D 38)

Opening times : from mid June to mid Sept.

5 ha (288 pitches)

Tariff : (2013 Price) 37,40€ ♣♣ ⊕ 🔲 🔢 (10A) – Extra per person 7€ Reservation fee 25€

Rental rates : (2013 Price) (from mid April to mid Sept.) ⚡ 76 🚐. Per night from 40 to 141€ – Per week from 283 to 989€ Reservation fee 25€

There is an attractive swimming area.

Surroundings : 🏕 ♀♀
Leisure activities : 🍽 ✗ ⸚ 🏄 🎣 hammam, jacuzzi ⸚ 🔲 🏊 ⚂ multi-sports ground
Facilities : ♿ ⊶ 🍴 launderette 🚗
Nearby : 🚗

Longitude : -2.10997
Latitude : 46.8097
G P S

▲▲▲ APV Les Aventuriers de la Calypso ♣♣

📞 0251597966, www.camping-apv.com – limited spaces for one-night stay

Address : route de Notre-Dame-de-Monts, at Les Tonnelles (4.6km to the northwest)

Opening times : from beginning April to end Sept.

4 ha (284 pitches)

Tariff : 34,98€ ♣♣ ⊕ 🔲 🔢 (10A) – Extra per person 8,67€ Reservation fee 27€

Rental rates : (from beginning April to end Sept.) – 140 🚐 42 🏠. Per night from 60 to 83€ – Per week from 245 to 1008€ Reservation fee 27€

Few pitches for tents or caravans and some rental options are rather old.

Surroundings : 🏕 🏕 ♀
Leisure activities : 🍽 ✗ 🏛 ⊕ nighttime ⸚
⸚ jacuzzi ⸚ 🚴 ✗ 🔲 🏊 ⚂ multi-sports ground
Facilities : ♿ ⊶ 🚿 ⛺ 🧺 🍴 launderette 🚗

Longitude : -2.11533
Latitude : 46.81232
G P S

▲▲▲ Club Airotel l'Abri des Pins ♣♣

📞 0251588386, www.abridespins.com – limited spaces for one-night stay

Address : route de Notre-Dame-de-Monts (4km northwest on the D 38)

Opening times : from mid June to mid Sept.

3 ha (209 pitches)

Tariff : 37,40€ ♣♣ ⊕ 🔲 🔢 (10A) – Extra per person 7€ – Reservation fee 25€

Rental rates : (from mid April to mid Sept.) ⚡ – 52 🚐 23 🏠. Per night from 40 to 141€ – Per week from 283 to 989€ Reservation fee 25€

A pretty play and paddling pool area. Choose pitches away from the road in preference.

Surroundings : 🏕 ♀♀
Leisure activities : 🍽 ✗ 🏛 ⸚ 🏄 🎣 hammam, jacuzzi ⸚ ✗ 🔲 🏊 ⚂
Facilities : ♿ ⊶ 🚿 ⛺ 🧺 🍴 launderette 🚗
Nearby : 🚗

Longitude : -2.10997
Latitude : 46.8097
G P S

▲▲ Le Vieux Ranch

📞 0251588658, www.levieuxranch.com

Address : chemin de la Parée du Jonc (4.3km to the northwest)

5 ha (242 pitches) undulating, flat, grassy, sandy

Rentals : ⚡ – 15 🚐 – 8 🏠 .

A gently undulating attractive location, 200m from the beach.

Surroundings : 🏕 🏕 ♀♀
Leisure activities : 🍽 🏛 🎣 ⸚ 🚴 🏊 ⚂ entertainment room
Facilities : ♿ ⊶ 🚿 ⛺ 🧺 🍴 launderette
Nearby : ✗ 🚗

Longitude : -2.11351
Latitude : 46.80717
G P S

The Michelin classification (▲▲▲ ... ▲) is totally independent of the official star classification system awarded by the local prefecture or other official organisation.

 Flower Plein Sud ♂♀

℘ 0251591040, www.campingpleinsud.com

Address : 246 route de Notre-Dame-de-Monts (4km to the northwest, on the D 38)

Opening times : from mid April to mid Sept.

2 ha (110 pitches) flat, grassy, sandy

Tariff : 29€ ♂♀ 🚐 📧 🔌 (6A) – Extra per person 5€ – Reservation fee 20€

Rental rates : (from mid April to mid Sept.) 🏊 – 30 🛖 – 2 canvas bungalows – 2 tent lodges. Per night from 38 to 107€ Per week from 230 to 750€ – Reservation fee 20€

An linear site with well marked-out pitches.

Surroundings : 🗺 ꝑ
Leisure activities : 🏆 🏃 🏄 🚴 ⛷
multi-sports ground
Facilities : ♿ o⃕ ♨ 🎏 ♻ 🍽 launderette

| G P S | Longitude : -2.11093 |
| | Latitude : 46.8103 |

🏔 La Forêt

℘ 0251588463, www.hpa-laforet.com

Address : 190 chemin de la Rive (5.5km to the northwest, follow the signs for Notre-Dame-de-Monts and take turning to the left)

Opening times : from beginning April to mid Sept.

1 ha (61 pitches)

Tariff : 34,90€ ♂♀ 🚐 📧 🔌 (10A)
Extra per person 5,50€ – Reservation fee 30€

Rental rates : (from beginning April to mid Sept.) – 16 🛖.
Per week from 299 to 779€ – Reservation fee 30€

🚐 borne 18€ – 10 📧 18€

Pretty trees and shrubs; an eco-friendly campsite.

Surroundings : 🗺 ꝑ
Leisure activities : 🏠 🏃 🚴 ⛷
Facilities : ♿ o⃕ ♨ 🎏 ♻ 🍽 🔲

| G P S | Longitude : -2.12993 |
| | Latitude : 46.81828 |

⛺ La Davière-Plage

℘ 0251582799, www.daviereplage.com

Address : 197 route de Notre-Dame-de-Monts (3km to the northwest, on the D 38)

Opening times : from mid April to end Sept.

3 ha (174 pitches)

Tariff : (2013 Price) 26,60€ ♂♀ 🚐 📧 🔌 (10A)
Extra per person 5,75€ – Reservation fee 20€

Rental rates : (2013 Price) (from mid April to end Sept.) 🏊 30 🛖 – 6 canvas bungalows. Per night 150€ – Per week from 290 to 715€ – Reservation fee 20€

🚐 borne 12€ – 20 📧 12€ – 🚐8€

Divided into 2 separate campsites; choose pitches away from the road in preference.

Surroundings : 🗺 ꝑ
Leisure activities : 🍴 🏠 🏃 🚴 ⛷
Facilities : ♿ o⃕ (July–Aug.) ♨ 🍽
launderette ♻
Nearby : 🏆

| G P S | Longitude : -2.10085 |
| | Latitude : 46.8054 |

Sud

 La Yole ♂♀

℘ 0251586717, www.vendee-camping.eu – limited spaces for one-night stay

Address : chemin des Bosses, at Orouet (7km southeast)

Opening times : from mid April to end Sept.

5 ha (369 pitches)

Tariff : 38,50€ ♂♀ 🚐 📧 🔌 (16A) – Extra per person 7,20€ Reservation fee 29€

Rental rates : (from mid April to end Sept.) 🏊 – 56 🛖. Per week from 260 to 950€ – Reservation fee 29€

A green, well-kept setting with flowers and plenty of shade from a beautiful nearby pine wood.

Surroundings : 🏊 🗺 ꝑ
Leisure activities : 🏆 🍴 🏠 🎮 🏃 jacuzzi
🏇 🚴 🎱 ⛷ ⛺
Facilities : ♿ o⃕ 🔲 ♨ 🎏 ♻ 🍽 launderette
♻ ♻

🏔 Les Jardins de l'Atlantique

℘ 0251580574, www.camping-jardins-atlantique.com limited spaces for one-night stay

Address : 100 rue de la Caillauderie (5.5km to the northeast)

Opening times : Permanent

5 ha (318 pitches) undulating, relatively flat, flat, sandy

Tariff : (2013 Price) 24,90€ ♂♀ 🚐 📧 🔌 (6A) – Extra per person 5,70€ Reservation fee 20€

Rental rates : (2013 Price) Permanent – 69 🛖 – 2 apartments. Per night from 49 to 100€ – Per week from 300 to 715€ Reservation fee 20€

Divided into 2 separate sections on both sides of the road, with a pretty covered paddling pool, perfect for young children.

Surroundings : 🗺 ꝑ
Leisure activities : 🏆 🍴 🏠 🎮 ♨♨ hammam,
jacuzzi 🏇 🚴 ⛷ multi-sports ground
Facilities : ♿ o⃕ ♨ 🍽 launderette ♻ ♻

| G P S | Longitude : -2.02751 |
| | Latitude : 46.76972 |

🏔 Le Both d'Orouet

℘ 0251586037, http://www.camping-lebothdorouet.com

Address : 77 avenue d'Orouët (6.7km southeast on the D 38, follow the signs for St-Hilaire-de-Riez, near a stream)

Opening times : from beginning April to end Sept.

4,4 ha (200 pitches)

Tariff : (2013 Price) 26€ ♂♀ 🚐 📧 🔌 (10A) – Extra per person 5€ – Reservation fee 15€

Rental rates : (2013 Price) (from beginning April to end Sept.) 31 🛖 – 19 🏠. Per night from 26 to 34€ – Per week from 287 to 686€ – Reservation fee 15€

🚐 borne

A leafy, green setting; there's a games room in an old barn attached to the farmhouse dating back to 1875.

Surroundings : 🗺 ꝑ
Leisure activities : 🏠 jacuzzi 🏇 ⛷ 🎣
multi-sports ground
Facilities : ♿ o⃕ 🔲 ♨ 🎏 ♻ 🍽 launderette
Nearby : 🏆 🍴

| G P S | Longitude : -1.99759 |
| | Latitude : 46.76495 |

⚐ Campéole les Sirènes

📞 02 51 58 01 31, http://vendee-camping.info

Address : avenue des Demoiselles (to the southeast, 500m from the beach)

Opening times : from beginning April to mid Sept.

15 ha/5 for camping (470 pitches) undulating, flat, sandy

Tariff : (2013 Price) 28,50€ ✶✶ ⛟ 🅿 🔌 (10A) Extra per person 7,80€ – Reservation fee 25€

Rental rates : (from beginning April to mid Sept.) ⛳ (2 mobile homes) – 52 🚐 – 80 canvas bungalows. – Reservation fee 25€ 🚐 borne

A pleasant, natural setting in Les Pays de Monts (regional pine forest), although the sanitary facilities are rather old.

Surroundings : 🌲 ♨️ Leisure activities : 🍴🎮🚴🛶⛵ multi-sports ground Facilities : 🚿 ⊶ 🍴 launderette Nearby : 🍴	**G P S** Longitude : -2.0548 Latitude : 46.7799

⚐ Le Logis

📞 02 51 58 60 67, www.camping-saintjeandemonts.com – limited spaces for one-night stay ⛳

Address : 4 chemin du Logis (4.3km southeast on the D 38, follow the signs for St-Gilles-Croix-de-Vie)

Opening times : from mid April to mid Sept.

0,8 ha (44 pitches) terraced, flat, grassy

Tariff : (2013 Price) 24,70€ ✶✶ ⛟ 🅿 🔌 (10A) – Extra per person 5€ Reservation fee 16€

Rental rates : (2013 Price) (from mid April to mid Sept.) ⛳ 12 🚐 – 2 gîtes. Per week 600€ – Reservation fee 16€ 🚐 borne 21€

Choose the pitches away from the road in preference.

Surroundings : ⛱ Leisure activities : 🏊🛶🛶⛵ (small swimming pool) Facilities : 🚿 ⊶ 🍴 📶 Nearby : 🍴🍴 🎣	**G P S** Longitude : -2.01308 Latitude : 46.77953

ST-JULIEN-DE-CONCELLES

44450 – Michelin map **316** H4 – pop. 6 839 – alt. 24
▶ Paris 384 – Nantes 19 – Angers 89 – La Roche-sur-Yon 80

⚐ Le Chêne

📞 02 40 54 12 00, www.campingduchene.fr

Address : 1 route du Lac (located 1.5km east along the D 37 (diversion), near the small lake)

Opening times : Permanent

2 ha (100 pitches) flat, grassy

Tariff : (2013 Price) ✶ 4,60€ ⛟ 2,10€ 🅿 4,10€ – 🔌 (16A) 3,30€

Rental rates : (2013 Price) Permanent – 25 🚐. Per night from 46 to 88€ – Per week from 60 to 595€ 🚐 1 🅿 4,80€

An attractive location, lots of green space; beside a lake.

Surroundings : ⛱ ♨️ Leisure activities : 🍴🏊🛶🛶 🎾 🖼 (open air in season) Facilities : 🚿 ⊶ 🍴launderette 🛒 Nearby : 🍴 🎣 pedalos	**G P S** Longitude : -1.37098 Latitude : 47.2492

ST-JULIEN-DES-LANDES

85150 – Michelin map **316** F8 – pop. 1 331 – alt. 59
▶ Paris 445 – Aizenay 17 – Challans 32 – La Roche-sur-Yon 24

⚐ Les Castels La Garangeoire ♟♟

📞 02 51 46 65 39, www.camping-la-garangeoire.com

Address : head 2.8km north along the D 21

Opening times : from mid April to end Sept.

200 ha/10 for camping (356 pitches) undulating, terraced, flat, grassy

Tariff : 39,50€ ✶✶ ⛟ 🅿 🔌 (16A) – Extra per person 8,30€ Reservation fee 25€

Rental rates : (from mid April to end Sept.) ⛳ (1 mobile home) 22 🚐 – 25 🏠. Per night from 41 to 189€ – Per week from 289 to 1 320€ – Reservation fee 25€

An extensive, charming site in the grounds of a château, with meadows, lakes and woods.

Surroundings : 🌲⛱ ♨️ Leisure activities : 🍴🍴🏊🎮🛶⛵ jacuzzi 🛶🚴🎾🎣🖼🏹⛵ pedalos 🚣 multi-sports ground Facilities : 🚿 ⊶ 🛁🧺🍴launderette 🛒 refrigerators	**G P S** Longitude : -1.71359 Latitude : 46.66229

⚐ Sunêlia Village de La Guyonnière ♟♟

📞 02 51 46 62 59, http://www.camping-guyonniere.com/

Address : head 2.4km northwest along the D 12, follow the signs for Landevieille then continue 1.2km along the road to the right not far from the lake at Le Jaunay

Opening times : from mid April to end Sept.

30 ha (294 pitches)

Tariff : (2013 Price) 22,90€ ✶✶ ⛟ 🅿 🔌 (10A) – Extra per person 8€ Reservation fee 20€

Rental rates : (from mid April to end Sept.) ⛳ – 86 🚐 25 🏠 – 4 tent lodges. Per night from 39 to 118€ – Per week from 273 to 826€ – Reservation fee 20€ 🚐 borne 13,90€ – 5 🅿 13,90€

A leafy, green location; animal park nearby.

Surroundings : 🌲 ♨️ Leisure activities : 🍴🍴🏊🎮🛶🎣 hammam, jacuzzi 🛶🚴🎾🎣🖼🏹⛵🏹 multi-sports ground, spa centre Facilities : 🚿 ⊶ 🏛🛁🍴launderette 🛒	**G P S** Longitude : -1.74963 Latitude : 46.65258

⚐ Yelloh! Village Château La Forêt ♟♟

📞 02 51 46 62 11, www.chateaulaforet.com

Address : located 0.5 km northeast along the D 55, follow the signs for Martinet

Opening times : from end April to beginning Sept.

50 ha/5 for camping (209 pitches)

Tariff : 39€ ✶✶ ⛟ 🅿 🔌 (10A) – Extra per person 7€

Rental rates : (from end April to beginning Sept.) – 26 🚐 – 5 🏠 1 🛏 – 1 cabin in the trees – 3 canvas bungalows – 1 tent lodge Per night from 31 to 159€ – Per week from 217 to 1 173€

In a wooded setting in the grounds of the château and its outbuildings..

Surroundings : 🌲⛱ ♨️ Leisure activities : 🍴🍴🏊🎮 daytime 🛶🛶🚴🎾🎣🖼🏹 disco, zip wire Facilities : 🚿 ⊶ 🛁🧺🍴launderette 🛒🛒	**G P S** Longitude : -1.71135 Latitude : 46.64182

ST-LAURENT-SUR-SÈVRE

85290 – Michelin map **316** K6 – pop. 3 442 – alt. 121
▶ Paris 365 – Angers 76 – Bressuire 36 – Cholet 14

Le Rouge Gorge

025167 86 39, www.camping-lerougegorge-vendee.com

Address : route de La Verrie (located 1km west along the D 111)

Opening times : from mid March to mid Oct.

 ha (93 pitches)

Tariff : (2013 Price) 22,30€ ♟ ♟ 🚐 🔲 🔌 (13A)
Extra per person 3,90€ – Reservation fee 10€

Rental rates :   (2013 Price) (from mid March to mid Nov.)
🛖 7 🏠 – 13 🏡 – 4 tent lodges. Per night from 55 to 92€
Per week from 245 to 685€ – Reservation fee 10€

🚐 borne

A pleasant setting with lots of green space and plenty of shade.

Surroundings : 🏕 ♨♨
Leisure activities : 🎣 ⛵ 🏊 zip wire
Facilities : 🚿 🔌 🍴 🏕 🧺 launderette 🧼
Nearby : 🎿

Longitude : -0.90307
Latitude : 46.95788

ST-MICHEL-EN-L'HERM

85580 – Michelin map **316** I9 – pop. 2 129 – alt. 9
▶ Paris 453 – Luçon 15 – La Rochelle 46 – La Roche-sur-Yon 47

Les Mizottes

025130 23 63, www.campinglesmizottes.fr

Address : 41 rue des Anciens Quais (800m southwest along the
D 746, follow the signs for l'Aiguillon-sur-Mer)

Opening times : from beginning April to end Sept.

 ha (150 pitches) flat, grassy

Tariff : 26,88€ ♟ ♟ 🚐 🔲 🔌 (6A) – Extra per person 4,92€

Rental rates : (from beginning April to end Sept.) 🚿 (1 mobile
home) – 40 🏠 – 3 canvas bungalows. Per night from 40 to 75€
Per week from 200 to 720€ – Reservation fee 20€

🚐 2 🔲 26€

High-quality service and leisure facillities.

Surroundings : 🏞 🏕 ♨
Leisure activities : 🍴 ✖ 🎣 🏇 🚴 🏊 🎿
multi-sports ground, entertainment room
Facilities : 🚿 🔌 🏕 🍴 launderette 🧼

Longitude : -1.25482
Latitude : 46.34943

ST-PÈRE-EN-RETZ

44320 – Michelin map **316** D4 – pop. 4 113 – alt. 14
▶ Paris 425 – Challans 54 – Nantes 45 – Pornic 13

Le Grand Fay

0240217289, www.camping-granfay.com

Address : rue du Grand Fay (take the eastern exit along the D 78,
follow the signs for Frossay then continue 500m down the turning
to the right)

1,2 ha (76 pitches)

Rentals : 6 🏠 .

*In a quiet residential area, behind the municipal sports centre
and near a lake.*

Surroundings : ♨♨
Leisure activities : ⛵ 🏊 🎿
Facilities : 🚿 🔌 launderette
Nearby : ✖✖

Longitude : -2.03654
Latitude : 47.20266

ST-PHILBERT-DE-GRAND-LIEU

44310 – pop. 7 806 – alt. 10
▶ Paris 407 – nantes 27 – La Roche-sur-Yon 57 – Angers 112

La Boulogne

0240788879, www.camping-la-boulogne.com

Address : 1 avenue de Nantes

Opening times : from beginning April to end Oct.

4,5 ha (180 pitches) flat, grassy

Tariff : (2013 Price) 14,40€ ♟ ♟ 🚐 🔲 🔌 (10A) –
Extra per person 3,70€ – Reservation fee 15€

Rental rates : (2013 Price) (from beginning April to end Oct.)
1 caravan – 10 🏠 – 10 canvas bungalows. Per night
from 50 to 100€ – Per week from 210 to 535€ – Reservation
fee 15€

🚐 borne – 10 🔲 14,40€

Beside the Boulogne river and near a pleasant lake.

Surroundings : ♨♨
Leisure activities : ⛵ 🏊
Facilities : 🚿 🔌 🏛 🏕 🍴 launderette
Nearby : jacuzzi 🎿 🛶 ⛷ 🎵

Longitude : -1.64027
Latitude : 47.0419

ST-RÉVÉREND

85220 – Michelin map **316** F7 – pop. 1 323 – alt. 19
▶ Paris 453 – Aizenay 20 – Challans 19 – La Roche-sur-Yon 36

Le Pont Rouge

025154 68 50, www.camping-lepontrouge.com

Address : rue Georges Clemenceau (take the southwestern exit along
the D 94 and take the road to the right; beside a stream)

2,2 ha (73 pitches)

Rentals : 13 🏠 – 1 🏡 – 7 canvas bungalows – (mobile homes
with/without sanitary facilities).

A green, well-kept setting, with a range of rental options.

Surroundings : 🏞 🏕 ♨♨
Leisure activities : 🍴 ✖ 🎵 nighttime ⛵ 🏊
Facilities : 🚿 🔌 🏕 🍴 launderette 🧼

Longitude : -1.83448
Latitude : 46.69366

ST-VINCENT-SUR-JARD

85520 – Michelin map **316** G9 – pop. 1 205 – alt. 10
▶ Paris 454 – Challans 64 – Luçon 34 – La Rochelle 70

Chadotel La Bolée d'Air

025190 36 05, http://chadotel.com/camping-saint-vincent-sur-jard/la-bolee-d-air/

Address : route du Bouil (situated 2km east along the D 21 follow the
signs for Longeville and take a right turn)

Opening times : from beginning April to end Sept.

5,7 ha (280 pitches) flat, grassy

Tariff : 30,50€ ♟ ♟ 🚐 🔲 🔌 (10A) – Extra per person 6€ – Reservation
fee 25€

Rental rates : (from beginning April to end Sept.) – 39 🏠
8 🏡. Per night from 50 to 82€ – Per week from 170 to 860€
Reservation fee 25€

Choose the pitches away from the road in preference.

Surroundings : 🏕 ♨♨
Leisure activities : 🍴 🎣 🎳 🍸 ⛵ 🏇 🚴 ✖ 🎯
🎿 🏊 ⛷ multi-sports ground
Facilities : 🚿 🔌 🏕 🎾 🍴 launderette 🧼

Longitude : -1.52622
Latitude : 46.41978

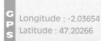

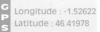

STE-LUCE-SUR-LOIRE

44980 – Michelin map **316** H4 – pop. 11 679 – alt. 9
▶ Paris 378 – Nantes 7 – Angers 82 – Cholet 58

⚠ Belle Rivière

🖉 02 40 25 85 81, www.camping-belleriviere.com

Address : route des Perrières (situated 2km northeast along the D 68, follow the signs for Thouaré; at La Gicquelière, take turning to the right for 1km; direct access to a branch of the Loire river)

Opening times : Permanent

3 ha (110 pitches) flat, grassy

Tariff : ✝ 4,50€ ⟷ 2,15€ 🔲 5,20€ – 🔌 (10A) 3,90€
Rental rates : Permanent 🚐 – 4 🛖. Per night from 65 to 88€
Per week from 334 to 540€ – Reservation fee 15€
🚰 borne 5€ – 9 🔲 16,35€
Pleasant, leafy setting with a great variety of trees and shrubs. A bus stop for town.

Surroundings : 🛏 ♨♨
Leisure activities : 🏇🏊 🏃
Facilities : 🚿 ☕ (June–Aug.) 🏢 🚮 📶 launderette
Nearby : 🛶 🏇
G P S Longitude : -1.45574
Latitude : 47.254

SAUMUR

49400 – Michelin map **317** I5 – pop. 28 070 – alt. 30
▶ Paris 300 – Angers 67 – Châtellerault 76 – Cholet 70

🏔 Flowers L'Île d'Offard 👥

🖉 02 41 40 30 00, www.cvtloisirs.com

Address : Bd de Verden (access via the town centre, on an island in the Loire river)

Opening times : from beginning March to mid Nov.

4,5 ha (258 pitches) flat, grassy

Tariff : (2013 Price) 30,90€ ✝✝ ⟷ 🔲 🔌 (10A) Extra per person 6,50€
Reservation fee 10€
Rental rates : (2013 Price) (from beginning March to mid Nov.) 🚐 – 50 🛖 – 10 tent lodges – 9 tents on stilts. Per night from 49 to 122€ – Per week from 190 to 854€ – Reservation fee 20€
🚰 borne
A pleasant location at the tip of the island with a view of the château.

Surroundings : ⟷ 🛏 ♨
Leisure activities : 🍴 ✕ 🎬 🗓daytime 🏃
🏇🏊🛶 🎣
Facilities : 🚿 ☕ 🏢 🚮 🚮 📶 🍴 launderette
🎣
Nearby : ✕
G P S Longitude : -0.0656
Latitude : 47.26022

LA SELLE-CRAONNAISE

53800 – Michelin map **310** C7 – pop. 931 – alt. 71
▶ Paris 316 – Angers 68 – Châteaubriant 32 – Château-Gontier 29

🏔 Base de Loisirs de la Rincerie

🖉 02 43 06 17 52, http://www.la-rincerie.com

Address : 3.5km northwest along the D 111, D 150, follow the signs for Ballots and take turning to the left

Opening times : from mid March to mid Oct.

120 ha/5 for camping (50 pitches) relatively flat, flat, grassy

Tariff : 14,20€ ✝✝ ⟷ 🔲 🔌 (10A) – Extra per person 3,20€

Rental rates : (from mid March to mid Oct.) 🚐 – 1 🛖 – 1 🏠
4 canvas bungalows. Per night from 36 to 103€ – Per week from 226 to 293€
🚰 borne 2€
Near a small lake, plenty of water-based activities.

Surroundings : 🞂 ≼
Leisure activities : 🗓daytime 🏇 🏇
Facilities : 🚿 ☕ 🏢 🚮 🚮 📶
At the leisure/activities centre : 🏊 🚣 🚲 🎣 🛶
G P S Longitude : -1.06528
Latitude : 47.86631

SILLÉ-LE-GUILLAUME

72140 – Michelin map **310** I5 – pop. 2 361 – alt. 161
▶ Paris 230 – Alençon 39 – Laval 55 – Le Mans 35

🏔 Indigo Les Molières

HUTTOPIA

🖉 02 43 20 16 12, www.camping-indigo.com

Address : at Sillé-Plage (head 2.5km north along the D 5, D 105, D 203 and take the road to the right)

Opening times : from end April to mid Sept.

3,5 ha (133 pitches) flat, grassy

Tariff : (2013 Price) 25,40€ ✝✝ ⟷ 🔲
🔌 (10A) – Extra per person 5,10€
Reservation fee 22€
Rental rates : (2013 Price) (from end April to mid Sept.) – 12 🛖 – 25 tent lodges. Per night from 43 to 91€
Per week from 211 to 637€
Reservation fee 22€
🚰 borne 7€
In the forest, near a small lake and two ponds.

Surroundings : 🞂 ♨♨
Leisure activities : 🏠
Facilities : 🚿
Nearby : 🍴 ✕ 🞂 🎣 🏇 pedalos
G P S Longitude : -0.12917
Latitude : 48.18333

SILLÉ-LE-PHILIPPE

72460 – Michelin map **310** L6 – pop. 1 091 – alt. 35
▶ Paris 195 – Beaumont-sur-Sarthe 25 – Bonnétable 11 – Connerré 15

🏔 Les Castels Le Château de Chanteloup

🖉 02 43 27 51 07, www.chateau-de-chanteloup.com

Address : at Chanteloup (situated 2km southwest along the D 301, follow the signs for Le Mans)

Opening times : from end May to end Aug..

20 ha (100 pitches) relatively flat, flat, grassy, sandy, pond, natural setting among trees and bushes

Tariff : 37,60€ ✝✝ ⟷ 🔲 🔌 (10A) – Extra per person 9,30€
Rental rates : (from end May to end Aug..) – 3 apartments – 6 tent lodges – 2 gîtes. Per night from 80 to 120€ – Per week from 590 to 735€

Surroundings : 🞂 ♨♨
Leisure activities : 🍴 ✕ 🎬 🗓 🏊 🚲 🛶
Facilities : ☕ 🚮 🍴 launderette 🎣
G P S Longitude : 0.34012
Latitude : 48.10461

SOULLANS

85300 – Michelin map **316** E7 – pop. 4 058 – alt. 12

▶ Paris 443 – Challans 7 – Noirmoutier-en-l'Île 46 – La Roche-sur-Yon 48

⚠ Municipal le Moulin Neuf

📞 02 51 68 00 24, camping-soullans@orange.fr

Address : rue Saint-Christophe (take the northern exit along the D 69, follow the signs for Challans and take the turning to the right)

Opening times : from mid June to mid Sept.

1,2 ha (80 pitches) flat, grassy

Tariff : (2013 Price) 9,50€ ★★ ⇌ 🔲 🔌 (4A) – Extra per person 2,50€

Near the town, a small and peaceful site with clearly marked-out pitches but average sanitary facilities.

Surroundings : 🔊 🗔 🔉
Facilities : 👤 ⟲ 🔳
Nearby : 🍴

GPS Longitude : -1.89566
Latitude : 46.79817

TALMONT-ST-HILAIRE

85440 – Michelin map **316** G9 – pop. 6 829 – alt. 35

▶ Paris 448 – Challans 55 – Luçon 38 – La Roche-sur-Yon 30

⚠ Yelloh! Village Le Littoral

📞 02 51 22 04 64, www.campinglelittoral.com

Address : at Le Porteau (9.5km southwest along the D 949, D 4a, after Querry-Pigeon, take right turn onto D 129, follow coast road to les Sables-d'Olonne; 100m from the ocean)

Opening times : from beginning April to mid Sept.

9 ha (483 pitches) relatively flat, flat, grassy, sandy

Tariff : 45€ ★★ ⇌ 🔲 🔌 (10A) – Extra per person 6€

Rental rates : (from mid April to mid Sept.) 👤 (1 mobile home) 🅿 – 184 🛏 – 19 🏠. Per night from 39 to 214€ – Per week from 273 to 1498€

🚰 borne

An attractive site with upmarket rental options and a pedestrian-only area. Free shuttle to the beaches.

Surroundings : 🗔 🔉
Leisure activities : 🍴 🍴 🎱 🎯 👫 jacuzzi 🚲 🍴 🔲 🏊 ⛵ multi-sports ground
Facilities : 👤 ⟲ 🕌 🔥 🔥 🚿 🍴 launderette 🔥 🔥

GPS Longitude : -1.70222
Latitude : 46.45195

⚠ Odalys Vitalys Les Cottages St-Martin

(rental of mobile homes and gîtes only)

📞 02 51 21 90 00, www.odalys-vacances.com

3,5 ha flat

Rentals : 42 🛏 – 15 apartments.

A mobile home village for rental and owner-occupiers.

Surroundings : 🔊 🗔
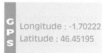
Leisure activities : 🛏 👫 🎱 🚲 🍴 🔲 🏊
Facilities : 👤 ⟲ 🍴 launderette
Nearby : 🏊 🍴 🍴 🔥

GPS Longitude : -1.70181
Latitude : 46.45254

The prices listed were supplied by the campsite owners in 2013 (if prices were not available, those from the previous year are given). The fees should be regarded as basic charges and may fluctuate with inflation.

⚠ Le Paradis

📞 02 51 22 22 36, www.camping-leparadis85.com

Address : rue de la Source (3.7km west along the D 949, follow the signs for Les Sables-d'Olonne, turn left onto D 4a, follow the signs for Querry-Pigeon and take the road to the right)

Opening times : from end March to mid Nov.

4,9 ha (148 pitches) terraced, relatively flat, flat, grassy, sandy

Tariff : (2013 Price) 26€ ★★ ⇌ 🔲 🔌 (10A) – Extra per person 4,50€
Reservation fee 20€

Rental rates : (2013 Price) (from beginning March to end Nov.) 60 🛏 – 15 🏠 – 8 canvas bungalows. Per night from 20 to 130€
Per week from 140 to 910€ – Reservation fee 20€

🚰 12 🔲 26€

A sloping site, well shaded in places with a range of rental options.

Surroundings : 🔊 🗔 🔉🔉
Leisure activities : 🍴 🍴 🎯 nighttime ⛵ 🔲 (open air in season), multi-sports ground
Facilities : 👤 ⟲ (July-Aug.) ⬜ 🔥 🍴 launderette 🔥

GPS Longitude : -1.65491
Latitude : 46.46462

THARON-PLAGE

44730 – Michelin map **316** C5

▶ Paris 444 – Nantes 59 – St-Nazaire 25 – Vannes 94

⚠ La Riviera

📞 02 28 53 54 88, www.campinglariviera.com – limited spaces for one-night stay

Address : rue des Gâtineaux (east of the resort, along the D 96, follow the signs for St-Michel-Chef-Chef)

Opening times : from beginning March to end Nov.

6 ha (250 pitches)

Tariff : 28€ ★★ ⇌ 🔲 🔌 (10A) – Extra per person 5€ – Reservation fee 15€

Rental rates : (from mid April to mid Nov.) – 2 🛏 – 5 🏠. Per night from 47 to 107€ – Per week from 330 to 750€
Reservation fee 15€

A mobile home village for owner-occupiers but with some places for tents and caravans.

Surroundings : 🗔
Leisure activities : 🍴 🛏 jacuzzi ⛵ 🏊 multi-sports ground
Facilities : 👤 ⟲ 🕌 🔥 🚿 🍴 🔳

GPS Longitude : -2.15087
Latitude : 47.16492

TENNIE

72240 – Michelin map **310** I6 – pop. 1 023 – alt. 100

▶ Paris 224 – Alençon 49 – Laval 69 – Le Mans 26

⚠ Municipal de la Vègre

📞 02 43 20 59 44, camping.tennie.fr – limited spaces for one-night stay

Address : rue Andrée Le Grou (take the western exit along the D 38, follow the signs for Ste-Suzanne)

2 ha (83 pitches) flat, grassy

Rentals : 5 🏠 – 1 studio – 1 apartment.

Plleasant setting beside a river and a lake.

Surroundings : 🔊 🗔 🔉🔉
Leisure activities : 🛏 ⛵ 🍴 🎣 🏊
Facilities : 👤 ⟲ 🔥 🔳
Nearby : 🍴 🦆

GPS Longitude : -0.07874
Latitude : 48.10705

LA TRANCHE-SUR-MER

85360 – Michelin map **316** H9 – pop. 2 715 – alt. 4
▶ Paris 459 – Luçon 31 – Niort 100 – La Rochelle 64

⚤ Club Airotel Le Jard ≗

✆ 0251274379, www.campingdujard.fr ✖

Address : 123 boulevard de Lattre de Tassigny (at La Grière-Plage, 3.8km along the road to L'Aiguillon)

Opening times : from mid May to mid Sept.

6 ha (350 pitches) flat, grassy

Tariff : 33€ ⚤ ⇔ 🅴 🔖 (10A) – Extra per person 7€

Rental rates : (from beginning May to mid Sept.) ✖ – 60 🏠. Per week from 220 to 865 €

A pleasant site with good sanitary facilities.

Surroundings : ⌂ ♉♉
Leisure activities : ▮ ✗ 🏛 ☉ ⚞ ⚲ ⟲
⚥ ✖ ⚞ 🎱 ⚲ ⚤
Facilities : ⚤ ☛ 🍴 🛀 🚽 ♨ launderette ⚤
⚤

G P S Longitude : -1.38694
Latitude : 46.34788

⚤ Les Préveils ≗

✆ 0251303052, www.lespreveils.pep79.net

Address : avenue Sainte Anne (at La Grière-Plage, follow the signs for L'Aiguillon for 4.2km)

Opening times : from end March to end Sept.

4 ha (180 pitches) undulating

Tariff : 34€ ⚤ ⇔ 🅴 🔖 (10A) – Extra per person 7€

Rental rates : (from end March to end Sept.) ⚤ (1 mobile home) 30 🏠 – 5 🏠 – 6 🛏 – 17 apartments. Per night from 55 to 65€ Per week from 755 to 880€ – Reservation fee 18€

A pleasant site 200m from the beach.

Surroundings : ⌂ ♉♉
Leisure activities : ✗ 🏛 ⚞ ⚲ ⚲ jacuzzi
⚥ 🎱 multi-sports ground, entertainment room
Facilities : ⚤ ☛ 🍴 🛀 ♨ launderette ⚤

G P S Longitude : -1.3936
Latitude : 46.34398

⚤ Baie d'Aunis

✆ 0251274736, www.camping-baiedaunis.com ✖ (July–Aug..)

Address : 10 rue du Pertuis Breton (take the eastern exit, follow the signs for l'Aiguillon)

Opening times : from end April to mid Sept.

2,5 ha (149 pitches)

Tariff : 35,10€ ⚤ ⇔ 🅴 🔖 (10A) – Extra per person 7,50€ – Reservation fee 30€

Rental rates : (from end April to mid Sept.) ✖ – 10 🏠 – 9 🏠. Per week from 350 to 850€ – Reservation fee 30€

🚐 borne

50m from the beach, but choose the pitches away from the road.

Surroundings : ⌂ ♉♉
Leisure activities : ▮ ✗ 🏛 ⚥ 🎱
Facilities : ⚤ ☛ 🍴 🛀 ♨ launderette ⚤
Nearby : ✖ 🎣 ♦

Routes nationales are main roads and their identifying numbers begin with N or RN. Routes départementales are generally quieter roads and begin with D or DN.

TRIAIZE

85580 – Michelin map **316** I9 – pop. 1 011 – alt. 3
▶ Paris 446 – Fontenay-le-Comte 38 – Luçon 9 – Niort 71

⚤ Municipal

✆ 0251561276, www.paysnedelamer.fr

Address : rue du Stade (in the village)

Opening times : from beginning July to end Aug.

2,7 ha (70 pitches) flat, grassy, stony, pond

Tariff : (2013 Price) ⚤ 2,55€ ⇔ 1,75€ 🅴 2,15€ – 🔖 (42A) 2,60€ Reservation fee 35€

Rental rates : (2013 Price) Permanent – 6 🏠. Per night from 60 to 80€ – Per week from 210 to 410€ – Reservation fee 35€

Surroundings : 🌳 ⌂
Leisure activities : ⚥ 🎣
Facilities : ⚤ ☛ 🚽 🛀
Nearby : ✖

G P S Longitude : -1.20152
Latitude : 46.39515

To visit a town or region, use the MICHELIN Green Guides.

LA TURBALLE

44420 – Michelin map **316** A3 – pop. 4 515 – alt. 6
▶ Paris 457 – La Baule 13 – Guérande 7 – Nantes 84

⚤ Municipal les Chardons Bleus

✆ 0240628060, www.camping-laturballe.fr

Address : boulevard de La Grande Falaise (2.5km to the south)

Opening times : from end March to end Sept.

5 ha (300 pitches)

Tariff : 23,30€ ⚤ ⇔ 🅴 🔖 (10A) – Extra per person 5,10€ – Reservation fee 10€

Rental rates : (from mid Jan. to mid Dec.) ⚤ (2 chalets) – 10 🏠 Per week from 275 to 653€ – Reservation fee 10€

🚐 29 🅴 20,15€

For lovers of wide, open spaces, near the beach.

Surroundings : 🌳 ⌂ ⚠
Leisure activities : ▮ ✗ 🏛 ⚥ 🎱
Facilities : ⚤ ☛ 🛀 ♨ launderette ⚤ ⚤
Nearby : ⚲ ⚞ fitness trail

G P S Longitude : -2.50048
Latitude : 47.32832

⚤ Parc Ste-Brigitte

✆ 0240248891, www.campingsaintebrigitte.com

Address : chemin des Routes (3km southeast, follow the signs for Guérande)

Opening times : from beginning April to end Sept.

10 ha/4 for camping (150 pitches) relatively flat, flat, grassy, pond

Tariff : ⚤ 6,70€ ⇔ 3,45€ 🅴 7,65€ – 🔖 (10A) 6,65€ – Reservation fee 16€

Rental rates : (from beginning April to end Sept.) – 16 🏠 Per night from 55 to 95€ – Per week from 380 to 760€ Reservation fee 16€

🚐 borne

Pretty grounds and manor house; the ageing facilities are fortunately well maintained.

Surroundings : 🌳 ♍♍
Leisure activities : ✗ 🏛 ⚥ ⚲ 🎱 (open air in season) 🎣
Facilities : ⚤ ☛ 📺 🛀 🚽 ♨ launderette ⚤

G P S Longitude : -2.4717
Latitude : 47.34254

VAIRÉ

85150 – Michelin map **316** F8 – pop. 1 474 – alt. 49
▶ Paris 448 – Challans 31 – La Mothe-Achard 9 – La Roche-sur-Yon 27

⚠ Le Roc

✆ 02 51 33 71 89, www.campingleroc.com

Address : route de Brem-sur-Mer (located 1.5km northwest along the D 32, follow the signs for Landevieille and turn left towards Brem-sur-Mer)

Opening times : from beginning March to mid Nov.

1,4 ha (100 pitches)

Tariff : (2013 Price) 27€ ✱✱ ⇔ 国 ⚡ (10A) – Extra per person 5€

Rental rates : (2013 Price) (from beginning March to mid Nov.) 26 🚐 – 3 🏠 – 2 canvas bungalows. Per night 80€ – Per week from 180 to 735€ – Reservation fee 20€

🚰 borne 10€ – 3 国 10€

A shaded setting, but choose the pitches away from the road.

Surroundings : 🚋 ⚲
Leisure activities : 🍷 ✗ 🎣 🛥 🏊 (small swimming pool) 🚣
Facilities : & ⚿ (Jul.-Aug.) 🏢 🚿 ⚘ launderette

Longitude : -1.76785
Latitude : 46.60815

VARENNES-SUR-LOIRE

49730 – Michelin map **317** J5 – pop. 1 898 – alt. 27
▶ Paris 292 – Bourgueil 15 – Chinon 22 – Loudun 30

⚠⚠ Les Castels Domaine de la Brèche 🔱

✆ 02 41 51 22 92, www.domainedelabreche.com

Address : 5 Impasse de la Brèche (6km west along the D 85, RD 952, follow the signs for Saumur, and take the road to the right; beside the lake)

Opening times : from mid April to mid Sept.

14 ha/7 for camping (201 pitches)Tariff : 40€ ✱✱ ⇔ 国 ⚡ (16A) Extra per person 9€ – Reservation fee 10€

Rental rates : (from mid April to mid Sept.) – 34 🚐 – 1 cabin in the trees. Per night from 24 to 189€ – Per week from 165 to 1 322€ Reservation fee 10€

🚰 borne

A pleasant site and setting beside a lake.

Surroundings : 🏞 🚋 ⚲
Leisure activities : 🍷 ✗ 🎦 🎣 🏹 🚴 ✗ 🏊 🚣 🛶 🏇 multi-sports ground
Facilities : & ⚿ 🚿 🚽 ⚘ 🏢 🛁 🚣

Longitude : 0.00213
Latitude : 47.24837

VENDRENNES

85250 – Michelin map **316** J7 – pop. 1 447 – alt. 97
▶ Paris 392 – Nantes 65 – La Roche-sur-Yon 30 – Niort 95

⚠ La Motte

✆ 02 51 63 59 67, www.camping-lamotte.com

Address : at La Motte (0.4km to the northeast)

Opening times : Permanent

3,5 ha (83 pitches) flat, grassy

Tariff : 20,20€ ✱✱ ⇔ 国 ⚡ (16A) – Extra per person 3,50€

Rental rates : Permanent – 32 🚐 – 5 🏠 . Per night from 50 to 180€ – Per week from 220 to 1 000€

Green, floral setting arranged around a small ornamental lake.

Surroundings : 🏞 🚋
Leisure activities : 🍷 ✗ 🎦 ⚙daytime 🛥 🚣 bowling
Facilities : & ⚿ 🏢 🚿 ⚘ launderette 🛁

Longitude : -1.11854
Latitude : 46.82587

VIHIERS

49310 – Michelin map **317** F6 – pop. 4 275 – alt. 100
▶ Paris 334 – Angers 45 – Cholet 29 – Saumur 40

⚠ Municipal de la Vallée du Lys

✆ 02 41 75 00 14, www.vihiers.fr

Address : route du Voide (take the western exit along the D 960, follow the signs for Cholet then take the D 54 to the right, following signs for Valanjou; beside the Lys river)

Opening times : from mid June to mid Sept.

0,3 ha (30 pitches) flat, grassy

Tariff : (2013 Price) ✱ 2€ ⇔ 国 2,55€ – ⚡ (6A) 1,95€

🚰 5 国

Surroundings : 🏞 ⚲
Leisure activities : 🎦 🛥 🏃
Facilities : &. 🚿

Longitude : -0.54034
Latitude : 47.1471

VILLIERS-CHARLEMAGNE

53170 – Michelin map **310** E7 – pop. 1 052 – alt. 105
▶ Paris 277 – Angers 61 – Châteaubriant 61 – Château-Gontier 12

⚠⚠ Village Vacances Pêche

✆ 02 43 07 71 68, vvp.villiers.charlemagne@wanadoo.fr

Address : Village des Haies (take the western exit along the D 4, follow the signs for Cossé-le-Vivien and take road to the left near the stadium)

Opening times : Permanent

9 ha/1 campable (20 pitches) flat, grassy

Tariff : 16,90€ ✱✱ ⇔ 国 ⚡ (16A) – Extra per person 6€

Rental rates : Permanent – 12 🏠 . Per week from 200 to 575€

🚰 borne

A pleasant site for angling, with chalets situated virtually on top of the water.

Surroundings : 🏞 ← 🚋 ⚲
Leisure activities : 🎦 ⚙daytime 🛥 🚴 🎣
Facilities : & 🚿 – 20 individual sanitary facilities (🏢 🚿 🚽 wc) 🛁 ⚘ 🏢 refrigerators
Nearby : ✗ 🎳

Longitude : -0.68233
Latitude : 47.9208

YVRÉ-L'ÉVÊQUE

72530 – Michelin map **310** K6 – pop. 4 412 – alt. 57
▶ Paris 204 – Nantes 194 – Le Mans 8 – Alençon 66

⚠ Onlycamp Le Pont Romain

✆ 02 43 82 25 39, www.onlycamp.fr

Address : at La Châtaigneraie (leave the village via the the Roman bridge, then take the road to the left, continue for 200m)

Opening times : from mid March to mid Nov.

2,5 ha (80 pitches) flat, grassy

Tariff : (2013 Price) 19,70€ ✱✱ ⇔ 国 ⚡ (16A) – Extra per person 4€

Rental rates : (2013 Price) (from mid March to mid Nov.) Ⓟ 5 🚐 – 5 🏠 – 3 canvas bungalows. Per night from 49 to 129€ Per week from 319 to 629€

🚰 borne 4€ – 14 国 19,70€

Surroundings : ⚲
Leisure activities : 🎦 🛥 🚣
Facilities : ⚿ Ⓟ 🏢 🚿 ⚘ launderette 🛁
Nearby : 🛁 🍷 ✗

Longitude : 0.27972
Latitude : 48.01944

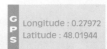

PICARDY

H. Lenain / hemis.fr

Are you ready for an action-packed journey through Picardy's fair and historic lands? The region that gave Gaul – now France – her first Christian king, Clovis, is renowned for its wealthy Cistercian abbeys, splendid Gothic cathedrals and flamboyant town halls, along with deeply poignant reminders of two world wars. If you are in the mood to explore the countryside, take a boat trip through the floating gardens of Amiens or explore the botanical reserve of Marais de Cessière. Try a spot of birdwatching on the Somme estuary or at Marquenterre bird sanctuary. Spend time relaxing in unspoilt hills, woods, pastures and vineyards. Picardy has a rich culinary history, so where better to try *soupe aux hortillonages* (vegetable gardener's soup), the famous *agneau pré-salé* (lamb fattened on the salt marshes), a plate of smoked eel or duck pâté, or a dessert laced with Chantilly cream. 'Drink well, eat well and do nothing', to quote Lafleur, the famous 19th-century Amiens puppet.

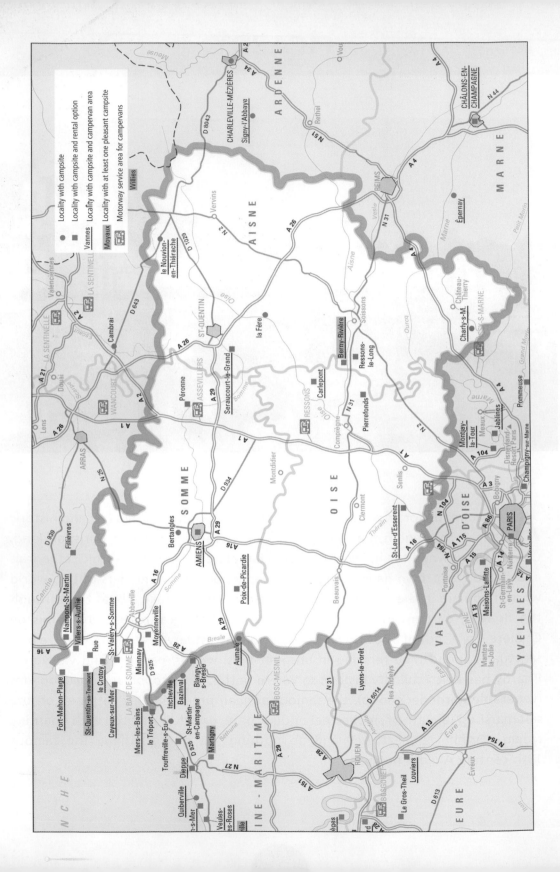

Locality with campsite
Locality with campsite and rental option
Locality with campsite and campervan area
Locality with at least one pleasant campsite
Motorway service area for campervans

AMIENS

80000 – Michelin map **301** G8 – pop. 133 998 – alt. 34
▶ Paris 135 – Lille 122 – Beauvais 62 – Arras 74

⚠ Sites et Paysages Le Parc des Cygnes

📞 03 22 43 29 28, www.parcdescygnes.com

Address : 111 avenue des Cygnes (to the northeast, rue du Grand-Marais – from the bypass (rocade), take exit 40 for Amiens Longpré)

Opening times : from beginning April to mid Oct.

3,2 ha (145 pitches)

Tariff : 27,70€ ♣♣ 🚗 🔲 🔋 (10A) – Extra per person 6,70€
Reservation fee 13,50€

Rental rates : (from beginning April to mid Oct.) ✂ – 9 🚐.
Per night from 47 to 107€ – Per week from 349 to 660€
Reservation fee 13,50€

🚰 borne 4,20€ – 5 🔲 11,50€ – 🚢 11,50€

There's a bus to the town centre.

Surroundings : ♀
Leisure activities : 🍸🏠 🏇🚴♂ 🗻
Facilities : 🚻 ⚡ 🔲 🛁 🗑 ❄ 🍴 launderette
Nearby : 🏊

GPS Longitude : 2.25918
Latitude : 49.92118

BERNY-RIVIÈRE

02290 – Michelin map **306** A6 – pop. 604 – alt. 49
▶ Paris 100 – Compiègne 24 – Laon 55 – Noyon 28

⚠⚠⚠ La Croix du Vieux Pont 🏠🏠

📞 03 23 55 50 02, www.la-croix-du-vieux-pont.com – limited spaces for one-night stay

Address : rue de la Fabrique (located 1.5km south on the D 91, at the entrance to Vic-sur-Aisne; beside the Aisne river)

Opening times : Permanent

34 ha (520 pitches)

Tariff : 29€ ♣♣ 🚗 🔲 🔋 (6A) – Extra per person 9€

Rental rates : 11 gîtes. Per week from 400 to 1 160€

🚰 borne

Surroundings : 🌲🚃♀
Leisure activities : 🍸🍴🏠 🏊🏇♀ 🛶 jacuzzi 🚴♂ 🚴 🎾 🗻 ⛷ ⛵ (fresh water) 🏄🐎🏇 disco, pedalos, multi-sports ground
Facilities : 🚻 ⚡ 🔲 🛁 🗑 ❄ 🍴 launderette 🛒🚿

GPS Longitude : 3.1284
Latitude : 49.40495

BERTANGLES

80260 – Michelin map **301** G8 – pop. 591 – alt. 95
▶ Paris 154 – Abbeville 44 – Amiens 11 – Bapaume 49

⚠ Le Château

📞 03 60 65 68 36, www.camping-bertangles.fr

Address : rue du Château (in the village)

Opening times : from beginning April to mid Sept.

0,7 ha (33 pitches) flat, grassy

Tariff : 21€ ♣♣ 🚗 🔲 🔋 (5A) – Extra per person 4,50€

Set in an orchard near the château

Surroundings : 🌲🚃♀
Leisure activities : 🏇♀
Facilities : 🚻 ⚡ 🗑 🔲

GPS Longitude : 2.30131
Latitude : 49.97167

CARLEPONT

60170 – Michelin map **305** J3 – pop. 1 41[..]
▶ Paris 103 – Compiègne 19 – Ham 30 – P[..]

⚠ Les Araucarias

📞 03 44 75 27 39, www.camping-les-araucaria[..]
for one-night stay

Address : 870 rue du Général Leclerc (take the [..] along the D 130, follow the signs for Compiègne[..]

Opening times : from beginning April to end Oct.

1,2 ha (60 pitches)

Tariff : ♣ 3,30€ 🚗 2,10€ 🔲 3,30€ – 🔋 (10A) 3€

Rental rates : Permanent – 6 🚐 – 2 🏠. Per night from 60 to 90€
Per week from 200 to 400€

🚰 borne 3€ – 2 🔲 15,10€

This site has a wide variety of vegetation and plants around the camping area.

Surroundings : 🌲🚃♀♀
Leisure activities : 🏇♀
Facilities : 🚻 ⚡ 🔲 🍴 launderette

GPS Longitude : 3.01836
Latitude : 49.50728

In order for the guide to remain wholly objective, the selection of campsites is made on an entirely independent basis.

CAYEUX-SUR-MER

80410 – Michelin map **301** B6 – pop. 2 813 – alt. 2
▶ Paris 217 – Abbeville 29 – Amiens 82 – Le Crotoy 26

⚠⚠⚠ Les Galets de la Mollière 🏠🏠

📞 03 22 26 61 85, www.campinglesgaletsdelamolliere.com

Address : at Mollière, rue Faidherbe (3.3km northeast along the D 102, follow coastal road)

Opening times : from end March to beginning Nov.

6 ha (198 pitches)

Tariff : 33€ ♣♣ 🚗 🔲 🔋 (10A) – Extra per person 7€ – Reservation fee 12€

Rental rates : Permanent – 39 🚐. Per night from 74 to 106€
Per week from 280 to 742€ – Reservation fee 12€

🚰 borne 5€

Surroundings : 🌲🚃
Leisure activities : 🍸🍴🏠 🏇♀ 🎾 ⛷
Facilities : 🚻 ⚡ 🛁 🍴 launderette

GPS Longitude : 1.52608
Latitude : 50.20275

⚠ Le Bois de Pins

📞 03 22 26 71 04, www.campingleboisdepins.com – limited spaces for one-night stay

Address : at Brighton, avenue Guillaume-le-Conquérant (situated 2km northeast along the D 102, coast road, 500m from the sea)

Opening times : from beginning April to beginning Nov.

4 ha (163 pitches) flat, grassy

Tariff : 27€ ♣♣ 🚗 🔲 🔋 (10A) – Extra per person 7€ – Reservation fee 10€

Surroundings : 🌲🚃
Leisure activities : 🏠 🏇♀
Facilities : 🚻 ⚡ 🔲 🍴 launderette
Nearby : 🍸🍴

GPS Longitude : 1.51709
Latitude : 50.19725

...SUR-MARNE

...Michelin map **306** B9 – pop. 2 741 – alt. 63
...Paris 82 – Château-Thierry 14 – Coulommiers 33 – La Ferté-sous-
...Jarre 16

⚠ Municipal des Illettes

📞 03 23 82 12 11, www.charly-sur-marne.fr

Address : route de Pavant (south of the town, 200m from the D 82 (recommended route)

Opening times : from beginning April to end Sept.

1,2 ha (43 pitches)

Tariff : 17,50 € ✲✲ 🚗 📺 🔌 (10A) – Extra per person 4 €
🚐 borne – 🔋 🔌 17,50 €

Surroundings : 🔲 🌳🌳
Leisure activities : 🏠
Facilities : ⚿ ⚡ 🔲 🔲 🔲 🍴 launderette
Nearby : 🍴 🔳

G P S Longitude : 3.28209
Latitude : 48.97369

The Michelin classification (⚠⚠⚠ ... ⚠) is totally independent of the official star classification system awarded by the local prefecture or other official organisation.

LE CROTOY

80550 – Michelin map **301** C6 – pop. 2 265 – alt. 1
▶ Paris 210 – Abbeville 22 – Amiens 75 – Berck-sur-Mer 29

⚠⚠⚠ Kawan Village Le Ridin

WAECHTER

📞 03 22 27 03 22, www.campingleridin. com – limited spaces for one-night stay

Address : at Mayocq (3km north following signs for St-Quentin-en-Tourmont and take the road to the right)

Opening times : from beginning April to end Sept.

4,5 ha (162 pitches) flat, grassy

Tariff : 31 € ✲✲ 🚗 📺 🔌 (10A) – Extra per person 5,50 € – Reservation fee 15 €

Rental rates : (from beginning April to end Sept.) – 33 🚐. Per night from 52 to 108 € – Per week from 260 to 756 € Reservation fee 15 €
🚐 borne

Surroundings : 🌳 🔲 🌳
Leisure activities : 🍴 🍴 🏠 🎣 jacuzzi 🚣 🚴 🏊
Facilities : ⚿ ⚡ 🔲 🔲 🍴 launderette 🔲

G P S Longitude : 1.63182
Latitude : 50.23905

⚠⚠ Flower Les Aubépines

WAECHTER

📞 03 22 27 01 34, www.camping-lesaubepines.com – limited spaces for one-night stay

Address : at St-Firmin, 800 rue de la Maye (4km to the north, follow the signs for St-Quentin-en-Tourmont and take road to the left)

Opening times : from beginning April to beginning Nov.

2,5 ha (196 pitches)

Tariff : 31 € ✲✲ 🚗 📺 🔌 (10A) – Extra per person 6 € – Reservation fee 6 €

Rental rates : (from beginning April to beginning Nov.) – 45 🚐. Per night from 50 to 147 € – Per week from 250 to 1029 € Reservation fee 6 €
🚐 borne – 5 📺 16 €

Surroundings : 🌳 🔲 🌳
Leisure activities : 🏠 🚣 🚴 🏊
Facilities : ⚿ ⚡ 🔲 🔲 🔲 🍴 launderette

G P S Longitude : 1.61139
Latitude : 50.24955

⚠⚠⚠ Les Trois Sablières

📞 03 22 27 01 33, www.camping-les-trois-sablieres.com – limited spaces for one-night stay

Address : 1850 rue de la Maye (4km to the northwest, follow the signs for St-Quentin-en-Tourmont and take the road to the left, 400m from the beach)

Opening times : from beginning April to beginning Nov.

1,5 ha (97 pitches)

Tariff : 24 € ✲✲ 🚗 📺 🔌 (10A) – Extra per person 6,50 €

Rental rates : (from beginning April to beginning Nov.) 18 🚐 – 2 🏠 – 2 gîtes. Per night from 60 to 100 € – Per week from 280 to 700 €
🚐 borne 8 € – 🔋 12 €
In a green setting with flowers.

Surroundings : 🌳 🔲 🌳
Leisure activities : 🍴 🏠 🎣 🚣 🚴 🏊
Facilities : ⚿ ⚡ 🔲 🍴 launderette

G P S Longitude : 1.59883
Latitude : 50.24825

LA FÈRE

02800 – Michelin map **306** C5 – pop. 3 012 – alt. 54
▶ Paris 137 – Compiègne 59 – Laon 24 – Noyon 31

⚠ Municipal du Marais de la Fontaine

📞 03 23 56 82 94

Address : rue Vauban (via the town centre towards Tergnier and take a right turn at the sports centre; near a branch of the Oise river)

Opening times : from beginning April to end Sept.

0,7 ha (26 pitches) flat, grassy

Tariff : ✲ 2,50 € 🚗 2 € 📺 2,50 € – 🔌 (10A) 3,50 €

Surroundings : 🔲 🌳
Facilities : ⚿ ⚡ 🔲 🔲
Nearby : 🍴

G P S Longitude : 3.36353
Latitude : 49.6654

Routes nationales are main roads and their identifying numbers begin with N or RN. Routes départementales are generally quieter roads and begin with D or DN.

FORT-MAHON-PLAGE

80120 – Michelin map **301** C5 – pop. 1 311 – alt. 2
▶ Paris 225 – Abbeville 41 – Amiens 90 – Berck-sur-Mer 19

⚠⚠⚠ Club Airotel Le Royon

📞 03 22 23 40 30, www.campingleroyon.com – limited spaces for one-night stay

Address : 1271 route de Quend (located 1km to the south)

Opening times : from mid March to beginning Nov.

4 ha (399 pitches)

Tariff : 35 € ✲✲ 🚗 📺 🔌 (6A) – Extra per person 7 € – Reservation fee 12 €

Rental rates : (from mid March to beginning Nov.) 🚐 – 84 🚐. Per night from 80 to 112€ – Per week from 360 to 790€ Reservation fee 12€

🚐 borne 3€ – 8 📧 19€

Surroundings : 🔲 ♀
Leisure activities : 🍸🚣✂🖼⛵ entertainment room
Facilities : ♿ ⚐🚽 🍳🍴 launderette
Nearby : ⛺

Longitude : 1.57963
Latitude : 50.33263

⚏ Le Vert Gazon

🕿 03 22 23 37 69, www.camping-levertgazon.com – limited spaces for one-night stay

Address : 741 route de Quend

Opening times : from beginning April to beginning Oct.

2,5 ha (130 pitches) flat, grassy

Tariff : 26,50€ 🚹🚹 🚗 📧 💧 (6A) – Extra per person 7€ – Reservation fee 10€

Rental rates : (from beginning April to beginning Oct.) ♿ (1 mobile home) – 1 caravan – 16 🚐 – 5 🏠 – 5 gîtes. Per night from 95€ – Per week from 349 to 649€ – Reservation fee 10€

🚐 borne 5€ – 2 📧 26,50€

Surroundings : 🔲
Leisure activities : 🍸🖼🚣🚴⛵
Facilities : ♿⚐🚽🍳🍴 launderette

Longitude : 1.57374
Latitude : 50.33438

MERS-LES-BAINS

80350 – Michelin map **301** B7 – pop. 3 124 – alt. 3
▶ Paris 217 – Amiens 89 – Rouen 99 – Arras 130

⚏ Flower Le Domaine du Rompval

🕿 02 35 84 43 21, www.campinglerompval.com

Address : at Blengues (situated 2km to the northeast)

Opening times : from beginning April to end Sept.

3 ha (132 pitches) flat, grassy

Tariff : 31,20€ 🚹🚹 🚗 📧 💧 (8A) – Extra per person 5€ – Reservation fee 6€

Rental rates : (from beginning April to end Sept.) – 25 🚐 5 studios. Per night from 59 to 115€ – Per week from 255 to 805€ Reservation fee 15€

🚐 borne
Some colourful and unusual rental accommodation.

Surroundings : ♀
Leisure activities : 🍸🖼🚣🚴⛵ (open air in season)
Facilities : ♿⚐🚽🍴 launderette

Longitude : 1.4154
Latitude : 50.0773

MIANNAY

80132 – Michelin map **301** D7 – pop. 568 – alt. 15
▶ Paris 191 – Amiens 63 – Arras 104 – Rouen 109

⚠ Sites et Paysages Le Clos Cacheleux

🕿 03 22 19 17 47, www.camping-lecloscacheleux.fr

Address : route de Bouillancourt-sous-Miannay

Opening times : from mid March to mid Oct.

8 ha (100 pitches)

Tariff : 27,10€ 🚹🚹 🚗 📧 💧 (10A) – Extra per person 5,60€ – Reservation fee 12€

Rental rates : (from beginning April to mid Oct.) 🚐 – 4 cabins in the trees – 1 gîte. Per night from 80 to 130€ – Per week from 560 to 910€ – Reservation fee 12€

🚐 14 📧 18,90€ – 🔌💧12,50€

In the grounds of a working farm (cattle-rearing).

Surroundings : 🔲 ♀
Leisure activities : 🚣
Facilities : ♿⚐🍳🍴 launderette
Nearby : 🍸✕🖼🚶🚣🖼 (open air in season) activities at the Le Val de Trie, opposite

Longitude : 1.71536
Latitude : 50.08646

MOYENNEVILLE

80870 – Michelin map **301** D7 – pop. 667 – alt. 92
▶ Paris 194 – Abbeville 9 – Amiens 59 – Blangy-sur-Bresle 22

⚏ Le Val de Trie 👥

🕿 03 22 31 48 88, www.camping-levaldetrie.fr

Address : 1 rue des Sources at Bouillancourt-sous-Miannay (3km northwest along the D 86; beside a stream)

Opening times : from beginning April to beginning Oct.

2 ha (100 pitches) flat, grassy, small lake

Tariff : 27,10€ 🚹🚹 🚗 📧 💧 (10A) – Extra per person 5,60€ – Reservation fee 12€

Rental rates : (from beginning April to beginning Oct.) ♿ (chalet) – 19 🚐 – 5 🏠. Per night from 49 to 155€ – Per week from 343 to 1085€ – Reservation fee 12€

🚐 10 📧 22,10€

Surroundings : 🌊 🔲 ♀
Leisure activities : 🍸✕🖼🚶🚣🖼 (open air in season)
Facilities : ♿⚐🆑🍳🍴 launderette

Longitude : 1.71508
Latitude : 50.08552

Do not confuse:
⚠ to ⚏ : MICHELIN classification with
★ to ★★★★★ : official classification

NAMPONT-ST-MARTIN

80120 – Michelin map **301** D5 – pop. 260 – alt. 10
▶ Paris 214 – Abbeville 30 – Amiens 79 – Boulogne-sur-Mer 52

⚏ Kawan Village La Ferme des Aulnes

🕿 03 22 29 22 69, www.fermedesaulnes.com – limited spaces for one-night stay

Address : at Fresne, 1 rue du Marais (3km southwest along the D 85e, follow the signs for Villier-sur-Authie)

Opening times : from beginning April to beginning Nov.

4 ha (120 pitches)

Tariff : 27€ 🚹🚹 🚗 📧 💧 (10A) – Extra per person 7€

Rental rates : (from beginning April to beginning Nov.) – 18 🚐. Per night from 70 to 160€ – Per week from 390 to 790€

🚐 borne – 12 📧 21€

In the buildings of an old Picardy farmhouse.

Surroundings : 🌊 🔲 ♀
Leisure activities : 🍸✕🖼 (piano bar) 🛀♨ jacuzzi 🚣🖼 (open air in season), entertainment room
Facilities : ♿⚐🆑🍳🍴 launderette

Longitude : 1.71201
Latitude : 50.33631

LE NOUVION-EN-THIÉRACHE

02170 – Michelin map **306** E2 – pop. 2 809 – alt. 185
▶ Paris 198 – Avesnes-sur-Helpe 20 – Le Cateau-Cambrésis 19 – Guise 21

⚠ Municipal du Lac de Condé

✆ 03 23 98 98 58, www.camping-thierache.com

Address : promenade Henri d'Orléans (situated 2km south along the D 26 and take the road to the left)

Opening times : from beginning April to end Sept.

1,3 ha (56 pitches) flat and relatively flat

Tariff : 11,90€ ✱✱ ⟵ 🅴 (8A) – Extra per person 3,40€
🚐 borne 2€ – 3 🅴 9€

On the edge of the forest, near a lake and a leisure park.

Surroundings : 🏞 ⌁	G P S	Longitude : 3.78271
Leisure activities : 🏛		Latitude : 50.00561
Facilities : 🚻 ⊶ 🔥		
Nearby : 🍷 🗙 🏖 🅼 🎿 🚣 bowling, mountain biking		

PÉRONNE

80200 – Michelin map **301** K8 – pop. 7 981 – alt. 52
▶ Paris 141 – Amiens 58 – Arras 48 – Doullens 54

⚠ Port de Plaisance

✆ 03 22 84 19 31, www.camping-plaisance.com

Address : take the southern exit, following the signs for Paris, between the marina and the commercial port; beside the Canal de la Somme

Opening times : from beginning March to end Oct.

2 ha (90 pitches)

Tariff : 30,10€ ✱✱ ⟵ 🅴 (10A) – Extra per person 4€
Rental rates : (from beginning March to end Oct.) – 4 🏠. Per night from 78€ – Per week from 287 to 513€

Surroundings : ⌁ 🌳🌳	G P S	Longitude : 2.93237
Leisure activities : 🍷 🏛 🏖 🚲 🎿		Latitude : 49.91786
Facilities : 🚻 ⊶ 🔥 🌊 ⚲ 💧 launderette		
Nearby : 🐟 ⚓		

PIERREFONDS

60350 – Michelin map **305** I4 – pop. 1 969 – alt. 81
▶ Paris 82 – Beauvais 78 – Compiègne 15 – Crépy-en-Valois 17

⚠ Municipal de Batigny

✆ 03 44 42 80 83, www.lecoeurdelaforet.fr

Address : rue de l'Armistice (take northwestern exit along the D 973, follow the signs for Compiègne)

Opening times : from beginning April to mid Oct.

1 ha (60 pitches)

Tariff : 16€ ✱✱ ⟵ 🅴 (6A) – Extra per person 5€
Rental rates : (from beginning April to mid Oct.) 🚿 – 2 🏠. Per night from 50 to 90€ – Per week from 350 to 630€

Attractive trees and shrubs decorate the site.

Surroundings : ⌁ 🌳🌳	G P S	Longitude : 2.97962
Leisure activities : 🏖		Latitude : 49.35194
Facilities : ⊶ 🌊 🌊 ⚲ 💧 🔥		
Nearby : 🗙		

POIX-DE-PICARDIE

80290 – Michelin map **301** E9 – pop. 2 388 – alt. 106
▶ Paris 133 – Abbeville 45 – Amiens 31 – Beauvais 46

⚠ Municipal le Bois des Pêcheurs

✆ 03 22 90 11 71, www.ville-poix-de-picardie.fr

Address : route de Verdun (take the western exit along the D 919, follow the signs for Formerie, beside a stream)

Opening times : from beginning April to end Sept.

2 ha (135 pitches) flat, grassy

Tariff : (2013 Price) ✱ 2€ ⟵ 14€ – 🅴 (6A) 4€
Rental rates : (from beginning April to end Sept.) – 2 . Per night from 90 to 120€ – Per week from 250 to 300€
🚐 borne 2€ – 3 🅴 9€

Surroundings : ⌁ 🌊	G P S	Longitude : 1.9743
Leisure activities : 🏛 🏖 🚲		Latitude : 49.75
Facilities : 🚻 ⊶ 🌊 CC 💧 launderette		
Nearby : 🗙 🖼		

Michelin classification:

🏔🏔🏔🏔 *Extremely comfortable, equipped to a very high standard*

🏔🏔🏔 *Very comfortable, equipped to a high standard*

🏔🏔 *Comfortable and well equipped*

🏔 *Reasonably comfortable*

⛺ *Satisfactory*

RESSONS-LE-LONG

02290 – Michelin map **306** A6 – pop. 756 – alt. 72
▶ Paris 97 – Compiègne 26 – Laon 53 – Noyon 31

🏔🏔 La Halte de Mainville

✆ 03 23 74 26 69, www.lahaltedemainville.com

Address : 18 r.du Routy (take the northeastern exit)

Opening times : from mid Jan. to beginning Dec.

5 ha (155 pitches) flat, grassy, small lake

Tariff : 20,50€ ✱✱ ⟵ 🅴 (8A) – Extra per person 4€
Rental rates : (from beginning April to mid Oct.) – 2 🚐 – 2 🏠. Per night 130€ – Per week 460€

Surroundings : ⌁ 🌊	G P S	Longitude : 3.15186
Leisure activities : 🏛 🏖 🎿 🐟		Latitude : 49.39277
Facilities : 🚻 ⊶ 🌊 🖼 🌊 ⚲ 💧 launderette		

RUE

80120 – Michelin map **301** D6 – pop. 3 095 – alt. 9
▶ Paris 212 – Abbeville 28 – Amiens 77 – Berck-Plage 22

⚠ Les Oiseaux

✆ 03 22 25 71 82, www.campingbaiesomme.com – limited spaces for one-night stay

Address : 3.2km south along the D 940, follow the signs for Le Crotoy and take the Chemin de Favières to the left; near a stream

1,2 ha (71 pitches) flat, grassy

Rentals : 2 🚐 – 5 gîtes.

Surroundings : ⌁ 🌊	G P S	Longitude : 1.66872
Leisure activities : 🏛		Latitude : 50.25264
Facilities : 🚻 ⊶ 🌊 💧 🔥		

ST-LEU-D'ESSERENT

60340 – Michelin map **305** F5 – pop. 4 708 – alt. 50
▶ Paris 57 – Beauvais 38 – Chantilly 7 – Creil 9

⚠ Campix

📞 03 44 56 08 48, www.campingcampix.com

Address : rue Pasteur (take the northern exit along the D 12, follow the signs for Cramoisy then continue 1.5km along the turning to the right and then a road)

Opening times : from mid March to end Nov.

6 ha (160 pitches) undulating, terraced, flat, grassy, stony

Tariff : ♦ 7€ ⇌ 🔲 7€ – 🔌 (6A) 4€

Rental rates : Permanent – 4 caravans – 7 🏠. Per night from 55 to 115€ – Per week from 385 to 805€

🚐 borne 6€

In a shaded old quarry overlooking the town and the Oise river.

Surroundings : 🐟 ⌂ ♨♨	
Leisure activities : ✗ 🎣 ⛵ 🚲 ⛵	**GPS** Longitude : 2.42728
Facilities : 🚻 ⚷ 🔌 🏧 ♨ 🍴 launderette 🚿	Latitude : 49.22484

ST-QUENTIN-EN-TOURMONT

80120 – Michelin map **301** C6 – pop. 305
▶ Paris 218 – Abbeville 29 – Amiens 83 – Berck-sur-Mer 24

⚠⚠ Le Champ Neuf

📞 03 22 25 07 94, www.camping-lechampneuf.com – limited spaces for one-night stay

Address : 8 rue du Champ Neuf

Opening times : from beginning April to mid Oct.

8 ha/4,5 for camping (157 pitches)

Tariff : 31,50€ ♦♦ ⇌ 🔲 🔌 (10A) – Extra per person 6,50€ – Reservation fee 10€

Rental rates : (from beginning April to mid Oct.) – 34 🛖 2 🏠. Per night from 71 to 84€ – Per week from 270 to 620€ Reservation fee 10€

🚐 borne

The site has an indoor water park.

Surroundings : 🐟 ⌂ ♀	
Leisure activities : ▼ ✗ 🎣 ♨ ⛵ ⛵ 🚲 🏊 ⛵ multi-sports ground, entertainment room	**GPS** Longitude : 1.60153 Latitude : 50.26978
Facilities : 🚻 ⚷ 🏧 ♨ 🍴 launderette 🚿	

To make the best possible use of this guide, please read pages 2–15 carefully.

ST-VALERY-SUR-SOMME

80230 – Michelin map **301** C6 – pop. 2 873 – alt. 27
▶ Paris 206 – Abbeville 18 – Amiens 71 – Blangy-sur-Bresle 45

⚠⚠ Club Airotel Le Walric

📞 03 22 26 81 97, www.campinglewalric.com – limited spaces for one-night stay

Address : route d'Eu (to the west along the D 3)

Opening times : from end March to beginning Nov.

5,8 ha (286 pitches)

Tariff : 35€ ♦♦ ⇌ 🔲 🔌 (6A) – Extra per person 7€ – Reservation fee 12€

Rental rates : (from end March to beginning Nov.) – 80 🛖. Per night from 74 to 111€ – Per week from 280 to 777€ Reservation fee 12€

🚐 borne

Surroundings : ⌂ ♀	
Leisure activities : ▼ 🎣 ⛵ ⛵ ✗ ⛵	**GPS** Longitude : 1.61791
Facilities : 🚻 ⚷ 🏧 ♨ 🍴 launderette	Latitude : 50.1839
Nearby : 🏊	

SERAUCOURT-LE-GRAND

02790 – Michelin map **306** B4 – pop. 787 – alt. 102
▶ Paris 148 – Chauny 26 – Ham 16 – Péronne 28

⚠ Le Vivier aux Carpes

📞 03 23 60 50 10, www.camping-picardie.com

Address : 10 rue Charles Voyeux (to the north along the D 321, near the post office, 200m from the Somme)

Opening times : from beginning March to end Oct.

2 ha (60 pitches) flat, grassy

Tariff : 22,50€ ♦♦ ⇌ 🔲 🔌 (10A) – Extra per person 4€

Rental rates : (from beginning March to end Oct.) – 1 🛖 – 2 🏠 2 canvas bungalows. Per night from 50 to 75€ – Per week from 300 to 450€

🚐 borne 4€

In a pleasant location beside the lakes.

Surroundings : 🐟 ⌂ ♨♨	
Leisure activities : 🎣 ⛵	**GPS** Longitude : 3.21435
Facilities : 🚻 ⚷ 🔌 🏧 🍴 launderette	Latitude : 49.78272
Nearby : 🏊	

VILLERS-SUR-AUTHIE

80120 – Michelin map **301** D6 – pop. 411 – alt. 5
▶ Paris 215 – Abbeville 31 – Amiens 80 – Berck-sur-Mer 16

⚠⚠ Kawan Village Le Val d'Authie 👥

GRANDIN

📞 03 22 29 92 47, www.valdauthie.fr – limited spaces for one-night stay

Address : 20 route de Vercourt (take the southern exit of the town)

Opening times : from beginning April to beginning Oct.

7 ha/4 for camping (170 pitches)

Tariff : 25€ ♦♦ ⇌ 🔲 🔌 (6A) – Extra per person 6€

Rental rates : (from beginning April to beginning Oct.) – 24 🏠. Per night from 55 to 120€ – Per week from 380 to 1140€

🚐 borne – 6 🔲 20€

Attractive decorative shrubs.

Surroundings : 🐟 ⌂ ♨♨	
Leisure activities : ▼ ✗ 🎣 ♨ 🏓 ⛵ 🏊 hammam ⛵ 🚲 ✗ 🏊 (open air in season) fitness trail multi-sports ground entertainment room	**GPS** Longitude : 1.69486 Latitude : 50.31356
Facilities : 🚻 ⚷ 🔌 ♨ 🚿 ♨ 🍴 launderette	

We have selected the best campsites in France with our usual care, listing those with the best facilities in the most pleasant surroundings.

POITOU-CHARENTES

Names such as Cognac, Angoulême or La Rochelle all echo through France's history, but there's just as much to appreciate in the Poitou-Charentes region today. Visit a thalassotherapy resort and allow the seawater to revive your spirits and tone aching muscles, or soak up the sun on the region's sandy beaches, where the scent of pine trees mingles with the fresh sea breezes. The best way to discover the region's attractive coastal islands is by bike; explore the country lanes lined with tiny blue and white cottages and colourful hollyhocks. Back on the mainland, take a trip on the canals of the marshy – and mercifully mosquito-free – Marais Poitevin, or 'Green Venice', with its poplar trees and green duckweed. You will have earned a drop of Cognac or a glass of the local apéritif, a fruity, ice-cold Pineau des Charentes. For a multimedia experience and a trip into the future of the moving image, head to Futuroscope, a hugely popular award-winning theme park located in Poitiers.

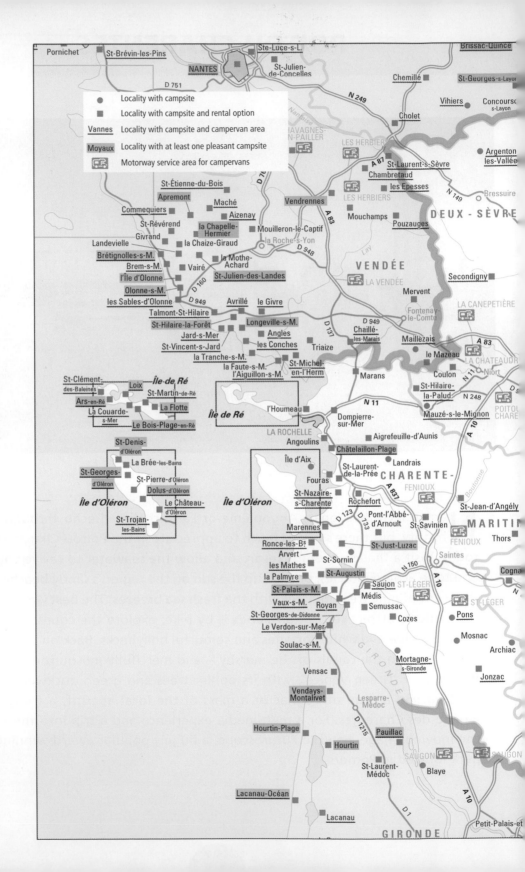

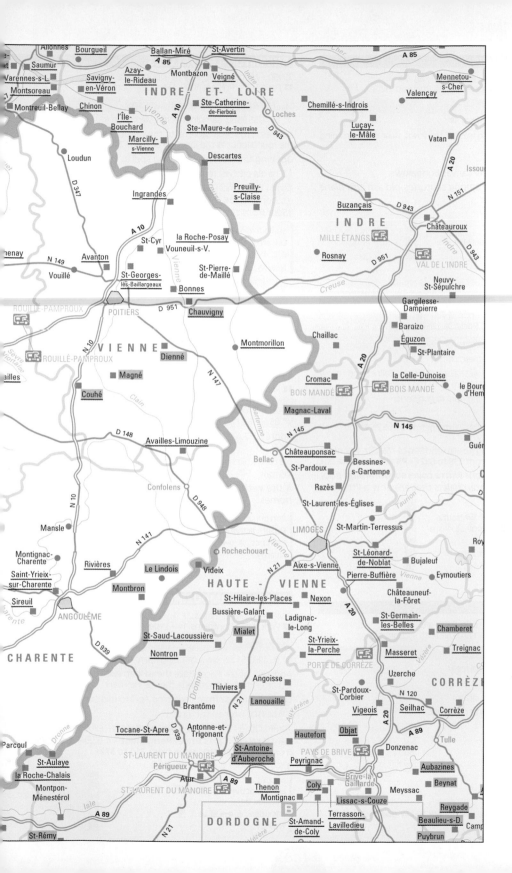

AIGREFEUILLE-D'AUNIS

17290 – Michelin map **324** E3 – pop. 3 682 – alt. 20
▶ Paris 457 – Niort 50 – Rochefort 22 – La Rochelle 25

⚠ La Taillée

𝒫 05 46 35 50 88, www.lataillee.com ✸

Address : 3 rue du Bois Gaillard (east of the town, near the swimming pool)

2 ha (80 pitches) flat, grassy

Rentals : ✸ **🅿** – 28 🛏 – 10 canvas bungalows.

A pleasant wooded setting among centuries-old ash and plane trees.

Surroundings : 🏞 ♡♡
Leisure activities : 🎳 ⛵ m
Facilities : & ⚬ ♨ ⛲ launderette
Nearby : ⛴

GPS	Longitude : -0.92682
	Latitude : 46.11514

ANGOULINS

17690 – Michelin map **324** D3 – pop. 3 720 – alt. 15
▶ Paris 481 – Poitiers 148 – La Rochelle 12 – Niort 73

⚠ Les Chirats - La Platère

𝒫 05 46 56 94 16, www.campingleschirats.fr

Address : rue du Chay (1.7km west along the r. des Salines and follow the signs for the customs post, 100m from the beach)

Opening times : from beginning April to end Sept.

4 ha (232 pitches)

Tariff : 28,60€ ⚥ ⛟ 🔌 (12A) – Extra per person 5,35€
Reservation fee 20€

Rental rates : (from beginning April to end Sept.) – 35 🏠. Per night from 49 to 87€ – Per week from 338 to 682€– Reservation fee 20€

The site is in 3 distinct sections with a covered swimming pool, used as a spa in season; rental chalets that are now a little old.

Surroundings : ⌂ ♡♡
Leisure activities : ♟ 🎳 📺 🎣 ≋ jacuzzi ⛵ m 🏊 (small swimming pool) 🏊 spa centre
Facilities : & ⚬ ♨ 🚿 ⛲ 🍴 🔲 🗑
Nearby : 🏇

GPS	Longitude : -1.13076
	Latitude : 46.104

ARCHIAC

17520 – Michelin map **324** I6 – pop. 812 – alt. 111
▶ Paris 514 – Angoulême 49 – Barbezieux 15 – Cognac 22

⚠ Municipal

𝒫 05 46 49 10 46, archiacmairie@free.fr

Address : 7 rue des Voituriers

1 ha (44 pitches) terraced, flat, grassy

Close to the municipal sports complex.

Surroundings : 🏞 ⌂ ♡♡
Leisure activities : 🎳
Facilities : 🔲
Nearby : ⛴ 🏊 🏊

GPS	Longitude : -0.30467
	Latitude : 45.52322

ARGENTON-LES-VALLEES

79150 – Michelin map **322** D3 – pop. 1 588
▶ Paris 367 – Poitiers 100 – Niort 89 – Nantes 102

⚠ Municipal du lac d'Hautibus

𝒫 05 49 65 95 08, campinghautibus@orange.fr

Address : rue de la Sablière (to the west of the town - access near the roundabout at the junction of the D 748 and D 759)

Opening times : from beginning April to end Sept.

1,5 ha (64 pitches) terraced, relatively flat, grassy

Tariff : (2013 Price) ⚥ 2,35€ ⛟ 2€ 🔲 2,20€ – 🔌 (6A) 2,70€
🚐 borne 5,10€

150m from the lake, with direct access (picturesque site).

Surroundings : ≼ ⌂ ♀
Leisure activities : 🎳
Facilities : & 🚿 🍴 launderette
Nearby : ⛾ 🏊 ⛵ boats to hire

GPS	Longitude : -0.45164
	Latitude : 46.98764

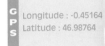

This guide is updated regularly, so buy your new copy every year!

ARVERT

17530 – Michelin map **324** D5 – pop. 3 100 – alt. 20
▶ Paris 513 – Marennes 16 – Rochefort 37 – La Rochelle 74

⚠ Le Presqu'Île

𝒫 05 46 36 81 76, campinglepresquile.com

Address : 7 rue des Aigrettes (north of the town, 150m from the D 14)

0,8 ha (60 pitches) flat, grassy

Rentals : ✸ – 3 🛏.

A site with pleasant shade and many owner-occupied mobile homes.

Surroundings : ♡♡
Leisure activities : 🎳 ⛵
Facilities : & ⚬ 🍴 🔲
Nearby : ⛾

GPS	Longitude : -1.12725
	Latitude : 45.74526

AVAILLES-LIMOUZINE

86460 – Michelin map **322** J8 – pop. 1 314 – alt. 142
▶ Paris 410 – Confolens 14 – L'Isle-Jourdain 15 – Niort 100

⚠ le Parc

𝒫 05 49 48 51 22, www.campingleparc.net

Address : at Les Places (take the eastern exit along the D 34, to the left after the bridge; beside the Vienne river)

Opening times : from beginning April to mid Oct.

2,7 ha (100 pitches) flat, grassy

Tariff : (2013 Price) 13€ ⚥ ⛟ 🔲 🔌 (10A) – Extra per person 3,30€

Rental rates : (2013 Price) Permanent – 4 🛏 – 3 🏠. Per night from 48 to 57€ – Per week from 310 to 372€
🚐 borne 4€ – 8 🔲 4€ – 🚐 🔌8€

Surroundings : 🏞 ♡♡
Leisure activities : 🎳 ⛵ m 🏊 🏊 pedalos 🏄
Facilities : & ⚬ 🍴 🔲 🗑 🔲
Nearby : ⛾

GPS	Longitude : 0.65829
	Latitude : 46.12401

To visit a town or region, use the MICHELIN Green Guides.

AVANTON

86170 – Michelin map **322** H5 – pop. 1 819 – alt. 110
▶ Paris 337 – Poitiers 12 – Niort 84 – Châtellerault 37

🏕 Du Futur

📞 05 49 54 09 67, www.camping-du-futur.com

Address : 9 rue des Bois (1.3km southwest along the D 757, follow the signs for Poitiers and take turning to the right after the level crossing)

Opening times : from beginning April to beginning Nov.

4 ha/1,5 (68 pitches) flat, grassy

Tariff : (2013 Price) 23,30€ ✶✶ 🚗 🔲 🔌 (10A) – Extra per person 3,80€ – Reservation fee 10€

Rental rates : (2013 Price) (from beginning April to end Oct.) 🚐 – 1 caravan – 14 🏠. Per night from 60 to 95€ – Per week from 322 to 525€ – Reservation fee 15€

🚐 borne 4,50€

Surroundings : 🛒 ♨
Leisure activities : ▮ 🚤 🏖 ♨
Facilities : 👨‍🦽 🔌 🍴 launderette

GPS Longitude : 0.30124
Latitude : 46.65638

BONNES

86300 – Michelin map **322** J5 – pop. 1 688 – alt. 70
▶ Paris 331 – Châtellerault 25 – Chauvigny 7 – Poitiers 25

🏕 Municipal

📞 05 49 56 44 34, www.campingbonnes86.fr

Address : 13 rue de la Varenne (south of the town; beside the Vienne river)

Opening times : from beginning June to beginning Sept.

1,2 ha (56 pitches) flat, grassy

Tariff : ✶ 3€ 🚗 1,30€ 🔲 2,60€ – 🔌 (15A) 2,80€

Rental rates : Permanent 👨‍🦽 (1 mobile home) – 6 🏠. Per night from 45 to 65€ – Per week from 170 to 298€

🚐 borne 3€

Surroundings : 🛒 ♨
Leisure activities : 🚤 🚲 ✂
Facilities : 👨‍🦽 🍴 launderette
Nearby : 🏊 ⛷

GPS Longitude : 0.59856
Latitude : 46.60182

The guide covers all 22 regions of France – see the map and list of regions on pages 4–5.

CHÂTELAILLON-PLAGE

17340 – Michelin map **324** D3 – pop. 6 081 – alt. 3
▶ Paris 482 – Niort 74 – Rochefort 22 – La Rochelle 19

🏕 Port Punay

📞 05 46 56 01 53, www.camping-port-punay.com

Address : quartier des Boucholeurs, allée Bernard Moreau

Opening times : from mid April to end Sept.

3 ha (157 pitches) flat, grassy

Tariff : 33,50€ ✶✶ 🚗 🔲 🔌 (10A) – Extra per person 6,50€ – Reservation fee 18€

Rental rates : (from mid April to end Sept.) 👨‍🦽 (1 mobile home) – 37 🏠 – 4 tent lodges. Per night from 43 to 105€ – Per week from 295 to 960€ – Reservation fee 18€

🚐 borne

Both shady and sunny pitches 200m from the beach and the port.

Surroundings : 🏖 🛒 ♨
Leisure activities : ▮ ✕ 🏖 🏄 🚤 🚲 ♨
Facilities : 👨‍🦽 🔌 🍴 launderette ⚰ ♨

GPS Longitude : -1.0846
Latitude : 46.05352

🏕 Club Airotel 2 Plages - Village Corsaire

📞 05 46 56 27 53, www.2plages.com

Address : avenue d'Angoulins (follow the signs for La Rochelle; 300m from the beach)

Opening times : from beginning May to mid Sept.

4,5 ha (265 pitches) flat, grassy

Tariff : 32€ ✶✶ 🚗 🔲 🔌 (10A) – Extra per person 6,30€ – Reservation fee 18€

Rental rates : (from mid April to mid Sept.) 👨‍🦽 (1 mobile home) 115 🏠. Per night from 52 to 134€ – Per week from 364 to 938€ Reservation fee 18€

Choose the pitches away from the road and the railway line.

Surroundings : 🛒 ♨
Leisure activities : ▮ ✕ 🏖 🚤 ♨ multi-sports ground
Facilities : 👨‍🦽 🔌 🍴 launderette ⚰ ♨
Nearby : 🚲

GPS Longitude : -1.09344
Latitude : 46.08441

🏕 L'Océan

📞 05 46 56 87 97, www.campingocean17.com

Address : avenue d'Angoulins (1.3km north along the D 202, follow the signs for La Rochelle and take a right turn)

3 ha (97 pitches) flat, grassy

A pretty, naturally filtered, landscaped lake.

Surroundings : 🏖 ♨
Leisure activities : 🏊 🚤 🛶 (lake), entertainment room
Facilities : 👨‍🦽 🔌 🍴 launderette

GPS Longitude : -1.09412
Latitude : 46.08818

CHAUVIGNY

86300 – Michelin map **322** J5 – pop. 6 848 – alt. 65
▶ Paris 333 – Bellac 64 – Le Blanc 36 – Châtellerault 30

🏕 Municipal de la Fontaine

📞 05 49 46 31 94, www.chauvigny.fr

Address : rue de la Fontaine (take the northern exit along the D 2, follow the signs for La Puye and take turning to the right; beside a stream)

Opening times : from beginning April to end Sept.

2,8 ha (102 pitches)

Tariff : ✶ 2,50€ 🚗 1,80€ 🔲 1,80€ – 🔌 (16A) 2,95€

Rental rates : Permanent – 1 🏠 – 4 🏡 – 5 studios. Per night from 17 to 22€ – Per week from 210 to 570€

🚐 borne – 10 🔲 7€

Municipal gardens with a water feature.

Surroundings : ≤ Medieval city, several castles ♨
Leisure activities : 🏊 🚤
Facilities : 👨‍🦽 🔌 🚿 ⚰ ♨ 🍴 launderette
Nearby : 🎣

COGNAC

16100 – Michelin map **324** I5 – pop. 18 729 – alt. 25
▶ Paris 478 – Angoulême 45 – Bordeaux 120 – Libourne 116

⚠ Municipal

𝒫 05 45 32 13 32, www.campingdecognac.com

Address : boulevard de Châtenay (2.3km north along the D 24, follow the signs for Boutiers; between the Charente and the Solençon rivers)

Opening times : from beginng May to mid Sept.

2 ha (160 pitches) flat, grassy

Tariff : (2013 Price) 19,20€ ✦✦ ⇦ 🔲 ⚡ (6A) – Extra per person 6,10€
Rental rates : (2013 Price) (from beginning May to mid Sept.) ⚓ (1 mobile home) – 8 🏠 – 2 canvas bungalows. Per night from 30 to 45 € – Per week from 170 to 490 €

A lovely grass area, part well shaded.

Surroundings : ⌷ ♤♤	
Leisure activities : ⚓🏊🎣	**G** Longitude : -0.30726
Facilities : ⚓ ⚡ (July –Aug.) ⚿⚡⚓♨🔲	**P** Latitude : 45.70926
Nearby : ♈ ✕	**S**

COUHÉ

86700 – Michelin map **322** H7 – pop. 1 885 – alt. 140
▶ Paris 370 – Confolens 58 – Montmorillon 61 – Niort 65

⛰ Sites et Paysages Les Peupliers ▲♣

𝒫 05 49 59 21 16, www.lespeupliers.fr

Address : avenue de Paris (situated 1km north, follow the signs for Poitiers; at Valence)

Opening times : from beginning May to end Sept.

16 ha/6 for camping (160 pitches)

Tariff : ✦ 8€ ⇦ 🔲 13,50€
⚡ (10A) 4,50€

Rental rates : Permanent – 25 🚐 – 18 🏠. Per night from 50 to 85 € – Per week from 240 to 1 110 €
🚮 borne – ⛟ 14€

Located in a wooded setting with a picturesque river running through it.

Surroundings : ♤⌷♤♤	
Leisure activities : ♈✕🏠⚡🏊🎣 🏊🎣	**G** Longitude : 0.18222
Facilities : ⚓⚡♨⚿⚡ launderette ⚓	**P** Latitude : 46.31222
⚓	**S**

COULON

79510 – Michelin map **322** C7 – pop. 2 211 – alt. 6
▶ Paris 418 – Fontenay-le-Comte 25 – Niort 11 – La Rochelle 63

⚠ La Venise Verte ▲♣

𝒫 05 49 35 90 36, www.camping-laveniseverte.fr

Address : 178 route des Bords de Sèvre (2.2km southwest along the D 123, follow the signs for Vanneau; beside a canal and near the Sèvre Niortaise river)

Opening times : from beginning April to end Oct.

2,2 ha (140 pitches) flat, grassy

Tariff : (2013 Price) 27,50€ ✦✦ ⇦ 🔲 ⚡ (10A)
Extra per person 6,50€ – Reservation fee 10€

Rental rates : (2013 Price) (from beginning April to end Oct.)
8 🚐 – 16 🏠. Per night from 46 to 95€ – Per week from 315 to 765 € – Reservation fee 10€

A site that is making great ecological efforts.

Surroundings : ♤♤	
Leisure activities : ♈✕🏠⚡🏊🏊🚲🎣🏊 ♨	**G** Longitude : -0.60889
Facilities : ⚓⚡♨⚓⚿⚡🔲⚓	**P** Latitude : 46.31444
Nearby : 🎣	**S**

COZES

17120 – Michelin map **324** E6 – pop. 1 973 – alt. 43
▶ Paris 494 – Marennes 41 – Mirambeau 35 – Pons 26

⚠ Municipal le Sorlut

𝒫 05 46 90 75 99, www.villedecozes.fr

Address : rue des Chênes (to the north, near the old station, behind the Champion supermarket)

Opening times : from mid April to mid Oct.

1,4 ha (120 pitches) flat, grassy

Tariff : ✦ 2,68€ ⇦ 🔲 2,83€ – ⚡ (10A) 2,78€
Rental rates : Permanent ⚓ (1 chalet) ♨ – 8 🏠. Per night from 66 to 80€ – Per week from 509 to 566€

Pleasantly shady pitches, comfortable chalets and the municipal swimming pool is adjacent to the campsite.

Surroundings : 🌳♤♤	
Leisure activities : 🏊	**G** Longitude : -0.83728
Facilities : ⚓ ⚡ (July –Aug.) ⚿ 🔲	**P** Latitude : 45.58649
Nearby : 🏊 🏊🎣	**S**

In order for the guide to remain wholly objective, the selection of campsites is made on an entirely independent basis.

DIENNE

86410 – Michelin map **322** J6 – pop. 508 – alt. 112
▶ Paris 362 – Poitiers 26 – Niort 107 – Limoges 107

⛰ DéfiPlanet au Domaine de Dienné

𝒫 05 49 45 87 63, www.domaine-de-dienne.fr – limited spaces for one-night stay

Address : at La Boquerie (RN 147)

Opening times : from mid Feb. to beginning Jan.

47 ha/1 for camping (19 pitches) lake, forest

Tariff : 39€ ✦✦ ⇦ 🔲 ⚡ (16A) – Extra per person 7,50€
Rental rates : (from mid Feb. to beginning Jan.) ⚓ ⓟ
24 caravans – 7 🏠 – 8 yurts – 24 cabins in the trees – 2 gîtes 5 'mushroom' houses – 5 'fairy' houses. Per night from 74 to 208€ Per week from 370 to 1 040€

A vast wooded estate offering a number of activities, nearly a dozen accommodation options of the more unusual kind and some pitches for tents and caravans.

Surroundings : 🌳♤	
Leisure activities : ♈✕🏠⚡🍴🏛	**G**
hammam, jacuzzi 🏊🚲🎣🏊🏊🐎	
horse riding centre, zip wire, spa centre,	**P** Longitude : 0.56024
entertainment room	Latitude : 46.44614
Facilities : ⚓⚡ⓟ🏛⚿ launderette ⚓	**S**

BOUCHER

DOMPIERRE-SUR-MER

7139 – Michelin map **324** H5
▶ Paris 465 – Poitiers 132 – La Rochelle 9 – La Roche-sur-Yon 84

⚠ Aire Naturelle Le Verger

📞 05 46 34 91 00 -, www.campingleverger17.com

Address : 27 rue Jean-Pierre Pigot (2km northwest along the D 107)

Opening times : from mid June to beginning Sept.

,5 ha (25 pitches) flat, grassy

Tariff : ✚ 5€ ⇔ 🗐 7€ – (½) (10A) 5€

Rental rates : (from mid June to beginning Sept.) ⚡ – 2 caravans.
Per week from 420 to 560€

Pitches in the shade of young apricot, cherry and apple trees.

Surroundings : 🌳 ♀
Facilities : ᕙ ⊶ 🖾 🗄

GPS Longitude : -1.05428
Latitude : 46.17787

FOURAS

7450 – Michelin map **324** D4 – pop. 4 092 – alt. 5
▶ Paris 485 – Châtelaillon-Plage 18 – Rochefort 15 – La Rochelle 34

▲▲▲ Municipal le Cadoret 🏕🏕

📞 05 46 82 19 19, www.campings-fouras.com

Address : boulevard de Chaterny (North coast; beside the Anse de Fouras, 100m from the beach)

Opening times : Permanent

,5 ha (498 pitches)

Tariff : 27,70€ 🏕🏕 ⇔ 🗐 (½) (10A) – Extra per person 5,70€
Reservation fee 25€

Rental rates : (from end March to beginning Nov.) ⚡ (2 mobile homes) – 19 🚐. Per week from 270 to 620€ – Reservation fee 25€

Beside the sea, near the sea fishing piers and the beautiful, wide beach 50m away.

Surroundings : 🗀 ♀♀
Leisure activities : 🍽 🗙 🖾 🗄 🏊 multi-sports ground
Facilities : ᕙ ⊶ 🏛 🗄 launderette 🗄
Nearby : 🗙 🎣 ♦

GPS Longitude : -1.08714
Latitude : 45.99296

L'HOUMEAU

7137 – Michelin map **324** C2 – pop. 2 073 – alt. 19
▶ Paris 478 – Poitiers 145 – La Rochelle 6 – Niort 83

▲▲ Au Petit Port de l'Houmeau

📞 05 46 50 90 82, www.aupetitport.com

Address : rue des Sartières (take the northeastern exit along the D 106, follow the signs for Nieul-sur-Mer, via the ring road (périphérique) towards Île de Ré and take the exit for Lagord-l'Houmeau)

2 ha (132 pitches)

Rentals : ⚡ (1 chalet) – 55 🚐 – 15 🏠.

Numerous rental options include some rather old chalets and newer mobile homes equipped to a good standard, clad in wood.

Surroundings : 🗀 ♀♀
Leisure activities : 🍽 🗙 🖾 🏊
Facilities : ᕙ ⊶ 🗄 launderette 🗄
Nearby : 🗙 🎣

GPS Longitude : -1.1883
Latitude : 46.19566

ÎLE-D'AIX

17123 – Michelin map **324** C3 – pop. 227 – alt. 10
▶ Paris 486 – Poitiers 152 – La Rochelle 31 – Niort 78

⚠ Le Fort de la Rade

📞 05 46 84 28 28, fortdelarade.ifrance.com

Address : situated at la Pointe Ste-Catherine, 300m from the beach at L'Anse de la Croix

3 ha (70 pitches) flat, grassy

In the grounds of the Fort de la Rade, surrounded by fortified walls; reserved for tents.

Surroundings : 🌳
Leisure activities : 🗙 🖾 🏊 ♦
Facilities : ᕙ ⊶ 🗄 – no electrical hook-up
Nearby : 🏊 ♀ 🚴

GPS Longitude : -1.17657
Latitude : 46.00935

ÎLE DE RÉ

17 – Michelin map **324**

Ars-en-Ré 17590 – Michelin map **324** A2 – pop. 1 321 – alt. 4
▶ Paris 506 – Fontenay-le-Comte 85 – Luçon 75 – La Rochelle 34

▲▲▲ Club Airotel le Cormoran 🏕🏕

📞 05 46 29 46 04, www.cormoran.com

Address : route de Radia (located 1km west)

Opening times : from mid April to end Sept.

3 ha (142 pitches) flat, grassy

Tariff : (2013 Price) 52,60€ 🏕🏕 ⇔ 🗐 (½) (10A)
Extra per person 13,25€ – Reservation fee 25€

Rental rates : (2013 Price) (from mid April to end Sept.) ⚡ (1 mobile home) – 97 🚐 – 2 tent lodges. Per night from 87 to 137€ – Per week from 279 to 1 428€ – Reservation fee 35€
🚐 borne 4€

An attractive site with flowers, near vineyards, forest and salt marshes.

Surroundings : 🌳 🗀 ♀
Leisure activities : 🍽 🗙 🖾 🗄 🏊 🏄 ⛵ 🏊
🚴 🎿 🏊 multi-sports ground
Facilities : ᕙ ⊶ 🏛 🗄 launderette 🗄

GPS Longitude : -1.53026
Latitude : 46.21136

Le Bois-Plage-en-Ré 17580 – Michelin map **324** B2 – pop. 2 364 – alt. 5
▶ Paris 494 – Fontenay-le-Comte 74 – Luçon 64 – La Rochelle 23

▲▲▲ Sunêlia Interlude 🏕🏕

📞 05 46 09 18 22, www.interlude.fr

Address : 8 route de Gros Jonc (2.3km southeast)

Opening times : from mid April to end Sept.

7,5 ha (387 pitches) undulating, flat, grassy, sandy

Tariff : 49€ 🏕🏕 ⇔ 🗐 (½) (10A) – Extra per person 10€ – Reservation fee 30€

Rental rates : (from mid April to end Sept.) ⚡ (1 mobile home) 194 🚐 – 5 tent lodges. Per night from 86 to 235€ – Per week from 602 to 1 645€ – Reservation fee 30€
🚐 borne 11€ – 🚐 11€

150m from the beach.

Surroundings : 🌳 🗀 ♀
Leisure activities : 🍽 🗙 🖾 🗄 🏊 🏄 ⛵
hammam, jacuzzi 🚴 🎿 🏊 (small swimming pool) 🏊 🏄 multi-sports ground, spa centre
Facilities : ᕙ ⊶ 🏛 🗄 🗄 🗄 launderette 🏊 🗄
Nearby : 🗙 ♦

GPS Longitude : -1.3793
Latitude : 46.17472

⚶ Les Varennes

☎ 05 46 09 15 43, www.les-varennes.com

Address : at Raise Maritaise (1.7km southeast, 300m from the beach)

Opening times : from mid April to mid Sept.

2,5 ha (145 pitches) flat, grassy

Tariff : 36€ ♥♥ ⟷ 🔲 (10A) – Extra per person 9€ – Reservation fee 20€
Rental rates : (from mid April to mid Sept.) – 85 🚐. Per week from 320 to 1114€ – Reservation fee 20€
Mobile homes and pitches in the shade of a pretty pine wood.

Surroundings : 🏖 ♉♉
Leisure activities : 🍸 🏊 🚲🖼 (open air in season)
Facilities : 🚿 ⊶ 🖂 ⛺ ☕ launderette 🧺
Nearby : 🍴

G P S Longitude : -1.38306
Latitude : 46.17829

La Couarde-sur-Mer 17670 – Michelin map **324** B2 – pop. 1 248 – alt. 1
▶ Paris 497 – Fontenay-le-Comte 76 – Luçon 66 – La Rochelle 26

⚶ L'Océan 👥

☎ 05 46 29 87 70, www.campingocean.com

Address : 50 r.d'Ars (at La Passe)

Opening times : from mid April to end Sept.

9 ha (338 pitches) flat, grassy

Tariff : (2013 Price) 49€ ♥♥ ⟷ 🔲 – (10A) 10€
Extra per person 11€ – Reservation fee 32€
Rental rates : (2013 Price) (from mid April to end Sept.) 🚿 (1 mobile home) 🚫 – 167 🚐. Per night from 42 to 202€ Per week from 294 to 1414€ – Reservation fee 32€
🚐 borne 8€
High-quality rental options surrounding a charming swimming area. At the bottom of the site there are 2 natural salt-water pools that are perfect for fishing.

Surroundings : 🏖 ⛱ ♉♉
Leisure activities : 🍸🏊 🏓 🚲 🎾 🖼 hammam, jacuzzi ⚽ multi-sports ground, spa centre, entertainment room
Facilities : 🚿 ⊶ 🖂 ⛺ 🧺 ☕ launderette 🧺

G P S Longitude : -1.46737
Latitude : 46.20447

⚶ La Tour des Prises

☎ 05 46 29 84 82, www.lesprises.com

Address : chemin de la Griffonerie (1.8km northwest along the D 735, turn off to the right)

Opening times : from beginning April to end Sept.

2,5 ha (140 pitches) flat, grassy

Tariff : 37€ ♥♥ ⟷ 🔲 (16A) – Extra per person 4,70€ – Reservation fee 14€
Rental rates : (from beginning April to end Sept.) – 50 🚐. Per night from 60 to 90€ – Per week from 295 to 725€ Reservation fee 20€
🚐 borne 10,50€ – 25 🔲 10,50€ – 🚌 10,50€
Enclosed by a pretty wall of local stone and surrounded by vines.

Surroundings : 🏖 ⛱ ♉♉
Leisure activities : 🏊 ⚽ 🚲🖼 (open air in season)
Facilities : 🚿 ⊶ ⛺ ☕ launderette 🧺

G P S Longitude : -1.4447
Latitude : 46.20473

La Flotte 17630 – Michelin map **324** C2 – pop. 2 918 – alt. 4
▶ Paris 489 – Fontenay-le-Comte 68 – Luçon 58 – La Rochelle 17

⚶ Camp'Atlantique Les Peupliers 👥

☎ 02 51 20 41 94, www.camp-atlantique.com – limited spaces for one-night stay

Address : RD 735, route de Rivedoux (1.3km southeast)

Opening times : from beginning April to end Sept.

4,5 ha (220 pitches) flat, grassy

Tariff : 41€ ♥♥ ⟷ 🔲 (10A) – Extra per person 6€ – Reservation fee 25€
Rental rates : (from beginning April to end Sept.) 🚿 (2 mobile homes) – 144 🚐. Per week from 269 to 1189€ – Reservation fee 25€
🚐 borne – 20 🔲 41€
Located at the entrance to the village of La Flotte, with a good number of mobile homes and owner-occupiers, but few tent or caravan pitches.

Surroundings : 🏖 ⛱ ♉
Leisure activities : 🍸 🍴 🏊 ⛹ 🏓 ⛳ 🏖 hammam, jacuzzi ⚽ 🚲 🎾 ⚽ multi-sports ground, entertainment room
Facilities : 🚿 ⊶ ⛺ ☕ launderette 🧺

G P S Longitude : -1.308
Latitude : 46.1846

⚶ La Grainetière 👥

☎ 05 46 09 68 86, www.la-grainetiere.com

Address : chemin des Essards (to the west of the town, follow the signs for Saint-Martin-de-Ré, recommended route via the D 735)

Opening times : from beginning April to end Sept.

2,3 ha (140 pitches) flat, sandy

Tariff : (2013 Price) 44,50€ ♥♥ ⟷ 🔲 (10A) – Extra per person 9€ Reservation fee 15€
Rental rates : (2013 Price) (from beginning April to end Sept. 70 🚐. Per night from 70 to 115€ – Per week from 252 to 1020€ Reservation fee 15€
Choose the pitches furthest away from the road.

Surroundings : ♉♉
Leisure activities : 🍴 🏊 🏓 jacuzzi ⚽ 🚲 🖼 (open air in season)
Facilities : 🚿 ⊶ ⛺ ☕ launderette 🧺 🧺

G P S Longitude : -1.34412
Latitude : 46.18747

Loix 17111 – Michelin map **324** B2 – pop. 731 – alt. 4
▶ Paris 505 – Fontenay-le-Comte 84 – Luçon 74 – La Rochelle 33

⚶ Flower Les Ilates 👥

☎ 05 46 29 05 43, www.camping-loix.com

Address : at Le Petit Boucheau, route du Grouin (take the eastern exit, 500m from the ocean)

Opening times : from beginning April to end Sept.

4,5 ha (228 pitches) flat, grassy

Tariff : 44€ ♥♥ ⟷ 🔲 (10A) – Extra per person 9€ – Reservation fee 10€
Rental rates : (from beginning April to end Sept.) 🚿 (2 chalets) 78 🚐 – 22 tent lodges – 34 gîtes. Per night from 42 to 163€ Per week from 210 to 1141€ – Reservation fee 20€
🚐 borne 8€
Rental options of varying degrees of comfort and design, suitable for large families.

Surroundings : 🏖 ⛱ ♉
Leisure activities : 🍸 🍴 🏓 jacuzzi ⚽ 🚲 🎾 🏊
Facilities : 🚿 ⊶ ⛺ 🧺 ☕ launderette 🧺

G P S Longitude : -1.42608
Latitude : 46.22756

St-Clément-des-Baleines 17590 – Michelin map **324** A2 – pop. 721 – alt. 2

▣ Paris 509 – Fontenay-le-Comte 89 – Luçon 79 – La Rochelle 38

⋀⋀⋀ Club Airotel La Plage ♠♠

✆ 05 46 29 42 62, www.la-plage.com

Address : 408 rue du Chaume

Opening times : from beginning April to mid Sept.

2,7 ha (140 pitches) flat, grassy

Tariff : (2013 Price) ✝ 16€ ⇦ ▣ – ⚡ (10A) 5,90€ – Reservation fee 25€

Rental rates : (2013 Price) (from beginning April to end Sept.) ⚿ (1 mobile home) Ⓟ – 89 🚐 – 2 tent lodges. Per night from 87 to 247€ – Per week from 229 to 1428€ – Reservation fee 35€

⛟ borne 4€

100m from the beach, but choose those pitches the furthest away from the road.

Surroundings : 🏊 🗺
Leisure activities : ♈ ✗ 🎬 🎯 🚣 🏓 ⛵
🏄 🚲 🏊 multi-sports ground
Facilities : ⚿ ⚬ 🅿 🚿 launderette ⛽
Nearby : 🎾 ⛳ 🚣

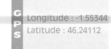

Longitude : -1.55344
Latitude : 46.24112

St-Martin-de-Ré 17410 – Michelin map **324** B2 – pop. 2 585 – alt. 14

▣ Paris 493 – Fontenay-le-Comte 72 – Luçon 62 – La Rochelle 22

⋀ Municipal

✆ 05 46 09 21 96, www.saint-martin-de-re.fr

Address : rue du Rempart (situated in the town)

5 ha (200 pitches) terraced, flat, grassy

Rentals : 21 🚐.

Set amidst the town's fortifications and close to the centre.

Surroundings : ⛳⛳
Leisure activities : ✗ 🎬 🚣
Facilities : ⚿ ⚬ 🏛 launderette

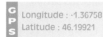

Longitude : -1.36758
Latitude : 46.19921

ÎLE D'OLÉRON

17 – Michelin map **324**

La Brée-les-Bains 17840 – Michelin map **324** B3 – pop. 758 – alt. 5

▣ Paris 531 – Marennes 32 – Rochefort 53 – La Rochelle 90

⋀⋀⋀ Antioche d'Oléron

✆ 05 46 47 92 00, www.camping-antiochedoleron.com

Address : route de Proires (located 1km northwest along the D 273 Follow the signs for St Denis and take a right turn, 150m from the beach)

Opening times : from beginning April to end Sept.

2,5 ha (129 pitches) flat, grassy

Tariff : 40,20€ ✝✝ ⇦ ▣ ⚡ (16A) – Extra per person 9,40€ Reservation fee 22€

Rental rates : (from beginning April to end Sept.) – 45 🚐. Per night from 52 to 145€ – Per week from 237 to 1015€ Reservation fee 22€

Pitches in both the shade and full sun and several luxurious mobile homes.

Surroundings : 🗺 ⛳
Leisure activities : ✗ 🎬 jacuzzi 🚣 🏊 🎯
Facilities : ⚿ ⚬ 🅿 🚿 launderette ⛽
Nearby : 🎾

Longitude : -1.35773
Latitude : 46.02033

Le Château-d'Oléron 17480 – Michelin map **324** C4 – pop. 3 930 – alt. 9

▣ Paris 507 – Marennes 12 – Rochefort 33 – La Rochelle 70

⋀⋀⋀ La Brande ♠♠

✆ 05 46 47 62 37, www.camping-labrande.com

Address : route des Huîtres (2.5km to the northwest, 250m from the sea)

Opening times : from beginning April to mid Nov.

4 ha (199 pitches) flat, grassy

Tariff : 44€ ✝✝ ⇦ ▣ ⚡ (10A) – Extra per person 8,20€ – Reservation fee 20€

Rental rates : (from beginning April to mid Nov.) ⚿ (4 chalets) 40 🚐 – 40 🏡 – 1 tent lodge. Per night from 50 to 95€ Per week from 250 to 1250€ – Reservation fee 20€

⛟ borne 7,50€ – 20 ▣ 16,50€

Both shaded and sunny pitches are available.

Surroundings : ⛳⛳
Leisure activities : ♈ ✗ 🎬 🎯 🚣 ⛵
hammam, jacuzzi 🚣 🚲 🏓 🏊 (open air in season) 🏄 🏊 multi-sports ground
Facilities : ⚿ ⚬ – 6 individual sanitary facilities (🚿 wc) 🚿 🅿 🚿 launderette 🏊 ⛽

Longitude : -1.21607
Latitude : 45.90464

⋀⋀⋀ Club Airotel Oléron ♠♠

✆ 05 46 47 61 82, www.camping-airotel-oleron.com

Address : 19 rue de la Libération (1.8km southwest following signs for St-Trojan and turn left onto r. de la Libération)

Opening times : from beginning April to end Sept.

15 ha/4 for camping (133 pitches) flat and relatively flat, grassy

Tariff : (2013 Price) 19,70€ ✝✝ ⇦ ▣ ⚡ (10A) Extra per person 4,50€ – Reservation fee 16€

Rental rates : (from beginning March to end Oct.) – 2 caravans 50 🚐 – 20 🏡. Per week from 320 to 860€ – Reservation fee 16€

⛟ borne

Activities based around the riding centre at the camp site.

Surroundings : 🏊 🗺 ⛳⛳
Leisure activities : ♈ ✗ 🎬 🎯 🚣 🚴 🏓 ⛵
🏊 🏊 🏇 horse riding centre, multi-sports ground
Facilities : ⚿ ⚬ 🅿 🚿 launderette ⛽

Longitude : -1.20791
Latitude : 45.88444

⋀⋀ Fief-Melin

✆ 05 46 47 60 85, www.camping.fiefmelin.com

Address : rue des Alizés (1.7km west following signs for St-Pierre-d'Oléron then turn right and continue for 600m)

Opening times : from beginning May to end Sept.

2,2 ha (144 pitches) flat, grassy

Tariff : 32,10€ ✝✝ ⇦ ▣ ⚡ (10A) – Extra per person 4,90€

Rental rates : (from beginning April to end Oct.) – 28 🚐. Per week from 255 to 785€

Surroundings : 🏊 🗺 ⛳
Leisure activities : 🎬 🎯 🚣 🚲 🏊 (open air in season), multi-sports ground
Facilities : ⚬ 🚿 🏊

Longitude : -1.21408
Latitude : 45.89371

Do not confuse:
⋀ *to* ⋀⋀⋀ *: MICHELIN classification with*
★ *to* ★★★★★ *: official classification*

Dolus-d'Oléron 17550 – Michelin map **324** C4 – pop. 3 176 – alt. 7
▶ Paris 511 – Marennes 17 – Rochefort 39 – La Rochelle 75

🏔 Ostréa

📞 05 46 47 62 36, www.camping-ostrea.com

Address : route des Huitres (3.5km east)

Opening times : from beginning April to end Sept.

2 ha (110 pitches) flat, grassy

Tariff : 32,70 € 🛉🛉 🚐 🗉 🔌 (6A) –Extra per person 8,10 €
Reservation fee 20 €

Rental rates : (from beginning April to end Sept.) – 25 🛖.
Per week from 320 to 720 € – Reservation fee 20 €

🚰 borne 5 €

On the east coast, very close to the sea. Choose the pitches away from the road.

Surroundings : 🏞 🎿🎿
Leisure activities : 🏓 🏊🏊 🖼 (open air in season)
Facilities : 🔥 ⚬🗝 🏺🚻 launderette 🍴 🚲

GPS Longitude : -1.22402
Latitude : 45.91299

🏔 Indigo Oléron Les Chênes Verts 🚶🚶

Indigo

📞 05 46 75 32 88, www.camping-indigo.com

Address : 9 Passe de l'Écuissière (Côte Ouest (west side of the island), 3.2km southwest along the D 126)

Opening times : from beginning June to end Sept.

3 ha (120 pitches) undulating, flat, grassy

Tariff : 30,60 € 🛉🛉 🚐 🗉 🔌 (10A) Extra per person 5,90 € – Reservation fee 22 €

Rental rates : (from beginning June to end Sept.) – 45 tent lodges. Per night from 53 to 100 € – Per week from 260 to 700 € – Reservation fee 22 €

🚰 borne 7 €

In a wooded and undulating setting near the sea.

Surroundings : 🏞 🎿🎿🎿
Leisure activities : ✖ 🎇nighttime 🏃 🎿🎿 🏹archery
Facilities : 🔥 ⚬🗝 🏺🚻 launderette 🚲

GPS Longitude : -1.27575
Latitude : 45.88727

🏔 La Perroche Leitner

📞 05 46 75 37 33, www.camping-leitner-oleron.jimdo.com

Address : 18 rue du Renclos-de-la-Perroche (4km southwest, at La Perroche)

Opening times : from mid April to mid Sept.

1,5 ha (100 pitches) flat, grassy

Tariff : (2013 Price) 30,80 € 🛉🛉 🚐 🗉 🔌 (10A) Extra per person 7,80 € – Reservation fee 14 €

🚰 borne 5,50 € – 25 🗉 30,80 €

In an attractive location close to the sea, with a choice of shady or sunny pitches.

Surroundings : 🏞 🎿🎿
Leisure activities : 🏊🏊
Facilities : 🔥 ⚬🗝 🏺🚻 🖼
Nearby : 🍷 ✖

GPS Longitude : -1.3031
Latitude : 45.9016

St-Denis-d'Oléron 17650 – Michelin map **324** B3 – pop. 1 336 – alt. 9
▶ Paris 527 – Marennes 33 – Rochefort 55 – La Rochelle 92

🏔 Village Vacances Les Hameaux des Marines

(rental of chalets only)

📞 05 46 36 45 59, www.chalets-en-france.com

Address : rue de Seulières (situated 300m from the beach)

Opening times : Permanent

2,5 ha flat

Rental rates : 🔥 (1 chalet) – 48 🛖. Per night from 60 to 90 € Per week from 330 to 1025 € – Reservation fee 13 €

A pleasant, small chalet village, all featuring lovely large covered terraces.

Surroundings : 🏞 ♀
Leisure activities : 🏓 🏃 🎿🎿 🖼 (open air in season)
Facilities : ⚬🗝 🏛 🚻 launderette

GPS Longitude : -1.39169
Latitude : 46.01354

🏔 Les Seulières

📞 05 46 47 90 51, www.campinglesseulieres.com

Address : 1371 route des Seulières - Les Huttes (3.5km southwest, follow the signs for Chaucre; 400m from the beach)

Opening times : from beginning April to end Oct.

2,4 ha (120 pitches) flat, grassy

Tariff : 22 € 🛉🛉 🚐 🗉 🔌 (10A) – Extra per person 4 € – Reservation fee 15 €

Rental rates : (from beginning April to end Oct.) – 2 🛖 8 🛖 Per night from 50 to 60 € – Per week from 300 to 600 € Reservation fee 15 €

Sunny or shaded pitches are available in a peaceful, family oriented setting.

Surroundings : 🏞 🎿🎿
Leisure activities : 🎿 🏓
Facilities : 🔥 ⚬🗝 🏺🚻 launderette
Nearby : 🍴

GPS Longitude : -1.38512
Latitude : 46.0034

St-Georges-d'Oléron 17190 – Michelin map **324** C4 – pop. 3 497 – alt. 10
▶ Paris 527 – Marennes 27 – Rochefort 49 – La Rochelle 85

🏔 Camping-Club Verébleu 🚶🚶

MONDAMERT

📞 05 46 76 57 70, www.verebleu.tm.fr
🏊

Address : at La Jousselinière (1.7km southeast along the D 273 and turn left, following signs for Sauzelle)

Opening times : from beginning June to mid Sept.

7,5 ha (324 pitches) flat, grassy

Tariff : (2013 Price) 42 € 🛉🛉 🚐 🔌 (13A) – Extra per person 11 € Reservation fee 25 €

Rental rates : (2013 Price) (from beginning June to mid Sept.) 🔥 (1 chalet) 🏊 – 76 🛖 – 68 🛖 Per night from 50 to 185 € – Per week from 350 to 1290 € – Reservation fee 25 €

🚰 borne – 160 🗉 33 €

Divided into two separate sections with tents, caravans and rental options surrounding a swimming and play area themed around Fort Boyard.

Surroundings : 🏊 ⌂ 🎠
Leisure activities : 🎣 🏓 🚣 🚴 🏊 🎱 ⛵
multi-sports ground
Facilities : 🚿 ⚬ 🚻 🧺 🚰 💧 launderette 🚐 🚗

GPS Longitude : -1.31759
Latitude : 45.97111

Domaine des 4 Vents

📞 05 46 76 65 47, www.camping-oleron-4vents.com

Address : at La Jousselinière (2km southeast along the D 273 and turn left, following signs for Sauzelle)

Opening times : from end June to end Aug.

7 ha (300 pitches) flat, grassy

Tariff : (2013 Price) 30€ ♦♦ 🚐 🔲 💡 (10A) – Extra per person 6,30€ Reservation fee 20€

Rental rates : (2013 Price) (from mid April to mid Sept.) – 80 🚐. Per week from 250 to 880€ – Reservation fee 20€

🚐 borne 4€ – 5 🔲 22€ – 🚐 10€

Sunny or shaded pitches with a large number of owner-occupied mobile homes.

Surroundings : 🏊 ⌂ 🎠
Leisure activities : ✗ 🏠 🏓 🚣 ⛵
multi-sports ground
Facilities : 🚿 ⚬ 🧺 🚰 💧 launderette 🚗

GPS Longitude : -1.31995
Latitude : 45.96973

Oléron Loisirs

rental of mobile homes, chalets and canvas bungalows only)

📞 05 46 76 50 20, www.oleron-loisirs.com – traditional camp. spaces also available

Address : at La Jousselinière (1.9km southeast along the D 273 and turn left, following signs for Sauzelle)

Opening times : from mid April to end Sept.

8 ha (321 pitches) flat, grassy

Rental rates : 🚿 (1 mobile home) 🚳 – 200 🚐 – 10 🏠 13 canvas bungalows. Per night from 42 to 95€ – Per week from 130 to 910€ – Reservation fee 25€

A mobile home park, including many with owner-occupiers.

Surroundings : 🏊 ⌂ 🎠
Leisure activities : 🎣 🏠 🎣 🏓 🚣 🚴 🏊 ⛵
🚣 ⛵ multi-sports ground, entertainment room
Facilities : 🚿 ⚬ 🧺 💧 launderette 🚐 🚗

GPS Longitude : -1.31435
Latitude : 45.97062

La Campière

📞 05 46 76 72 25, www.la-campiere.com

Address : chemin de l'Achenau (5.4km southwest following signs for Chaucre and take road to the left)

Opening times : from mid April to end Sept.

1,7 ha (66 pitches) flat, grassy

Tariff : 34,80€ ♦♦ 🚐 🔲 💡 (10A) – Extra per person 8€ – Reservation fee 17€

Rental rates : (from mid April to end Sept.) – 1 🚐 – 12 🏠 3 tent lodges. Per week from 200 to 840€ – Reservation fee 19€

🚐 borne

In a pleasant, leafy setting with a small wine bar where you can taste the local produce.

Surroundings : 🏊 🎠
Leisure activities : 🎣 🏠 🏓 🚣 🚴 🏊 (small swimming pool)
Facilities : 🚿 ⚬ 🧺 🚰 💧 launderette

GPS Longitude : -1.38198
Latitude : 45.99108

Côte Ouest

Club Airotel Les Gros Joncs

📞 05 46 76 52 29, www.camping-les-gros-joncs.com – limited spaces for one-night stay

Address : 850 route de Ponthezière - Les Sables Vignier (5km southwest, 300m from the sea)

Opening times : from mid March to mid Nov.

5 ha (253 pitches) terraced, flat, sandy

Tariff : 50,50€ ♦♦ 🚐 🔲 💡 (10A) – Extra per person 13,30€ Reservation fee 8€

Rental rates : Permanent 🚿 (5 chalets) – 114 🚐 – 96 🏠. Per night from 83 to 208€ – Per week from 368 to 1455€ Reservation fee 8€

🚐 borne – 🚐 17€

A partially covered swimming area, good quality rental options and some pitches for tents and caravans, with old sanitary facilities.

Surroundings : 🏊 ⌂ 🎠
Leisure activities : 🎣 ✗ 🏠 🎣 🏓 🚴 🏊
hammam, jacuzzi 🚣 🚴 🚣 🏊 ⛵ spa centre, entertainment room
Facilities : 🚿 ⚬ 🧺 🚰 💧 launderette 🚐 🚗

GPS Longitude : -1.379
Latitude : 45.95342

St-Pierre-d'Oléron 17310 – Michelin map **324** C4 – pop. 6 532 – alt. 8
▶ Paris 522 – Marennes 22 – Rochefort 44 – La Rochelle 80

Aqua 3 Masses

📞 05 46 47 23 96, www.campingles3masses.com – limited spaces for one-night stay

Address : at Le Marais-Doux (4.3km southeast)

3 ha (130 pitches) flat, grassy

Rentals : 🚿 (1 chalet) – 35 🚐 – 12 🏠.

A pleasant setting with flowers and good-quality rental options.

Surroundings : 🏊 ⌂ 🎠
Leisure activities : ✗ 🏠 🚣 🚴 🏊 (open air in season) 🏊
Facilities : 🚿 ⚬ 🧺 💧 launderette 🚗

GPS Longitude : -1.29226
Latitude : 45.91815

St-Trojan-les-Bains 17370 – Michelin map **324** C4 – pop. 1 471 – alt. 5
▶ Paris 509 – Marennes 16 – Rochefort 38 – La Rochelle 74

La Combinette

📞 05 46 76 00 47, www.combinette-oleron.com

Address : 36 avenue des Bris (located 1.5km southwest)

Opening times : from beginning April to mid Oct.

4 ha (208 pitches) undulating, flat, grassy, sandy

Tariff : 32,30€ ♦♦ 🚐 🔲 💡 (10A) – Extra per person 9,50€ Reservation fee 25€

Rental rates : (from beginning April to mid Oct.) – 10 🚐 19 🏠 – 9 studios. Per night from 80 to 110€ – Per week from 299 to 1 060€ – Reservation fee 25€

An undulating site with shade and good quality services.

Surroundings : 🏊 🎠
Leisure activities : 🎣 ✗ 🏠 🏓 🚴 🏊 ⛳
hammam, jacuzzi 🚣 🚴 🏊 multi-sports ground
Facilities : 🚿 ⚬ 🧺 🚰 💧 🏠 🚐 🚗
Nearby : 🚳

GPS Longitude : -1.2159
Latitude : 45.82958

🏔 Indigo Oléron Les Pins 👥👤

📞 05 46 76 02 39, www.camping-indigo.com

Address : 11 avenue des Bris (to the southwest)

Opening times : from end April to mid Sept.

5 ha (160 pitches) undulating, flat, grassy, sandy

Tariff : (2013 Price) 28€ 👤👤 🚐 📧 🔌 (10A) – Extra per person 5,40€ Reservation fee 22€

Rental rates : (2013 Price) (from end April to mid Sept.) – 56 tent lodges. Per night from 48 to 103€ – Per week from 235 to 721€ – Reservation fee 22€

🚰 borne 7€

A natural setting, but choose the pitches away from the road.

Surroundings : 🌳
Leisure activities : 🏃 🏊 🏄 🎣
Facilities : 👤 ☎ 🚿 🍴 launderette 🧺

GPS	Longitude : -1.21413
	Latitude : 45.83128

INGRANDES

86220 – Michelin map **322** J3 – pop. 1 784 – alt. 50
▶ Paris 305 – Châtellerault 7 – Descartes 18 – Poitiers 41

🏔 Les Castels Le Petit Trianon de Saint Ustre

📞 05 49 02 61 47, www.petit-trianon.com

Address : 1 rue du Moulin de St-Ustre (3km to the northeast; at St-Ustre)

Opening times : from mid April to mid Sept.

4 ha (95 pitches)

Tariff : 33,60€ 👤👤 🚐 📧 🔌 (10A) – Extra per person 8,50€ Reservation fee 10€

Rental rates : (from mid April to mid Sept.) – 23 🚐 – 3 studios 1 cabin in the trees – 6 tipis – 2 gîtes. Per night from 39 to 139€ Per week from 220 to 973€ – Reservation fee 10€

🚰 borne – 4 📧 29,30€

A pleasant setting around a small château with a range of rental options.

Surroundings : 🌊 ⛰ 🌳
Leisure activities : 🎮 🏊 ⛰ 🎣
Facilities : 👤 ☎ 🚿 🍴 📧 🧺

GPS	Longitude : 0.58653
	Latitude : 46.88779

JONZAC

17500 – Michelin map **324** H7 – pop. 3 488 – alt. 40 – ♨
▶ Paris 512 – Angoulême 59 – Bordeaux 84 – Cognac 36

🏔 Les Castors

📞 05 46 48 25 65, www.campingcastors.com

Address : 8 rue de Clavelaud (located 1.5km southwest along the D 19, follow the signs for Montendre and take the road to the right)

Opening times : from mid March to mid Nov.

3 ha (120 pitches) flat and relatively flat, grassy

Tariff : 22€ 👤👤 🚐 📧 🔌 (6A) – Extra per person 5,50€ – Reservation fee 8€

Rental rates : (from mid March to mid Nov.) – 61 🚐 – 6 🏠 1 canvas bungalow. Per night from 42 to 118€ – Per week from 240 to 650€ – Reservation fee 10€

🚰 borne 3,20€

The part of the site near the swimming pools is well shaded, another part is in the sun, with well-equipped mobile homes.

Surroundings : 🌳 ♨
Leisure activities : 🍴 🛁 jacuzzi 🏊 🚴 🎣 🏊 multi-sports ground
Facilities : 👤 ☎ 🚿 🍴 launderette 🧺

GPS	Longitude : -0.44712
	Latitude : 45.43009

LANDRAIS

17290 – Michelin map **324** E3 – pop. 680 – alt. 12
▶ Paris 455 – Niort 48 – Rochefort 23 – La Rochelle 32

🏔 le Pré Maréchat

📞 05 46 27 73 69, www.cc-plaine-aunis.fr

Address : take northwestern exit along the D 112, follow the signs for Aigrefeuille-d'Aunis and take road to the left, 120m from a lake

Opening times : from mid June to mid Sept.

0,6 ha (37 pitches) flat, grassy

Tariff : 👤 2,50€ 🚐 1,50€ 📧 3€ – 🔌 (30A) 2€

Surroundings : 🌊 🌳 ♨
Leisure activities : 🏊 🎣
Facilities : 👤 🧺
Nearby : 🎣

GPS	Longitude : -0.86536
	Latitude : 46.06963

LE LINDOIS

16310 – Michelin map **324** N5 – pop. 343 – alt. 270
▶ Paris 453 – Angoulême 41 – Confolens 34 – Montbron 12

🏔 L'Étang

📞 05 45 65 02 67, www.campingdeletang.com

Address : route de Rouzède (500m southwest along the D 112)

Opening times : from beginning April to beginning Nov.

10 ha/1,5 (29 pitches) relatively flat

Tariff : 23,50€ 👤👤 🚐 📧 🔌 (16A) – Extra per person 5€

In a pleasantly wild and rural setting with plenty of trees beside a lake.

Surroundings : 🌊 🌳 ♨♨♨
Leisure activities : 🍴 🍽 🏖 (beach) 🚣 boats to hire
Facilities : 👤 ☎ 🚿 🍴 🧺

GPS	Longitude : 0.58555
	Latitude : 45.73974

LOUDUN

86200 – Michelin map **322** G2 – pop. 7 089 – alt. 120
▶ Paris 311 – Angers 79 – Châtellerault 47 – Poitiers 55

🏔 Municipal de Beausoleil

📞 05 49 98 15 38, http://www.ville-loudun.fr

Address : chemin de l'Étang (2.5km take the northern exit along the D 347, towards Angers take road to the left after the level crossing; beside a stream and near a lake)

0,6 ha (33 pitches)

Surroundings : 🌳 ♨
Leisure activities : 🏊
Facilities : 👤 🚿

GPS	Longitude : 0.06175
	Latitude : 47.00334

MAGNÉ

36160 – Michelin map **322** I6 – pop. 622 – alt. 121
▸ Paris 375 – Poitiers 29 – Niort 82 – Angoulême 94

⛺ Les Cabanes du Parc de la Belle

(rental of cabins in the trees only)
☎ 05 49 87 80 86, www.parcdelabelle.com
Address : rue Anatole de Briey (in town centre, opposite the church)
Opening times : Permanent
10 ha
Rental rates : 🚫 – 14 cabins in the trees. Per night from 99 to 270€

In a magnificent park: breakfast and park visit included in the price. Packed lunches available.

Surroundings : 🐟 ♒		G P S	Longitude : 0.39212
Leisure activities : 🏇			Latitude : 46.35716
Facilities : 🚿 🏪 🎳			
Nearby : 🍷 🍴			

MANSLE

16230 – Michelin map **324** L4 – pop. 1 543 – alt. 65
▸ Paris 421 – Angoulême 26 – Cognac 53 – Limoges 93

⛺ Municipal Le Champion

☎ 05 45 20 31 41, campinglechampionmansle@gmail.com
Address : rue de Watlington (take the northeastern exit along the D 18, follow the signs for Ruffec and take a right turn)
2 ha (120 pitches) flat, grassy

Near the small town, and close to a race course (horses) and a canoe centre, beside the Charente river.

Surroundings : 🐟 🗔 ♒		G P S	Longitude : 0.18178
Leisure activities : 🏊			Latitude : 45.87801
Facilities : 🚿 🚰 🏖 🖼			
Nearby : 🍴 🛶 🏇 🌳			

MARANS

17230 – Michelin map **324** E2 – pop. 4 623 – alt. 1
▸ Paris 461 – Fontenay-le-Comte 28 – Niort 56 – La Rochelle 24

⛺ Municipal du Bois Dinot

☎ 05 46 01 10 51, www.ville-marans.fr
Address : route de Nantes (500m north along the N 137, 80m from the Marans-La Rochelle canal)
7 ha/3 for camping (170 pitches) flat, grassy
Rentals : ♿ (1 chalet) – 12 🏠.

In the heart of a wooded park with a former velodrome for lovers of 2-wheeled transport.

Surroundings : 🗔 ♒		G P S	Longitude : -0.98945
Leisure activities : 🏇			Latitude : 46.31583
Facilities : ♿ 🚰 🏖 🍽 launderette			
Nearby : 🛶 🚣 pedalos			

Some information or pricing may have changed since the guide went to press. We recommend you check the price list online in advance or at the entrance to the campsite and enquire about possible restrictions.

MARENNES

17320 – Michelin map **324** D5 – pop. 5 608 – alt. 10
▸ Paris 494 – Pons 61 – Rochefort 22 – Royan 31

⛺ Au Bon Air

☎ 05 46 85 02 40, www.aubonair.com
Address : 9 avenue Pierre Voyer (2.5km to the west; at Marennes-Plage)
Opening times : from beginning April to end Sept.
2,4 ha (126 pitches) flat, grassy, sandy
Tariff : 27,70€ ★★ 🚗 🔲 🔌 (16A) – Extra per person 6,30€
Reservation fee 18€
Rental rates : (from beginning April to end Sept.) – 16 🚐 5 🏠. Per night from 35 to 77€ – Per week from 249 to 821€
Reservation fee 18€
🚐 borne 2€ – 🚿 🔲16€

Close to the beach (200m), pitches in the shade with some owner-occupier mobile homes.

Surroundings : 🗔 ♒		G P S	Longitude : -1.13442
Leisure activities : 🍷 🎦 🏇 🏊			Latitude : 45.81882
Facilities : ♿ 🚰 🏖 🔥 🍽 launderette			

For more information on visiting particular towns or regions, consult the relevant regional MICHELIN Green Guide. We also recommend you use the appropriate Michelin regional map to locate your selected campsite, to calculate distances and to work out the best route.

LES MATHES

17570 – Michelin map **324** D5 – pop. 1 719 – alt. 10
▸ Paris 514 – Marennes 18 – Rochefort 40 – La Rochelle 76

⛺ La Pinède 🏊

Cie Bel Air

☎ 05 46 22 45 13, www.campinglapinede.com – limited spaces for one-night stay
Address : 2103 route de la Fouasse (3km to the northwest)
8 ha (372 pitches) flat and relatively flat, grassy
Rentals : ♿ – 192 🚐 – 10 🏠.

A large swimming area, partially covered, with several pitches for tents and caravans, but choose those furthest away from the road.

Surroundings : 🐟 🗔 ♒			
Leisure activities : 🍷 🍴 🎦 🏊 🏇 🎣 🚣 🏹 🚲 🎱 🏊 archery multi-sports ground		G P S	Longitude : -1.17568
Facilities : ♿ 🚰 🏖 – 4 individual sanitary facilities (🚿 💧 🚽 wc) 🔥 🍽 launderette 🏊 🏖			Latitude : 45.72784
Nearby : amusement park			

▲▲▲ L'Estanquet ♣♣

℘ 05 46 22 47 32, www.campinglestanquet.com

Address : route de la Fouasse (3.5km to the northwest)

Opening times : from beginning April to end Sept.

6 ha (387 pitches)

Tariff : 37,50€ ✦✦ ⇌ 🔲 ⚡ (10A) – Extra per person 6€ – Reservation fee 20€

Rental rates : (from beginning April to end Sept.) – 226 🛖 10 🚐 – 20 canvas bungalows. Per night from 43 to 141€ Per week from 189 to 987€ – Reservation fee 20€

A good choice of mobile homes at a water park, with free use of the covered swimming pool and play area at the Les Sables de Cordouan campsite 200m away.

Surroundings : 🏕 ⚜⚜
Leisure activities : ♈ ✕ 🏵 ⛹ 🚣 🚴 🎾 ⚓
⚓ multi-sports ground
Facilities : ♿ ⚓ 🛁 🚿 ♨ launderette 🔌
🚿
Nearby : 🎡 amusement park

Longitude : -1.17661
Latitude : 45.73214
G P S

▲▲▲ L'Orée du Bois ♣♣

℘ 05 46 22 42 43, www.camping-oree-du-bois.fr – limited spaces for one-night stay

Address : 225 route de la Bouverie (3.5km to the northwest, at La Fouasse)

Opening times : from end May to mid Sept.

6 ha (429 pitches) flat

Tariff : 46€ ✦✦ ⇌ 🔲 ⚡ (6A) – Extra per person 10,50€ – Reservation fee 25€

Rental rates : (from end May to mid Sept.) – 170 🛖. Per night from 45 to 80€ – Per week from 225 to 1390€ – Reservation fee 25€

Tent and caravan pitches with refurbished individual sanitary facilities and several luxurious mobile homes.

Surroundings : 🏕 ⚜⚜
Leisure activities : ♈ ✕ 🏠 🏵 ⛹ 🚣 🚴 🎾
⚓ multi-sports ground
Facilities : ♿ ⚓ 🛁 🚿 – 40 individual sanitary facilities (🚿 🛁 🚽 wc) ♨ launderette 🔌 🚿

Longitude : -1.17905
Latitude : 45.72998
G P S

▲ Les Sables de Cordouan

℘ 05 32 09 04 08, www.campingsablesdecordouan.com – limited spaces for one-night stay

Address : route de la Fouasse (situated 3.6km northwest)

Opening times : from beginning April to mid Oct.

3 ha (150 pitches) flat

Tariff : (2013 Price) 37,50€ ✦✦ ⇌ 🔲 ⚡ (10A) – Extra per person 6€ Reservation fee 20€

Rental rates : (from beginning April to mid Oct.) – 30 🛖. Per night from 46 to 138€ – Per week from 219 to 966€ Reservation fee 20€

Campers can also make use of all the services and entertainment provided at the the Estanquet campsite (200m). Not many pitches for tents and caravans.

Surroundings : 🏕 ⚜⚜
Leisure activities : 🚣 🎣
Facilities : ♿ ⚓ ♨ launderette
Nearby : 🔌 ♈ ✕ ⚓ 🎡 amusement park

Longitude : -1.17563
Latitude : 45.73022
G P S

▲ Monplaisir

℘ 05 46 22 50 31, www.campingmonplaisirlesmathes.fr

Address : 26 avenue de La Palmyre (southwestern exit)

Opening times : from beginning April to end Sept.

2 ha (114 pitches) flat, grassy

Tariff : (2013 Price) 24,50€ ✦✦ ⇌ 🔲 ⚡ (10A) Extra per person 6,50€

🚰 borne 4€

Only pitches for tents and caravans – no rental options.

Surroundings : ⚜⚜
Leisure activities : 🏠 ⚓ 🎣
Facilities : ♿ ⚓ 🛁 ♨ launderette
Nearby : ♈ ✕ 🚴 🏇 ⚓

Longitude : -1.15563
Latitude : 45.71541
G P S

MAUZÉ-SUR-LE-MIGNON

79210 – Michelin map **322** B7 – pop. 2 758 – alt. 30
◪ Paris 430 – Niort 23 – Rochefort 40 – La Rochelle 43

▲ Municipal le Gué de la Rivière

℘ 05 49 26 30 35, www.ville-mauze-mignon.fr – 🏠

Address : rue du Port (located 1km northwest along the D 101, follow the signs for St-Hilaire-la-Palud and take the turning to the left; between the Mignon river and the canal)

Opening times : from mid May to beginning Sept.

1,5 ha (75 pitches) flat, grassy

Tariff : ♦ 2,55€ ⇌ 🔲 2,65€ – ⚡ (10A) 3,55€

🚰 borne 4€

Surroundings : 🌲 🏕 ⚜⚜
Leisure activities : 🏠
Facilities : ⚓

Longitude : -0.67959
Latitude : 46.19968
G P S

The prices listed were supplied by the campsite owners in 2013 (if prices were not available, those from the previous year are given). The fees should be regarded as basic charges and may fluctuate with inflation.

MÉDIS

17600 – Michelin map **324** E6 – pop. 2 698 – alt. 29
◪ Paris 498 – Marennes 28 – Mirambeau 48 – Pons 39

▲▲▲ Sites et Paysages Le Clos Fleuri

℘ 05 46 05 62 17, www.le-clos-fleuri.com

Address : 8 impasse du Clos Fleuri (situated 2km southeast along the D 117e 3)

Opening times : from beginning June to mid Sept.

3 ha (120 pitches) flat and relatively flat, grassy

Tariff : 38,50€ ✦✦ ⇌ 🔲 ⚡ (10A) – Extra per person 9,50€ Reservation fee 20€

Rental rates : (from beginning June to mid Sept.) 🎾 – 4 🛖 10 🚐. Per night from 50 to 120€ – Per week from 290 to 760€ Reservation fee 20€

A pleasant rural setting with ample shade from a variety of trees.

Surroundings : 🌲 🏕 ⚜⚜
Leisure activities : ♈ ✕ 🏠 🛎 🚣 🏇 ⚓
Facilities : ♿ ⚓ 🛁 ♨ launderette 🔌 🚿

Longitude : -0.94633
Latitude : 45.63003
G P S

MONTBRON

16220 – Michelin map **324** N5 – pop. 2 161 – alt. 141
▶ Paris 460 – Angoulême 29 – Nontron 25 – Rochechouart 38

🏕 Les Castels Les Gorges du Chambon 🧍🧍

✆ 05 45 70 71 70, www.camping-gorgesduchambon.com

Address : at Le Chambon (4.4km east along the D 6, follow the signs for Piégut-Pluviers, then take left turn for 3.2km along the D 163, follow the signs for Ecuras and take the road to the right; 80m from the Tardoir river (direct access)

Opening times : from end April to mid Sept.

28 ha/7 for camping (132 pitches) flat, grassy

Tariff : (2013 Price) 33,40€ ★★ ⛺ 🔲 🔌 (10A)
Extra per person 9,10€ – Reservation fee 10€

Rental rates : (2013 Price) (from mid April to mid Sept.) ♿
(1 mobile home) – 15 🚐 – 8 🏠 – 4 canvas bungalows
4 tent lodges – 1 gîte. Per night from 28 to 99€ – Per week from 196 to 693€ – Reservation fee 20€

In a pretty, wooded green setting spread out around on an old landscaped and renovated farmhouse.

Surroundings : 🐾 ⛰ ☍ 🌳🌳
Leisure activities : 🍴 ✗ 🎯 🏸 🏃 🚴 ⛳
🛶 🏊 ⛵
Facilities : ♿ ⛽ 🗑 ⛲🚰 launderette 🚿 ⛏
Nearby : 🐎

G P S — Longitude : 0.5593
Latitude : 45.65945

MONTIGNAC-CHARENTE

16330 – Michelin map **324** K5 – pop. 731 – alt. 50
▶ Paris 432 – Angoulême 17 – Cognac 42 – Rochechouart 66

🏕 Municipal les Platanes

✆ 05 45 39 89 16, mairie.montignac-chte@orange.fr – 🏠

Address : 25 avenue de la Boixe (200m northwest along the D 115, follow the signs for Aigré)

Opening times : from beginning June to end Aug.

1,5 ha (100 pitches) flat, grassy

Tariff : ★ 5,25€ ⛺ 🔲 – 🔌 (12A) 6,10€

Choose the shady pitches furthest away from the road.

Surroundings : 🌳🌳
Leisure activities : 🎯
Facilities : ♿ ⛽
Nearby : 🏊 🛶

G P S — Longitude : 0.11797
Latitude : 45.78189

MONTMORILLON

86500 – Michelin map **322** L6 – pop. 6 410 – alt. 100
▶ Paris 354 – Bellac 43 – Le Blanc 32 – Chauvigny 27

🏕 Municipal de l'Allochon

✆ 05 49 91 02 33, www.ville-montmorillon.fr

Address : 31 avenue Fernad-Tribot (take the southeastern exit along the D 54, follow the signs for Le Dorat; 50m from the Gartempe river, beside a stream)

Opening times : from beginning March to end Oct.

2 ha (80 pitches) terraced, flat, grassy

Tariff : ★ 1,71€ ⛺ 1€ 🔲 1€ – 🔌 (10A) 3,49€
🚰 borne

Surroundings : 🌳🌳
Leisure activities : 🎯 🏃
Facilities : ♿ ⛽ 🗑 ⛲🚰 ⛏ 🏠
Nearby : 🏊 🛶 🎣

G P S — Longitude : 0.87526
Latitude : 46.42038

MORTAGNE-SUR-GIRONDE

17120 – Michelin map **324** F7 – pop. 1 027 – alt. 51
▶ Paris 509 – Blaye 59 – Jonzac 30 – Pons 26

🏕 Municipal Bel Air

✆ 05 46 91 48 84, www.mortagne-sur-gironde

Address : towards the port

Opening times : from mid May to end Sept.

1 ha (20 pitches) terraced, flat, grassy

Tariff : 11,60€ ★★ ⛺ 🔲 🔌 (45A) – Extra per person 3€
🚰 borne 7,50€

Several pitches have a panoramic view of the estuary and the marina.

Surroundings : 🐾 ⛰ ☍ 🌳🌳
Leisure activities : 🏃
Facilities : ♿ ⛽🗑 ⛲ 🚿 ⛏ 🏠

G P S — Longitude : -0.79147
Latitude : 45.47974

We value your opinion and welcome your feedback.
Do email us at campingfrance@tp.michelin.com

MOSNAC

17240 – Michelin map **324** G6 – pop. 476 – alt. 23
▶ Paris 501 – Cognac 34 – Gémozac 20 – Jonzac 11

🏕 Municipal les Bords de la Seugne

✆ 05 46 70 48 45, mosnac@mairie17.com

Address : 34 rue de la Seugne (in the village; beside the river)

Opening times : from mid April to mid Oct.

0,9 ha (33 pitches) flat, grassy

Tariff : (2013 Price) ★ 3€ ⛺ 🔲 3€ – 🔌 (0A) 3€

In the village, very simple but attractive; a small site beside the pretty little church.

Surroundings : 🐾 ⛰ Église Saint-Saturnin,
Mosnac ☍ 🌳🌳
Leisure activities : 🛶
Facilities : ⛽🗑 ⛲ 🏠

G P S — Longitude : -0.52293
Latitude : 45.5058

LA PALMYRE

17570 – Michelin map **324** C5
▶ Paris 524 – Poitiers 191 – La Rochelle 77 – Rochefort 46

🏕 Village Siblu Bonne Anse Plage

(rental of mobile homes only)

✆ 05 46 22 40 90, www.siblu.fr/bonneanse

Address : avenue de la Coubre (situated 2km west along the D 25, 400m from the beach)

Opening times : from end May to mid Sept.

18 ha (613 pitches) undulating

Rental rates : (2013 Price) – 500 🚐. Per night from 50 to 213€
Per week from 350 to 1 491€ – Reservation fee 15€
🚰 6 🔲 20€

A mobile home park, most of which belong to owner-occupiers.

Surroundings : ☍ 🌳🌳
Leisure activities : 🍴 ✗ 🎯 🏸 🏋 🏃 🚴 🐎
🏊 ⛵ climbing wall multi-sports ground
Facilities : ♿ ⛽ ⛏ launderette 🚿 ⛏-

G P S — Longitude : -1.19983
Latitude : 45.69843

⛰ Yelloh! Village Parc de la Côte Sauvage ♣♣

𝒫 05 46 22 40 18, www.parc-cote-sauvage.com ✄

Address : at la Coubre (3km west along the D 25)

Opening times : from mid April to mid Sept.

14 ha (400 pitches) undulating, flat, relatively flat, grassy, sandy

Tariff : 49€ ♣♣ ⛺ 🔲 [♿] (10A) – Extra per person 9€

Rental rates : (from mid April to mid Sept.) ✄ – 200 🛏. Per night from 54 to 213€ – Per week from 378 to 1491€

🚐 borne – 🔌 [♿]20€

A wooded setting very near the beach and the la Coubre lighthouse.

Surroundings : 🏖 🛌 ♨♨
Leisure activities : ♈ ✕ 🏠 ♒ 🏃 🛶 🏊 🚴 🏓 🎣 multi-sports ground
Facilities : ♿ ⚡ 🏺 ⛺ ♈ launderette 🧺 🚿

GPS Longitude : -1.22769
Latitude : 45.69584

⛰ Beausoleil

𝒫 05 46 22 30 03, www.campingbeausoleil.com

Address : 20 avenue de la Coubre (take the northwestern exit, 500m from the beach)

Opening times : from beginning June to end Aug.

4 ha (244 pitches) undulating, flat, grassy, sandy

Tariff : (2013 Price) 31,50€ ♣♣ ⛺ 🔲 [♿] (10A)
Extra per person 3,80€ – Reservation fee 17€

Rental rates : (2013 Price) (from beginning April to mid Sept.) 15 🛏 – 2 canvas bungalows. Per week from 197 to 760€ Reservation fee 17€

Tranquil, family-oriented establishment with owner-occupiers and a further hundred or so pitches for tents or caravans.

Surroundings : ♨♨
Leisure activities : 🏠 🛶 🏊 (small swimming pool)
Facilities : ♿ ⚡ 🏺 ♈ launderette 🧺 🚿

GPS Longitude : -1.18301
Latitude : 45.69242

PARTHENAY

79200 – Michelin map **322** E5 – pop. 10 338 – alt. 175
▶ Paris 377 – Bressuire 32 – Châtellerault 79 – Fontenay-le-Comte 69

⛰ Le Bois Vert

𝒫 05 49 64 78 43, www.camping-boisvert.com

Address : 14 rue Boisseau (take the southwestern exit follow the signs for La Roche-sur-Yon and take a right turn after the bridge over the Thouet; near a lake)

Opening times : from beginning April to end Oct.

2 ha (86 pitches) flat, grassy

Tariff : 28€ ♣♣ ⛺ 🔲 [♿] (10A) – Extra per person 6,50€ – Reservation fee 10€

Rental rates : (from beginning April to end Oct.) ♿ – 14 🛏 4 canvas bungalows. Per night from 35 to 91€ – Per week from 175 to 637€ – Reservation fee 10€

🚐 borne 8€ – 🔌 [♿]27,50€

Surroundings : 🛌 ♨
Leisure activities : ♈ 🏠 🏃 🚴 🛶
Facilities : ♿ ⚡ 🏺 ♨ ♈ launderette
Nearby : ✕ 🚿 🛶 ✗ 🎣

GPS Longitude : -0.2675
Latitude : 46.64194

PONS

17800 – Michelin map **324** G6 – pop. 4 446 – alt. 39
▶ Paris 493 – Blaye 64 – Bordeaux 97 – Cognac 24

⛰ Les Moulins de la Vergne

𝒫 05 46 94 11 49, www.moulinsdelavergne.nl

Address : 9 impasse du Moulin de la Vergne (situated 2km north along the D 234, towards Colombiers)

Opening times : Permanent

3 ha/1 for camping (51 pitches) flat, grassy

Tariff : 25€ ♣♣ ⛺ 🔲 [♿] (10A) – Extra per person 4€

🚐 5 🔲 25€

The bar-restaurant at the mill has an attractive terrace; good quality chalet rentals.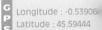

Surroundings : 🏖 ♨
Leisure activities : ♈ ✕ 🏠 🛶 🎣
Facilities : ⚡ ♈ launderette 🚿

GPS Longitude : -0.53906
Latitude : 45.59444

⛺ Municipal le Paradis

𝒫 05 46 91 36 72, ville.pons@smic17.fr

Address : avenue du Paradis (to the west near the swimming pool)

1 ha (60 pitches) flat, grassy

A lovely grass area and a good amount of shade in a simple but very pleasant site.

Surroundings : ♨♨
Leisure activities : 🏠
Facilities : ♿ ⚡ 🏺 ♨ ♈ 🔲
Nearby : 🛶 🏊

GPS Longitude : -0.5553
Latitude : 45.57793

PONT-L'ABBÉ-D'ARNOULT

17250 – Michelin map **324** E5 – pop. 1 716 – alt. 20
▶ Paris 474 – Marennes 23 – Rochefort 19 – La Rochelle 59

⛰ Parc de la Garenne

𝒫 05 46 97 01 46, www.lagarenne.net

Address : 24 avenue Bernard Chambenoit (take the southeastern exit along the D 125, follow the signs for Soulignonne)

2,7 ha (111 pitches) flat, grassy

Rentals : 30 🛏 – 2 canvas bungalows.

Well shaded in part, some leisure activities and very simple sanitary facilities.

Surroundings : 🏖 🛌 ♨
Leisure activities : 🏠 🛶 🚴 ✗ multi-sports ground
Facilities : ♿ ⚡ 🏺 ♨ ♈ launderette 🚿
Nearby : 🛶

GPS Longitude : -0.87096
Latitude : 45.82729

PRAILLES

79370 – Michelin map **322** E7 – pop. 666 – alt. 150
▶ Paris 394 – Melle 15 – Niort 23 – St-Maixent-l'École 13

⛺ Le Lambon

𝒫 05 49 32 85 11, www.lelambon.com

Address : au Plan d'eau du Lambon (2.8km southeast)

Opening times : from beginning April to end Sept.

1 ha (50 pitches) terraced, flat and relatively flat, grassy

Tariff : 12,90€ ♣♣ ⛺ 🔲 [♿] (16A) – Extra per person 4,70€

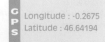

Rental rates : (from beginning April to end Oct.) – 7 🏠 – 39 gîtes. Per night from 67 to 87€ – Per week from 177 to 416€

🚰 borne

200m from a boating centre where a number of activities are offered.

Surroundings : 🏞 ♀♀
Facilities : 🚿 🗑 🍴 launderette
Nearby : 🍴 🍽 🏛 🚣 🎿 🏊 🏖 (beach) 🎣 sports trail

| GPS | Longitude : -0.20753 |
| | Latitude : 46.30055 |

RIVIÈRES

16110 – Michelin map **324** M5 – pop. 1 833 – alt. 75
▶ Paris 445 – Poitiers 108 – Angoulême 26 – Limoges 84

⛺ des Flots

☎ 06 48 51 18 90, www.campinglesflots.16.hebergratuit.com

Address : 714 rue des Flots

Opening times : from mid April to mid Oct.

1 ha (45 pitches) flat, grassy, stony

Tariff : 16,60€ ★★ 🚐 🔌 🔋 (16A) – Extra per person 3,50€
Reservation fee 5€

Rental rates : Permanent – 2 🏕. Per night from 50 to 70€ – Per week from 250 to 380€ – Reservation fee 15€

🚰 borne 2€ – 5 🔲 16,60€

Beside the river and close to the Château de La Rochefoucauld.

Surroundings : 🏞 🏕 ♀
Leisure activities : 🎣
Facilities : 🚿 🗑 🍴
Nearby : 🏊

| GPS | Longitude : 0.3809 |
| | Latitude : 45.74507 |

ROCHEFORT

17300 – Michelin map **324** E4 – pop. 25 317 – alt. 12 – ⚓
▶ Paris 475 – Limoges 221 – Niort 62 – La Rochelle 38

⛺ Le Bateau

☎ 05 46 99 41 00, www.campinglebateau.com

Address : rue des Pêcheurs D'Islande (near the Charente river, along the western bypass (bd Bignon) and follow the signs for Port Neuf, near the aquatic centre)

Opening times : from beginning April to end Oct.

5 ha/1,5 (133 pitches)

Tariff : 15,50€ ★★ 🚐 🔌 🔋 (10A) – Extra per person 4,50€
Reservation fee 15€

Rental rates : (from beginning April to end Oct.) – 39 🏕. Per night from 55 to 108€ – Per week from 290 to 630€ – Reservation fee 15€

🚰 47 🔲 15,50€ – 🚐 🔋15,50€

Many spa bathers in search of peace and quiet come to this site with good access to water.

Surroundings : 🏞 🏕 ♀
Leisure activities : 🍴 🍽 🏛 🚣 🎿 🎣
Facilities : 🚿 🛒 🗑 🔥 🍴 launderette
Nearby : 🎣

| GPS | Longitude : -0.9962 |
| | Latitude : 45.94834 |

*The classification (1 to 5 tents, **black** or **red**) that we award to selected sites in this guide is our own system. It should not be confused with the classification (1 to 5 stars) of official organisations.*

⛺ Municipal Le Rayonnement

☎ 05 46 82 67 70, camping.municipal@ville-rochefort.fr

Address : 3 avenue de la Fosse aux Mâts (near the town centre)

Opening times : from beginning March to end Nov.

2 ha (138 pitches) flat, fine gravel, grassy

Tariff : 16,29€ ★★ 🚐 🔌 🔋 (15A) – Extra per person 2,70€
Reservation fee 30€

Rental rates : (from end Jan. to end Nov.) 🦽 (1 mobile home) 17 🏕. Per week from 245 to 346€ – Reservation fee 30€

🚰 borne – 30 🔲 3€

Surroundings : 🏕 ♀♀
Leisure activities : 🏛 🚣 🚲
Facilities : 🦽 🛒 🗑 🔥 🔥 🍴 launderette

| GPS | Longitude : -0.95835 |
| | Latitude : 45.93 |

LA ROCHE-POSAY

86270 – Michelin map **322** K4 – pop. 1 556 – alt. 112 – ⚓
▶ Paris 325 – Le Blanc 29 – Châteauroux 76 – Châtellerault 23

⛰ Club Airotel La Roche-Posay Vacances 👥

☎ 05 49 86 21 23, www.larocheposay-vacances.com

Address : route de Lésigny (located 1.5km north along the D 5, near the racecourse; beside the Creuse river)

Opening times : from mid April to end Sept.

5,5 ha (200 pitches)

Tariff : 33€ ★★ 🚐 🔌 🔋 (10A) – Extra per person 8€

Rental rates : (from mid April to end Sept.) – 78 🏕. Per night from 49 to 128€ – Per week from 343 to 896€

🚰 10 🔲 20€

Attractively marked out pitches arranged around a partially covered water park.

Surroundings : 🏞 🏕 ♀♀
Leisure activities : 🏛 🎱 🎿 🚣 🚲 🔲 🏊
🏊 🎣 boats to hire 🛶
Facilities : 🦽 🛒 🗑 🔥 🍴 launderette 🚿
Nearby : 🏇

| GPS | Longitude : 0.80963 |
| | Latitude : 46.7991 |

RONCE-LES-BAINS

17390 – Michelin map **324** D5
▶ Paris 505 – Marennes 9 – Rochefort 31 – La Rochelle 68

⛰ Village Siblu La Pignade

(rental of mobile homes only)

☎ 05 46 36 15 35, www.camping-lapignade.com

Address : 45 avenue du Monard (located 1.5km to the south)

Opening times : from end May to mid Sept.

15 ha (482 pitches) flat

Rental rates : 🦽 🚳 – 100 🏕. Per night from 47 to 179€
Per week from 308 to 1 323€ – Reservation fee 15€

A mobile home park, most of which belong to owner-occupiers.

Surroundings : 🏞 🏕 ♀
Leisure activities : 🍴 🍽 🎱 🎿 🚣 🎠 🔲
(open air in season) 🏊 multi-sports ground
entertainment room
Facilities : 🛒 🍴 launderette 🔥 🚿
Nearby : 🚲 🎿 quad biking

| GPS | Longitude : -1.16204 |
| | Latitude : 45.7863 |

⛰ La Clairière ♠♣

📞 05 46 36 36 63, www.camping-la-clairiere.com – limited spaces for one-night stay

Address : rue du Bois de la Pesse (3.6km south along the D 25, follow the signs for Arvert and take turning to the right)

Opening times : from end June to beginning Sept.

12 ha/4 for camping (292 pitches) undulating, flat, grassy, sandy

Tariff : 36€ ♦♦ ⇔ ▣ ⅏ (10A) – Extra per person 8€ – Reservation fee 22€

Rental rates : (from beginning April to end Sept.) ⬳ – 25 ⬚ 8 ⬚. Per night from 85€ – Per week from 325 to 855€ Reservation fee 22€

⬚ borne 3€

Spacious and in a shaded setting, undulating, sometimes a little 'natural'.

Surroundings : 🌲 ♨♨
Leisure activities : ▾ ✕ 🏠 ⊙nighttime ⅋
🛶 🎿 🏊 massages
Facilities : ♿ ⛽ 🔧 ‼ launderette 🚿 ⛽
Nearby : 🐎
GPS Longitude : -1.16844
Latitude : 45.77502

⛰ Les Pins ♠♣

📞 05 46 36 07 75, http://www.activ-loisirs.com – limited spaces for one-night stay

Address : 16 avenue Côte de Beauté (located 1km to the south)

Opening times : from beginning April to beginning Oct.

1,5 ha (81 pitches)

Tariff : 38€ ♦♦ ⇔ ▣ ⅏ (16A) – Extra per person 7€ – Reservation fee 20€

Rental rates : (from beginning April to beginning Nov.) – 33 ⬚ 23 ⬚ – 14 canvas bungalows – 1 gîte. Per night from 76 to 159€ Per week from 204 to 899€ – Reservation fee 20€

Various rental options at varying degrees of comfort and price.

Surroundings : ♨♨
Leisure activities : 🏠 ⅋ 🎿 🚲🖼(open air in season) entertainment room
Facilities : ♿ ⛽ 🔧 ‼ launderette ⛽
Nearby : ✕
GPS Longitude : -1.15862
Latitude : 45.78875

ROYAN

17200 – Michelin map **324** D6 – pop. 18 259 – alt. 20
▶ Paris 504 – Bordeaux 121 – Périgueux 183 – Rochefort 40

⛰ Le Royan

📞 05 46 39 09 06, www.le-royan.com

Opening times : from beginning April to mid Oct.

3,5 ha (194 pitches)

Tariff : (2013 Price) 36€ ♦♦ ⇔ ▣ – Extra per person 9,50€ Reservation fee 20€

Rental rates : (2013 Price) (from beginning April to mid Oct.) 34 ⬚ – 13 ⬚ – 12 mobile homes (without sanitary facilities). Per week from 215 to 815 € – Reservation fee 20€

Various rental options and degrees of comfort; pitches are well marked out, but choose those furthest away from the road.

Surroundings : ⬚ ♨♨
Leisure activities : ▾ ✕ 🏠 🎿 🏊 🏐
Facilities : ♿ ⛽ 🔧 ⛽ ‼ launderette 🚿 ⛽
GPS Longitude : -1.04207
Latitude : 45.64456

⛰ Campéole Clairefontaine ♠♣

📞 05 46 39 08 11, www.campingclairefontaine.com

Address : at Pontaillac, rue du Colonel Lachaux (400m from the beach)

Opening times : from beginning April to end Sept.

5 ha (246 pitches) flat, grassy

Tariff : (2013 Price) 20,70€ ♦♦ ⇔ ▣ ⅏ (10A)
Extra per person 4,80€ – Reservation fee 25€

Rental rates : (2013 Price) (from beginning April to end Sept.) ♿ (1 mobile home) – 33 ⬚ – 40 ⬚ – 50 canvas bungalows – (30 with sanitary facilities and 20 without). Per night from 31 to 65€ Per week from 217 to 1 253€ – Reservation fee 25€

⬚ borne

A pleasant, green site with a good games area; close to shops (300m).

Surroundings : 🌲 ♨♨
Leisure activities : ▾ ✕ 🏠 ⊙ ⅋ 🎿 🏊 🏐 multi-sports ground
Facilities : ♿ ⛽ 🔧 ‼ launderette 🚿 ⛽
Nearby :, casino
GPS Longitude : -1.04977
Latitude : 45.63094

⛰ Le Chant des Oiseaux

📞 05 46 39 47 47, www.camping-royan-chantdesoiseaux.com

Address : 19 rue des Sansonnets (2.3km to the northwest)

Opening times : from mid April to end Sept.

2,5 ha (150 pitches)

Tariff : 19€ ♦♦ ⇔ ▣ ⅏ (5A) – Extra per person 3,90€ – Reservation fee 5€

Rental rates : (from mid April to beginning Oct.) – 36 ⬚ Per night from 126 to 142€ – Per week from 190 to 900€ Reservation fee 16€

⬚ borne – 8 ▣ 19€ – 🔌 ⅏15€

High-quality rental options, some offering accommodation on a hotel-style basis.

Surroundings : 🌲 ♨♨
Leisure activities : ✕ 🏠 ⊙nighttime ⅋ 🏊
Facilities : ♿ ⛽ 🔧 🔧 ‼ launderette 🚿
GPS Longitude : -1.02872
Latitude : 45.6466

ST-AUGUSTIN-SUR-MER

17570 – Michelin map **324** D5 – pop. 1 219 – alt. 10
▶ Paris 512 – Marennes 23 – Rochefort 44 – La Rochelle 81

⛰ Le Logis du Breuil

📞 05 46 23 23 45, www.logis-du-breuil.com

Address : 36 rue du Centre (located to the southeast along the D 145, follow the signs for Royan)

Opening times : from beginning May to end Sept.

30 ha/8,5 for camping (390 pitches) undulating, flat, grassy, wood

Tariff : 31,80€ ♦♦ ⇔ ▣ ⅏ (10A) – Extra per person 7,95€ Reservation fee 10€

Rental rates : (from beginning May to end Sept.) – 7 ⬚ – 1 ⬚ 5 apartments. Per week from 290 to 750€ – Reservation fee 20€

On the edge of the St Augustin forest, with vast green spaces and meadows. Ideal for relaxation or ball games.

Surroundings : 🌲 ♨♨
Leisure activities : ▾ ✕ 🏠 🎿 🚲 🏐 🏊 multi-sports ground
Facilities : ♿ ⛽ 🔧 – 4 individual sanitary facilities (🚿 🚽 wc) ‼ launderette 🚿 ⛽
GPS Longitude : -1.09612
Latitude : 45.67445

ST-CYR

6130 – Michelin map **322** I4 – pop. 1 024 – alt. 62
◼ Paris 321 – Poitiers 18 – Tours 85 – Joué 82

▲▲▲ Flower Lac de St-Cyr

𝒫 05 49 62 57 22, www.campinglacdesaintcyr.com

Address : parc de St-Cyr (located 1.5km northeast along the D 4,
82, follow the signs for Bonneuil-Matours and take road to the left,
near a lake - from N10, access via La Tricherie)

Opening times : from beginning April to beginning Oct.

,4 ha (198 pitches) flat, grassy

Tariff : 30€ ♦♦ ⬅ 🔲 (10A) – Extra per person 3€

Rental rates : (from beginning April to beginning Oct.) – 32 🚐
yurts – 3 tent lodges. Per night from 35 to 120€ – Per week
from 175 to 840€

Surroundings : ≤ ⌂ 🎿 ⚠
Leisure activities : ✗ 🏠 🎣 🏕 🏂 🚴
✂
Facilities : 🔥 ☛ 🚿 🛁 🚰 🍴 launderette 🔌 🚿
Nearby : 🍸 🏊 🎣 🚣 pedalos

ST-GEORGES-DE-DIDONNE

7110 – Michelin map **324** D6 – pop. 5 055 – alt. 7
◼ Paris 505 – Blaye 84 – Bordeaux 117 – Jonzac 56

▲▲▲ Bois-Soleil 👫👤

𝒫 05 46 05 05 94, www.bois-soleil.com 🌐 (from end June to end Aug)

Address : 2 avenue de Suzac (situated to the south along the D 25,
follow the signs for Meschers-sur-Gironde)

Opening times : from beginning April to beginning Oct.

0 ha (453 pitches) undulating, terraced, flat, grassy

Tariff : 47€ ♦♦ ⬅ 🔲 (16A) – Reservation fee 30€

Rental rates : (from beginning April to beginning Oct.) 🌐
9 🚐 – 8 🏠 – 7 studios. Per night from 30 to 200€ – Per week
from 180 to 1350€ – Reservation fee 30€
🚰 borne 5€

The site is in 3 sections: one section with 200 owner-occupier
mobile homes, one with good shade and some pitches near
the road, and a tranquil section with rentals on terraces with a
panoramic view of the sea.

Surroundings : ⌂ 🎿 ⚠
Leisure activities : 🍸 ✗ 🏠 🎣 🏕 🏂
hammam 🏕 🚴 ✂ 🏊 multi-sports ground
Facilities : 🔥 ☛ 🚿 🛁 🚰 – 6 individual
sanitary facilities (🚿 🚽 wc) 🔌 🚿 🍴
launderette 🔌 🚿
Nearby : 🐎

ST-GEORGES-LÈS-BAILLARGEAUX

6130 – Michelin map **322** I4 – pop. 3 888 – alt. 100
◼ Paris 329 – Poitiers 12 – Joué 89 – Châtellerault 23

▲▲▲ Kawan Village Le Futuriste

𝒫 05 49 52 47 52, www.camping-le-futuriste.fr

Address : rue du Château (south of the town, access via the D 20)

Opening times : Permanent

ha (112 pitches) small lake

Tariff : ♦ 3,50€ ⬅ 4,30€ 🔲 24,70€ – (6A) 4,40€ – Reservation
fee 15€

Rental rates : Permanent 🌐 – 4 🚐 – 6 🏠. Per night
from 75 to 106€ – Per week from 418 to 833€ – Reservation fee
15€
🚰 borne 6€

Surroundings : ≤ Futuroscope ⌂ 🎿
Leisure activities : 🍸 ✗ 🏠 🏕 🏂 🚣
multi-sports ground
Facilities : 🔥 ☛ 🚿 🛁 🚰 🍴 launderette
🚿

GPS
Longitude : 0.39543
Latitude : 46.66468

ST-HILAIRE-LA-PALUD

79210 – Michelin map **322** B7 – pop. 1 603 – alt. 15
◼ Paris 436 – Poitiers 104 – Niort 24 – La Rochelle 41

▲▲▲ Le Lidon

𝒫 05 49 35 33 64, www.le-lidon.com

Address : at Lidon (3km west along the D 3 follow the signs for
Courçon and take road to the left, at the canoeing centre)

Opening times : from mid April to mid Sept.

3 ha (140 pitches) flat, grassy

Tariff : 28€ ♦♦ ⬅ 🔲 (10A) Extra per person 6,50€ – Reservation
fee 13,50€

Rental rates : (from mid April to mid Sept.) – 1 caravan – 3 🏠
4 canvas bungalows – 9 tent lodges. Per night from 44 to 96€
Per week from 220 to 672€ – Reservation fee 13,50€
🚰 borne 4€

Surroundings : 🏝 🎿
Leisure activities : 🍸 ✗ 🏠 🚴 🏊 🚣 boats
to hire 🏊
Facilities : 🔥 ☛ 🚿 🛁 🚰 🍴 launderette 🚿

GPS
Longitude : -0.74324
Latitude : 46.28379

These symbols are used for a campsite that is exceptional
in its category:

▲▲▲...▲ *Particularly pleasant setting, quality*
          and range of services available

🏝🏝   *Tranquil, isolated site – quiet site,*
          particularly at night

≤≤   *Exceptional view – interesting or panoramic*
          view

ST-JEAN-D'ANGÉLY

17400 – Michelin map **324** G4 – pop. 7 581 – alt. 25
◼ Paris 444 – Angoulême 70 – Cognac 35 – Niort 48

▲▲▲ Val de Boutonne

𝒫 05 46 32 26 16, campingcharentemaritime17.com

Address : 56 quai de Bernouet (take the northwestern exit, follow
the signs for La Rochelle, then take left turning onto Av. du Port
(D 18))

1,8 ha (99 pitches) flat, grassy

Rentals : 13 🚐 – 5 🏠.
🚰 borne

A pleasant, simple site; only basic sanitary facilities, but not far
from a good boating centre.

Surroundings : 🏝 🎿
Leisure activities : 🏠 🏕 🚴 🏊
Facilities : 🔥 ☛ 🚿 🛁 🍴 launderette
Nearby : 🍸 ✗ 🏐 🏊 🚣 watersports centre

GPS
Longitude : -0.53638
Latitude : 45.94877

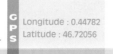

GPS
Longitude : 0.44782
Latitude : 46.72056

GPS
Longitude : -0.98629
Latitude : 45.58371

ST-JUST-LUZAC

17320 – Michelin map **324** D5 – pop. 1 838 – alt. 5
▶ Paris 502 – Rochefort 23 – La Rochelle 59 – Royan 26

 Les Castels Séquoia Parc

𝒫 05 46 85 55 55, www.sequoiaparc.com

Address : at La Josephtrie (2.7km northwest along the D 728, follow the signs for Marennes and take the road to the right)

Opening times : from mid May to beginning Sept.

45 ha/28 for camping (460 pitches) flat, grassy

Tariff : 55€ ♣ ♣ ⇜ 回 ⑭ (10A)
Extra per person 10€ – Reservation fee 30€

Rental rates : (from mid May to beginning Sept.) ♿ ⇝ – 320 🚐 40 🏠. Per night from 44 to 98€ Per week from 308 to 1687€

Pretty swimming area near the outbuildings of a château in a park with a variety of trees and flowers.

Surroundings : 🐾 ⛱ ♀♀
Leisure activities : 🍷 ✕ 🏛 🎣 ✳ 🛶 🚴 ⛷ 🎿 🛶 wildlife park, tourist information multi-sports ground
Facilities : ♿ ⌁ 🛁 🚿 🍴 launderette 🛒 🏊

GPS Longitude : -1.06046
Latitude : 45.81173

ST-LAURENT-DE-LA-PRÉE

17450 – Michelin map **324** D4 – pop. 1 814 – alt. 7
▶ Paris 483 – Rochefort 10 – La Rochelle 31

Domaine des Charmilles

𝒫 05 46 84 00 05, www.domainedescharmilles.com

Address : at Fouras, 1541 route de l'Océan (2.2km northwest along the D 214e 1, follow the signs for Fouras and turn right onto D 937, follow the signs for La Rochelle)

Opening times : from end April to mid Sept.

5 ha (270 pitches) flat, grassy

Tariff : 34€ ♣ ♣ ⇜ 回 ⑭ (10A) – Extra per person 6€ – Reservation fee 25€

Rental rates : (from end April to mid Sept.) ⇝ (July–Aug.) 75 🚐 – 18 🏠. Per night from 37 to 133€ – Per week from 259 to 929€ – Reservation fee 25€

There are pitches for tents or caravans.

Surroundings : ⛱ ♀♀
Leisure activities : 🍷 🏛 🌙 nighttime ✳ 🛶 🚲 🏊 🎿 multi-sports ground
Facilities : ♿ ⌁ 🛁 🚿 🍴 launderette 🏊 🛒

GPS Longitude : -1.05034
Latitude : 45.99052

Le Pré Vert

𝒫 05 46 84 89 40, www.camping-prevert.com

Address : rue du Petit Loir (2.3km northeast along the D 214, follow the signs for la Rochelle; at St-Pierre – take the expressway, Fouras exit)

3 ha (168 pitches) terraced, flat, grassy

Rentals : 50 🚐.

Plenty of mobile homes but few pitches for tents and caravans, laid out around a naturally filtered pool.

Surroundings : ⛱ ♀♀
Leisure activities : ✕ 🏛 ✳ 🛶 🏊 (pool)
Facilities : ♿ ⌁ 🛁 🚿 🍴 launderette 🛒

GPS Longitude : -1.01917
Latitude : 45.99046

ST-NAZAIRE-SUR-CHARENTE

17780 – Michelin map **324** D4 – pop. 1 124 – alt. 14
▶ Paris 491 – Fouras 27 – Rochefort 13 – La Rochelle 49

L'Abri-Cotier

𝒫 05 46 84 81 65, www.camping-la-rochelle.net

Address : 26 La Bernardière (located 1km southwest along the D 125e1)

Opening times : from beginning April to end Sept.

1,8 ha (100 pitches)

Tariff : 24,80€ ♣ ♣ ⇜ 回 ⑭ (6A) – Extra per person 5,20€ – Reservation fee 20€

Rental rates : (from beginning April to end Sept.) ♿ (1 mobile home) – 30 🚐 – 5 🏠. Per week from 255 to 725€ – Reservation fee 20€

🚰 borne 3€

A good amount of shade, marked-out pitches and both new and slightly older rental accommodation.

Surroundings : 🐾 ⛱ ♀♀
Leisure activities : 🍷 ✕ 🏛 🛶 🖼 (open air in season)
Facilities : ♿ ⌁ 🛁 🍴 launderette 🛒 refrigerators

GPS Longitude : -1.05856
Latitude : 45.93349

The Michelin classification (⌂⌂⌂⌂… ⌂) is totally independent of the official star classification system awarded by the local prefecture or other official organisation.

ST-PALAIS-SUR-MER

17420 – Michelin map **324** D6 – pop. 3 926 – alt. 5
▶ Paris 512 – La Rochelle 82 – Royan 6

Côte de Beauté

𝒫 05 46 23 20 59, www.camping-cote-de-beaute.com

Address : 157 avenue de la Grande Côte (2.5km to the northwest, 50m from the sea)

Opening times : from mid April to end Sept.

1,7 ha (115 pitches) flat, grassy

Tariff : 33,10€ ♣ ♣ ⇜ 回 ⑭ (6A) – Extra per person 5,10€ Reservation fee 23€

Rental rates : (from mid April to end Sept.) – 13 🚐 – 1 tent lodge. Per night from 29 to 92€ – Per week from 200 to 645€ Reservation fee 23€

🚰 borne

Some pitches above the road have a panoramic view of the ocean.

Surroundings : ⛱ ♀
Leisure activities : 🏛 🛶
Facilities : ♿ ⌁ 🛁 🍴 🖼
Nearby : 🏊 🍷 ✕ 🛒

GPS Longitude : -1.1191
Latitude : 45.64973

ST-PIERRE-DE-MAILLÉ

36260 – Michelin map **322** L4 – pop. 925 – alt. 79
▶ Paris 333 – Le Blanc 22 – Châtellerault 32 – Chauvigny 21

⚠ Municipal Le Grand Pré

🖉 05 49 48 64 11, www.camping-saintpierredemaille.com/

Address : 16 route de Vicq (take northwestern exit along the D 11; beside the Gartempe river)

3 ha (93 pitches)

Rentals : 4 canvas bungalows – 5 tent lodges.
Sports camps and groups are welcome.

Surroundings : 🐾 ♨️
Leisure activities : ⛳🏊🎣 guided walks ✤
Facilities : launderette

GPS Longitude : 0.83897
Latitude : 46.68463

ST-SAVINIEN

17350 – Michelin map **324** F4 – pop. 2 413 – alt. 18
▶ Paris 457 – Rochefort 28 – La Rochelle 62 – St-Jean-d'Angély 15

⛰ L'Île aux Loisirs

🖉 05 46 90 35 11, www.ilesauxloirs.com

Address : 102 rue de St-Savinien (500m west along the D 18, follow the signs for Pont-l'Abbé-d'Arnoult; between the Charente river and the canal, 200m from a small lake)

Opening times : from beginning April to end Sept.

1,8 ha (82 pitches) flat, grassy

Tariff : (2013 Price) 17,80€ ✶✶ 🚐 🔌 (10A) – Extra per person 5,70€ – Reservation fee 16€

Rental rates : (from beginning April to end Sept.) – 17 . Per night from 64 to 86€ – Per week from 273 to 585€ Reservation fee 16€

🛢 🛒 17,80€

Surroundings : ⌂ ♨️
Leisure activities : 🍽✗🏊🚲✤
Facilities : ♿ ☕ ☆🚰 launderette ♨
Nearby : ✂🏔🏊🎣⚓ sports trail

GPS Longitude : -0.68427
Latitude : 45.87786

ST-SORNIN

17600 – Michelin map **324** E5 – pop. 303 – alt. 16
▶ Paris 495 – Marennes 13 – Rochefort 24 – La Rochelle 60

⚠ Le Valerick

🖉 05 46 85 15 95, www.camping-le-valerick.fr

Address : 1 La Mauvinière (1.3km northeast along the D 118, follow the signs for Pont-l'Abbé)

Opening times : from beginning April to end Sept.

1,5 ha (50 pitches) flat and relatively flat, grassy, wood

Tariff : 20,60€ ✶✶ 🚐 🔌 (6A) – Extra per person 4,40€

Rental rates : (from beginning April to end Sept.) ✗ – 2 .
Per week 650€

An undulating site, very well maintained with basic sanitary facilities.

Surroundings : ♨️
Leisure activities : ✗🏊
Facilities : ♿ ☕ 🚮🚰📶

GPS Longitude : -0.96521
Latitude : 45.77446

ST-YRIEIX-SUR-CHARENTE

16710 – Michelin map **324** K5 – pop. 7 025 – alt. 53
▶ Paris 451 – Poitiers 114 – Angoulême 7 – La Rochelle 142

⛰ du Plan d'Eau

🖉 05 45 92 14 64, www.camping-angouleme.fr

Address : 1 rue du Camping

Opening times : from beginning April to end Oct.

6 ha (148 pitches) flat, grassy, stony

Tariff : 19,30€ ✶✶ 🚐 🔌 (10A) – Extra per person 4,55€

Rental rates : (from beginning April to end Oct.) ♿ (1 mobile home) – 15 🏠. Per night from 36 to 82€ – Per week from 198 to 517€

🛢 borne 2,50€ – 14 🔲 9€

Located near Angoulême town centre with a bus stop for trips to town.

Surroundings : 🐾 ⌂
Leisure activities : 🎯🚣🚲 multi-sports ground
Facilities : ♿ ☕ 🍴 ☆🚰 launderette
Nearby : 🚂 hammam jacuzzi 🏊 (beach) 🏄🎣💧 watersports centre

GPS Longitude : 0.13808
Latitude : 45.67652

Key to rentals symbols :

12 🏠   *Number of mobile homes*
20 🏡   *Number of chalets*
6 🛏   *Number of rooms to rent*
Per night   *Minimum/maximum rate per night*
30–50€
Per week   *Minimum/maximum rate per week*
300–1,000€

SAUJON

17600 – Michelin map **324** E5 – pop. 6 636 – alt. 7
▶ Paris 499 – Poitiers 165 – La Rochelle 71 – Saintes 28

⛰ Lac de Saujon ▲⁑

🖉 05 46 06 82 99, www.campingsaujon.com

Address : voie des Tourterelles

Opening times : from beginning April to mid Oct.

3,7 ha (150 pitches) flat, grassy

Tariff : 24,50€ ✶✶ 🚐 🔌 (10A) – Extra per person 5€ – Reservation fee 19€

Rental rates : (from beginning March to mid Nov.) ✗ – 36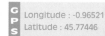
4 🏡 – 4 canvas bungalows. Per night 100 € – Per week from 190 to 680€ – Reservation fee 19€

🛢 borne 5€ – 13 🔲 12€ – 🛒 🔌11,40€

A pleasant site beside a large lake; a high standard of rental accommodation.

Surroundings : 🐾
Leisure activities : 🍽✗🎯🚶🚣🚲
Facilities : ♿ ☕ ☆🚮🚰 launderette 🏊 ☆
Nearby : 🎣🏊🏊🐎 fitness trail

GPS Longitude : -0.93848
Latitude : 45.68282

SECONDIGNY

79130 – Michelin map **322** D5 – pop. 1 773 – alt. 177
▶ Paris 391 – Bressuire 27 – Champdeniers 15 – Coulonges-sur-l'Autize 22

Le Moulin des Effres

☎ 05 49 95 61 97, www.campinglemoulindeseffres.fr

Address : take the southern exit along the D 748, follow the signs for Niort and take road to the left, near a lake

Opening times : from mid April to end Sept.

2 ha (90 pitches)

Tariff : (2013 Price) 18€ ✻✻ ⬅ 🅴 🚰 (6A) – Extra per person 3,70€ Reservation fee 10€

Rental rates : (2013 Price) (from mid April to end Sept.) – 17 🚍 3 tipis – 2 tent lodges. Per week from 154 to 616€ – Reservation fee 10€

🚐 borne 5€

Surroundings : 🏊 🛏 🔆🔆
Leisure activities : 🏛 🚲 🛶 ⛷
Facilities : 🔆 🚿 (Jun-Aug) ⛺ 🚾 🔳
Nearby : 🍽 ✕ 🛶 🎿 🎯 🚣 pedalos

G P S Longitude : -0.41418
Latitude : 46.60421

SEMUSSAC

17120 – Michelin map **324** E6 – pop. 1 998 – alt. 36
▶ Paris 520 – Poitiers 187 – La Rochelle 85 – Angoulême 111

Le 2 B

☎ 05 46 05 95 16, www.camping-2b.com

Address : 9 chemin des Bardonneries (3.8km east along the D 730, follow the signs for St-Georges-de-Didonne)

Opening times : from beginning April to end Sept.

1,8 ha (93 pitches)

Tariff : 24€ ✻✻ ⬅ 🅴 🚰 (10A) – Extra per person 5€ – Reservation fee 12€

Rental rates : (from beginning April to end Sept.) – 20 🚍. Per night from 37 to 92€ – Per week from 250 to 650€

Choose the pitches away from the road if possible.

Surroundings : 🔆🔆
Leisure activities : 🍽 ✕ 🏛 🛶 🎯 🎿 ⛷
Facilities : 🔆 🚾 ⛺ 🚾 launderette

G P S Longitude : -0.94793
Latitude : 45.6041

SIREUIL

16440 – Michelin map **324** K6 – pop. 1 189 – alt. 26
▶ Paris 460 – Angoulême 16 – Barbezieux 24 – Cognac 35

Nizour

☎ 05 45 90 56 27, www.campingdunizour.com

Address : 2 route de la Charente (located 1.5km southeast along the D 7, follow the signs for Blanzac, turn left before the bridge; 120m from the Charente river (direct access))

Opening times : from mid April to end Sept.

1,6 ha (56 pitches) flat, grassy

Tariff : 20,50€ ✻✻ ⬅ 🅴 🚰 (6A) – Extra per person 4,75€ Reservation fee 8€

Rental rates : (from mid May to beginning Sept.) 🎿 – 5 🚍. Per week 537€ – Reservation fee 8€

🚐 borne 5€ – 1 🅴 10€

Choose the pitches furthest away from the road in preference.

Surroundings : 🛏 🔆🔆
Leisure activities : 🍽 🏛 🛶 🚲 🎿 ⛷
Facilities : 🔆 🚿 ⛺ launderette
Nearby : 🎿 ⚓

G P S Longitude : 0.02418
Latitude : 45.60688

THORS

17160 – Michelin map **324** I5 – pop. 418 – alt. 23
▶ Paris 466 – Angoulême 53 – Cognac 84 – Limoges 143

Le Relais de l'Étang

☎ 05 46 58 26 81, www.paysdematha.com

Address : route de Cognac (heading north on the D 121, turn off right, rue de Pilori, rte de Matha, near a lake)

0,8 ha (25 pitches)

Rentals : 3 🚍.

A small, simple site, laid out in a semi-circle around a lake.

Surroundings : 🏊 🛏 🔆🔆
Leisure activities : 🛶
Facilities : 🔆 🚿 ⛺ 🚾 launderette
Nearby : 🍽 ✕ 🎯 🏖 (beach) 🚣 pedalos

G P S Longitude : -0.30822
Latitude : 45.83662

VAUX-SUR-MER

17640 – Michelin map **324** D6 – pop. 3 835 – alt. 12
▶ Paris 514 – Poitiers 181 – La Rochelle 75 – Rochefort 44

Le Nauzan-Plage

☎ 05 46 38 29 13, www.campinglenauzanplage.com

Address : 39 avenue de Nauzan-Plage (500m from the beach)

Opening times : from beginning May to end Sept.

3,9 ha (239 pitches) flat, grassy

Tariff : 38,10€ ✻✻ ⬅ 🅴 🚰 (10A) – Extra per person 8,50€ Reservation fee 20€

Rental rates : Permanent – 37 🚍. Per night from 36 to 96€ Per week from 150 to 1120€ – Reservation fee 20€

🚐 borne 8€ – 3 🅴 10€ – 🚌 🚰10€

The site is beside a park and is crossed by a pretty stream.

Surroundings : 🛏 🔆
Leisure activities : 🍽 ✕ 🏛 🕐daytime 🛶 ⛷
Facilities : 🔆 🚿 ⛺ 🚾 launderette 🚿 ⛺
Nearby : ✕ 🖼 🚣

G P S Longitude : -1.07196
Latitude : 45.64295

Le Val-Vert

☎ 05 46 38 25 51, www.val-vert.com

Address : 108 avenue Fréderic Garnier (to the southwest of the town)

Opening times : from mid April to end Sept.

3 ha (181 pitches) terraced, flat, grassy, stony

Tariff : ✻ ⬅ 🅴 32,70€ – 🚰 (10A) 6,20€ – Reservation fee 16€
Rental rates : (from mid April to end Sept.) – 34 🚍 – 37 🏠 Per week from 250 to 799€ – Reservation fee 16€
🚐 borne
Beside a pretty park, lake and stream.

Surroundings : 🛏 🔆🔆
Leisure activities : ✕ 🏛 🛶 🚲 🎿
Facilities : 🔆 🚿 🅴 ⛺ 🚾 launderette ⛺
Nearby : ✕ 🖼 🚣

G P S Longitude : -1.06299
Latitude : 45.64357

VOUILLÉ

86190 – Michelin map **322** G5 – pop. 3 498 – alt. 118
▶ Paris 345 – Châtellerault 46 – Parthenay 34 – Poitiers 18

🔺 Municipal

📞 05 49 51 90 10, www.vouille86.fr

Address : chemin de la Piscine (located in the town; beside the Auxance river)

Opening times : from beginning June to end Aug.

0,5 ha (48 pitches) flat, grassy

Tariff : (2013 Price) 👤 3,80 € 🚗 2,50 € 🔲 2,50 € – 🔌 (10A) 5 €

Surroundings :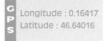
Leisure activities : 🛶 🏊 🎣
Facilities : 🚿 🔧 ✉ 🔲
Nearby : ✗

G
P Longitude : 0.16417
S Latitude : 46.64016

VOUNEUIL-SUR-VIENNE

86210 – Michelin map **322** J4 – pop. 1 981 – alt. 58
▶ Paris 316 – Châtellerault 12 – Chauvigny 20 – Poitiers 27

⛰ Les Chalets de Moulière – (exclusive rental chalets)

📞 05 49 85 84 40, www.camping-les-chalets-de-mouliere-vouneuil-sur-vienne – traditional camp. spaces also available

Address : rue des Ardentes (take the eastern exit along the D 15, follow the signs for Monthoiron and take turning to the left, 60m from the Vienne (direct access)

1,5 ha flat

Rental rates : ♿ (1 chalet) – 24 🏠.

Welcomes summer camps.

Leisure activities : 🛖 🚲 🎣
Facilities : � 🚽 🔲 🚿
Nearby : ✗ 🎣

G
P Longitude : 0.5445
S Latitude : 46.71965

PROVENCE-ALPES-CÔTE D'AZUR

B. Jaubert / age fotostock

A new day dawns in sun-drenched Provence. As the fishmongers tell jokes, chat and sell their freshly-caught fish under clear blue skies, you cannot help but fall in love with the relaxed, happy-go-lucky spirit of Marseilles. In the countryside beyond, the sun casts its first amber rays across the ochre walls of a hilltop village and over the glorious fields of lavender in the valley below. The steady chirping of the cicadas is interrupted only by the gentle sound of sheep bells ringing in the hills. Slow down to the gentle pace of the villagers and join them as they gather within the refreshingly cool walls of a local café. However, by 2pm you may begin to wonder where everyone has gone. On hot afternoons, most people exercise their traditional right to a siesta, even those who frequent the chic beaches of St Tropez and in the seaside cabins of the Camargue. Fear not, it will soon be time to wake up and prepare for a serious game of *pétanque* and a chilled glass of pastis.

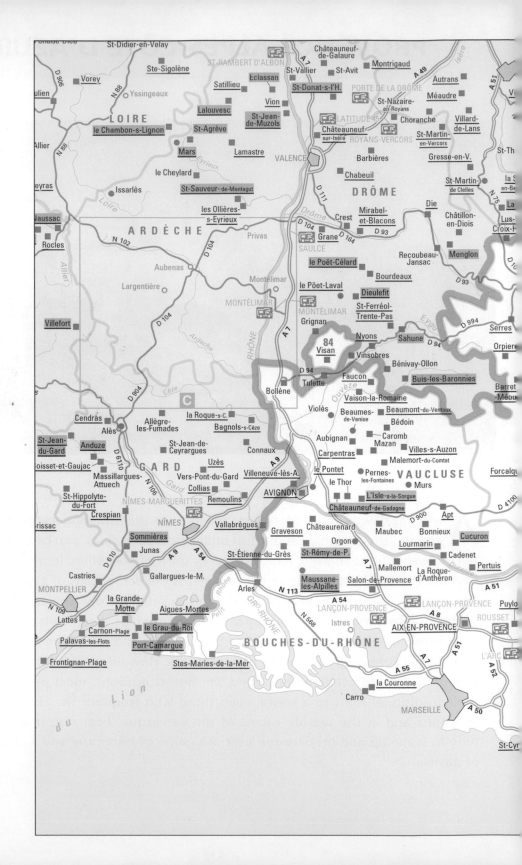

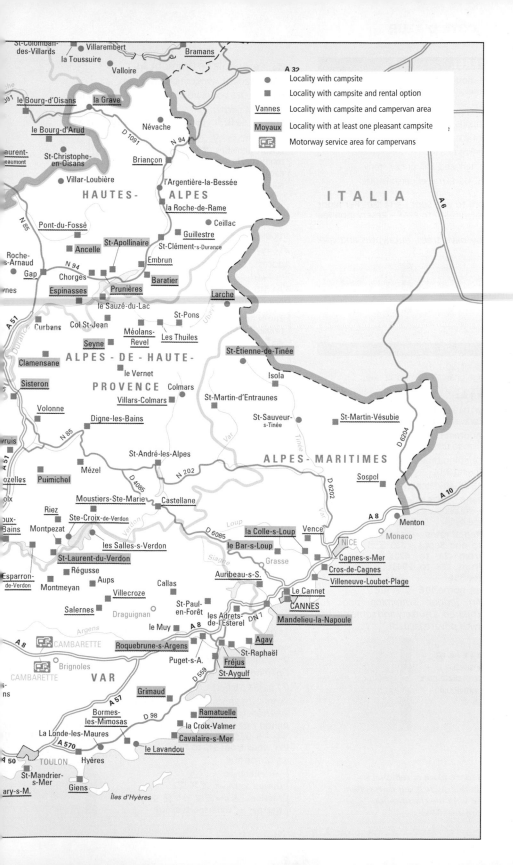

Legend

- Locality with campsite
- Locality with campsite and rental option
- Vannes — Locality with campsite and campervan area
- Moyaux — Locality with at least one pleasant campsite
- Motorway service area for campervans

St-Colomban-des-Villards
Villarembert
la Toussuire
Valloire
Bramans
A 32
le Bourg-d'Oisans
la Grave
D 1091
Névache
N 94
le Bourg-d'Arud
...aurent-...eaumont
St-Christophe-en-Oisans
Briançon
Villar-Loubière
l'Argentière-la-Bessée
HAUTES- ALPES
la Roche-de-Rame
ITALIA
A 6
D 091
Pont-du-Fossé
Ceillac
Guillestre
St-Apollinaire
Ancelle
St-Clément-s-Durance
N 85
Roches-s-Arnaud
N 94
Embrun
Gap
Chorges
Baratier
Espinasses
Prunières
le Sauzé-du-Lac
Larche
...rnes
A 57
Curbans
Col St-Jean
St-Pons
A 57
Méolans-Revel
Les Thuiles
Seyne
St-Étienne-de-Tinée
Clamensane
ALPES - DE - HAUTE-
le Vernet
Isola
Sisteron
PROVENCE
Colmars
St-Martin-d'Entraunes
Volonne
Villars-Colmars
St-Sauveur-s-Tinée
St-Martin-Vésubie
D 6204
Digne-les-Bains
Var
...ruis
A 57
St-André-les-Alpes
ALPES - MARITIMES
...ozelles
Puimichel
Mézel
N 202
Tinée
D 6202
Sospel
A 10
...olx
Moustiers-Ste-Marie
Castellane
A 8
Menton
Riez
Ste-Croix-de-Verdon
Loup
la Colle-s-Loup
Vence
NICE
Monaco
...ux-...Bains
Montpezat
D 4085
D 6085
le Bar-s-Loup
Cagnes-s-Mer
les Salles-s-Verdon
Grasse
Cros-de-Cagnes
Esparron-de-Verdon
St-Laurent-du-Verdon
Siagne
Auribeau-s-S.
Villeneuve-Loubet-Plage
Régusse
Montmeyan
Aups
Callas
Le Cannet
Villecroze
St-Paul-en-Forêt
CANNES
Salernes
Draguignan
les Adrets-de-l'Esterel
DN 7
Mandelieu-la-Napoule
Argens
le Muy
A 8
A 8
CAMBARETTE
Roquebrune-s-Argens
Agay
St-Raphaël
Brignoles
Puget-s-A.
Fréjus
CAMBARETTE
VAR
A 57
D 559
St-Aygulf
Grimaud
Bormes-les-Mimosas
D 98
Ramatuelle
la Croix-Valmer
La Londe-les-Maures
A 570
Cavalaire-s-Mer
le Lavandou
TOULON
Hyères
A 50
St-Mandrier-s-Mer
...ary-s-M.
Giens
Îles d'Hyères

LES ADRETS-DE-L'ESTEREL

83600 – Michelin map **340** P4 – pop. 2 063 – alt. 295
▶ Paris 881 – Cannes 26 – Draguignan 44 – Fréjus 17

⛰ Les Philippons

📞 04 94 40 90 67, www.lesphilippons.com

Address : 378 route de l'Argentière (head 3km east along the D 237)

Opening times : from mid April to end Sept.

5 ha (150 pitches) very uneven, terraced, flat, grassy, stony

Tariff : 32,30€ ✶✶ 🚗 🔲 ⚡ (10A) – Extra per person 6,20€
Reservation fee 20€

Rental rates : (from mid April to end Sept.) – 14 🏠. Per night from 43 to 128€ – Per week from 301 to 896€ – Reservation fee 30€

A natural setting shaded by olive trees, eucalyptus and cork oaks.

Surroundings : ⟦symbols⟧	
Leisure activities : 🍷 ✕ ⛵ 🏊	**G** Longitude : 6.84002
Facilities : 🚿 🍳 🍽 launderette 🧺 refrigerators	**P S** Latitude : 43.52876

AGAY

83530 – Michelin map **340** Q5 – alt. 20
▶ Paris 880 – Cannes 34 – Draguignan 43 – Fréjus 12

⛰ Esterel Caravaning ♨️

📞 04 94 82 03 28, www.esterel-caravaning.fr

Address : avenue des Golfs (situated 4km to the northwest)

Opening times : from beginning April to end Sept.

15 ha (405 pitches)

Tariff : 55€ ✶✶ 🚗 🔲 ⚡ (16A)
Extra per person 11€ – Reservation fee 40€

Rental rates : (from beginning April to end Sept.) – 330 🚐. Per night from 24 to 420€ – Per week from 168 to 2940€ – Reservation fee 35€

🚐 borne 10€ – 2 🔲 10€

An indoor swimming pool for children, a nursery and some pitches with private jacuzzi!

Surroundings : ⟦symbols⟧	
Leisure activities : 🍷 ✕ 🎮 🏊 🏋️ hammam ⛵ 🚴 ⚽ 🏓 🏊 disco, multi-sports ground, spa centre, skate park	**G** Longitude : 6.83256
Facilities : 🚿 🍳 🔲 🍳 – 18 individual sanitary facilities (🚿 🚽 wc) 🧺 🍽 launderette 🧺	**P S** Latitude : 43.45419
Nearby : squash	

LAROCHE

⛰ Campéole Le Dramont ♨️

📞 04 94 82 07 68, www.camping-mer.com

Address : 986 boulevard de la 36ème Division du Texas

6,5 ha (374 pitches)

Rentals : 56 🚐 – 56 🏠 – 65 canvas bungalows

Surroundings : ⟦symbols⟧	
Leisure activities : 🍷 ✕ 🎮 🏊 ⛵ multi-sports ground	**G** Longitude : 6.84835
Facilities : 🚿 🍳 🔲 🍳 🍽 launderette 🧺 🍳	**P S** Latitude : 43.41782
Nearby : scuba diving	

⛰ Village Vacances Vallée du Paradis ♨️

(mobile home rentals only)

📞 04 94 82 16 00, www.camping-vallee-du-paradis.fr

Address : avenue du Gratadis (located 1km to the northwest; beside the Agay)

3 ha flat

Rentals : 198 🚐.

Surroundings : ⟦symbols⟧	
Leisure activities : 🍷 ✕ 🎮 🏊 🏋️ ⛳ 🏊 ⛵ 🏊 🚴	**G** Longitude : 6.85285
Facilities : 🚿 🍳 🍳 🍽 launderette 🧺 🍳	**P S** Latitude : 43.43546
Nearby : ⚓	

⛰ Les Rives de l'Agay

📞 04 94 82 02 74, www.lesrivesdelagay.com

Address : 575 avenue du Gratadis (700m to the northwest; beside the Agay river and 500m from the beach)

Opening times : from mid March to beginning Nov.

2 ha (171 pitches)

Tariff : 48€ ✶✶ 🚗 🔲 ⚡ (6A) – Extra per person 7€ – Reservation fee 20€

Rental rates : (from mid March to beginning Nov.) – 43 🚐. Per night from 39 to 52€ – Per week from 347 to 986 € Reservation fee 20€

Surroundings : ⟦symbols⟧	
Leisure activities : ✕ 🎮 🏊 scuba diving	**G** Longitude : 6.85263
Facilities : 🚿 🍳 🔲 🍳 🧺 🍽 launderette 🧺 🍳	**P S** Latitude : 43.43408
Nearby : ⚓	

⛰ Agay-Soleil

📞 04 94 82 00 79, www.agay-soleil.com ⚡

Address : 1152 boulevard de la Plage (700m east on the D 559, follow the signs for Cannes)

Opening times : from end March to beginning Nov.

0,7 ha (53 pitches)

Tariff : (2013 Price) 33,40€ ✶✶ 🚗 🔲 ⚡ (6A) – Extra per person 5,80€ Reservation fee 16€

Rental rates : (2013 Price) (from end March to beginning Nov.) ⚡ – 5 🚐 – 2 🏠 – 1 apartment. Per night from 60 to 120€ Per week from 310 to 760€

🚐 borne 10€

Surroundings : ⟦symbols⟧	
Leisure activities : 🍷 ✕ 🎮	**G** Longitude : 6.86822
Facilities : 🚿 🍳 🔲 🍳 🍳 🍳	**P S** Latitude : 43.43333
Nearby : 🏄 watersports centre	

*The classification (1 to 5 tents, **black** or red) that we award to selected sites in this guide is our own system. It should not be confused with the classification (1 to 5 stars) of official organisations.*

⚠ Royal-Camping

☎ 04 94 82 00 20, www.royalcamping.net

Address : rue Louise Robinson (located 1.5km west along the D 559, follow the signs for St Raphael and take turning to the left)

Opening times : from mid Feb. to beginning Nov.

4,6 ha (45 pitches)

Tariff : (2013 Price) 33,50€ ♥♥ ⇔ ▣ ฿ (6A) – Extra per person 7€ Reservation fee 20€

Rental rates : (2013 Price) (from mid Feb. to beginning Nov.) ▯▯▯. Per night from 45 to 105€ – Per week from 320 to 740€ Reservation fee 20€

Surroundings : ♡♡ ⛰
Leisure activities : 🎱
Facilities : ⚓ ⚒ 🍴
Nearby : ▣ ⛵ 🍴 ✕ ⛴

GPS | Longitude : 6.85707
| Latitude : 43.42027

This guide is not intended as a list of all the camping sites in France; its aim is to provide a selection of the best sites in each category.

AIX-EN-PROVENCE

13100 – Michelin map **340** H4 – pop. 141 895 – alt. 206
➤ Paris 752 – Aubagne 39 – Avignon 82 – Manosque 57

⚠ Chantecler

☎ 04 42 26 12 98, www.campingchantecler.com

Address : 41 avenue du Val-Saint-André (2.5km southeast, access via Cours Gambetta – from the A8, take exit 31 for Aix - Val-St-André)

Opening times : Permanent

8 ha (240 pitches) undulating, terraced, flat, grassy, stony

Tariff : (2013 Price) ♥ 6,70€ ⇔ ▣ 7,50€ – ฿ (10A) 4,20€

Rental rates : (2013 Price) Permanent – 38 ▯▯▯ – 10 🏠. Per week from 434 to 807€

🚐 borne

◀ view of Mont Ste-Victoire from some pitches.

Surroundings : ⌒ ♡♡♡
Leisure activities : 🍴 ✕ 🎱 🏃 ⛷ 🏊
Facilities : ♿ ⚓ ⚒ ⛴ 🍴 launderette 🛶

GPS | Longitude : 5.47416
| Latitude : 43.51522

ANCELLE

05260 – Michelin map **334** F5 – pop. 854 – alt. 1 340 – Winter sports : 1 350/1 807m
➤ Paris 665 – Gap 17 – Grenoble 103 – Orcières 18

⚠ Les Auches

☎ 04 92 50 80 28, www.lesauches.com

Address : Les Auches (take the northern exit following signs for Pont du Fossé and take turning to the right.)

Opening times : from beginning April to mid Nov.

2 ha (67 pitches) terraced, relatively flat, grassy

Tariff : 24€ ♥♥ ⇔ ▣ ฿ (6A) – Extra per person 4,80€

Rental rates : Permanent ⚒ – 11 ▯▯▯ – 11 🏠 – 4 studios 1 apartment – 2 canvas bungalows. Per week from 245 to 686€ Reservation fee 15€

Surroundings : ♨ ≤ ♡♡
Leisure activities : ✕ 🎱 🏃 jacuzzi ⛷ 🏊
Facilities : ♿ ⚓ ⚒ 🍴 launderette

GPS | Longitude : 6.21075
| Latitude : 44.62435

APT

84400 – Michelin map **332** F10 – pop. 11 405 – alt. 250
➤ Paris 728 – Aix-en-Provence 56 – Avignon 54 – Carpentras 49

⚠ Le Lubéron

☎ 04 90 04 85 40, www.campingleluberon.com

Address : avenue de Saignon (situated 2km southeast along the D 48)

Opening times : from beginning April to end Sept.

5 ha (110 pitches) terraced, flat and relatively flat, grassy, fine gravel

Tariff : 25,50€ ♥♥ ⇔ ▣ ฿ (6A) – Extra per person 7€ – Reservation fee 18€

Rental rates : (from beginning April to end Sept.) – 8 ▯▯▯ – 20 🏠 6 tent lodges – 1 gîte. Per night from 72 to 108€ – Per week from 224 to 900€ – Reservation fee 18€

Surroundings : ♨ ≤ ♡♡
Leisure activities : 🍴 ✕ ⛷ 🏊
Facilities : ♿ ⚓ 🍴 ⛴ 🍴 launderette

GPS | Longitude : 5.41327
| Latitude : 43.86632

⚠ Les Cèdres

☎ 04 90 74 14 61, www.camping-les-cedres.fr

Address : take northwestern exit along the D 22, follow the signs for Rustrel

Opening times : from mid Feb. to beginning Nov.

1,8 ha (75 pitches)

Tariff : ♥ 2,70€ ⇔ 5,40€ – ฿ (10A) 3,50€

Rental rates : (from beginning April to mid Oct.) – 4 canvas bungalows. Per night from 34 to 38 € – Per week from 225 to 260€ Reservation fee 34€

🚐 borne 4€

Surroundings : ♀
Leisure activities : 🎱 ⛷ climbing wall
Facilities : ♿ ⚓ 🍴 ⛴ ▣ refrigerators
Nearby : 🏊

GPS | Longitude : 5.4013
| Latitude : 43.87765

The prices listed were supplied by the campsite owners in 2013 (if prices were not available, those from the previous year are given). The fees should be regarded as basic charges and may fluctuate with inflation.

L'ARGENTIÈRE-LA-BESSÉE

05120 – Michelin map **334** H4 – pop. 2 328 – alt. 1 024
➤ Paris 696 – Briançon 17 – Embrun 33 – Gap 74

⚠ Municipal Les Écrins

☎ 04 92 23 03 38, www.camping-les-ecrins.com

Address : avenue Pierre Sainte (head 2.3km south along the N 94, follow the signs for Gap, and take D 104 to the right)

3 ha (71 pitches)

A young and sporty crowd comes here for the numerous whitewater activities.

Surroundings : ≤ ⌒ ♀
Leisure activities : 🎱 ⛷ ✕ 🛶
Facilities : ♿ ⚓ 🍴 🍴 ▣ 🛶
Nearby : 🎿 🏊 ⛴ (river) rafting and canyoning

GPS | Longitude : 6.55823
| Latitude : 44.77687

ARLES

13200 – Michelin map **340** C3 – pop. 52 979 – alt. 13
▶ Paris 719 – Aix-en-Provence 77 – Avignon 37 – Cavaillon 44
O : 14 km via N 572 rte de St-Gilles and D 37 on the left

⛰ Crin Blanc 👥

📞 04 66 87 48 78, www.camping-crin-blanc.com ✂

Address : at the hamlet des Saliers (located to the southwest of Saliers along the D 37)

Opening times : from beginning April to end Sept.

4,5 ha (170 pitches)

Tariff : 24€ 👫 🚗 📖 🔌 (10A) – Extra per person 5,50€ – Reservation fee 10€

Rental rates : (from beginning April to end Sept.) ✂ – 120 🚐. Per night from 63 to 85€ – Per week from 199 to 850€ Reservation fee 19€

Surroundings : 🗺
Leisure activities : 🍸 ✕ 🏛 ⛳ 🏊 🎾 🎣 ⛷ ⛸
Facilities : ♿ ☎ 🚻 🚮 🚿 🍴 launderette 🧺 🚰
Nearby : 🏇

GPS Longitude : 4.47392
Latitude : 43.66149

AUBIGNAN

84810 – Michelin map **332** D9 – pop. 4 861 – alt. 65
▶ Paris 675 – Avignon 31 – Carpentras 7 – Orange 21

⛰ Le Brégoux

📞 04 90 62 62 50, www.camping-lebregoux.fr

Address : 410 chemin du Vas (800m southeast along the D 55, follow the signs for Caromb and take the road to the right.)

Opening times : from beginning March to end Oct.

3,5 ha (170 pitches) flat, grassy

Tariff : 👤 3,85€ 🚗 📖 3,75€ 🔌 (10A) 3,80€

Rental rates : (from beginning March to end Oct.) – 5 🚐. Per week from 315 to 535€

Surroundings : 🌳🌳
Leisure activities : 🏛 ⛳ 🎾
Facilities : ☎ 🚿 🍴 launderette

GPS Longitude : 5.03609
Latitude : 44.09808

AUPS

83630 – Michelin map **340** M4 – pop. 2 083 – alt. 496
▶ Paris 818 – Aix-en-Provence 90 – Castellane 71 – Digne-les-Bains 78

⛰ International Camping

📞 04 94 70 06 80, www.internationalcamping-aups.com

Address : 495 route de Fox-Amphoux (head 500m west along the D 60)

Opening times : from beginning April to end Sept.

4 ha (190 pitches)

Tariff : (2013 Price) 👤 7,80€ 🚗 📖 6,80€ – 🔌 (10A) 6,20€

Rental rates : (2013 Price) Permanent – 25 🚐. Per week from 570€
A picturesque and well-kept setting.

Surroundings : 🏊 🗺 ⛵
Leisure activities : ✕ 🎾 ⛷ disco
Facilities : ☎ 🚿 🍴 📷 🚰

GPS Longitude : 6.21705
Latitude : 43.62465

AURIBEAU-SUR-SIAGNE

06810 – Michelin map **341** C6 – pop. 2 945 – alt. 85
▶ Paris 900 – Cannes 15 – Draguignan 62 – Grasse 9

⛰ Le Parc des Monges

📞 04 93 60 91 71, www.parcdesmonges.com

Address : 635 chemin du Gabre (head 1.4km northwest along the D 509, follow the signs for Tanneron)

Opening times : from end April to end Sept.

1,3 ha (54 pitches)

Tariff : 👤 6€ 🚗 4,20€ 📖 32€ – 🔌 (10A) 6,50€

Rental rates : (from end April to end Sept.) ✂ – 6 🚐 – 8 🏠 Per week from 765 to 795€

🚐 borne 8€

Beside the Siagne river.

Surroundings : 🏊 🗺 🌳🌳
Leisure activities : jacuzzi ⛷
Facilities : ♿ ☎ 🚮 🚿 🚰 🍴 📷
Nearby : 🍸 ✕ 🚰 ⛵ 🏊

GPS Longitude : 6.90252
Latitude : 43.60659

AVIGNON

84000 – Michelin map **332** B10 – pop. 89 592 – alt. 21
▶ Paris 682 – Aix-en-Provence 82 – Arles 37 – Marseille 98

⛰ Aquadis Loisirs Le Pont d'Avignon

📞 04 90 80 63 50, www.aquadis-loisirs.com

Address : 10 chemin de la Barthelasse (take northwestern exit, follow the signs for Villeneuve-lès-Avignon across the Édouard-Daladier bridge and take a right turn, on the Île-de-la-Barthelasse)

Opening times : from beginning March to end Nov.

8 ha (300 pitches)

Tariff : 24,55€ 👫 🚗 📖 🔌 (10A) – Extra per person 5,60€ Reservation fee 9,90€

Rental rates : (from beginning March to end Nov.) – 10 canvas bungalows. Per night from 49 to 88€ – Per week from 250 to 620€ Reservation fee 19,80€

🚐 borne 18€ – 90 📖 18€ – 🚐 14€

Surroundings : 🗺 🌳🌳
Leisure activities : 🍸 ✕ 🏛 ⛳ 🎾 ⛷
Facilities : ♿ ☎ 🅿 🍴 launderette 🧺 🚰

GPS Longitude : 4.7971
Latitude : 43.95331

BARATIER

05200 – Michelin map **334** G4 – pop. 511 – alt. 855
▶ Paris 704 – Marseille 214 – Gap 39 – Digne 90

⛰ Les Airelles

📞 04 92 43 11 57, www.lesairelles.com

Address : route des Orres (1.2km southeast along the D 40, follow the signs for Les Orres and take turning to the right)

Opening times : from beginning June to mid Sept.

5 ha/4 for camping (130 pitches) terraced, flat and relatively flat, grassy, stony

Tariff : 👤 6,80€ 🚗 📖 7,80€ – 🔌 (10A) 5€

Rental rates : (from beginning June to mid Sept.) – 8 caravans 16 ⬚ – 32 ⬚ – 3 tent lodges. Per night from 60 to 103 € Per week from 310 to 720 €

Surroundings : ⬚ ⬚
Leisure activities : ♟ ✕ ⬚ ⬚ daytime  ⬚ multi-sports ground
Facilities : ⬚ ⬚ ⬚ launderette

GPS Longitude : 6.50164
Latitude : 44.5291

⛰ Le Verger

☎ 06 81 93 06 15, www.campingleverger.fr – limited spaces for one-night stay

Address : chemin de Jouglar (take the western exit; recommended route for caravans is via the village)

Opening times : Permanent

4,3 ha/2,5 for camping (110 pitches)

Tariff : (2013 Price) 17 € ♟ ♟ ⬚ ⬚ ⬚ (10A) – Extra per person 5,50 € Reservation fee 14 €

Rental rates : (2013 Price) Permanent – 14 ⬚ – 14 gîtes. Per night from 85 to 105 € – Per week from 425 to 715 € – Reservation fee 14 €

Surroundings : ⬚ ⬚ ⬚
Leisure activities : ♟ ✕ ⬚ ⬚
Facilities : ⬚ ⬚ ⬚ ⬚
Nearby : ✕ ⬚ ⬚

GPS Longitude : 6.40143
Latitude : 44.5374

⛰ Les Deux Bois

☎ 04 92 43 54 14, www.camping-les2bois.com

Address : route de Pra Fouran (access to the town along the D 204)

Opening times : from mid May to mid Sept.

2,5 ha (100 pitches) terraced, sloping, flat, grassy, stony

Tariff : 21,80 € ♟ ♟ ⬚ ⬚ ⬚ (10A) – Extra per person 5,40 € Reservation fee 15 €

Rental rates : Permanent ⬚ – 4 ⬚. Per night from 73 to 125 € Per week from 350 to 880 € – Reservation fee 15 €

⬚ 3 ⬚ 16,70 €

Luxurious mobile home rentals, open all year.

Surroundings : ⬚ ⬚
Leisure activities : ♟ ✕ 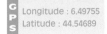 ⬚
Facilities : ⬚ ⬚ ⬚ ⬚ ⬚ ⬚
Nearby : ✕ ⬚

GPS Longitude : 6.49207
Latitude : 44.53837

⛰ Les Grillons

☎ 04 92 43 32 75, www.lesgrillons.com

Address : route de la Madeleine (located 1km north along the D 40, D 340 and take road to the left)

Opening times : from mid May to mid Sept.

1,5 ha (95 pitches)

Tariff : 22,50 € ♟ ♟ ⬚ ⬚ ⬚ (16A) – Extra per person 5,40 € Reservation fee 10 €

Rental rates : (from mid May to mid Sept.) – 16 ⬚. Per night from 56 to 84 € – Per week from 266 to 675 € – Reservation fee 13 €

Surroundings : ⬚ ⬚
Leisure activities : ✕ ⬚
Facilities : ⬚ ⬚ ⬚ launderette

GPS Longitude : 6.49755
Latitude : 44.54689

Some campsites benefit from proximity to a municipal leisure centre.

05300 – Michelin map **334** C7 – pop. 220 – alt. 640
▶ Paris 700 – Laragne-Montéglin 14 – Sault 46 – Séderon 21

⛰ Les Gorges de la Méouge

☎ 04 92 65 08 47, www.camping-meouge.com

Address : Le Serre (take the eastern exit along the D 942, follow the signs for Laragne-Montéglin and take the road to the right, near the Méouge river)

Opening times : from beginning May to end Sept.

3 ha (115 pitches) flat, grassy

Tariff : 18,80 € ♟ ♟ ⬚ ⬚ ⬚ (10A) – Extra per person 5,70 €
Rental rates : (from beginning May to end Sept.) – 13 ⬚. Per night from 62 to 87 € – Per week from 439 to 611 €

⬚ borne 2 € – ⬚ 10 €

Surroundings : ⬚ ⬚
Leisure activities : ⬚ ⬚
Facilities : ⬚ ⬚ ⬚ ⬚ ⬚ ⬚

GPS Longitude : 5.73822
Latitude : 44.26078

Routes nationales are main roads and their identifying numbers begin with N or RN. Routes départementales are generally quieter roads and begin with D or DN.

06620 – Michelin map **341** C5 – pop. 2 805 – alt. 320
▶ Paris 916 – Cannes 22 – Grasse 10 – Nice 31

⛰ Les Gorges du Loup

☎ 04 93 42 45 06, www.lesgorgesduloup.com

Address : 965 chemin des Vergers (located 1km northeast along the D 2210, then continue 1km along the Chemin des Vergers)

Opening times : from beginning April to end Sept.

1,6 ha (70 pitches) very uneven, terraced, flat, grassy, stony

Tariff : 30 € ♟ ♟ ⬚ ⬚ ⬚ (10A) – Extra per person 5,50 € – Reservation fee 15 €

Rental rates : (from beginning April to end Sept.) – 5 ⬚ – 10 ⬚ 1 studio. Per week from 320 to 730 € – Reservation fee 15 €

Small terraces, many shaded by centuries-old olive trees.

Surroundings : ⬚ ⬚ ⬚
Leisure activities : ⬚ ⬚ ⬚
Facilities : ⬚ ⬚ ⬚ ⬚ ⬚

GPS Longitude : 6.99527
Latitude : 43.70183

84190 – Michelin map **332** D9 – pop. 2 283 – alt. 100
▶ Paris 666 – Avignon 34 – Nyons 39 – Orange 23

⛰ Municipal de Roquefiguier

☎ 04 90 62 95 07, www.mairie-de-beaumes-de-venise – ⬚

Address : route de Lafare (take the northern exit along the D 90, follow the signs for Malaucène and take a right turn; beside the Salette river)

Opening times : from beginning March to end Oct.

1,5 ha (63 pitches) terraced, relatively flat, grassy, stony

Tariff : (2013 Price) ♟ 2,80 € ⬚ 1,90 € ⬚ 3,35 € – ⬚ (16A) 3,10 €

Surroundings : ⬚ ⬚ ⬚
Leisure activities : ⬚
Facilities : ⬚ ⬚ ⬚ ⬚ ⬚ refrigerators
Nearby : ✕

GPS Longitude : 5.03448
Latitude : 44.12244

BEAUMONT-DU-VENTOUX

84340 – Michelin map **332** E8 – pop. 317 – alt. 360
▶ Paris 676 – Avignon 48 – Carpentras 21 – Nyons 28

⚠ Mont-Serein

🖉 04 90 60 49 16, www.camping-ventoux.com – alt. 1400

Address : at the Mont-Serein ski resort (20km east along the D 974 and take the D 164a, r. du Mont-Ventoux via Malaucène)

Opening times : Permanent

1,2 ha (60 pitches)

Tariff : ★ 5€ 🚐 🗉 9€ – ⁅⁆ (16A) 3€

Rental rates : Permanent – 7 🏠. Per night from 125 to 270€ Per week from 290 to 600€

🚐 borne 4€ – 30 🗉 9€

In an attractive elevated location.

Surroundings : 🏞 ≼ Mont Ventoux and the Alps 🏕	**GPS** Longitude : 5.25898
Leisure activities : 🛖 🎿	Latitude : 44.1811
Facilities : 🔌 🎭 🛁 🚾 🍴 🖭 🏊	

BÉDOIN

84410 – Michelin map **332** E9 – pop. 3 132 – alt. 295
▶ Paris 692 – Avignon 43 – Carpentras 16 – Vaison-la-Romaine 21

⚠ Municipal la Pinède

🖉 04 90 65 61 03, camping.municipal@bedoin.fr

Address : chemin des Sablières (take the western exit following signs for Crillon-le-Brave and take the road to the right, next to the municipal swimming pool)

Opening times : from mid March to end Oct.

6 ha (121 pitches)

Tariff : 15€ ★★ 🚐 🗉 ⁅⁆ (16A) – Extra per person 3,40€

Rental rates : (from mid March to end Oct.) – 3 🏠. Per week from 290 to 470€

Surroundings : 🎾🎾	**GPS** Longitude : 5.17261
Facilities : ♿ 🔌 🛁 🖭	Latitude : 44.12486
Nearby : 🍴 🏊	

BOLLÈNE

84500 – Michelin map **332** B8 – pop. 13 885 – alt. 40
▶ Paris 634 – Avignon 53 – Montélimar 34 – Nyons 35

⚠ La Simioune

🖉 04 90 63 17 91, www.la-simioune.fr

Address : quartier de Guffiage (5km northeast following signs for Lambisque (access on the D 8 along the old road to Suze-la-Rousse following the Lez) and take road to the left)

Opening times : Permanent

2 ha (80 pitches) terraced, flat, sandy

Tariff : 22,50€ ★★ 🚐 🗉 ⁅⁆ (10A) – Extra per person 4,50€

Rental rates : Permanent – 2 🛖 – 4 🏠. Per night from 80 to 100€ – Per week from 350 to 550€

Wooden, ranch-style buildings.

Surroundings : 🏞 🎾🎾	**GPS** Longitude : 4.74848
Leisure activities : 🍴 🏊 🐎	Latitude : 44.28203
Facilities : ♿ 🔌 🛁 🍴 🖭 🛒	

BONNIEUX

84480 – Michelin map **332** E11 – pop. 1 424 – alt. 400
▶ Paris 721 – Aix-en-Provence 49 – Apt 12 – Cavaillon 27

⚠ Le Vallon

🖉 04 90 75 86 14, www.campinglevallon.com

Address : route de Ménerbes (take the southern exit along the D 3 and turn off left)

Opening times : from mid March to mid Oct.

1,3 ha (80 pitches) terraced, flat, grassy, stony, wood

Tariff : 22,80€ ★★ 🚐 🗉 ⁅⁆ (10A) – Extra per person 4€ – Reservation fee 10€

Rental rates : (from mid March to mid Oct.) 🚫 – 1 🛖 – 3 yurts 5 canvas bungalows. Per night from 53 to 80€ – Per week from 320 to 490€ – Reservation fee 10€

Surroundings : 🏞 ≼ 🏕 🎾	**GPS** Longitude : 5.22838
Facilities : 🔌 🛁 🚾 🍴 🖭	Latitude : 43.81881
Nearby : 🏇 🍴	

BORMES-LES-MIMOSAS

83230 – Michelin map **340** N7 – pop. 7 321 – alt. 180
▶ Paris 871 – Fréjus 57 – Hyères 21 – Le Lavandou 4

🏔 Le Camp du Domaine ▲▲

CAILLAT

🖉 04 94 71 03 12, www.campdudomaine.com 🚫 (from mid July to mid Aug)

Address : at La Favière, 2581 route de Bénat (situated 2km to the south, near the port)

Opening times : from beginning April to end Oct.

38 ha (1200 pitches) very uneven, terraced, flat, stony, rocks

Tariff : (2013 Price) 48€ ★★ 🚐 🗉 ⁅⁆ (16A) – Extra per person 11€ Reservation fee 27€

Rental rates : (2013 Price) (from beginning April to end Oct.) 🚫 50 🛖 – 100 🏠. Per night from 130 to 150€ – Per week from 530 to 1215€ – Reservation fee 27€

🚐 borne 35€ – 150 🗉 35€

A secluded site on an undulating, wooded area close to the beach. Excursions organised out of season

Surroundings : 🏕 🎾🎾 ⛰	
Leisure activities : 🍴 🍽 🛖 🎮 🏓 🏇 🎿 🎾 multi-sports ground	**GPS** Longitude : 6.35129
Facilities : ♿ 🔌 🛁 🛏 🚾 🍴 launderette 🖭 🛒 refrigerated food storage facilities	Latitude : 43.11788
Nearby : 🛶 pedalos	

🏔 Manjastre

🖉 04 94 71 03 28, www.campingmanjastre.com

Address : 150 chemin des Girolles (5km northwest sur N 98, follow the signs for Cogolin)

Opening times : Permanent

3,5 ha (120 pitches) terraced, flat and relatively flat, stony

Tariff : 28,80€ ★★ 🚐 🗉 ⁅⁆ (10A) – Extra per person 6,40€ Reservation fee 15€

🚐 borne 6€ – 8 🗉 15€

An attractive layout of terraces among mimosas and cork oaks.

Surroundings : 🏞 🚃 ♨♨
Leisure activities : 🍴 ✕ ⚽ 🏊
Facilities : & ⚡ cc 📶 🍽 ♨ 🚿 ♨ launderette 🚿

GPS Longitude : 6.32153
Latitude : 43.16258

BRIANÇON

05100 – Michelin map **334** H2 – pop. 11 574 – alt. 1 321 – Winter sports : 1 200/2 800m
▶ Paris 681 – Digne-les-Bains 145 – Embrun 48 – Grenoble 89

⚞ Les 5 Vallées

🕻 04 92 21 06 27, www.camping5vallees.com

Address : St-Blaise (situated 2km south along the N 94)

Opening times : from beginning June to mid Sept.

5 ha (180 pitches)

Tariff : 🚶 7,70€ ⚙ 2,90€ 🔲 4,80€ – [⚡] (10A) 5,70€

Rental rates : (from mid Dec. to end Sept.) ✂ – 31 🚐. Per week from 422 to 760€

🚰 borne

Surroundings : ♨♨
Leisure activities : 🏠 ⚽ 🏊
Facilities : & ⚡ 🍽 ♨ launderette 🏊 🚿
Nearby : ✎

GPS Longitude : 6.69323
Latitude : 45.11898

CADENET

84160 – Michelin map **332** F11 – pop. 4 061 – alt. 170
▶ Paris 734 – Aix-en-Provence 33 – Apt 23 – Avignon 63

⚞ Homair Vacances Val de Durance

🕻 04 90 68 37 75, www.homair.com

Address : 570 avenue du Club Hippique (2.7km southwest along the D 943, follow the signs for Aix, turn right onto D 59 and take road to the left)

10 ha/2,4 for camping (232 pitches)

Rentals : 220 🚐.

Beside a small lake and 300m from the Durance river.

Surroundings : 🏞 ⚓ 🚃 ♨♨
Leisure activities : 🍴 ✕ 🏠 🌞 daytime 🏃 ⚽ 🏊 🛶 ✎ multi-sports ground
Facilities : & ⚡ 🚿 🍽 ♨ 🔲 🏊 🚿

GPS Longitude : 5.35515
Latitude : 43.71957

CAGNES-SUR-MER

06800 – Michelin map **341** D6 – pop. 48 024 – alt. 20
▶ Paris 915 – Antibes 11 – Cannes 21 – Grasse 25

⚞ La Rivière

🕻 04 93 20 62 27, www.campinglariviere06.fr

Address : 168 chemin des Salles (3.5km to the north; beside the Cagne river)

Opening times : from mid March to mid Oct.

1,2 ha (90 pitches)

Tariff : 25€ 🚶🚶 ⚙ 🔲 [⚡] (6A) – Extra per person 4€

Rental rates : (from beginning April to end Sept.) ✂ – 4 🚐. Per week from 240 to 430€

Surroundings : 🏞 🚃 ♨♨
Leisure activities : ✕ 🏠 ⚽ 🏊
Facilities : ⚡ 🚿 🏊 🚿

GPS Longitude : 7.14283
Latitude : 43.69581

⚞ Le Colombier

🕻 04 93 73 12 77, www.campinglecolombier.com ✂ (July–Aug.)

Address : 35 chemin Sainte Colombe (head 2km north towards the hills by the road to Vence)

Opening times : from beginning April to end Sept.

0,5 ha (33 pitches) flat and relatively flat, grassy, gravelled

Tariff : 29,50€ 🚶🚶 ⚙ 🔲 [⚡] (10A) – Extra per person 6€ – Reservation fee 8€

Rental rates : (from beginning April to end Sept.) ✂ – 2 🚐 1 studio. Per week from 230 to 590€ – Reservation fee 8€

🚰 borne – 4 🔲 29,50€ – 🚐 25,50€

The swimming pool is across the road.

Surroundings : 🏞 🚃 ♨♨
Leisure activities : 🏠 🏊 (small swimming pool)
Facilities : & ⚡ 🚿 ♨ launderette, refrigerators

GPS Longitude : 7.13893
Latitude : 43.67107

CALLAS

83830 – Michelin map **340** O4 – pop. 1 813 – alt. 398
▶ Paris 872 – Castellane 51 – Draguignan 14 – Toulon 94

⚞ Les Blimouses

🕻 04 94 47 83 41, www.campinglesblimouses.com

Address : 3km south along the D 25 and take D 225, follow the signs for Draguignan

Opening times : from beginning March to end Dec.

6 ha (170 pitches) terraced, flat and relatively flat, grassy, stony

Tariff : 29€ 🚶🚶 ⚙ 🔲 [⚡] (6A) – Extra per person 4€

Rental rates : (from beginning March to end Dec.) – 32 🚐 7 🏠. Per night from 39 to 75€ – Per week from 250 to 790€

Surroundings : 🏞 🚃 ♨♨
Leisure activities : ✕ ⚽ 🏊 ✎
Facilities : & ⚡ 🚿 🔲 🏊 🚿

GPS Longitude : 6.53242
Latitude : 43.57456

The guide covers all 22 regions of France – see the map and list of regions on pages 4–5.

CANNES

06400 – Michelin map **341** D6 – pop. 73 372 – alt. 2
▶ Paris 898 – Aix-en-Provence 149 – Marseille 160 – Nice 33

⚞ Le Parc Bellevue

🕻 04 93 47 28 97, www.parcbellevue.com

Address : at la Bocca, 67 avenue Maurice Chevalier (to the north, behind the municipal stadium)

Opening times : from beginning April to end Sept.

5 ha (250 pitches) very uneven, terraced, flat, grassy, gravelled

Tariff : 30€ 🚶🚶 ⚙ 🔲 [⚡] (6A) – Extra per person 4,25€

Rental rates : (from beginning April to end Sept.) – 50 🚐. Per week from 220 to 730€

🚰 borne

Choose the pitches away from the road in preference.

Surroundings : 🚃 ♨♨
Leisure activities : ✕ 🏠 ⚽ 🏊
Facilities : & ⚡ cc 🚿 🍽 ♨ 🔲 🚿

GPS Longitude : 6.96042
Latitude : 43.55617

LE CANNET

06110 – Michelin map **341** C6 – pop. 41 725 – alt. 80
▶ Paris 909 – Marseille 180 – Nice 39 – Monaco 54

⚠ Le Ranch

℘ 04 93 46 00 11, www.leranchcamping.fr

Address : at Aubarède, chemin St. Joseph (located 1.5km northwest along the D 9 then take bd. de l'Esterel to the right)

Opening times : from mid April to mid Oct.

2 ha (130 pitches) terraced, flat and relatively flat, grassy, stony

Tariff : (2013 Price) 🕴 7€ 🚗 3€ 🔲 19€ 🔋 (6A) – Reservation fee 15€
Rental rates : (from mid April to mid Oct.) – 11 🚐 – 5 🏠 – 2 ⛺.
Reservation fee 15€

🚽 borne 5€
Choose the pitches away from the road in preference.

Surroundings : 🏞 ♨♨
Leisure activities : 🎣 🏊‍♂️ 🎳 (small swimming pool)
Facilities : ♿ ☛ 🏛 ⛲ 🚿 🍴 launderette 🍽

Longitude : 6.97698
Latitude : 43.56508

CAROMB

84330 – Michelin map **332** D9 – pop. 3 185 – alt. 95
▶ Paris 683 – Avignon 37 – Carpentras 10 – Malaucène 10

⚠ Le Bouquier

℘ 04 90 62 30 13, www.lebouquier.com

Address : avenue Charles de Gaulle (located 1.5km north along the D 13)

1,5 ha (50 pitches) terraced, flat, stony, gravelled
Rentals : 3 🚐.

Surroundings : 🏞 ♨
Leisure activities : 🏊 (small swimming pool)
Facilities : ♿ ☛ 🅿 🏛 🚿 🍴 🔲

Longitude : 5.10994
Latitude : 44.12396

CARPENTRAS

84200 – Michelin map **332** D9 – pop. 29 271 – alt. 102
▶ Paris 679 – Avignon 30 – Cavaillon 28 – Orange 24

⚠ Flower Lou Comtadou

℘ 04 90 67 03 16, www.campingloucomtadou.com

Address : 881 avenue Pierre de Coubertin (located 1.5km southeast along the D 4, follow the signs for St-Didier and take turning to the right, near the sports centre)

Opening times : from beginning March to end Oct.

1 ha (99 pitches) small lake

Tariff : 17€ 🕴🕴 🚗 🔲 🔋 (6A) – Extra per person 4,50€ – Reservation fee 15€

Rental rates : (from beginning March to end Oct.) – 20 🚐 2 canvas bungalows – 3 tent lodges. Per night from 44 to 105€ Per week from 308 to 735€ – Reservation fee 15€

🚽 borne

Surroundings : 🏞 ♨♨
Leisure activities : 🎣 🏊‍♂️
Facilities : ♿ ☛ ⛲ 🚿 🍴 🔲
Nearby : 🍴 🎳 🔲

Longitude : 5.05429
Latitude : 44.04417

CARRO

13500 – Michelin map **340** F6
▶ Paris 787 – Marseille 44 – Aix-en-Provence 51 – Martigues 13

⚠ Yelloh! Village Les Chalets de la Mer

(chalet rental only)

℘ 04 42 80 73 46, www.semovim-martigues.com

Address : rue de la Tramontane

3 ha flat

Rentals : ♿ (8 chalets) – 78 🏠.
Around 20 of the chalets offer accommodation on a hotel-style basis, with half board available.

Surroundings : 🏊 🏞 ♨♨
Leisure activities : 🍴 🍽 🎳 🌙 nighttime 🤸 🎠 ♨ 🏊‍♂️ 🎳
Facilities : ♿ ☛ launderette 🍽

Longitude : 5.04117
Latitude : 43.33291

Some campsites benefit from proximity to a municipal leisure centre.

CASTELLANE

04120 – Michelin map **334** H9 – pop. 1 553 – alt. 730
▶ Paris 797 – Digne-les-Bains 54 – Draguignan 59 – Grasse 64

⚠ Les Castels Le Domaine du Verdon 👥

℘ 04 92 83 61 29, www.camp-du-verdon.com

Address : Domaine de la Salaou (Camp du Verdon)

Opening times : from mid May to mid Sept.

9 ha (500 pitches) flat, grassy

Tariff : 48€ 🕴🕴 🚗 🔲 🔋 (16A) – Extra per person 14€ – Reservation fee 20€
Rental rates : (from mid May to mid Sept.) ♿ – 135 🚐 – 4 🏠.
Per night from 52 to 156€ – Per week from 364 to 1 092€
Reservation fee 20€

🚽 borne

Surroundings : 🏊 🏞 ♨♨
Leisure activities : 🍴 🍽 🎳 🌙 🤸 🎠 🚲 🛶 🏊 🎳
Facilities : ♿ ☛ ⛲ 🚿 🍴 launderette 🍽 🍽 🍴 refrigerated food storage facilities

Nearby : rafting and canyoning

Longitude : 6.49402
Latitude : 43.83895

⚠ RCN Les Collines de Castellane

℘ 04 92 83 68 96, www.rcn.fr/collinesdecastellane – pitches accessed via steep slope, help moving caravans onto and off pitches avilable on request – alt. 1 000

Address : route de Grasse (7km southeast along the N 85; at La Garde)

Opening times : from mid April to end Sept.

7 ha (200 pitches)

Tariff : 43,95€ 🕴🕴 🚗 🔲 🔋 (12A) – Extra per person 5,50€ – Reservation fee 19,50€
Rental rates : (from end April to end Sept.) – 32 🚐 – 4 🏠 – 2 tent lodges. Per night from 33 to 171€ – Per week from 231 to 1 197€. Reservation fee 19,50€

Surroundings : 🏊 🏞 ♨♨
Leisure activities : 🍴 🍽 🎳 🤸 🎠 🎳 🏊 🎳
Facilities : ♿ ☛ ⛲ 🚿 🍴 🔲 🍽

Longitude : 6.56994
Latitude : 43.8244

⚏ International Camping

✆ 04 92 83 66 67, www.camping-international.fr

Address : route Napoléon

Opening times : from end March to beginning Oct.

5 ha (274 pitches) flat and relatively flat, stony, grassy

Tariff : 35€ ✶✶ ⇌ ▣ ⚡ (10A) – Extra per person 6€ – Reservation fee 10€

Rental rates : (from end March to beginning Oct.) – 32  10 🏠. Per night from 35 to 130€ – Per week from 275 to 825€ Reservation fee 10€

🚐 borne

Surroundings : ▭ ⚲	
Leisure activities : ♟ ✗ ⌂ 🚲⛷ ⛵	**G** Longitude : 6.49796
Facilities : 🚿 ⚲ cc 🛁 🔥 ☂ ⚐ ⚟ ▣ ⚟ 🛒	**P** Latitude : 43.85866
refrigerated food storage facilities	**S**
Nearby : 🐎	

⚏ La Colle

✆ 04 92 83 61 57, www.camping-lacolle.com

Address : 2.5km southwest along the D 952, follow the signs for Moustiers-Ste-Marie and take GR 4 to the right

Opening times : from beginning April to end Sept.

3,5 ha/1 for camping (41 pitches) terraced, flat and relatively flat, grassy, stony

Tariff : 23€ ✶✶ ⇌ ▣ ⚡ (10A) – Extra per person 5,80€

Rental rates : (from beginning April to end Sept.) 🚿 – 12  1 🏠. Per night from 38 to 63€ – Per week from 266 to 610€

In a wild setting, beside a stream, peaceful and natural.

Surroundings : ▨ ≤ ▭ ⚲	
Leisure activities : ⌂ 🚲	**G** Longitude : 6.49312
Facilities : 🚿 ⚲ ☂ ⚐ ⚟ ▣	**P** Latitude : 43.83864
Nearby : adventure park	**S**

⚏ Notre-Dame

✆ 04 92 83 63 02, www.camping-notredame.com

Address : route des Gorges du Verdon (500m southwest along the D 952, follow the signs for Moustiers-Ste-Marie; beside a stream)

Opening times : from beginning April to mid Oct.

0,6 ha (44 pitches) flat, grassy

Tariff : (2013 Price) 23,50€ ✶✶ ⇌ ▣ ⚡ (6A) – Extra per person 6€ Reservation fee 9€

Rental rates : (2013 Price) (from beginning April to mid Oct.) 🚿 11 . Per night from 45 to 95€ – Per week from 315 to 610€ Reservation fee 9€

🚐 borne 6€ – 🔌 ⚡ 14,50€

Surroundings : ≤	
Leisure activities : ⚓	**G** Longitude : 6.50425
Facilities : 🚿 ⚲ ⚐	**P** Latitude : 43.84545
Nearby : adventure park	**S**

Key to rentals symbols :

12	*Number of mobile homes*
20 🏠	*Number of chalets*
6 🛏	*Number of rooms to rent*
Per night 30–50€	*Minimum/maximum rate per night*
Per week 300–1,000€	*Minimum/maximum rate per week*

83240 – Michelin map **340** O6 – pop. 6 731 – alt. 2

▶ Paris 880 – Draguignan 55 – Fréjus 41 – Le Lavandou 21

⚏ Cros de Mouton

✆ 04 94 64 10 87, www.crosdemouton.com – pitches accessed via steep slope, help moving caravans onto and off pitches avilable on request

Address : chemin du Cros de Mouton (located 1.5km to the northwest)

Opening times : from mid March to beginning Nov.

5 ha (199 pitches) very uneven, terraced, flat, stony

Tariff : ✶ 9,20€ ⇌ ▣ 9,20€ – ⚡ (10A) 4,90€ – Reservation fee 20€

Rental rates : (from mid March to beginning Nov.) – 58 15 🏠. Per night from 65 to 108€ – Per week from 395 to 1030€ Reservation fee 20€

Surroundings : ▨ ≤ Baie de Cavalaire ▭ ⚲⚲	
Leisure activities : ♟ ✗ ⌂ 🛥 ⛵	**G** Longitude : 6.51662
Facilities : 🚿 ⚲ ☂ ⚐ ⚟ ▣ ⚟ 🛒	**P** Latitude : 43.18243
	S

05600 – Michelin map **334** I4 – pop. 307 – alt. 1 640 – Winter sports : 1 700/2 500m

▶ Paris 729 – Briançon 50 – Gap 75 – Guillestre 14

⚏ Les Mélèzes

✆ 04 92 45 21 93, www.campingdeceillac.com

Address : La Rua des Reynauds (1.8km southeast)

Opening times : from beginning June to beginning Sept.

3 ha (100 pitches)

Tariff : ✶ 6,60€ ⇌ ▣ 7€ – ⚡ (16A) 5€

Pleasant location and setting beside the Mélezet river.

Surroundings : ▨ ≤ ⚲	
Leisure activities : ⛷	**G** Longitude : 6.78843
Facilities : ⚲ ▥ 🛁 ☂ ⚐ ▣	**P** Latitude : 44.65389
	S

To visit a town or region, use the MICHELIN Green Guides.

84470 – Michelin map **332** C10 – pop. 3 249 – alt. 90

▶ Paris 701 – Marseille 95 – Avignon 14 – Nîmes 58

⚏ Le Fontisson

✆ 04 90 22 59 77, www.campingfontisson.com

Address : 1125 route d'Avignon (near the exit from town along the follow the signs for Avignon and take road to the right)

Opening times : from beginning April to mid Oct.

2 ha (55 pitches)

Tariff : 31€ ✶✶ ⇌ ▣ ⚡ (10A) – Extra per person 7,30€ – Reservation fee 10€

Rental rates : (from beginning April to mid Oct.) – 19 4 canvas bungalows. Per night from 85 to 860€ – Per week from 95 to 470€ – Reservation fee 15€

🚐 borne 26€

Surroundings : ▨ ▭ ⚲⚲	
Leisure activities : ⌂ 🛥 ✗ 🔥 ⛵ multi- sports ground	**G** Longitude : 4.93297
Facilities : 🚿 ⚲ ⚐ ⚟ ▣	**P** Latitude : 43.92846
	S

CHÂTEAURENARD

13160 – Michelin map **340** E2 – pop. 14 971 – alt. 37
▶ Paris 692 – Avignon 10 – Carpentras 37 – Cavaillon 23

⚠ La Roquette

✆ 04 90 94 46 81, www.camping-la-roquette.com

Address : 745 avenue Jean-Mermoz (located 1.5km east along the D 28, follow the signs for Noves and take a right turn, near the swimming pool - from A 7 take exit Avignon-Sud)

Opening times : from beginning April to beginning Nov.

2 ha (74 pitches) flat, grassy

Tariff : 25 € ♦♦ ⇔ 🔲 🅷 (10A) – Extra per person 6 €

Rental rates : (from beginning April to beginning Nov.) 13 🛖. Per night from 40 to 110 € – Per week from 280 to 890 € Reservation fee 12 €

Surroundings : 🖵 ♀
Leisure activities : ⛊ ✗ 🛶 🏊
Facilities : ⟁ ⊶ ⌀ ⟟ ▥

G P S Longitude : 4.87017
Latitude : 43.88328

To make the best possible use of this guide, please read pages 2–15 carefully.

CHORGES

05230 – Michelin map **334** F5 – pop. 2 567 – alt. 864
▶ Paris 676 – Embrun 23 – Gap 18 – Savines-le-Lac 12

⚠ Municipal

✆ 04 92 50 67 72, www.baiestmichel.com

Address : baie St-Michel (4.5km southeast along the N 94, follow the signs for Briançon, 200m from the lake at Serre-Ponçon)

2 ha (110 pitches) terraced, flat, grassy, stony
Rentals : ⟁ (1 chalet) – 10 🛖.

Surroundings : 🌲 ≤ ♀
Leisure activities : 🛆 🛶 ≌ (lake)
Facilities : ⟁ ⊶ ⟟
Nearby : ⛊ ✗ 🛠 🛶 🦆 pedalos

G P S Longitude : 6.32379
Latitude : 44.5283

CLAMENSANE

04250 – Michelin map **334** ⌐7 – pop. 166 – alt. 694
▶ Paris 720 – Avignon 180 – Grenoble 158 – Marseille 152

⚠ Le Clot du Jay en Provence

✆ 04 92 68 35 32, www.clotdujay.com

Address : route de Bayons (located 1km east along the D 1, follow the signs for Bayons, near the Sasse river)

Opening times : from mid April to end Sept.

6 ha/3 for camping (50 pitches) very uneven, terraced, flat, grassy, stony, pond

Tariff : 25 € ♦♦ ⇔ 🔲 🅷 (10A) – Extra per person 5 € – Reservation fee 9 €

Rental rates : (from mid April to end Sept.) – 8 🛖 – 11 🛖 2 canvas bungalows. Per night from 52 to 70 € – Per week from 225 to 680 € – Reservation fee 9 €

Surroundings : 🌲 🖵 ♀♀
Leisure activities : ⛊ ✗ 🛶 🏊 🛷
Facilities : ⟁ ⊶ ⌀ ⟟ ▥ ⟱
Nearby : 🦆

G P S Longitude : 6.0845
Latitude : 44.3226

LA COLLE-SUR-LOUP

06480 – Michelin map **341** D5 – pop. 7 640 – alt. 90
▶ Paris 919 – Antibes 15 – Cagnes-sur-Mer 7 – Cannes 26

🏔 Sites et Paysages Les Pinèdes 👥

✆ 04 93 32 98 94, www.lespinedes.com

Address : route du Pont de Pierre (located 1.5km west along the D 6, follow the signs for Grasse, 50m from the Loup river)

Opening times : from end March to end Sept.

3,8 ha (155 pitches) very uneven, terraced, flat, grassy, fine gravel

Tariff : 43,70 € ♦♦ ⇔ 🔲 🅷 (10A) – Extra per person 6,20 € Reservation fee 20 €

Rental rates : (from end March to end Sept.) – 32 🛖 – 9 🛖 Per night from 55 to 165 € – Per week from 350 to 1230 € Reservation fee 20 €

🚐 borne 6 € – 🔌 🅷 14 €

Surroundings : 🖵 ♀♀
Leisure activities : ⛊ 🎮 🏓 🛶 🏊 multi-sports ground
Facilities : ⊶ ▦ 🛁 ⟱ ⟟ launderette 🗄 refrigerated food storage facilities
Nearby : ✗ ≌ 🐴 leisure park

G P S Longitude : 7.08337
Latitude : 43.68177

🏔 Le Vallon Rouge

✆ 04 93 32 86 12, www.auvallonrouge.com – limited spaces for one-night stay

Address : route de Gréolières (3.5km west along the D 6, follow the signs for Grasse; beside the Loup river)

Opening times : from mid April to end Sept.

3 ha (103 pitches) terraced, flat, grassy, sandy, fine gravel

Tariff : 44,30 € ♦♦ ⇔ 🔲 🅷 (10A) – Extra per person 6 € – Reservation fee 20 €

Rental rates : (from mid April to end Sept.) – 36 🛖 – 21 🛖 6 tent lodges. Per night 130 € – Per week from 295 to 1050 € Reservation fee 20 €

🚐 borne 4 € – 30 🔲 38 €

Surroundings : 🌲 🖵 ♀♀
Leisure activities : ✗ 🎮 🏓 🏊 ≌ multi-sports ground
Facilities : ⟁ ⊶ 🛁 ⟱ ⟟ launderette 🗄

G P S Longitude : 7.07324
Latitude : 43.68452

In order for the guide to remain wholly objective, the selection of campsites is made on an entirely independent basis.

COLMARS

04370 – Michelin map **334** H7 – pop. 385 – alt. 1 235
▶ Paris 816 – Marseille 206 – Digne-les-Bains 71 – Embrun 94

⚠ Aire Naturelle les Pommiers

✆ 04 92 83 41 56, www.camping-pommier.com – alt. 1 250

Address : Les Buissières (300m to the south)

1 ha (25 pitches) terraced, flat and relatively flat, grassy

Surroundings : 🌲 ≤ ♀♀
Facilities : ⟁ ⊶ ▥

G P S Longitude : 6.62132
Latitude : 44.17747

COL-ST-JEAN

04340 – Michelin map **334** G6 – alt. 1 333 – Winter sports : 1 300/2 500m

▶ Paris 709 – Barcelonnette 34 – Savines-le-Lac 31 – Seyne 10

⚞⚞⚞ Yelloh! Village L'Étoile des Neiges ♣♟

✆ 04 92 35 01 29, www.etoile-des-neiges.com – alt. 1 300

Address : at the Col St-Jean ski resort (800m south along the D 207 and turn right onto D 307)

Opening times : from end May to beginning Sept.

3 ha (150 pitches) terraced, flat, grassy, stony

Tariff : 39€ ♣♣ ⇌ 🗉 🕅 (10A) – Extra per person 8€

Rental rates : (and from end May to beginning Sept) 🛇 (July–Aug.) – 60 ⌂🕱 – 26 🕮 – 5 apartments – 4 gîtes. Per night from 31 to 171€ – Per week from 217 to 1 197€

> Surroundings : 🌤 ⟜ ⟅
> Leisure activities : 🍴 ✗ 🏠 🏦 🛖 🛝 ⅃⅃ 💆 🌊
> hammam, jacuzzi 🛶 🎿 ☃ multi-sports ground, spa centre
> Facilities : 🖿 ⚷ 🏧 ♨ 🛁 🚿 🛒 🍴 launderette 🚿
>
> Nearby : 🏊 🚲 🏇 adventure park
>
> **GPS** Longitude : 6.348
> Latitude : 44.40927

LA COURONNE

13500 – Michelin map **340** F5

▶ Paris 786 – Marseille 42 – Aix-en-Provence 49 – Martigues 11

⚞⚞⚞ Le Mas ♣♟

✆ 04 42 80 70 34, www.camping-le-mas.com – limited spaces for one-night stay

Address : chemin de Sainte Croix (4km southeast along the D 49, follow the signs for Sausset-les-Pins and take a right turn; near the beach at Ste-Croix)

Opening times : from mid March to mid Nov.

5,5 ha (300 pitches) terraced, flat, grassy, stony

Tariff : 43€ ♣♣ ⇌ 🗉 🕅 (10A) – Extra per person 9€ – Reservation fee 20€

Rental rates : (from mid March to mid Nov.) 🛇 – 151 ⌂🕱 45 🕮. Per week from 224 to 1 386€ – Reservation fee 20€

🚐 borne 10€

Some pitches with a sea view.

> Surroundings : 🌤 ♀♀
> Leisure activities : 🍴 ✗ 🏠 🏦 🛖 🛶 ☃
> multi-sports ground
> Facilities : 🖿 ⚷ 🍴 launderette 🚿
> Nearby : 🏊
>
> **GPS** Longitude : 5.07349
> Latitude : 43.33168

⚞⚞⚞ Yelloh! Village La Côte Bleue

✆ 04 42 42 81 00, www.semovim-martigues.com

Address : chemin de la Batterie

Opening times : from beginning July to end Sept.

5 ha (200 pitches) terraced, flat, stony, sandy

Tariff : (2013 Price) 33€ ♣♣ ⇌ 🗉 🕅 (10A) – Extra per person 5€ – Reservation fee 15,50€

Rental rates : (2013 Price) (from beginning July to end Sept.) 79 ⌂🕱. Per night from 36 to 144€ – Per week from 252 to 1 008€ Reservation fee 15,50€

> Surroundings : 🌤 ♀♀
> Leisure activities : ✗ 🏠 🛖
> Facilities : 🖿 ⚷ 🍴 launderette 🏊 🚿
>
> **GPS** Longitude : 5.05639
> Latitude : 43.33067

⚞ Flower Le Marius

CAVALIER

✆ 04 42 80 70 29, www.camping-marius.com

Address : plage de la Saulce (3km southeast along the D 49)

2 ha (113 pitches)

Rental rates : 🖿 (2 chalets) – 37 ⌂🕱 15 canvas bungalows (with/without sanitary facilities)

> Surroundings : 🌤 ⟜ ♀♀
> Leisure activities : 🍴 ✗ 🛶 🚲 🏄
> Facilities : 🖿 🛁 launderette 🚿
>
> **GPS** Longitude : 5.06744
> Latitude : 43.33512

⚞ Les Mouettes

✆ 04 42 80 70 01, www.campinglesmouettes.fr – limited spaces for one-night stay

Address : 16 chemin de la Quiétude (4km southeast along the D 49, follow the signs for Sausset, along the r. du Tamaris, near the beach at Ste-Croix)

2 ha (131 pitches) terrace, flat, stony

Rentals : 23 ⌂🕱 – 20 🕮 – 10 studios.

Some pitches with a sea view.

> Surroundings : 🌤 ♀♀
> Leisure activities : 🍴 ✗
> Facilities : 🖿 ⚷ 🛁 🛒 🍴 launderette
> Nearby : 🏊
>
> **GPS** Longitude : 5.07618
> Latitude : 43.33024

LA CROIX-VALMER

83420 – Michelin map **340** O6 – pop. 3 351 – alt. 120

▶ Paris 873 – Brignoles 70 – Draguignan 48 – Fréjus 35

⚞⚞⚞ Sélection Camping ♣♟

✆ 04 94 55 10 30, www.selectioncamping.com 🛇

Address : 12 boulevard de la Mer (2.5km southwest along the D 559, follow the signs for Cavalaire and take road to the right at the roundabout)

Opening times : from mid March to mid Oct.

4 ha (205 pitches) terraced, flat, grassy, stony

Tariff : 42€ ♣♣ ⇌ 🗉 🕅 (10A) – Extra per person 11€ – Reservation fee 30€

Rental rates : (from mid March to mid Oct.) 🛇 – 50 ⌂🕱 15 gîtes. Per night from 52 to 150€ – Reservation fee 30€

> Surroundings : 🌤 ⟜ ♀♀
> Leisure activities : 🍴 ✗ 🕘daytime 🛖 🛶
> 🎣 ☃ multi-sports ground, entertainment room
> Facilities : 🖿 ⚷ 🏧 🛁 🍴 launderette 🏊 🚿
>
> **GPS** Longitude : 6.55501
> Latitude : 43.19439

These symbols are used for a campsite that is exceptional in its category:

⚞⚞⚞…⚞ *Particularly pleasant setting, quality and range of services available*

🌤🌤 *Tranquil, isolated site – quiet site, particularly at night*

⟜⟜ *Exceptional view – interesting or panoramic view*

CROS-DE-CAGNES

06800 – Michelin map **341** D6
▶ Paris 923 – Marseille 194 – Nice 12 – Antibes 11

ᴍᴀ Homair Vacances Green Park ♣♣

✆ 04 93 07 09 96, www.homair.com – limited spaces for one-night stay

Address : 159 bis chemin du Vallon des Vaux (3.8km to the north)

Opening times : from mid April to end Sept.

5 ha (156 pitches) very uneven, terraced, flat, grassy, fine gravel

Tariff : 31€ ♥♥ ⛺ 🔲 💡 (6A) – Extra per person 8€ – Reservation fee 20€

Rental rates : (from mid April to end Sept.) ♿ (2 chalets) – 59 🛖 59 🏠. Per night from 22 to 180€ – Per week from 154 to 1 260€ Reservation fee 20€

A free shuttle service to the beaches July–Aug.

Surroundings : 🏖 🚏 ♀
Leisure activities : ♈ ✕ 🏠 ☺ 🏃 ⛵ 🚴 🏊 multi-sports ground
Facilities : ♿ ⚡ 🔲 🚿 🚰 🚽 launderette 🛁
Nearby : ⛵ 🍴 🏊

G	Longitude : 7.1569
P	
S	Latitude : 43.68904

ᴍᴀ Le Val Fleuri

✆ 04 93 31 21 74, www.campingvalfleuri.fr

Address : 139 chemin du Vallon des Vaux (3.5km to the north)

Opening times : from beginning April to end Sept.

1,5 ha (93 pitches)

Tariff : (2013 Price) 30€ ♥♥ ⛺ 🔲 💡 (10A) – Extra per person 4€

Rental rates : (2013 Price) (from beginning April to end Sept.) 11 🛖 – 1 studio – 1 apartment. Per night from 50 to 65€ Per week from 280 to 610€
🚐 borne

A free shuttle service to the beach July–Aug.

Surroundings : 🏖 🚏 ♀♀
Leisure activities : ♈ 🏃 🏊
Facilities : ♿ ⚡ 🚿 🔲
Nearby : ✕

G	Longitude : 7.15577
P	
S	Latitude : 43.68745

ᴍᴀ Homair Vacances Le Todos

✆ 04 93 07 09 96, www.homair.com – limited spaces for one-night stay
Address : 159bis chemin du Vallon des Vaux (3.8km to the north)

1,6 ha (68 pitches)

Rentals : 44 🛖 – 9 🏠.

A free shuttle service to the beach July–Aug.

Surroundings : 🏖 🚏 ♀♀
Leisure activities : 🏃 🏊
Facilities : ♿ ⚡ 🚽 launderette 🛁
Nearby : ♈ ✕ 🛁 🏠 ☺ 🏃 🚴 ✕ 🏊

G	Longitude : 7.1569
P	
S	Latitude : 43.68904

CUCURON

84160 – Michelin map **332** F11 – pop. 1 844 – alt. 350
▶ Paris 739 – Aix-en-Provence 34 – Apt 25 – Cadenet 9

ᴀ Le Moulin à Vent

✆ 04 90 77 25 77, http://www.le-moulin-a-vent.com

Address : chemin de Gastoule (located 1.5km south along the D 182; follow the signs for Villelaure then continue 800m along the turning to the left)

Opening times : from beginning April to beginning Oct.

2,2 ha (80 pitches)

Tariff : 19,50€ ♥♥ ⛺ 🔲 💡 (10A) – Extra per person 5€
Rental rates : (from beginning April to beginning Oct.) 🚫 – 1 🛖 4 🏠. Per night from 64 to 69€ – Per week from 412 to 540€
🚐 borne 5€

In a setting among vineyards.

Surroundings : 🏖 ≼ 🚏 ♀♀
Leisure activities : 🏠 🚣 🏃
Facilities : ♿ ⚡ 🚿 🚽 🔲 🛁 refrigerators

G	Longitude : 5.44484
P	
S	Latitude : 43.75641

CURBANS

05110 – Michelin map **334** E6 – pop. 418 – alt. 650
▶ Paris 717 – Marseille 171 – Digne-les-Bains 78 – Gap 20

ᴍᴀ Le Lac

✆ 04 92 54 23 10, www.au-camping-du-lac.com – limited spaces for one-night stay

Address : at Le Fangeas

Opening times : end April to end Oct.

5,2 ha (140 pitches)

Tariff : 28€ ♥♥ ⛺ 🔲 💡 (10A) – Extra per person 6€ – Reservation fee 14€

Rental rates : Permanent – 50 🛖. Per night from 45 to 117€ Per week from 240 to 820€ – Reservation fee 14€

The site has a Hautes-Alpes post code (05), but is actually located in the Alpes-de-Haute-Provence (04).

Surroundings : ≼ ♀
Leisure activities : ♈ ✕ 🎮 nighttime ✕ 🏊 🏄 🎣 multi-sports ground
Facilities : ⚡ 🚽 launderette 🛁

G	Longitude : 6.0299
P	
S	Latitude : 44.42452

Do not confuse:
▲ to ᴍᴀ : *MICHELIN classification with*
★ to ★★★★★ : *official classification*

DIGNE-LES-BAINS

04000 – Michelin map **334** F8 – pop. 17 172 – alt. 608 – ♨
▶ Paris 744 – Aix-en-Provence 109 – Antibes 140 – Avignon 167

ᴍᴀ Les Eaux Chaudes

✆ 04 92 32 31 04, www.campingleseauxchaudes.com

Address : 32 avenue des Thermes (located 1.5km southeast along the D 20; beside a stream)

Opening times : from mid April to mid Oct.

3,7 ha (90 pitches)

Tariff : 26,50€ ♥♥ ⛺ 🔲 💡 (10A) – Extra per person 6,80€ – Reservation fee 15€

Rental rates : (from beginning April to end Oct.) – 52 🛖 4 🏠. Per night from 52 to 123€ – Per week from 364 to 861€ Reservation fee 18€
🚐 borne 4,50€

Surroundings : ≼
Leisure activities : 🏠 🏃 🏊
Facilities : ♿ ⚡ 🔲 🚰 🚽 🚿
Nearby : ✕

G	Longitude : 6.2507
P	
S	Latitude : 44.08656

EMBRUN

05200 – Michelin map **334** G5 – pop. 6 188 – alt. 871
▶ Paris 706 – Barcelonnette 55 – Briançon 48 – Digne-les-Bains 97

⚠ Municipal de la Clapière

☎ 04 92 43 01 83, www.camping-embrun-clapiere.com
Address : avenue du Lac (2.5km southwest along the N 94, follow the signs for Gap and take a right turn; at the leisure and activity park)
Opening times : from end April to end Sept.
6,5 ha (291 pitches) terraced, flat, grassy, fine gravel
Tariff : (2013 Price) 22,64€ ✦✦ ⇌ 🅴 (16A) – Extra per person 5,70€
Rental rates : (2013 Price) Permanent – 6 🚐 – 14 🏠. Per night from 87 to 97€ – Per week from 330 to 740€
🚐 borne
A pleasant leisure and activity park with direct access in season.

Surroundings : 𝕭𝕭
Leisure activities : 🎬 🌙nighttime 🏊
Facilities : 🚿 🚰 🍴launderette
Nearby : 🍴✗ 🚣 🎿 🏊 🅼 🏞 🏖 (lake) 🚵 🛶 pedalos
GPS Longitude : 6.47875 Latitude : 44.55075

ESPARRON-DE-VERDON

04800 – Michelin map **334** D10 – pop. 433 – alt. 397
▶ Paris 795 – Barjols 31 – Digne-les-Bains 58 – Gréoux-les-Bains 13

⚠ Le Soleil

☎ 04 92 77 13 78, www.camping-le-soleil.com 🐾
Address : 1000 chemin de la Tuilière (take the southern exit along the D 82, follow the signs for Quinson, then continue 1km along the right turn)
Opening times : from mid April to mid Oct.
2 ha (100 pitches) very uneven, terraced, stony, fine gravel
Tariff : 26€ ✦✦ ⇌ 🅴 (6A) – Extra per person 6,75€ – Reservation fee 15€
Rental rates : (from mid April to mid Oct.) 🐾 – 12 🚐 – 2 canvas bungalows. Per night from 30 to 85€ – Per week from 120 to 620€ Reservation fee 20€
🚐 borne 5€ – 🚿 27€
In a pleasant setting beside a lake.

Surroundings : 𝕭 🚐 𝕭𝕭 ⛰
Leisure activities : 🍴✗ 🎬 🏊 🚣
Facilities : 🚿 🚰 🅿 🍴 🏞 🖲 🏖 🚵
Nearby : 🛶 pedalos
GPS Longitude : 5.97062 Latitude : 43.73439

ESPINASSES

05190 – Michelin map **334** F6 – pop. 665 – alt. 630
▶ Paris 689 – Chorges 19 – Gap 25 – Le Lauzet-Ubaye 23

⚠ La Viste

☎ 04 92 54 43 39, www.laviste.fr – alt. 900
Address : le Belvédère de Serre-Ponçon (head 5.5km northeast along the D 900b, take the D 3 following signs for Chorges and turn left onto D 103)
Opening times : from mid May to mid Sept.
4,5 ha/2,5 for camping (170 pitches) terraced, undulating, flat, grassy, stony
Tariff : (2013 Price) ✦ 7€ ⇌ 🅴 7€ – (5A) 3,70€ – Reservation fee 15€

Rental rates : (2013 Price) (from mid May to mid Sept.) – 10 🚐 30 🏠. Per night from 48 to 62€ – Per week from 690 to 880€ Reservation fee 15€
🚐 borne
In an attractive location overlooking the Lac de Serre-Ponçon.

Surroundings : 🏔 ⇐ mountains, lake and Barrage de Serre-Ponçon (dam) 𝕭𝕭
Leisure activities : 🍴✗ 🎬daytime 🏊 🚣
Facilities : 🚿 🚰 🍴 launderette 🏖 🚵
Nearby : 🏖 (lake) 🎿 water skiing
GPS Longitude : 6.26832 Latitude : 44.47613

FAUCON

84110 – Michelin map **332** D8 – pop. 414 – alt. 350
▶ Paris 677 – Marseille 152 – Avignon 59 – Montélimar 68

⚠ L'Ayguette

☎ 04 90 46 40 35, www.ayguette.com
Address : take the eastern exit along the D 938, follow the signs for Nyons and continue 4.1 km to the right along the D 71, follow the signs for St Romains-Viennois then take the D 86
Opening times : from mid April to end Sept.
2,8 ha (100 pitches) undulating, flat, grassy, stony
Tariff : 31€ ✦✦ ⇌ 🅴 (10A) – Extra per person 5,50€ – Reservation fee 6€
Rental rates : (from mid April to end Sept.) – 24 🚐. Per week from 231 to 693€ – Reservation fee 12€
🚐 borne
In a natural setting.

Surroundings : 𝕭 🚐 𝕭𝕭
Leisure activities : ✗ 🏊 🚣
Facilities : 🚿 🚰 🍴 🖲 🚵
GPS Longitude : 5.12933 Latitude : 44.26215

FORCALQUIER

04300 – Michelin map **334** C9 – pop. 4 640 – alt. 550
▶ Paris 747 – Aix-en-Provence 80 – Apt 42 – Digne-les-Bains 50

⚠ Indigo Forcalquier

☎ 04 92 75 27 94, www.camping-indigo.com
Address : route de Sigonce (take the eastern exit on D 16)
Opening times : from mid April to end Sept.
2,9 ha (115 pitches) terraced, flat and relatively flat, grassy, stony
Tariff : (2013 Price) 27,80€ ✦✦ ⇌ 🅴 (10A) – Extra per person 6,20€ – Reservation fee 22€
Rental rates : (2013 Price) (from mid April to end Sept.) 🅿 – 33 🚐 4 🏠 – 19 tent lodges. Per night from 46 to 112€ – Per week from 225 to 784€ – Reservation fee 22€
🚐 borne 7€

Surroundings : 🚐 𝕭𝕭
Leisure activities : ✗ 🎬 🏊 🚵 🚣
Facilities : 🚿 🚰 🖲 🚵 🍴 🖲 🚵
Nearby : 🍽
GPS Longitude : 5.78723 Latitude : 43.96218

HUTTOPIA

FRÉJUS

83600 – Michelin map **340** P5 – pop. 52 203 – alt. 20
▶ Paris 868 – Brignoles 64 – Cannes 40 – Draguignan 31

⚞⚟ La Baume - La Palmeraie ♁♀

☎ 0494198888, www.labaume-lapalmeraie.com – limited spaces for one-night stay

Address : 3775 rue des Combattants d'Afrique du Nord (4.5km north along the D 4; follow the signs for Bagnols-en-Forêt)

Opening times : from beginning April to end Sept.

26 ha/20 for camping (780 pitches)

Tariff : (2013 Price) 51€ ♛♛ ⇌ 回 ⚡ (6A) – Extra per person 14€ – Reservation fee 33€

Rental rates : (2013 Price) (from beginning April to end Sept.) ♿ 171 ⏚ – 182 apartments. Per night from 37 to 222€ – Per week from 259 to 2030€ – Reservation fee 33€

A large swimming area.

Surroundings : ⛱ 𝄞
Leisure activities : ⛴ ✕ 🎦 ⚐ (open-air theatre) ⛹ 👣 hammam, jacuzzi 🚴 🏸 🎱 🏊 ♨ disco skate park
Facilities : ♿ ⚲ ▥ 🛁 🚿 🚰 ⛾ launderette 🛆 ⛽

Longitude : 6.72319
Latitude : 43.46655

⚞⚟⚟ Yelloh! Village Domaine du Colombier ♁♀

☎ 0494515601, www.clubcolombier.com – limited spaces for one-night stay

Address : 1052 rue des Combattants en Afrique du Nord (situated 2km north along the D 4; follow the signs for Bagnols-en-Forêt)

Opening times : from beginning April to mid Oct.

10 ha (400 pitches) terraced, undulating, flat, grassy

Tariff : 62€ ♛♛ ⇌ 回 ⚡ (16A) – Extra per person 9€

Rental rates : (from beginning April to mid Oct.) – 156 ⏚ 125 ⏠. Per night from 39 to 389€ – Per week from 273 to 2723€ 🚰 borne

Themed village rental options (African, Malibu…)!

Surroundings : ⟨ ⛱
Leisure activities : ⛴ ✕ 🎦 ⚐ ⛹ 👣 jacuzzi 🚴 🏸 🏊 ♨ disco
Facilities : ♿ ⚲ ▥ 🛁 🚿 🚰 ⛾ launderette 🛆 ⛽

Longitude : 6.72688
Latitude : 43.44588

⚞⚟⚟ Sunêlia Holiday Green

☎ 0494198830, www.holidaygreen.com – limited spaces for one-night stay

Address : rue des Anciens Combattants d'Afrique du Nord

Opening times : from beginning April to end Sept.

15 ha (680 pitches) very uneven, terraced, flat, grassy, stony

Tariff : 55€ ♛♛ ⇌ 回 ⚡ (16A) – Extra per person 10€ – Reservation fee 40€

Rental rates : (from beginning April to end Sept.) 🏊 – 300 ⏚ 14 ⏠. Per night from 57 to 309€ – Per week from 399 to 2793€ Reservation fee 40€

Surroundings : ⛱ ⛰ 𝄞
Leisure activities : ⛴ ✕ 🎦 ⚐ ⛹ hammam, jacuzzi 🚴 🏸 🏊 ♨ disco, multi-sports ground
Facilities : ♿ ⚲ ⛾ launderette 🛆 ⛽

Longitude : 6.71683
Latitude : 43.48481

⚞⚟ La Pierre Verte ♁♀

☎ 0494408830, www.campinglapierreverte.com

Address : rue des Anciens Combattants d'Afrique du Nord (6.5km north along the D 4, follow the signs for Bagnols-en-Forêt and take the road to the right)

Opening times : from mid April to end Sept.

28 ha (440 pitches) very uneven, terraced, flat, grassy, stony, rocks

Tariff : 45€ ♛♛ ⇌ 回 ⚡ (10A) – Extra per person 10€ – Reservation fee 25€

Rental rates : (from mid April to end Sept.) – 200 ⏚. Per night from 40 to 195€ – Per week from 280 to 1365€ – Reservation fee 25€

Surroundings : ⛱ ⛰ 𝄞
Leisure activities : ⛴ ✕ 🎦 ⚐ ⛹ 🚴 🏸 🎱 🔥 🏊 ♨ multi-sports ground
Facilities : ♿ ⚲ 🛁 🚿 ⛾ launderette 🛆 ⛽

Longitude : 6.72054
Latitude : 43.48382

⚞⚟ La Plage d'Argens

Cie Bel Air

☎ 0494511497, www.laplagedargens.fr

Address : 541 RD (route Départementale) 559 (3km south along the N 98, direct access to the beach)

Opening times : from beginning April to end Oct.

7 ha (500 pitches) flat, grassy

Tariff : 38€ ♛♛ ⇌ 回 ⚡ (5A) Extra per person 7€ – Reservation fee 35€

Rental rates : (from beginning April to mid Oct.) – 66 ⏚ – 8 tent lodges. Per night from 70 to 115€ – Per week from 287 to 1260€ Reservation fee 35€ 🚰 borne 5€

Beside the Argens river, with direct access to the beach. Choose the pitches away from the road.

Surroundings : 𝄞
Leisure activities : ⛴ ✕ 🎦 🚴 🏊
Facilities : ♿ ⚲ 🛁 ⛾ launderette 🛆 ⛽

Longitude : 6.72489
Latitude : 43.4087

⚞⚟ Les Pins Parasols

☎ 0494408843, www.lespinsparasols.com

Address : 3360 rue des Combattants d'Afrique du Nord (4km north along the D 4, follow the signs for Bagnols-en-Forêt)

Opening times : from beginning April to end Sept.

4,5 ha (189 pitches) terraced, flat, grassy, stony

Tariff : 30,70€ ♛♛ ⇌ 回 ⚡ (6A) – Extra per person 6,80€

Rental rates : (from beginning April to end Sept.) 🏊 – 9 ⏚. Per night from 32 to 111€ – Per week from 221 to 778€

Pretty pitches laid out on terraces lie among shady pine trees.

Surroundings : ⛱ 𝄞
Leisure activities : ✕ 🎦 🚴 🏊 ♨
Facilities : ♿ ⚲ 🚽 ▥ 🛁 – 48 individual sanitary facilities (🚿 🛁 🚽 wc) ⛾ 🖳 🛆 ⛽

Longitude : 6.72531
Latitude : 43.464

GAP

05000 – Michelin map **334** E5 – pop. 39 243 – alt. 735
▶ Paris 665 – Avignon 209 – Grenoble 103 – Sisteron 52

⚠️ Alpes-Dauphiné

☎ 04 92 51 29 95, www.alpesdauphine.com – alt. 850

Address : route Napoléon (3km north along the N 85, follow the signs for Grenoble)

Opening times : from mid April to mid Oct.

10 ha/6 for camping (185 pitches)

Tariff : 26,20€ ♣♣ ⛺ 🔲 🔌 (6A) – Extra per person 7€ – Reservation fee 20€

Rental rates : (from mid April to mid Oct.) – 40 🚐 – 15 🏠 – 2 gîtes. Per night from 50 to 90€ – Per week from 310 to 690€ – Reservation fee 20€

🚐 borne 6€

Surroundings : 🏊🏊
Leisure activities : 🍸 ✗ 🛖 jacuzzi 🚵 ⛷
Facilities : 🚿 ⚬🗝 🏛 🅿️ ⛺ 🚰 launderette
GPS Longitude : 6.08255 | Latitude : 44.58022

The Michelin classification (⚠️⚠️⚠️... ⚠️) is totally independent of the official star classification system awarded by the local prefecture or other official organisation.

GIENS

83400 – Michelin map **340** L7
▶ Paris 869 – Marseille 93 – Toulon 29 – La Seyne-sur-Mer 37

⚠️ La Presqu'île de Giens 👥

☎ 04 94 58 22 86, www.camping-giens.com – 📮

Address : 153 route de la Madrague

Opening times : from beginning April to beginning Oct.

7 ha (460 pitches) terraced, flat, grassy, stony

Tariff : (2013 Price) 34€ ♣♣ ⛺ 🔲 🔌 (16A) – Extra per person 8,30€

Rental rates : (from beginning April to beginning Oct.) – 69 🚐 – 50 🏠. Per night from 75 to 165€ – Per week from 371 to 1 155€ – Reservation fee 17€

🚐 borne

Surroundings : 🛏️ 🏊🏊
Leisure activities : 🍸 ✗ 🛖 🎣 daytime 🚴 🚵
Facilities : ⚬🗝 🏛 ⛺ 🚰 launderette 🚿 🚿
Nearby : bowling
GPS Longitude : 6.14332 | Latitude : 43.04084

⚠️ La Tour Fondue

☎ 04 94 58 22 86, www.camping-latourfondue.com – 📮

Address : avenue des Arbanais

Opening times : from beginning April to beginning Nov.

2 ha (140 pitches) flat, grassy

Tariff : 30,50€ ♣♣ ⛺ 🔲 🔌 (10A) – Extra per person 8,30€

Rental rates : (from beginning April to beginning Nov.) – 21 🚐. Per night from 75 to 114€ – Per week from 371 to 798€ – Reservation fee 17€

🚐 borne

Surroundings : 🛏️ 🏊
Leisure activities : 🛖
Facilities : ⚬🗝 🚰 launderette
Nearby : 🚿 🍸 ✗ 🤿 scuba diving
GPS Longitude : 6.15569 | Latitude : 43.02971

LA GRAVE

05320 – Michelin map **334** F2 – pop. 493 – alt. 1 526 – Winter sports : 1 450/3 250m
▶ Paris 642 – Briançon 38 – Gap 126 – Grenoble 80

⚠️ La Meije

ROMAGNE

☎ 06 08 54 30 84, www.camping-delameije.com

Address : head east towards Briançon along the D 1091; beside the Romanche river

Opening times : from mid May to mid Sept.

2,5 ha (50 pitches) terrace, flat and relatively flat, grassy

Tariff : 19,60€ ♣♣ ⛺ 🔲 🔌 (6A)

Extra per person 3,30€
🚐 10 🔲 19,60€

The site has a magnificent view of the La Grave glacier

Surroundings : 🌊 ⛰️ 🏊🏊
Leisure activities : 🎿 🎣 🎣 🏊
Facilities : 🚿 ⚬🗝 🚐 ⛺ 🚰 🅿️
Nearby : 🚣 rafting and canyoning
GPS Longitude : 6.30911 | Latitude : 45.04526

⚠️ Le Gravelotte

☎ 04 76 79 93 14, www.camping-le-gravelotte.com

Address : 1.2km west along the D 1091, follow the signs for Grenoble and take road to the left; beside the Meije river

Opening times : from mid June to end Sept.

4 ha (75 pitches) flat, grassy

Tariff : 14€ ♣♣ ⛺ 🔲 🔌 (10A) – Extra per person 3,70€

An attractive location at the foot of the mountains and beside the Romanche river.

Surroundings : ⛰️ 🏊
Leisure activities : 🍸 🎣 🏊
Facilities : 🚿 ⚬🗝 🚰 🅿️
GPS Longitude : 6.29697 | Latitude : 45.04328

A 'quartier' is a district or area of a town or village.

GRAVESON

13690 – Michelin map **340** D2 – pop. 3 875 – alt. 14
▶ Paris 696 – Arles 25 – Avignon 14 – Cavaillon 30

⚠️ Les Micocouliers

☎ 04 90 95 81 49, http://www.lesmicocouliers.fr

Address : 445 route de Cassoulen (1.2km southeast along the D 28, follow the signs for Châteaurenard and turn right onto D 5, follow the signs for Maillane)

Opening times : from mid March to mid Oct.

3,5 ha (118 pitches) flat, grassy

Tariff : (2013 Price) 30€ ♣♣ ⛺ 🔲 🔌 (10A) – Extra per person 7,50€ – Reservation fee 10€

Rental rates : (2013 Price) Permanent 🏕️ – 5 🚐. Per night from 60 to 101€ – Per week from 390 to 710€ – Reservation fee 17€

🚐 borne 6€

Surroundings : 🛏️ 🏊
Leisure activities : 🚵 🏊
Facilities : 🚿 ⚬🗝 🚰 🅿️
GPS Longitude : 4.78111 | Latitude : 43.84389

GRÉOUX-LES-BAINS

04800 – Michelin map **334** D10 – pop. 2 510 – alt. 386 – ♨
▶ Paris 783 – Aix-en-Provence 55 – Brignoles 52 – Digne-les-Bains 69

🔺 Yelloh! Village le Verdon Parc 👥

Cie Bel Air

✆ 0492780808, www.
campingverdonparc.fr ✗ (July–Aug.)
Address : domaine de la Paludette
(600m south along the D 8, follow the
signs for St-Pierre and take the turning
to the left after the bridge; beside the
Verdon river)

Opening times : from beginning April
to end Oct.

8 ha (280 pitches) terraced, flat, grassy,
stony, gravelled

Tariff : 36€ ♣♣ ⇌ 🔲 🔱 (16A)
Extra per person 6€

Rental rates : (from beginning April
to end Oct.) ♿ (2 mobile homes)
✗ – 150 🚐 – 8 tent lodges.
Per night from 39 to 174 € – Per week
from 273 to 1218€
🚰 borne – 15 🔲 18€ – 🚐 🔱16€

Surroundings : ⛰ 🚗 ♨
Leisure activities : ♟ ✗ 🎬 ⛱ daytime 🏃
⚽ 🏓 🏊 ⛵ multi-sports ground
Facilities : ♿ ⚡ 🚿 🚽 launderette ⛟
refrigerators
GPS Longitude : 5.884
Latitude : 43.75205

🔺 La Pinède

✆ 0492780547, www.camping-lapinede-04.com
Address : route de Saint-Pierre (located 1.5km south along the D 8,
200m from the Verdon river)
Opening times : from beginning March to end Nov.
3 ha (160 pitches) terraced, flat and relatively flat, stony, fine gravel
Tariff : 24,70€ ♣♣ ⇌ 🔲 🔱 (10A) – Extra per person 5€
Rental rates : (from beginning March to end Nov.) – 56 🚐.
Per night from 33 to 107€ – Per week from 232 to 750€
🚰 borne 4€

Surroundings : ⛰ ≤ 🚗 ♨
Leisure activities : ♟ ✗ 🎬 ⛱ 🏊
Facilities : ♿ ⚡ 🚿 🚽 🔲
Nearby : 🎣
GPS Longitude : 5.88294
Latitude : 43.74848

🔺 Verseau

✆ 0492776710, www.camping-le-verseau.com
Address : 113 chemin Gaspard de Besse (1.2km south along the D 8,
follow the signs for St-Pierre and take the road to the right, near the
Verdon river)
Opening times : from mid March to mid Nov.
2,5 ha (120 pitches) flat and relatively flat, grassy, stony
Tariff : (2013 Price) 23,50€ ♣♣ ⇌ 🔲 🔱 (16A)
Extra per person 4,50€
Rental rates : (2013 Price) (from mid March to mid Nov.) – 47 🚐
13 🏠. Per week from 268 to 1790€

Surroundings : ⛰ ≤ 🚗 ♨
Leisure activities : ♟ 🎬 ⛱ 🏊
entertainment room
Facilities : ♿ ⚡ 🚿 🚽 🔲 refrigerators
GPS Longitude : 5.88199
Latitude : 43.75152

GRIMAUD

83310 – Michelin map **340** O6 – pop. 4 309 – alt. 105
▶ Paris 861 – Brignoles 58 – Fréjus 32 – Le Lavandou 32

🔺 Les Prairies de la Mer 👥

✆ 0494790909, www.riviera-villages.com
Address : at Saint-Pons-les-Mûres (RN 98)
20 ha (1500 pitches)
Rentals : 🅿 – 150 🚐 – 150 🏠.
🚰 borne

Surroundings : ≤ St Tropez and the gulf 🚗
♨♨
Leisure activities : ♟ ✗ 🎬 ⛱ 🏃 🎣 🚢
hammam jacuzzi ⚽ 🏓 ✗ ⛵ 🏊 disco,
scuba diving, multi-sports ground, spa
centre
Facilities : ⚡ 🚿 ⛺ 🚽 🚽 launderette ⛟
🚿 ⛟
GPS Longitude : 6.58241
Latitude : 43.28086

🔺 Domaine des Naïades 👥

✆ 0494556780, www.lesnaiades.com – limited spaces for one-night
stay
Address : at Saint-Pons-les-Mûres
Opening times : from beginning April to mid Oct.
27 ha/14 for camping (492 pitches) terraced, flat, grassy, sandy
Tariff : (2013 Price) 58€ ♣♣ ⇌ 🔲 🔱 (10A) – Extra per person 8€
Rental rates : (2013 Price) (from mid April to mid Oct.) – 226 🚐
Per night from 49 to 252€ – Per week from 343 to 1764€
🚰 borne 2,50€

Surroundings : 🚗 ♨♨
Leisure activities : ♟ ✗ 🎬 🏃 ⚽ 🚴 🏊 ⛵
Facilities : ♿ ⚡ 🚿 🚽 launderette ⛟ 🚿
GPS Longitude : 6.57937
Latitude : 43.28517

*A chambre d'hôte is a guesthouse or B & B-style accom-
modation.*

GUILLESTRE

05600 – Michelin map **334** H5 – pop. 2 308 – alt. 1 000
▶ Paris 715 – Barcelonnette 51 – Briançon 36 – Digne-les-Bains 114

🔺 Parc Le Villard

✆ 0492450654, www.camping-levillard.com
Address : route des campings, Le Villard (situated 2km west along
the D 902a, follow the signs for Gap; beside the Chagne river)
Opening times : from beginning June to mid Sept.
3,2 ha (120 pitches) flat and relatively flat, grassy, stony
Tariff : (2013 Price) 26,50€ ♣♣ ⇌ 🔲 🔱 (10A) – Extra per person 6€
Rental rates : (2013 Price) (from mid Feb. to beginning Sept.) ✗
17 🚐 – 5 🏠 – 2 canvas bungalows. Per night from 45 to 80€
Per week from 285 to 800€ – Reservation fee 8€
The site occupies both sides of a small road.

Surroundings : ≤ ♨
Leisure activities : ✗ 🎬 ⛱ ✗ 🏓 🎣 🏊
Facilities : ♿ ⚡ 🚿 🚽 launderette ⛟
refrigerators
GPS Longitude : 6.62687
Latitude : 44.65895

⚠ St-James-les-Pins

☎ 04 92 45 08 24, www.lesaintjames.com

Address : route des Campings (head 1.5km west following signs for Risoul and take turning to the right)

Opening times : from beginning Jan. to end Oct.

2,5 ha (100 pitches)

Tariff : 19,60€ ♣♣ ⇔ 🔲 🗲 (10A) – Extra per person 3,50€
Rental rates : Permanent – 10 🚐 – 13 🏠 – 10 🛏. Per night from 55 to 75€ – Per week from 293 to 670€
🚽 borne 4,60€
the site is crossed by the Chagne mountain stream.

Surroundings : ❄ 🎾	
Leisure activities : 🏛 🏖 🏊 multi-sports ground	**G**
Facilities : 👤 ⚡ 🏛 🚿 🍴 launderette	**P** **S**
Nearby : 🍽 🛶	Longitude : 6.63293 Latitude : 44.65685

⚠ La Rochette

☎ 04 92 45 02 15, www.campingguillestre.com

Address : route des Campings (head 1km west following signs for Risoul and take turning to the right)

Opening times : from beginning May to end Sept.

4 ha (190 pitches) flat and relatively flat, stony, grassy

Tariff : (2013 Price) 18,90€ ♣♣ ⇔ 🔲 🗲 (10A) – Extra per person 4€ Reservation fee 9€
🚽 borne

Surroundings : ⇜ 🎾	
Leisure activities : 🏛 🏖 🏊	**G**
Facilities : 👤 ⚡ 📮 🚿 🍴 launderette 🚽	**P** **S**
Nearby : 🍽 🛶 🍴 🛶	Longitude : 6.63845 Latitude : 44.65895

HYÈRES

83400 – Michelin map **340** L7 – pop. 54 686 – alt. 40
▣ Paris 851 – Aix-en-Provence 102 – Cannes 123 – Draguignan 78

⚠ Les Palmiers 👥 (mobile home rentals only)

☎ 04 94 66 39 66, www.camping-les-palmiers.fr

Address : rue du Ceinturon, L'Ayguade

Opening times : from mid March to mid Oct.

5,5 ha

Rental rates : 345 🚐. Per night from 47 to 134€ – Per week from 343 to 1645€ – Reservation fee 30€

Surroundings : 🌊 ⊏ 🎾	
Leisure activities : 🍸 🍽 🏛 🌙 nighttime 🏃 🛁 ♨ hammam 🏖 🚴 ✂ 🛶 🛝 🛶	**G**
Facilities : 👤 ⚡ 🚿 🍴 launderette 🚽 🛒	**P** **S** Longitude : 6.16725 Latitude : 43.10344

⚠ Le Ceinturon 3

☎ 04 94 66 32 65, www.ceinturon3.fr – 🅵🅁

Address : 2 rue des Saraniers (5km southeast, 100m from the sea; at Ayguade-Ceinturon)

Opening times : from mid April to end Sept.

2,5 ha (200 pitches)

Tariff : 37,85€ ♣♣ ⇔ 🔲 🗲 (10A) – Extra per person 6,25€
Rental rates : (from mid April to end Sept.) 🏖 – 1 🚐 40 🏠. Per night from 47 to 118€ – Per week from 330 to 824€ Reservation fee 16€

Surroundings : 🎾	
Leisure activities : 🍸 🍽 🏖	**G**
Facilities : 👤 ⚡ ✉ 🏛 🚿 🍴 launderette 🚽 🛒	**P** **S**
Nearby : ✂	Longitude : 6.16962 Latitude : 43.10109

L'ISLE-SUR-LA-SORGUE

84800 – Michelin map **332** D10 – pop. 18 936 – alt. 57
▣ Paris 693 – Apt 34 – Avignon 23 – Carpentras 18

⚠ Club Airotel La Sorguette

☎ 04 90 38 05 71, www.camping-sorguette.com

Address : 871 route d'Apt (located 1.5km southeast along the N 100; near the Sorgue)

Opening times : from mid March to mid Oct.

2,5 ha (164 pitches)

Tariff : 28,10€ ♣♣ ⇔ 🔲 🗲 (10A) – Extra per person 8,10€ Reservation fee 20€
Rental rates : (from mid March to mid Oct.) 👤 (1 mobile home) 30 🚐 – 3 yurts – 1 tipi – 3 tent lodges. Per night from 46 to 95€ Per week from 287 to 791€ – Reservation fee 20€
🚽 borne 7€ – 3 🔲 14€ – 🚽 11€

Surroundings : 🎾	
Leisure activities : 🍽 🏛 🏃 🏖 🚴 🛶 🛝 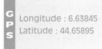	**G**
Facilities : 👤 ⚡ 🍴 launderette 🚽 🛒 refrigerated food storage facilities	**P** **S** Longitude : 5.07192 Latitude : 43.9146

This guide is not intended as a list of all the camping sites in France; its aim is to provide a selection of the best sites in each category.

ISOLA

06420 – Michelin map **341** D2 – pop. 748 – alt. 873
▣ Paris 897 – Marseille 246 – Nice 76 – Cuneo 79

⚠ Le Lac des Neiges

☎ 04 93 02 18 16, www.princiland.fr – alt. 875

Address : route de St-Etienne-de-Tinée (located 1km north of the village along the D 2205)

3 ha (98 pitches)

Rentals : 🏖 – 1 🚐 – 4 🛏 – 2 studios – 2 gîtes.

Surroundings : ⊏ 🎾	
Leisure activities : 🍸 🍽 🏛 🏖 🛶 🚴 🛶 pedalos 🛶	**G**
Facilities : 👤 ⊙ 🏛 🚿 ♨ 🍴 🛒	**P** **S** Longitude : 7.03912 Latitude : 44.18898
Nearby : ✂	

Michelin classification:

⚠⚠⚠⚠	*Extremely comfortable, equipped to a very high standard*
⚠⚠⚠	*Very comfortable, equipped to a high standard*
⚠⚠⚠	*Comfortable and well equipped*
⚠⚠	*Reasonably comfortable*
⚠	*Satisfactory*

LARCHE

04530 – Michelin map **334** J6 – pop. 74 – alt. 1 691
▶ Paris 760 – Barcelonnette 28 – Briançon 81 – Cuneo 70

⚠ Domaine des Marmottes

✆ 04 92 84 33 64, www.camping-marmottes.fr

Address : Malboisset (800m southeast down a turning to the right; beside the Ubayette river)

Opening times : from beginning June to end Sept.

2 ha (52 pitches)

Tariff : 🕴 8€ 🚗 🗉 – 🔌 (10A) 3,50€
🚰 borne

Surroundings : 🏕 ◁ ⌂ 🌳🌳
Leisure activities : ✗
Facilities : ♿ ⚬ ⚏ 🕨 launderette
Nearby : 🍸

GPS Longitude : 6.85257
Latitude : 44.44615

LE LAVANDOU

83980 – Michelin map **340** N7 – pop. 5 747 – alt. 1
▶ Paris 873 – Cannes 102 – Draguignan 75 – Fréjus 61

⚠ Beau Séjour

✆ 04 94 71 25 30, campingbeausejourvar.com

Address : la Grande Bastide (located 1.5km to the southwest)

Opening times : from mid April to end Sept.

1,5 ha (135 pitches)

Tariff : 24,44€ 🕴🕴 🚗 🗉 🔌 (10A) – Extra per person 6€
🚰 10 🗉 22,94€
Attractive and shaded marked-out pitches.

Surroundings : ⌂ 🌳🌳
Leisure activities : 🍸 ✗
Facilities : ♿ ⚬ ⚏ 🕨 ⚏

GPS Longitude : 6.35165
Latitude : 43.13497

LA LONDE-LES-MAURES

83250 – Michelin map **340** M7 – pop. 9 910 – alt. 24
▶ Paris 861 – Bormes-les-Mimosas 11 – Cuers 31 – Hyères 10

⚠ Les Moulières

✆ 04 94 01 53 21, www.campinglesmoulieres.com – ℝ

Address : 15 chemin de la Garenne, Le Puits de Magne (situated 2.5km southeast; follow the signs for Port-de-Miramar and take turning to the right)

Opening times : from end May to beginning Sept.

3 ha (250 pitches) flat, grassy

Tariff : 35,50€ 🕴🕴 🚗 🗉 🔌 (6A) – Extra per person 8€

Surroundings : 🏕 🌳
Leisure activities : 🍸 ✗ ⚏ ✂
Facilities : ♿ ⚬ ⚏ 🕨 🗉 ⚏

GPS Longitude : 6.23526
Latitude : 43.12236

The prices listed were supplied by the campsite owners in 2013 (if prices were not available, those from previous year are given). The fees should be regarded as basic charges and may fluctuate with inflation.

LOURMARIN

84160 – Michelin map **332** F11 – pop. 1 000 – alt. 224
▶ Paris 732 – Aix-en-Provence 37 – Apt 19 – Cavaillon 73

⚠ Les Hautes Prairies

✆ 04 90 68 02 89, www.campinghautesprairies.com

Address : route de Vaugines (700m east along the D 56)

Opening times : from beginning April to end Sept.

3,6 ha (158 pitches) flat and relatively flat, grassy, stony

Tariff : 28€ 🕴🕴 🚗 🗉 🔌 (10A) – Extra per person 5€ – Reservation fee 18€

Rental rates : (from beginning April to end Sept.) – 15 🛏 – 15 🏠 6 🛏. Per night from 55 to 120€ – Per week from 300 to 800€ Reservation fee 18€
🚰 borne 3€

Surroundings : ⌂ 🌳
Leisure activities : 🍸 ✗ ⚏ ✂
Facilities : ♿ ⚬ ⚏ 🕨 🗉 ⚏

GPS Longitude : 5.37291
Latitude : 43.76784

MALEMORT-DU-COMTAT

84570 – Michelin map **332** D9 – pop. 1 461 – alt. 208
▶ Paris 688 – Avignon 33 – Carpentras 11 – Malaucène 22

⚠ Font Neuve

✆ 04 90 69 90 00, www.campingfontneuve.com

Address : quartier Font-Neuve (1.6km southeast along the D 5, follow the signs for Méthanis and take road to the left)

Opening times : from mid April to end Sept.

1,5 ha (54 pitches) terraced, flat and relatively flat, grassy, stony

Tariff : 22,80€ 🕴🕴 🚗 🗉 🔌 (6A) – Extra per person 5€ – Reservation fee 10€

Rental rates : (from mid April to end Sept.) – 5 🏠. Per night from 70€ – Per week from 300 to 480€ – Reservation fee 10€

Surroundings : 🏕 ◁ ⌂ 🌳🌳
Leisure activities : ✗ ⚏ ✂ ⚏
Facilities : ♿ ⚬ ⚏ 🗉 ⚏ 🕨 🗉 ⚏

GPS Longitude : 5.17098
Latitude : 44.0142

MALLEMORT

13370 – Michelin map **340** G3 – pop. 5 925 – alt. 120
▶ Paris 716 – Aix-en-Provence 34 – Apt 38 – Cavaillon 20

⚠ Durance Luberon

✆ 04 90 59 13 36, www.campingduranceluberon.com – for caravans, access via town centre not advised, acces via N 7 and D 561, signs for Charleval

Address : at the Domaine du Vergon (2.8km southeast along the D 23, 200m from the canal, towards the power station – from the A 7 take exits 26 and 7)

Opening times : from beginning April to end Sept.

4 ha (110 pitches) flat, grassy

Tariff : (2013 Price) 26,50€ 🕴🕴 🚗 🗉 – Extra per person 6€
Rental rates : (2013 Price) (from beginning April to end Sept.) 8 🛏. Per night from 55 to 72€ – Per week from 380 to 700€ Reservation fee 15€

Surroundings : 🏕 ⌂ 🌳🌳
Leisure activities : ✗ ⚏ ⚏
Facilities : ♿ ⚬ ⚏ 🗉 🗉 ⚏ 🗉 🕨 🗉 ⚏
Nearby : 🐎

GPS Longitude : 5.20492
Latitude : 43.72091

MANDELIEU-LA-NAPOULE

06210 – Michelin map **341** C6 – pop. 21 764 – alt. 4
▶ Paris 890 – Brignoles 86 – Cannes 9 – Draguignan 53

⚠ Les Cigales

✆ 04 93 49 23 53, www.lescigales.com

Address : 505 avenue de la Mer (at Mandelieu)

Opening times : Permanent

2 ha (115 pitches)

Tariff : 40,20€ ✶✶ ⚊ 🖳 🔌 (6A) – Extra per person 8,60€
Reservation fee 25€

Rental rates : (from beginning March to beginning Nov.)
30 🛏 – 9 studios. Per night from 68 to 165€ – Per week
from 400 to 990€ – Reservation fee 25€

🚐 borne

A green 'oasis' in the town; beside the Siagne river.

Surroundings : 🌳 ⌂ ♨♨
Leisure activities : ⚓ 🛝
Facilities : & ⚊ 🎫 🛁 ☂ 🚰 🚿 launderette
Nearby : 🍷 ✗ 🚴 🎠 🎿 ⚓

| | G P S | Longitude : 6.9424 |
| | | Latitude : 43.53883 |

⚠ Les Pruniers - Les Bungalows du Golfe

✆ 04 93 49 99 23, www.bungalow-camping.com

Address : 118 rue de la Pinéa (via the av. de la Mer)

Opening times : from beginning Feb. to beginning Nov.

0,8 ha (64 pitches)

Tariff : (2013 Price) 24,40€ ✶✶ ⚊ 🖳 🔌 (10A) – Extra per person 5€

Rental rates : (2013 Price) (from beginning Feb. to mid Nov.)
36 studios. Per night from 40 to 96€ – Per week from 280 to 670€

The site has a swimming pool beside the Siagne river.

Surroundings : 🌳 ⌂ ♨♨
Leisure activities : 🎫 ⚓ 🛝
Facilities : ⚊ 🚰 🖳 🛁
Nearby : 🍷 ✗ 🎿 ⚓

| | G P S | Longitude : 6.94349 |
| | | Latitude : 43.53503 |

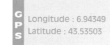

*We value your opinion and welcome your feedback.
Do email us at campingfrance@tp.michelin.com*

MAUBEC

84660 – Michelin map **332** D10 – pop. 1 877 – alt. 120
▶ Paris 706 – Aix-en-Provence 68 – Apt 25 – Avignon 32

⚠ Municipal Les Royères du Prieuré

✆ 04 90 76 50 34, www.campingmaubec-luberon.com

Address : 52 chemin de la Combe St-Pierre (south of the town)

Opening times : from beginning April to mid Oct.

1 ha (93 pitches) terraced, flat, grassy, stony

Tariff : ✶ 3,50€ ⚊ 2,30€ 🖳 2,30€ – 🔌 (10A) 4€ – Reservation
fee 10€

Rental rates : (from beginning April to mid Oct.) 🚿 – 3 🛏 – 2 🛌
1 gîte. Per night from 70 to 80€ – Per week from 450 to 520€
Reservation fee 10€

Lovely terraces with plenty of shade.

Surroundings : 🌳 ≤ ♨♨
Facilities : ⚊ 🚰 🛁

| | G P S | Longitude : 5.1326 |
| | | Latitude : 43.84032 |

MAUSSANE-LES-ALPILLES

13520 – Michelin map **340** D3 – pop. 2 076 – alt. 32
▶ Paris 712 – Arles 20 – Avignon 30 – Marseille 81

⚠ Municipal les Romarins

✆ 04 90 54 33 60, www.maussane.com/spip.php?article79

Address : avenue des Alpilles (take the northern exit along the D 5,
follow the signs for St-Rémy)

Opening times : from mid March to mid Oct.

3 ha (145 pitches)

Tariff : (2013 Price) 21€ ✶✶ ⚊ 🖳 🔌 (10A) – Extra per person 6€

🚐 borne

Note that the reception is at the tourist office.

Surroundings : ⌂ ♨♨
Leisure activities : 🎫 ⚓ 🍴
Facilities : & ⚊ 🛁 ☂ 🚰 🚿 launderette
Nearby : 🛝

| | G P S | Longitude : 4.8093 |
| | | Latitude : 43.72104 |

*There are several different types of sani-station
('borne' in French) – sanitation points providing
fresh water and disposal points for grey water.
See page 12 for further details.*

MAZAN

84380 – Michelin map **332** D9 – pop. 5 641 – alt. 100
▶ Paris 684 – Avignon 35 – Carpentras 9 – Cavaillon 30

⚠ Le Ventoux

✆ 04 90 69 70 94, www.camping-le-ventoux.com

Address : 1348 chemin de la Combe (3km north along the D 70,
follow the signs for Caromb then take the road to the left, follow the
signs for Carpentras, recommended route via D 974)

0,7 ha (49 pitches)

Rentals : 16 🛏 .

Surroundings : 🌳 ≤ Mont Ventoux ♨♨
Leisure activities : 🍷 ✗ ⚓ 🛝
Facilities : & ⚊ 🎫 🛁 🚰 launderette 🛁

| | G P S | Longitude : 5.11378 |
| | | Latitude : 44.0805 |

MENTON

06500 – Michelin map **341** F5 – pop. 28 848
▶ Paris 966 – Marseille 218 – Nice 32 – Antibes 55

⚠ Municipal St-Michel

✆ 04 93 35 81 23, www.menton.fr – acces difficult for caravans and
campervans – 🚫

Address : chemin du Parc de St-Michel (follow the signs for Les
Ciappes de Castellar, Plateau St-Michel)

Opening times : from beginning April to end Oct.

2 ha (131 pitches) terraced, flat, grassy, fine gravel

Tariff : ✶ 4,25€ ⚊ 4,60€ 🖳 4,90€ – 🔌 (16A) 3€

*Shady pitches under centuries-old olive trees, but the sanitary
facilities are not very good.*

Surroundings : ♨♨
Leisure activities : 🍷 ✗
Facilities : ⚊ 🖳 🛁 refrigerated food sto-
rage facilities

| | G P S | Longitude : 7.498 |
| | | Latitude : 43.77906 |

MÉOLANS-REVEL

04340 – Michelin map **334** H6 – pop. 333 – alt. 1 080
▶ Paris 787 – Marseille 216 – Digne-les-Bains 74 – Gap 64

⛰ Le Rioclar 👥

📞 0492811032, www.rioclar.com – alt. 1 073

Address : D 900 (located 1.5km east, follow the signs for
Barcelonnette, near the Ubaye et a small lake)

Opening times : from mid May to beginning Sept.

8 ha (200 pitches) terraced, flat, grassy, stony

Tariff : (2013 Price) 27,30€ ♦♦ ⇔ ▤ (½) (10A) – Extra per person 6€
Reservation fee 18€

Rental rates : (2013 Price) ⚡ – 25 🚐 – 3 🏠. Per night
from 57 to 78€ – Per week from 390 to 700€ – Reservation fee 18€

In a pleasant location and setting.

Surroundings : 🌿 ⛱ ♨♨
Leisure activities : 🍴✗ 🎪 ☺ 🏇 🎯 🚴 ⚽
🏓 ⛷ rafting and canyoning 🚣 multi-sports
ground
Facilities : 🚿 ⛽ 🛁 🚾 🌐 🧺 🍴
Nearby : 🏊 (lake)

Longitude : 6.53172
Latitude : 44.39928

⛰ Domaine Loisirs de l'Ubaye

📞 0492810196, www.loisirsubaye.com – alt. 1 073

Address : D 900 (3km east, follow the signs for Barcelonnette, beside
the Ubaye river)

Opening times : from beginning May to mid Oct.

9,5 ha (267 pitches)

Tariff : 24€ ♦♦ ⇔ ▤ (½) (6A) – Extra per person 6€ – Reservation
fee 15€

Rental rates : (from mid Feb. to mid Oct.) – 19 🚐 – 19 🏠.
Per week from 310 to 700€ – Reservation fee 15€

🚐 borne 24€

Surroundings : ⛱ ♨♨
Leisure activities : ✗ 🎪 ☺ daytime 🏇 🚴
⚽ ⛷
Facilities : 🚿 ⛽ ▥ 🛁 🚾 🧊 🍴 launderette
🧺 🍴
Nearby : rafting and canyoning

Longitude : 6.54638
Latitude : 44.39645

To visit a town or region, use the MICHELIN Green Guides.

MÉZEL

04270 – Michelin map **334** F8 – pop. 680 – alt. 585
▶ Paris 745 – Barrême 22 – Castellane 47 – Digne-les-Bains 15

⛰ La Célestine

📞 0492355254, www.camping-lacelestine.fr

Address : route de Manosque (3km south along the D 907; beside
the Asse river)

Opening times : from beginning May to end Sept.

2,4 ha (100 pitches) flat, grassy

Tariff : 23€ ♦♦ ⇔ ▤ (½) (10A) – Extra per person 5€

Rental rates : (from beginning May to end Sept.) – 8 🚐.
Per night from 79€ – Per week from 490 to 590€

Surroundings : ♨♨
Leisure activities : 🍴 🎪 🏇 🚴 🏊 (pool)
quad biking
Facilities : 🚿 ⛽ 🧺

Longitude : 6.19183
Latitude : 43.97002

MONTMEYAN

83670 – Michelin map **340** L4 – pop. 543 – alt. 480
▶ Paris 832 – Marseille 88 – Toulon 87 – Draguignan 46

⛺ Château de l'Éouvière

📞 0494807554, www.leouviere.com

Address : route de Taverne (500m south along the D 13)

30 ha/5 for camping (81 pitches)

Rentals : 10 🚐 – 2 apartments.

Surroundings : 🌳 ♨♨
Leisure activities : 🎪 🏊
Facilities : 🚿 ⛽ 🍴 🌐 🍴

Longitude : 6.06035
Latitude : 43.63819

*The pitches of many campsites are marked out with low
hedges of attractive bushes and shrubs.*

MONTPEZAT

04500 – Michelin map **334** E10
▶ Paris 806 – Digne-les-Bains 54 – Gréoux-les-Bains 23
– Manosque 37

⛰ Village Center Côteau de la Marine

Interaview Production

📞 0825002030, www.campings.village-center.fr

Address : at Vauvert, route de
Baudinard (situated 2km southeast)

Opening times : from end April to
end Sept.

12 ha (283 pitches)

Tariff : 33€ ♦♦ ⇔ ▤ (½) (10A)
Extra per person 6€

Rental rates : (from end April to end Sept.) – 177 🚐 – 46 tent
lodges. Per night from 29 to 110€ – Per week from 420 to 1071€
Reservation fee 30€

Surroundings : 🌿 ≤ ⛱ ♨
Leisure activities : 🍴✗ 🎪 ☺ daytime 🏇 🚴
⚽ ⛷ pedalos, electric boats 🚣
Facilities : ⛽ 🌐 🍴 🧊 🧺 🍴

Longitude : 6.09818
Latitude : 43.74765

MOUSTIERS-STE-MARIE

04360 – Michelin map **334** F9 – pop. 718 – alt. 631
▶ Paris 783 – Aix-en-Provence 90 – Castellane 45 – Digne-les-
Bains 47

⛰ Le Vieux Colombier

📞 0492746189, www.lvcm.fr

Address : quartier St Michel (800m to the south)

Opening times : from end April to end Sept.

2,7 ha (70 pitches) terraced, relatively flat, grassy, stony

Tariff : (2013 Price) 22€ ♦♦ ⇔ ▤ (½) (6A) – Extra per person 5,80€
Reservation fee 9€

Rental rates : (2013 Price) (from end April to end Sept.) – 13 🚐.
Per night from 42 to 568€ – Per week from 230 to 610€
Reservation fee 9€

🚐 borne 7€

Surroundings : ≤ ⛱ ♨
Leisure activities : 🎪
Facilities : 🚿 ⛽ 🛁 🍴 🍴
Nearby : ✗

Longitude : 6.22166
Latitude : 43.83956

⛰ St-Jean

𝒫 04 92 74 66 85, www.camping-st-jean.fr

Address : quartier Saint Jean (located 1km southwest along the D 952, follow the signs for Riez; beside the Maïre river)

Opening times : from end March to mid Oct.

,6 ha (125 pitches)

Tariff : (2013 Price) 23,30€ ♟ ♟ ⇔ 🔲 ⚡ (10A) – Extra per person 6,10€ – Reservation fee 10€

Rental rates : (2013 Price) (from end March to mid Oct.) – 12 🚐 ? canvas bungalows. Per night from 38 to 95€ – Per week from 250 to 650€ – Reservation fee 10€

🚐 borne 4€

Surroundings : ≫ ≤ ♒

Leisure activities : 🛶 ♩ m

Facilities : ♿ o━ ⚄ ⚲ ♈ 📷

Nearby : ≈

G P S Longitude : 6.21496
Latitude : 43.84366

⛰ Manaysse

𝒫 04 92 74 66 71, www.camping-manaysse.com

Address : quartier Manaysse (900m southwest along the D 952, follow the signs for Riez)

Opening times : from beginning April to end Oct.

,6 ha (97 pitches) terraced, sloping, flat, grassy, gravelled

Tariff : (2013 Price) ♟ 3,70€ ⇔ 🔲 3,50€ – ⚡ (10A) 3,50€

Rental rates : (2013 Price) (from mid June to mid Sept.) – 1 gîte.

🚐 borne 10,90€ – 5 🔲 10,90€

Surroundings : ♒

Leisure activities : 🛶 ♩

Facilities : ♿ o━ ⚄ 🆑 ♈ ♈ 📷

G P S Longitude : 6.21494
Latitude : 43.84452

Key to rentals symbols :

12 🚐		*Number of mobile homes*
20 🏠		*Number of chalets*
6 🛏		*Number of rooms to rent*
Per night 30–50€		*Minimum/maximum rate per night*
Per week 300–1,000€		*Minimum/maximum rate per week*

MURS

34220 – Michelin map **332** E10 – pop. 428 – alt. 510

▶ Paris 704 – Apt 17 – Avignon 48 – Carpentras 26

⛰ Municipal des Chalottes

𝒫 04 90 72 60 84, www.communedemurs-vaucluse.fr

Address : take the southern exit along the D 4, follow the signs for Apt then continue 1.8km to the right, after the VVF holiday village

Opening times : from end March to mid Sept.

4 ha (50 pitches) very uneven, relatively flat to hilly, stony

Tariff : ♟ 3,50€ ⇔ 🔲 4€ – ⚡ (2A) 2€

A wooded setting in a pleasant location.

Surroundings : ≫ ≤ ♒

Leisure activities : 🛶

Facilities : ♿ o━ (July–Aug.) ⚲ ♈

G P S Longitude : 5.22749
Latitude : 43.93864

LE MUY

83490 – Michelin map **340** O5 – pop. 8 983 – alt. 27

▶ Paris 853 – Les Arcs 9 – Draguignan 14 – Fréjus 17

⛰ Les Cigales ♟♟

𝒫 04 94 45 12 08, www.camping-les-cigales-sud.fr

Address : 4 chemin de Jas de la Paro (3km southwest, access via the junction with the A 8 and take the road to the right before the toll road)

22 ha (585 pitches) very uneven, terraced, flat, grassy, stony, rocks

Rentals : 187 🚐 – 41 🏠.

In a pleasant wooded setting.

Surroundings : ▭ ♒

Leisure activities : ♟ ✕ 🎬 (July–Aug.) 🏃 jacuzzi 🛶 ⚲ ⛷ 🐎 forest trail, multi-sports ground

Facilities : ♿ o━ ⚄ ♈ launderette 🖳 🚐 refrigerators

G P S Longitude : 6.54355
Latitude : 43.46225

⛰ RCN Le Domaine de la Noguière

𝒫 04 94 45 13 78, www.rcn.nl

Address : 1617 route de Fréjus

Opening times : from mid March to end Oct.

11 ha (350 pitches)

Tariff : 50,50€ ♟ ♟ ⇔ 🔲 ⚡ (6A) – Extra per person 5,75€ – Reservation fee 19,95€

Rental rates : (from mid March to end Oct.) – 35 🚐. Per night from 35 to 172€ – Per week from 245 to 1204€ – Reservation fee 19,95€

Surroundings : ▭

Leisure activities : ♟ ✕ 🎬 daytime 🛶 ⚽ ⛷ ⛰ ≈ multi-sports ground

Facilities : o━ 🆑 ♈ ♈ launderette 🖳

Nearby : 🚐

G P S Longitude : 6.59222
Latitude : 43.46828

NANS-LES-PINS

83860 – Michelin map **340** J5 – pop. 4 123 – alt. 380

▶ Paris 794 – Aix-en-Provence 44 – Brignoles 26 – Marseille 42

⛰ Domaine de La Sainte Baume ♟♟

𝒫 04 94 78 92 68, www.saintebaume.com

Address : quartier Delvieux Sud (900m north along the D 80 and take a right turn, from the A 8: take exit St-Maximin-la-Ste-Baume)

Opening times : from beginning April to end Sept.

8 ha (250 pitches) flat and relatively flat, grassy, stony

Tariff : 22€ ♟ ♟ ⇔ 🔲 ⚡ (10A) – Extra per person 8€

Rental rates : (from beginning April to end Sept.) 🌿 – 150 🚐. Per night from 37 to 52€ – Per week from 217 to 1246€ Reservation fee 20€

Surroundings : ≫ ▭ ♒

Leisure activities : ✕ 🛶 🎬 🏃 jacuzzi 🛶 ⚽ ♩ ⛷ ⛰ disco, multi-sports ground

Facilities : ♿ o━ 🆑 ⚲ ♈ launderette 🖳 🚐

Nearby : 🐎

G P S Longitude : 5.78808
Latitude : 43.37664

The guide covers all 22 regions of France – see the map and list of regions on pages 4–5.

NÉVACHE

05100 – Michelin map **334** H2 – pop. 339 – alt. 1 640 – Winter sports : 1 400/2 000m
▶ Paris 693 – Bardonècchia 18 – Briançon 21

⚠ Fontcouverte

✆ 0492213821, m.goiran@orange.fr – access difficult for caravans – alt. 1 860 – ㅐ

Address : 1 lot. de l'Aiguille Rouge (6.2km northwest along the D 301t, Vallée de la Clarée)

Opening times : from beginning June to end Sept.

2 ha (100 pitches) terraced, flat and relatively flat, grassy, stony

Tariff : 10€ ✶✶ ⇌ 🔲 💲 (0A) – Extra per person 2,80€

In a pleasant location at the end of the valley and beside a mountain stream.

Surroundings : 🌄 ≤ 🏕 ♨♨
Leisure activities : 🌾
Facilities : ♿ ⚡ 🚿 🏊
Nearby : ✗

GPS Longitude : 6.69323
Latitude : 45.11898

NIOZELLES

04300 – Michelin map **334** D9 – pop. 237 – alt. 450
▶ Paris 745 – Digne-les-Bains 49 – Forcalquier 7 – Gréoux-les-Bains 33

🏕 Sites et Paysages Moulin de Ventre 👥

✆ 0492786331, www.moulin-de-ventre.com

Address : 2.5km east along the N 100, follow the signs for La Brillanne

Opening times : from beginning April to end Sept.

28 ha/3 for camping (124 pitches) terraced, flat and relatively flat, grassy

Tariff : 34,50€ ✶✶ ⇌ 🔲 💲 (10A) – Extra per person 7€ – Reservation fee 23€

Rental rates : (from beginning April to end Sept.) – 12 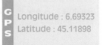 5 🏠 – 2 apartments – 2 tent lodges. Per night from 43 to 108€ Per week from 220 to 1020€ – Reservation fee 23€
🚰 borne – 🔋 💲14,50€
Beside the Lauzon river and a small lake.

Surroundings : 🌄 🗐 ♨♨
Leisure activities : 🍴✗ 🎣 🕐daytime (July–Aug.) 🧒🏊 🌾
Facilities : ♿ ⚡ 🛁 🚿 🍴 launderette ♨
Nearby : pedalos

GPS Longitude : 5.86798
Latitude : 43.9333

ORGON

13660 – Michelin map **340** F3 – pop. 3 055 – alt. 90
▶ Paris 709 – Marseille 72 – Avignon 29 – Nîmes 98

🏕 La Vallée Heureuse

✆ 0490441713, www.camping-lavalleeheureuse.com

Address : quartier Lavau (situated 2km to the south, follow the signs for Sénas then take left turning along the D 73D)

Opening times : from beginning April to end Sept.

8 ha (80 pitches)

Tariff : (2013 Price) 16€ ✶✶ ⇌ 🔲 💲 (16A) – Extra per person 5€ Reservation fee 17€
🚰 🔋14,40€

On a remarkable natural site.

Surroundings : 🌄 ≤ 🗐 ♨♨
Leisure activities : 🎣 🚣 🌾
Facilities : ♿ ⚡ 🚿🍴 launderette, refrigerated food storage facilities
Nearby : ✗ 🎣 🌾

GPS Longitude : 5.03956
Latitude : 43.7817

ORPIERRE

05700 – Michelin map **334** C7 – pop. 326 – alt. 682
▶ Paris 689 – Château-Arnoux 47 – Digne-les-Bains 72 – Gap 55

🏕 Les Princes d'Orange

✆ 0492662253, www.campingorpierre.com

Address : Le Flonsaine (300m south of the town, 150m from the Céans river)

Opening times : from beginning April to end Oct.

20 ha/4 for camping (120 pitches) very uneven, terraced, flat, grassy, stony

Tariff : 36€ ✶✶ ⇌ 🔲 💲 (10A) – Extra per person 10,20€ Reservation fee 10€

Rental rates : (from beginning April to end Oct.) – 36 🚐 Per night from 57 to 118€ – Per week from 399 to 826€ Reservation fee 12€

🚰 borne 5€ – 11 🔲 24€ – 🔋 💲13€

Surroundings : 🌄 ≤ Orpierre and the mountains ♨♨
Leisure activities : 🍴✗ 🎣 🧒🏊 🌾
Facilities : ♿ ⚡ 🛁🍴 launderette
Nearby : 🚴

GPS Longitude : 5.69652
Latitude : 44.31077

PERNES-LES-FONTAINES

84210 – Michelin map **332** D10 – pop. 10 454 – alt. 75
▶ Paris 685 – Apt 43 – Avignon 23 – Carpentras 6

⚠ Municipal de la Coucourelle

✆ 0490664555, ville-pernes-les-fontaines.fr

Address : 391 avenue René Char (located 1km east along the D 28, follow the signs for St-Didier, at the sports centre)

1 ha (40 pitches) flat, grassy

A leafy, green setting with trees and shrubs.

Surroundings : 🌄 🗐 ♀
Leisure activities : 🧒
Facilities : ♿ ⚡ 🛁 🚿 🍴 📦
Nearby : ✂ 🏊

GPS Longitude : 5.0677
Latitude : 43.99967

PERTUIS

84120 – Michelin map **332** G11 – pop. 18 706 – alt. 246
▶ Paris 747 – Aix-en-Provence 23 – Apt 36 – Avignon 76

🏕 Franceloc Domaine les Pinèdes du Luberon 👥

✆ 0490791098, www.campings-franceloc.fr/accueil-camping-les_pinedes_du_luberon

Address : avenue Pierre Augier (situated 2km east along the D 973)

5 ha (220 pitches) terraced, flat, grassy, stony

Rentals : ♿ (1 mobile home) – 140 🚐 – 6 🏠 – 8 tent lodges.
🚰 borne

Surroundings : 🗐 ♨♨
Leisure activities : 🍴✗ 🎣 🕐 🧒 🏊 🌾 🏊
Facilities : ♿ ⚡ 🛁 🚿 🍴 launderette
Nearby : ✂

GPS Longitude : 5.5253
Latitude : 43.68979

PEYRUIS

04310 – Michelin map **334** D8 – pop. 2 615 – alt. 402
▣ Paris 727 – Digne-les-Bains 30 – Forcalquier 20 – Manosque 29

⚠ Les Cigales (mobile home rentals only)

✆ 04 92 68 16 04, www.camping-lescigales.fr

Address : south of the town; near the stadium and a stream

Opening times : Permanent

1 ha relatively flat, grassy

Rental rates : 6 . Per night from 30 to 99€ – Per week from 210 to 693€ – Reservation fee 30€

Surroundings : ⟵ ⌂ ♀	
Leisure activities : 🏌	**G** Longitude : 5.93645
Facilities : ♿ ⛽ ⌂ 🏛 🍴 🚿 🔲	**P** Latitude : 44.0228
Nearby : 🍽 🎿 sports trail	**S**

PONT-DU-FOSSÉ

05260 – Michelin map **334** F4 – pop. 980
▣ Paris 673 – Marseille 204 – Gap 24 – Grenoble 102

⚠ Le Diamant

✆ 04 92 55 91 25, www.campingdiamant.com

Address : at Pont du Fossé (800m southwest along the D 944, follow the signs for Gap)

Opening times : Permanent

1 ha (100 pitches) flat, grassy

Tariff : 23,80€ ♥♥ 🚐 🔲 🔌 (20A) – Extra per person 4,80€

Rental rates : Permanent – 15 . Per night from 30 to 75€ – Per week from 210 to 550€

🚰 borne 19,80€ – 10 🔲 19,80€

Beside the Drac river.

Surroundings : ♀♀	
Leisure activities : 🏛 🏌 ♟ 🧗 climbing wall	**G** Longitude : 6.2197
Facilities : ♿ ⛽ ⌂ 🚿 🔲 🍴 launderette 🧺	**P** Latitude : 44.66535 **S**

The information in the guide may have changed since going to press.

LE PONTET

04130 – Michelin map **332** C10 – pop. 16 891 – alt. 40
▣ Paris 688 – Marseille 100 – Avignon 5 – Aix 83

⚠ Le Grand Bois

✆ 04 90 31 37 44, www.campinglegrandbois.webeasysite.fr

Address : 1340 chemin du Grand Bois (3km northeast along the D 62, follow the signs for Vedène and take turning to the left, at a place called La Tapy, from the A 7 take the Avignon-Nord exit)

Opening times : from mid May to mid Sept.

3,5 ha (100 pitches) flat, grassy

Tariff : ♥ 6€ 🚐 2€ 🔲 8€ – 🔌 (5A) 3€

🚰 borne 3€

pleasant wooded site.

Surroundings : ⌂ ♀♀	
Leisure activities : 🏛 🎿	**G** Longitude : 4.8836
Facilities : ♿ ⛽ ⌂ 🍴 🚿 🔲	**P** Latitude : 43.97455 **S**

PRUNIÈRES

05230 – Michelin map **334** F5 – pop. 287 – alt. 1 018
▣ Paris 681 – Briançon 68 – Gap 23 – Grenoble 119

⚠ Le Roustou

✆ 04 92 50 62 63, www.campingleroustou.com – 🚰

Address : 4km south along the N 94

Opening times : from beginning May to end Sept.

11 ha/6 for camping (180 pitches) terraced, undulating, flat and relatively flat, grassy, fine gravel

Tariff : ♥ 7,50€ 🚐 🔲 7,90€ – 🔌 (6A) 4,10€

Rental rates : (from beginning May to end Sept.) – 27 🏠. Per night from 52 to 149€ – Per week from 367 to 1047€ Reservation fee 12€

🚰 borne

Surroundings : ⌂ ⟵ ⌂ ♀♀ ⛰	
Leisure activities : 🍴 ✕ 🏛 🏌 🍽 🎿 🛶	**G** Longitude : 6.34111
Facilities : ♿ ⛽ 🚿 🍴 🔲 🧺	**P** Latitude : 44.5225
Nearby : ⚓	**S**

PUGET-SUR-ARGENS

83480 – Michelin map **340** P5 – pop. 6 722 – alt. 17
▣ Paris 863 – Les Arcs 21 – Cannes 41 – Draguignan 26

⚠ La Bastiane 👥

✆ 04 94 55 55 94, www.labastiane.com

Address : 1056 chemin de Suvière (2.50km to the north)

Opening times : from mid April to end Oct.

4 ha (170 pitches) terraced, flat, grassy, stony

Tariff : 47€ ♥♥ 🚐 🔲 🔌 (10A) – Extra per person 9€ – Reservation fee 30€

Rental rates : (from mid April to end Oct.) – 78  – 6 🏠 18 canvas bungalows. Per night from 89 to 199€ – Per week from 623 to 1393€ – Reservation fee 30€

Surroundings : 🌲 ♀♀	
Leisure activities : 🍴 ✕ 🏛 ♟ 🏌 🚲 🍽 🎿 disco, multi-sports ground	**G** Longitude : 6.67837
Facilities : ♿ ⛽ 🏛 🚿 🍴 launderette 🧺	**P** Latitude : 43.46975
Nearby : 🐎	**S**

PUIMICHEL

04700 – Michelin map **334** E9 – pop. 253 – alt. 723
▣ Paris 737 – Avignon 140 – Grenoble 175 – Marseille 112

⚠ Les Matherons

✆ 04 92 79 60 10, www.campinglesmatherons.com

Address : 3km southwest along the D 12, follow the signs for Oraison and take the gravel road to the right

Opening times : from end April to end Sept.

70 ha/4 for camping (27 pitches) terraced, flat and relatively flat, grassy, stony

Tariff : ♥ 5,25€ 🚐 🔲 9€ – 🔌 (3A) 3,25€

Rental rates : (Permanent) – 2 . Per week from 290 to 550€

In a wild, natural setting among woods and chirping cicadas.

Surroundings : 🌲 ♀♀	
Leisure activities : 🏌	**G** Longitude : 6.00763
Facilities : ⛽ 🅿 🔲 🔲 🍴 🔲 🧺	**P** Latitude : 43.96035 **S**

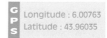

PUYLOUBIER

13114 – Michelin map **340** J4 – pop. 1 798 – alt. 380
▶ Paris 775 – Aix-en-Provence 26 – Rians 38 – St-Maximin-la-Ste-Baume 19

⚠ Municipal Cézanne

✆ 0442663633, www.le-cezanne.com

Address : chemin Philippe Noclercq (take the eastern exit along the D 57, by the stadium)

Opening times : from mid March to beginning Nov.

1 ha (50 pitches) terraced, relatively flat, grassy, stony

Tariff : ♣ 5,50€ ⬗ 2€ 🔲 3€ – (10A) 3,50€

Rental rates : (from mid March to end Oct.) – 4 🚐 – 2 gîtes. Per night from 50 to 90€ – Per week from 380 to 480€
🚰 borne 3€ – 3 🔲 14€ – 🚿10€
Situated at the foot of Mont Ste-Victoire.

Surroundings : 🏞 ♨
Leisure activities : ✂
Facilities : ⚷ 🍴 🔥
GPS Longitude : 5.68227
Latitude : 43.527

A 'quartier' is a district or area of a town or village.

RAMATUELLE

83350 – Michelin map **340** O6 – pop. 2 240 – alt. 136
▶ Paris 873 – Fréjus 35 – Hyères 52 – Le Lavandou 34

⛰ Le Kon Tiki 👥

✆ 0494559696, www.riviera-villages.com – limited spaces for one-night stay

Address : plage de Pampelonne

Rentals : 100 🚐 – 200 🏠.

Surroundings : ♀ ⛰
Leisure activities : ♣ ✗ 🏠 🎯 🏃 ⛷ ⛸
hammam jacuzzi ♨ ⛱ (beach) 🤿 🏊
scuba diving, spa centre
Facilities : ⚷ 🏢 🔥 🚿 🍴 launderette
🏪
Nearby : 🐎
GPS Longitude : 6.65852
Latitude : 43.23147

⛰ Yelloh! Village les Tournels 👥

✆ 0494559090, www.tournels.com

Address : route de Camarat

Opening times : from beginning March to end Oct.

20 ha (975 pitches) very uneven, terraced, flat, grassy, stony

Tariff : 63€ ♣♣ ⬗ 🔲 (10A)
– Extra per person 8€

Rental rates : (from beginning April to end Oct.) – 263 🚐 – 86 🏠. Per night from 39 to 319€
Per week from 273 to 2233€
🚰 borne 5€
An upmarket indoor water park.

Surroundings : ⛰ 🏞 ♨
Leisure activities : ♣ ✗ 🎯(amphitheatre) 🏃
🏋 ⛸ hammam, jacuzzi ♨ 🚴 🏄 ✂ ⛷
disco, multi-sports ground, spa centre
Facilities : ♿ ⚷ 🏢 🔥 🚿 🍴 launderette
🏪 refrigerated food storage facilities
GPS Longitude : 6.65112
Latitude : 43.20537

⛰ La Toison d'Or 👥

✆ 0494798354, www.riviera-villages.com

Address : route des Tamaris

5 ha (500 pitches)

Rentals : 176 🚐 – 50 lodges.

Surroundings : ♀ ⛰
Leisure activities : ♣ ✗ 🏠 🎯 🏃 🏋 ⛸
hammam, jacuzzi ♨ ✂ ⛱ 🏊 scuba diving,
spa centre
Facilities : ⚷ 🔥 🚿 🍴 launderette 🏪
GPS Longitude : 6.66007
Latitude : 43.23884

⛰ Campéole la Croix du Sud 👥

✆ 0494555123, www.campeole.com – limited spaces for one-night stay

Address : route des Plages

3 ha (120 pitches) terraced, flat, grassy, stony, sandy

Rentals : 17 🚐 – 11 🏠.

Surroundings : 🏞 ♨
Leisure activities : ♣ ✗ 🏃 🚴 🚲 ⛷
Facilities : ♿ ⚷ 🔥 🍴 🔲
GPS Longitude : 6.64104
Latitude : 43.21426

RÉGUSSE

83630 – Michelin map **340** L4 – pop. 2 067 – alt. 545
▶ Paris 838 – Marseille 113 – Toulon 94 – Digne-les-Bains 75

⛰ Homair Vacances Les Lacs du Verdon 👥

✆ 0494701795, www.homair.com

Address : domaine de Roquelande

17 ha (400 pitches)

Rentals : 296 🚐.

Surroundings : ⛰ ♨
Leisure activities : ♣ ✗ 🏠 🎯 🏃 🚴 🚲 ✂
🏋 ⛷ multi-sports area
Facilities : ⚷ 🏢 🔥 🍴 launderette 🏪
Nearby : 🐎
GPS Longitude : 6.15073
Latitude : 43.66041

RIEZ

04500 – Michelin map **334** E10 – pop. 1 783 – alt. 520
▶ Paris 792 – Marseille 105 – Digne-les-Bains 41 – Draguignan 64

⚠ Rose de Provence

✆ 0492777545, www.rose-de-provence.com

Address : rue Edouard Dauphin

Opening times : from mid April to beginning Oct.

1 ha (91 pitches) terrace, flat, grassy, gravelled

Tariff : (2013 Price) 21,30€ ♣♣ ⬗ 🔲 (6A) – Extra per person 5,80€
Reservation fee 10€

Rental rates : (2013 Price) Permanent – 7 🚐 – 2 🏠 – 2 canvas bungalows. Per night from 30 to 85€ – Per week from 210 to 595€ – Reservation fee 15€
🚰 borne

Surroundings : 🏞 ♨
Leisure activities : jacuzzi ♨
Facilities : ♿ ⚷ 🔥 🔲 refrigerated food storage facilities
Nearby : ✂
GPS Longitude : 6.09922
Latitude : 43.81307

LA ROCHE-DE-RAME

05310 – Michelin map **334** H4 – pop. 830 – alt. 1 000
🡒 Paris 701 – Briançon 22 – Embrun 27 – Gap 68

⛰ Le Verger

📞 04 92 20 92 23, www.campingleverger.com
Address : Les Gillis (head 1.2km northwest along the N 94, follow the signs for Briançon)
Opening times : Permanent
1,6 ha (50 pitches) terraced, relatively flat, grassy
Tariff : (2013 Price) 19,80€ ⭐⭐ 🚐 🔲 🔌 (10A)
Extra per person 5,30€
Rental rates : (2013 Price) 6 🚐 – 1 🏠 – 1 gîte. Per night from 50 to 65€ – Per week from 350 to 490€
🚐 borne 3,50€ – 5 🔲
Pitches in the shade of cherry and apricot trees.

Surroundings : 🐟 ≤ 🌳
Leisure activities : 🎣 🛶
Facilities : 🚻 🚿 🍽 �''' launderette

G P S Longitude : 6.57951
Latitude : 44.7581

⛰ Municipal du Lac

📞 06 10 03 57 28, www.campingdulac05.fr
Address : RN 94 La Roche de Rame (take the southern exit)
1 ha (95 pitches)
Rentals : 2 🏠 – 2 canvas bungalows – 1 gîte

Surroundings : ≤ 🌳
Leisure activities : 🍽
Facilities : 🚻 🚿 �''' 🛁
Nearby : 🍴 🏊 🏊 (lake) 🚣 pedalos

G P S Longitude : 6.58145
Latitude : 44.74673

LA ROCHE DES ARNAUDS

05400 – Michelin map **334** D5 – pop. 1 372 – alt. 945
🡒 Paris 672 – Corps 49 – Gap 15 – St-Étienne-en-Dévoluy 33

⛰ Au Blanc Manteau

📞 04 92 57 82 56, www.campingaublancmanteau.fr – alt. 900 – 🏠
Address : route de Ceuze (1.3km southwest along the D 18; beside a mountain stream)
Opening times : Permanent
4 ha (40 pitches)
Tariff : (2013 Price) 18€ ⭐⭐ 🚐 🔲 🔌 (20A) – Extra per person 4,50€

Surroundings : ❄ 🐟 ≤ 🚗
Leisure activities : 🍽 🎣 🛶 🚲 🏐 🎿
Facilities : 🚻 🚿 🚐 🍽 🛁 🖳 🚿

G P S Longitude : 5.95085
Latitude : 44.54962

ROQUEBRUNE-SUR-ARGENS

83520 – Michelin map **340** O5 – pop. 12 708 – alt. 13
🡒 Paris 862 – Les Arcs 18 – Cannes 49 – Draguignan 23

🏔 Domaine de la Bergerie ♨

📞 04 98 11 45 45, www.domainelabergerie.com – limited spaces for one-night stay
Address : Vallée du Fournel - route du Col de Bougnon (head 8km southeast along the D 7, follow the signs for St-Aygulf and turn right into D 8; beside some lakes)
Opening times : from end April to end Sept.
60 ha (700 pitches) very uneven, terraced, flat, grassy, stony
Tariff : 52,30€ ⭐⭐ 🚐 🔲 🔌 (10A) – Extra per person 11,50€
Reservation fee 25€

Rental rates : (from mid March to mid Nov.) – 300 🚐. Per night from 54 to 214€ – Per week from 378 to 1498€ – Reservation fee 25€

Surroundings : 🌳🌳
Leisure activities : 🍽 🍴 🎭 (open-air theatre) 🏃 🏊 hammam, jacuzzi 🛥 🚲 🏐 🏓 🛶 🎿 🚣 disco, multi-sports ground, entertainment room
Facilities : 🚻 🚿 🚐 🛁 🖳 �''' launderette 🚿 🚿

G P S Longitude : 6.67535
Latitude : 43.39879

🏔 Les Pêcheurs ♨

SMONCINI

📞 04 94 45 71 25, www.camping-les-pecheurs.com
Address : 700m northwest along the D 7
Opening times : from beginning April to end Sept.
3,3 ha (220 pitches) flat, grassy
Tariff : 47,50€ ⭐⭐ 🚐 🔲 🔌 (10A)
Extra per person 9€ – Reservation fee 22€
Rental rates : (from beginning April to end Sept.) – 31 🚐 – 20 🏠 – 1 cottage on stilts. Per night from 47 to 157€ – Per week from 315 to 1095€ – Reservation fee 22€
🚐 borne
In a pleasant wooded setting with flowers, beside the Argens river and a small lake across the road.

Surroundings : 📺 🌳🌳🌳
Leisure activities : 🍴 🎣 🎭 daytime 🏃 🏊 hammam, jacuzzi 🛥 🏐 🛶 🚣 pedalos 🎿
Facilities : 🚻 🚿 🖳 🛁 �''' launderette 🚿 🚿
Nearby : 🏊

G P S Longitude : 6.63354
Latitude : 43.45094

🏔 Lei Suves

📞 04 94 45 43 95, www.lei-suves.com – limited spaces for one-night stay
Address : quartier du Blavet (head 4km north along the D 7 and take underpass under A 8)
Opening times : from beginning April to mid Oct.
7 ha (310 pitches) terraced, flat, grassy, stony
Tariff : 50,40€ ⭐⭐ 🚐 🔲 🔌 (6A) – Extra per person 10,80€
Reservation fee 25€
Rental rates : (from beginning April to mid Oct.) 🎿 – 30 🚐.
Per week from 385 to 1050€ – Reservation fee 25€
🚐 borne
In a pleasant wooded setting; well kept.

Surroundings : 🐟 📺 🌳🌳
Leisure activities : 🍽 🍴 🎭 (open-air theatre) 🏃 🛥 🏐 🛶 multi-sports ground
Facilities : 🚻 🚿 🛁 🖳 �''' launderette 🚿 🚿

G P S Longitude : 6.63882
Latitude : 43.47821

*The classification (1 to 5 tents, **black** or **red**) that we award to selected sites in this guide is our own system. It should not be confused with the classification (1 to 5 stars) of official organisations.*

⛺ Moulin des Iscles

📞 04 94 45 70 74, www.campingdesiscles.com

Address : chemin du Moulin des Iscles (head 1.8km east along the D 7, follow the signs for St-Aygulf and take road to the left)

Opening times : from beginning April to end Sept.

1,5 ha (90 pitches) flat, grassy

Tariff : 26,70€ ♠♣ 🚗 🅴 ⚡ (6A) – Extra per person 3,50€ – Reservation fee 15€

Rental rates : (from beginning April to end Sept.) – 5 🚐 – 1 🛏 3 studios – 2 apartments. Per night from 68 to 112€ – Per week from 350 to 780€ – Reservation fee 15€

Beside the Argens river.

Surroundings : 🏞 🎣
Leisure activities : ✗ 🏛 🎣 🎣
Facilities : ♿ ⛽ 🆑 🚿 🚻 🍴 🧺 🚮

GPS Longitude : 6.65784
Latitude : 43.44497

LA ROQUE-D'ANTHÉRON

13640 – Michelin map **340** G3 – pop. 5 143 – alt. 183
▶ Paris 726 – Aix-en-Provence 29 – Cavaillon 34 – Manosque 60

⛰ Village Center Les Iscles

(mobile home rentals only)

📞 08 25 00 20 30, www.village-center.com

Address : at La Durance (head 3km south along the D 23)

Opening times : from beginning April to end Sept.

10 ha (269 pitches)

Rental rates : 267 🚐. Per night from 31 to 81€ – Per week from 587 to 931€

Surroundings : 🏞 🎣
Leisure activities : 🍴 ✗ 🎣 🏃 🚣 🎣 🛶 (river) ⛵ 🎣
Facilities : ⛽ 🆑 🍴 launderette 🚮 🚿

GPS Longitude : 5.32099
Latitude : 43.72819

ST-ANDRÉ-LES-ALPES

04170 – Michelin map **334** H9 – pop. 930 – alt. 914
▶ Paris 786 – Castellane 20 – Colmars 28 – Digne-les-Bains 43

⛺ Municipal les Iscles

📞 04 92 89 02 29, camping-les-iscles.com – alt. 894

Address : chemin des Iscles (located 1km south along the N 202, follow the signs for Annot and take the turning to the left, 300m from the Verdon river)

2,5 ha (200 pitches)

Rentals : ♿ (1 mobile home) 🐾 – 16 🚐 .

In a pleasant pine wood.

Surroundings : 🏞 🎣
Leisure activities : 🏛 🏃
Facilities : ♿ ⛽ 🚿 🍴 🚮
Nearby : 🎣 🏃 sports trail

GPS Longitude : 6.50844
Latitude : 43.9612

Some campsites benefit from proximity to a municipal leisure centre.

ST-APOLLINAIRE

05160 – Michelin map **334** G5 – pop. 117 – alt. 1 285
▶ Paris 684 – Embrun 19 – Gap 27 – Mont-Dauphin 37

⛺ Campéole Le Clos du Lac

📞 04 92 44 27 43, www.camping-closdulac.com – access difficult for caravans and campervans – alt. 1 450

Address : route des Lacs (2.3km northwest along the D 509; 50m from the small lake at St-Apollinaire)

2 ha (68 pitches)

Rentals : 18 🚐 .

In an attractive elevated location.

Surroundings : 🏞 ◄ Lac de Serre-Ponçon and mountains 🌳
Leisure activities : 🎣 jacuzzi 🏃
Facilities : ⛽ 🚿 📮
Nearby : 🍷 ✗ 🚿 🏃 🏊 (lake) 🎣

GPS Longitude : 6.34642
Latitude : 44.56127

This guide is updated regularly, so buy your new copy every year!

ST-AYGULF

83370 – Michelin map **340** P5
▶ Paris 872 – Brignoles 69 – Draguignan 35 – Fréjus 6

⛰ L'Étoile d'Argens ♣♣

📞 04 94 81 01 41, www.etoiledargens.com

Address : chemin des Étangs (5km northwest along the D 7, follow the signs for Roquebrune-sur-Argens and turn right onto the D 8; beside the Argens river)

Opening times : from beginning June to end Sept.

11 ha (493 pitches) flat, grassy

Tariff : 63€ ♠♣ 🚗 🅴 ⚡ (10A) – Extra per person 10€ – Reservation fee 30€

Rental rates : (from beginning April to end Sept.) 🐾 – 105 🚐 Per night from 40 to 225€ – Per week from 280 to 1600€ – Reservation fee 30€

Pretty, spacious pitches with shade. River shuttle service to the beaches (duration: 30 min).

Surroundings : 🏞 🚐 🎣
Leisure activities : 🍷 ✗ 🎣 🏃 jacuzzi 🏃 🚴 🎣 🏃 🏊 disco, multi-sports ground
Facilities : ♿ ⛽ 🍴 🚿 🚮 🍴 launderette 🚮 🚿
Nearby : ⚓

GPS Longitude : 6.70562
Latitude : 43.41596

⛰ Au Paradis des Campeurs

📞 04 94 96 93 55, www.paradis-des-campeurs.com – 🏠

Address : La Gaillarde-Plage (2.5km south along the N 98, follow the signs for Ste-Maxime)

Opening times : from beginning April to end Sept.

6 ha/3,5 for camping (180 pitches)

Tariff : 35€ ♠♣ 🚗 🅴 ⚡ (6A) – Extra per person 6€

Rental rates : (from beginning April to end Sept.) 🐾 – 16 🚐

Some pitches have a sea view and direct access to the beach.

Surroundings : 🚐 🌳
Leisure activities : 🍷 ✗ 🏛 🏃
Facilities : ♿ ⛽ 🆑 🚿 🚮 🍴 launderette 🚮 🚿
Nearby : disco

GPS Longitude : 6.71235
Latitude : 43.366

⚠ Sandaya Résidence du Campeur

℘ 0494810159, www.sandaya.fr – limited spaces for one-night stay

Address : 189 Les Grands Châteaux-de-Villepey (3km northwest along the D 7, follow the signs for Roquebrune-sur-Argens)

Opening times : from mid April to mid Oct.

⬜ ha (451 pitches) grassy

Tariff : (2013 Price) 62€ ✦ ✦ ⬅ 🔲 🔌 (10A) – Extra per person 7€ – Reservation fee 30€

Rental rates : (2013 Price) (from mid April to mid Oct.) – 265 🚐 ⬜ tent lodges. Per night from 40 to 135€ – Per week from 525 to 1582€ – Reservation fee 30€

Surroundings : 🗔 ♨ ♨

Leisure activities : 🍽 🗙 🖼 🎮 🏃 🏊 🚴 🎣 🏓 ♨ 🎯 multi-sports ground

Facilities : ⊶ – 451 individual sanitary facilities (🗔 ♨ 🚻 wc) 🚿 🧺 launderette 🗑🚃

Nearby : open-air cinema

	Longitude : 6.70875
G P S	Latitude : 43.40867

⚠ Les Lauriers Roses

℘ 0494812446, www.info-lauriersroses.com – pitches accessed via steep slope, help moving caravans onto and off pitches avilable on request

Address : Les Grands Châteaux de Villepey (3km northwest along the D 7)

Opening times : from end April to end Sept.

⬜ ha (95 pitches) very uneven, terraced, flat, grassy, stony

Tariff : 46€ ✦ ✦ ⬅ 🔲 🔌 (10A) – Extra per person 9,75€ – Reservation fee 15€

Rental rates : (from end April to end Sept.) 🚿 – 15 🚐. Per night from 50 to 200€ – Per week from 285 to 1380€ – Reservation fee 15€

🚰 borne 40€ – 1 🔲 46€

Surroundings : 🐾 ♨ ♨

Leisure activities : 🖼 🏊 🎣

Facilities : ⚕ ⊶ 🚿 🗑 🧺 🎯

	Longitude : 6.70923
G P S	Latitude : 43.40471

⚠ Vaudois

℘ 0494813770, www.campingdevaudois.com

Address : 4.5km northwest along the D 7, follow the signs for Roquebrune-sur-Argens; 300m from a small lake

Opening times : from beginning May to end Sept.

⬜ ha (110 pitches) flat, grassy

Tariff : (2013 Price) 30,50€ ✦ ✦ ⬅ 🔲 🔌 (10A) – Extra per person 6,90€

Rental rates : (2013 Price) (from beginning May to end Sept.) 🚿 🚐. Per week from 215 to 660€

Surroundings : ♨ ♨

Leisure activities : 🖼 🏊

Facilities : ⚕ ⊶ 🚿 🧺 🗑

Nearby : 🏊

	Longitude : 6.69214
G P S	Latitude : 43.41084

ST-CLÉMENT-SUR-DURANCE

05600 – Michelin map **334** H5 – pop. 285 – alt. 872

▶ Paris 715 – L'Argentière-la-Bessée 21 – Embrun 13 – Gap 54

⚠ Les Mille Vents

℘ 0492451090

Address : located 1km east along the N 94, follow the signs for Briançon and take D 994d to the right after the bridge and the white water sports centre

⬜ ha (100 pitches)

Rentals : 3 🏠 .

Beside the river.

Surroundings : ≤ ♨

Leisure activities : 🎣 🏊

Facilities : ⚕ ⊶ 🗑 🚿 🗑

Nearby : 🗙 rafting and canyoning

	Longitude : 6.6618
G P S	Latitude : 44.66362

ST-CYR-SUR-MER

83270 – Michelin map **340** J6 – pop. 11 865 – alt. 10

▶ Paris 810 – Bandol 8 – Brignoles 70 – La Ciotat 10

⚠ Le Clos Ste-Thérèse

℘ 0494321221, www.clos-therese.com – pitches accessed via steep slope, help moving caravans onto and off pitches avilable on request – limited spaces for one-night stay

Address : 3.5km southeast along the D 559

Opening times : from beginning April to end Sept.

4 ha (123 pitches) very uneven, terraced, flat, grassy, stony

Tariff : 33,20€ ✦ ✦ ⬅ 🔲 🔌 (10A) – Extra per person 6,50€ – Reservation fee 23€

Rental rates : (from beginning April to end Sept.) – 7 🚐 23 🏠 – 5 canvas bungalows. Per night 126€ – Per week from 226 to 880€ – Reservation fee 23€

🚰 borne

Surroundings : 🗔 ♨ ♨

Leisure activities : 🍽 🖼 🏊 🎣 spa facilities

Facilities : ⚕ ⊶ 🗑 🚿 🗑 🎯

Nearby : 🗙

	Longitude : 5.72951
G P S	Latitude : 43.15955

ST-ÉTIENNE-DE-TINÉE

06660 – Michelin map **341** C2 – pop. 1 311 – alt. 1 147

▶ Paris 788 – Grenoble 226 – Marseille 262 – Nice 90

⚠ Municipal du Plan d'Eau

℘ 0493024157, mairie@saintetiennedetinee.fr

Address : route du col de la Bonette (500m north of the town)

0,5 ha (23 pitches)

Situated beside the Tinée river, overlooking a small but pretty lake. Reserved for tents.

Surroundings : 🐾 ≤ 🗔

Leisure activities : 🖼 🏖 (beach) 🏊

Facilities : ⊶ 🅿 no electrical hook-up

Nearby : fitness trail

	Longitude : 6.92299
G P S	Latitude : 44.25858

ST-ÉTIENNE-DU-GRÈS

13103 – Michelin map **340** D3 – pop. 2 202 – alt. 7

▶ Paris 706 – Arles 16 – Avignon 24 – Les Baux-de-Provence 15

⚠ Municipal du Grès

℘ 0490490003, campingalpilles.com

Address : avenue du Dr-Barberin (take the northwestern exit along the D 99, follow the signs for Tarascon; near the stadium, 50m from the Vigueira)

Opening times : Permanent

0,6 ha (40 pitches)

Tariff : (2013 Price) 17€ ✦ ✦ ⬅ 🔲 🔌 (16A) – Extra per person 3,50€

🚰 borne 4€

Surroundings : 🗔 ♨ ♨

Facilities : ⊶ 🗑 🗑 🚿 🧺 launderette

	Longitude : 4.71772
G P S	Latitude : 43.78628

ST-LAURENT-DU-VERDON

04500 – Michelin map **334** E10 – pop. 92 – alt. 468
▶ Paris 797 – Marseille 118 – Digne-les-Bains 59 – Avignon 166

⚑ La Farigoulette

📞 0492744162, www.camping-la-farigoulette.com

Address : lake St Laurent (located 1km north follow signs along the C 1 for Montpezat)

Opening times : from mid May to mid Sept.

14 ha (200 pitches)

Tariff : (2013 Price) 31,60€ ✹✹ ⇌ 🅴 🅷 (5A) – Extra per person 5,10€ Reservation fee 15€

Rental rates : (2013 Price) (from mid May to mid Sept.) – 25 🚐. Per night from 40 to 130€ – Per week from 280 to 910€ Reservation fee 20€

🚐 borne

Surroundings : 🏊 ⛵ ♨️
Leisure activities : ✗ ⊙ daytime ⛷ 🏋 🛶 pedalos 🏌 multi-sports ground
Facilities : ⊶ 🚿🍴 launderette ♨️ 🔄 🚿

G P S Longitude : 6.0777
Latitude : 43.73407

ST-MANDRIER-SUR-MER

83430 – Michelin map **340** K7 – pop. 5 773 – alt. 1
▶ Paris 836 – Bandol 20 – Le Beausset 22 – Hyères 30

⚑ Homair Vacances La Presqu'île

(mobile home rentals only)

📞 0494307470, www.homair.com

Address : quartier Pin Rolland (2.5km west, carr. D 18 and follow the signs for La Pointe de Marégau (headland), near the marina)

Opening times : from mid March to beginning Oct.

2,5 ha very uneven, terraced, flat, stony

Rental rates : 125 🚐. Per night from 24 to 190€ – Per week from 168 to 1330€ – Reservation fee 20€

Surroundings : ♨️
Leisure activities : 🍴 ✗ ⊙ ⛷ 🏋 🛶 🔫 🏊
Facilities : 🚿 ⊶ 🆑 🍴 🔄 🚿
Nearby : 🔫

G P S Longitude : 5.90577
Latitude : 43.07655

ST-MARTIN-D'ENTRAUNES

06470 – Michelin map **341** B3 – pop. 83 – alt. 1 050
▶ Paris 778 – Annot 39 – Barcelonnette 50 – Puget-Théniers 44

⚑ Le Prieuré

📞 0493055499, http://www.le-prieure.com – alt. 1 070 🏊

Address : route des Blancs (located 1km east along the D 2202, follow the signs for Guillaumes then continue 1.8km along the road to the left, after the bridge over the Var)

Opening times : from beginning May to end Sept.

12 ha/1,5 (35 pitches) terraced, flat and relatively flat, grassy

Tariff : (2013 Price) ✹ 4,80€ ⇌ 🅴 7,80€ – 🅷 (10A) 3,50€ Reservation fee 10€

Rental rates : (2013 Price) Permanent 🏊 – 8 🏠 – 4 canvas bungalows – 1 tent lodge – 9 gîtes. Per night from 45 to 78€ Per week from 315 to 540€ – Reservation fee 10€

Surroundings : 🏊 ⬕ ♨️
Leisure activities : ✗ 🎱 ⛷ 🏋 🔫 🏊 (small swimming pool)
Facilities : ⊶ 🍴 🔄 🚿

G P S Longitude : 6.76283
Latitude : 44.14895

ST-MARTIN-VESUBIE

06450 – Michelin map **341** E3 – pop. 1 325 – alt. 1 000
▶ Paris 899 – Marseille 235 – Nice 65 – Cuneo 140

⚑ À la Ferme St-Joseph

📞 0670519014, www.camping-alafermestjoseph.com

Address : to the southeast of the town along the D 2565 follow the signs for Roquebillière, near Saint-Martin-Vésubie

Opening times : from end April to end Sept.

0,6 ha (50 pitches)

Tariff : 24,20€ ✹✹ ⇌ 🅴 🅷 (6A) – Extra per person 4,80€ Reservation fee 10€

Rental rates : (from end April to end Sept.) 🏊 – 3 🛏. Per night 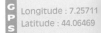 from 50 to 86€ – Per week from 342 to 594€ – Reservation fee 10€

🚐 borne

Surroundings : 🏊 ⬕ ♨
Facilities : ⊙ (July–Aug.) 🔄 🍴 🅱
Nearby : 🔫 🏊

G P S Longitude : 7.25711
Latitude : 44.06469

ST-PAUL-EN-FORÊT

83440 – Michelin map **340** P4 – pop. 1 616 – alt. 310
▶ Paris 884 – Cannes 46 – Draguignan 27 – Fayence 10

⚑ Le Parc 👥

📞 0494761535, www.campingleparc.com

Address : 83440 St Paul en Foret (3km north along the D 4, follow the signs for Fayence then take the road to the right)

Opening times : from beginning March to mid Oct.

3 ha (100 pitches) terraced, flat, grassy, stony

Tariff : (2013 Price) 36€ ✹✹ ⇌ 🅴 🅷 (10A) – Extra per person 7,20€

Rental rates : (2013 Price) (from beginning April to end Sept 30 🚐 – 4 🏠 – 2 tent lodges – 1 gîte. Per night from 43 to 82 Per week from 190 to 960€ – Reservation fee 25€

Surroundings : 🏊 🎵
Leisure activities : ✗ 🎱 ⊙ daytime ⛷ 🏋 🔫 🏊
Facilities : 🚿 ⊶ 🍴 🚿🍴 launderette 🚿
Nearby : 🐎

G P S Longitude : 6.68979
Latitude : 43.58445

ST-PONS

04400 – Michelin map **334** H6 – pop. 742 – alt. 1 157
▶ Paris 797 – Marseille 227 – Digne-les-Bains 84 – Gap 74

⚑ Village Vacances Le Loup Blanc du Riou

(chalet rentals only)

📞 0492814497, www.leloupblanc.com

Address : located 1km southwest, behind Ubaye aerodrome

Opening times : Permanent

2 ha

Rental rates : 8 🏠 – 8 gîtes. Per night from 75 to 95 € – Per wee from 295 to 760€

A pleasant small chalet village, shaded by a pine wood.

Surroundings : 🏊 ⬕ ♨️
Leisure activities : 🎱 🏋 🏊
Facilities : ⊶ 🅿 🍴 🔄 🅱
Nearby : ✗ 🐎 adventure park

G P S Longitude : 6.6122
Latitude : 44.39107

ST-RAPHAËL

83700 – Michelin map **340** P5 – pop. 34 269

▶ Paris 870 – Aix-en-Provence 121 – Cannes 42 – Fréjus 4

Les Castels Douce Quiétude 👥

📞 04 94 44 30 00, www.douce-quietude.com – limited spaces for one-night stay

Address : 3435 boulevard Jacques Baudino (take northeastern exit towards Valescure then continue 3km - from A8, take exit 38)

Opening times : from beginning April to mid Oct.

10 ha (400 pitches) terraced, undulating, flat, grassy, stony

Tariff : 59€ ✳✳ 🚗 🔲 🔌 (16A) – Extra per person 11,50€
Reservation fee 30€

Rental rates : (from beginning April to mid Oct.) – 258 🚐. Per night from 37 to 263€ – Per week from 259 to 1841€
Reservation fee 30€

Surroundings : 🌿 �� 🛈🛈
Leisure activities : 🍸✕🎯👫🎿⛴ hammam, jacuzzi 🚴🎣✕🏹🎿 disco
Facilities : 🚿🚻🔲🔌🚿🍴 launderette 🚰🚿

Do not confuse:
🔺 to 🔺🔺🔺 : MICHELIN classification with
★ to ★★★★★ : official classification

ST-RÉMY-DE-PROVENCE

13210 – Michelin map **340** D3 – pop. 10 458 – alt. 59

▶ Paris 702 – Arles 25 – Avignon 20 – Marseille 89

Monplaisir

📞 04 90 92 22 70, www.camping-monplaisir.fr

Address : chemin de Monplaisir (800m northwest along the D 5, Follow the signs for Maillane and take road to the left)

Opening times : from beginning March to end Oct.

2,8 ha (140 pitches)

Tariff : 32,90€ ✳✳ 🚗 🔲 🔌 (10A) – Extra per person 8,10€
Reservation fee 17€

Rental rates : (from beginning March to end Oct.) 🚐 – 12 🚐. Per week from 350 to 750€ – Reservation fee 17€
🚐 borne

A pleasant site with flowers, set around a Provençal mas (traditional house).

Surroundings : 🌿 🗒 🛈🛈
Leisure activities : 🍸✕🏠🚴🎿
Facilities : 🚿🚻🔲🚿🍴 launderette 🚰🚿

Pégomas

📞 04 90 92 01 21, www.campingpegomas.com

Address : 3 avenue Jean Moulin (take the eastern exit along the D 99a, follow the signs for Cavaillon and take the turning to the left, at intersection of the Chemin de Pégomas et av. Jean-Moulin towards D 30, follow the signs for Noves)

Opening times : from mid March to mid Oct.

2 ha (105 pitches) flat, grassy

Tariff : (2013 Price) 29€ ✳✳ 🚗 🔲 🔌 (6A) – Extra per person 8€ –
Reservation fee 17€

Rental rates : (2013 Price) (from mid May to mid Oct.) 🚐 – 6 🚐
6 🏠. Per week from 360 to 500€
🚐 borne

Surroundings : 🗒 🛈🛈
Leisure activities : 🍸🚴🎿
Facilities : 🚿🚻🔲🚿🍴 launderette, refrigerated food storage facilities
Nearby : ✕

Longitude : 4.84099
Latitude : 43.78838

ST-SAUVEUR-SUR-TINÉE

06420 – Michelin map **341** D3 – pop. 336 – alt. 500

▶ Paris 816 – Auron 31 – Guillaumes 42 – Isola 2000 28

Municipal

📞 04 93 02 03 20, mairie.st-sauveur-sur-tinee@wanadoo.fr – 🏠

Address : quartier Les Plans (800m north on the D 30, follow the signs for Roubion, before the bridge, beside the Tinée river)

Opening times : from mid June to mid Sept.

0,37 ha (20 pitches) terraced, flat, stony, fine gravel

Tariff : (2013 Price) 16,50€ ✳✳ 🚗 🔲 🔌 (3A) – Extra per person 4,50€

A footpath offers direct access to the village.

Surroundings : 🌿 ⟨ 🗒 🛈🛈
Facilities : 🚿 🅿 🚿🛇🖼
Nearby : 🚴✕🎣 fitness trail

Longitude : 7.10611
Latitude : 44.08722

STE-CROIX-DE-VERDON

04500 – Michelin map **334** E10 – pop. 124 – alt. 530

▶ Paris 780 – Brignoles 59 – Castellane 59 – Digne-les-Bains 51

Municipal les Roches

📞 04 92 77 78 99, www.blog4ever.com

Address : route du Lac (located 1km northeast of the village, 50m from the lake at Ste-Croix – caravans are not permitted through village)

Opening times : from beginning April to end Sept.

6 ha (233 pitches) terraced, undulating, flat, grassy, fine gravel

Tariff : (2013 Price) 19,80€ ✳✳ 🚗 🔲 🔌 (10A) – Extra per person 4€
Reservation fee 30€
🚐 9 🔲 19,80€

Shaded by olive and almond trees.

Surroundings : ⟨🛈🛈
Facilities : 🚿🚿🖼 refrigerated food storage facilities
Nearby : ✕🚣💧 pedalos

Longitude : 6.15381
Latitude : 43.76043

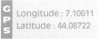

Michelin classification:
🔺🔺🔺🔺 *Extremely comfortable, equipped to a very high standard*
🔺🔺🔺 *Very comfortable, equipped to a high standard*
🔺🔺🔺 *Comfortable and well equipped*
🔺🔺 *Reasonably comfortable*
🔺 *Satisfactory*

PROVENCE-ALPES-CÔTE D'AZUR

STES-MARIES-DE-LA-MER

13460 – Michelin map **340** B5 – pop. 2 308 – alt. 1
▶ Paris 761 – Aigues-Mortes 31 – Arles 40 – Marseille 131

⚠ Sunêlia Le Clos du Rhône

℘ 04 90 97 85 99, www.camping-leclos.fr

Address : route d'Aigues-Mortes (head 2km west along the D 38 and take the turning to the left)

Opening times : from beginning April to mid Nov.

7 ha (420 pitches)

Tariff : 31,50€ ✱✱ ⬅ ▣ ⚡ (16A) – Extra per person 9€

Rental rates : (from beginning April to mid Nov.) ♿ (1 mobile home) – 91 🚐 – 14 tent lodges. Per night from 28 to 120€ – Per week from 170 to 1210€

⬅ borne – 101 ▣ 20€

Near the Petit Rhône river and the beach.

Surroundings : ♀ ⚠
Leisure activities : ✗ 🏠 🎯 ⛱ 🎣
Facilities : ♿ ⊶ �Ⅲ ⛺ ♨ ⚐ ⚑ launderette ⚑ refrigerated food storage facilities
Nearby : 🐎 boat trips on the Rhône

GPS Longitude : 4.40231
Latitude : 43.44996

SALERNES

83690 – Michelin map **340** M4 – pop. 3 574 – alt. 209
▶ Paris 830 – Aix-en-Provence 81 – Brignoles 33 – Draguignan 23

⚠ Municipal les Arnauds

℘ 04 94 67 51 95, www.village-vacances-lesarnauds.com

Address : quartier Les Arnauds (take the northwestern exit along the D 560, follow the signs for Sillans-la-Cascade and take the turning to the left)

Opening times : from beginning May to end Sept.

2 ha (52 pitches) flat, grassy

Tariff : (2013 Price) 27,50€ ✱✱ ⬅ ▣ ⚡ (10A) Extra per person 7,50€

Rental rates : Permanent – 6 studios – 14 apartments.

⬅ 52 ▣ 27,50€

Access to the village by a footpath along the Bresque river.

Surroundings : 🌲 ⟷ 〰
Leisure activities : 🏠 🚤 ⛱ 🎣 (river)
Facilities : ♿ ⊶ ⛺ ♨ ⚐ ⚑ launderette refrigerated food storage facilities

GPS Longitude : 6.2257
Latitude : 43.56623

These symbols are used for a campsite that is exceptional in its category:

⚠⚠⚠...⚠ *Particularly pleasant setting, quality and range of services available*

🌲 *Tranquil, isolated site – quiet site, particularly at night*

≪≪ *Exceptional view – interesting or panoramic view*

LES SALLES-SUR-VERDON

83630 – Michelin map **340** M3 – pop. 231 – alt. 440
▶ Paris 790 – Brignoles 57 – Digne-les-Bains 60 – Draguignan 49

⚠ Les Pins

℘ 04 98 10 23 80, www.campinglespins.com

Address : take the southern exit along the D 71 then continue 1.2km along the road to the right; 100m from the Lac de Ste-Croix

Opening times : from beginning April to mid Oct.

3 ha/2 for camping (104 pitches) terraced, flat, grassy, stony

Tariff : (2013 Price) ✱ 5,95€ ⬅ ▣ 6€ – ⚡ (6A) 6,15€ – Reservation fee 25€

⬅ borne

In an attractive, shaded setting, near a pine wood, with direct access to the village.

Surroundings : 🌲 ⟷ 〰
Leisure activities : 🏠 🚤
Facilities : ♿ ⊶ ⛺ ♨ ⚐ ⚑ launderette refrigerated food storage facilities
Nearby : 🏊 🎣 ⚐ fitness trail

GPS Longitude : 6.2084
Latitude : 43.77603

The pitches of many campsites are marked out with low hedges of attractive bushes and shrubs.

SALON-DE-PROVENCE

13300 – Michelin map **340** F4 – pop. 42 440 – alt. 80
▶ Paris 720 – Aix-en-Provence 37 – Arles 46 – Avignon 50

⚠ Nostradamus

℘ 04 90 56 08 36, www.camping-nostradamus.com

Address : route d'Eyguières (5.8km northwest along the D 17 and turn left onto D 72D)

Opening times : from beginning March to end Oct.

2,7 ha (83 pitches) flat, grassy

Tariff : (2013 Price) 27,65€ ✱✱ ⬅ ▣ ⚡ (6A) – Extra per person 6,20€ Reservation fee 20€

Rental rates : (2013 Price) (from beginning March to end Oct.) 18 🚐. Per night from 40 to 186€ – Per week from 230 to 982€ Reservation fee 20€

⬅ borne 5€

Beside a canal.

Surroundings : 🌲 ⟷ 〰
Leisure activities : 🏠 🚤 🎣
Facilities : ♿ ⊶ ⧉Ⅲ ♨ ⚐ ⚑ launderette

GPS Longitude : 5.06229
Latitude : 43.68401

SANARY-SUR-MER

83110 – Michelin map **340** J7 – pop. 16 806 – alt. 1
▶ Paris 824 – Aix-en-Provence 75 – La Ciotat 23 – Marseille 55

⚠ Campasun Mas de Pierredon ♠♦

℘ 04 94 74 25 02, www.campasun.eu

Address : 652 chemin Raoul Coletta (3km to the north, follow the signs for Ollioules and take the turning to the left after the motorway bridge)

Opening times : from mid April to end Sept.

6 ha/2,5 for camping (122 pitches) terraced, flat, grassy, stony

Tariff : 48,50€ ✱✱ ⬅ ▣ ⚡ (10A) – Extra per person 9,50€ Reservation fee 25€

Rental rates : (from mid April to end Sept.) – 44 ⬛ – 14 🏠. Per night from 43 to 190€ – Per week from 217 to 1140€ – Reservation fee 25€

🚐 borne 5€ – 9 ▣ 25,30€

Surroundings : 🛆 ♤♤
Leisure activities : 🍴 ✗ 🏟 🏃 ⛸ ✂ ♪
🎿
Facilities : ♿ ⛟ 🛁 ♨ ☂ ♆ 🔲 🚿

G P S Longitude : 5.81452 Latitude : 43.13159

🏕 Campasun Parc Mogador ♣♣

📞 04 94 74 53 16, www.campasun.eu 🚫 (July–Aug.)

Address : 167 chemin de Beaucours

Opening times : from end March to beginning Nov.

3 ha (180 pitches) terraced, flat, grassy, stony

Tariff : 48,50€ ♥♥ 🚐 ▣ ♨ (10A) – Extra per person 9,50€ – Reservation fee 25€

Rental rates : (from end March to beginning Nov.) 🚫 (July–Aug.) – 76 ⬛ – 6 🏠. Per night from 43 to 172€ – Per week from 217 to 1030€ – Reservation fee 25€

🚐 borne 5€

Surroundings : 🛆 🛆 ♤♤
Leisure activities : ✗ 🏟 🏃 🎿 🎿
bowling
Facilities : ♿ ⛟ 🛁 ♨ ☂ ♆ launderette 🚿

G P S Longitude : 5.78777 Latitude : 43.12367

LE SAUZÉ-DU-LAC

05160 – Michelin map **334** F6 – pop. 129 – alt. 1 052
▶ Paris 697 – Barcelonnette 35 – Digne-les-Bains 74 – Gap 40

🏕 La Palatrière

📞 04 92 44 20 98, www.lapalatriere.com

Address : site des Demoiselles Coiffées (4.6km south along the D 954, follow the signs for Savines-Lac)

Opening times : from beginning May to end Sept.

3 ha (30 pitches) terraced, flat, grassy, stony

Tariff : (2013 Price) 24,50€ ♥♥ 🚐 ▣ ♨ (5A) – Extra per person 7€

Rental rates : (from beginning April to end Oct.) – 6 ⬛ – 10 🏠. Per night from 49 to 110€ – Per week from 250 to 760€

An attractive location overlooking the Lac de Serre-Ponçon.

Surroundings : 🛆 ← Lac de Serre-Ponçon and the mountains ♤♤
Leisure activities : 🍴 ✗ 🏟 jacuzzi 🎿 🎿
Facilities : ♿ ⛟ 🔲 ♨ 🔲

G P S Longitude : 6.34543 Latitude : 44.49909

SERRES

05700 – Michelin map **334** C6 – pop. 1 308 – alt. 670
▶ Paris 670 – Die 68 – Gap 41 – Manosque 89

🏕 Domaine des Deux Soleils ♣♣

📞 04 92 67 01 33, www.domaine-2soleils.com – alt. 800

Address : avenue Des Pins - La Flamenche (800m southeast along the N 75, follow the signs for Sisteron then continue 1km along the turning to the left; at Super-Serres)

Opening times : from mid April to mid Oct.

26 ha/12 for camping (72 pitches) terraced, flat, grassy, stony

Tariff : 19,90€ ♥♥ 🚐 ▣ ♨ (6A) – Extra per person 3,50€ – Reservation fee 22,75€

Rental rates : (from mid April to mid Oct.) – 12 ⬛ – 13 🏠. Per night from 40 to 90€ – Per week from 495 to 690€ – Reservation fee 22,75€

🚐 10 ▣ 19,90€

Many pitches are set among trees, shrubs and bushes in a wild and natural setting.

Surroundings : 🛆 🛆 ♤
Leisure activities : ✗ 🏃 🎿 🎿 multi-sports ground
Facilities : ♿ ⛟ ♨ ♆ 🔲 🚿

G P S Longitude : 5.72767 Latitude : 44.4203

SEYNE

04140 – Michelin map **334** G6 – pop. 1 434 – alt. 1 200
▶ Paris 719 – Barcelonnette 43 – Digne-les-Bains 43 – Gap 54

🏕 Les Prairies

📞 04 92 35 10 21, www.campinglesprairies.com

Address : at Haute Gréyère, chemin Charcherie (located 1km south along the D 7, follow the signs for Auzet and take road to the left; beside the Blanche river)

Opening times : from beginning May to mid Sept.

3,6 ha (100 pitches) open site, flat, grassy, stony

Tariff : 23,90€ ♥♥ 🚐 ▣ ♨ (10A) – Extra per person 5,60€ – Reservation fee 16€

Rental rates : (from beginning May to mid Sept.) – 8 ⬛ – 8 🏠. Per night from 250 to 540€ – Per week from 270 to 600€ – Reservation fee 16€

🚐 borne

Surroundings : 🛆 ← ▱ ♤♤
Leisure activities : 🍴 ✗ 🏟 🎿 🎿
Facilities : ♿ ⛟ 🔲 🛆 launderette 🚿
Nearby : 🍴 🔲

G P S Longitude : 6.35972 Latitude : 44.34262

Routes nationales are main roads and their identifying numbers begin with N or RN. Routes départementales are generally quieter roads and begin with D or DN.

SISTERON

04200 – Michelin map **334** D7 – pop. 7 427 – alt. 490
▶ Paris 704 – Barcelonnette 100 – Digne-les-Bains 40 – Gap 52

🏕 Municipal des Prés-Hauts

📞 04 92 61 19 69, www.sisteron.fr

Address : 44 chemin des Prés Hauts (3km north following signs for Gap and take D 951 to the right, follow the signs for La Motte-du-Caire, near the Durance river)

Opening times : from beginning April to end Sept.

4 ha (141 pitches)

Tariff : 25€ ♥♥ 🚐 ▣ ♨ (10A) – Extra per person 4€ – Reservation fee 10€

Rental rates : (from beginning May to mid Sept.) – 10 ⬛. Per week from 320 to 590€

🚐 18 ▣ 25€

Pitches well marked out in a green setting.

Surroundings : 🛆 ← ▱ ♤
Leisure activities : 🏟 🎿 🎿 ✂ 🔲
Facilities : ♿ ⛟ 🔲 🛆 ☂ ♆ 🔲

G P S Longitude : 5.93645 Latitude : 44.21432

SOSPEL

06380 – Michelin map **341** F4 – pop. 3 523 – alt. 360
▶ Paris 967 – Breil-sur-Roya 21 – L'Escarène 22 – Lantosque 42

⚠ Domaine Ste-Madeleine

⌂ 04 93 04 10 48, www.camping-sainte-madeleine.com

Address : route de Moulinet (4.5km northwest along the D 2566, follow the signs for Le Col de Turini)

Opening times : from beginning April to end Sept.

3 ha (90 pitches)

Tariff : (2013 Price) 25 € ⚤ 🚐 ▣ ⚡ (10A) – Extra per person 4,80 €
Rental rates : (2013 Price) (from beginning April to end Sept.)
🚿 (July–Aug.) – 3 🚐 – 10 🏠. Per night from 65 to 100 €
Per week from 320 to 620 €
🚰 borne 3 €

Surroundings : ⌂ ≤ 🎋
Leisure activities : ⟰
Facilities : ⚿ ⚿ ⚿ ⚿ ⚿

Longitude : 7.41575
Latitude : 43.8967

LE THOR

84250 – Michelin map **332** C10 – pop. 8 099 – alt. 50
▶ Paris 688 – Avignon 18 – Carpentras 16 – Cavaillon 14

⚠ FranceLoc Domaine Le Jantou

⌂ 04 90 33 90 07, www.campings-franceloc.fr

Address : 535 chemin des Coudelières (head 1.2km west via the northern exit towards Bédarrides; direct access to the Sorgue, recommended route via the D 1 (bypass)

Opening times : from beginning April to mid Sept.

6 ha/4 for camping (195 pitches) flat, grassy

Tariff : (2013 Price) 33 € ⚤ 🚐 ▣ ⚡ (10A) – Extra per person 7 €
Rental rates : (2013 Price) (from beginning April to mid Sept.)
7 caravans – 146 🚐 – 6 🏠 – 6 canvas bungalows. Per night from 33 to 151 € – Per week from 133 to 1 099 €

Surroundings : ⌂ 🎋
Leisure activities : 🏛 🏊 🛶 🎯 ⟰ ⚑
Facilities : ⚿ ⚿ 🏛 🍴 ⚿ ⚿ launderette
🍴 refrigerators

Longitude : 4.98282
Latitude : 43.92969

For more information on visiting particular towns or regions, consult the relevant regional MICHELIN Green Guide. We also recommend you use the appropriate Michelin regional map to locate your selected campsite, to calculate distances and to work out the best route.

LES THUILES

04400 – Michelin map **334** H6 – pop. 374 – alt. 1 130
▶ Paris 752 – Marseille 221 – Digne-les-Bains 82 – Gap 62

⚠ Le Fontarache

⌂ 04 92 81 90 42, www.camping-fontarache.fr – alt. 1 108

Address : Les Thuiles Basses (take the eastern exit of the town, D 900 follow the signs for Barcelonnette, near the Ubaye river)

Opening times : from beginning June to mid Sept.

6 ha (150 pitches)

Tariff : 24,80 € ⚤ 🚐 ▣ ⚡ (6A) – Extra per person 5 € – Reservation fee 12 €

Rental rates : (from beginning June to mid Sept.) – 16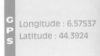
2 🏠. Per night from 36 to 93 € – Per week from 250 to 660 €
Reservation fee 12 €
🚰 borne 5 € – 🚰 11 €

Surroundings : ≤ ⌂ 🎋
Leisure activities : 🍴 🍽 🏊 multi-sports ground
Facilities : ⚿ ⚿ 🍴 launderette
Nearby : 🏊 ✕ 🍴 🚣 (river) rafting and canyoning

Longitude : 6.57537
Latitude : 44.3924

We have selected the best campsites in France with our usual care, listing those with the best facilities in the most pleasant surroundings.

VAISON-LA-ROMAINE

84110 – Michelin map **332** D8 – pop. 6 153 – alt. 193
▶ Paris 664 – Avignon 51 – Carpentras 27 – Montélimar 64

⚠ FranceLoc Le Carpe Diem 👥

⌂ 04 90 36 02 02, www.camping-carpe-diem.com

Address : route de St-Marcellin (situated 2km southeast at the intersection of the D 938 (rte de Malaucène) and the D 151)

Opening times : from beginning April to beginning Nov.

10 ha/6,5 for camping (232 pitches) terraced, flat and relatively flat, grassy

Tariff : (2013 Price) 39 € ⚤ 🚐 ▣ ⚡ (10A) – Extra per person 7 €
Reservation fee 27 €

Rental rates : (2013 Price) (from beginning April to beginning Nov.) – 183 🚐 – 14 🏠 – 1 cabin in the trees – 8 canvas bungalows. Per night from 37 to 166 € – Per week from 147 to 1 211 € – Reservation fee 27 €
🚰 borne

An original reconstruction of an amphitheatre beside the swimming pool.

Surroundings : ⌂ ⌂ 🎋
Leisure activities : 🍴 ✕ 🏛 🎮 🎯 🏊 ⚑ 🏋
🏊 🛶 ⟰
Facilities : ⚿ ⚿ 🍴 ⚿ 🏊 🍴 refrigerated food storage facilities

Longitude : 5.08945
Latitude : 44.23424

⚠ Le Soleil de Provence

⌂ 04 90 46 46 00, www.camping-soleil-de-provence.fr

Address : quartier Trameiller (3.5km northeast along the D 938, follow the signs for Nyons)

4 ha (153 pitches) terraced, flat and relatively flat, grassy, stony
Rentals : 🚿 – 26 🚐 .

Surroundings : ≤ Ventoux and mountains of Nyons ⌂ 🌿
Leisure activities : 🏛 🏊 🏊 ⟰
Facilities : ⚿ ⚿ 🏛 🍴 ⚿ 🔲

Longitude : 5.10616
Latitude : 44.26838

⚠ Théâtre Romain

⌂ 04 90 28 78 66, www.camping-theatre.com

Address : quartier des Arts – Chemin du Brusquet (to the northeast of the town, recommended route via the bypass (rocade)

Opening times : from mid March to beginning Nov.

1,2 ha (75 pitches) flat, grassy, fine gravel

Tariff : ✤ 8 € 🚐 ▣ 9 € – ⚡ (10A) 4,50 € – Reservation fee 11 €

Rental rates : (from mid March to beginning Nov.) – 9 🚐.
Per night from 35 to 95€ – Per week from 220 to 650€
Reservation fee 11€
🚰 borne 5€ – 🚽14€

Surroundings : �︎ ♀♀
Leisure activities : 🏖 🚣 🛝 (small swimming pool)
Facilities : 🚻 ⛽ 🛁 🧺 ⟁ 🍽 🔲
Nearby : 🍴

GPS Longitude : 5.07843
Latitude : 44.24505

VENCE

06140 – Michelin map **341** D5 – pop. 19 183 – alt. 325
🅿 Paris 923 – Antibes 20 – Cannes 30 – Grasse 24

🏕 Domaine de la Bergerie

🖉 04 93 58 09 36, www.camping-domainedelabergerie.com

Address : 1330 chemin de la Sine (4km west along the D 2210, follow the signs for Grasse and take road to the left)

Opening times : from end March to mid Oct.

30 ha/13 for camping (450 pitches) terraced, flat, grassy, stony

Tariff : 32€ ✶✶ 🚐 🔲 [≉] (5A)
Extra per person 5,20€ – Reservation fee 15€
Rental rates : (from end March to mid Oct.) 🏠 – 6 cabins and 2 chalets (without sanitary facilities). Per night from 30,40 to 41,40€ – Per week from 250 to 460€ – Reservation fee 15€

🚰 borne 5€

In a very pleasant natural setting spread out around an old but attractively restored sheep farm.

Surroundings : 🛥 �︎ ♫♫♫
Leisure activities : 🍴🍽 🚣 🎾 🛝
Facilities : 🚻 ⛽ 🖵 🛁 ⟁ 🧺 launderette 🛒 🚿
Nearby : sports trail

GPS Longitude : 7.08981
Latitude : 43.71253

LE VERNET

04140 – Michelin map **334** G7 – pop. 123 – alt. 1 200
🅿 Paris 729 – Digne-les-Bains 32 – La Javie 16 – Gap 68

🏕 Lou Passavous

🖉 04 92 35 14 67, www.loupassavous.com

Address : route Roussimal (800m north following signs for Roussimat ; beside the Bès river)

Opening times : from beginning May to mid Sept.

1,5 ha (60 pitches) open site, flat and relatively flat, grassy, stony
Tariff : 22,50€ ✶✶ 🚐 🔲 [≉] (6A) – Extra per person 5,25€
Reservation fee 12,50€
Rental rates : (from beginning May to mid Sept.) 🏠 – 2 🚐.
Per week from 450 to 640 € – Reservation fee 13,50€

Surroundings : 🛥 ≤ ♀
Leisure activities : 🍽 🍴 🚣
Facilities : 🚻 ⛽ 🖵🏛 🛁 ⟁ 🍽 🔲 🛒
Nearby : 🎾 🛝 🚵 🐎

GPS Longitude : 6.39139
Latitude : 44.28194

VEYNES

05400 – Michelin map **334** C5 – pop. 3 166 – alt. 827
🅿 Paris 660 – Aspres-sur-Buëch 9 – Gap 25 – Sisteron 51

🏕 Les Prés

🖉 04 92 57 26 22, www.camping-les-pres.com – alt. 960

Address : Le Petit Vaux (3.4km northeast along the D 994 follow the signs for Gap, then continue 5.5km along the D 937 following signs for Superdevoluy and take road to the left via the bridge over the Béoux)

Opening times : from mid March to mid Nov.

0,35 ha (25 pitches)

Tariff : 18,30€ ✶✶ 🚐 🔲 [≉] (10A) – Extra per person 4€
Rental rates : Permanent 🏠 – 4 🚐 – 3 canvas bungalows.
Per night from 45 to 110€ – Per week from 120 to 480€

Surroundings : 🛥 ≤ ♀
Facilities : 🚻 ⛽ 🍽 🔲

GPS Longitude : 5.84995
Latitude : 44.58842

The guide covers all 22 regions of France – see the map and list of regions on pages 4–5.

VILLAR-LOUBIÈRE

05800 – Michelin map **334** E4 – pop. 48 – alt. 1 026
🅿 Paris 648 – La Chapelle-en-Valgaudémar 5 – Corps 22 – Gap 43

🏕 Municipal Les Gravières

🖉 04 92 55 35 35, http://www.sudrafting.fr/camping-villar-loubiere.html

Address : 700m east following signs for La Chapelle-en-Valgaudémar and take the road to the right

Opening times : from mid June to mid Sept.

2 ha (50 pitches) flat, grassy, stony, wood

Tariff : (2013 Price) ✶ 2,80€ 🚐 3€ 🔲 3,60€ – [≉] (3A) 4,20€

An ideal destination for whitewater sports fans.

Surroundings : 🛥 ≤ ♀♀
Leisure activities : 🏖 🎾 🛶 rafting and canyoning
Facilities : 🚻 ⛽ (July–Aug.) 🔲

GPS Longitude : 6.1464
Latitude : 44.82373

VILLARS-COLMARS

04370 – Michelin map **334** H7 – pop. 246 – alt. 1 225
🅿 Paris 774 – Annot 37 – Barcelonnette 46 – Colmars 3

🏕 Le Haut-Verdon

🖉 04 92 83 40 09, www.lehautverdon.com – access via Col d'Allos strictly not advised

Address : 0.6km south along the D 908, follow the signs for Castellane ; beside the Verdon river

Opening times : from beginning May to end Sept.

3,5 ha (109 pitches)

Tariff : 28€ ✶✶ 🚐 🔲 [≉] (6A) – Extra per person 10€ – Reservation fee 15€

Rental rates : Permanent – 7 🚐 – 4 🏠. Per night 75 €
Per week 700 € – Reservation fee 15€
🚰 borne 3€

Surroundings : ≤ �︎ ♀♀
Leisure activities : 🍽 🍴 🏖 🚣 🎾 🛝 🛥
Facilities : ⛽ 🏛 🍽 🛒

GPS Longitude : 6.60573
Latitude : 44.1604

VILLECROZE

83690 – Michelin map **340** M4 – pop. 1 128 – alt. 300
▶ Paris 835 – Aups 8 – Brignoles 38 – Draguignan 21

⚠ Le Ruou ♣♣

🔗 04 94 70 67 70, www.leruou.com – limited spaces for one-night stay

Address : 309 RD (route Départementale) 560 (5.4km southeast along the D 251, follow the signs for Barbebelle and take D 560, follow the signs for Flayosc, recommended route via the D 560)

Opening times : from mid April to mid Oct.

4,3 ha (134 pitches) very uneven, terraced, flat, grassy

Tariff : (2013 Price) 39€ ♣♣ 🚐 🔲 🔌 (10A) – Extra per person 7€ Reservation fee 25€

Rental rates : (2013 Price) (from mid April to mid Oct.) – 39 🛖 19 🏠 – 26 canvas bungalows. Per night from 34 to 142€ Per week from 238 to 994€ – Reservation fee 25€

🚾 borne 5€

Pretty pitches arranged on terraces.

Surroundings : ◁ 🖭
Leisure activities : 🍴 🍽 🏠 🏸 🏊 🎣 🛶 ⛷
Facilities : ♿ ⚡ ♨ 🍴 launderette 🚿

G P S Longitude : 6.29796
       Latitude : 43.55343

VILLENEUVE-LOUBET-PLAGE

06270 – Michelin map **341**
▶ Paris 919 – Marseille 191 – Nice 24 – Monaco 38

⚠ La Vieille Ferme

🔗 04 93 33 41 44, www.vieilleferme.com

Address : 296 boulevard des Groules (2.8km south along the N 7, follow the signs for Antibes and take a right turn)

Opening times : Permanent

2,9 ha (153 pitches) terraced, flat, grassy, fine gravel

Tariff : 36€ ♣♣ 🚐 🔲 🔌 (10A) – Extra per person 6€ – Reservation fee 28€

Rental rates : Permanent – 32 🏠. Per night from 55 to 80€ Per week from 365 to 960€ – Reservation fee 28€

🚾 borne

Surroundings : 🖭
Leisure activities : 🍴 🏠 🌀 daytime jacuzzi 🏊 🔲 (open-air in season)
Facilities : ♿ ⚡ 🍴 ♨ 🚿 🍴 launderette 🚿 refrigerated food storage facilities

G P S Longitude : 7.12579
       Latitude : 43.61967

⚠ Parc des Maurettes

🔗 04 93 20 91 91, www.parcdesmaurettes.com

Address : 730 avenue du Dr Lefèbvre (along the N 7)

Opening times : from beginning Jan. to mid Nov.

2 ha (140 pitches) terraced, flat, grassy, gravelled, stony

Tariff : (2013 Price) 39,40€ ♣♣ 🚐 🔲 🔌 (16A) Extra per person 5,70€ – Reservation fee 25€

Rental rates : (2013 Price) (from beginning Jan. to mid Nov.) 14 🏠 – 2 🛏 – 3 studios. Per night from 60 to 128€ – Per week from 378 to 765€ – Reservation fee 25€

🚾 borne 6€ – 5 🔲 16,40€

A pleasant spa and relaxation area.

Surroundings : 🖭
Leisure activities : 🏠 🛁 jacuzzi 🏊
Facilities : ♿ ⚡ 🅿 🍴 ♨ 🚿 🍴 launderette

G P S Longitude : 7.12964
       Latitude : 43.63111

⚠ L'Hippodrome

🔗 04 93 20 02 00, www.camping-hippodrome.com

Address : 5 avenue des Rives (400m from the beach, behind the Géant Casino commercial centre)

Opening times : Permanent

0,8 ha (46 pitches) flat, grassy, fine gravel

Tariff : 34€ ♣♣ 🚐 🔲 🔌 (10A) – Extra per person 5,50€ – Reservation fee 20€

Rental rates : Permanent – 15 studios. – Reservation fee 20€

🚾 borne

Surroundings : 🖭
Leisure activities : 🏠 🏊 🔲 (open-air in season)
Facilities : ♿ ⚡ 🌳 🍴 ♨ 🚿 🍴 launderette, refrigerators
Nearby : 🍴

G P S Longitude : 7.13771
       Latitude : 43.64199

VILLES-SUR-AUZON

84570 – Michelin map **332** E9 – pop. 1 296 – alt. 255
▶ Paris 694 – Avignon 45 – Carpentras 19 – Malaucène 24

⚠ Les Verguettes

🔗 04 90 61 88 18, www.provence-camping.com

Address : route de Carpentras (take the western exit along the D 942)

Opening times : from beginning April to beginning Oct.

2 ha (88 pitches) terraced, flat and relatively flat, grassy, stony

Tariff : 32,50€ ♣♣ 🚐 🔲 🔌 (10A) – Extra per person 7,50€ Reservation fee 23€

Rental rates : (from beginning April to beginning Oct.) – 8 🛖 Per night from 48 to 60€ – Per week from 260 to 736€ Reservation fee 23€

🚾 borne

Surroundings : 🌿 ◁ Mont Ventoux 🖭
Leisure activities : 🏠 🏓 🎱 🏊
Facilities : ♿ ⚡ 🍴 ♨ 🚿 🍴 📻 🌳 refrigerators

G P S Longitude : 5.22834
       Latitude : 44.05686

*The classification (1 to 5 tents, **black** or **red**) that we award to selected sites in this guide is our own system. It should not be confused with the classification (1 to 5 stars) of official organisations.*

VIOLÈS

84150 – Michelin map **332** C9 – pop. 1 546 – alt. 94
▶ Paris 659 – Avignon 34 – Carpentras 21 – Nyons 33

⚠ Les Favards

🔗 04 90 70 90 93, www.favards.com

Address : route d'Orange (1.2km west along the D 67)

Opening times : from mid April to beginning Oct.

20 ha/1,5 (49 pitches) flat, grassy

Tariff : (2013 Price) ♣ 5,80€ 🚐 🔲 5€ – 🔌 (10A) 3,25€

In the grounds of a vineyard

Surroundings : 🌿 ◁ 🖭 ♀
Leisure activities : 🍴 🏊
Facilities : ♿ ⚡ 🌳 🍴 📻 refrigerated food storage facilities

G P S Longitude : 4.93528
       Latitude : 44.16229

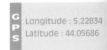

VISAN

84820 – Michelin map **332** C8 – pop. 1 956 – alt. 218
🞐 Paris 652 – Avignon 57 – Bollène 19 – Nyons 20

⚠ L'Hérein

𝄞 04 90 41 95 99, www.campingvisan.com

Address : route de Bouchet (located 1km west along the D 161, follow the signs for Bouchet; near a stream)

Opening times : from end March to mid Oct.

3,3 ha (75 pitches)

Tariff : (2013 Price) 16€ 🏃🏃 ⇔ 🔲 [⚡] (6A) – Extra per person 4,50€

Reservation fee 10€

Rental rates : (2013 Price) (from end March to mid Oct.) – 6 🚐. Per night from 45 to 65€ – Per week from 285 to 380€ Reservation fee 10€

🚰 borne – 120 🔲 11,50€

Surroundings : 🏞 ⌂ 🎿🎿
Leisure activities : ✗ 🏛 🚣🎣 ⛰ 🛝
Facilities : ♿ ⚷ 🏍 🚿 ⚒ ¶ 🔲 ⛴

Longitude : 4.93601
Latitude : 44.31236

VOLONNE

04290 – Michelin map **334** E8 – pop. 1 658 – alt. 450
🞐 Paris 718 – Château-Arnoux-St-Aubin 4 – Digne-les-Bains 29 – Forcalquier 33

🏔 Sunêlia L'Hippocampe ♠♣

𝄞 04 92 33 50 00, www.l-hippocampe.com

Address : route Napoléon (500m southeast along the D 4)

Opening times : from end April to end Sept.

8 ha (447 pitches) flat, grassy, fruit trees

Tariff : 30€ 🏃🏃 ⇔ 🔲 [⚡] (10A) – Extra per person 7€ – Reservation fee 30€

Rental rates : (from end April to end Sept.) – 182 🚐 – 30 🏠 16 canvas bungalows. Per night from 35 to 214€ – Per week from 245 to 1 498€ – Reservation fee 30€

🚰 borne 5€ – 10 🔲 8€ – 🚐 [⚡]11€

In a pleasant setting, beside the Durance river.

Surroundings : 🏞 ⌂ 🎿🎿
Leisure activities : ¶ ✗ 🏊 🚣 🎣 🛶 🎿 🛝 disco, pedalos 🎪 entertainment room
Facilities : ♿ ⚷ 🔲 ⛴ 🚿 ⚒ ¶ launderette 🏊 ⛴

Longitude : 6.0173
Latitude : 44.1054

Key to rentals symbols:

12 🚐	*Number of mobile homes*	
20 🏠	*Number of chalets*	
6 🛏	*Number of rooms to rent*	
Per night 30–50€	*Minimum/maximum rate per night*	
Per week 300–1,000€	*Minimum/maximum rate per week*	

VOLX

04130 – Michelin map **334** D9 – pop. 2 953 – alt. 350
🞐 Paris 748 – Digne-les-Bains 51 – Forcalquier 15 – Gréoux-les-Bains 22

⚠ La Vandelle

𝄞 04 92 79 35 85, www.camping-lavandelle.com

Address : avenue de la Vandelle (1.3km southwest of the town)

2 ha (50 pitches)

Rentals : 2 canvas bungalows – 1 tent lodge.

Surroundings : 🏞 🎿🎿
Leisure activities : 🎿
Facilities : ♿ ⚷ ¶ 🔲

Longitude : 5.83162
Latitude : 43.869

RHÔNE-ALPES

G. Labriet / Photononstop

Rhône-Alpes is a region of contrasts and a cultural crossroads. Its lofty peaks are a snow-covered paradise for skiers, climbers and hikers, drawn by the beauty of its shimmering glaciers and tranquil lakes; stylish Chamonix and Courchevel set the tone and the pace in cool Alpine chic. Descend from the roof of Europe, past herds of cattle on the mountain pastures and into the bustle of the Rhône valley. From Roman roads to speedy TGVs, playing host to the main arteries between north and south has forged the region's reputation for economic drive. Holidaymakers may rush through Rhône-Alpes in summer but those in the know linger to enjoy its culinary specialities. The region boasts a host of Michelin-starred restaurants: three-starred trendsetters and the legendary neighbourhood *bouchons* (small, family-run bistros) of Lyon, capital of this gastronomic paradise, make it a compulsory stop. Enjoy a Bresse chicken, cheese and sausages from Lyon and a glass of Côtes du Rhône.

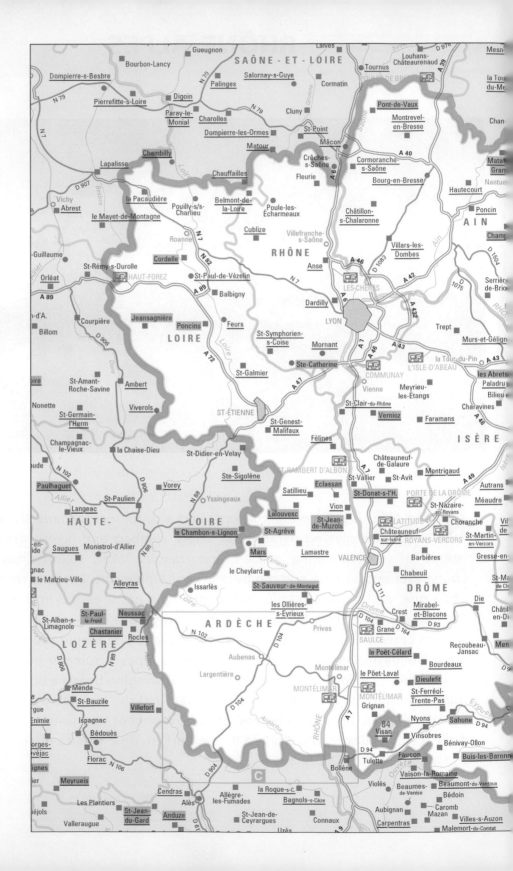

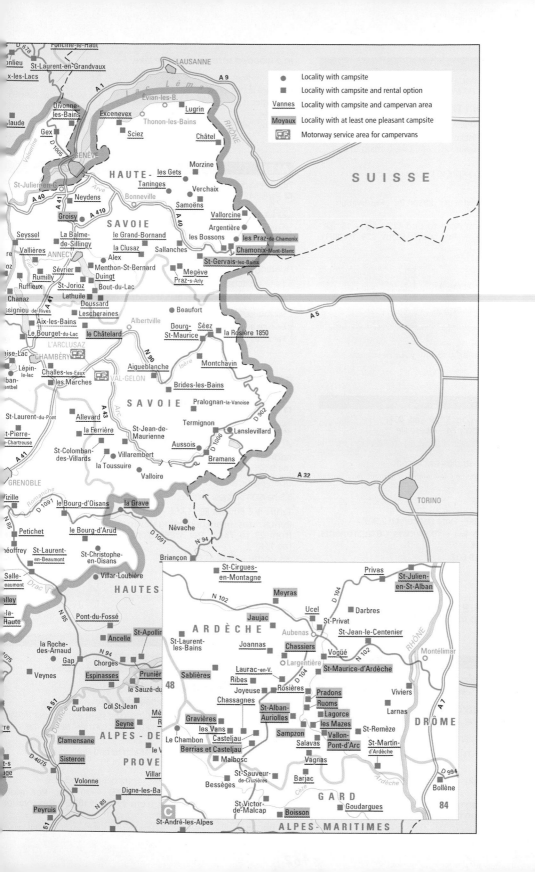

Legend:
- Locality with campsite
- Locality with campsite and rental option
- **Vannes** Locality with campsite and campervan area
- **Moyaux** Locality with at least one pleasant campsite
- Motorway service area for campervans

LAUSANNE

Foncine-le-Haut
D 678
St-Laurent-en-Grandvaux
onlieu
x-les-Lacs
Divonne-les-Bains
Évian-les-B.
Lugrin
Excenevex
Thonon-les-Bains
Sciez
Châtel
Gex
GENÈVE
SUISSE
St-Julien-en-G.
HAUTE-
les Gets
Morzine
Neydens
Taninges
Verchaix
Bonneville
Groisy
Samoëns
SAVOIE
Vallorcine
Argentière
Seyssel
le Grand-Bornand
les Bossons
les Praz-de-Chamonix
La Balme-de-Sillingy
la Clusaz
Sallanches
Chamonix-Mont-Blanc
Vallières
ANNECY
Alex
St-Gervais-les-Bains
oz
Sévrier
Menthon-St-Bernard
Megève
Rumilly
Duingt
Praz-s-Arly
Ruffieux
St-Jorioz
Bout-du-Lac
Chanaz
Lathuile
ssignieu de-Rives
Doussard
Lescheraines
Beaufort
Aix-les-Bains
Albertville
A 5
Le Bourget-du-Lac
le Châtelard
Dourg-St-Maurice
Séez
la Rosière 1850
L'ARCLUSAZ
aise-Lac
CHAMBÉRY
N 90
Lépin-le-lac
Challes-les-Eaux
VAL-GELON
Aigueblanche
Montchavin
ntbel
les Marches
Isère
St-Laurent-du-Pont
Brides-les-Bains
SAVOIE
Allevard
Pralognan-la-Vanoise
t-Pierre-e-Chartreuse
la Ferrière
Termignon
St-Jean-de-Maurienne
Lanslevillard
St-Colomban-des-Villards
Villarembert
Aussois
la Toussuire
Bramans
Valloire
GRENOBLE
Vizille
le Bourg-d'Oisans
la Grave
D 1091
Petichet
le Bourg-d'Arud
Névache
éoffrey
St-Laurent-en-Beaumont
St-Christophe-en-Oisans
N 94
Briançon
Salle-eaumont
Villar-Loubière
HAUTES-
alley
la-Haute
Pont-du-Fossé
N 85
Ancelle
St-Apolli
la Roche-des-Arnaud
N 94
Chorges
Gap
Veynes
Prunier
Espinasses
le Sauzé-du
48
A 51
Curbans
Col St-Jean
Mé
Seyne
R
Clamensane
ALPES-DE-
re
Sisteron
le V
PROVE
Villar
Volonne
Digne-les-Ba
Peyruis
N 85
St-André-les-Alpes
51

(Inset map — département Ardèche / Gard):

St-Cirgues-en-Montagne
Privas
Meyras
St-Julien-en-St-Alban
N 102
Ucel
Jaujac
Darbres
St-Privat
ARDÈCHE
Aubenas
St-Jean-le-Centenier
St-Laurent-les-Bains
Joannas
Chassiers
Vogüé
N 102
Montélimar
Largentière
St-Maurice-d'Ardèche
Sablières
Laurac-en-V.
D 104
Viviers
Ribes
Rosières
Joyeuse
Pradons
Larnas
Chassagnes
Ruoms
DRÔME
Gravières
St-Alban-Auriolles
Lagorce
les Vans
les Mazes
St-Remèze
Le Chambon
Casteljau
Sampzon
Vallon-Pont-d'Arc
St-Martin-d'Ardèche
Berrias et Casteljau
Salavas
Malbosc
Vagnas
D 994
St-Sauveur-de-Cruzières
Barjac
Bollène
Bessèges
GARD
84
St-Victor-de-Malcap
Boisson
Goudargues
ALPES-MARITIMES

LES ABRETS

38490 – Michelin map **333** G4 – pop. 3 186 – alt. 398
▶ Paris 514 – Aix-les-Bains 45 – Belley 31 – Chambéry 38

▲▲▲ Kawan Village Le Coin Tranquille ▲▲

✆ 0476321348, www.coin-tranquille.com

Address : 6 chemin des Vignes (head 2.3km east along the N 6, follow the signs for Le Pont-de-Beauvoisin and take turning to the left)

Opening times : from beginning April to beginning Nov.

4 ha (180 pitches)

Tariff : 36€ ♛♛ ⇔ 🔲 ⚡ (6A) – Extra per person 8€ – Reservation fee 16€

Rental rates : (from beginning April to end Oct.) ℗ – 15 🏠. Per night from 84 to 108€ – Per week from 329 to 861€ Reservation fee 31€

🚐 borne

> Surroundings : 🏊 ⊏⊐ ◗◗
> Leisure activities : ▮ ✗ 🏛 ⊙daytime ⛷
> 🛶 🚲 🏊
> Facilities : ⅄ ⛟ 📶 ⅂ ▯ launderette ⬚
> ⬚

GPS	Longitude : 5.6084 Latitude : 45.54139

This guide is updated regularly, so buy your new copy every year!

AIGUEBLANCHE

73260 – Michelin map **333** M4 – pop. 3 129 – alt. 461
▶ Paris 641 – Lyon 174 – Chambéry 74 – Albertville 25

▲ Marie-France

✆ 0609473230, www.camping-studios-savoie.com

Address : 453 avenue de Savoie

Opening times : Permanent

0,5 ha (30 pitches)

Tariff : 13,80€ ♛♛ ⇔ 🔲 ⚡ (10A) – Extra per person 2,80€

Rental rates : Permanent – 5 ⊨ – 10 studios – 6 apartments. Per night 90€ – Per week 350€

🚐 borne 5€ – 5 🔲 9,60€ – 🚐9,60€

> Surroundings : ← ⊏⊐ ◗◗
> Leisure activities : ⅃ℴ
> Facilities : ⅄ ⛟ ▯ ▯
> At the leisure/activities centre : ▮ ✗ 🍴
> 🛶 ✗ ▯ ▯ ⅂ ⬚ ◗ 🐎 sports trail

GPS	Longitude : 6.48946 Latitude : 45.50924

AIX-LES-BAINS

73100 – Michelin map **333** I3 – pop. 26 819 – alt. 200 – ⚓
▶ Paris 539 – Annecy 34 – Bourg-en-Bresse 115 – Chambéry 18

▲▲▲ International du Sierroz

✆ 0479618989, www.camping-sierroz.com

Address : boulevard Robert Barrier (2.5km to the northwest)

Opening times : from mid March to mid Nov.

5 ha (290 pitches)

Tariff : 25,20€ ♛♛ ⇔ 🔲 ⚡ (10A) – Extra per person 5,30€ Reservation fee 12€

Rental rates : (from mid March to mid Nov.) – 34 🚐. Per week from 283 to 676€ – Reservation fee 12€

🚐 borne 5€

In a wooded setting, near the lake.

> Surroundings : ⊏⊐ ◗◗
> Leisure activities : ▮ 🏛
> Facilities : ⅄ ⛟ 📶 ⅂ ⬚ ⅂ ▯ launderette
> ⬚ 🍴
> Nearby : 🏊 🎣 ⛵

GPS	Longitude : 5.88628 Latitude : 45.70104

ALEX

74290 – Michelin map **328** K5 – pop. 980 – alt. 589
▶ Paris 545 – Albertville 42 – Annecy 12 – La Clusaz 20

▲ La Ferme des Ferrières

✆ 0450028709, www.camping-des-ferrieres.com

Address : located 1.5km west along the D 909, follow the signs for Annecy and take the road to the right

Opening times : from beginning June to end Sept.

5 ha (200 pitches)

Tariff : 15,80€ ♛♛ ⇔ 🔲 ⚡ (5A) – Extra per person 2,80€

> Surroundings : 🏊 ← ◗
> Leisure activities : ▮ 🏛 🛶
> Facilities : ⅄ ⛟ 🚐 ⅂ ▯

GPS	Longitude : 6.22346 Latitude : 45.89015

ALLEVARD

38580 – Michelin map **333** J5 – pop. 3 768 – alt. 470 – ⚓
▶ Paris 593 – Albertville 50 – Chambéry 33 – Grenoble 40

▲▲▲ Clair Matin

✆ 0476975519, www.camping-clair-matin.com

Address : 20 rue des Pommiers (take the southwestern exit along the D 525, follow the signs for Grenoble)

Opening times : from mid April to mid Oct.

5,5 ha (200 pitches) terraced, flat and relatively flat, grassy

Tariff : ♛ 3,60€ ⇔ 🔲 13,45€ – ⚡ (10A) 5,50€ – Reservation fee 8€

Rental rates : (from beginning May to mid Oct.) – 29 🚐. Per night from 29 to 75€ – Per week from 202 to 526€ – Reservation fee 13€

🚐 borne – 10 🔲 13€ – 🚐11€

> Surroundings : 🏊 ← ◗◗
> Leisure activities : ✗ 🏛 ⅂
> Facilities : ⅄ ⛟ ⅂ ⬚ ▯ launderette

GPS	Longitude : 6.06591 Latitude : 45.38869

ANSE

69480 – Michelin map **327** H4 – pop. 5 604 – alt. 170
▶ Paris 436 – L'Arbresle 17 – Bourg-en-Bresse 57 – Lyon 27

▲▲▲ Les Portes du Beaujolais

✆ 0474671287, www.camping-beaujolais.com

Address : 495 avenue Jean Vacher (take the southeastern exit, follow the signs for Lyon and 600m along the road turn left before the bridge)

Opening times : from beginning March to end Oct.

7,5 ha (198 pitches) flat, grassy

Tariff : 29,50€ ♛♛ ⇔ 🔲 ⚡ (16A) – Extra per person 5,20€

Rental rates : Permanent – 35 🚐 – 30 🏠. Per night from 65 to 130€ – Per week from 299 to 1189€ – Reservation fee 5€

🚐 borne

At the point where the Azergues and Saône rivers meet.

Surroundings : 🌲 🏊
Leisure activities : 🍽 ✕ 🏠 🚡 hammam, jacuzzi 🚴‍♂️🚲 🏊 ♨ spa centre
Facilities : 🛁 ⛽ [CC] 🎰 ♨ 🚰 🚿 🛖 🏠 🚮
Nearby : 🎣

G P S	Longitude : 4.72616
	Latitude : 45.94106

ARGENTIÈRE

74400 – Michelin map **328** O5 – alt. 1 252
▶ Paris 619 – Annecy 106 – Chamonix-Mont-Blanc 10 – Vallorcine 10

🏔 Le Glacier d'Argentière

📞 04 50 54 17 36, www.campingchamonix.com

Address : 161 chemin des Chosalets (located 1km south following signs for Chamonix, 200m from the Arve river)

1 ha (80 pitches)

Surroundings : ⛰ 🏊
Leisure activities : 🏠
Facilities : 🛁 ⛽ launderette

G P S	Longitude : 6.92363
	Latitude : 45.9747

ARTEMARE

01510 – Michelin map **328** H5 – pop. 1 112 – alt. 245
▶ Paris 506 – Aix-les-Bains 33 – Ambérieu-en-Bugey 47 – Belley 18

🏔 Sites et Paysages Le Vaugrais

📞 04 79 87 37 34, www.camping-le-vaugrais.fr

Address : at Cerveyrieu, 2 chemin le Vaugrais (700m west along the D 69d, follow the signs for Belmont, beside the Séran river)

Opening times : from beginning March to mid Dec.

1 ha (33 pitches) flat, grassy

Tariff : (2013 Price) 18€  (10A) – Extra per person 3,50€
Reservation fee 7€

Surroundings : ⛰ 🌲 🏊
Leisure activities : 🍽 🏠 🚴‍♂️🚲 🏊 🚣
Facilities : 🛁 ⛽ 🎰 🚿 🛖 🏠

G P S	Longitude : 5.68383
	Latitude : 45.87465

AUSSOIS

73500 – Michelin map **333** N6 – pop. 677 – alt. 1 489
▶ Paris 670 – Albertville 97 – Chambéry 110 – Lanslebourg-Mont-Cenis 17

🏔 Municipal la Buidonnière

📞 04 79 20 35 58, www.camping-aussois.com

Address : route de Cottériat (take the southern exit along the D 215, follow the signs for Modane and take road to the left)

Opening times : Permanent

4 ha (160 pitches) terraced, relatively flat, grassy, stony

Tariff : 🚶 6,70€ 🚗 – 🔌 (10A) 5,90€
🚐 borne 2€
A free shuttle service operates to the ski lifts.

Surroundings : ❄ 🏊 ⛰ Parc de la Vanoise 🌲
Leisure activities : 🏠 🚴‍♂️ 🎿 🏊 (pool) sports trail
Facilities : 🛁 ⛽ 🎰 🛖 launderette

G P S	Longitude : 6.74586
	Latitude : 45.22432

AUTRANS

38880 – Michelin map **333** G6 – pop. 1 676 – alt. 1 050 – Winter sports : 1 050/1 650m
▶ Paris 586 – Grenoble 36 – Romans-sur-Isère 58 – St-Marcellin 47

🏔 **Yelloh! Village au Joyeux Réveil** 👥

📞 04 76 95 33 44, www.camping-au-joyeux-reveil.fr

Address : at Le Château (take the northeastern exit following signs for Montaud and take a right turn)

Opening times :

1,5 ha (100 pitches) flat, grassy

Tariff : 43€ (6A) – Extra per person 8€ – Reservation fee 15€

Rental rates : (from beginning May to end Sept.) – 30 🚐. Per night from 39 to 165€ – Per week from 315 to 1 134€
Reservation fee 15€
🚐 borne 5€
Some luxury rental options.

Surroundings : ⛰
Leisure activities : ✕ 🏠 🚶 🚡 hammam, jacuzzi 🚴‍♂️ 🏊 🏊 ♨ spa centre
Facilities : 🛁 ⛽ 🎰 🚿 🛖 🏠 🚮

G P S	Longitude : 5.54844
	Latitude : 45.17555

BALBIGNY

42510 – Michelin map **327** E5 – pop. 2 809 – alt. 331
▶ Paris 423 – Feurs 10 – Noirétable 44 – Roanne 29

🏔 La Route Bleue

📞 04 77 27 24 97, http://camping-de-la-route-bleue.fr

Address : at Pralery (2.8km northwest along the N 82 and turn left onto D 56, follow the signs for St-Georges-de-Baroille)

Opening times : from mid March to end Oct.

2 ha (100 pitches) flat and relatively flat, grassy

Tariff : 19,80€  (10A) – Extra per person 5€
Rental rates : (from beginning April to end Oct.) – 2 🚐. Per night from 45 to 85€ – Per week from 290 to 580€ – Reservation fee 15€
In a pleasant location beside the Loire river.

Surroundings : 🎣 🏊
Leisure activities : 🍽 ✕ 🏠 🏊 🚣
Facilities : 🛁 ⛽ 🛖 launderette

G P S	Longitude : 4.15725
	Latitude : 45.82719

LA BALME-DE-SILLINGY

74330 – Michelin map **328** J5 – pop. 4 891 – alt. 480
▶ Paris 524 – Dijon 250 – Grenoble 111 – Lons-le-Saunier 136

🏔 La Caille

📞 04 50 68 85 21, www.domainedelacaille.com

Address : 18 chemin de la Caille (4km north on N 508 towards Frangy and take the road to the right)

Opening times : from beginning May to end Sept.

4 ha/1 for camping (30 pitches) flat and relatively flat, grassy

Tariff : (2013 Price) 26€ 🚶🚶 🚗 🔲 🔌 (13A) – Extra per person 6€
Rental rates : Permanent 🅿 – 12 🚐 – 12 🏠 – 2 gîtes. Per night from 80 to 120€ – Per week from 250 to 699€ – Reservation fee 20€
🚐 borne – 3 🔲 21€

Surroundings : 🏊 🌲 🏊
Leisure activities : 🍽 ✕ 🏠 🏊 🎾 🏊
Facilities : 🛁 ⛽ 🛖 🏠 🚮

G P S	Longitude : 6.03609
	Latitude : 45.97828

BARBIÈRES

26300 – Michelin map **332** D4 – pop. 771 – alt. 426
▶ Paris 586 – Lyon 124 – Valence 23 – Grenoble 79

⛰ Le Gallo-Romain

☎ 04 75 47 44 07, www.legalloromain.net

Address : route du Col de Tourniol (1.2km southeast along the D 101; beside the Barberolle river)

Opening times : from end April to end Sept.

3 ha (62 pitches) terrace, flat and relatively flat, grassy, stony

Tariff : 35 € ★★ ⬅ 🔲 🅿 (6A) – Extra per person 6,50 € – Reservation fee 15 €

Surroundings : 🐟 ⟨ ▱ ♒♒ Leisure activities : ▼ ✕ 🏛 ⛵ 🛶 Facilities : ⅙ �o━ ▥ ♨⛲ launderette ⚓ refrigerators	**GPS** Longitude : 5.15092 Latitude : 44.94456

BEAUFORT

73270 – Michelin map **333** M3 – pop. 2 206 – alt. 750
▶ Paris 601 – Albertville 21 – Chambéry 72 – Megève 37

⛺ Municipal Domelin

☎ 04 79 38 33 88, camping-beaufort@orange.fr

Address : in the town (RD 925)

Opening times : from beginning June to end Sept.

2 ha (100 pitches) flat and relatively flat, grassy

Tariff : (2013 Price) ★ 3,72 € ⬅ 2,30 € 🔲 3,10 € – 🅿 (10A) 3,10 €

Surroundings : 🐟 ⟨ ♒ Facilities : ⅙ o━ (July-Aug.) launderette Nearby : ☲ ⛲ ⛰ 🛶 sports trail	**GPS** Longitude : 6.56403 Latitude : 45.7218

BELMONT-DE-LA-LOIRE

42670 – Michelin map **327** F3 – pop. 1 515 – alt. 525
▶ Paris 405 – Chauffailles 6 – Roanne 35 – St-Étienne 108

⛺ Municipal les Écureuils

☎ 04 77 63 72 25, www.belmontdelaloire.fr

Address : at the leisure/activities centre by the lake (1.4km west along the D 4, follow the signs for Charlieu and take road to the left, 300m from a lake)

Opening times : from beginning May to end Sept.

0,6 ha (28 pitches) terraced, relatively flat to hilly, grassy, gravelled

Tariff : ★ 2,30 € ⬅ 1,18 € 🔲 1,41 € – 🅿 (5A) 2,40 €
Rental rates : Permanent – 9 🏠. Per night from 43 to 75 € Per week from 250 to 448 €
🚐 2 🔲
Situated beside a leisure and activity park.

Surroundings : 🐟 ▱ Leisure activities : ⛲⬆ Facilities : 🗑 📷 Nearby : ✂ 🛶	**GPS** Longitude : 4.33819 Latitude : 46.1662

In order for the guide to remain wholly objective, the selection of campsites is made on an entirely independent basis.

BENIVAY-OLLON

26170 – Michelin map **332** E8 – pop. 66 – alt. 450
▶ Paris 689 – Lyon 227 – Valence 126 – Avignon 71

⛰ Domaine de l'Écluse

☎ 04 75 28 07 32, www.campecluse.com

Address : at Barastrage (1km south on the D 347)

Opening times : from mid April to end Sept.

4 ha (75 pitches) undulating, terraced, flat, grassy, stony, fine gravel

Tariff : 30 € ★★ ⬅ 🔲 🅿 (6A) – Extra per person 6 € – Reservation fee 30 €

Rental rates : (from mid April to end Sept.) ⅙ ⚞ – 12 🚐 12 🏠 – 2 gîtes. Per night from 60 to 120 € – Per week from 300 to 770 € – Reservation fee 30 €

Shaded by cherry trees, surrounded by vineyards and beside a stream.

Surroundings : 🐟 ⟨ ▱ ♒♒ Leisure activities : ▼ ✕ 🏛 ⛵ 🛶 🛷 🛶 Facilities : ⅙ o━ 🗑 ♨⛲ 📷	**GPS** Longitude : 5.18545 Latitude : 44.30298

The guide covers all 22 regions of France – see the map and list of regions on pages 4–5.

BERRIAS-ET-CASTELJAU

07460 – Michelin map **331** H7 – pop. 643 – alt. 126
▶ Paris 668 – Aubenas 40 – Largentière 29 – St-Ambroix 18

⛰ Les Cigales

☎ 04 75 39 30 33, www.camping-cigales-ardeche.com

Address : at La Rouvière (1km to the northeast, follow the signs for Casteljau)

Opening times : from beginning April to end Sept.

3 ha (110 pitches) terraced, flat and relatively flat, grassy

Tariff : 27 € ★★ ⬅ 🔲 🅿 (10A) – Extra per person 5,50 € – Reservation fee 15 €

Rental rates : (from beginning April to end Sept.) – 23 🚐 7 🏠 – 5 gîtes. Per night from 60 € – Per week from 250 to 610 € Reservation fee 15 €

Shaded pitches, on terraces with a pleasant swimming pool.

Surroundings : 🐟 ♒♒ Leisure activities : ▼ 🏛 ⛵ ✂ ⛵ Facilities : ⅙ o━ 🗑 ♨⛲ 📷 ⚓	**GPS** Longitude : 4.21133 Latitude : 44.37829

⛰ La Source 👥

☎ 04 75 39 39 13, www.camping-source-ardeche.com

Address : at La Rouvière (situated 1.5km northeast, follow the signs for Casteljau)

Opening times : from end April to mid Sept.

2,5 ha (93 pitches)

Tariff : 23,30 € ★★ ⬅ 🔲 🅿 (6A) – Extra per person 6,50 €
Rental rates : (from end April to mid Sept.) – 22 🚐 – 4 🏠. Per week 785 €

Various rental options with chalets of a good standard, a pleasant swimming pool area on a site bordered by a stream, Le Gravierou.

Surroundings : 🐟 ▱ ♒♒ Leisure activities : ✕ 🏛 ⛪ ⛵ 🛶 Facilities : ⅙ o━ 🗑 ♨⛲ 📷 ⚓	**GPS** Longitude : 4.20646 Latitude : 44.37725

BILIEU

38850 – Michelin map **333** G5 – pop. 1 232 – alt. 580
▶ Paris 526 – Belley 44 – Chambéry 47 – Grenoble 38

△ Municipal Bord du Lac

📞 04 76 06 67 00, http://campingleborddulac.fr – limited spaces for one-night stay

Address : at Le Petit Bilieu (1.9km west, follow the signs for Charavines, recommended route via the D 50d and D 90)

1,3 ha (81 pitches)

Surroundings : 🐟 ≤ ⌆⌆ △
Leisure activities : 🎣
Facilities : ὅ ⌐ 🏢 🍴 🖼
Nearby : ⚓

GPS	Longitude : 5.5312
	Latitude : 45.44615

There are several different types of sani-station ('borne' in French) – sanitation points providing fresh water and disposal points for grey water. See page 12 for further details.

LES BOSSONS

74400 – Michelin map **328** O5 – alt. 1 005
▶ Paris 614 – Lyon 222 – Annecy 89 – Thonon 99

⛰ Les Deux Glaciers

📞 04 50 53 15 84, www.les2glaciers.com

Address : 80 route des Tissières-les-Bossons (follow the signs for Le Tremplin-Olympique)

1,6 ha (130 pitches)

Rentals : 🚫 – 2 🚐 – 4 🏠.

A pleasant setting near the glaciers.

Surroundings : ❄ ≤ ⌆⌆
Leisure activities : ✗
Facilities : ὅ ⌐ 🏢 🍴 launderette 🚿

GPS	Longitude : 6.83684
	Latitude : 45.90228

BOURDEAUX

26460 – Michelin map **332** D6 – pop. 621 – alt. 426
▶ Paris 608 – Crest 24 – Montélimar 42 – Nyons 40

⛰ Yelloh! Village Les Bois du Châtelas

📞 04 75 00 60 80, www.chatelas.com

Address : route de Dieulefit (1.4km southwest along the D 538)

Opening times : from mid April to mid Sept.

17 ha/7 for camping (80 pitches) terraced, relatively flat, stony, grassy

Tariff : 18€ ✱✱ ⚘ 🔌 💧 (10A) – Extra per person 6€

Rental rates : (from beginning April to mid Sept.) – 3 🚐 88 🏠 – 3 tipis – 8 tent lodges – 1 gîte. Per night from 35 to 201€ Per week from 245 to 1 407€

🚽 borne 1€ – 🚿 💧16€

A panoramic view of the chalets and restaurant.

Surroundings : 🐟 ≤ 🏕
Leisure activities : 🍷✗ 🎱 🏊 hammam,
jacuzzi 🚣 🚴 🎮 🏓 🏐 multi-sports ground
Facilities : ὅ ⌐ 🏢 🍴 🚿 🖼 🍳
Nearby : 🎿 🐎

GPS	Longitude : 5.12783
	Latitude : 44.57832

LE BOURG-D'ARUD

38520 – Michelin map **333** J8
▶ Paris 628 – L'Alpe-d'Huez 25 – Le Bourg-d'Oisans 15 – Les Deux-Alpes 29

⛰ Le Champ du Moulin

📞 04 76 80 07 38, www.champ-du-moulin.com

Address : take the western exit along the D 530

Opening times : from mid Dec. to end April and from beginning June to mid Sept.

1,5 ha (80 pitches) open site, flat, grassy, stony

Tariff : 28,20€ ✱✱ ⚘ 🔌 💧 (10A) – Extra per person 6,10€ – Reservation fee 17€

Rental rates : (from mid Dec. to end April and from beginning June to mid Sept.) – 4 🚐 – 10 🏠 – 2 canvas bungalows. Per night from 42 to 99€ – Per week from 294 to 693€ Reservation fee 17€

🚽 borne – 20 🔌 22,40€ – 🚿 11€

Surrounded by the Oisans mountains and beside the Vénéon river.

Surroundings : ❄ 🐟 🌳
Leisure activities : 🍷✗ 🎱 🏕 🎣
Facilities : ὅ ⌐ 🏢 🍳 🍴 🖼 🚿
At the leisure/activities centre : : 🎿 🎿 🚣
🚣 rafting and canyoning

GPS	Longitude : 6.11986
	Latitude : 44.98596

LE BOURG-D'OISANS

38520 – Michelin map **333** J7 – pop. 3 381 – alt. 720
▶ Paris 614 – Briançon 66 – Gap 95 – Grenoble 52

⛰ Sites et Paysages À la Rencontre du Soleil

📞 04 76 79 12 22, www.alarencontredusoleil.com

Address : route de l'Alpe d'Huez (1.7km to the northeast)

Opening times : Permanent

1,6 ha (73 pitches) flat, grassy

Tariff : 40€ ✱✱ ⚘ 🔌 💧 (10A) – Extra per person 7,80€ – Reservation fee 20€

Rental rates : Permanent 🅿 – 4 caravans – 14 🚐 – 11 🏠. Per week from 230 to 840€ – Reservation fee 20€

🚽 2 🔌 30€ – 🚿 💧16€

Surroundings : ≤ 🏕 ⌆⌆
Leisure activities : ✗ 🎱 🚣 🏊 (open air in season), multi-sports ground
Facilities : ⌐ 🍳 🍴 launderette 🚿

GPS	Longitude : 6.03716
	Latitude : 45.06296

⛰ Les Castels Le Château de Rochetaillée 👥

📞 04 76 11 04 40, www.camping-le-chateau.fr

Address : at Rochetaillée, chemin de Bouthéon

Opening times : from mid May to mid Sept.

2,6 ha (135 pitches) flat, grassy

Tariff : 41,80€ ✱✱ ⚘ 🔌 💧 (10A) – Extra per person 9,30€ – Reservation fee 19€

Rental rates : Permanent – 48 🚐 – 3 🛏. Per night from 54 to 128€ – Per week from 230 to 840€ – Reservation fee 19€

🚽 borne 18€ – 5 🔌 18€ – 🚿 💧18€

Surroundings : ≤ 🏕 ⌆⌆
Leisure activities : 🍷✗ 🎱 🎮 🏓 🎯 🎣 🏊
hammam, jacuzzi 🚣 🚴 🧗 🍴 climbing wall
Facilities : ὅ ⌐ 🍳 🚿 🍴 launderette
🖼 🚿

GPS	Longitude : 6.00512
	Latitude : 45.11543

RCN Belledonne

0476800718, www.rcn-belledonne.fr

Address : at Rochetaillée

Opening times : from end April to mid Sept.

3,5 ha (180 pitches) flat, grassy

Tariff : 44,95€ ✱✱ ⊶ 回 ⚡ (10A) – Extra per person 5,40€
Reservation fee 19,95€

Rental rates : (from mid April to mid Sept.) – 24 ⛺. Per night from 39 to 159€ – Per week from 273 to 1113€ – Reservation fee 19,95€

borne

The whole site is very green with plenty of flowers.

Surroundings : ◁ ♨♨
Leisure activities : ▼ ✗ 🏛 ⊙ ⥈ hammam 🚣 🚲 ✗ 🛶 sports trail
Facilities : ♿ ⊶ ☑ CC 🎏 ♨ launderette 🐟 🚿

Longitude : 6.01095
Latitude : 45.11331

Le Colporteur ♣♣

0476791144, www.camping-colporteur.com

Address : at Le Mas du Plan (south of the town, access via r. de la Piscine)

Opening times : from beginning April to end Sept.

3,3 ha (135 pitches) flat, grassy

Tariff : (2013 Price) ⊶ ⚡ (16A) – Reservation fee 17€

Rental rates : (from beginning April to end Sept.) – 4 caravans 4 ⛺ – 30 🏠. Per night from 26 to 115€ – Per week from 370 to 740 € – Reservation fee 17€

Beside a small river.

Surroundings : 🏞 ◁ 🖿 ♨♨
Leisure activities : ▼ ✗ 🏛 🏃 🚣
Facilities : ♿ ⊶ (season) ♨ 🎏 🚿
Nearby : 🛶 ✗

Longitude : 6.03546
Latitude : 45.0527

La Cascade

0476800242, www.lacascadesarenne.com

Address : located 1.5km to the northeast, follow the signs for L'Alpe-d'Huez, near the Sarennes river

Opening times : from mid Dec. to end Sept.

2,4 ha (140 pitches)

Tariff : (2013 Price) 34,10€ ✱✱ ⊶ 回 ⚡ (16A)
Extra per person 8,40€

Rental rates : (from mid Dec. to end Sept.) ⚞ – 18 🏠. Per night from 54 to 173€ – Per week from 756 to 1091€

Surroundings : ❄ ◁ 🖿 ♨♨
Leisure activities : 🏛 🚣 🛶
Facilities : ⊶ 🎏 ♨ 🚿 🖾

Longitude : 6.03988
Latitude : 45.06446

BOURG-EN-BRESSE

01000 – Michelin map **328** E3 – pop. 39 586 – alt. 251
▶ Paris 424 – Annecy 113 – Besançon 152 – Chambéry 120

Municipal de Challes

0474453721, www.bourgenbresse.fr

Address : 5 allée du Centre Nautique (take northeastern exit following signs for Lons-le-Saunier; by the swimming pool)

Opening times : from beginning April to mid Oct.

1,3 ha (120 pitches)

Tariff : 16,10€ ✱✱ ⊶ 回 ⚡ (6A) – Extra per person 3,50€

---

borne
Pitches are pleasantly shaded.

Surroundings : ♨♨
Leisure activities : ✗
Facilities : ⊶ 🎏 🚿 ♨ 🖾
Nearby : 🛶

Longitude : 5.2403
Latitude : 46.20905

BOURGET-DU-LAC

73370 – Michelin map **333** I4 – pop. 4 277 – alt. 240
▶ Paris 531 – Aix-les-Bains 10 – Annecy 44 – Chambéry 13

International l'Île aux Cygnes

0479250176, www.camping-bourget-lac.fr

Address : 501 boulevard E.Coudurier (located 1km to the north; beside the lake)

Opening times : from end April to end Sept.

2,5 ha (267 pitches)

Tariff : (2013 Price) 22,60€ ✱✱ ⊶ 回 ⚡ (10A) – Extra per person 5€
Reservation fee 15€

Rental rates : (from end April to end Sept.) – 4 ⛺ – 4 🏠. Per night from 91 to 147€ – Per week from 375 to 760€ Reservation fee 15€

borne 2€ – 29 回 5,90€ – ⚡ 12€

The campervan pitches are at the entrance to the campsite.

Surroundings : ◁ ♨♨
Leisure activities : ✗ 🏛 ⊙ daytime 🚣 🚲 ⤳
Facilities : ⊶ ♨ 🎏 🚿 ♨ launderette 🐟 🚿
Nearby : 🖾 ✗ 🏊 🛶 🐟 ⚓ ⚓

Longitude : 5.86308
Latitude : 45.65307

Routes nationales are main roads and their identifying numbers begin with N or RN. Routes départementales are generally quieter roads and begin with D or DN.

BOURG-ST-MAURICE

73700 – Michelin map **333** N4 – pop. 7 650 – alt. 850 – Winter sports : at Les Arcs : 1 600/3 226m
▶ Paris 635 – Albertville 54 – Aosta 79 – Chambéry 103

Le Versoyen

0479070345, www.leversoyen.com

Address : route des Arcs road RD 119 (take the northeastern exit along the N 90, follow the signs for Séez then continue 500m along the turning to the right, near a mountain stream)

Opening times : from end May to end Oct. and mid Dec to mid Apr

3,5 ha (200 pitches)

Tariff : ✱ 5,60€ ⊶ 1€ 回 5,10€ – ⚡ (10A) 5,80€ – Reservation fee 10€

Rental rates : (from end May to end Sept. and mid Dec to mid April) ⚞ – 2 caravans – 11 ⛺. Per night from 35 to 65€ Per week from 200 to 550€ – Reservation fee 10€

borne 3€ – 20 回 15,20€

A free shuttle service to the funicular railway.

Surroundings : ❄ 🏞 ◁ ♀
Leisure activities : 🏛 🚣
Facilities : ⊶ 🎏 ♨ launderette
At the leisure/activities park : ✗ 🖿 🛶 🛶 🐎 sports trail

Longitude : 6.78373
Latitude : 45.6221

BOUT-DU-LAC

74210 – Michelin map **328** K6
▶ Paris 553 – Albertville 29 – Annecy 17 – Megève 43

 International du Lac Bleu

✆ 0450443018, www.camping-lac-bleu.com

Address : route de la Plage (follow the signs for Albertville)

3,3 ha (221 pitches)

Rentals : ✂ – 32 🚐 .

A pleasant location beside the lake (beach).

Surroundings : ⇐ ⌑ ♡♡ ⚠
Leisure activities : ♟ ✗ 🌳 🚣
Facilities : ♿ ☛ ♨ ⁗ launderette ⚲
Nearby : ⛱ ✗ ♏ 🎣 🛶 ⚓ paragliding

G P S Longitude : 6.21648 Latitude : 45.79103

*The Michelin classification (⛰⛰⛰ ... ⛰) is totally
independent of the official star classification system
awarded by the local prefecture or other official
organisation.*

BRAMANS

73500 – Michelin map **333** N6 – pop. 388 – alt. 1 200
▶ Paris 673 – Albertville 100 – Briançon 71 – Chambéry 113

 Municipal Le Val d'Ambin

✆ 0479050305, www.camping-bramansvanoise.com

Address : 602 route de l'église (700m northeast - access is
recommended via Le Verney, on the N6)

Opening times : from end April to end Oct.

4 ha (166 pitches) open site, undulating, terraced, flat, grassy, pond

Tariff : 16,10€ ✴ ✴ 🚐 🔲 ⚡ (8A) – Extra per person 3,40€

Rental rates : Permanent – 1 caravan – 10 🏠 – 5 tent lodges.
Per night from 34 to 150€ – Per week from 175 to 675€

🚰 borne 2€

In an attractive panoramic location.

Surroundings : 🏞 ⇐
Leisure activities : 🎱 🚴 ✗
Facilities : ♿ ☛ (July–Aug.) ⁙ 🚿 ⁗ ⁗ launderette

G P S Longitude : 6.78144 Latitude : 45.22787

BRIDES-LES-BAINS

73570 – Michelin map **333** M5 – pop. 560 – alt. 580
▶ Paris 612 – Albertville 32 – Annecy 77 – Chambéry 81

⛰ La Piat

✆ 0479552274, www.camping-brideslesbains.com

Address : avenue du Comte Greyfié de Bellecombe

Opening times : from mid April to mid Oct.

2 ha (60 pitches)

Tariff : 15,20€ ✴ ✴ 🚐 🔲 ⚡ (10A) – Extra per person 3,40€

Rental rates : (from mid April to mid Oct.) – 5 🚐 . Per night
from 32 to 46€ – Per week from 222 to 322€

🚰 borne 2,50€

Surroundings : ⇐ ♀
Facilities : ♿ ☛ ⁙ 🚿 ⁗ launderette

G P S Longitude : 6.56172 Latitude : 45.453

BUIS-LES-BARONNIES

26170 – Michelin map **332** E8 – pop. 2 291 – alt. 365
▶ Paris 685 – Carpentras 39 – Nyons 29 – Orange 50

 La Fontaine d'Annibal

✆ 0475280312, vacances-baronnies.com

Address : route de Séderon (located 1km to the north, road to the
left just after the bridge over the Ouvèze.)

Opening times : from beginning April to end Oct.

(50 pitches)

Tariff : 23,50€ ✴ ✴ 🚐 🔲 ⚡ (10A) – Extra per person 3,50€

Rental rates : Permanent ♿ – 2 🚐 – 8 🏠 – 26 🛏 – 8 apartments
4 canvas bungalows. Per night from 48 to 110€ – Per week
from 280 to 770€

Surroundings : ⌑ ♀
Leisure activities : 🎱 🚣
Facilities : ♿ ☛ ⁙ 🚿 🚿 🚿 ⁗ launderette
Nearby : ♟ 🎣

G P S Longitude : 5.28187 Latitude : 44.28438

⛰ La Via Natura Les Éphélides

✆ 0475281015, www.ephelides.com

Address : quartier Tuves (1.4km southwest along av. de Rieuchaud)

Opening times : from beginning May to mid Sept.

2 ha (40 pitches)

Tariff : 24,90€ ✴ ✴ 🚐 🔲 ⚡ (16A) – Extra per person 4,70€ –
Reservation fee 12€

Rental rates : (from beginning April to mid Oct.) – 1 caravan
6 🚐 – 5 🏠 . Per night from 35 to 72 € – Per week
from 340 to 660€ – Reservation fee 12€

Shaded by cherry trees, near the Ouvèze. Site welcomes dogs.

Surroundings : 🏞 ⇐ ♀
Leisure activities : ✗ 🚴 🚣
Facilities : ♿ ☛ 🚿 📷
Nearby : ✗ 🐎 skateboarding

G P S Longitude : 5.26793 Latitude : 44.21875

⛰ Domaine de la Gautière

✆ 0475280268, www.camping-lagautiere.com

Address : at La Gautière (5km southwest along the D 5, then take a
right turn)

Opening times : from beginning April to end Oct.

6 ha/3 for camping (40 pitches)

Tariff : 23,10€ ✴ ✴ 🚐 🔲 ⚡ (10A) – Extra per person 5,80€ –
Reservation fee 10€

Rental rates : (from beginning April to end Oct.) – 9 🚐 – 3 🏠 .
Per week from 280 to 750€ – Reservation fee 15€

🚰 borne 3€ – 🔌 10€

Largely shaded by olive trees.

Surroundings : 🏞 ⇐ ♀
Leisure activities : 🎱 🚴 🚣
Facilities : ♿ ☛ 🚿 ⁗ 📷

G P S Longitude : 5.24258 Latitude : 44.2517

*For more information on visiting particular towns or
regions, consult the relevant regional MICHELIN Green
Guide. We also recommend you use the appropriate
Michelin regional map to locate your selected campsite,
to calculate distances and to work out the best route.*

CASTELJAU

07460 – Michelin map **331** H7
▶ Paris 665 – Aubenas 38 – Largentière 28 – Privas 69

▲▲▲ La Rouveyrolle

🕿 0475390067, www.campingrouveyrolle.fr – limited spaces for one-night stay

Address : hamlet : La Rouveyrolle (to the east of the village)

Opening times : from beginning April to end Oct.

3 ha (100 pitches)

Tariff : (2013 Price) 33,90€ ✦✦ 🚐 🗐 ⚡ (6A) – Extra per person 9€
Reservation fee 25€

Rental rates : (2013 Price) (from beginning April to end Oct.)
64 🚐. Per night from 90 to 157€ – Per week from 245 to 1106€
Reservation fee 25€

Plenty of space in a natural setting beside the river, a range of well-equipped and high-quality mobile homes, but also some rather old sanitary facilities.

Surroundings : 🌊 ⌂ ♨♨
Leisure activities : ▾ ✗ 🏛 🛶 🦺 jacuzzi
🛥 🎣 🎳 🏓
Facilities : 🚿 ☡ ⚑ launderette 🗑 🚿

GPS Longitude : 4.22222
Latitude : 44.39583

▲▲ Bel Air (mobile home rentals only)

🕿 0475393639, www.camping-belair-ardeche.com

Address : at Les Tournaires (500m to the north, follow the signs for Chaulet-Plage)

Opening times : from beginning April to mid Nov.

1,5 ha (60 pitches)

Rental rates : 37 🚐. Per night 85€ – Per week 990€
🚐 borne 19€

A mobile home park, some very well equipped and some owner-occupiers, sometimes located a little too close together.

Surroundings : 🌊 ♨♨
Leisure activities : ▾ ✗ 🏛 🦺
Facilities : 🚿 ☡ ⚑ 🗑 🚿
Nearby : 🎳 🎣

GPS Longitude : 4.21574
Latitude : 44.4006

▲ Chaulet Plage

🕿 0475393027, www.chaulet-plage.com

Address : Terres du Moulin (600m to the north, follow the signs for Chaulet-Plage)

1,5 ha (62 pitches)

Rentals : 6 🏠 – 6 apartments – military tents.

Pitches on terraces that descend to the snackbar beside the Chassezac river.

Surroundings : 🌊 ♨♨
Leisure activities : ▾ ✗ 🎳 🎣 🏓
Facilities : 🚿 ☡ ⚑ launderette 🗑 🚿

GPS Longitude : 4.21528
Latitude : 44.40453

▲ Le Pousadou

🕿 0475390405, www.pousadou.fr

Address : Domaine de Cassagnole, at Les Tournaires

Opening times : from beginning April to end Sept.

23 ha/1,7 (52 pitches) flat, grassy

Tariff : 24€ ✦✦ 🚐 🗐 ⚡ (10A) – Extra per person 2€

In the heart of the domain vineyards, near the river; reception is in the cellar.

Surroundings : 🌊 ≤ ♨♨
Leisure activities : 🎳 🎣
Facilities : 🚿 ⚑ – 52 individual sanitary facilities (🚿 🗑 🚽 wc) 🚰

GPS Longitude : 4.21788
Latitude : 44.40158

CHABEUIL

26120 – Michelin map **332** D4 – pop. 6 568 – alt. 212
▶ Paris 569 – Crest 21 – Die 59 – Romans-sur-Isère 18

▲▲ FranceLoc Le Grand Lierne

🕿 0475598314, www.grandlierne.com 🚫 (July–Aug.)

Address : 5km northeast along the D 68, follow the signs for Peyrus, turn left onto D 125 and turn right onto D 143 – from A 7, Valence-Sud exit towards Grenoble

Opening times : from end April to mid Sept.

3,6 ha (216 pitches)

Tariff : 39€ ✦✦ 🚐 🗐 ⚡ (10A) – Extra per person 7€ – Reservation fee 27€

Rental rates : (from end April to mid Sept.) 🚫 – 173 🚐
6 🏠 – 8 tent lodges. Per night from 37 to 166€ – Per week from 147 to 1211€ – Reservation fee 27€
🚐 borne

Numerous rental options and pitches for tents and caravans in a wooded setting, with facilities suitable for families.

Surroundings : 🌊 ⌂ ♨♨
Leisure activities : ▾ ✗ 🏛 🎲 🦺 🚲 🎯
🛥 🎣 🏓
Facilities : 🚿 ☡ 🚿 ⚑ launderette 🗑 🚿
refrigerated food storage facilities

GPS Longitude : 5.065
Latitude : 44.91572

The prices listed were supplied by the campsite owners in 2013 (if prices were not available, those from the previous year are given). The fees should be regarded as basic charges and may fluctuate with inflation.

CHALLES-LES-EAUX

73190 – Michelin map **333** I4 – pop. 5 073 – alt. 310 – ♨
▶ Paris 566 – Albertville 48 – Chambéry 6 – Grenoble 52

▲▲ Municipal le Savoy

🕿 0479729731, www.camping-challesleseaux.com

Address : avenue du Parc (take the r. Denarié, 100m from the N 6)

Opening times : from beginning April to end Sept.

2,8 ha (88 pitches)

Tariff : ✦ 4€ 🚐 1,75€ 🗐 5€ – ⚡ (10A) 3,30€
Rental rates : (from beginning April to end Sept.) – 2 🚐 – 6 🏠
3 canvas bungalows. Per night from 35 to 80€ – Per week from 205 to 530€ – Reservation fee 15€
🚐 borne – 22 🗐 17,30€

Pretty pitches lined with hedges, near a small lake.

Surroundings : ⌂ ♨
Leisure activities : 🏛 🦺 🚲
Facilities : 🚿 ☡ 🚿 🚰 🚽 🗑
Nearby : 🍴 🎳

GPS Longitude : 5.98418
Latitude : 45.55152

CHAMONIX-MONT-BLANC

74400 – Michelin map **328** O5 – pop. 9 054 – alt. 1 040
▶ Paris 610 – Albertville 65 – Annecy 97 – Aosta 57

⚠ L'Île des Barrats

☎ 04 50 53 51 44, www.campingdesbarrats.com – ⛺

Address : 185 chemin de l'Île des Barrats (to the southwest of the town, 150m from the Arve river)

Opening times : from beginning June to mid Sept.

0,8 ha (56 pitches)

Tariff : 31€ ✶✶ ⬅ 🅴 🅗 (10A) – Extra per person 6,50€

Rental rates : (from mid Dec. to mid Sept.) ⬚ – 4 🏠. Per week from 700 to 1 €

⛽ borne 8€

Surroundings : ⟨ Mont Blanc mountain range and glaciers ⌐ ♀
Leisure activities : 🎿
Facilities : ♿ ⊶ ⬚ ⬚ ⬚ laundrette

Longitude : 6.86135
Latitude : 45.91463

CHAMPDOR

01110 – Michelin map **328** G4 – pop. 462 – alt. 833
▶ Paris 486 – Ambérieu-en-Bugey 38 – Bourg-en-Bresse 51 – Hauteville-Lompnes 6

⚠ Municipal le Vieux Moulin

☎ 06 50 54 28 98, www.champdor.jimdo.com

Address : route de Corcelles (800m northwest along the D 57a)

Opening times : Permanent

1,6 ha (62 pitches) flat, grassy

Tariff : (2013 Price) 14,70€ ✶✶ ⬅ 🅴 🅗 (12A) – Extra per person 3,30€

Rental rates : Permanent ⬚ – 2 yurts – 1 gîte. Per night from 60€ Per week from 280 to 340€

⛽ borne

In the Le Bugey hills close to natural lakes – one for swimming, one for fishing.

Surroundings : ⟨ ⟨
Leisure activities : 🎿 ⟵
Facilities : ♿ ⊶ (July-Aug.) ⬚ ⬚ ⬚
Nearby : ✕ ⬚ (pool) ⟨

Longitude : 5.59138
Latitude : 46.023

CHANAZ

73310 – Michelin map **333** H3 – pop. 510 – alt. 232
▶ Paris 521 – Aix-les-Bains 21 – Annecy 53 – Bellegarde-sur-Valserine 44

⚠ Municipal des Îles

☎ 04 79 54 58 51, www.campingdechanaz.fr – limited spaces for one-night stay

Address : at base de Loisirs (leisure centre), located 1km west along the D 921, follow the signs for Culoz and take road to the left after the bridge, 300m from the Rhône (small lake and marina)

1,5 ha (103 pitches)

Rentals : 18 🏠.

Near a picturesque village and the Canal de Savière.

Surroundings : ⟨ ♀
Leisure activities : 🎿
Facilities : ♿ ⊶ ⬚ ⬚ ⬚ ⬚
Nearby : ⬚ ✕ ⟵ ⬚ ⬚ (small swimming pool) ⟨ ⚓

Longitude : 5.79378
Latitude : 45.8091

CHANCIA

01590 – Michelin map **321** D8 – pop. 237 – alt. 320
▶ Paris 452 – Bourg-en-Bresse 48 – Lons-le-Saunier 46 – Nantua 30

⚠ Municipal les Cyclamens

☎ 04 74 75 82 14, www.camping-chancia.com – limited spaces for one-night stay

Address : La Presqu'île (located 1.5km southwest along the D 60e and take road to the left, where the Ain and the Bienne rivers meet)

2 ha (155 pitches) flat, grassy

On a tiny peninsula in the Lac de Coiselet; a rural site surrounded by beautiful cliffs.

Surroundings : ⟨ ⟨ ♀
Leisure activities : 🎿 ⟵
Facilities : ♿ ⊶ ⬚ ⬚ launderette
Nearby : ⬚ ⟨ ⚓

Longitude : 5.6311
Latitude : 46.34203

To visit a town or region, use the MICHELIN Green Guides.

CHARAVINES

38850 – Michelin map **333** G5 – pop. 1 758 – alt. 500
▶ Paris 534 – Belley 47 – Chambéry 49 – Grenoble 40

⚠ Les Platanes

☎ 04 76 06 64 70, www.camping-lesplatanes.com

Address : 85 rue du Camping (take the northern exit along the D 50d, 150m from the lake)

1 ha (67 pitches) flat, grassy

Rentals : ⬚ – 10 🏠.

Surroundings : ♀♀
Leisure activities : ✕ 🎿
Facilities : ♿ ⊶ ⬚ ⬚ ⬚
Nearby : ⬚ ✕ ⬚ (beach) ⟨ ⚓ pedalos

Longitude : 5.51545
Latitude : 45.43096

CHASSAGNES

07140 – Michelin map **331** H7
▶ Paris 644 – Lyon 209 – Privas 67 – Nîmes 85

⛰ Domaine des Chênes

☎ 04 75 37 37 37 35, www.domaine-des-chenes.fr – limited spaces for one-night stay

Address : at Chassagnes Haut

Opening times : from beginning April to end Sept.

2,5 ha (122 pitches) flat, grassy, stony

Tariff : 32€ ✶✶ ⬅ 🅴 🅗 (10A) – Extra per person 6€ – Reservation fee 25€

Rental rates : (from beginning April to end Sept.) – 45 🏠. Per night from 37 to 180€ – Per week from 259 to 1260€ Reservation fee 25€

⛽ borne 19€

Varied rental options, including some high-quality mobile homes, some owner-occupiers, and pitches for tents and caravans.

Surroundings : ⟨ ⟨ ⌐ ♀♀
Leisure activities : ⬚ ✕ 🎿 ⟵ ⬚ hammam, jacuzzi ⬚
Facilities : ♿ ⊶ ⬚ ⬚ ⬚
Nearby : ⬚

Longitude : 4.13218
Latitude : 44.39899

⚤ Lou Rouchétou

✆ 0475373313, www.lou-rouchetou.com

Address : at Chassagnes bas (follow the signs for Les Vans along the D 104)

1,5 ha (120 pitches)

Rentals : 20 🚐.

Plenty of natural spaces around the pitches.

Surroundings : 🛶 ≤ 𝟢𝟢
Leisure activities : ♈ ✕ ⚓ ⛵ 🏊
Facilities : ⅋ ⊶ 🚾 🍳 🧺 🗑 🚿
Nearby : ♒

GPS Longitude : 4.17125
Latitude : 44.41087

CHASSIERS

07110 – Michelin map **331** H6 – pop. 1 008 – alt. 340
▶ Paris 643 – Aubenas 16 – Largentière 4 – Privas 48

⚤ Sunêlia Domaine Les Ranchisses ♣♠

✆ 0475883197, www.lesranchisses.fr

Address : route de Rocher (1.6km to the northwest, access via the D 5, follow the signs for Valgorge)

Opening times : from mid April to end Sept.

6 ha (226 pitches) terraced, flat and relatively flat, grassy

Tariff : 49€ ♈♈ 🚐 🔲 🚰 (10A) – Extra per person 10€ – Reservation fee 15€

Rental rates : (from mid April to end Sept.) – 101 🚐 – 3 gîtes. Per night from 37 to 192€ – Per week from 259 to 1344€ Reservation fee 30€

🚰 borne

In 2 separate sections on either side of the road, linked by a tunnel. Choose the more peaceful pitches near the river with better shade. Well-equipped spa area.

Surroundings : ⛺ 𝟢𝟢 ⛰
Leisure activities : ♈ ✕ ⚓ 🎯 🏹 🎿 hammam, jacuzzi ⚓ ✂ 🎱 🏊 🏊 ⚓ ♒ multi-sports ground, spa centre, skate park
Facilities : ⅋ ⊶ 🚾 🍳 🚿 🍳 🍴 launderette 🗑 🚿

GPS Longitude : 4.28536
Latitude : 44.56137

CHÂTEAUNEUF-DE-GALAURE

26330 – Michelin map **332** C2 – pop. 1 557 – alt. 253
▶ Paris 531 – Annonay 29 – Beaurepaire 19 – Romans-sur-Isère 27

⚤ Iris Parc Le Château de Galaure

✆ 0475686522, www.chateaudegalaure.com

Address : route de St-Vallier (800m southwest along the D 51)

Opening times : from end April to end Sept.

12 ha (400 pitches) flat, grassy

Tariff : 39€ ♈♈ 🚐 🔲 🚰 (6A) – Extra per person 7,50€

Rental rates : (from end April to end Sept.) – 148 🚐 105 canvas bungalows. Per night from 25 to 141€ – Per week from 120 to 987€ – Reservation fee 20€

A pleasant, lush, green site and plenty of shade.

Surroundings : 𝟢𝟢
Leisure activities : ♈ ✕ ⚓ 🎯 ⚓ 🏊 🎿 skateboarding
Facilities : ⅋ ⊶ 🚾 🍳 🗑 🚿 🚿
Nearby : ✂ 🎱 ♒ fitness trail

GPS Longitude : 4.95644
Latitude : 45.23029

CHÂTEAUNEUF-SUR-ISÈRE

26300 – Michelin map **332** C3 – pop. 3 707 – alt. 118
▶ Paris 561 – Lyon 98 – Valence 13 – Privas 55

⚤ Sunêlia Le Soleil Fruité ♣♠

✆ 0475841970, www.lesoleilfruite.com ✂ (from beginning July to end Aug)

Address : at Les Pêches (4km, take exit 14 Valence Nord towards Châteauneuf sur Isère, continue along the D 877; near the "Les Folies du Lac" cabaret)

Opening times : from end April to mid Sept.

4 ha (138 pitches) flat, grassy

Tariff : 33,90€ ♈♈ 🚐 🔲 🚰 (10A) – Extra per person 7,80€ Reservation fee 16€

Rental rates : (from end April to mid Sept.) ✂ – 34 🚐. Per week from 294 to 896€ – Reservation fee 16€

🚰 borne 3€

Surroundings : 🛶 ⛺ 𝟢
Leisure activities : ♈ ✕ ⚓ 🎯 🎣 🎿 🏹 🎿
Facilities : ⊶ 🍳 🍴 launderette 🗑 🚿

GPS Longitude : 4.89372
Latitude : 44.99707

These symbols are used for a campsite that is exceptional in its category:

⚤ ... ⚤   *Particularly pleasant setting, quality and range of services available*

🛶🛶   *Tranquil, isolated site – quiet site, particularly at night*

≤≤   *Exceptional view – interesting or panoramic view*

CHÂTEL

74390 – Michelin map **328** O3 – pop. 1 213 – alt. 1 180 – Winter sports : 1 200/2 100m
▶ Paris 578 – Annecy 113 – Évian-les-Bains 34 – Morzine 38

⚤ L'Oustalet ♣♠

✆ 0450732197, www.oustalet.com – alt. 1 110

Address : 1428 route des Freinets (head 2km southwest following the signs for Le Col de Bassachaux; beside the Dranse river)

Opening times : from mid Junee to beginning Sept. and from mid Dec to mid Apr

3 ha (100 pitches)

Tariff : 35€ ♈♈ 🚐 🔲 🚰 (6A) – Extra per person 6,20€ – Reservation fee 10€

Rental rates : (from mid Junee to beginning Sept. and from mid Dec. to mid April) ✂ – 16 🚐 – 1 apartment. Per night from 65 to 120€ – Per week from 380 to 730€ – Reservation fee 10€

🚰 borne 6€ – 14 🔲

A pleasant location in the Vallée d'Abondance.

Surroundings : ❄ ≤
Leisure activities : ♈ ⚓ 🎯 daytime 🎯 🚠 ⚓ ✂ 🎱 🏊
Facilities : ⅋ ⊶ 🏧 🍳 🍴 launderette
Nearby : ✕ 🚿 🚲 ⛷

GPS Longitude : 6.82981
Latitude : 46.25755

LE CHÂTELARD

73630 – Michelin map **333** J3 – pop. 645 – alt. 750
▶ Paris 562 – Aix-les-Bains 30 – Annecy 30 – Chambéry 35

⚠ Les Cyclamens

☏ 0479548019, www.camping-cyclamens.com

Address : head towards the northwestern exit and take road to the left, follow the signs for Le Champet

Opening times : from beginning April to end Oct.

0,7 ha (34 pitches) flat, grassy

Tariff : (2013 Price) ♦ 3,80€ ⇔ 🚗 5€ – (½) (10A) 3,10€ – Reservation fee 4€

Rental rates : (from beginning April to end Oct.) – 1 cabin in the trees. Per night from 75 to 95€ – Per week from 525 to 600€

🚐 borne 4€ – 2 🗐 12,60€

Surroundings : 🏞 ⩽ ♨♨
Leisure activities : 🏛 ⛵
Facilities : ♿ ⚡ 🚿 ♨🍴 🗐

GPS	Longitude : 6.13263
	Latitude : 45.68782

CHÂTILLON-EN-DIOIS

26410 – Michelin map **332** F5 – pop. 561 – alt. 570
▶ Paris 637 – Die 14 – Gap 79 – Grenoble 97

🏔 VivaCamp le Lac Bleu

☏ 0475218530, www.lacbleu-diois.com

Address : quartier la Touche (4km southwest along the D 539, follow the signs for Die and take D 140, follow the signs for Menglon, take road to the left before the bridge)

9 ha/3 for camping (90 pitches) flat, grassy, stony

Rentals : 77 🛖 – 77 🏠 – 9 canvas bungalows.

Surroundings : ⩽ ♀ ⛰
Leisure activities : 🍴✗ 🏛 🏊 🏃 jacuzzi ⛵ 🎣 🚣 ✈
Facilities : ♿ ⚡ 🚿 ♨🍴 🗐 🌊 🚗

GPS	Longitude : 5.45332
	Latitude : 44.68457

CHÂTILLON-SUR-CHALARONNE

01400 – Michelin map **328** C4 – pop. 4 899 – alt. 177
▶ Paris 418 – Bourg-en-Bresse 28 – Lyon 55 – Mâcon 28

🏔 Municipal du Vieux Moulin

☏ 0474550479, www.camping-vieuxmoulin.com – limited spaces for one-night stay

Address : rue Jean Jaurès (take southeastern exit along the D 7, follow the signs for Chalamont; beside the Chalaronne, 150m from a lake - direct access)

Opening times : from beginning May to end Sept.

3 ha (140 pitches) flat, grassy

Tariff : (2013 Price) ♦ 4,99€ ⇔ 🚗 2,70€ 🗐 4,37€ – (½) (10A) 4,37€ Reservation fee 10,40€

Rental rates : (from beginning May to end Sept.) – 5 🏠. Per week from 318 to 435€ – Reservation fee 10,40€

🚐 borne 5,62€ – 19 🗐 17€

In a shaded green setting beside a river.

Surroundings : 🏞 ♀♀
Leisure activities : 🏛 ⛵🏃 🏐 multi-sports ground
Facilities : ♿ ⚡ ♨🍴 🗐
Nearby : 🍴✗ 🎣 🚣 🏊

GPS	Longitude : 4.96228
	Latitude : 46.11654

CHAUZON

07120 – Michelin map **331** I7 – pop. 341 – alt. 128
▶ Paris 649 – Aubenas 20 – Largentière 14 – Privas 51

🏔 La Digue

☏ 0475396357, www.camping-la-digue.fr – access difficult for caravans

Address : at Les Aires (located 1km east of the town, 100m from the Ardèche river (direct access)

Opening times : from beginning April to end Sept.

7 ha/3 for camping (141 pitches) terraced, flat, grassy

Tariff : (2013 Price) 36,90€ ♦♦ ⇔ 🗐 (½) (10A) Extra per person 7,50€ – Reservation fee 11€

Rental rates : (from beginning April to end Sept.) – 37 🛖 8 🏠. Per night from 35 to 140€ – Per week from 249 to 979€ Reservation fee 11€

Shady pitches, some good quality mobile home rentals.

Surroundings : 🏞 ♀♀
Leisure activities : 🍴✗ 🏃 🏐 🎣 🚣 ⛵
Facilities : ♿ ⚡ 🛏 ♨🍴 🗐 🌊

GPS	Longitude : 4.37337
	Latitude : 44.48437

LE CHEYLARD

07160 – Michelin map **331** I4 – pop. 3 289 – alt. 450
▶ Paris 598 – Aubenas 50 – Lamastre 21 – Privas 47

⚠ Municipal Le Cheylard

☏ 0475290953, www.camping-le-cheylard.com

Address : at Le Vialon

Opening times : from beginning April to end Sept.

1,5 ha (61 pitches) flat and relatively flat, grassy

Tariff : 13,50€ ♦♦ ⇔ 🗐 (½) (3A) – Extra per person 3€

Rental rates : (from beginning April to end Sept.) 🚫 – 1 🛖 4 canvas bungalows – 1 gîte. Per night from 45 to 85€ – Per week from 170 to 500€

Surroundings : 🏞 ♀♀
Facilities : ♿ ⚡ 🍴 🗐 🚗

GPS	Longitude : 4.42011
	Latitude : 44.9155

CHORANCHE

38680 – Michelin map **333** F7 – pop. 132 – alt. 280
▶ Paris 588 – La Chapelle-en-Vercors 24 – Grenoble 52 – Romans-sur-Isère 32

🏔 Le Gouffre de la Croix

☏ 0476360713, www.camping-choranche.com 🚫 (July-Aug.)

Address : at Combe Bernard (to the southeast of the town, follow the signs for Chatelas; beside the Bourne river)

Opening times : from mid May to mid Sept.

2,5 ha (52 pitches) open site, terraced, flat, grassy

Tariff : 23,50€ ♦♦ ⇔ 🗐 (½) (6A) – Extra per person 4,50€ Reservation fee 22,50€

Rental rates : (from mid May to mid Sept.) 🚫 – 2 🛖 – 2 🏠. Per week from 330 to 470€ – Reservation fee 22,50€

In a natural wooded setting at the bottom of the valley.

Surroundings : 🏞 ⩽♀♀
Leisure activities : 🍴 🚣 🏐
Facilities : ♿ ⚡ 🚿 ♨ 🗐

GPS	Longitude : 5.39447
	Latitude : 45.06452

LA CLUSAZ

74220 – Michelin map **328** L5 – pop. 1 876 – alt. 1 040 – Winter sports : 1 100/2 600m
▶ Paris 564 – Albertville 40 – Annecy 32 – Bonneville 26

⚠ FranceLoc Le Plan du Fernuy

✆ 04 50 02 44 75, www.franceloc.fr

Address : 1800 route des Confins (located 1.5km to the east)

Opening times : from mid Dec. to end April and from mid Junee to mid Sept.

1,3 ha (80 pitches) terraced, relatively flat, grassy, gravelled

Tariff : 33€ ✸✸ 🚗 🔲 🔌 (13A) – Extra per person 6€ – Reservation fee 27€

Rental rates : (from mid Dec. to end April and from mid Junee to mid Sept.) 🏠 – 18 🚐 – 12 🏡 – 1 studio – 3 apartments. Per night from 61 to 110€ – Per week from 299 to 2240€ Reservation fee 27€

🚰 borne 10€

An attractive indoor swimming pool and pleasant location at the foot of Les Aravis mountains.

Surroundings : ❄ ⛷ ⇐ 🗭 💧
Leisure activities : 🍽 🛋 🛶 🖼
Facilities : ♿ ☎ 🎫 🅿 🚿 🚮 🍴 launderette

G P S	Longitude : 6.45174
	Latitude : 45.90948

The pitches of many campsites are marked out with low hedges of attractive bushes and shrubs.

CORDELLE

42123 – Michelin map **327** D4 – pop. 896 – alt. 450
▶ Paris 409 – Feurs 35 – Roanne 14 – St-Just-en-Chevalet 27

⚠ De Mars

✆ 04 77 64 94 42, www.camping-de-mars.com

Address : Presqu'ile de Mars (4.5km south along the D 56 and take the road to the right)

Opening times : from beginning April to mid Oct.

1,2 ha (63 pitches) terraced, flat and relatively flat, grassy

Tariff : 28,50€ ✸✸ 🚗 🔲 🔌 (10A) – Extra per person 7,80€ – Reservation fee 14€

Rental rates : (from mid April to mid Oct.) ♿ (1 mobile home) 12 🚐 – 2 🏡 – 2 canvas bungalows. Per night from 45 to 110€ Per week from 315 to 770€ – Reservation fee 14€

🚰 47 🔲 28,50€ – 🛒 14€

In an attractive location overlooking the Loire river gorges.

Surroundings : ⛰ ⇐ 🗭 💧
Leisure activities : 🍽 🗙 🛋 🛶 🚲 🛫
Facilities : ♿ ☎ 🎫 🚿 🚮 🍴 launderette 🛁
Nearby : 🛶

G P S	Longitude : 4.06101
	Latitude : 45.91668

The Michelin classification (⚠⚠⚠ ... ⚠) is totally independent of the official star classification system awarded by the local prefecture or other official organisation.

CORMORANCHE-SUR-SAÔNE

01290 – Michelin map **328** B3 – pop. 1 051 – alt. 172
▶ Paris 399 – Bourg-en-Bresse 44 – Châtillon-sur-Chalaronne 23 – Mâcon 10

⚠ Le Lac

✆ 03 85 23 97 10, www.lac-cormoranche.com

Address : at Les Luizants (take the western exit along the D 51a and continue 1.2km along the turning to the right; at the leisure and activity park)

Opening times : from beginning May to end Sept.

48 ha/4,5 for camping (117 pitches) flat, grassy, sandy, wood

Tariff : 20,80€ ✸✸ 🚗 🔲 🔌 (10A) – Extra per person 5,35€ Reservation fee 6€

Rental rates : (from beginning May to end Sept.) 🏠 – 9 🚐 12 🏡 – 4 tipis. Per night from 43 to 95€ – Per week from 158 to 565€ – Reservation fee 6€

🚰 borne

Trees and shrubs surround the pitches, near a small but pretty lake.

Surroundings : 🗭 💧
Leisure activities : 🍽 🗙 🛶 🚲 🎣 🏊 (beach) 🎏 🎱 entertainment room
Facilities : ♿ ☎ 🚿 🚮 🍴 launderette 🛁

G P S	Longitude : 4.82573
	Latitude : 46.25105

Key to rentals symbols:

12 🚐	Number of mobile homes
20 🏡	Number of chalets
6 🛏	Number of rooms to rent
Per night 30–50€	Minimum/maximum rate per night
Per week 300–1,000€	Minimum/maximum rate per week

CREST

26400 – Michelin map **332** D5 – pop. 7 857 – alt. 196
▶ Paris 585 – Die 37 – Gap 129 – Grenoble 114

⚠ Les Clorinthes 👥

✆ 04 75 25 05 28, www.lesclorinthes.com

Address : quai Soubeyran (take the southern exit along the D 538 then take the road to the left after the bridge, near the Drôme river and the sports centre)

Opening times : from end April to mid Sept.

4 ha (160 pitches)

Tariff : 24,40€ ✸✸ 🚗 🔲 🔌 (6A) – Extra per person 6,90€ Reservation fee 21€

Rental rates : (from end April to mid Sept.) – 10 🚐 – 4 🏡 2 canvas bungalows. Per night from 50 to 70€ – Per week from 329 to 672€ – Reservation fee 21€

Surroundings : ⇐ 💧
Leisure activities : 🍽 🗙 🛋 🕹 daytime 🏃 🛶 🚲 🏊
Facilities : ♿ ☎ 🚿 🍴 launderette
Nearby : 🍴 🐎

G P S	Longitude : 5.0277
	Latitude : 44.724

CUBLIZE

69550 – Michelin map **327** F3 – pop. 1 242 – alt. 452

▶ Paris 422 – Amplepuis 7 – Chauffailles 29 – Roanne 30

⚑ Campéole le Lac des Sapins

✆ 0474895283, www.campinglacdessapins.com – limited spaces for one-night stay

Address : rue du Lac (800m to the south; beside the Reins stream and 300m from the lake (direct access)

Opening times : from beginning April to end Sept.

4 ha (174 pitches) flat, grassy

Tariff : (2013 Price) 22€ ♦♦ ⇌ 🗉 ⚡ (6A)

Rental rates : (2013 Price) (from beginning April to end Sept.) 24 🚐 – 26 🏠 – 6 tent lodges. Per night from 55 to 140€ Per week from 399 to 896€

🚽 borne

Surroundings : 🏞 ≤ 🗔	
Leisure activities : 🚣🚴✂ multi-sports ground	**G P S** Longitude : 4.37849
Facilities : ♿ ⚡ 🛁 ✂ ▾ 🚿 launderette	Latitude : 46.0132
At the leisure/activities centre : 🏋 🏊 🏄	

CULOZ

01350 – Michelin map **328** H5 – pop. 2 920 – alt. 248

▶ Paris 512 – Aix-les-Bains 24 – Annecy 55 – Bourg-en-Bresse 88

⚑ Le Colombier

✆ 0479871900, http://camping.colombier.free.fr

Address : Ile de Verbaou (1.3km east, at junction of D 904 and D 992; beside a stream)

1,5 ha (81 pitches)

Rentals : 5 🚐.

Near a leisure centre.

Surroundings : ≤ 🗔 🌳	
Leisure activities : 🛈 🚣🚴	**G P S** Longitude : 5.79346
Facilities : ♿ ⚡ 🛁 ✂ ▾ 🚿 launderette 🚮	Latitude : 45.85158
Nearby : ✂ 📷 🏋 🏊	

DARBRES

07170 – Michelin map **331** J6 – pop. 252 – alt. 450

▶ Paris 618 – Aubenas 18 – Montélimar 34 – Privas 21

⚑ Les Lavandes

✆ 0475942065, www.les-lavandes-darbres.com

Address : in the village

Opening times : from mid April to end Sept.

1,5 ha (70 pitches) terraced, flat, grassy, stony

Tariff : 28,90€ ♦♦ ⇌ 🗉 ⚡ (6A) – Extra per person 4,20€ Reservation fee 15€

Rental rates : (from mid April to end Sept.) – 12 🏠. Per night from 53 to 59€ – Per week from 260 to 650€ – Reservation fee 15€

Near the centre of the village, with an attractive view from the bar's terrace, swimming pool; some elevated pitches.

Surroundings : 🏞 🌳	
Leisure activities : 🛈 ✗ 🚣 🏊	**G P S** Longitude : 4.50402
Facilities : ⚡ 🛁 🚿 launderette 🚮	Latitude : 44.64701

DARDILLY

69570 – Michelin map **327** H5 – pop. 8 384 – alt. 338

▶ Paris 457 – Lyon 13 – Villeurbanne 21 – Vénissieux 26

⚑ Indigo International Lyon

HUTTOPIA

✆ 0478356455, www.camping-indigo.com

Address : Poroute de Lyon (10km northwest along the N 6, follow the signs for Mâcon – from the A 6, take the Limonest exit)

Opening times : Permanent

6 ha (150 pitches) flat, grassy

Tariff : (2013 Price) 27,75€ ♦♦ ⇌ 🗉 ⚡ (10A) – Extra per person 4,85€ Reservation fee 22€

Rental rates : Permanent – 6 caravans 41 🚐 – 7 tent lodges. Per night from 39 to 108€ – Per week from 191 to 605€ – Reservation fee 22€

🚽 borne 7€

Surroundings : 🌳	
Leisure activities : 🛈 ✗ 🛶 🚣 🏊	**G P S** Longitude : 4.76125
Facilities : ♿ ⚡ 🏪 🛁 🚿 launderette	Latitude : 45.81817

DIE

26150 – Michelin map **332** F5 – pop. 4 357 – alt. 415

▶ Paris 623 – Gap 92 – Grenoble 110 – Montélimar 73

⚑ Le Glandasse

✆ 0475220250, www.camping-glandasse.com

Address : quartier de la Maldrerie (1km southeast along the D 93, follow the signs for Gap then take the road to the right, beside the Drôme river)

Opening times : from mid April to end Sept.

3,5 ha (120 pitches) flat and relatively flat, grassy, stony

Tariff : 25,50€ ♦♦ ⇌ 🗉 ⚡ (10A) – Extra per person 5,50€ Reservation fee 10€

Rental rates : (from mid April to end Sept.) – 2 🚐 – 15 🏠. Per night from 40 to 81€ – Per week from 280 to 567€ Reservation fee 10€

Note for access: maximum height 2.80m.

Surroundings : 🏞 ≤ 🗔 🌳	
Leisure activities : ✗ 🛶 🎣 jacuzzi 🚣 🚴 🏋 🏊 🏓	**G P S** Longitude : 5.38403
Facilities : ♿ ⚡ 🛁 🚿 launderette 🚮	Latitude : 44.73993

⚑ Le Riou Merle

✆ 0475222131, www.camping-lerioumerle.com

Address : route de Romeyer (head north along the D 742)

Opening times : from beginning April to mid Oct.

2,5 ha (97 pitches) flat, grassy

Tariff : 24€ ♦♦ ⇌ 🗉 ⚡ (10A) – Extra per person 5,80€

Rental rates : (from beginning April to mid Oct.) – 9 🚐 – 3 🏠. Per night from 50 to 85€ – Per week from 252 to 600€

🚽 borne

Surroundings : 🗔 🌳	
Leisure activities : 🛈 ✗ 🛶 🏊	**G P S** Longitude : 5.37776
Facilities : ⚡ 📷 🚿 launderette 🚮	Latitude : 44.75441

DIEULEFIT

26220 – Michelin map **332** D6 – pop. 3 028 – alt. 366
▶ Paris 614 – Crest 30 – Montélimar 29 – Nyons 30

⚞ Huttopia Dieulefit

HUTTOPIA

✆ 04 75 54 63 94, www.huttopia.com

Address : quartier d'Espeluche (3km north along the D 540 follow the signs for Bourdeaux then take the road to the left)

Opening times : from mid April to beginning Nov.

17 ha (140 pitches) undulating, flat, grassy

Tariff : 45€ ♟♟ ⟺ 🔲 🄵 (10A)
Extra per person 7,50€ – Reservation fee 22€

Rental rates : (from mid April to beginning Nov.) – 20 🏠 – 20 tent lodges. Per night from 64 to 170€ Per week from 336 to 1190€ – Reservation fee 22€

🚰 borne 7€

Surroundings : ⤳
Leisure activities : ✕ 🏛 ⛵ ⤵
Facilities : ⚷ ⛲ launderette ⤴

GPS Longitude : 5.05826
Latitude : 44.53987

Some information or pricing may have changed since the guide went to press. We recommend you check the price list online in advance or at the entrance to the campsite and enquire about possible restrictions.

⚞ Le Domaine des Grands Prés

✆ 04 75 49 94 36, www.lesgrandspres-dromeprovencale.com

Address : quartier les Grands Prés (take the western exit along the D 540, follow the signs for Montélimar, near the Jabron - direct access to the town along the pedestrian path)

Opening times : from end March to beginning Nov.

1,8 ha (91 pitches) flat, grassy

Tariff : 23€ ♟♟ ⟺ 🔲 🄵 (10A) – Extra per person 7€ – Reservation fee 5€

Rental rates : (from end March to beginning Nov.) – 9 caravans 5 🏠 – 6 yurts – 1 cabin in the trees – 2 tipis – 3 canvas bungalows – 4 tent lodges – 1 gîte. Per night from 35 to 125€ Per week from 199 to 799€ – Reservation fee 5€

Surroundings : ⤳ ≈≈
Leisure activities : 🏛 ⤵
Facilities : ⚷ ⛲ 🏧 ⤴ launderette
Nearby : ✕ ⤵

GPS Longitude : 5.06149
Latitude : 44.52141

There are several different types of sani-station ('borne' in French) – sanitation points providing fresh water and disposal points for grey water. See page 12 for further details.

DIVONNE-LES-BAINS

01220 – Michelin map **328** J2 – pop. 7 926 – alt. 486 – ⚜
▶ Paris 488 – Bourg-en-Bresse 129 – Genève 18 – Gex 9

⚞ Indigo Divonne - Le Fleutron

HUTTOPIA

✆ 04 50 20 01 95, www.camping-indigo.com

Address : 2465 Vie de L'Etraz (3km to the north, after Villard)

8 ha (253 pitches) terraced, flat and relatively flat, stony, grassy

Rentals : 5 caravans – 15 🚐 – 10 🏠 30 tent lodges.

🚰 borne

In a wooded setting with a mountain to the rear.

Surroundings : ⤳ ≈≈
Leisure activities : ♟ ✕ 🏛 🏃 ⛵ ⤵ 🚲 🎾 ⤵
Facilities : ⚷ ⚷ 🏧 ⤴ ⤴ ⛲ launderette ⤴ ⤴

GPS Longitude : 6.1178
Latitude : 46.37137

DOUSSARD

74210 – Michelin map **328** K6 – pop. 3 473 – alt. 456
▶ Paris 555 – Albertville 27 – Annecy 20 – La Clusaz 36

⚞⚞ Campéole la Nublière ♟♟

✆ 04 50 44 33 44, www.campeole.com

Address : 30 allée de la Nublière (located 1.8km to the north)

Opening times : from mid April to end Sept.

9,2 ha (467 pitches)

Tariff : 28€ ♟♟ ⟺ 🔲 🄵 (6A) – Extra per person 7,50€ – Reservation fee 25€

Rental rates : (from mid April to end Sept.) – 56 🚐 – 10 🏠 40 canvas bungalows. Per night from 32 to 94€ – Per week from 274 to 1010€ – Reservation fee 25€

🚰 borne

Pleasant location beside the lake (beach).

Surroundings : ♨ ⚠
Leisure activities : ♟ ✕ 🏃 ⛵ ≈≈ ⤵ entertainment room
Facilities : ⚷ ⚷ ⤴ ⤴ 🄵 🏧 ⤴
Nearby : ⤴ 🎾 🏧 ⤴ ⛵ paragliding

GPS Longitude : 6.21763
Latitude : 45.79014

⚞ La Ferme de Serraz

✆ 04 50 44 30 68, www.campinglaserraz.com

Address : rue de la Poste (in the town, take the eastern exit near the post office)

3,5 ha (197 pitches) flat, grassy
Rental rates : 40 🚐

Surroundings : ≤ ≈≈
Leisure activities : ♟ ✕ 🏛 ⛵ 🚲 ⤵
Facilities : ⚷ ⚷ ⤴ ⤴ ⤴ launderette

GPS Longitude : 6.22588
Latitude : 45.77508

DUINGT

74410 – Michelin map **328** K6 – pop. 891 – alt. 450
▶ Paris 548 – Albertville 34 – Annecy 12 – Megève 48

⛰ Municipal les Champs Fleuris

✆ 0450685731, www.camping-duingt.com

Address : 631 voie Romaine - Les Perris (located 1km west)

Opening times : from mid April to mid Sept.

1,3 ha (112 pitches) terraced, flat and relatively flat, grassy

Tariff : 21,90€ ✶✶ ⟺ 🅴 (4) (10A) – Extra per person 5,80€

Rental rates : (from mid April to mid Sept.) – 6 🚐 – 2 tent lodges. Per night from 60 to 98€ – Per week from 395 to 730€

🚐 borne 4€ – 30 🅴 17,50€

Surroundings : ⟨
Leisure activities :
Facilities : ⛱ ⟿ ⛺ ⛟ launderette

GPS	Longitude : 6.18882
	Latitude : 45.82658

We value your opinion and welcome your feedback.
Do email us at campingfrance@tp.michelin.com

ECLASSAN

07370 – Michelin map **331** K3 – pop. 910 – alt. 420
▶ Paris 534 – Annonay 21 – Beaurepaire 46 – Condrieu 42

⛰ La Via Natura L'Oasis

✆ 0475345623, www.oasisardeche.com – pitches accessed via steep slope, help moving caravans onto and off pitches avilable on request

Address : at Le Petit Chaléat (4.5km northwest, follow the signs for Fourany and take road to the left)

Opening times : from end April to beginning Sept.

4 ha (63 pitches) terraced, flat, grassy, stony

Tariff : (2013 Price) 28€ ✶✶ ⟺ 🅴 (4) (6A) – Extra per person 4€ – Reservation fee 8€

Rental rates : (from end April to beginning Sept.) – 4 🚐 – 12 🏠 4 canvas bungalows – 6 tent lodges. Per night from 28 to 102€ Per week from 232 to 714€ – Reservation fee 8€

Pitches on natural-style terraces, some beside the Ay river.

Surroundings : ⟨
Leisure activities : ⛱
Facilities : ⛱ ⟿

GPS	Longitude : 4.73944
	Latitude : 45.17889

EXCENEVEX

74140 – Michelin map **328** L2 – pop. 988 – alt. 375
▶ Paris 564 – Annecy 71 – Bonneville 42 – Douvaine 9

⛰ Campéole La Pinède

✆ 0450728505, www.camping-lac-leman.info – limited spaces for one-night stay

Address : 10 avenue de la Plage (located 1km southeast along the D 25)

Opening times : from mid April to mid Sept.

12 ha (619 pitches)

Tariff : (2013 Price) ✶ ⟺ 🅴 24,20€ – (4) (16A) 4,30€ – Reservation fee 25€

Rental rates : (from mid April to mid Sept.) – 84 🚐 – 20 🏠 56 canvas bungalows. Per night from 27 to 145€ – Per week from 187 to 1015€– Reservation fee 25€

🚐 borne – 25,70€

Pleasant wooded site close to a beach on Lake Geneva.

Surroundings :
Leisure activities : jacuzzi (open air in season), multi-sports ground
Facilities : ⛱ ⟿ launderette
Nearby : ⟿ pedalos

GPS	Longitude : 6.35799
	Latitude : 46.34543

FARAMANS

38260 – Michelin map **333** D5 – pop. 906 – alt. 375
▶ Paris 518 – Beaurepaire 12 – Bourgoin-Jallieu 35 – Grenoble 60

⛰ Municipal des Eydoches

✆ 0474542178, mairie.faramans@wanadoo.fr – limited spaces for one-night stay

Address : 515 avenue des Marais (take the eastern exit along the D 37, follow the signs for La Côte-St-André)

Opening times : Permanent

1 ha (60 pitches) flat, grassy

Tariff : (2013 Price) ✶ 4€ ⟺ 🅴 5,60€ – (4) (5A) 3,40€

Rental rates : Permanent – 2 🏠. Per night from 60 to 70€ Per week from 220 to 300€

🚐 borne 6,60€ – 2 🅴 12€

Surroundings :
Facilities : ⛱
Nearby :

GPS	Longitude : 5.17563
	Latitude : 45.39348

Michelin classification:

⛰⛰⛰⛰ *Extremely comfortable, equipped to a very high standard*
⛰⛰⛰ *Very comfortable, equipped to a high standard*
⛰⛰ *Comfortable and well equipped*
⛰ *Reasonably comfortable*
⛰ *Satisfactory*

FÉLINES

07340 – Michelin map **331** K2 – pop. 1 475 – alt. 380
▶ Paris 520 – Annonay 13 – Beaurepaire 31 – Condrieu 24

⛰ Bas-Larin

✆ 0475348793, www.camping-bas-larin.com

Address : 88 route de Larin-le-Bas (situated 2km southeast, along the N 82, follow the signs for Serrières and take the road to the right)

Opening times : from end April to beginning Sept.

1,5 ha (67 pitches) terraced, relatively flat to hilly, grassy

Tariff : 21,80€ ✶✶ ⟺ 🅴 (4) (10A) – Extra per person 3,50€

Rental rates : (from beginning April to end Sept.) – 10 🚐 – 1 🏠 3 canvas bungalows. Per night from 40 to 85€ – Per week from 220 to 599€

🚐 10 🅴 18€

The pitches on terraces are well shaded, but choose those furthest away from the road (a former national highway).

Surroundings :
Leisure activities :
Facilities : ⛱

GPS	Longitude : 4.74665
	Latitude : 45.3086

LA FERRIÈRE

38580 – Michelin map **333** J6 – pop. 226 – alt. 926
▶ Paris 613 – Lyon 146 – Grenoble 52 – Chambéry 47

⚑ Neige et Nature

✆ 04 76 45 19 84, www.neige-nature.fr – alt. 900

Address : chemin de Montarmand (to the west of the village; beside the Bréda river)

Opening times : from mid May to mid Sept.

1,2 ha (45 pitches) terraced, flat and relatively flat, grassy

Tariff : 22,70€ ✶✶ 🚗 ▣ ⚡ (10A) – Extra per person 5,90€
Rental rates : Permanent – 2 🚐 – 2 🏠. Per night from 60 to 80€
Per week from 325 to 570€
🚰 borne – 20 ▣ 18,30€
A green, well-kept setting.

Surroundings : ⚵ ≤ ⌂ 👤
Leisure activities : 🏠
Facilities : 🚿 ⚮ 🚻 🏕 ⏚ ℐ 📮 ♨
Nearby : ≋ (pool)

| | Longitude : 6.08331 |
| G P S | Latitude : 45.3184 |

FEURS

42110 – Michelin map **327** E5 – pop. 7 741 – alt. 343
▶ Paris 433 – Lyon 69 – Montbrison 24 – Roanne 38

⚑ Municipal du Palais

✆ 04 77 26 43 41, mairie.camping@feurs.fr –

Address : route de Civens (take the northern exit along the N 82, follow the signs for Roanne and take a right turn)

Opening times : from beginning April to end Oct.

5 ha (385 pitches)

Tariff : (2013 Price) ✶ 3€ 🚗 2,60€ ▣ 3,10€ – ⚡ (16A) 3,50€
🚰 30 ▣ 15,40€
In a peaceful area, just round the corner from the town centre.

Surroundings : 👤👤
Leisure activities : 🏊
Facilities : 🚿 ⚮ 🚻 ⏚ ℐ 🚰 ♨
Nearby : 🍴 🏊

| | Longitude : 4.22572 |
| G P S | Latitude : 45.75429 |

FLEURIE

69820 – Michelin map **327** H2 – pop. 1 250 – alt. 320
▶ Paris 410 – Bourg-en-Bresse 46 – Chauffailles 44 – Lyon 58

⚑ VivaCamp la Grappe Fleurie

✆ 04 74 69 80 07, www.beaujolais-camping.com

Address : rue de la Grappe Fleurie (600m south of the town along the D 119e and take a right turn.)

Opening times : from mid April to mid Oct.

2,5 ha (85 pitches) flat, grassy

Tariff : 29,40€ ✶✶ 🚗 ▣ ⚡ (10A) – Extra per person 6€ – Reservation fee 15€
Rental rates : (from mid April to mid Oct.) – 20 🚐 – 4 🏠 – 2 🛏
3 canvas bungalows. Per night from 45 to 123€ – Per week from 315 to 861€ – Reservation fee 25€
In the heart of a vineyard.

Surroundings : ⚵ ≤ ⌂ 👤
Leisure activities : 🏊 🍴 🏊
Facilities : 🚿 ⚮ ⏚ ℐ launderette
Nearby : 🏊 🍴

| | Longitude : 4.7001 |
| G P S | Latitude : 46.18854 |

LES GETS

74260 – Michelin map **328** N4 – pop. 1 254 – alt. 1 170 – Winter sports : 1 170/2 000m
▶ Paris 579 – Annecy 77 – Bonneville 33 – Chamonix-Mont-Blanc 60

⚑ Le Frêne

✆ 04 50 75 80 60, www.alpensport-hotel.com – alt. 1 315 – 🛒

Address : at Les Cornus (take the southwestern exit along the D 902 then continue 2.3km, following signs for Les Platons to the right)

Opening times : from end June to beginning Sept.

0,3 ha (32 pitches)

Tariff : 26€ ✶✶ 🚗 ▣ ⚡ (4A) – Extra per person 7,50€
🚰 borne 6€

Surroundings : ⚵ ≤ Aiguille du Midi, Mt Blanc mountain range ⌂
Leisure activities : 🏠 🏊 🏊
Facilities : 🚿 ⚮ ⏚ ℐ 🚰 ♨ 📮

| | Longitude : 6.64296 |
| G P S | Latitude : 46.15065 |

GEX

01170 – Michelin map **328** J3 – pop. 9 882 – alt. 626
▶ Paris 490 – Genève 19 – Lons-le-Saunier 93 – Pontarlier 110

⚑ Municipal les Genêts

✆ 04 50 42 84 57, www.pays-de-gex.org

Address : route de Divonne-les-Bains (located 1km east along the D 984 and take the road to the right)

Opening times : from beginning May to end Sept.

3,3 ha (140 pitches)

Tariff : (2013 Price) ✶ 4,20€ 🚗 ▣ 6,20€ – ⚡ (16A) 3,35€
Rental rates : (from beginning May to end Sept.) – 4 🚐
Per week from 260 to 498€
🚰 borne 3€ – 96 ▣ 18,35€
Pretty situation between Lake Geneva and the Jura mountains.

Surroundings : ≤ ⌂
Leisure activities : 🍴 🏠 🏊 🚲
Facilities : 🚿 ⚮ 🚻 🏕 ⏚ ℐ 🚲 launderette
Nearby : 🍴 🏊

| | Longitude : 6.06841 |
| G P S | Latitude : 46.33564 |

LE GRAND-BORNAND

74450 – Michelin map **328** L5 – pop. 2 195 – alt. 934 – Winter sports : 1 000/2 100 m
▶ Paris 564 – Albertville 47 – Annecy 31 – Bonneville 23

⚑ L'Escale

✆ 04 50 02 20 69, www.campinglescale.com

Address : route de la Patinoire (east of the town, near the church, near the Borne river)

Opening times : from mid May to mid Sept.

2,8 ha (149 pitches) terraced, flat and relatively flat, grassy, stony

Tariff : 22€ ✶✶ 🚗 ▣ ⚡ (5A) – Extra per person 6€ – Reservation fee 12€
Rental rates : Permanent – 30 🚐 – 32 🏠 – 2 🛏 – 15 studios 15 apartments. Per night from 40 to 90€ – Per week from 295 to 695€ – Reservation fee 12€ – 🚰 borne – 20 ▣ 22€
A pleasant water and play park.

Surroundings : ❄ ⚵ ≤
Leisure activities : 🍴 🍴 🏠 jacuzzi 🏊 🍴 🏊 🏊
Facilities : 🚿 ⚮ 🏕 ⏚ ℐ 🚰 ♨ launderette 🚲
Nearby : 🏂 🏊 sports trail

| | Longitude : 6.42817 |
| G P S | Latitude : 45.94044 |

⛺ Le Clos du Pin

☎ 04 50 02 70 57, www.le-clos-du-pin.com – alt. 1 015 – limited spaces for one-night stay

Address : 1.3km east, following the signs for Le Bouchet; beside the Borne river

Opening times : from mid Junee to mid Sept. and from beg Dec to mid May

1,3 ha (61 pitches)

Tariff : (2013 Price) 28,85 € ♣♦ ⇌ 🅴 🕮 (10A)
Extra per person 5,04 € – Reservation fee 8 €

Rental rates : (from mid Junee to mid Sept. and from beg Dec to mid May) – 10 🚐 – 1 apartment. – Reservation fee 8 €

🅿 borne

Surroundings : ❄ 🦌 ≼ Chaîne des Aravis mountains
Leisure activities : 🎱
Facilities : ♿ ⚲ ☒ 🏧 ♨ ⚗ 🚰 launderette

| GPS | Longitude : 6.44281 |
| | Latitude : 45.93971 |

GRANE

26400 – Michelin map **332** C5 – pop. 1 730 – alt. 175
▶ Paris 583 – Crest 10 – Montélimar 34 – Privas 29

🏕 Flower Les Quatre Saisons

☎ 04 75 62 64 17, www.camping-4saisons.com

Address : take the southeastern exit, 900m along the D 113, follow the signs for la Roche-sur-Grâne

Opening times : from beginning April to end Sept.

2 ha (80 pitches) terraced, flat and relatively flat, grassy, sandy

Tariff : 31,50 € ♣♦ ⇌ 🅴 🕮 (6A) – Extra per person 5 €

Rental rates : Permanent – 4 🚐 – 11 🏠 – 4 tent lodges. Per night from 42 to 117 € – Per week from 210 to 819 €

🅿 borne

Surroundings : 🦌 ≼ 🌳 ⚘
Leisure activities : 🍹 ⚗ 🏊
Facilities : ♿ ⚲ 🆑 🏧 ♨ ⚗ 🚰 launderette 🐾
Nearby : 🍴

| GPS | Longitude : 4.92671 |
| | Latitude : 44.72684 |

GRAVIÈRES

07140 – Michelin map **331** G7 – pop. 391 – alt. 220
▶ Paris 636 – Lyon 213 – Privas 71 – Nîmes 92

⛺ Le Mas du Serre

☎ 04 75 37 33 84, www.campinglemasduserre.com

Address : at Le Serre (1.3km southeast along the D 113 and take the road to the left, 300m from the Chassezac)

Opening times : from beginning April to end Sept.

1,5 ha (75 pitches) terraced, flat and relatively flat, grassy

Tariff : ♦ 7 € ⇌ 🅴 22 € – 🕮 (6A) 3,50 €

Rental rates : (from beginning April to end Sept.) – 6 🚐. Per night from 53 to 93 € – Per week from 370 to 650 €

🅿 borne 5 €

An attractive site set around an old mas (regional-style house).

Surroundings : 🦌 ≼ ⚘
Leisure activities : 🏊 🏊
Facilities : ♿ ⚲ 🆑 🏧 📱
Nearby : 🏊

| GPS | Longitude : 4.1016 |
| | Latitude : 44.41475 |

GRESSE-EN-VERCORS

38650 – Michelin map **333** G8 – pop. 394 – alt. 1 205 – Winter sports : 1 300/1 700m
▶ Paris 610 – Clelles 22 – Grenoble 48 – Monestier-de-Clermont 14

🏔 Les 4 Saisons

☎ 04 76 34 30 27, www.camping-les4saisons.com

Address : 1.3km southwest, at La Ville

Opening times : from beginning May to mid Oct. and from Christmas to end March

2,2 ha (90 pitches) terraced, flat, grassy, fine gravel, stony

Tariff : 24,70 € ♣♦ ⇌ 🅴 🕮 (10A) – Extra per person 5,15 € Reservation fee 6 €

Rental rates : (from beginning May to mid Oct. and from Christmas to end March) 🏊 – 9 🚐 – 3 🏠. Per week from 402 to 704 € – Reservation fee 16 €

🅿 borne 5 €

In a pleasant location at the foot of the Massif du Vercors plateau and mountains.

Surroundings : ❄ 🦌 ≼ Massif du Vercors mountains
Leisure activities : 🍹 🍴 🎱 🏊 🏊
Facilities : ♿ ⚲ 🏧 🚰 launderette
Nearby : 🐾 🍴

| GPS | Longitude : 5.55559 |
| | Latitude : 44.8965 |

GRIGNAN

26230 – Michelin map **332** C7 – pop. 1 564 – alt. 198
▶ Paris 629 – Crest 46 – Montélimar 25 – Nyons 25

🏔 Les Truffières

☎ 04 75 46 93 62, www.lestruffieres.com 🏊

Address : 1100 chemin Belle-Vue-d'Air, quartier Nachony (situated 2km southwest along the D 541, follow the signs for Donzère and take the D 71, follow the signs for Chamaret)

Opening times : from mid April to mid Sept.

1 ha (85 pitches) flat, grassy, stony, wood

Tariff : 26,20 € ♣♦ ⇌ 🅴 🕮 (10A) – Extra per person 5 € – Reservation fee 12 €

Rental rates : (from mid April to mid Sept.) 🏊 – 12 🚐. Per night from 55 to 95 € – Per week from 230 to 760 € – Reservation fee 12 €

A wooded setting.

Surroundings : 🦌 🌳 ⚘⚘
Leisure activities : 🍴 🎱 🏊 🏊
Facilities : ♿ ⚲ 🏧 🚰 📱

| GPS | Longitude : 4.89121 |
| | Latitude : 44.41163 |

GROISY

74570 – Michelin map **328** K4 – pop. 2 976 – alt. 690
▶ Paris 534 – Dijon 228 – Grenoble 120 – Lons-le-Saunier 146

⛺ Le Moulin Dollay

☎ 04 50 68 00 31, www.moulindollay.fr

Address : 206 rue du Moulin Dollay (situated 2km southeast, junction of D 2 and N 203; beside a stream, at a place called Le Plot)

Opening times : from beginning May to end Sept.

3 ha (30 pitches)

Tariff : 20 € ♣♦ ⇌ 🅴 🕮 (6A) – Extra per person 5 €
🅿 borne 5 € – 6 🅴 15 € – 🚐 🕮 15 €

Surroundings : 🌳 ⚘
Leisure activities : 🎱 🏊
Facilities : ♿ ⚲ 🏧 🏧 ♨ ⚗ 🚰 launderette

| GPS | Longitude : 6.19076 |
| | Latitude : 46.00224 |

HAUTECOURT

01250 – Michelin map **328** F4 – pop. 760 – alt. 370
▶ Paris 442 – Bourg-en-Bresse 20 – Nantua 24 – Oyonnax 33

⚠ L'Île de Chambod

𝒫 04 74 37 25 41, www.campingilechambod.com

Address : 3232 route du Port (4.5km southeast along the D 59, follow the signs for Poncin then take the turning to the left, 300m from the Ain (small lake)

Opening times : from mid April to end Sept.

2,4 ha (110 pitches) flat, grassy

Tariff : ★ 4,90 € ⬅ 2,90 € 🅴 3,50 € – 🔌 (10A) 3,90 €

Rental rates : (from mid April to end Sept.) – 7 🚐 – 4 canvas bungalows. Per night from 27 to 86 € – Per week from 154 to 602 € Reservation fee 18,50 €

🚰 borne 2 €

Surroundings : ⪉ ▱ ℺	
Leisure activities : ⛄ ✕ ☖ ⚓	GPS
Facilities : ♿ ⛟ ♨♒ 🖼	Longitude : 5.42819
Nearby : ⚓ ⚓ sports trail	Latitude : 46.12761

ISSARLÈS

07470 – Michelin map **331** G4 – pop. 165 – alt. 946
▶ Paris 574 – Coucouron 16 – Langogne 36 – Le Monastier-sur-Gazeille 18

⚠ La Plaine de la Loire

𝒫 06 24 49 22 79, www.campinglaplainedelaloire.fr – alt. 900

Address : Le Moulin du Lac - Pont de Laborie (3km west along the D 16, follow the signs for Coucouron and take the road to the left before the bridge, beside the Loire river)

Opening times : from mid May to end Sept.

1 ha (50 pitches) flat, grassy

Tariff : 16 € ★★ ⬅ 🅴 🔌 (10A) – Extra per person 3,50 €

Perfect for those in search of peace, nature and fishing.

Surroundings : ⪉ ⪉ ℺℺	
Leisure activities : ✕ ⚓ ⚓ ⚓ ⚓	GPS
Facilities : ⛟ ♒♒♨	Longitude : 4.05207
	Latitude : 44.818

This guide is not intended as a list of all the camping sites in France; its aim is to provide a selection of the best sites in each category.

JAUJAC

07380 – Michelin map **331** H6 – pop. 1 212 – alt. 450
▶ Paris 612 – Privas 44 – Le Puy-en-Velay 81

⚠ Bonneval

𝒫 04 75 93 27 09, www.campingbonneval.com ✉ 07380 Fabras

Address : at Les Plots at Fabras (situated 2km northeast along the D 19 and take D 5, follow the signs for Pont-de-Labeaume, 100m from the Lignon river and basalt columns)

Opening times : from mid April to end Sept.

3 ha (60 pitches) terraced, flat and relatively flat, grassy

Tariff : 26,70 € ★★ ⬅ 🅴 🔌 (6A) – Extra per person 6 €

Rental rates : (from mid April to end Oct.) – 4 🚐 – 1 🏠 – 1 tent lodge – 3 gîtes. Per week from 280 to 660 €

Pitches in both sun and shade, various rental options and a good standard of sanitary facilities suitable for families.

Surroundings : ⪉ ⪉ Chaîne du Tanargue mountains ℺	
Leisure activities : ⛄ ⚓ ⚓ ⚓	GPS
Facilities : ♿ ⛟ (season) ▱✉🖼 ♨♒ 🖼	Longitude : 4.25825
Nearby : ⚓	Latitude : 44.64168

JEANSAGNIÈRE

42920 – Michelin map **327** C5 – pop. 84 – alt. 1 050
▶ Paris 440 – Lyon 111 – St-Étienne 84 – Clermont-Ferrand 88

⚠ Village de la Droséra (chalet rentals only)

𝒫 04 77 24 81 44, www.ladrosera.fr

Address : at La Droséra

Opening times : Permanent

16 ha

Rental rates : (2013 Price) – 7 🏠. Per night 60 € – Per week 350 €

Pretty wooden chalets in a mountain park.

Surroundings : ⪉ ⪉ of the Monts du Forez ℺℺	
Leisure activities : ☖ ⚓ ⚓ walking trails	GPS
Facilities : ⛟ ✉	Longitude : 3.83592
	Latitude : 45.73928

JOANNAS

07110 – Michelin map **331** H6 – pop. 342 – alt. 430
▶ Paris 650 – Aubenas 23 – Largentière 8 – Privas 55

⚠ La Marette

𝒫 04 75 88 38 88, www.lamarette.com

Address : route de Valgorge (2.4km west along the D 24, after La Prade)

4 ha (97 pitches)

Rentals : 2 caravans – 24 🚐 – 19 🏠.

Numerous small, individual terraces in a natural setting and well shaded.

Surroundings : ⪉ ▱ ℺℺	
Leisure activities : ⛄ ✕ ☖ ⚓ ⚓ ⚓	GPS
Facilities : ♿ ⛟ ♨♒ 🖼 ⚓	Longitude : 4.22913
	Latitude : 44.56662

⚠ Le Roubreau

𝒫 04 75 88 32 07, www.leroubreau.com

Address : route de Valgorge (1.4km west along the D 24 and take road to the left)

Opening times : from mid April to mid Sept.

3 ha (100 pitches) flat and relatively flat, grassy, stony

Tariff : 29,50 € ★★ ⬅ 🅴 🔌 (4A) – Extra per person 6,50 € Reservation fee 7,50 €

Rental rates : (from mid April to mid Sept.) – 14 🚐 – 15 🏠 2 canvas bungalows. Per night from 29 to 67 € – Per week from 200 to 770 € – Reservation fee 7,50 €

🚰 borne 5 €

Well-shaded pitches and rental options beside the Roubreau river, with good sanitary facilities.

Surroundings : ⪉ ▱ ℺℺	
Leisure activities : ⛄ ✕ ☖ ⚓ ⚓ ⚓ ⚓	GPS
Facilities : ♿ ⛟ ♨♒ 🖼 ⚓	Longitude : 4.23865
	Latitude : 44.55964

JOYEUSE

07260 – Michelin map **331** H7 – pop. 1 640 – alt. 180
▶ Paris 650 – Alès 54 – Mende 97 – Privas 55

⚠ La Nouzarède

☎ 04 75 39 92 01, www.camping-nouzarede.fr

Address : north of the town along the rte du Stade, 150m from the Beaume river (direct access)

Opening times : from beginning April to end Sept.

4 ha (103 pitches)

Tariff : 28,60€ ★★ ⇔ 🗉 ⚡ (10A) – Extra per person 6,50€ – Reservation fee 14,50€

Rental rates : (from beginning April to end Sept.) – 27 🏕 – Per night from 53 to 109€ – Per week from 260 to 765€ – Reservation fee 14,50€

Opposite a well-equipped horse and pony centre, good sanitary facilities.

Surroundings : 🗔 🕆🕆
Leisure activities : 🍸 ✗ 🏠 🛶🛱 🌊 🐎
Facilities : & ⊶ ⫿⫿ 🛁🛠🐾 🍴 🔟 🏃
Nearby : ✗💦 🏊 🚤

Longitude : 4.23526
Latitude : 44.48368

LAGORCE

07150 – Michelin map **331** I7 – pop. 700 – alt. 120
▶ Paris 648 – Aubenas 23 – Bourg-St-Andéol 34 – Privas 54

⚠⚠⚠ Les Castels Domaine de Sévenier

(chalet rentals only)

☎ 04 75 88 29 44, www.sevenier.net

Address : quartier Sévenier (1.6km south along the D 1, follow signs for Vallon-Pont-d'Arc)

Opening times : from beginning April to mid Nov.

4 ha undulating

Rental rates : & (3 chalets) – 56 🏠. Per night from 55 to 297 € – Per week from 385 to 2079€ – Reservation fee 20€

An attractive chalet site, some equipped for very young children or large families, some on a hotel-style basis.

Surroundings : 🌊
Leisure activities : 🍸 ✗ 🛶🛱 🌊
Facilities : ⊶ ⫿⫿ 🍴 🔟 🏃

Longitude : 4.41153
Latitude : 44.4338

LALLEY

38930 – Michelin map **333** H9 – pop. 205 – alt. 850
▶ Paris 626 – Grenoble 63 – La Mure 30 – Sisteron 80

⚠ Sites et Paysages Belle Roche

☎ 04 76 34 75 33, www.camping-belleroche.com – alt. 860

Address : chemin de Combe Morée (head south of the town following signs for Mens and take the road to the right)

Opening times : from beginning April to beginning Oct.

2,4 ha (60 pitches) terrace, flat, grassy, stony

Tariff : 25€ ★★ ⇔ 🗉 ⚡ (10A) – Extra per person 7 €

Rental rates : (from beginning April to beginning Oct.) 6 🏕 – 1 tent lodge. Per night from 45 to 95€ – Per week from 225 to 680€ – Reservation fee 15€

🚰 borne 5€ – 🚐 12€

In a pleasant location opposite the village.

Surroundings : 🌊 ≤ 🗔 🎋
Leisure activities : 🍸 ✗ 🎣 🛶🛱 🌊 multi-sports ground
Facilities : & ⊶ 🍴 launderette 🏃
Nearby : ✗

Longitude : 5.67889
Latitude : 44.75472

LALOUVESC

07520 – Michelin map **331** J3 – pop. 496 – alt. 1 050
▶ Paris 553 – Annonay 24 – Lamastre 25 – Privas 80

⚠ Municipal le Pré du Moulin

☎ 04 75 67 84 86, www.lalouvesc.com

Address : chemin de l'Hermuzière (north of the village)

Opening times : from mid May to end Sept.

2,5 ha (70 pitches) terraced, relatively flat, grassy

Tariff : ★ 2,60€ ⇔ 1,80€ 🗉 – ⚡ (10A) 3,30€

Rental rates : (from mid May to end Sept.) – 5 🏕 – 5 tree houses and 10 huts (without sanitary facilities). Per night from 28 to 49€ – Per week from 188 to 343€

🚰 borne 2€

Various rental options, some with rather old, simple facilities.

Surroundings : 🌊 🎋
Leisure activities : 🛶🛱 🐎 ✗
Facilities : & ⊶ 🛁 🍴 🔟 🏃

Longitude : 4.53392
Latitude : 45.12388

The Michelin classification (⚠⚠⚠ … ⚠) is totally independent of the official star classification system awarded by the local prefecture or other official organisation.

LAMASTRE

07270 – Michelin map **331** J4 – pop. 2 501 – alt. 375
▶ Paris 577 – Privas 55 – Le Puy-en-Velay 72 – Valence 38

⚠⚠⚠ Le Retourtour

☎ 04 75 06 40 71, www.campingderetourtour.com

Address : 1 rue de Retourtour

Opening times : from mid April to end Sept.

2,9 ha (130 pitches)

Tariff : 23,96€ ★★ ⇔ 🗉 ⚡ (13A) – Extra per person 4,98€ – Reservation fee 10€

Rental rates : (from mid April to end Sept.) – 15 🏕 – 3 canvas bungalows – 2 gîtes. Per night from 59 to 89€ – Per week from 224 to 595€ – Reservation fee 10€

🚰 borne – 🚐 10,56€

Well-shaded pitches, near a small lake.

Surroundings : 🌊 🕆🕆
Leisure activities : 🍸 ✗ 🏠 🎣 🛶🛱 🏃
Facilities : & ⊶ 🛁🌿 🍴 🔟 🏃
Nearby : 💦 (beach)

Longitude : 4.56483
Latitude : 44.99164

LANSLEVILLARD

73480 – Michelin map **333** O6 – pop. 457 – alt. 1 500 – Winter sports : 1 400/2 800m
▶ Paris 689 – Albertville 116 – Briançon 87 – Chambéry 129

⛰ Caravaneige Municipal

✆ 0479059052, www.camping-valcenis.com/
Address : rue sous l'Eglise (southwestern exit, follow the signs for Lanslebourg; beside rapids)
3 ha (100 pitches)

Surroundings : ❄ ≤	
Leisure activities : ⛱ ✕ 🏠 🛶 🚣	**G** Longitude : 6.90928
Facilities : ♿ ⊶ ▥ launderette 🧺	**P** Latitude : 45.29057
Nearby : ✕ 🛶	**S**

A chambre d'hôte is a guesthouse or B & B-style accommodation.

LARNAS

07220 – Michelin map **331** J7 – pop. 97 – alt. 300
▶ Paris 631 – Aubenas 41 – Bourg-St-Andéol 12 – Montélimar 24

⛰ FranceLoc Le Domaine d'Imbours 👥

✆ 0475543950, www.domaine-imbours.com
Address : 2.5km southwest along the D 262 - for caravans, from Bourg-St-Andéol go via St-Remèze and Mas du Gras (D 4, D 362 and D 262)
Opening times : from beginning April to end Sept.
270 ha/10 for camping (694 pitches) flat and relatively flat, grassy, stony
Tariff : (2013 Price) 37€ ✱✱ 🚐 🔲 ⚡ (6A) – Extra per person 7€
Reservation fee 27€
Rental rates : (2013 Price) (from beginning April to end Sept.) 4 caravans – 350 🚐 – 50 🏠 – 32 tent lodges – 100 gîtes hotel (96 rooms). Per night from 33 to 117€ – Per week from 133 to 1274€ – Reservation fee 27€

Surroundings : 🏞 ⚶⚶	
Leisure activities : ⛱ ✕ 🏠 🎱 🏊 🚣 🚴 ✕ 🛶 🏘 🏊 ⛷ multi-sports ground	**G** Longitude : 4.5764
Facilities : ♿ ⊶ 🚿 🍽 🛒 🧺	**P** Latitude : 44.4368
Nearby : 🐎	**S**

LATHUILE

74210 – Michelin map **328** K6 – pop. 960 – alt. 510
▶ Paris 554 – Albertville 30 – Annecy 18 – La Clusaz 38

⛰ Les Fontaines

✆ 0450443122, www.campinglesfontaines.com
Address : 1295 route de Chaparon (situated 2km to the north at Chaparon)
Opening times : from end April to end Sept.
3 ha (170 pitches)
Tariff : 29,50€ ✱✱ 🚐 🔲 ⚡ (5A) – Extra per person 7,50€
Reservation fee 16€
Rental rates : (from end April to end Sept.) – 50 🚐 – 3 🏠. Per week from 250 to 810€ – Reservation fee 16€

Surroundings : 🏞 ⚶⚶	
Leisure activities : ⛱ ✕ 🏠 🎱 🏊 🏊 multi-sports ground	**G** Longitude : 6.20444
Facilities : ♿ ⊶ 🚿 launderette 🧺	**P** Latitude : 45.80037
	S

⛰ L'Idéal

✆ 0450443297, www.campingideal.com
Address : 715 route de Chaparon (located 1.5km to the north)
Opening times : from end April to mid Sept.
3,2 ha (300 pitches)
Tariff : (2013 Price) 34,20€ ✱✱ 🚐 🔲 ⚡ (10A)
Extra per person 7,50€
Rental rates : (from end April to mid Sept.) ♿ (1 mobile home 🚗 (from end June to beginning Sept.) – 73 🚐 – 1 studio 7 apartments. Per night from 130 to 150€ – Per week from 200 to 810€ – Reservation fee 18€
Situated around an attractive swimming area.

Surroundings : 🏞 ≤ ⚶	
Leisure activities : ⛱ ✕ 🏠 🎱jacuzzi 🚣 ✕ 🛶 🏊 🏊 multi-sports ground	**G** Longitude : 6.20582
Facilities : ♿ ⊶ 🚿 🍽 launderette 🧺 🧺	**P** Latitude : 45.79537
	S

⛰ La Ravoire

✆ 0450443780, www.camping-la-ravoire.fr
Address : route de la Ravoire (2.5km to the north)
2 ha (110 pitches) flat, grassy
Rentals : 🚗 – 16 🚐 – 4 🏠.
In a beautiful green setting near the lake.

Surroundings : ≤ ⚶⚶	
Leisure activities : ⛱ ✕ 🏠 🚣 🏊 🏊 multi-sports ground	**G** Longitude : 6.20975
Facilities : ♿ ⊶ 🚿 🧺 🚻 🍽 launderette	**P** Latitude : 45.80244
Nearby : 🛶	**S**

⛰ Le Taillefer

✆ 0450443030, www.campingletaillefer.com
Address : 1530 route de Chaparon (situated 2km to the north, at Chaparon)
Opening times : from beginning May to end Sept.
1 ha (32 pitches)
Tariff : 23,50€ ✱✱ 🚐 🔲 ⚡ (6A) – Extra per person 6€

Surroundings : ≤ ⚶	
Leisure activities : ⛱ 🏠 🚣 🚴	**G** Longitude : 6.20565
Facilities : ♿ ⊶ 🚿 🍽 launderette	**P** Latitude : 45.80231
	S

A 'quartier' is a district or area of a town or village.

LAURAC-EN-VIVARAIS

07110 – Michelin map **331** H6 – pop. 885 – alt. 182
▶ Paris 646 – Alès 60 – Mende 102 – Privas 50

⛰ Les Châtaigniers

✆ 0475368626, www.chataigniers-laurac.com
Address : at Prends-toi Garde (to the southeast of the town, recommended route via the D 104)
Opening times : from beginning April to end Sept.
1,2 ha (71 pitches)
Tariff : 23€ ✱✱ 🚐 🔲 – ⚡ (10A) 4€ – Extra per person 4€
Rental rates : (from beginning April to end Sept.) 🚗 (from beginning July to end Aug.) – 12 🚐. Per night from 50 to 65€ Per week from 290 to 650€

🚗 5 🔲

The upper part of the site has the most shade, the lower part has marked out pitches.

Surroundings : 🛝🛝
Leisure activities : 🎣 ⛵ 🛷
Facilities : ♿ ⛽ 🚿 ⛺ 🅿

GPS Longitude : 4.29497
Latitude : 44.50429

LÉPIN-LE-LAC

73610 – Michelin map **333** H4 – pop. 407 – alt. 400
▶ Paris 555 – Belley 36 – Chambéry 24 – Les Échelles 17

🏕 Le Curtelet

📞 0479441122, www.camping-le-curtelet.com

Address : 1.4km to the northwest

Opening times : from mid May to end Sept.

1,3 ha (94 pitches)

Tariff : 23,40€ ✶✶ 🚐 🔲 🗲 (10A) – Extra per person 5,10€
Reservation fee 10€

Surroundings : ≤ 🏖 🛝
Leisure activities : 🍹 ⛵ 🏊 ❨
Facilities : ♿ ⛽ (July-Sept.) 🚿 ⛺ 🛁 launde-rette
Nearby : 🍴 🛖

GPS Longitude : 5.77916
Latitude : 45.54002

LESCHERAINES

73340 – Michelin map **333** J3 – pop. 731 – alt. 649
▶ Paris 557 – Aix-les-Bains 26 – Annecy 26 – Chambéry 29

🏔 Municipal l'Île

📞 0479638000, www.savoie-camping.com

Address : at base de Loisirs (leisure centre) Les Îles du Chéran (2.5km southeast along the D 912, follow the signs for Annecy and take the turning to the right, 200m from the Chéran)

Opening times : from end April to end Sept.

7,5 ha (250 pitches)

Tariff : 16,30€ ✶✶ 🚐 🔲 🗲 (10A) – Extra per person 4,35€
Reservation fee 10€

Rental rates : (from end April to end Sept.) – 12 🚍 – 5 🏠 gîtes. Per night from 36 to 77€ – Per week from 250 to 580€
🚐 borne 1,50€ – 10 🔲 4€ – 🔌🗲15€

Beside a small lake, surrounded by woods and mountains.

Surroundings : 🌳 ≤ 🏖 ⛰
Leisure activities : 🏛
Facilities : ♿ ⛽ 🚿 🛁 🗑 🛁 launderette
At the leisure/activities centre : 🍹 🍴 🛁 🍴
🛖 🏊 🛷 🐎 pedalos

GPS Longitude : 6.11207
Latitude : 45.70352

LUGRIN

74500 – Michelin map **328** N2 – pop. 2 260 – alt. 413
▶ Paris 584 – Annecy 91 – Évian-les-Bains 8 – St-Gingolph 12

🏔 Vieille Église

📞 0450760195, www.campingvieilleeglise.fr

Address : 53 route des Préparraux (situated 2km west, at Vieille-Église)

Opening times : from mid April to mid Oct.

1,6 ha (100 pitches)

Tariff : 26,90€ ✶✶ 🚐 🔲 🗲 (10A) – Extra per person 7,40€
Reservation fee 5€

Rental rates : (from mid April to mid Oct.) – 25 🚍 – 1 🛏
1 studio – 2 apartments. Per night from 45 to 60€ – Per week from 290 to 795€ – Reservation fee 5€
🚐 borne 7€ – 🔌🗲21€

Surroundings : ≤ 🏡 🛝
Leisure activities : 🛖 🏊
Facilities : ♿ ⛽ 🔌 🗑 🚿 🛁 launderette

GPS Longitude : 6.64655
Latitude : 46.40052

LUS-LA-CROIX-HAUTE

26620 – Michelin map **332** H6 – pop. 507 – alt. 1 050
▶ Paris 638 – Alès 207 – Die 45 – Gap 49

🏔 Champ la Chèvre

📞 0492585014, www.campingchamplachevre.com

Address : to the southeast of the town, near the swimming pool

Opening times : from end April to end Sept.

3,6 ha (100 pitches)

Tariff : 23,60€ ✶✶ 🚐 🔲 🗲 (6A) – Extra per person 6,90€
Reservation fee 15€

Rental rates : Permanent – 4 🚍 – 8 🏠 – 2 tent lodges. Per night from 35 to 111€ – Per week from 215 to 780€ – Reservation fee 15€
🚐 borne 5€ – 2 🔲 23,60€

Surroundings : 🌳 ≤ 🛝
Leisure activities : 🏛 🏊 (open air in season)
Facilities : ♿ ⛽ 🔌 🗑 🛁 🗑
Nearby : 🐎

GPS Longitude : 5.70998
Latitude : 44.6629

MALBOSC

07140 – Michelin map **331** G7 – pop. 152 – alt. 450
▶ Paris 644 – Alès 45 – La Grand-Combe 29 – Les Vans 19

🏔 Le Moulin de Gournier

📞 0475373550, www.camping-moulin-de-gournier.com

Address : le Gournier (7km northeast along the D 216, follow the signs for Les Vans)

4 ha/1 for camping (29 pitches)

Rentals : 1 🏠.

Pitches on terraces that descend to the Ganière river.

Surroundings : 🌳 🏡 🛝🛝
Leisure activities : 🏓 🚴 🏊 ❨
Facilities : ♿ ⛽ 🗑 🛁

GPS Longitude : 4.0943
Latitude : 44.36566

LES MARCHES

73800 – Michelin map **333** I5 – pop. 2 453 – alt. 328
▶ Paris 572 – Albertville 43 – Chambéry 12 – Grenoble 44

🏔 La Ferme du Lac

📞 0479281348, www.campinglafermedulac.fr

Address : located 1km southwest along the N 90, follow the signs for Pontcharra and take the D 12 to the right

2,6 ha (100 pitches) flat, grassy

Rentals : 🚫 – 9 🚍 – 1 🏠.

Surroundings : 🏡 🛝🛝
Leisure activities : 🏛 🏊
Facilities : ♿ ⛽ 🚿 🛁 🗑

GPS Longitude : 5.99327
Latitude : 45.49595

MARS

07320 – Michelin map **331** H3 – pop. 279 – alt. 1 060
▶ Paris 579 – Annonay 49 – Le Puy-en-Velay 44 – Privas 71

⚠ La Prairie

✆ 0475302447, www.camping-laprairie.com

Address : at Laillier (to the northeast of the town along the D 15, follow the signs for St-Agrève and take road to the left)

Opening times : from mid May to mid Sept.

0,6 ha (30 pitches)

Tariff : ✿ 3,30€ ⌁ 1,50€ 🅴 4,50€ – ⚡ (6A) 3€

Rental rates : (from mid May to mid Sept.) – 1 🛖. Per night 150€ Per week 750€

🚐 borne 4€

Well-kept pitches, positioned around the house.

Surroundings : ⛰ ◁
Leisure activities : ✗ 🚣 🚲
Facilities : ⚖ ⌐ 🚿 ▥
Nearby : ✗ 18-hole golf course

Longitude : 4.32632
Latitude : 45.02393

MASSIGNIEU-DE-RIVES

01300 – Michelin map **328** H6 – pop. 591 – alt. 295
▶ Paris 516 – Aix-les-Bains 26 – Belley 10 – Morestel 37

⚠ VivaCamp le Lac du Lit du Roi

✆ 0479421203, www.camping-savoie.com

Address : at La Tuillère (2.5km north following signs for Belley and take the road to the right)

Opening times : from mid April to end Sept.

4 ha (120 pitches)

Tariff : (2013 Price) 28€ ✿✿ ⌁ 🅴 ⚡ (10A) – Extra per person 6,50€ Reservation fee 15€

Rental rates : (from mid April to end Sept.) – 30 🚐 – 5 🛖 2 tipis – 3 canvas bungalows. Per night from 44 to 123€ Per week from 264 to 861€ – Reservation fee 20€

🚐 5 🅴 28€

In a pleasant location beside a lake formed by the Rhône river.

Surroundings : ⛰ ◁ lake and hills ⌂ 🌳 ⚠
Leisure activities : ✗ 🚣 🚲 🎾 🏊 ⛵ pedalos ⛵
Facilities : ⚖ ⌐ 🅴 🚿 ▥

Longitude : 5.77001
Latitude : 45.76861

MATAFELON-GRANGES

01580 – Michelin map **328** G3 – pop. 653 – alt. 453
▶ Paris 460 – Bourg-en-Bresse 37 – Lons-le-Saunier 56 – Mâcon 75

⚠ Les Gorges de l'Oignin

✆ 0474768097, www.gorges-de-loignin.com

Address : rue du Lac (900m south of the village, neare the Oignin river)

Opening times : from mid April to end Sept.

2,6 ha (128 pitches)

Tariff : 25,40€ ✿✿ ⌁ 🅴 ⚡ (10A) – Extra per person 5,20€ Reservation fee 16€

Rental rates : (from mid April to end Sept.) – 2 🚐 – 10 🛖. Per night from 50 to 95€ – Per week from 266 to 662€ Reservation fee 16€

🚐 20 🅴 25,40€

Near a lake.

Surroundings : ◁
Leisure activities : ✗ ✗ 🚣 🏊
Facilities : ⚖ ⌐ ▥ 🚿 ♨ 🚾 ▥
Nearby : 🏊

Longitude : 5.55723
Latitude : 46.25534

This guide is updated regularly, so buy your new copy every year!

LES MAZES

07150 – Michelin map **331** I7
▶ Paris 669 – Lyon 207 – Privas 58 – Nîmes 83

⚠⚠ La Plage Fleurie ▲▲

✆ 0475880115, www.laplagefleurie.com

Address : 3.5km west

Opening times : from end April to beginning Sept.

12 ha/6 for camping (300 pitches) terraced, flat and relatively flat, grassy

Tariff : (2013 Price) 45,90€ ✿✿ ⌁ 🅴 ⚡ (10A) Extra per person 9,35€ – Reservation fee 20€

Rental rates : (from end April to beginning Sept.) – 170 🚐 32 canvas bungalows. Per night from 54 to 183€ – Per week from 378 to 1 281€ – Reservation fee 25€

🚐 borne

Located beside the Ardèche river, with a sandy beach and an area of grass and several luxurious mobile homes.

Surroundings : ⛰ ◁ 🌳🌳
Leisure activities : ✗ ✗ 🎬 🎮 🏊 🚣 🏊 ⛵ (beach) ⛵ ⛵
Facilities : ⚖ ⌐ 🚿 ♨ 🅴 🚾 🍴

Longitude : 4.3546
Latitude : 44.40837

⚠⚠ Beau Rivage

✆ 0475880354, www.beaurivage-camping.com

Address : on the D 579

Opening times : from end April to mid Sept.

2 ha (100 pitches)

Tariff : 33€ ✿✿ ⌁ 🅴 ⚡ (10A) – Extra per person 5,90€ – Reservation fee 16€

Rental rates : (from end April to mid Sept.) 🎾 – 14 🚐. Per night from 70 € – Per week from 390 to 785€ – Reservation fee 23€

Located among the vineyards on the banks of the Ardèche river, the perfect place for some peace and quiet.

Surroundings : ⛰ ⌐ 🌳🌳
Leisure activities : ✗ 🎬 🚣 🏊 ⛵ ⛵
Facilities : ⚖ ⌐ 🚿 ♨ 🅴 🚾

Longitude : 4.3649
Latitude : 44.4103

⚠⚠ Arc-en-Ciel ▲▲

✆ 0475880465, www.arcenciel-camping.com

Address : on the D 579

5 ha (218 pitches)

Rentals : 66 🚐 – 4 canvas bungalows – 10 tent lodges – 2 gîtes

Beside the Ardèche river with a sandy beach and grassy area. A wide range of local rental options of various levels of comfort.

Surroundings : ⛰ 🌳🌳
Leisure activities : ✗ ✗ 🎬 🚣 🏊 ⛵ (beach) ⛵ ⛵
Facilities : ⚖ ⌐ 🚿 ♨ 🅴 🚾 🍴

Longitude : 4.3512
Latitude : 44.41177

MÉAUDRE

8112 – Michelin map **333** G7 – pop. 1 321 – alt. 1 012 – Winter sports : 1 000/1 600m
▶ Paris 588 – Grenoble 38 – Pont-en-Royans 26 – Tullins 53

⚠ Les Buissonnets

𝒫 0476952104, www.camping-les-buissonnets.com – limited spaces for one-night stay

Address : at Les Grangeons (500m northeast along the D 106 and take turning to the right, 200m from the Méaudret river)

Opening times : Permanent

2,8 ha (100 pitches)

Tariff : 22,10€ ♥♥ ⇌ 🅴 🔌 (10A) – Extra per person 5,25€
Rental rates : Permanent ⚡ (from beginning Dec. to end Oct.)
🅿 – 10 �🚐 – 3 🏠. Per week from 290 to 466€
🚰 borne 5€ – 40 🅴 15,80€ – 🛁14,50€

Surroundings : ❄ 🚣 ≤ ⛱
Leisure activities :
Facilities : 🚿 ⊶ ▥ 🍽 ☕ ⛺
Nearby : ✂ 🛶

GPS Longitude : 5.53243
Latitude : 45.12955

⚠ Les Eymes

𝒫 0476952485, www.camping-les-eymes.com

Address : 3.8km north along the D 106c, follow the signs for Autrans and take turning to the left

Opening times : from beginning May to end Sept.

2,3 ha (40 pitches)

Tariff : 20€ ♥♥ ⇌ 🅴 🔌 (10A) – Extra per person 7€ – Reservation fee 2€
Rental rates : Permanent – 7 �🚐 – 3 🏠. Per night from 53 to 97€
Per week from 318 to 582€ – Reservation fee 10€
🚰 borne 5€ – 3 🅴 17€

Surroundings : 🚣 ≤
Leisure activities : ✕ 🛶
Facilities : 🚿 ⊶ ▥ ☕ 🍽 ⛺ 🚮 ⚡

GPS Longitude : 5.51574
Latitude : 45.14468

MEGÈVE

74120 – Michelin map **328** M5 – pop. 3 907 – alt. 1 113 – Winter sports : 1 113/2 350m
▶ Paris 598 – Albertville 32 – Annecy 60 – Chamonix-Mont-Blanc 33

⚠ Bornand

𝒫 0450930086, www.camping-megeve.com – alt. 1 060

Address : 57 route du Grand Bois – Demi quartier (3km northeast along the N 212, follow the signs for Sallanches and the Rte de la télécabine (cable car) to the right)

Opening times : from mid Junee to end Aug.

1,5 ha (80 pitches)

Tariff : (2013 Price) ♥ 3,90€ ⇌ 🅴 4,50€ – 🔌 (6A) 3,60€
Rental rates : Permanent ⚡ – 4 🏠. Per week from 315 to 565€
🚰 borne 3€

Surroundings : ≤ ⛱
Leisure activities : 🖼
Facilities : 🚿 ⊶ 🍽 launderette
Nearby : ✕

GPS Longitude : 6.64161
Latitude : 45.87909

MENGLON

26410 – Michelin map **332** F6 – pop. 406 – alt. 550
▶ Paris 645 – Lyon 183 – Valence 80 – Grenoble 90

🔺 L'Hirondelle ♥♥

𝒫 0475218208, www.campinghirondelle.com

Address : bois de Saint Ferréol (2.8km northwest along the D 214 and D 140, follow the signs for Die, near the D 539 (recommended route)

Opening times : from end April to mid Sept.

7,5 ha (180 pitches) undulating, flat, grassy

Tariff : ♥ 9,75€ ⇌ 🅴 15,70€ – 🔌 (6A) 4,60€ – Reservation fee 18,50€
Rental rates : (from beginning April to end Sept.) – 20 �🚐 – 24 🏠
4 canvas bungalows – 9 tent lodges. Per night from 41 to 135€
Per week from 292 to 950€ – Reservation fee 18,50€
A pleasant site and setting beside the Bez river.

Surroundings : 🚣 ≤ ⛲ 🎲
Leisure activities : 🍸 ✕ 🖼 ☾nighttime 🏃
🏋 🐎 🛶 ≈ (river) 🎯 multi-sports ground
Facilities : 🚿 ⊶ 🆒 ☕ 🍽 launderette 🚮 🚰

GPS Longitude : 5.44746
Latitude : 44.68143

MENTHON-ST-BERNARD

74290 – Michelin map **328** K5 – pop. 1 876 – alt. 482
▶ Paris 552 – Lyon 148 – Annecy 9 – Genève 51

⚠ Le Clos Don Jean

𝒫 0450601866, www.clos-don-jean.com

Address : 435 route du Clos-Don-Jean

Opening times : from beginning June to end Aug.

1 ha (60 pitches)

Tariff : (2013 Price) 19€ ♥♥ ⇌ 🅴 🔌 (6A) – Extra per person 4,50€
Rental rates : (from beginning June to mid Sept.) 9 �🚐.
Per night from 65 to 80€ – Per week from 285 to 505 €

Surroundings : 🚣 ≤ ⛱
Leisure activities : 🖼
Facilities : ⊶ 🚮 ⛺

GPS Longitude : 6.19699
Latitude : 45.86298

MEYRAS

07380 – Michelin map **331** H5 – pop. 842 – alt. 450
▶ Paris 609 – Aubenas 17 – Le Cheylard 54 – Langogne 49

🔺 Sites et Paysages Domaine de La Plage

𝒫 0475364059, www.lecampingdelaplage.com – limited spaces for one-night stay

Address : at Neyrac-les-Bains (3km southwest along the N 102, follow the signs for Le Puy-en-Velay)

Opening times : from end March to end Oct.

0,8 ha (45 pitches)

Tariff : (2013 Price) 35€ ♥♥ ⇌ 🅴 – Extra per person 3,50€
Rental rates : (2013 Price) (from end March to end Oct.) – 27 �🚐
12 🏠 – 7 gîtes. Per week from 250 to 810€
Below the road, choose pitches beside the Ardèche river.

Surroundings : ≤ ⛲ 🎲
Leisure activities : 🍸 ✕ 🖼 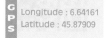 🚴 🛶 ≈ 🎣
multi-sports ground, entertainment room
Facilities : 🚿 ⊶ ▥ ☕ 🍽 launderette
🚰

GPS Longitude : 4.26067
Latitude : 44.67315

To make the best possible use of this guide, please read pages 2–15 carefully.

⛰ Le Ventadour

☎ 0475941815, www.leventadour.com

Address : at the Pont de Rolandy (3.5km southeast, along the N 102, follow the signs for Aubenas; beside the Ardèche river)

Opening times : from mid April to beginning Oct.

3 ha (115 pitches)

Tariff : 28,40€ ♟♟ ⛟ 🔲 ⚡ (10A) – Extra per person 6€ – Reservation fee 15€

Rental rates : (from mid April to beginning Oct.) – 17 🚐. Per night from 89 to 149€ – Per week from 199 to 780€ Reservation fee 15€

Choose pitches beside the river, futher away from the road.

Surroundings : 🛏 ♀	G
Leisure activities : ♟ ✗ ⛵ 🚲 ⛆ (beach) 🎣	P
Facilities : 🚿 ⚷ 🔲 🍴 launderette 🚐	S

Longitude : 4.28291
Latitude : 44.66757

MEYRIEU-LES-ÉTANGS

38440 – Michelin map **333** E4 – pop. 839 – alt. 430
▶ Paris 515 – Beaurepaire 31 – Bourgoin-Jallieu 14 – Grenoble 78

⛰ Base de Loisirs du Moulin

☎ 0474593034, www.camping-meyrieu.com

Address : route de Saint-Anne (800m southeast along the D 56b, follow the signs for Châtonnoy and turn left towards Ste-Anne; near a small lake)

1 ha (58 pitches)

Rentals : ℗ – 3 🚐 – 11 🏠.

Pitches on terraces looking out over the lake.

Surroundings : 🌲 🛏 ♀♀	G
Leisure activities : 🎣 👟 🎣	P
Facilities : 🚿 ⚷ 🚐 🚻 🔲	S
Nearby : ♟ ✗ 🚐 🚐 🎣 ⛆ pedalos	

Longitude : 5.20175
Latitude : 45.5152

To visit a town or region, use the MICHELIN Green Guides.

MIRABEL-ET-BLACONS

26400 – Michelin map **332** D5 – pop. 904 – alt. 225
▶ Paris 595 – Crest 7 – Die 30 – Dieulefit 33

⛰ Gervanne

☎ 0475400020, www.gervanne-camping.com

Address : quartier Bellevue (situated where the Drôme and the Gervanne rivers meet, at Blacons)

Opening times : from beginning April to end Sept.

3,7 ha (150 pitches)

Tariff : (2013 Price) 29,50€ ♟♟ ⛟ 🔲 ⚡ (6A) – Extra per person 7,30€ Reservation fee 15€

Rental rates : (from beginning April to end Sept.) 🚿 (1 chalet) 🚐 – 3 caravans – 3 🚐 – 18 🏠. Per night from 64 to 87€ Per week from 301 to 854€ – Reservation fee 15€

🚐 borne 4€ – 3 🔲 17,30€

A green setting beside the Gervanne and Drôme rivers.

Surroundings : 🌲 ♀♀ ⛰	G
Leisure activities : ♟ ✗ 🎣 🚲 🚲 🎣	P
Facilities : 🚿 ⚷ 🍴 launderette 🚐 🚐	S
Nearby : fitness trail	

Longitude : 5.08917
Latitude : 44.71083

MONTCHAVIN

73210 – Michelin map **333** N4
▶ Paris 672 – Lyon 206 – Chambéry 106 – Albertville 57

⛺ Caravaneige de Montchavin

☎ 0479078323, www.montchavin-lescoches.com – alt. 1 250

Address : at Montchavin

Opening times : from beginning Nov. to end Sept.

1,33 ha (90 pitches)

Tariff : 22€ ♟♟ ⛟ 🔲 ⚡ (6A) – Extra per person 5,30€

Rental rates : Permanent 🚿 – 2 🚐. Per night from 95 Per week from 285 to 665€

🚐 borne 5€

A superb location and view.

Surroundings : ❄ 🌲 ≪ Vallée de la Tarentaise and mountains ♀	G
Leisure activities : 🎣	P
Facilities : 🚿 ⚷ 🔲 🍴 launderette	S
Nearby : 🚐 ♟ ✗ 🎣 🎣 skating rink	

Longitude : 6.73933
Latitude : 45.56058

These symbols are used for a campsite that is exceptional in its category:

⛰⛰⛰...⛰ *Particularly pleasant setting, quality and range of services available*

🦢🦢 *Tranquil, isolated site – quiet site, particularly at night*

≪≪ *Exceptional view – interesting or panoramic view*

MONTREVEL-EN-BRESSE

01340 – Michelin map **328** D2 – pop. 2 363 – alt. 215
▶ Paris 395 – Bourg-en-Bresse 18 – Mâcon 25 – Pont-de-Vaux 22

⛰ La Plaine Tonique 👥

☎ 0474308052, www.laplainetonique. com

Address : at Base de Loisirs (leisure centre, (500m east along the D 28)

Opening times : from mid April to mid Sept.

27 ha/15 for camping (548 pitches)

Tariff : 16,10€ ♟♟ ⛟ 🔲 ⚡ (10A) Extra per person 7,30€

Rental rates : (from mid April to mid Sept.) 🚿 – 5 🚐 – 57 🏠 – 15 🏠 3 studios – 15 apartments – 8 tipis 1 gîte. Per week from 400 to 844€

🚐 borne 2€ – 5 🔲 15€

Beside a lake and an attractive swimming area.

Surroundings : 🛏 ♀ ⛰	G
Leisure activities : ♟ ✗ 🎣 🌳 👟 🎣 🚲	
🎣 🎣 🔲 🚿 🦢 💧 sports trail	P
Facilities : 🚿 ⚷ 🚐 🚐 🚻 🍴 🔲 🚐 🚐	S

Longitude : 5.136
Latitude : 46.33902

MONTRIGAUD

6350 – Michelin map **332** D2 – pop. 496 – alt. 462
Paris 560 – Lyon 97 – Valence 51 – Grenoble 75

▲ La Grivelière

☎ 0475717071, www.lagriveliere.com

ddress : route de Roybon

pening times : from beginning April to end Sept.

6 ha (59 pitches) flat, grassy

riff : 25,50€ ♟♟ ⇔ 🖳 (6A) – Extra per person 4,50€
eservation fee 10€

ntal rates : (from beginning April to end Sept.) – 2 caravans
– 1 – 2 canvas bungalows. Per night from 40 to 55€
er week from 250 to 710€ – Reservation fee 10€

2 🖳 14€

Surroundings :
Leisure activities : ♟ ✕ 🏠 ⚓
Facilities : 🚿 launderette

| | Longitude : 5.16711 |
|G P S| Latitude : 45.22176 |

MORNANT

0440 – Michelin map **327** H6 – pop. 5 438 – alt. 380
Paris 478 – Givors 12 – Lyon 26 – Rive-de-Gier 13

▲ Municipal de la Trillonière

☎ 0478441647, www.ville-mornant.fr

dress : boulevard Général de Gaulle (southern exit, junction of
30 and D 34, near a stream)

pening times : from beginning May to end Sept.

ha (60 pitches) flat and relatively flat, grassy

riff : (2013 Price) 16,40€ ♟♟ ⇔ 🖳 (10A) – Extra per person 4€
borne – 59 🖳 16,40€ – 🚐 15,58€

the foot of the medieval old town; bus stop for Lyon.

Facilities : 🚿
Nearby : ✕ 🏊 🏞

| | Longitude : 4.67073 |
|G P S| Latitude : 45.61532 |

MORZINE

110 – Michelin map **328** N3 – pop. 2 930 – alt. 960 – Winter sports :
000/2 100m
Paris 586 – Annecy 84 – Chamonix-Mont-Blanc 67 – Cluses 26

▲ Les Marmottes

0450757444, www.campinglesmarmottes.com – alt. 938

ldress : at Essert-Romand (3.7km northwest along the D 902,
low the signs for Thonon-les-Bains and take D 329 to the left)

ening times : from end June to beginning Sept. and from mid
c to end Mar

ha (26 pitches)

riff : 27€ ♟♟ ⇔ 🖳 (6A) – Extra per person 7€

ntal rates : (from end June to beginning Sept. and from
d Dec. to end Mar.) – 2 🖳 – 1 – 1 studio. Per week
m 383 to 585€

huttle service to the centre of Morzine.

urroundings :
eisure activities : 🏠
acilities : 🚿 launderette

| | Longitude : 6.67725 |
|G P S| Latitude : 46.19487 |

MURS-ET-GELIGNIEUX

01300 – Michelin map **328** G7 – pop. 236 – alt. 232
Paris 509 – Aix-les-Bains 37 – Belley 17 – Chambéry 42

▲ Île de la Comtesse

☎ 0479872333, www.ile-de-la-comtesse.com

Address : located 1km southwest on the D 992

Opening times : from end April to beginning Sept.

3 ha (100 pitches)

Tariff : 31€ ♟♟ ⇔ 🖳 (6A) – Extra per person 6€ – Reservation
fee 14€

Rental rates : (from end April to beginning Sept.) – 25 🖳
11 – 6 canvas bungalows. Per night from 50 to 120€ –
Per week from 350 to 850€ – Reservation fee 28€

borne 5€

Near the Rhône river (small lake).

Surroundings :
Leisure activities : ♟ ✕ 🏠 ⚓ 🚲 🏞
Facilities : ♿ 🚿 launderette
Nearby :

| | Longitude : 5.64876 |
|G P S| Latitude : 45.63993 |

NEYDENS

74160 – Michelin map **328** J4 – pop. 1 486 – alt. 560
Paris 525 – Annecy 36 – Bellegarde-sur-Valserine 33 – Bonneville 34

▲ La Colombière

☎ 0450351314, www.camping-la-colombiere.com

Address : 166 chemin Neuf (east of the town)

Opening times : from beginning April to mid Nov.

2,5 ha (156 pitches)

Tariff : 37€ ♟♟ ⇔ 🖳 (10A) – Extra per person 6€ – Reservation
fee 12€

Rental rates : Permanent – 29 🖳 – 8 . Per night
from 70 to 150€ – Per week from 310 to 889€ – Reservation
fee 12€

borne 5€ – 2 🖳 14€ – 🚐 19€

Surroundings :
Leisure activities : ♟ ✕ 🏠 daytime ⚓
🚲 🏊 (small swimming pool)
Facilities : ♿ 🚿 launderette

| | Longitude : 6.10578 |
|G P S| Latitude : 46.11997 |

NOVALAISE-LAC

73470 – pop. 1 712 – alt. 427
Paris 524 – Belley 24 – Chambéry 21 – Les Échelles 24

▲ Le Grand Verney

☎ 0479360254, www.camping-legrandverney.info – limited spaces
for one-night stay

Address : Le Neyret (1.2km southwest along the C 6)

Opening times : from end April to beginning Oct.

2,5 ha (112 pitches)

Tariff : 18,50€ ♟♟ ⇔ 🖳 (10A) – Extra per person 4,50€

Rental rates : (from beginning April to end Oct.) – 20 🖳.
Per night from 65 to 80 € – Per week from 310 to 620 €

Surroundings :
Leisure activities : 🏊
Facilities : ♿ 🚿

| | Longitude : 5.78371 |
|G P S| Latitude : 45.5683 |

NYONS

26110 – Michelin map **332** D7 – pop. 7 104 – alt. 271
▶ Paris 653 – Alès 109 – Gap 106 – Orange 43

⚠ L'Or Vert

℘ 0475262485, www.camping-or-vert.com – ℞ ✗ (from beginning July to end Aug.)

Address : at Aubres, quai de la Charité (3km northeast along the D 94, follow the signs for Serres; beside the Eygues)

Opening times : from beginning April to end Sept.

1 ha (79 pitches) small orchard

Tariff : (2013 Price) 24,50€ ★★ ⇌ 🗉 🚰 (6A) – Extra per person 5,60€
Rental rates : Permanent ✗ (from beginning April to end Sept.) – 1 🚐 – 7 🏠. Per night from 45 to 85€ – Per week from 250 to 770€ – Reservation fee 10€
🚰 borne 17,20€

Surroundings : ⇐ 🗔 ♀♀
Leisure activities : ✗ 🖾 ⚴ ≌ ✗
Facilities : ⊶ ⌿ ♨ ⁇ 📷 refrigerators

G P S Longitude : 5.16272
Latitude : 44.37273

⚠ Les Terrasses Provençales

℘ 0475279236, www.lesterrassesprovencales.com

Address : Les Barroux - Novezan (7km northwest along the D 538, then take the D 232 to the right)

2,5 ha (70 pitches)
Rentals : ✗ – 10 🚐.

Surroundings : ≲ ⇐ ♀
Leisure activities : ⵟ ✗ 🖾 ⚴ ≌
Facilities : ⅋ ⊶ ♨ ⌀ ⁇ launderette

G P S Longitude : 5.08047
Latitude : 44.40949

LES OLLIÈRES-SUR-EYRIEUX

07360 – Michelin map **331** J5 – pop. 927 – alt. 200
▶ Paris 593 – Le Cheylard 28 – Lamastre 33 – Montélimar 53

⚠ VivaCamp le Mas de Champel ⚤

℘ 0475662323, www.masdechampel.com

Address : at the Domaine de Champel (north of the town along the D 120, follow the signs for la Voulte-sur-Rhône and take the road to the left, near L'Eyrieux)

Opening times : from mid April to end Sept.

4 ha (95 pitches)

Tariff : (2013 Price) 29,10€ ★★ ⇌ 🗉 🚰 (10A)
Extra per person 6,90€ – Reservation fee 15€

Rental rates : (from end April to end Sept.) – 35 🚐 – 1 tipi 9 canvas bungalows. Per night from 48 to 128€ – Per week from 155 to 896€ – Reservation fee 25€

Various rental options of varying degrees of comfort; pleasant small beach beside the river.

Surroundings : ≲ ⇐ ♀♀
Leisure activities : ⵟ ✗ 🖾 🕐 nighttime ⚴
≋ jacuzzi ⚴ ⚴ ≌ ≌ ⚭
Facilities : ⅋ ⊶ ⫿ ♨ ⁇ launderette ⌀

G P S Longitude : 4.6146
Latitude : 44.80603

⚠ FranceLoc Domaine des Plantas ⚤

℘ 0475662153, http://campingplantas.franceloc.fr/fr/accueil.htm

Address : 3km east of the town via narrow road, access near the bridge; beside the Eyrieux river

Opening times : from end April to mid Sept.

27 ha/7 for camping (172 pitches)

Tariff : 40€ ★★ ⇌ 🗉 🚰 (8A) – Extra per person 4,50€ – Reservation fee 27€

Rental rates : (from end April to mid Sept.) – 2 caravans – 91 🚐 21 🏠 – 4 tent lodges. Per night from 37 to 151€ – Per week from 147 to 1099€ – Reservation fee 27€
🚰 borne
Various rental and accommodation options.

Surroundings : ≲ ⇐ 🗔 ♀♀
Leisure activities : ⵟ ✗ 🖾 ⚴ ⚴ ⚴ 🔲 ≌
≌ ⚭
Facilities : ⅋ ⊶ ♨ ⁇ launderette ≋ ⌀
Nearby : ⚘

G P S Longitude : 4.63565
Latitude : 44.8087

⚠ Eyrieux-Camping ⚤

℘ 0475663008, www.eyrieuxcamping.com

Address : at La Feyrère (take the eastern exit along the D 120, follow the signs for La Voulte-sur-Rhône and take the road to the right; 100m from the Eyrieux river (direct access)

Opening times : from beginning April to mid Nov.

3 ha (94 pitches)

Tariff : 31,40€ ★★ ⇌ 🗉 🚰 (10A) – Extra per person 6,70€ – Reservation fee 15€

Rental rates : (from beginning April to mid Nov.) ⅋ (1 mobile home) – 25 🚐 – 25 🏠 – 11 canvas bungalows. Per night from 41 to 136€ – Per week from 287 to 955€ – Reservation fee 15€

Various rental options; the facilites range from basic to more luxurious.

Surroundings : ≲ ⇐ 🗔 ♀♀
Leisure activities : ⵟ ✗ ⚴ ⚴ ⚴ ⚴ ⚴ 🔲 ⯑
≌ ⚭ multi-sports ground
Facilities : ⅋ ⊶ ⁇ launderette ⌀
refrigerators

G P S Longitude : 4.63072
Latitude : 44.80764

LA PACAUDIÈRE

42310 – Michelin map **327** C2 – pop. 1 078 – alt. 363
▶ Paris 370 – Lapalisse 24 – Marcigny 21 – Roanne 25

⚠ Municipal Beausoleil

℘ 0477641150, lapacaudiere@wanadoo.fr

Address : at Beausoleil (700m east along the D 35, follow the signs for Vivans and take a right turn, near the sports field and the college)

Opening times : from beginning May to end Sept.

1 ha (35 pitches)

Tariff : ★ 3,80€ ⇌ 1,75€ 🗉 2€ – 🚰 (6A) 3,10€
Rental rates : (from beginning April to end Sept.) – 5 🏠 1 apartment. Per night 73€ – Per week 352€
🚰 borne 12,75€ – 30 🗉 12,75€
On the outskirts of the village, a beautiful swimming pool and a pretty chalet village.

Surroundings : 🗔
Leisure activities : 🖾 ⚴ ✗ ⚴ ≌ ⚴
Facilities : ⅋ ⊶ ⌿ ♨ ⚭ ⁇ 📷

G P S Longitude : 3.87236
Latitude : 46.17562

Routes nationales are main roads and their identifying numbers begin with N or RN. Routes départementales are generally quieter roads and begin with D or DN.

PALADRU

38850 – Michelin map **333** G5 – pop. 1 044 – alt. 503
▶ Paris 523 – Annecy 84 – Chambéry 47 – Grenoble 43

⚠ Le Calatrin

✆ 04 76 32 37 48, www.camping-paladru.fr

Address : 799 rue de la Morgerie (near the exit from town, towards Charavines)

Opening times : from beginning April to end Sept.

2 ha (60 pitches)

Tariff : 21€ ♣♣ ⬛ 🅿 (10A) – Extra per person 7,50€

Rental rates : (from beginning April to end Sept.) – 2 canvas bungalows. Per night from 35 to 75€ – Per week from 210 to 520€

🚐 2 🅿 11€

Surroundings : ⚲ ≤
Leisure activities : 🎣 ⚓
Facilities : ♿ ⚡ 🚿 💧 🏠
Nearby : ▼ ✗ 🏊 (beach)

Longitude : 5.54673
Latitude : 45.47077

PETICHET

38119 – Michelin map **333** H7
▶ Paris 592 – Le Bourg-d'Oisans 41 – Grenoble 30 – La Mure 11

⚠ Ser-Sirant

✆ 04 76 83 91 97, www.sersirant.fr

Address : at the lake Laffrey Petichet (take the eastern exit and take road to the left)

Opening times : from end April to end Sept.

2 ha (100 pitches)

Tariff : 25,40€ ♣♣ ⬛ 🅿 (10A) – Extra per person 5,90€
Reservation fee 9€

Rental rates : (from end April to end Sept.) – 6 🚍 – 6 🏠. Per night from 67 to 100€ – Per week from 280 to 660€
Reservation fee 16€

🚐 borne 1,50€ – 3 🅿 9€ – ⛟ 12€

Surroundings : ⚲ ≤
Leisure activities : ▼ 🎣 ⚲ 🏊 ⚓ boats to hire
Facilities : ⚡ 💧 launderette
Nearby : 💧

Longitude : 5.77759
Latitude : 45.00038

LE POËT-CÉLARD

26460 – Michelin map **332** D6 – pop. 133 – alt. 590
▶ Paris 618 – Lyon 156 – Valence 53 – Avignon 114

⚠ Club Airotel Le Couspeau

✆ 04 75 53 30 14, www.couspeau.com – alt. 600

Address : quartier Bellevue (1.3km southeast along the D 328A)

Opening times : from beginning April to mid Sept.

6 ha (133 pitches)

Tariff : (2013 Price) 39€ ♣♣ ⬛ 🅿 (6A) – Extra per person 8€
Reservation fee 16€

Rental rates : (from mid April to mid Sept.) – 14 🚍 – 31 🏠 – 6 tent lodges. Per night from 45 to 142€ – Per week from 315 to 994€ – Reservation fee 20€

🚐 borne

In an elevated, panoramic location.

Surroundings : ⚲ ≤ 🏠 💧
Leisure activities : ▼ ✗ 🏊 🚴 ⚲ 🎣 🖼 (small swimming pool) 🏊 ⚲ multi-sports ground, water park
Facilities : ♿ ⚡ 🏠 🚿 💧 launderette ⚲ ⚲

Longitude : 5.11152
Latitude : 44.59641

LE POËT-LAVAL

26160 – Michelin map **332** D6 – pop. 922 – alt. 311
▶ Paris 619 – Crest 35 – Montélimar 25 – Nyons 35

⚠ Municipal Lorette

✆ 04 75 91 00 62, www.campinglorette.fr

Address : quartier Lorette (located 1km east along the D 540, follow the signs for Dieulefit)

Opening times : from beginning May to end Sept.

2 ha (60 pitches)

Tariff : 15,10€ ♣♣ ⬛ 🅿 (6A) – Extra per person 3,40€

🚐 borne

Beside the Jabron river.

Surroundings : ≤ ⚲
Leisure activities : 🏊 🏊 ⚓
Facilities : ♿ ⚲ 💧 🏠
Nearby : ✗

Longitude : 5.02277
Latitude : 44.52922

PONCIN

01450 – Michelin map **328** F4 – pop. 1 618 – alt. 255
▶ Paris 456 – Ambérieu-en-Bugey 20 – Bourg-en-Bresse 28 – Nantua 25

⚠ Vallée de l'Ain

✆ 04 74 35 72 11, www.campingvalleedelain.com – limited spaces for one-night stay

Address : route d'Allement (500m northwest along the D 91 and D 81, follow the signs for Meyriat, near the Ain river)

Opening times : from beginning April to end Sept.

1,5 ha (89 pitches) flat, grassy

Tariff : 21,60€ ♣♣ ⬛ 🅿 (10A) – Extra per person 5€ – Reservation fee 12€

Rental rates : (from beginning April to end Sept.) – 4 🚍 3 🏠. Per night from 35 to 45€ – Per week from 230 to 600€ Reservation fee 12€

🚐 borne 5€ – 20 🅿 12€

Surroundings : ⚲
Leisure activities : ▼ ✗ 🏊 ⚲
Facilities : ⚡ 💧 🏠
Nearby : ✗ 🏊 ⚓

Longitude : 5.40407
Latitude : 46.08996

PONCINS

42110 – Michelin map **327** D5 – pop. 869 – alt. 339
▶ Paris 446 – Lyon 77 – St-Étienne 50 – Clermont-Ferrand 109

⚠ Village Vacances Le Nid Douillet

(chalet rentals only)

✆ 04 77 27 80 36, www.le-nid-douillet.com

Address : at Les-Baraques-des-Rotis, route de Montbrison-es-Baraques-des-Rotis

Opening times : Permanent

2 ha flat, grassy

Rental rates : (2013 Price) – 6 🏠. Per night from 50 to 125€ Per week from 325 to 500€

Chalets set in a lush green landscape.

Surroundings : ⚲
Leisure activities : ✗ 🎣 🏊
Facilities : 💧 🏠
Nearby : 🐎

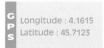

Longitude : 4.1615
Latitude : 45.7123

PONT-DE-VAUX

01190 – Michelin map **328** C2 – pop. 2 187 – alt. 177
▶ Paris 380 – Bourg-en-Bresse 40 – Lons-le-Saunier 69 – Mâcon 24

Champ d'Été

📞 03 85 23 96 10, www.camping-champ-dete.com

Address : 800m northwest along the D 933, towards Mâcon and take the road to the right, near a small lake

Opening times : from beginning May to mid Oct.

3,5 ha (150 pitches) flat, grassy

Tariff : ♦ 4€ ⇔ 🖭 8€ – ⚡ (10A) 13€

Rental rates : (from beginning March to end Nov.) – 30 🏠
1 gîte. Per night from 135 to 270€ – Per week from 235 to 605€

🚰 borne 2€

Leisure activities : 🏛 🚣 🎮 🏊 ⛷
Facilities : 👍 ⌀ 🏕 🚻 🖼
Nearby : 🎣

G P S	Longitude : 4.93301 Latitude : 46.42966

Aux Rives du Soleil 👥

📞 03 85 30 33 65, www.rivesdusoleil.com

Address : at Le Port

Opening times : from mid April to mid Oct.

8 ha (160 pitches) flat, grassy

Tariff : ♦ 6,50€ ⇔ 3€ 🖭 7€ – ⚡ (6A) 3,50€ – Reservation fee 15€

Rental rates : (from mid April to end Sept.) – 11 🚐 – 8 canvas bungalows. Per night from 26 to 94€ – Per week from 182 to 658€ Reservation fee 15€

On a peninsula at the confluence of the Saône and Reyssouze rivers.

Surroundings : ♀ ⛰
Leisure activities : 🍴 ✕ 🏛 🌳 🧗 🚣 🚴 🏊
🏄 🎣 🐎
Facilities : 👍 ⌀ 🏕 🚻 launderette 🚿

G P S	Longitude : 4.89892 Latitude : 46.44701

Les Ripettes

📞 03 85 30 66 58, www.camping-les-ripettes.com

Address : at Les Tourtes

Opening times : from beginning April to end Sept.

2,5 ha (54 pitches) flat, grassy

Tariff : 20,50€ ♦♦ ⇔ 🖭 ⚡ (10A) – Extra per person 4€

Rental rates : (from beginning April to end Sept.) 👍 🚿 – 1 🚐.
Per night from 40 to 60€ – Per week from 280 to 420€

🚰 3 🖭 17€

A very well-kept camping area with lots of green space.

Surroundings : 🏡 ♀
Leisure activities : 🏊
Facilities : ⌀ 🏕 🚻 launderette

G P S	Longitude : 4.98073 Latitude : 46.44449

Key to rentals symbols:

12	🚐	*Number of mobile homes*
20	🏠	*Number of chalets*
6	🛏	*Number of rooms to rent*
Per night 30–50€		*Minimum/maximum rate per night*
Per week 300–1,000€		*Minimum/maximum rate per week*

POUILLY-SOUS-CHARLIEU

42720 – Michelin map **327** D3 – pop. 2 582 – alt. 264
▶ Paris 393 – Charlieu 5 – Digoin 43 – Roanne 15

Municipal les Ilots

📞 04 77 60 80 67, www.pouillysoucharlieu.fr

Address : route de Marcigny (take the northern exit along the D 482, follow the signs for Digoin and take right turn; beside the Sornin river)

Opening times : from mid May to mid Sept.

1 ha (50 pitches) flat, grassy

Tariff : ♦ 2,45€ ⇔ 🖭 2,35€ – ⚡ (16A) 3,30€

A family atmosphere; situated a little out of town.

Surroundings : 🌳 ♀
Leisure activities : 🏛 🚴
Facilities : 👍 ⌀ 🏕 🚻 🖼
Nearby : ✂ 🎣

G P S	Longitude : 4.11135 Latitude : 46.15101

We have selected the best campsites in France with our usual care, listing those with the best facilities in the most pleasant surroundings.

POULE-LES-ÉCHARMEAUX

69870 – Michelin map **327** F3 – pop. 1 045 – alt. 570
▶ Paris 446 – Chauffailles 17 – La Clayette 25 – Roanne 47

Municipal les Écharmeaux

📞 06 79 30 46 62, www. poulelesecharmeaux.eu

Address : to the west of the village

0,5 ha (21 pitches) terraced, flat, grassy

Pitches arranged on individual terraces looking out over a lake.

Surroundings : 🌳 ◁ 🏡
Leisure activities : ✂
Facilities : ⌀ 🖼
Nearby : 🎣

G P S	Longitude : 4.4598 Latitude : 46.14871

PRADONS

07120 – Michelin map **331** I7 – pop. 421 – alt. 124
▶ Paris 647 – Aubenas 20 – Largentière 16 – Privas 52

Les Coudoulets 👥

📞 04 75 93 94 95, www.coudoulets.com

Address : chemin de l'Ardèche (to the northwest of the town)

Opening times : from mid April to mid Sept.

3,5 ha/2,5 for camping (123 pitches)

Tariff : 35€ ♦♦ ⇔ 🖭 ⚡ (16A) – Extra per person 7,20€ – Reservation fee 10€

Rental rates : (from mid April to mid Sept.) – 26 🚐 – 4 gîtes.
Per night from 40 to 110€ – Per week from 280 to 740€ Reservation fee 10€

🚰 borne

Well shaded and near the river, with good sanitary facilities; entertainment for the family.

Surroundings : 🌳 🏡 ♀♀
Leisure activities : 🍴 ✕ 🌳 daytime 🧗 🚣
🏊 🏄 🚲
Facilities : 👍 ⌀ 🏕 🚻 launderette

G P S	Longitude : 4.3572 Latitude : 44.47729

🏔 Le Pont

✆ 04 75 93 93 98, www.campingdupontardeche.com

Address : chemin du Cirque de Gens (300m west along the D 308, follow the signs for Chauzon)

Opening times : from beginning April to end Sept.

2 ha (80 pitches)Tariff : 34€ ♛♛ 🚗 🔲 🔌 (10A) – Extra per person 7€ Reservation fee 10€

Rental rates : (from beginning April to end Sept.) – 16 🚐 3 🏠. Per night from 45 to 65€ – Per week from 252 to 854€ Reservation fee 10€

Choose the pitches near the steps down to the Ardèche river, further from the road.

Surroundings : 🔲 ♤♤
Leisure activities : 🍴✗ 🛖 🛶 🏊 🚣
Facilities : 👤 ⚡ 🍴 🔲

	GPS
Longitude : 4.35337	
Latitude : 44.47392	

🏔 Laborie 👥

✆ 04 75 39 72 26, www.campingdelaborie.com

Address : route de Ruoms (1.8km northeast along the follow the signs for Aubenas)

Opening times : from mid April to mid Sept.

3 ha (100 pitches) flat, grassy

Tariff : 31€ ♛♛ 🚗 🔲 🔌 (10A) – Extra per person 5,20€ – Reservation fee 10€

Rental rates : (from mid April to mid Sept.) 🏊 – 13 🚐. Per week 760€ – Reservation fee 10€

Choose pitches near the river, furthest away from the road.

Surroundings : ♤♤♤
Leisure activities : 🍴 🛖 🏃 🛶 🏊 🚣
Facilities : 👤 ⚡ 🍴 🔲

	GPS
Longitude : 4.3783	
Latitude : 44.48161	

PRALOGNAN-LA-VANOISE

73710 – Michelin map **333** N5 – pop. 754 – alt. 1 425 – Winter sports : 1 410/2 360m

▶ Paris 634 – Albertville 53 – Chambéry 103 – Moûtiers 28

🏔 Le Parc Isertan

✆ 04 79 08 75 24, www.camping-isertan.com

Address : quartier Isertan (south of the town)

Opening times : and from mid dec to mid Apr

4,5 ha (180 pitches) open site, terraced, flat, grassy, stony

Tariff : 36€ ♛♛ 🚗 🔲 🔌 (10A) – Extra per person 6,50€ – Reservation fee 5€

Rental rates : (from end May to end Sept. and from mid Dec. to mid April) – 3 🏠 – 4 tent lodges – 1 gîte. Per night from 30 to 40€ Per week from 190 to 1 090€ – Reservation fee 5€

A pleasant location beside a mountain stream.

Surroundings : ❄ 🌿 ⛰
Leisure activities : 🍴✗ 🛖 🏊
Facilities : 👤 ⚡ 🔲 🍴 🏊
Nearby : 🛶 🎿 🏃 🚣 ⛷ climbing

	GPS
Longitude : 6.72883	
Latitude : 45.37189	

*The classification (1 to 5 tents, **black** or red) that we award to selected sites in this guide is our own system. It should not be confused with the classification (1 to 5 stars) of official organisations.*

LES PRAZ-DE-CHAMONIX

74400 – Michelin map **328** O5 – alt. 1 060
▶ Paris 620 – Lyon 237 – Annecy 104 – Aosta / Aoste 61

🏔 La Mer de Glace

✆ 04 50 53 44 03, www.chamonix-camping.com – 🇫🇷

Address : 200 chemin de la Bagna (at Les Bois, 80m from the Arveyron (direct access)

Opening times : from end April to end Sept.

2 ha (150 pitches)

Tariff : ♛ 8€ 🚗 🔲 8,90€ – 🔌 (10A) 3€

Surroundings : 🌿 ⛰ valley and Mont Blanc mountain range 🔲 ♤
Leisure activities : 🛖
Facilities : 👤 ⚡ 🚿 🔲 🍴 launderette

	GPS
Longitude : 6.89142	
Latitude : 45.93846	

PRAZ-SUR-ARLY

74120 – Michelin map **328** M5 – pop. 1 353 – alt. 1 036
▶ Paris 609 – Lyon 179 – Annecy 55 – Genève 75

🏔 Les Prés de l'Arly

✆ 06 10 44 02 33, www.campinglespresdelarly.com – limited spaces for one-night stay

Address : at Les Thouvassieres

Opening times : Permanent

1 ha (81 pitches)

Tariff : ♛ 5€ 🚗 🔲 3€ – 🔌 (10A) 9€

Rental rates : Permanent – 2 🚐 – 1 🏠 – 1 studio – 3 apartments 1 tipi. Per night from 40 to 200€ – Per week from 300 to 700€
🚐 borne 10€ – 3 🔲 10€ – 🚰 8€

Surroundings : ❄ 🌿 ⛰
Leisure activities : 🛖 🛶
Facilities : ⚡ 🚿 🔲 🏊 🍴 🔲
Nearby : 🎿 🏃 🚣 climbing wall

	GPS
Longitude : 6.57047	
Latitude : 45.83762	

PRIVAS

07000 – Michelin map **331** J5 – pop. 8 461 – alt. 300
▶ Paris 596 – Alès 107 – Mende 140 – Montélimar 34

🏔 Kawan Village Ardèche Camping 👥

✆ 04 75 64 05 80, www.ardechecamping.fr

Address : boulevard de Paste (located 1.5km south along the D 2, follow the signs for Montélimar; beside the Ouvèze river)

Opening times : from mid April to end Sept.

5 ha (170 pitches)

Tariff : 32€ ♛♛ 🚗 🔲 🔌 (10A) – Extra per person 9€ – Reservation fee 20€

Rental rates : (from mid April to end Sept.) – 2 caravans – 26 🚐 18 🏠 – 4 canvas bungalows – 4 tent lodges. Per night from 50 to 120€ – Per week from 252 to 875€ – Reservation fee 20€
🚐 borne 5€ – 🚰 🔌 15€

Near the town centre with facilities suitable for families with young children.

Surroundings : 🌿 ⛰ ♤
Leisure activities : 🍴✗ 🏃 🛶 🏊 🚣 ⛷ multi-sports ground
Facilities : 👤 ⚡ 🔲 🍴 🔲 🏊

	GPS
Longitude : 4.59698	
Latitude : 44.72597	

RECOUBEAU-JANSAC

26310 – Michelin map **332** F6 – pop. 240 – alt. 500
▶ Paris 637 – La Chapelle-en-Vercors 55 – Crest 51 – Die 14

▲▲▲ Le Couriou

✆ 0475213323, www.lecouriou.fr

Address : at Combe Lambert (head 700m northwest along the D 93, follow the signs for Dié)

7 ha/4,5 for camping (138 pitches) terraced, flat and relatively flat, grassy, gravelled, stony, wood

Rentals : 22 ▭ – 15 ▭.

Swimming area and a small but pretty chalet village.

Surroundings : ≤ ▭ ♨
Leisure activities : ♟ ✗ ▭ ⛵ jacuzzi ⚓ ⛷ ⛵ multi-sports ground, spa centre
Facilities : ♿ ☕ ♨ ♟ launderette ♨

G P S Longitude : 5.41098
Latitude : 44.65689

RIBES

07260 – Michelin map **331** H7 – pop. 266 – alt. 380
▶ Paris 656 – Aubenas 30 – Largentière 19 – Privas 61

▲▲ Les Cruses

✆ 0475395469, www.campinglescruses.com

Address : at Le Champcros (located 1km southeast of the town, along the D 450)

Opening times : from beginning May to mid Sept.

0,7 ha (47 pitches)

Tariff : 30€ ⚤ ⚤ ⚗ ▤ ⚡ (6A) – Extra per person 7€ – Reservation fee 16,50€

Rental rates : (from mid April to mid Sept.) – 2 caravans 8 ▭ 18 ▭ – 2 gîtes. Per night from 60 to 131€ – Per week from 317 to 922€ – Reservation fee 16,50€

🚐 borne 2€ – 4 ▤ 17€ – 🚐 ⚡17€

In 2 distinct sections on either side of a small path; pitches that look out over the Ardeche vineyards.

Surroundings : 🌿 ♨
Leisure activities : ✗ ▭ jacuzzi ⚓ ⛷
Facilities : ☕ (July–Aug.) ♟ ♨ ♨ ♟ ▤ ♨

G P S Longitude : 4.20757
Latitude : 44.4927

The information in the guide may have changed since going to press.

LA ROSIÈRE 1850

73700 – Michelin map **333** O4 – alt. 1 850 – Winter sports : 1 100/2 600m
▶ Paris 657 – Albertville 76 – Bourg-St-Maurice 22 – Chambéry 125

▲ La Forêt

✆ 0479068621, www.camping-larosiere.com – alt. 1 730

Address : situated 2km south along the N 90, follow the signs for Bourg-St-Maurice - direct access to the village

Opening times : Permanent

1,5 ha (67 pitches)

Tariff : 29€ ⚤ ⚤ ⚗ ▤ ⚡ (10A) – Extra per person 6,50€ – Reservation fee 5€

Rental rates : Permanent 🏠 – 3 ▭ – 1 ▭. Per night from 55 to 80€ – Per week from 450 to 760€ – Reservation fee 5€

🚐 35 ▤ 29€

In an attractive location looking out over the valley.

Surroundings : ❄ 🌿 ≤ ♨
Leisure activities : ♟ ⚓ ⛷ (small swimming pool)
Facilities : ♿ ☕ ▥ ♟ ▤
Nearby : ✗

G P S Longitude : 6.85425
Latitude : 45.6234

Using the traditional Michelin classification method, the guide provides you with an easy, speedy reference for assessing the category of each site: 1 to 5 tents (see page 10).

ROSIÈRES

07260 – Michelin map **331** H7 – pop. 1 121 – alt. 175
▶ Paris 649 – Aubenas 22 – Largentière 12 – Privas 54

▲▲▲ Arleblanc

✆ 0475395311, www.arleblanc.com

Address : take the northeastern exit, follow the signs for Aubenas and proceed 2.8km along the road to the right, beside the Intermarché commercial centre

Opening times : from beginning April to beginning Nov.

10 ha/6 for camping (167 pitches) flat, grassy

Tariff : 31,50€ ⚤ ⚤ ⚗ ▤ ⚡ (6A) – Extra per person 7€ – Reservation fee 16€

Rental rates : (from beginning April to beginning Nov. 34 ▭ – 6 ▭ – 4 gîtes. Per night from 50 to 106€ – Per week from 300 to 750€ – Reservation fee 16€

An extensive site set around a 12th-century priory and beside the Beaume river. Ideal for swimming and fishing.

Surroundings : 🌿 ♨
Leisure activities : ♟ ✗ ⚓ ⛷ ♟ ⛷ ⛵ 🐟
Facilities : ♿ ☕ ▥ ♟ ♟ ♟ ♟ launderette ♟ ♨
Nearby : 🐎

G P S Longitude : 4.27221
Latitude : 44.46552

▲▲ La Plaine

✆ 0475395135, www.campinglaplaine.com

Address : at Les Plaines (700m northeast along the D 104)

4,5 ha/3,5 for camping (128 pitches)

Rentals : 54 ▭ – 2 ▭.

A good amount of shade for the pitches and a small pool for anglers.

Surroundings : ▭ ♨
Leisure activities : ♟ ▭ ⚓ ✗ ♟ ⛷ 🐟
Facilities : ♿ ☕ ♟ ♟ ▤

G P S Longitude : 4.26677
Latitude : 44.48608

▲▲ Les Platanes

✆ 0475395231, www.campinglesplatanesardeche.com

Address : at La Charve (take the northeastern exit, follow the signs for Aubenas and proceed 3.7km along the road to the right, beside the Intermarché commercial centre)

Opening times : from beginning April to mid Oct.

2 ha (90 pitches) flat, grassy

Tariff : (2013 Price) 28,50€ ⚤ ⚤ ⚗ ▤ ⚡ (16A)
Extra per person 5,10€

Rental rates : (from beginning April to mid Oct.) 🏠 – 27 ▭
Per night from 47 to 52€ – Per week from 250 to 760€

🚐 borne

Pitches for tents and caravans beside the river, beneath hack-berry trees; the mobile homes are across a small road.

Surroundings : 🐟 ⛰ ♨♨
Leisure activities : 🍷 ✕ 🎣 🚣 ⛵ 🛶
Facilities : ♿ ⚬ₘ ⊞ 👶 🎯 🔥 🧺 🚮

G P S Longitude : 4.27766
Latitude : 44.45702

⚠ Les Hortensias

📞 04 75 39 91 38, www.camping-leshortensias.com

Address : quartier Ribeyre-Bouchet (1.8km northwest along the D 104, follow the signs for Joyeuse, D 303, follow the signs for Vernon to the right, and take road to the left)

Opening times : from end May to mid Sept.

4 ha (43 pitches)

Tariff : 27 € ✶✶ 🚘 🗲 (10A) – Extra per person 4,60 €

Rental rates : (from end May to mid Sept.) 🐾 – 20 🚌 – 4 canvas bungalows – 1 gîte. Per week from 310 to 740 €

Surrounded by vineyards, a peaceful site, various rental options, but few pitches for tents and caravans

Surroundings : 🐟 🚃 ♨♨
Leisure activities : 🛶
Facilities : ♿ ⚬ₘ 🎯 ⊞
Nearby : ⛱ (river) 🐟

G P S Longitude : 4.23976
Latitude : 44.48755

RUFFIEUX

73310 – Michelin map **333** I2 – pop. 800 – alt. 282
▶ Paris 517 – Aix-les-Bains 20 – Ambérieu-en-Bugey 58 – Annecy 51

⚠ Saumont

📞 04 79 54 26 26, www.campingsaumont.com

Address : at Saumont (1.2km west, access on the D 991, near the carr. du Saumont, towards Aix-les-Bains and take the road to the right; beside a stream)

Opening times : from beginning April to end Oct.

4,6 ha (66 pitches)

Tariff : 20,50 € ✶✶ 🚘 🗲 (10A) – Extra per person 4,30 €
Reservation fee 10 €

Rental rates : (from beginning April to end Oct.) – 16 🚌 4 🏠. Per night from 40 to 98 € – Per week from 260 to 685 € Reservation fee 10 €

Surroundings : 🚃 ♨♨
Leisure activities : 🍷 🚣 🎾 🛶 ⚓
Facilities : ♿ ⚬ₘ ⊞ 👶 🔥 🧺 launderette

G P S Longitude : 5.88483
Latitude : 45.8491

RUMILLY

74150 – Michelin map **328** I5 – pop. 13 197 – alt. 334
▶ Paris 530 – Aix-les-Bains 21 – Annecy 19 – Bellegarde-sur-Valserine 37

⚠ Le Madrid

📞 04 50 01 12 57, www.camping-le-madrid.com

Address : route de Saint-Félix (3km southeast along the D 910, follow the signs for Aix-les-Bains then turn left onto D 3 and take D 53 to the right; 500m from a small lake)

Opening times : Permanent

3,2 ha (109 pitches)

Tariff : 26 € ✶✶ 🚘 🗲 (16A) – Extra per person 4 € – Reservation fee 15 €

Rental rates : Permanent – 3 🚌 – 23 🏠. Per night from 44 to 88 € Per week from 260 to 650 € – Reservation fee 15 €
🚐 borne 3 € – 4 🗲 19 €

Surroundings : 🚃 ♨♨
Leisure activities : 🍷 ✕ 🎪 🚣 🛶
Facilities : ♿ ⚬ₘ 🔲 👶 🔥 🧺 launderette 🚮 refrigerated food storage facilities
Nearby : ⛱ 🐟

G P S Longitude : 5.96239
Latitude : 45.84084

RUOMS

07120 – Michelin map **331** I7 – pop. 2 249 – alt. 121
▶ Paris 651 – Alès 54 – Aubenas 24 – Pont-St-Esprit 49

⛰⛰ Sunêlia Aluna Vacances 👤👤

📞 04 75 93 93 15, www.alunavacances.fr

Address : route de Lagorce (2km east along the D 559)

Opening times : from mid April to mid Sept.

10 ha (430 pitches) terraced, flat and relatively flat, grassy, stony

Tariff : 48 € ✶✶ 🚘 🗲 (10A)
Extra per person 11,60 € – Reservation fee 30 €

Rental rates : (from mid April to mid Sept.) ♿ (2 mobile homes) 230 🚌 – 2 tent lodges. Per night from 36 to 230 € – Per week from 252 to 1610 € – Reservation fee 30 €

The Aluna music festival is held every year in mid June, with 4 to 7 concerts every evening that attract crowds of up to 35 000 over the 3 days.

Surroundings : 🐟 🚃 ♨♨
Leisure activities : 🍷 ✕ 🎪 🎯 🏕 🎣 hammam, jacuzzi 🚣 🎾 🛶 ⚓ multi-sports ground, spa centre
Facilities : ⚬ₘ 👶 🔥 launderette 🚮 🚮
Nearby : 🐎

G P S Longitude : 4.3526
Latitude : 44.44962

⛰⛰ Yelloh! Village La Plaine 👤👤

📞 04 75 39 65 83, www.yellohvillage-la-plaine.com

Address : quartier la Grand Terre (3.5km to the south)

Opening times : from mid April to mid Sept.

4,5 ha (212 pitches) flat and relatively flat, grassy, sandy

Tariff : 47 € ✶✶ 🚘 🗲 (8A) – Extra per person 8 €

Rental rates : (from mid April to mid Sept.) 🐾 🅿 – 87 🚌. Per night from 39 to 156 € – Per week from 273 to 1092 €
🚐 borne

Near vineyards and the Ardèche river; the pitches are well shaded with some high-quality rentals.

Surroundings : 🐟 ⛰ ♨♨♨
Leisure activities : 🍷 ✕ 🎪 🎯 🏕 🎣 🚣 🚲 🎣 ⛱ 🛶 ⚓ multi-sports ground
Facilities : ♿ ⚬ₘ ⊞ 👶 🔥 🐾 🧺 launderette 🚮

G P S Longitude : 4.33596
Latitude : 44.42666

A chambre d'hôte is a guesthouse or B & B-style accommodation.

🏕 Domaine de Chaussy 👥

(rental of mobile homes & gîtes only, plus hotel)

☎ 0475939966, www.domainedechaussy.com

Address : quartier du Petit Chaussy (2.3km east along the D 559, follow the signs for Lagorce)

Opening times : from beginning April to mid Sept.

18 ha/5,5 for camping (250 pitches) undulating

Rental rates : 300 🚐 – 40 🛏 – 17 gîtes. Per night from 52 to 65 €
Per week from 352 to 1034 € – Reservation fee 20 €

Numerous sporting activities for the family.

Surroundings : 🌊 ♨
Leisure activities : ♈ ✕ 🎦 🎲 ⛷ 🏊
hammam, jacuzzi ⛷ 🎿 🏊 fitness
trail, mountain biking trail
Facilities : ♿ ⚡ 🚿 🍴 launderette 🏧 🚰
GPS Longitude : 4.36913
Latitude : 44.4472

🏕 RCN La Bastide en Ardèche 👥

☎ 0475396472, www.rcn.fr

Address : route d'Alès - D111, at the bridge (4km southwest, at Labastide)

Opening times : from beginning April to end Sept.

7 ha (300 pitches)

Tariff : 50,50 € 👫 🚗 🔲 ⚡ (6A) – Extra per person 5,65 €
Reservation fee 19,95 €

Rental rates : (from beginning April to end Sept.) – 40 🚐.
Per night from 37 to 73 € – Per week from 511 to 1204 €
Reservation fee 20 €

In an attractive location beside the Ardèche river with a sandy beach, but choose the pitches further away from the road.

Surroundings : ≤ ♨
Leisure activities : ♈ ✕ 🎦 ⛷ 🏊 🎿 ⛷
🏊 (beach)
Facilities : ♿ ⚡ 🚿 🚰 launderette
🏧 🚰
GPS Longitude : 4.32524
Latitude : 44.42326

🏕 La Grand'Terre 👥

☎ 0475396494, www.camping-lagrandterre.com

Address : 3.5km to the south

Opening times : from mid April to mid Sept.

10 ha (296 pitches)

Tariff : 39 € 👫 🚗 🔲 ⚡ (10A) – Extra per person 9 €
Rental rates : (from mid April to mid Sept.) –66 🚐. Per night from 42 to 148 € – Per week from 294 to 1036 €
🚰 borne 2 € – 6 🔲 16 €

Most of the pitches have a very wooded setting, with one great bonus: a beautiful beach beside the Ardèche river.

Surroundings : 🌊 💦
Leisure activities : ♈ ✕ 🎦 🎲 ⛷ 🎿 🚴 🏊
🎿 🏊 (beach) 🌊 multi-sports ground
Facilities : ♿ ⚡ 🚿 🍴 launderette 🏧 🚰
GPS Longitude : 4.33192
Latitude : 44.42522

🏕 La Chapoulière 👥

☎ 0475396498, www.lachapouliere.com

Address : 3.5km to the south

Opening times : from beginning April to mid Oct.

2,5 ha (164 pitches)

Tariff : 37,50 € 👫 🚗 🔲 ⚡ (10A) – Extra per person 9 €

Rental rates : (from beginning April to mid Oct.) 🏊 – 20 🚐
Per night from 43 to 60 € – Per week from 301 to 896 €
🚰 borne – 3 🔲 37,50 €

A lovely grassy area beside the Ardèche river, with some pitches overlooking the water.

Surroundings : 🌊 ♨
Leisure activities : ♈ ✕ 🎦 🎲 ⛷ 🎿 🏊 🎿
🌊 multi-sports ground
Facilities : ♿ ⚡ 🚿 🍴 🔲 🏧 🚰
GPS Longitude : 4.32972
Latitude : 44.43139

🏕 Sites et Paysages Le Petit Bois 👥

☎ 0475396072, www.campinglepetitbois.fr

Address : 87 rue du Petit Bois (800m north of the town, 80m from the Ardèche river)

Opening times : from beginning April to end Sept.

2,5 ha (110 pitches)

Tariff : 36 € 👫 🚗 🔲 ⚡ (10A) – Extra per person 7 € – Reservation fee 15 €

Rental rates : (from beginning April to mid Sept.) 🏊 – 21 🚐
18 🏠. Per night from 37 to 210 € – Per week from 259 to 1500 €
Reservation fee 15 €

🚰 borne 15 € – 🔋 ⚡14 €

Some rentals have a panoramic view over the Ardèche river, some are very well equipped with access to the river via a steep path.

Surroundings : 🌊 🔲 ♨
Leisure activities : ♈ ✕ 🎦 ⛷ 🏊 hammam
⛷ 🏊 (open air in season) 🎿 🎿 🌊
multi-sports ground
Facilities : ♿ ⚡ 🚿 🍴 launderette
GPS Longitude : 4.33789
Latitude : 44.45882

🏕 Les Paillotes en Ardèche

☎ 0475396205, www.campinglespaillotes.com – limited spaces for one-night stay

Address : chemin de l'Espédès (600m north along the D 579, follow the signs for Pradons and take road to the left)

Opening times : from beginning April to end Sept.

1 ha (45 pitches) flat, grassy

Tariff : 42 € 👫 🚗 🔲 ⚡ (10A) – Extra per person 8 €

Rental rates : (from beginning April to end Sept.) – 30 🚐
5 canvas bungalows – 2 gîtes. Per week from 180 to 945 €
Reservation fee 30 €

Well marked-out pitches but little space for tents and caravans, near a large canoeing centre.

Surroundings : 🔲 ♨
Leisure activities : ♈ ✕ ⛷ 🏊 🎿
Facilities : ♿ ⚡ 🚿 🚰 🚰 🍴 🔲
GPS Longitude : 4.34184
Latitude : 44.45938

⛺ Le Carpenty

☎ 0475397429, www.camping-ruoms-ardeche.com

Address : 3.6km south along the D 111

Opening times : from end March to end Sept.

0,7 ha (45 pitches)

Tariff : 27 € 👫 🚗 🔲 ⚡ (10A) – Extra per person 4 €

Rental rates : (from end March to end Sept.) – 28 🚐. Per night from 40 to 60 € – Per week from 205 to 680 €

A lovely green site beside the Ardèche river, but choose pitches away from the road and the bridge.

Surroundings : 🔲 ♨
Leisure activities : ♈ ✕ ⛷ 🏊 🎿
Facilities : ♿ ⚡ 🍴 🔲 🚰

GPS Longitude : 4.32842
Latitude : 44.42695

SABLIÈRES

07260 – Michelin map **331** G6 – pop. 144 – alt. 450
▶ Paris 629 – Aubenas 48 – Langogne 58 – Largentière 38

⛰ La Drobie

☎ 0475369522, www.ladrobie.com

Address : at Le Chambon (3km west along the D 220 and take turning to the right; beside the river, for caravans recommended route is via Lablachère along the D 4)

Opening times : from mid April to end Sept.

1,5 ha (80 pitches)

Tariff : 17€ ♥♥ ⬤ 🔲 (4) (10A) – Extra per person 5,50€ – Reservation fee 5€

Rental rates : (from mid April to end Oct.) – 3 🚐 – 10 ⌂ 1 gîte. Per night from 45 to 65€ – Per week from 410 to 550€ Reservation fee 5€

Beside the river where bathing is possible. The pitches (with good sanitary facilities) are shaded by oak and cherry trees. Restaurant offering local cuisine.

Surroundings : 🐟 ≼
Leisure activities : ♥ ✕ 🚣 ※ 🛝 ≋ 🎣
Facilities : &. ⚲ 🖥 ▥ 🏪

Longitude : 4.04863
Latitude : 44.54368

We have selected the best campsites in France with our usual care, listing those with the best facilities in the most pleasant surroundings.

SAHUNE

26510 – Michelin map **332** E7 – pop. 322 – alt. 330
▶ Paris 647 – Buis-les-Baronnies 27 – La Motte-Chalancon 22 – Nyons 16

⛰ Vallée Bleue

☎ 0475274442, www.lavalleebleue.com

Address : take the southwestern exit along the D 94, follow the signs for Nyons; beside the Eygues

Opening times : from beginning April to mid Sept.

3 ha (45 pitches)

Tariff : ♥ 6,50€ ⬤ 🔲 11€ – (4) (10A) 3,50€

Rental rates : (from beginning April to end Sept.) ⚡ – 2 ⌂. Per week from 350 to 850€

Surroundings : ≼ ♀
Leisure activities : ✕ 🚣 ▰ 🛝
Facilities : &. ⚲ 🖥▥ ▱ 🏪

Longitude : 5.26139
Latitude : 44.41148

ST-AGRÈVE

07320 – Michelin map **331** I3 – pop. 2 522 – alt. 1 050
▶ Paris 582 – Aubenas 68 – Lamastre 21 – Privas 64

⛰ Le Riou la Selle

☎ 0475302928, www.campinglerioulaselle.fr

Address : 2.8km southeast along the D 120, follow the signs for Cheylard, take the D 21, follow the signs for Nonières to the left and take the Chemin de la Roche to the right

Opening times : from end April to end Sept.

1 ha (29 pitches) terraced, flat and relatively flat, grassy

Tariff : (2013 Price) 22,50€ ♥♥ ⬤ 🔲 (4) (10A) – Extra per person 6€

Rental rates : (from end April to end Sept.) – 2 🚐 – 2 ⌂. Per night from 85 to 130€ – Per week from 300 to 590€

A peaceful site, part pleasantly situated among shrubs and bushes; rental options range from basic to more luxurious.

Surroundings : 🐟 🗔 ♀♀
Leisure activities : ♥ ✕ 🚣 🛝
Facilities : &. ⚲ (July–Aug.) ▥ 🏖 ▱ 🏪 🖥 🏪

Longitude : 4.40462
Latitude : 44.98892

We value your opinion and welcome your feedback. Do email us at campingfrance@tp.michelin.com

ST-ALBAN-AURIOLLES

07120 – Michelin map **331** H7 – pop. 994 – alt. 108
▶ Paris 656 – Alès 49 – Aubenas 28 – Pont-St-Esprit 55

⛰⛰⛰ Sunêlia Le Ranc Davaine 👥

PAILLET

☎ 0475396055, www.camping-ranc-davaine.fr

Address : route de Chandolas (2.3km southwest along the D 208, follow the signs for Chandolas)

Opening times : from mid April to mid Sept.

13 ha (435 pitches)

Tariff : 51€ ♥♥ ⬤ 🔲 (4) (10A) Extra per person 12,10€ – Reservation fee 30€

Rental rates : (from mid April to mid Sept.) &. (1 mobile home) ⚡ 250 🚐. Per night from 51 to 215€ Per week from 357 to 1505€ Reservation fee 30€

A good amount of shade is provided by oak trees, around a partially covered water and play park, with direct access to the river.

Surroundings : 🐟 🗔 ♀♀
Leisure activities : ♥ ✕ 🚣 ☷ 🕴 ⛷ ≋ hammam, jacuzzi 🚣 ※ 🔲 🛝 ≋ 🎣 disco 🎿 spa centre
Facilities : &. ⚲ ▥ 🏖 🖊 ▱ 🏪 launderette 🏪 ▱

Longitude : 4.26868
Latitude : 44.40014

⛰ Le Mas du Sartre

☎ 0475397174, www.camping-mas-du-sartre-07.com

Address : at Auriolles, 5 chemin de la Vignasse (1.8km northwest along the D 208)

Opening times : from beginning May to mid Sept.

1,6 ha (49 pitches)

Tariff : 28€ ♥♥ ⬤ 🔲 (4) (10A) – Extra per person 6,50€ – Reservation fee 5€

Rental rates : (from beginning May to mid Sept.) – 10 🚐 4 ⌂. Per night from 44 to 82€ – Per week from 305 to 580€ Reservation fee 5€

 borne 10€ – 5 🔲 10€ – 🛒 10€

Choose the pitches surrounded by shrubs and bushes, further away from the road.

Surroundings : 🗔 ♀♀
Leisure activities : ♥ ✕ 🚣 🚣 🛝 multi-sports ground
Facilities : &. ⚲ 🖥 🏪 🏪 refrigerators

Longitude : 4.31477
Latitude : 44.43418

ST-ALBAN-DE-MONTBEL

73610 – Michelin map **333** H4 – pop. 605 – alt. 400
▶ Paris 551 – Belley 32 – Chambery 21 – Grenoble 74

⚑ Base de Loisirs du Sougey ♦♦

✆ 0479360144, www.camping-sougey.com

Address : at Le Sougey (1.2km to the northeast, 300m from the lake)

Opening times : from beginning May to mid Sept.

4 ha (159 pitches)

Tariff : 27,60€ ♦♦ ⇌ 🔲 🔋 (10A) – Extra per person 4,20€

Rental rates : (from beginning May to mid Sept.) 🚫 – 7 🚍
8 🏠. Per night from 65 to 110€ – Per week from 290 to 730€

Surroundings : ▭ ♀	
Leisure activities : ▼ 🏠 🏃 🚴	**G** Longitude : 5.79069
Facilities : ♿ ⊶ 🛁 🚿 🍴 launderette 🦮	**P** Latitude : 45.55562
Nearby : 🏖 ✕ ✂ 🛥 🎣 ♨ pedalos	**S**

ST-AVIT

26330 – Michelin map **332** C2 – pop. 326 – alt. 348
▶ Paris 536 – Annonay 33 – Lyon 81 – Romans-sur-Isère 22

⚑ Domaine la Garenne

✆ 0475686226, www.domaine-la-garenne.com

Address : 156 chemin de Chablezin

Opening times : from beginning May to end Sept.

14 ha/6 for camping (112 pitches)

Tariff : (2013 Price) 30,50€ ♦♦ ⇌ 🔲 🔋 (6A) – Extra per person 6,50€
Reservation fee 10€

Rental rates : (from beginning May to end Sept.) 🚫 – 25 🚍
8 🏠. Per night from 60 to 120 € – Per week from 360 to 868€
Reservation fee 10€

Surroundings : 🌲 ⋜ ♀♀	
Leisure activities : ✕ 🏠 🏃 ⛷	**G** Longitude : 4.9549
Facilities : ♿ ⊶ 🛁 🍴 📷	**P** Latitude : 45.20176
Nearby : 🎣	**S**

ST-CHRISTOPHE-EN-OISANS

38520 – Michelin map **333** K8 – pop. 123 – alt. 1 470
▶ Paris 635 – L'Alpe-d'Huez 31 – La Bérarde 12 – Le Bourg-
d'Oisans 21

⚑ Municipal la Bérarde

✆ 0476792045– access narrow, sometimes only possible using
passing places – alt. 1 738

Address : at La Bérarde (10.5km southeast along the D 530; difficult
access for caravans (steep slope)

2 ha (165 pitches)

Very pleasant rural site beside the Vénéon river.

Surroundings : 🌲 ⋜ Parc National des Écrins ♀	
Leisure activities : 🏠 🎣	**G** Longitude : 6.29205
Facilities : ⊶ ▥ 📷	**P** Latitude : 44.93309
Nearby : 🏖 ▼ ✕	**S**

Some campsites benefit from proximity to a municipal leisure centre.

ST-CIRGUES-EN-MONTAGNE

07510 – Michelin map **331** G5 – pop. 248 – alt. 1 044
▶ Paris 586 – Aubenas 40 – Langogne 31 – Privas 68

⚑ Les Airelles

✆ 0475389249, www.camping-les-airelles.fr

Address : route de Lapalisse (take the northern exit along the D 160,
follow the signs for the Lac-d'Issarlès, right bank of the Vernason
river)

Opening times : from beginning April to end Oct.

0,7 ha (50 pitches)

Tariff : 16,50€ ♦♦ ⇌ 🔲 🔋 (6A) – Extra per person 4,50€

Rental rates : (from beginning April to mid Oct.) – 10 🚍 – 9 🛏
Per night from 45 to 55€ – Per week from 230 to 450€

🚐 borne 4€

Surroundings : 🌲 ⋜ ♀♀	
Leisure activities : ▼ ✕ 🏠 🛥 🎣	**G** Longitude : 4.0949
Facilities : ⊶ 🍴 launderette	**P** Latitude : 44.75648
Nearby : 🏃 ✂	**S**

ST-CLAIR-DU-RHÔNE

38370 – Michelin map **333** B5 – pop. 3 886 – alt. 160
▶ Paris 501 – Annonay 35 – Givors 26 – Le Péage-de-Roussillon 10

⚑ Le Daxia

✆ 0474563920, www.campingledaxia.com – 🇫🇷

Address : route du Péage - avenue du Plateau des Frères (2.7km
south along the D 4 and take road to the left, recommended route
via the N 7 and D 37)

Opening times : from beginning April to end Sept.

7,5 ha (120 pitches) flat, grassy

Tariff : (2013 Price) 22,75€ ♦♦ ⇌ 🔲 🔋 (6A)
Extra per person 4,70€ Reservation fee 15€

Rental rates : (from beginning April to end Sept.) 🚫 (from
beginning April to end Sept.) – 2 🏠. Per night from 60 to 75€
Per week from 270 to 495€ – Reservation fee 20€

🚐 borne

Pretty, marked out pitches; beside the Varèze river.

Surroundings : 🌲 ▭ ♀♀	
Leisure activities : ▼ ✕ 🏠 🏃 ♨ ⛷ 🎣	**G** Longitude : 4.78129
Facilities : ♿ ⊶ 🛁 🍴 📷 🦮	**P** Latitude : 45.42128
	S

ST-COLOMBAN-DES-VILLARDS

73130 – Michelin map **333** K6 – pop. 187 – alt. 1 100
▶ Paris 643 – Lyon 176 – Chambéry 76 – Grenoble 106

⚑ FranceLoc La Perrière

✆ 0479052860, www.campings-franceloc.fr

Address : at La Perrière

2 ha (46 pitches) terraced, flat, grassy, wood

Rentals : 10 🚍 – 6 🏠.

Surroundings : ⋜ Mountains and Pic du Puy Gris (2,950m) ♀	
Leisure activities : 🏃 ⛷	**G** Longitude : 6.22667
Facilities : ♿ ⊶ 🍴	**P** Latitude : 45.29417
Nearby : 🏖 ▼ ✕ 🛥 🐎 climbing, via ferrata (protected climbing route)	**S**

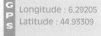

ST-DONAT-SUR-L'HERBASSE

26260 – Michelin map **332** C3 – pop. 3 825 – alt. 202
▶ Paris 545 – Grenoble 92 – Hauterives 20 – Romans-sur-Isère 13

🏕 Domaine du Lac de Champos

☎ 04 75 45 17 81, www.lacdechampos.com
Address : situated 2km northeast along the D 67
Opening times : from end April to mid Sept.
43 ha/6 for camping (60 pitches)
Tariff : 19€ ✹ ✹ ⇌ 🔲 🚿 (10A) – Extra per person 4€
Rental rates : (from beginning April to end Oct.) – 21 🏠 – 4 tent lodges. Per night from 28 to 78€ – Per week from 199 to 549€
Reservation fee 15€
🛏 5 🔲 16€ – ⛺11€

In a pleasant setting beside the Lac de Champos.

Surroundings : ⚲ 🏔
Leisure activities : ♟ ✗ 🛖 🏊 ✂ 🎿 🦢 pedal go-carts 🚵
Facilities : ♿ ⚷ 🚿 🍴 launderette

G P S	Longitude : 5.00543
	Latitude : 45.13615

🏕 Domaine des Ulèzes

☎ 04 75 47 83 20, www.camping-des-ulezes.fr
Address : route de Romans (take southeastern exit along the D 53 and take the road to the right; near the Herbasse river)
Opening times : from beginning April to end Oct.
2,5 ha (85 pitches) flat, grassy
Tariff : 20€ ✹ ✹ ⇌ 🔲 🚿 (10A) – Extra per person 4,80€
Rental rates : (from beginning April to end Oct.) – 9
3 canvas bungalows. Per night from 80 to 130€ – Per week from 415 to 680€
🛏 borne

Surroundings : 🦢 🍴 ⚲
Leisure activities : ✗ 🛖 🏊 ⛵ m 🦢
Facilities : ♿ ⚷ 🚿 🍴 🔲
Nearby : ♟ 🦢

G P S	Longitude : 4.99285
	Latitude : 45.11914

Do not confuse:
△ *to* 🏕 *: MICHELIN classification with*
★ *to* ★★★★★ *: official classification*

ST-FERRÉOL-TRENTE-PAS

26110 – Michelin map **332** E7 – pop. 228 – alt. 417
▶ Paris 634 – Buis-les-Baronnies 30 – La Motte-Chalancon 34 - Nyons 14

🏕 La Via Natura Le Pilat

☎ 04 75 27 72 09, www.campinglepilat.com
Address : route de Bourdeau (located 1km north along the D 70; beside a stream)
Opening times : from beginning April to end Sept.
1 ha (90 pitches)
Tariff : ✹ 7€ ⇌ 🔲 11€ – 🚿 (6A) 4€
Rental rates : (from beginning April to end Sept.) 🎿 – 21 🏠
2 gîtes. Per night from 50 to 95€ – Per week from 250 to 820€
🛏 borne – 3 🔲 14€

Surroundings : 🦢 ⚬ 🍴 ⚲
Leisure activities : ✗ 🛖 🏊 ⛷ 🎿 🦢
Facilities : ♿ ⚷ 🚿 🍴 🔲 🔷

G P S	Longitude : 5.21195
	Latitude : 44.43406

ST-GALMIER

42330 – Michelin map **327** E6 – pop. 5 596 – alt. 400
▶ Paris 457 – Lyon 82 – Montbrison 25 – Montrond-les-Bains 11

🏕 Campéole Val de Coise 👫

☎ 04 77 54 14 82, www.camping-valdecoise.com – limited spaces for one-night stay
Address : route de la Thiery (situated 2km east along the D 6 and take the road to the left; beside the Coise river)
Opening times : from mid April to mid Oct.
3,5 ha (92 pitches)
Tariff : (2013 Price) 20,30€ ✹ ✹ ⇌ 🔲 🚿 (16A)
Extra per person 5,70€
Rental rates : (from mid April to mid Oct.) – 11 🚐 – 5 🏠 4 canvas bungalows. Per night from 26 to 95€ – Per week from 181 to 665€
🛏 borne 1€

Located not far from the source of Badoit mineral water and the river.

Surroundings : ⚲
Leisure activities : 🏠 🚵 🏊 ⛷ 🚣 🦢
Facilities : ♿ ⚷ 🔲 🍴 launderette
Nearby : 🦢

G P S	Longitude : 4.33552
	Latitude : 45.59308

Michelin classification:

🏕🏕🏕🏕	*Extremely comfortable, equipped to a very high standard*
🏕🏕🏕	*Very comfortable, equipped to a high standard*
🏕🏕	*Comfortable and well equipped*
🏕	*Reasonably comfortable*
△	*Satisfactory*

ST-GENEST-MALIFAUX

42660 – Michelin map **327** F7 – pop. 2 916 – alt. 980
▶ Paris 528 – Annonay 33 – St-Étienne 16 – Yssingeaux 46

△ Municipal de la Croix de Garry

☎ 06 85 40 95 38, www.st-genest-malifaux.fr – alt. 928 – limited spaces for one-night stay
Address : at La Croix de Garry (Take the southern exit along the D 501, follow the signs for Montfaucon-en-Velay; near a lake and 150m from the Semène river)
Opening times : from mid April to mid Oct.
2 ha (85 pitches)
Tariff : 16€ ✹ ✹ ⇌ 🔲 🚿 (6A) – Extra per person 4€
Rental rates : Permanent ♿ (1 chalet) 🎿 – 8 🏠 – 4 ⛺ – 1 gîte.
Per night from 100€ – Per week from 280 to 400€
🛏 borne 16€

A small out of town site; beside a small lake that is ideal for fishing.

Surroundings : ⚬
Leisure activities : 🏊
Facilities : ♿ ⚷ 🔲 🍴 🔷
Nearby : 🎿 🦢

G P S	Longitude : 4.42258
	Latitude : 45.33357

ST-GERVAIS-LES-BAINS

74170 – Michelin map **328** N5 – pop. 5 673 – alt. 820 – ♨ – Winter sports : 1 400/2 000m
▶ Paris 597 – Annecy 84 – Bonneville 42 – Chamonix-Mont-Blanc 25

⚠ Les Dômes de Miage

𝒫 04 50 93 45 96, http://www.natureandlodge.fr – alt. 890

Address : 197 route des Contamines (situated 2km south along the D 902, at a place called les Bernards)

Opening times : from mid May to mid Sept.

3 ha (150 pitches) flat, grassy

Tariff : 29,80€ ♦♦ ⇌ 🅴 🅷 (10A) – Extra per person 5,80€ – Reservation fee 10€

Rental rates : Permanent 🚫 – 1 🏠. Per night 290€ – Per week 2030€ – Reservation fee 10€

🚐 borne – 10 🅴 25,50€

Surroundings : 🏞 ⩽	G	Longitude : 6.72022
Leisure activities : 🏄	P	Latitude : 45.87355
Facilities : & ⛟ 🌳🚿 launderette 🏧,	S	
Nearby : ♼ ✕ 🏇		

ST-JEAN-DE-MAURIENNE

73300 – Michelin map **333** L6 – pop. 8 374 – alt. 556
▶ Paris 641 – Lyon 174 – Chambéry 75 – St-Martin-d'Hères 105

⚠ Municipal les Grands Cols

𝒫 04 79 64 28 02, www.campingdesgrandscols.com

Address : 422 avenue du Mont Cenis

Opening times : from mid May to end Sept.

2,5 ha (80 pitches)

Tariff : 20€ ♦♦ ⇌ 🅴 🅷 (16A) – Extra per person 5€ – Reservation fee 7€

Rental rates : (from mid May to mid Sept.) – 7 🛖. Per night from 45 to 90€ – Per week from 250 to 550€ – Reservation fee 7€

Surroundings : ⩽ mountains	G	Longitude : 6.3515
Leisure activities : ✕ 🏕 🏄 multi-sports	P	Latitude : 45.2716
ground	S	
Facilities : ⛟ 🏖 🚿🌳 🅿		

ST-JEAN-DE-MUZOLS

07300 – Michelin map **331** K3 – pop. 2 444 – alt. 123
▶ Paris 541 – Annonay 34 – Beaurepaire 53 – Privas 62

⚠ Le Castelet

𝒫 04 75 08 09 48, www.camping-lecastelet.com

Address : 113 route du Grand Pont (2.8km southwest along the D 238, follow the signs for Lamastre; beside the Doux river and near the Tournon - St-Jean-de-Muzols railway station)

Opening times : from beginning April to mid Sept.

3 ha (66 pitches)

Tariff : (2013 Price) 25,50€ ♦♦ ⇌ 🅴 🅷 (10A) – Extra per person 6€ – Reservation fee 5€

Rental rates : (from beginning April to mid Sept.) – 3 🛖 – 4 🏠. Per night from 75€ – Per week from 388 to 610€ – Reservation fee 10€

🚐 borne

Pitches on terraces extending down to the river, below vineyards and the road.

Surroundings : 🏞 ⩽ 🍳	G	Longitude : 4.78564
Leisure activities : ♼ 🏕 🏄 ⊿ 🛶 🎣	P	Latitude : 45.0681
Facilities : & ⛟ 🧺 🏖🚿 🅿	S	

ST-JEAN-LE-CENTENIER

07580 – Michelin map **331** J6 – pop. 668 – alt. 350
▶ Paris 623 – Alès 83 – Aubenas 20 – Privas 24

⚠ Les Arches

𝒫 04 75 36 75 19, www.camping-les-arches.com

Address : at Le Cluzel (1.2km west along the D 458a and take D 258, follow the signs for Mirabel then take the road to the right)

Opening times : from end April to mid Sept.

10 ha/5 for camping (177 pitches)

Tariff : 29,70€ ♦♦ ⇌ 🅴 🅷 (10A) – Extra per person 6€

Rental rates : Permanent – 25 🛖 – 2 gîtes. Per night from 35 to 106€ – Per week from 250 to 745€ – Reservation fee 10€

🚐 borne – 🚰 25,50€

Pitches and rental options in both sun and shade, situated with a view of or beside a small natural pool, near a waterfall.

Surroundings : 🏞 🚡 🍳	G	Longitude : 4.52576
Leisure activities : ♼ ✕ 🏄 🚲 ⊿ 🛶	P	Latitude : 44.58759
Facilities : & ⛟ 🏖🚿 🖥 🅿	S	

The pitches of many campsites are marked out with low hedges of attractive bushes and shrubs.

ST-JORIOZ

74410 – Michelin map **328** J5 – pop. 5 716 – alt. 452
▶ Paris 545 – Albertville 37 – Annecy 9 – Megève 51

⚠ International du Lac d'Annecy

𝒫 04 50 68 67 93, www.camping-lac-annecy.com

Address : 1184 route d'Albertville (located 1km southeast)

Opening times : from end April to mid Sept.

2,5 ha (163 pitches) flat, grassy

Tariff : 34€ ♦♦ ⇌ 🅴 🅷 (10A) – Extra per person 6,90€ – Reservation fee 22€

Rental rates : (from end April to mid Sept.) 🚫 – 24 🛖 3 🏠. Per night from 42 to 140€ – Per week from 294 to 980€ Reservation fee 22€

Surroundings : 🍳	G	Longitude : 6.17845
Leisure activities : ♼ ✕ 🏕 jacuzzi 🏄 🚲	P	Latitude : 45.83078
⊿ 🏊 multi-sports ground	S	
Facilities : & ⛟ 🏖 🚿🌳 🅿 launderette		

⚠ Europa ♠♠

𝒫 04 50 68 51 01, www.camping-europa.com

Address : 1444 route d'Albertville (1.4km southeast)

Opening times : from end April to mid Sept.

3 ha (210 pitches)

Tariff : 38€ ♦♦ ⇌ 🅴 🅷 (6A) – Extra per person 7,90€ – Reservation fee 25€

Rental rates : (from end April to end Sept.) 🚫 – 55 🛖 4 🏠 Per night from 158 to 193€ – Per week from 304 to 996€ Reservation fee 25€

There's a charming swimming area.

Surroundings : ⩽ 🍳	G	Longitude : 6.18185
Leisure activities : ♼ ✕ 🖥 🏊♦ 🏄 🚲⊿ 🏊	P	Latitude : 45.83
multi-sports ground	S	
Facilities : & ⛟ 🏖🌳 🚿 🅿 launderette 🏧		

🏔 Le Solitaire du Lac

☏ 04 50 68 59 30, www.campinglesolitaire.com – access difficult

Address : 615 route de Sales (located 1km to the north)

Opening times : from beginning April to mid Sept.

3,5 ha (200 pitches) flat, grassy Tariff : 27,30€ ♣♣ ⇔ 🔲 🔁 (6A) – Extra per person 5,50€ – Reservation fee 8€

Rental rates : (from beginning April to beginning Sept.) 🚫 15 🔲. Per night from 59 to 75€ – Per week from 294 to 665€ Reservation fee 8€

🔁 borne ,30€

In a pleasant location near the lake (direct access).

Surroundings : 🔲 🔲 ⚠
Leisure activities : 🔲 🔲 ⚓
Facilities : 🔲 ⚙ 🔲 launderette 🔲

G P S Longitude : 6.14492
Latitude : 45.8407

ST-JULIEN-EN-ST-ALBAN

07000 – Michelin map **331** K5 – pop. 1 311 – alt. 131
▶ Paris 587 – Aubenas 41 – Crest 29 – Montélimar 35

🏔 L'Albanou

☏ 04 75 66 00 97, www.camping-albanou.com

Address : chemin de Pampelonne (head 1.4km east along the N 304, follow the signs for Pouzin and take the Celliers road to the right; near the Ouvèze river)

Opening times : from end April to end Sept.

1,5 ha (87 pitches) flat, grassy

Tariff : (2013 Price) 26€ ♣♣ ⇔ 🔲 🔁 (10A) – Extra per person 5€ Reservation fee 3€

Rental rates : (from end April to end Sept.) – 3 🔲. Per week from 320 to 650€ – Reservation fee 5€

🔁 borne – 6 🔲 22€

Attractive marked-out pitches.

Surroundings : 🔲 🔲
Leisure activities : jacuzzi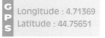
Facilities : 🔲 ⚙ 🔲

G P S Longitude : 4.71369
Latitude : 44.75651

ST-LAURENT-DU-PONT

38380 – Michelin map **333** H5 – pop. 4 496 – alt. 410
▶ Paris 560 – Chambéry 29 – Grenoble 34 – La Tour-du-Pin 42

🏔 Municipal les Berges du Guiers

☏ 04 76 55 20 63, www.camping-chartreuse.com

Address : avenue de la gare (take the northern exit along the D 520, follow the signs for Chambéry and take the turning to the left; beside the Guiers Mort – pedestrian walkway to village)

Opening times : from mid Junee to mid Sept.

1 ha (45 pitches) flat, grassy

Tariff : 17,50€ ♣♣ ⇔ 🔲 🔁 (5A) – Extra per person 5€ – Reservation fee 10€

Surroundings : 🔲
Facilities : 🔲 ⚙ 🔲
Nearby :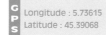

G P S Longitude : 5.73615
Latitude : 45.39068

In order for the guide to remain wholly objective, the selection of campsites is made on an entirely independent basis.

ST-LAURENT-EN-BEAUMONT

38350 – Michelin map **333** I8 – pop. 436 – alt. 900
▶ Paris 613 – Le Bourg-d'Oisans 43 – Corps 16 – Grenoble 51

🏔 Belvédère de l'Obiou

☏ 04 76 30 40 80, www.camping-obiou.com

Address : at Les Égats (1.3km southwest along the N 85)

Opening times : from mid April to mid Oct.

1 ha (45 pitches)

Tariff : 27,40€ ♣♣ ⇔ 🔲 🔁 (10A) – Extra per person 5,90€ Reservation fee 15€

Rental rates : (from beginning May to end Sept.) – 5 🔲 – 2 🔲. Reservation fee 15€

🔁 borne 5€ – 3 🔲 – 🔲 🔁 11€

Surroundings : 🔲
Leisure activities : ✗ 🔲 🔁 🔲
Facilities : 🔲 ⚙ 🔲 🔲 🔲
Nearby : 🍸

G P S Longitude : 5.83779
Latitude : 44.87597

ST-LAURENT-LES-BAINS

07590 – Michelin map **331** F6 – pop. 156 – alt. 840
▶ Paris 603 – Aubenas 64 – Langogne 30 – Largentière 52

🏔 Le Ceytrou

☏ 04 66 46 02 03, campingleceytrou.free.fr

Address : situated 2.1km to the southeast along the D 4

Opening times : from beginning April to mid Nov.

2,5 ha (60 pitches)

Tariff : 13€ ♣♣ ⇔ 🔲 🔁 (10A) – Extra per person 3,80€

Rental rates : (from beginning April to mid Nov.) – 12 🔲. Per night from 40 to 70€ – Per week from 150 to 420€

In a charming location in the heart of the Vivarais Cévenol mountains.

Surroundings : 🔲 🔲
Leisure activities : 🔲 ✗ 🔁 🔲 🔲
Facilities : 🔲 ⚙ 🔲 🔲

G P S Longitude : 3.97962
Latitude : 44.59922

ST-MARTIN-D'ARDÈCHE

07700 – Michelin map **331** I6 – pop. 886 – alt. 46
▶ Paris 641 – Bagnols-sur-Cèze 21 – Barjac 27 – Bourg-St-Andéol 13

🏔 Le Pontet 🔲

☏ 04 75 04 63 07, www.campinglepontet.com

Address : at Le Pontet (located 1.5km east along the D 290, follow the signs for St-Just and take road to the left)

Opening times : from beginning April to end Sept.

1,8 ha (97 pitches)

Tariff : 19,90€ ♣♣ ⇔ 🔲 🔁 (10A) – Extra per person 5,50€ Reservation fee 10€

Rental rates : (from beginning April to end Sept.) – 17 🔲. Per night from 45 to 80€ – Per week from 260 to 690€ Reservation fee 26€

🔁 borne 3€ – 4 🔲 8€ – 🔲 8€

Surrounded by vineyards with plenty of shade and with a swimming pool on the other side of the little road.

Surroundings : 🔲 🔲
Leisure activities : 🍸 ✗ 🔲 🔁
Facilities : 🔲 ⚙ 🔲 🔲 🔲

G P S Longitude : 4.58453
Latitude : 44.30409

ᗰ Les Gorges

✆ 0475046109, www.camping-des-gorges.com

Address : chemin de Sauze (located 1.5km to the northwest)

Opening times : from mid April to mid Sept.

3 ha (145 pitches)

Tariff : 40€ ★☆ ⬌ 🔲 ⚡ (10A) – Extra per person 8€ – Reservation fee 30€

Rental rates : (from mid April to mid Sept.) – 24 ⛺ – 1 gîte. Per night from 39 to 163€ – Per week from 273 to 1141€ Reservation fee 30€

🚐 borne

A well-shaded site with easy access to the banks of the Ardèche river.

Surroundings : 🏞 ⚬⚬
Leisure activities : 🍹 ✕ 🏞 🚣 🛶 ⚓ ➰ ✈
multi-sports ground
Facilities : 🚿 ⚬━🛒 🖤🍴 🗑 🚿🛁

Longitude : 4.55547
Latitude : 44.31155

ᗰ Indigo le Moulin

✆ 0475046620, www.camping-indigo.com

Address : take southeastern exit along the D 290, follow the signs for St-Just and take a right turn (D 200); beside the Ardèche river

Opening times : from mid April to end Sept.

6,5 ha (200 pitches)

Tariff : 31,90€ ★☆ ⬌ 🔲 ⚡ (10A) Extra per person 6,60€ – Reservation fee 22€

Rental rates : (from mid April to end Sept.) – 16 caravans – 47 tent lodges. Per night from 45 to 110€ Per week from 221 to 770€ Reservation fee 22€

🚐 borne 7€

Surroundings : ⚬
Leisure activities : ✕ 🏞 🚣 🛶 ⚓ ➰
Facilities : 🚿 ⚬━🛒 🚿🍴 🗑 🚿

Longitude : 4.57122
Latitude : 44.30035

ST-MARTIN-DE-CLELLES

38930 – Michelin map **333** G8 – pop. 157 – alt. 750
▶ Paris 616 – Lyon 149 – Grenoble 48 – St-Martin-d'Hères 49

⚠ La Chabannerie

✆ 0476340038, www.camping-isere.net

Address : Lotissement La Chabannerie

Opening times : from beginning May to end Sept.

2,5 ha (49 pitches)

Tariff : 23€ ★☆ ⬌ 🔲 ⚡ (10A) – Extra per person 5€

🚐 borne

Surroundings : 🌳 ⪬ 🏞 ⚬⚬
Leisure activities : 🏞 🛶
Facilities : ⚬━ 🚿 🖤🍴 🗑 🚿

Longitude : 5.61624
Latitude : 44.82574

Some campsites benefit from proximity to a municipal leisure centre.

ST-MARTIN-EN-VERCORS

26420 – Michelin map **332** F3 – pop. 378 – alt. 780
▶ Paris 601 – La Chapelle-en-Vercors 9 – Grenoble 51 – Romans-sur-Isère 46

⚠ La Porte St-Martin

✆ 0475455110, www.camping-laportestmartin.com

Address : take the northern exit along the D 103

Opening times : from beginning April to end Sept.

1,5 ha (66 pitches)

Tariff : (2013 Price) 18,90€ ★☆ ⬌ 🔲 ⚡ (10A) – Extra per person 7€

Rental rates : Permanent 🚫 – 3 ⛺ – 1 gîte. Per night from 50 to 120€ – Per week from 230 to 650€

🚐 borne 8€

Surroundings : ⪬ ⚬
Leisure activities : 🏞 🚲 🛶 (small swimming pool)
Facilities : 🚿 ⚬━ 🍴 🗑

Longitude : 5.44336
Latitude : 45.02456

ST-MAURICE-D'ARDÈCHE

07200 – Michelin map **331** I6 – pop. 312 – alt. 140
▶ Paris 639 – Aubenas 12 – Largentière 16 – Privas 44

ᗰ Le Chamadou 👥

✆ 0820366197, www.camping-le-chamadou.com ✉ 07120 Balazuc

Address : at Mas de Chaussy (500m from a lake)

Opening times : from beginning April to end Oct.

1 ha (86 pitches)

Tariff : 30,70€ ★☆ ⬌ 🔲 ⚡ (10A) – Extra per person 7€ – Reservation fee 14€

Rental rates : (from beginning April to end Oct.) 🚫 – 24 ⛺. Per night from 17 to 22€ – Per week from 240 to 1200€ Reservation fee 14€

In the heart of the Ardèche winegrowing area, with a pretty traditional stone farmhouse.

Surroundings : 🌿 ⪬ ⚬
Leisure activities : 🍹 ✕ 🏞 🎿 🚣 🏕 🛶 ➰
multi-sports ground
Facilities : 🚿 ⚬━ 🚿🍴 🗑
Nearby : ➰

Longitude : 4.40384
Latitude : 44.50826

To visit a town or region, use the MICHELIN Green Guides.

ST-NAZAIRE-EN-ROYANS

26190 – Michelin map **332** E3 – pop. 716 – alt. 172
▶ Paris 576 – Grenoble 69 – Pont-en-Royans 9 – Romans-sur-Isère 19

⚠ Municipal du Lac

✆ 0475484118, jm.combier@hotmail.fr

Address : 100B rue des Condamines (700m southeast, follow the signs for St-Jean-en-Royans)

1,5 ha (75 pitches)

Rentals : 2 tent lodges.

Beside the Bourne river where it widens to a small lake.

Surroundings : ⪬ ⚬⚬
Leisure activities : 🏞 ➰
Facilities : 🚿 ⚬━ 🍴 🗑

Longitude : 5.25368
Latitude : 45.05912

ST-PAUL-DE-VÉZELIN

42590 – Michelin map **327** D4 – pop. 303 – alt. 431
▶ Paris 415 – Boën 19 – Feurs 30 – Roanne 26

⚠ Arpheuilles

𝒫 04 77 63 43 43, www.camping-arpheuilles.com – access difficult for caravans

Address : 4km to the north, at Port Piset, near the river (and lake)

Opening times : from mid April to beginning Sept.

3,5 ha (80 pitches)

Tariff : 25,50€ ☂☂ ⟺ 🔲 🔌 (5A) – Extra per person 5€
Rental rates : (from mid April to mid Oct.) ⚡ – 4 🚐 – 7 🏠.
Per night from 60 to 130€ – Per week from 270 to 680€
🚐 5 🔲 14,50€
An attractive location in the steep valley of the Loire river, on a secluded and unspoilt site.

Surroundings : 🌲 ⟨ ♨ ⛰
Leisure activities : ♟ ✖ 🏛 ⛳ 🏊 🎣 🛶 ☸
Facilities : ♿ 🔌 🍳 🚿 🍴 launderette 🧺
Nearby : 🏊

In order for the guide to remain wholly objective, the selection of campsites is made on an entirely independent basis.

ST-PIERRE-DE-CHARTREUSE

38380 – Michelin map **333** H5 – pop. 999 – alt. 885 – Winter sports : 900/1 800m
▶ Paris 571 – Belley 62 – Chambéry 39 – Grenoble 28

⚠ Sites et Paysages De Martinière

𝒫 04 76 88 60 36, www.campingdemartiniere.com

Address : route du Col de Porte (3km southwest along the D 512, follow the signs for Grenoble)

Opening times : from beginning May to mid Sept.

1,5 ha (100 pitches)

Tariff : 26,90€ ☂☂ ⟺ 🔲 🔌 (10A) – Extra per person 6,30€
Reservation fee 8€
Rental rates : (from mid May to mid Sept.) ⚡ – 4 🚐 – 2 🏠.
Per week from 250 to 750€ – Reservation fee 8€
🚐 borne – 2 🔲 21,40€ – 🚱 11,50€
Pleasant location in the heart of Chartreuse.

Surroundings : ⟨ ♨
Leisure activities : 🏛 ⛳ 🏊
Facilities : 🔌 🍳 🚿 🍴 🧺
Nearby : ✖

ST-PRIVAT

07200 – Michelin map **331** I6 – pop. 1 588 – alt. 304
▶ Paris 631 – Lyon 169 – Privas 26 – Valence 65

⚠ Le Plan d'Eau

𝒫 04 75 35 44 98, www.campingleplandeau.fr

Address : route de Lussas (situated 2km southeast along the D 259)

Opening times : from mid April to beginning Sept.

3 ha (100 pitches)

Tariff : 31,50€ ☂☂ ⟺ 🔲 🔌 (8A) – Extra per person 5,50€
Reservation fee 20€

Rental rates : (from mid April to beginning Sept.) – 8 🚐
15 🏠. Per night from 33 to 128€ – Per week from 230 to 900€
Good shade cover; pitches near the Ardèche river.

Surroundings : 🌲 ⟨ ♨
Leisure activities : ♟ ✖ ⛳ 🏊 🏖 🛶
multi-sports ground
Facilities : ♿ 🔌 🍳 🍴 launderette

Longitude : 4.43296
Latitude : 44.61872

ST-REMÈZE

07700 – Michelin map **331** J7 – pop. 863 – alt. 365
▶ Paris 645 – Barjac 30 – Bourg-St-Andéol 16 – Pont-St-Esprit 27

⚠ Domaine de Briange

𝒫 04 75 04 14 43, www.campingdebriange.com

Address : route de Gras (situated 2km north along the D 362)

Opening times : from beginning May to mid Sept.

4 ha (80 pitches)

Tariff : ⟺🔲 32€ – 🔌 (6A) 5€
Rental rates : (from beginning March to mid Nov.) ♿ (1 chalet)
1 caravan – 24 🏠 – 1 cabin in the trees – 6 canvas bungalows.
Per night from 55 to 190€
Many different rental options, some of a high standard and many well spaced out.

Surroundings : 🌲 ♨
Leisure activities : ✖ ⛳ 🎮 🏊
Facilities : ♿ 🔌 🍴 🖼

Longitude : 4.5139
Latitude : 44.40615

⚠ La Résidence d'Été

𝒫 04 75 04 26 87, www.campinglaresidence.com

Address : rue de la Bateuse

1,6 ha (60 pitches) fruit trees

Rentals : 19 🚐.

Very close to the centre of the village; a lovely natural area beneath cherry trees.

Surroundings : ⟨ ♨
Leisure activities : ✖ ⛳ 🏊
Facilities : ♿ 🔌 🍴 🖼 🧺

Longitude : 4.50437
Latitude : 44.39105

ST-SAUVEUR-DE-CRUZIÈRES

07460 – Michelin map **331** H8 – pop. 535 – alt. 150
▶ Paris 674 – Alès 28 – Barjac 9 – Privas 81

⚠ La Claysse

𝒫 04 75 35 40 65, www.campingdelaclaysse.com – For caravans and campervans, access via the top of the village.

Address : at La Digue (To the northwest of the town; beside the river)

5 ha/1 for camping (60 pitches)

Rentals : ⚡ – 13 🚐.

Below the road, some pitches beside the river. Production and sale of olive oil.

Surroundings : 🏞 ♨
Leisure activities : ✖ 🏛 ⛳ 🚴 🏊 🏖 🛶
Facilities : ♿ 🔌 🍳 🍴 🖼
Nearby : climbing

Longitude : 4.25085
Latitude : 44.29984

ST-SAUVEUR-DE-MONTAGUT

07190 – Michelin map **331** J5 – pop. 1 144 – alt. 218
▶ Paris 597 – Le Cheylard 24 – Lamastre 29 – Privas 24

🏔 L'Ardéchois

🖉 0475666187, www.ardechois-camping.fr

Address : situated 8.5km west along the D 102, follow the signs for Albon

Opening times : from mid May to mid Sept.

37 ha/5 for camping (107 pitches)

Tariff : 32,50€ ✝✝ ⊜ 🗉 ⚡ (10A) – Extra per person 6,95€

Reservation fee 23€

Rental rates : (from mid May to mid Sept.) – 29 🛏 – 1 gîte. Per night from 50 to 100€ – Per week from 370 to 880€ Reservation fee 23€

🚐 borne

In 2 separate sections on either side of the road, with pitches beside the Glueyre river.

Surroundings : 🌿 ⩙ 🌳🌳
Leisure activities : ✝ 🗙 🏕 🏇 🚲 🛶 ⛵ 🎣
Facilities : 🚿 🔒 🆓 🏖 🍴 launderette 🧺

GPS Longitude : 4.52294
Latitude : 44.82893

ST-SYMPHORIEN-SUR-COISE

69590 – Michelin map **327** F6 – pop. 3 438 – alt. 558
▶ Paris 489 – Andrézieux-Bouthéon 26 – L'Arbresle 36 – Feurs 30

🏔 Hurongues

🖉 0478484429, www.camping-hurongues.com

Address : 3.5km west along the D 2, follow the signs for Chazelles-sur-Lyon, 400m from a small lake

3,6 ha (114 pitches) terraced

In a pleasant wooded setting based around a leisure park.

Surroundings : 🌿 🏕 🌳🌳
Leisure activities : 🏕 🏇
Facilities : 🔒 🏢 🏖 🍴
Nearby : 🗙 🏓 🎣

GPS Longitude : 4.4282
Latitude : 45.63481

ST-THÉOFFREY

38119 – Michelin map **333** H8 – pop. 444 – alt. 936
▶ Paris 595 – Le Bourg-d'Oisans 44 – Grenoble 33 – La Mure 10

🏔 Au Pré du Lac

🖉 0476839134, www.aupredulac.eu

Address : at the hamlet Pétichet

Opening times : from beginning March to end Oct.

3 ha (96 pitches) flat, grassy

Tariff : ✝ 4,80€ ⊜ 🗉 8€ – ⚡ (10A) 4,80€ – Reservation fee 8€
Rental rates : (from beginning March to end Oct.) – 4 🛏 – 2 🏠 1 gîte. Per week 610€ – Reservation fee 12,50€

Surroundings : ♀ ⛰
Leisure activities : ✝ 🗙 🏕 🏇 ⛵ 🎣 🛶
Facilities : 🚿 🔒 🏢 🏖 🍴 launderette 🧺
Nearby : ⚓

GPS Longitude : 5.77224
Latitude : 45.00454

The pitches of many campsites are marked out with low hedges of attractive bushes and shrubs.

ST-VALLIER

26240 – Michelin map **332** B2 – pop. 4 000 – alt. 135
▶ Paris 526 – Annonay 21 – St-Étienne 61 – Tournon-sur-Rhône 16

⛺ Municipal les Îsles de Silon

🖉 0475232217, www.saintvallier.com

Address : at Les Îles (situated to the north, near the Rhône river)

1,35 ha (92 pitches)
Rentals : 4 🛏 .

Surroundings : ⩙ 🏕 🌳🌳
Leisure activities : 🏊
Facilities : 🔒 🏢 🍴 🏖
Nearby : 🗙 🛶

GPS Longitude : 4.81237
Latitude : 45.1879

STE-CATHERINE

69440 – Michelin map **327** G6 – pop. 911 – alt. 700
▶ Paris 488 – Andrézieux-Bouthéon 38 – L'Arbresle 37 – Feurs 43

⛺ Municipal du Châtelard

🖉 0478818060, http://mairie-saintecatherine.fr – alt. 800 – limited spaces for one-night stay

Address : at Le Châtelard (situated 2km to the south)

Opening times : from beginning March to end Nov.

4 ha (61 pitches) terraced, flat, grassy

Tariff : ✝ 2,25€ ⊜ 🗉 2,55€ – ⚡ (6A) 2,80€

Surroundings : 🌿 ⩙ Mont Pilat and Monts du Lyonnais 🏕
Leisure activities : 🏕
Facilities : 🔒 🚻 🏖

GPS Longitude : 4.57344
Latitude : 45.58817

Routes nationales are main roads and their identifying numbers begin with N or RN. Routes départmentales are generally quieter roads and begin with D or DN.

SALAVAS

07150 – Michelin map **331** I7 – pop. 530 – alt. 96
▶ Paris 668 – Lyon 206 – Privas 58 – Nîmes 77

⛺ Le Péquelet

🖉 0475880449, lepequelet.com

Address : at Le Cros (take the southern exit along the D 579, follow the signs for Barjac and continue along the turning to the left for 2km)

Opening times : from beginning April to end Sept.

2 ha (60 pitches) flat, grassy

Tariff : 29,50€ ✝✝ ⊜ 🗉 ⚡ (10A) – Extra per person 8€ – Reservation fee 10€

Rental rates : (from beginning April to end Sept.) 10 🛏 – 7 🏠 – 2 canvas bungalows – 2 gîtes. Per night from 40 to 115€ – Per week from 250 to 800€ – Reservation fee 10€

🚐 borne – 💧 ⚡ 15€

Beside the Ardèche river and surrounded by vineyards.

Surroundings : 🌿 🏕 🌳🌳 ⛰
Leisure activities : 🏕 🛶 ⛵ 🎣 🏄
Facilities : 🔒 🏖 🍴 🏢

GPS Longitude : 4.39806
Latitude : 44.39075

SALLANCHES

74700 – Michelin map **328** M5 – pop. 15 619 – alt. 550
▶ Paris 585 – Annecy 72 – Bonneville 29 – Chamonix-Mont-Blanc 28

🏕 Village Center Les Îles

🕿 0825 00 53 18, http://campings.
village-center.fr/rhones-alpes/camping-
montagne-il

Address : 245 chemin de la Cavettaz
(situated 2km to the southeast; beside a
stream and 250m from a lake)

Opening times : from beginning April
to end Sept.

4,6 ha (260 pitches)

Tariff : 20 € ♣♣ 🚗 🔲 🗲 (10A)

Extra per person 4 €
Rental rates : (from beginning April to end Sept.) – 41 🚐
11 🏠. Per night from 26 to 70 € – Per week from 511 to 797 €
Reservation fee 30 €

Surroundings : ≼ ⌂ ♀♀
Leisure activities : ¶ 🕑 daytime
Facilities : 🕭 ⚬🗝 🔲 🖽 🖋 🕈 ¶ 🔲 🖳 🛒
Nearby : 🏖 🐟 🛶 🐎

GPS
Longitude : 6.65103
Latitude : 45.92404

LA SALLE-EN-BEAUMONT

38350 – Michelin map **333** I8 – pop. 297 – alt. 756
▶ Paris 614 – Le Bourg-d'Oisans 44 – Gap 51 – Grenoble 52

🏕 Le Champ Long

🕿 0476 30 41 81, www.camping-champlong.com – help moving
caravans onto and off pitches avilable on request

Address : at Le Champ-Long (2.7km southwest along the N 85, follow
the signs for la Mure and take road to the left)

Opening times : from beginning April to mid Oct.

5 ha (97 pitches)

Tariff : 25 € ♣♣ 🚗 🔲 🗲 (10A) – Extra per person 6 € – Reservation
fee 15 €

Rental rates : (from beginning April to mid Oct.) – 4 🚐 – 12 🏠
3 🛏. Per night from 60 to 100 € – Per week from 370 to 800 €
Reservation fee 15 €

🔲 borne 5 € – 🚰 13 €

Surroundings : 🌊 ≼ Lac du Sautet and
valley ⌂ ♀♀
Leisure activities : ¶ 🗙 🖼 🛶 🗲
Facilities : 🕭 ⚬🗝 ¶ launderette 🛒

GPS
Longitude : 5.84416
Latitude : 44.85725

SAMOËNS

74340 – Michelin map **328** N4 – pop. 2 311 – alt. 710
▶ Paris 598 – Lyon 214 – Annecy 82 – Genève 63

🏕 Club Airotel Le Giffre

🕿 0450 34 41 92, www.camping-samoens.com

Address : at La Glière

Opening times : from beginning Jan. to end Dec.

7 ha (312 pitches)

Tariff : 20,15 € ♣♣ 🚗 🔲 🗲 (10A) – Extra per person 4,30 €
Rental rates : Permanent 🏚 – 1 🚐 – 6 🏠 – 5 canvas
bungalows. Per night 70 € – Per week from 188 to 629 €
🔲 borne 5 € – 14 🔲 20,15 € – 🚰 11 €

In a pleasant location, near a lake and a leisure park.

Surroundings : ❄ ≼ ♀
Leisure activities : 🕑 🌊
Facilities : 🕭 ⚬🗝 🖽 🖋 🖥 🕈 ¶ 🔲
Nearby : ¶ 🗙 🛶 🐎 🛶 🏊 🏖 ⛷ 🛶 sports trail

GPS
Longitude : 6.71917
Latitude : 46.07695

SAMPZON

07120 – Michelin map **351** I7 – pop. 224 – alt. 120
▶ Paris 660 – Lyon 198 – Privas 56 – Nîmes 85

🏕 Yelloh! Village Soleil Vivarais 👥

🕿 0475 39 67 56, www.soleil-vivarais.com

Address : at the bridge (follow the signs for Vallon Pont d'Arc)

Opening times : from mid April to mid Sept.

12 ha (350 pitches)

Tariff : 51 € ♣♣ 🚗 🔲 🗲 (10A) – Extra per person 8 €
Rental rates : (from mid April to mid Sept.) – 249 🚐. Per night
from 39 to 152 € – Per week from 273 to 1064 €

*Near a lovely beach on the Ardèche river; mobile homes
ranging from good to a high standard of comfort.*

Surroundings : 🌊 ≼ ♀♀
Leisure activities : ¶ 🗙 🖼 🕑 🛶 🛶 🚴 🛶
🏊 🏖 (beach) 🐟 🐎
Facilities : 🕭 ⚬🗝 🔲 🖋 ¶ launderette 🖳 🛒

GPS
Longitude : 4.35528
Latitude : 44.42916

🏕 Le Mas de la Source

🕿 0475 39 67 98, www.campingmasdelasource.com

Address : La Tuillière

Opening times : from mid April to end Sept.

1,2 ha (30 pitches)

Tariff : 31,70 € ♣♣ 🚗 🔲 🗲 (6A) – Extra per person 6,60 €
Reservation fee 5 €
Rental rates : (from mid April to end Sept.) 🏚 – 8 🚐. Per night
from 40 to 100 € – Per week from 200 to 695 € – Reservation
fee 8 €

*On the Sampzon river peninsula; pleasant, shaded access to the
Ardèche river.*

Surroundings : 🌊 ⌂ ♀♀
Leisure activities : 🛶 🛶 🏊 🐟
Facilities : 🕭 ⚬🗝 🖋 ¶ 🖥

GPS
Longitude : 4.3466
Latitude : 44.42242

🏕 Sun Camping

🕿 0475 39 76 12, www.suncamping.com

Address : 10 chemin des Piboux (200m from the Ardèche)

Opening times : from mid April to mid Sept.

1,2 ha (70 pitches)

Tariff : (2013 Price) 31,70 € ♣♣ 🚗 🔲 🗲 (10A) – Extra per person 6 €
Reservation fee 8 €
Rental rates : (from mid April to mid Sept.) – 14 🚐. Per night
from 42 to 93 € – Per week from 294 to 651 € – Reservation
fee 13 €

*On the Sampzon river peninsula with good-quality mobile
home rentals.*

Surroundings : 🌊 ♀♀
Leisure activities : ¶ 🛶 🏊
Facilities : 🕭 ⚬🗝 (July–Aug.) 🖋 ¶ launderette
Nearby : 🖳 🗙 🛒

GPS
Longitude : 4.35352
Latitude : 44.42895

SATILLIEU

07290 – Michelin map **331** J3 – pop. 1 616 – alt. 485
▶ Paris 542 – Annonay 13 – Lamastre 36 – Privas 87

⚠ Municipal le Grangeon

🖉 0475678486, www.lalouvesc.com

Address : chemin de l'Hermuzière (head 1.1km southwest along the D 578a; follow the signs for Lalouvesc and take the turning to the left)

Opening times : from beginning May to end Sept.

1 ha (52 pitches)

Tariff : (2013 Price) 🚶 2,60€ 🚗 1,80€ 🔲 – 🔌 (10A) 3,30€
Rental rates : (from end May to beginning Sept.) – 5 🚐.
Per night from 28 to 49€ – Per week from 188 to 343€
🚰 borne 2€
Pitches and chalets with good shade, beside the Ay river and an attractive lake.

Surroundings : 🌿 ⛱ 🌳
Leisure activities : 🏠
Facilities : 🚿 ⚡ 🍴 🏍 💺
Nearby : 🏊 (fresh water)

G P S Longitude : 4.60389
Latitude : 45.14438

SCIEZ

74140 – Michelin map **328** L3 – pop. 5 269 – alt. 406
▶ Paris 561 – Abondance 37 – Annecy 69 – Annemasse 24

⚠ Le Chatelet

🖉 0450725260, www.camping-chatelet.com – limited spaces for one-night stay

Address : 658 chemin des Hutins Vieux (3km northeast along the N 5, follow the signs for Thonon-les-Bains and turn left onto the rte du Port at Sciez-Plage, 300m from the beach)

Opening times : from beginning April to end Oct.

2,5 ha (121 pitches)

Tariff : 22,50€ 🚶🚶 🚗 🔲 🔌 (10A) – Extra per person 5,60€
Reservation fee 8€
Rental rates : (from beginning March to end Nov.) ♿ (1 chalet) 12 🏠 – 2 tent lodges. Per night from 39 to 122€ – Per week from 256 to 854€ – Reservation fee 12€
🚰 borne 4€

Surroundings : 🌿
Leisure activities : 🏍 🚲
Facilities : 🚿 ⚡ 🍴 launderette
Nearby : 🍴 🏊 🛶 pedalos

G P S Longitude : 6.39705
Latitude : 46.34079

A 'quartier' is a district or area of a town or village.

SÉEZ

73700 – Michelin map **333** N4 – pop. 2 332 – alt. 904
▶ Paris 638 – Albertville 57 – Bourg-St-Maurice 4 – Moûtiers 31

⚠ Le Reclus

🖉 0479410105, www.campinglereclus.com

Address : route de Tignes (take northwestern exit along the N 90, follow the signs for Bourg-St-Maurice; beside the Reclus river)

Opening times : Permanent

1,5 ha (108 pitches)

Tariff : 19€ 🚶🚶 🚗 🔲 🔌 (10A) – Extra per person 4,20€ – Reservation fee 5€

Rental rates : Permanent – 1 caravan – 4 🚐 – 4 🏠
5 yurts – 1 apartment. Per night from 50 to 85€ – Per week from 300 to 590€ – Reservation fee 10€
🚰 borne 5€ – 6 🔲 12€ – 🚐 12€

Surroundings : ❄ 🌳
Leisure activities : 🍴 🏠
Facilities : 🚿 ⚡ 🏍 🍴 launderette

G P S Longitude : 6.78529
Latitude : 45.62577

SERRIÈRES-DE-BRIORD

01470 – Michelin map **328** F6 – pop. 1 143 – alt. 218
▶ Paris 481 – Belley 29 – Bourg-en-Bresse 57 – Crémieu 24

🏔 Le Point Vert

🖉 0474361345, www.camping-ain-bugey.com – limited spaces for one-night stay

Address : route du Point Vert (2.5km west, at the leisure and activity park)

1,9 ha (137 pitches) flat, grassy

Rentals : 6 🚐 .

Beside a small lake near the Rhône river.

Surroundings : 🌊 ⛰
Leisure activities : 🏠 🕐daytime 🎣 🏊
🚲 🏊 🛶
Facilities : 🚿 ⚡ 🍴 🍴 launderette 🚿
Nearby : 🍴 🍴 🛶 🏊 (beach) 🛶 pedalos

G P S Longitude : 5.42731
Latitude : 45.81633

SÉVRIER

74320 – Michelin map **328** J5 – pop. 3 835 – alt. 456
▶ Paris 541 – Albertville 41 – Annecy 6 – Megève 55

🏔 Le Panoramic

🖉 0450524309, www.camping-le-panoramic.com

Address : 22 chemin des Bernets (located 3.5km to the south)

Opening times : from end April to end Sept.

3 ha (209 pitches)

Tariff : (2013 Price) 23,50€ 🚶🚶 🚗 🔲 🔌 (10A) `
Extra per person 5,40€ – Reservation fee 10€
Rental rates : (from end April to end Sept.) – 18 🚐 – 17 🏠
4 studios – 3 apartments. Per night from 44 to 80€ – Per week from 260 to 810€ – Reservation fee 10€
🚰 borne 6€
In two separate sections, looking out over the lake.

Surroundings : ⬙ ⛱
Leisure activities : 🍴 🍴 🏠 🕐daytime 🏊
🚲 🏊
Facilities : 🚿 ⚡ 🍴 🍴 launderette 🚿 🚿
Nearby : 🐴

G P S Longitude : 6.1417
Latitude : 45.84308

🏔 Au Coeur du Lac

🖉 0450524645, www.campingaucoeurdulac.com

Address : 3233 route d'Albertville (located 1km to the south)

Opening times : from beginning April to end Sept.

1,7 ha (100 pitches)

Tariff : 28,60€ 🚶🚶 🚗 🔲 🔌 (5A) – Extra per person 5,50€
Rental rates : (from mid April to end Sept.) 🚫 – 10 🚐
Per night from 40 to 100€ – Per week from 270 to 690€
🚰 borne – 15 🔲 24,50€

n an attractive location near the lake (direct access)

Surroundings : ⪕ ⌂ ♨
Leisure activities : 🎣 daytime 🏇 🚴 ⛵
Facilities : ♿ ⚷ 🏇 👶🍴 launderette ⛟
Nearby : 🍴 🎣 🏇

G P S	Longitude : 6.14399
	Latitude : 45.85487

SEYSSEL

01420 – Michelin map **328** H5 – pop. 948 – alt. 258
▶ Paris 517 – Aix-les-Bains 33 – Annecy 41 – Genève 52

⛰ L' International

✆ 0450592847, www.camp-inter.fr

Address : chemin de la Barotte (2.4km southwest along the D 992, follow the signs for Culoz and take the road to the right)

Opening times : from mid April to end Sept.

1,5 ha (45 pitches)

Tariff : 26€ ✹✹ 🚗 🅴 (10A) – Extra per person 4,50€ – Reservation fee 10€

Rental rates : (from mid April to end Sept.) – 15 🚐. Per night from 55 to 99€ – Per week from 270 to 600€ – Reservation fee 15€

🚐 5 🅴 22€

A peaceful setting in the hills.

Surroundings : 🌄 ⪕ ⌂ ♨
Leisure activities : ✗ 🎣 🏇 🚴 🛶
Facilities : ⚷ 🍴 launderette ⛟

G P S	Longitude ; 5.82349
	Latitude : 45.94957

SEYSSEL

74910 – Michelin map **328** I5 – pop. 2 262 – alt. 252
▶ Paris 517 – Aix-les-Bains 32 – Annecy 40

⛰ Le Nant-Matraz

✆ 0450590368, campinglenantmatraz@bbox.fr

Address : 15 route de Genève (take the northern exit along the D 992)

1 ha (74 pitches)

Surroundings : ⪕ ⌂ ♨♨
Leisure activities : 🍴
Facilities : ⚷ 🏠

G P S	Longitude : 5.83574
	Latitude : 45.96339

TANINGES

74440 – Michelin map **328** M4 – pop. 3 414 – alt. 640
▶ Paris 570 – Annecy 68 – Bonneville 24 – Chamonix-Mont-Blanc 51

⛰ Municipal des Thézières

✆ 0450342559, www.taninges.com

Address : Les Vernays-sous-la-Ville (take the southern exit, follow the signs for Cluses; beside the Foron river, 150m from the Giffre river)

Opening times : Permanent

2 ha (113 pitches)

Tariff : (2013 Price) 14,70€ ✹✹ 🚗 🅴 (10A) Extra per person 2,80€

🚐 borne 4,80€ – 3 🅴 14,70€

Surroundings : 🌄 ⪕ ♨♨
Leisure activities :
Facilities : ♿ ⚷ 🍴 launderette ⛟
Nearby : 🎣 🏇 🎿

G P S	Longitude : 6.58837
	Latitude : 46.09866

TERMIGNON

73500 – Michelin map **333** N6 – pop. 423 – alt. 1 290
▶ Paris 680 – Bessans 18 – Chambéry 120 – Lanslebourg-Mont-Cenis 6

⛰ Les Mélèzes

✆ 0479205141, www.camping-termignon-lavanoisecom

Address : route du Doron (in the village; beside a mountain stream)

Opening times : Permanent

0,7 ha (66 pitches) flat, grassy

Tariff : 15,10€ ✹✹ 🚗 🅴 (10A) – Extra per person 5,60€

Rental rates : Permanent 🚐 – 4 🚐. Per night from 65 to 76€ Per week from 380 to 480€

Surroundings : 🌄 ⪕ ♨♨
Leisure activities : 🎣 🌊
Facilities : ♿ ⚷ (from mid June to mid Sept.) 🚐 🍴 🏠

G P S	Longitude : 6.81535
	Latitude : 45.27815

LA TOUSSUIRE

73300 – Michelin map **333** K6 – alt. 1 690
▶ Paris 651 – Albertville 78 – Chambéry 91 – St-Jean-de-Maurienne 16

⛰ Caravaneige du Col

✆ 0479830080, www.camping-du-col.com – alt. 1 640

Address : 1 km east of La Toussuire, on rte de St-Jean-de-Maurienne

Opening times : mid Junee to end Aug., and mid Dec to mid April

0,8 ha (40 pitches) flat, grassy

Tariff : (2013 Price) 26,40€ ✹✹ 🚗 🅴 – Extra per person 5,60€

Rental rates : (2013 Price) (mid June to end Aug., and mid Dec. to mid April) – 7 🚐 – 3 🏠 – 2 apartments. Per week from 210 to 780€

Free shuttle service to the ski resort.

Surroundings : ❄ ⪕ Les Aiguilles d'Arves (peaks)
Leisure activities : 🍴 ✗ 🎣 daytime 🚡 🏇 🛶
Facilities : ♿ ⚷ 🍴 🏠 🍴 launderette

G P S	Longitude : 6.2739
	Latitude : 45.25727

TREPT

38460 – Michelin map **333** E3 – pop. 1 741 – alt. 275
▶ Paris 495 – Belley 41 – Bourgoin-Jallieu 13 – Lyon 52

⛰ Sites et Paysages Les 3 Lacs du Soleil

✆ 0474929206, www.camping-les3lacsdusoleil.com

Address : at La Plaine Serrière (2.7km east along the D 517, follow the signs for Morestel and take the road to the right, near two lakes)

Opening times : from end April to mid Sept.

25 ha/3 for camping (160 pitches) flat, grassy

Tariff : 35,50€ ✹✹ 🚗 🅴 (6A) – Extra per person 7€

Rental rates : (from beginning April to mid Sept.) 🚐 – 30 🚐 7 🏠 – 18 canvas bungalows – 2 tent lodges. Per night from 44 to 126€ – Per week from 308 to 882€

Surroundings : 🌄 ♨ ⛰
Leisure activities : 🍴 ✗ 🎣 daytime 🏃 🏇 🎿 🛶 🏊 (beach) 🪂 🎣
Facilities : ♿ ⚷ 🍴 launderette

G P S	Longitude : 5.33447
	Latitude : 45.69039

TULETTE

26790 – Michelin map **332** C8 – pop. 1 915 – alt. 147
▶ Paris 648 – Avignon 53 – Bollène 15 – Nyons 20

⚠ Les Rives de l'Aygues

✆ 04 75 98 37 50, www.lesrivesdelaygues.com

Address : route de Cairanne (head 3km south along the D 193 and take road to the left)

Opening times : from beginning May to end Sept.

3,6 ha (100 pitches)

Tariff : (2013 Price) ♦ 5,80 € ⟋ 2,50 € ▣ 8,40 € – ⚡ (6A) 4,70 €
Reservation fee 10 €

Rental rates : (from beginning May to mid Sept.) ⤳ – 2 ⌂
6 ⌂. Per week from 279 to 720 € – Reservation fee 10 €

In a natural setting among vineyards.

Surroundings : ⟋ ⤳ ♙♙
Leisure activities : ♟ ✗ ⌂ ⟋ ⟍
Facilities : ♿ ⚲ ⟋ ⚐ ▣ ⟋

G P S Longitude : 4.933
Latitude : 44.2648

Some campsites benefit from proximity to a municipal leisure centre.

UCEL

07200 – Michelin map **331** I6 – pop. 1 929 – alt. 270
▶ Paris 626 – Aubenas 6 – Montélimar 44 – Privas 31

⛰ Domaine de Gil ♣♦

✆ 04 75 94 63 63, www.domaine-de-gil.com ⤳

Address : route de Vals (take northwestern exit along the D 578b)

Opening times : from end April to mid Sept.

4,8 ha/2 for camping (80 pitches)

Tariff : 38 € ♦♦ ⟋ ▣ ⚡ (10A) – Extra per person 6,50 € – Reservation fee 20 €

Rental rates : (from end April to mid Sept.) ⤳ – 52 ⌂. Per night from 110 to 350 € – Per week from 245 to 903 € – Reservation fee 20 €

⤇ borne

Well-shaded pitches and mobile homes with a very pleasant natural area beside the Ardèche river.

Surroundings : ⟋ ◁ ⤳ ♙♙ ⛰
Leisure activities : ♟ ✗ ⌂ ⟋ nighttime ⚶
jacuzzi ⟋ ⚵ ♩ ⟍ ⤳ ⚐ multi-sports
ground
Facilities : ♿ ⚲ ⟋ ⚐ ⟋ ⚐ launderette ⟋

G P S Longitude : 4.37959
Latitude : 44.64308

VAGNAS

07150 – Michelin map **331** I7 – pop. 521 – alt. 200
▶ Paris 670 – Aubenas 40 – Barjac 5 – St-Ambroix 20

⛰ La Rouvière-Les Pins

✆ 04 75 38 61 41, www.rouviere07.com

Address : at La Rouviere (take the southern exit following signs for Barjac then continue 1.5km along the road to the right)

Opening times : from beginning April to mid Sept.

2 ha (100 pitches)

Tariff : 24 € ♦♦ ⟋ ▣ ⚡ (10A) – Extra per person 6 € – Reservation fee 15 €

Rental rates : (from mid April to mid Sept.) – 2 ⌂ – 2 apartments
3 canvas bungalows. Per night from 125 to 170 € – Per week
from 240 to 720 € – Reservation fee 15 €

⤇ borne

A spacious site in the heart of the vineyards.

Surroundings : ⟋ ♙♙
Leisure activities : ♟ ⌂ ⟋ ⟍
Facilities : ♿ ⚲ ⟋ ⚐ ⟋ ▣ ⟋

G P S Longitude : 4.34194
Latitude : 44.3419

VALLIÈRES

74150 – Michelin map **328** I5 – pop. 1 393 – alt. 347
▶ Paris 533 – Lyon 132 – Annecy 30 – Genève 59

⛰ Les Charmilles

✆ 04 50 62 10 60, www.campingcharmilles.com

Address : 625 route de Val de Fier

Opening times : from beginning April to end Oct.

3 ha (81 pitches) flat, grassy

Tariff : 14 € ♦♦ ⟋ ▣ ⚡ (8A) – Extra per person 4 € – Reservation fee 10 €

Rental rates : (from beginning April to end Oct.) – 10 ⌂
10 ⌂. Per night from 50 to 60 € – Per week from 189 to 590 €
Reservation fee 10 €

⤇ 10 ▣ 13 € – ⚡13 €

Surroundings : ◁ ♙♙
Leisure activities : ♟ ✗ ⌂ ⟋ ⚵ ⟍
Facilities : ♿ ⚲ ⚐ ⟋ launderette

G P S Longitude : 5.9285
Latitude : 45.90286

VALLOIRE

73450 – Michelin map **333** L7 – pop. 1 299 – alt. 1 430 – Winter
sports : 1 430/2 600m
▶ Paris 664 – Albertville 91 – Briançon 52 – Chambéry 104

⚠ Ste Thècle

✆ 04 79 83 30 11, www.valloire.net

Address : route des Villards (north of the town, at the confluence of two mountain streams)

1,5 ha (81 pitches)

Surroundings : ❄ ⟋ ◁
Leisure activities : ⌂ ⟋
Facilities : ♿ ⚲ ▥ ▣
Nearby : ⚵ ⟋ ⛷ skating rink , bowling

G P S Longitude : 6.42872
Latitude : 45.16587

VALLON-PONT-D'ARC

07150 – Michelin map **331** I7 – pop. 2 337 – alt. 117
▶ Paris 658 – Alès 47 – Aubenas 32 – Avignon 81

⛰ Les Castels Nature Parc l'Ardéchois ♣♦

✆ 04 75 88 06 63, www.ardechois-camping.com

Address : route Touristique des Gorges de l'Ardèche (located 1.5km southeast along the D 290)

Opening times : from beginning April to end Sept.

5 ha (240 pitches) flat, grassy

Tariff : 55 € ♦♦ ⟋ ▣ ⚡ (6A)
Extra per person 10,90 € – Reservation fee 40 €

CHALVET

Rental rates : (from beginning April to end Sept.) – 25 🚐.
Per night from 69 to 126€ – Per week from 483 to 1250€
Reservation fee 40€

🚐 borne

In a green setting with some very well-equipped pitches and an attractive terraced layout, above the Ardèche river.

Surroundings : 🏊 ❮ 🏕 ♨♨ ⚲
Leisure activities : ♈ ✕ 🎱 🏕 🚶 🚣 ✺ 🏊
🏊 multi-sports ground
Facilities : ♿ ⚡ ▥ 🚿 🚮 ⚗ ♈ launderette
🚰 🚿
Nearby : ⛷

GPS Longitude : 4.39673
Latitude : 44.39672

🏕 Mondial-Camping 👥

📞 0475880044, www.mondial-camping.com

Address : route des Gorges de l'Ardèche (located 1.5km southeast)

Opening times : from beginning April to end Sept.

4 ha (240 pitches) flat, grassy

Tariff : 45,50€ ⚥⚥ 🚐 📺 🔌 (10A) – Extra per person 9,20€ –
Reservation fee 30€

Rental rates : (from beginning April to end Sept.) ✂ – 24 🚐.
7 canvas bungalows. Per night from 55 to 110€ – Per week
from 320 to 1080€ – Reservation fee 30€

A green site beside the Ardèche river, with some pitches well marked out.

Surroundings : ❮ ♨♨ ⚲
Leisure activities : ♈ ✕ 🎱 🏕 🚶 🚣 🏊 ✺
🏊 multi-sports ground
Facilities : ♿ ⚡ ▥ 🚿 🚮 ⚗ ♈ launderette
🚰
Nearby : ⛷

GPS Longitude : 4.40139
Latitude : 44.39695

🏕 La Roubine 👥

📞 0475880456, www.camping-roubine.com

Address : route de Ruoms (located 1.5km west)

Opening times : from mid April to mid Sept.

7 ha/4 for camping (135 pitches)

Tariff : 48€ ⚥⚥ 🚐 📺 🔌 (10A)
Extra per person 9,70€ – Reservation fee 30€

Rental rates : (from mid April to mid Sept.) ♿ (1 mobile home) ✂
38 🚐. Per night from 53 to 231€
Per week from 371 to 1617€ –
Reservation fee 30€

An attractive campsite beside the Ardèche river; some luxurious mobile homes and very good sanitary facilities.

Surroundings : 🏊 🏕 ♨♨ ⚲
Leisure activities : ♈ ✕ 🎱 🏕 🚶 ⛵ jacuzzi
🚣 ⛷ 🏊 multi-sports ground, spa centre
Facilities : ♿ ⚡ ▥ 🚿 ♈ launderette 🚰 🚿

GPS Longitude : 4.37835
Latitude : 44.40636

The pitches of many campsites are marked out with low hedges of attractive bushes and shrubs.

🏕 International

📞 0475880099, www.internationalcamping07.com

Address : La Plaine Salavas (located 1km southwest)

Opening times : from end April to end Sept.

2,7 ha (120 pitches)

Tariff : 40€ ⚥⚥ 🚐 📺 🔌 (10A) – Extra per person 8€ – Reservation fee 15€

Rental rates : (from mid April to end Sept.) – 14 🚐 – 2 🏠.
Per week from 250 to 810€ – Reservation fee 15€

🚐 borne

Choose the pitches away from the bridge and beside the Ardèche river.

Surroundings : 🏕 ♨♨ ⚲
Leisure activities : ♈ ✕ 🚣 🚣
Facilities : ♿ ⚡ 🚿 ♈ 📺 🚰 🚿

GPS Longitude : 4.38203
Latitude : 44.39925

🏕 L'Esquiras

📞 0475880416, www.camping-esquiras.com

Address : chemin du Fez (2.8km northwest along the D 579, follow the signs for Ruoms and take the road to the right after the Intermarché service station)

Opening times : from mid April to end Sept.

2 ha (106 pitches)

Tariff : (2013 Price) 32€ ⚥⚥ 🚐 📺 🔌 (10A) – Extra per person 7€
Reservation fee 15€

Rental rates : (from mid April to end Sept.) – 40 🚐. Per night
from 49 to 69€ – Per week from 250 to 920€ – Reservation fee 15€

🚐 borne 8€ – 6 📺 8€

A green setting with a plenty of room in which to unwind; good quality mobile homes.

Surroundings : 🏊 ❮ ♨♨
Leisure activities : ✕ 🎱 🚶 🚣
Facilities : ♿ ⚡ 🚿 ♈ 📺
Nearby : forest trail

GPS Longitude : 4.37913
Latitude : 44.41536

🏕 La Rouvière 👥

📞 0475371007, www.campinglarouviere.com

Address : route des Gorges Chames (6.6km southeast along the D 290; at Chames)

3 ha (153 pitches)

Rentals : 39 🚐 – 3 tent lodges.

Below the road, beside the Ardèche river with well-organised canoeing activities.

Surroundings : ♨♨ ⚲
Leisure activities : ✕ 🚶 🚣 ✺ 🏊
multi-sports ground
Facilities : ⚡ 🚿 ♈ 📺 🚰

GPS Longitude : 4.42649
Latitude : 44.37796

🏕 Le Midi

📞 0475880678, www.camping-midi.com

Address : route des Gorges de l'Ardèche (6.5km southeast along the D 290; at Chames)

1,6 ha (52 pitches)

Rentals : 4 🚐 – 5 tents (for groups).

Below the road, with well-organised canoeing activities and a spacious site near the river. Groups welcome.

Surroundings : 🏊 🏕 ♨♨ ⚲
Leisure activities : 🚣 ✺ 🏊
Facilities : ♿ ⚡ ♈ 📺 🚰
Nearby : ✕

GPS Longitude : 4.42093
Latitude : 44.37672

VALLORCINE

74660 – Michelin map **328** O4 – pop. 419 – alt. 1 260 – Winter sports : 1 260/1 400m
▶ Paris 628 – Annecy 115 – Chamonix-Mont-Blanc 19 – Thonon-les-Bains 96

⚠ Les Montets

🖉 0546756154, www.camping-montets.fr – alt. 1 300

Address : 671 route du Treuil, at Le Montet (2.8km southwest along the N 506, access via Chemin de la Gare, at Le Buet)

1,7 ha (75 pitches)

🚐 borne

A pleasant location beside a stream and near the Eau Noire river.

Surroundings : 🏞 ⩽ ♀
Leisure activities : ✗
Facilities : ⛏ ⊶ Ⓟ ▚ ▣
Nearby : ✂ 🎣

GPS Longitude : 6.92376
Latitude : 46.02344

LES VANS

07140 – Michelin map **331** G7 – pop. 2 805 – alt. 170
▶ Paris 663 – Alès 44 – Aubenas 37 – Pont-St-Esprit 66

⚠ Le Pradal

🖉 0475372516, www.camping-lepradal.com

Address : 1.5km west along the D 901

Opening times : from beginning April to end Sept.

1 ha (36 pitches)

Tariff : 🟊 6,50€ 🚗 ▣ 19€ – (⚡) (6A) 3,80€
Rental rates : (from beginning April to end Sept.) – 3 🛏 – 1 🏠.
Per night from 50 to 70€ – Per week from 200 to 630€
🚐 borne 7€ – 4 ▣ 19€ – ⛽ 19€

Numerous pitches on small, individual terraces surrounded by hedges.

Surroundings : ♀♀
Leisure activities : 🍴 🏞 🏊 multi-sports ground
Facilities : ⛏ ⊶ 🚿

GPS Longitude : 4.11023
Latitude : 44.40809

VERCHAIX

74440 – Michelin map **328** N4 – pop. 661 – alt. 800
▶ Paris 580 – Annecy 74 – Chamonix-Mont-Blanc 59 – Genève 52

⚠ Municipal Lac et Montagne

🖉 0450901012, www.mairie-verchaix.fr – alt. 660

Address : 1.8km south along the D 907; beside the Giffre river

Opening times : Permanent

2 ha (107 pitches)

Tariff : 🟊 2,50€ 🚗 2€ ▣ 3,50€ – (⚡) (10A) 4,50€

Surroundings : ⩽ ♀
Leisure activities : 🏄 ✂ 🎣
Facilities : ⛏ ⊶ ▥ launderette
Nearby : 🍴 ✗ 🐎

GPS Longitude : 6.67527
Latitude : 46.09001

A chambre d'hôte is a guesthouse or B & B-style accommodation.

VERNIOZ

38150 – Michelin map **333** C5 – pop. 1 182 – alt. 250
▶ Paris 500 – Annonay 38 – Givors 25 – Le Péage-de-Roussillon 12

⛰ Le Bontemps

🖉 0474578352, www.camping-lebontemps.com

Address : 5 impasse du Bontemps (4.5km east along the D 37 and take the road to the right; beside the Varèze river, at St-Alban-de-Varèze)

Opening times : from beginning April to end Sept.

6 ha (175 pitches)

Tariff : 32€ 🟊🟊 🚗 ▣ (⚡) (10A) – Extra per person 7€ – Reservation fee 10€

Rental rates : (from beginning April to end Sept.) – 8 🛏 3 🏠. Per night from 45 to 95€ – Per week from 320 to 800€ Reservation fee 10€

🚐 borne

Surroundings : 🏞 🛶 ♀♀
Leisure activities : 🍴 ✗ 🏞 🎲 🏖 🏇 🚴 ✂ 🏓 🏊 entertainment room
Facilities : ⛏ ⊶ ㏄ 🔥 🚿 ▚ launderette 🚻

GPS Longitude : 4.92836
Latitude : 45.42798

VILLARD-DE-LANS

38250 – Michelin map **333** G7 – pop. 4 031 – alt. 1 040
▶ Paris 584 – Die 67 – Grenoble 34 – Lyon 123

⛰ FranceLoc Domaine de L'Oursière

🖉 0476951477, www.camping-oursiere.fr

Address : avenue du Général de Gaulle (take the northern exit along the D 531, follow the signs for Grenoble; pedestrian path to village)

Opening times : from mid Dec. to end March and from mid May to end Sept.

4 ha (189 pitches)

Tariff : 22€ 🟊🟊 🚗 ▣ (⚡) (10A) – Extra per person 7€ – Reservation fee 11€

Rental rates : (from mid Dec. to end March and from mid May to end Sept.) – 48 🛏 – 3 🏠. Per night from 44 to 82€ – Per week from 175 to 700€ – Reservation fee 27€

🚐 borne 5€

Surroundings : ❄ ⩽
Leisure activities : 🏞 🏇 ▚ 🏊 🏖 ✂ spa facilities
Facilities : ⛏ ⊶ ▥ 🔥 🚿 ▣ 🚿
Nearby : 🎳 bowling

GPS Longitude : 5.55639
Latitude : 45.0775

VILLAREMBERT

73300 – Michelin map **333** K6 – pop. 253 – alt. 1 296
▶ Paris 647 – Aiguebelle 49 – Chambéry 87 – St-Jean-de-Maurienne 12

⚠ Municipal la Tigny

🖉 0479567465, mairie.villarembert@wanadoo.fr

Address : take the southern exit along the D 78 and take road to the left

Opening times : from beginning July to end Aug.

0,3 ha (27 pitches)

Tariff : 🟊 3,60€ 🚗 2,40€ ▣ 3€ – (⚡) (60A) 3€

In a green setting near a stream.

Surroundings : ⩽ ♀
Leisure activities : 🏇
Facilities : 🚿 ▣ 🚿 🚻

GPS Longitude : 6.28033
Latitude : 45.24581

VILLARS-LES-DOMBES

01330 – Michelin map **328** D4 – pop. 4 328 – alt. 281
▶ Paris 433 – Bourg-en-Bresse 29 – Lyon 37 – Villefranche-sur-Saône 29

⚠ Indigo Parc des Oiseaux ♠♣

🖉 04 74 98 00 21, www.parcdesoiseaux.com – limited spaces for one-night stay

Address : 164 avenue des Nations (southwestern exit, follow the signs for Lyon and take the turning to the left; near the swimming pool)

Opening times : from mid April to end Oct.

5 ha (191 pitches)

Tariff : (2013 Price) 24,90 € ★★ 🚐 🔲 🏕 (10A)
Extra per person 4,50 €

Rental rates : Permanent 🦅 – 4 caravans – 35 canvas bungalows. Per night from 45 to 95 € – Per week from 252 to 532 € Reservation fee 20 €

🚐 borne – 50 🔲 20,40 €

A pleasant setting in partial shade beside the Chalaronne river.

Surroundings : 🌳 ⌂ ⌒
Leisure activities : ✗ 🎱 🏃 💪 🚴 🎣
Facilities : ♿ 🚿 🔲 🛁 🍴 launderette
Nearby : ✗ 🎣 🛶 🏊

G P S Longitude : 5.03039
Latitude : 45.99749

This guide is updated regularly, so buy your new copy every year!

VINSOBRES

26110 – Michelin map **332** D7 – pop. 1 109 – alt. 247
▶ Paris 662 – Bollène 29 – Grignan 24 – Nyons 9

⚠ Franceloc Le Sagittaire ♠♣

🖉 04 75 27 00 00, www.campings-franceloc.fr

Address : at Le Pont de Mirabel (Junction of D 94 and D 4, near the Eygues (direct access)

Opening times : Permanent

14 ha/8 for camping (274 pitches)

Tariff : (2013 Price) 35 € ★★ 🚐 🔲 🏕 (10A) – Extra per person 8 € Reservation fee 27 €

Rental rates : Permanent – 6 caravans – 112 🏠 – 60 🏡 4 tipis. Per night from 35 to 116 € – Per week from 175 to 1512 € Reservation fee 27 €

An attractive swimming and play area.

Surroundings : ⛰ ⌂ ⌒
Leisure activities : ♟ ✗ 🎱 🏖 🏃 🏋 💪
🎱 🛶 🏊 🏄 (stretch of water) 🎿 🏹 multi-sports ground
Facilities : ♿ 🚿 🔲 🛁 🏕 🍴 launderette 🛁 🚿

G P S Longitude : 5.08002
Latitude : 44.22661

⚠ Municipal Chez Antoinette

🖉 04 75 27 61 65, camping-municipal@club-internet.fr

Address : quartier Champessier (located south of the town along the D 190; by the stadium)

1,9 ha (70 pitches)
Rental rates : – 1 🏠 .

Surroundings : ⛰ ⌒
Leisure activities : 💪
Facilities : ♿ 🚿 🍴 🔲 refrigerators

G P S Longitude : 5.06594
Latitude : 44.32912

VION

07610 – Michelin map **331** K3 – pop. 905 – alt. 128
▶ Paris 537 – Annonay 30 – Lamastre 34 – Tournon-sur-Rhône 7

⚠ L'Iserand

🖉 04 75 08 01 73, www.iserandcampingardeche.com

Address : 1307 rue Royale (located 1km north along the N 86, follow the signs for Lyon)

Opening times : from mid April to mid Sept.

1,3 ha (60 pitches)

Tariff : 20 € ★★ 🚐 🔲 🏕 (10A) – Extra per person 7 €
Rental rates : (from mid April to mid Sept.) 🦅 – 8 🏠 – 8 🏡. Per night from 50 to 70 € – Per week from 360 to 620 €
🚐 borne 20 € – 4 🔲 20 €
Choose pitches furthest away from the road.

Surroundings : ⛰ ⌒
Leisure activities : ✗ 💪 🏖 🏊
Facilities : ♿ 🚿 🔲 🍴 🔲 🚿

G P S Longitude : 4.80027
Latitude : 45.12117

VIZILLE

38220 – Michelin map **333** H7 – pop. 7 592 – alt. 270
▶ Paris 582 – Le Bourg-d'Oisans 32 – Grenoble 20 – La Mure 22

⚠ Le Bois de Cornage

Mairie Vizille

🖉 06 83 18 17 87, www.campingvizille.com

Address : chemin du Camping (take the northern exit towards the N 85, follow the signs for Grenoble and turn right onto av. de Venaria)

Opening times : from beginning April to end Oct.

2,5 ha (128 pitches)

Tariff : 21 € ★★ 🚐 🔲 🏕 (16A)
Extra per person 5,30 € – Reservation fee 10 €

Rental rates : Permanent – 22 🏠. Per night from 47 to 85 € Per week from 260 to 590 € – Reservation fee 10 €
🚐 borne 3 €
Partially shaded by centuries-old trees.

Surroundings : ⛰ ⌒
Leisure activities : ✗ 💪 🏊
Facilities : 🚿 🔲 🍴 🔲 🚿

G P S Longitude : 5.76948
Latitude : 45.08706

VOGÜÉ

07200 – Michelin map **331** I6 – pop. 917 – alt. 150
▶ Paris 638 – Aubenas 9 – Largentière 16 – Privas 40

⚠ Domaine du Cros d'Auzon ♠♣

🖉 04 75 37 04 14, www.domaine-cros-auzon.com

Address : 2.5km south along the D 579 and take the road to the right

18 ha/6 for camping (170 pitches)

Rental rates : ♿ (5 mobile homes) – 40 🏠 – 3 🏡 – 37 🛏 (hotel).

The lower part of the site is near the river with shaded pitches, the upper part contains the services: water park, restaurant, hotel.

Surroundings : ⛰ ⌂ ⌒
Leisure activities : ♟ ✗ 🎱 🏖 🏃 💪 ✗
🎱 🛶 🏊 🏄
Facilities : ♿ 🚿 🛁 🚿 🍴 launderette 🚿

G P S Longitude : 4.40678
Latitude : 44.53178

⚠ Les Roches

✆ 0475377045, www.campinglesroches.fr

Address : district Bausson (located 1.5km south along the D 579; at Vogüé-Gare, 200m from the Auzon and the Ardèche rivers)

Opening times : from beginning May to end Aug.

2,5 ha (100 pitches)

Tariff : (2013 Price) 30,50€ ♥♥ ⛺ 🚗 ▣ ⚡ (10A) – Extra per person 6,50€
Rental rates : (from beginning May to end Aug.) – 8 🚐. Per week from 350 to 650€
🚐 borne 4€

Shaded pitches on small terraces, in a wild setting among rocks.

Surroundings : 🌿 ♡♡
Leisure activities : ♀ 🏛 🚣 🏊
Facilities : ♿ ⚬🛒 🚿 ♨ launderette, refrigerators
Nearby : ≋

GPS Longitude : 4.41406
Latitude : 44.542

⚠ Les Peupliers

✆ 0475377147, www.campingpeupliers.com

Address : at Gourgouran (head 2km south along the D 579 and take the road to the right; at Vogüé-Gare)

Opening times : from beginning April to end Sept.

3 ha (100 pitches)

Tariff : 32,60€ ♥♥ 🚗 ▣ ⚡ (16A) – Extra per person 6,25€
Reservation fee 19€
Rental rates : (from beginning April to end Sept.) – 10 🚐 9 🏠. Per night from 40 to 160€ – Per week from 250 to 800€
Reservation fee 19€
🚐 borne 4,50€

Some pitches beside the Ardèche river and rental options, some a bit old.

Surroundings : 🌿 ♡♡
Leisure activities : ♀ ✗ 🚣 🏊 ≋ 🎣
Facilities : ⚬🛒 🚿 ♨ launderette

GPS Longitude : 4.411
Latitude : 44.53765

⚠ L'Oasis des Garrigues

✆ 0475370327, www.oasisdesgarrigues.com

Address : Quartier Brugière (situated 2km south along the D 579, take a right turn at the roundabout)

1,2 ha (61 pitches)

Rentals : 🚫 – 9 🚐 – 9 🏠.

Rentals of a varying degrees of comfort and some pitches for tents and caravans, some of which are well equipped (awning, fridge...)

Leisure activities : ♀ 🏊
Facilities : ♿ ⚬🛒 🚿 ♨ 📶 🖾
Nearby : ≋ 🎣

GPS Longitude : 4.41094
Latitude : 44.53841

⚠ Les Chênes Verts

✆ 0475377154, www.camping-chenesverts.com

Address : Champ Redon (1.7km southeast along the D 103)

Opening times : from beginning June to end Sept.

2,5 ha (37 pitches)

Tariff : 26€ ♥♥ 🚗 ▣ ⚡ (16A) – Extra per person 4€
Rental rates : (from beginning April to end Oct.) – 26 🏠. Per night from 55 to 120€ – Per week from 270 to 850€ – Reservation fee 30€

A well shaded site, laid out with terraces above the road, but few pitches for tents and caravans.

Surroundings : ♡♡
Leisure activities : ✗ 🚣 🏊
Facilities : ♿ ⚬🛒 🚿 📶 ♨ 🖾 🚿

GPS Longitude : 4.42075
Latitude : 44.54425

Do not confuse:
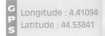
⚠ *to* ⚠⚠⚠ : *MICHELIN classification with*
★ *to* ★★★★★ : *official classification*

CANILLO

AD100 – Michelin map **343** H9 – pop. 4 826 – alt. 1531
▶ Andorra-la-Vella 13

🔺 Santa-Creu

℘ (00-376) 85 14 62, www.elsmeners.com

Address : near the town centre (beside the Valira-del-Orient river (left bank)

Opening times : from mid June to mid Sept.

0,5 ha

Tariff : ♦ 4,20€ 🚗 4,20€ 🗐 4,20€ [9] (5A)

The site is on a shaded field near the town centre.

Surroundings : ≤ ♀
Leisure activities : ♟
Facilities : ⅃ ⚭ ⤐ ⫏⊠ ¹⁄ 🔳

GPS Longitude : 1.59978
Latitude : 42.56579

🔺 Jan-Ramon

℘ (00-376) 75 14 54, www.elsmeners.com

Address : carretera General (400m northeast following signs for Port d'Envalira; beside the Valira-del-Orient river (left bank)

Opening times : from mid June to mid Sept.

0,6 ha flat, grassy

Tariff : ♦ 4,20€ 🚗 4,20€ 🗐 4,20€ [9] (6A)
Rental rates : Permanent ⚋ – 5 🏠. Per night from 73 to 83€
Per week from 511 to 581€

A pleasant and partially shaded site, but there is noise from the nearby road.

Surroundings : ≤ ♀
Leisure activities : ♟ ✕
Facilities : ⚭ ⫏⊠ ¹⁄ 🔳 ⤏

For more information on visiting particular towns or regions, consult the relevant regional MICHELIN Green Guide. We also recommend you use the appropriate Michelin regional map to locate your selected campsite, to calculate distances and to work out the best route.

GPS Longitude : 1.59975
Latitude : 42.56594

LA MASSANA

AD400 – Michelin map **343** H9 – pop. 9 744 – alt. 1241
▶ Andorra-la-Vella 6

🏔 Xixerella

℘ (00-376) 73 86 13, www.xixerellapark.com – alt. 1 450

Address : at Xixerella (3.5km northeast along the CG 4 then continue to Erts, taking turning on the left)

Opening times : from beginning Dec. to end Sept.

5 ha terraced, relatively flat, stony, grassy

Tarif : ♦ 6,60€ 🚗 6,60€ 🗐 13,20€ – [9] (6A) 6,60€
Rental rates : (from beginning Dec. to end Oct.) – 13 🏠 28 apartments. Per week from 972 to 1224€

A shaded grass area for tents and caravans; a range of rental options of good quality.

Surroundings : ≤ ♀♀
Leisure activities : ♟ ✕ 🖼 ≋ hammam, jacuzzi ⤢ ⼉ 🏊
Facilities : ⅃ ⚭ ⫏⊠ ▥ ¹⁄ launderette ⊿ ⤏

GPS Longitude : 1.48882
Latitude : 42.55327

ORDINO

AD300 – Michelin map **343** H9 – pop. 4 322 – alt. 1304
▶ Andorra-la-Vella 8

🏔 Borda d'Ansalonga

℘ (00-376) 85 03 74, www.campingansalonga.com

Address : carretera Général del Serrat (2.3km northwest along the rte du Circuit de Tristaina; beside the Valira-del-Nord river)

Opening times : from beginning June to mid Sept.

3 ha flat, grassy

Tarif : 25€ ♦♦ 🚗 🗐 [9] (10A) – Extra per person 7€

A shaded and grassy site, but choose the pitches near the stream and away from the road in preference.

Surroundings : ≤ ♀♀
Leisure activities : ♟ ✕ 🖼 ⤢ ⼉
Facilities : ⅃ ⚭ ⫏⊠ ▥ ¹⁄ launderette ⤏

GPS Longitude : 1.52162
Latitude : 42.56855

Michelin Travel Partner

Société par actions simplifiées au capital de 11 288 880 EUR
27 cours de l'Ile Seguin – 92100 Boulogne Billancourt (France)
R.C.S. Nanterre 433 677 721

No part of this publication may be reproduced in any form
without the prior permission of the publisher.

© Michelin Travel Partner
ISBN 978-2-067194-02-1

Layout: Jean-Luc Carnet
Translation: JMS Books llp (www.jmswords.com)
Layout of English edition: Chris Bell, cbdesign
Printed: February 2014
Printed and bound in Italy
Printed on paper from sustainable forests